Handbook of Corrosion Data

Edited by
Bruce D. Craig
Metallurgical Consultants, Inc.

ASM INTERNATIONAL®
Metals Park, OH 44073

Library of Congress Catalog Card Number: 89-083794

ISBN: 0-87170-361-0

SAN 204-7586

ASM INTERNATIONAL®
Metals Park OH 44073
Telephone: (216) 338-5151

PRINTED IN THE UNITED STATES OF AMERICA

Preface

The purpose of this book is to provide those involved with the corrosion of metals and alloys a starting point to quickly and easily assess the recent literature on metals in corrosive environments. This handbook is not intended to provide all of the data available in the literature on every environment that exists. The reader should appreciate the magnitude of such a task is beyond the limits of a simple reference. In fact, NIST-NACE have jointly sponsored such a database that is computerized and continually updated. This handbook presents data obtained from a literature search covering corrosion literature fronm 1985 to 1987. It is meant to provide a source for a quick overview of the most recent research literature. For certain environments (i.e. sulfuric acid), a significant amount of work has been performed over the years such that specific data or graphs have been adopted as classic reference material on the subject. These classic pieces have been included to aid the reader in "coming up to speed" on a specific environment.

This book is intended to provide a starting point from which more detailed analysis of the literature may be initiated to fuly evaluate the performance of metals in corrosive environments. It is by no means intended to act as a complete guide to the corrosion behavior of metals, rather it may aid in eliminating alloys that are obviously inappropriate. A book that presents primarily tables and graphs cannot include all of the important support data available in the original paper. Therefore, the original papers must be consulted for important parameters that affect corrosion such as test duration, solution composition, temperature, stress level, heat treatment, etc. Final selection of metals for a specific environment should be based on more detailed literature surveys and/or testing in the actual or a simulated environment.

Several excellent books are available that provide greater detail on the selection of metals for certain environments. One of the most extensive is the *Metals Handbook*, Volume 13, published by ASM International, which also includes key references on specific alloys and environments.

The Handbook of Corrosion Data is organized on the basis of environment (chemical compound) rather than along the lines of specific alloy systems. The latter is presented in summary fashion as a general overview at the beginning of this volume. However, the designer or applications engineer is more often faced with choosing an alloy for a specific environment. Therefore, more analysis may be necessary to provide a complete comparison. Books such as the *Corrosion Data Survey*, 5th Edition, MACE (1985) are an excellent complement to this handbook.

The reader is cautioned that corrosion is indeed a complex subject and that simply looking up the major chemical component in a system may not be sufficient to entirely define the alloys that are suitable for application. In fact, it is far more common that relatively small concentrations of other chemical constituents may be a more controling factor in the selection of materials than the major component. Thus, it is incumbent on the reader to consider all the chemical species expected in the environment as well as the effects of temperature, pressure, flow rate, etc. on corrosion.

As an additional aid, a listing is included that cross references common names of compounds to their actual chemical names, or other various terms used for certain compounds.

A brief introduction to corrosion concepts is included to provide those new to the corrosion field a short introduction to the terminology frequently used in the corrosion literature and the ways in which corrosion can manifest itself.

I extend my thanks and appreciation to David Anderson, National Institute of Standards and Technology; Steve Brubaker, E.I. DuPont Nemours, Inc.; Robert Kain, La Que Center for Corrosion Technology; Greg Kobrin, E.I. DuPont Nemours, Inc.; George Lai, Haynes International, Inc.; Bernard W. Lifka, Alcoa Technical Center; Thomas Spence, The Duriron Co., Inc; Narasi Sridhar, Haynes International, Inc.; and Dave Thomas, RMI Corporation; for their help and cooperation with this project.

Also, I would like to acknowledge the substantial contribution of Matthew J. Donachie, Jr., The Hartford Graduate Center, in the preparation of the material in Part 1 for Stainless Steels, Iron-Base Superalloys, Aluminum and Aluminum Alloys, Copper and Copper Alloys, Magnesium and Magnesium Alloys, Nickel and Nickel Alloys, Cobalt-Base Alloys and Superalloys, Titanium and Titanium Alloys.

It is the intent of the Technical Book Committee that revisions to this Handbook will be ongoing and begin immediately upon publication of this volume.

Denver, CO
August, 1989

Bruce D. Craig

Contents

Preface iii
Contents.. v
Expanded Contents viii
Chemical Listing xi
Conversion Rates xiii

Part I: Corrosion of Metals and Alloys

Corrosion Concepts 1
Pure Iron 2
Cast Irons 2
Carbon Steels 5
Low-Alloy Steels
Alloy Steels 8
Stainless Steels 8
    Austenitic Stainless Steels 12
    Martensitic Stainless Steels 12
    Ferritic Stainless Steels 13
    Precipitation-Hardening Stainless Steels 13
    Duplex Stainless Steels 13
Cast Steels 14
Iron-Base Superalloys 15
Aluminum and Aluminum Alloys 16
Copper and Copper Alloys 18
Magnesium and Magnesium Alloys 24
Lead and Lead Alloys 26
Zinc and Zinc Alloys 29
Tin and Tin Alloys 49
Nickel and Nickel Alloys 50
Cobalt-Base Alloys and Superalloys.......................... 52
Titanium and Titanium Alloys 53
Zirconium 62
Tantalum and Tantalum Alloys 66
Niobium and Niobium Alloys.................................. 71
Noble Metals and Alloys 73
    Silver 74
    Gold 76
    Platinum 76
    Palladium 77
Uranium... 80
Cemented Carbides.. 81
Metallic Glasses 83
References 84
Source Journals in Corrosion Science and Engineering ... 85
Bibliography 87

Part II: Corrosion Media

Acetaldehyde 105
Acetic Acid 106
Acetic Anhydride 116
Acetone 118
Adipic Acid.. 121
Aluminum Chloride 121
Aluminum Fluoride 123
Aluminum Hydroxide 124
Aluminum Sulfate 124
Ammonia... 126

Ammonium Carbonate 131
Ammonium Chloride... 132
Ammonium Fluoride... 134
Ammonium Hydroxide... 136
Ammonium Nitrate 138
Ammonium Phosphate 140
Ammonium Sulfate 141
Aqua Regia 143
Atmospheric Environments 145

Barium Carbonate 176
Barium Chloride... 176
Barium Hydroxide 178
Benzene 179
Benzoic Acid... 181
Boric Acid 182
Bromine 185
Butyl Alcohol 186
Butane 188

Cadmium Sulfate 190
Calcium Bromide 191
Calcium Chloride.. 192
Calcium Fluoride.. 196
Calcium Hydroxide 196
Calcium Hypochlorite 198
Camphor 200
Caprylic Acid 201
Carbon 201
Carbon Bisulfide 205
Carbon Dioxide.. 205
Carbon Monoxide 212
Carbon Tetrachloride 213
Carbonic Acid 216
Cellulose Acetate.. 217
Cesium Hydroxide 217
Chlorides 218
Chlorine 226
Chlorine Dioxide 234
Chlorine Water 236
Chloroacetic Acid 236
Chloroform 237
Chlorosulfonic Acid 238
Chromic Acid 239
Citric Acid... 242
Copals 246
Cresol 246
Cupric Chloride 247
Cupric Nitrate 249
Cupric Sulfate 250

Dichloroacetic Acid 252

Ether 253
Ethyl Alcohol 254
Ethyl Chloride 256
Ethylene Glycol 257

Fatty Acids 259
Ferric Chloride 261
Ferric Sulfate 267
Ferrous Chloride 269
Ferrous Sulfate 271

Fluorine 273
Fluosilicic Acid 274
Formaldehyde 275
Formic Acid 277

Gelatin 283
Gluconic Acid 284
Glycerol 285
Glycolic Acid 286

Hydrobromic Acid 287
Hydrochloric Acid 289
Hydrofluoric Acid 317
Hydrogen 330
Hydrogen Chloride 335
Hydrogen Cyanide 337
Hydrogen Peroxide 339
Hydrogen Sulfide 340
Hydroiodic Acid 350
Hypochlorites 351
Hypochlorous Acid 352

Iodine 352

Lactic Acid 354
Liquid Metals 356
Lithium Chloride 364

Magnesium Chloride 365
Magnesium Hydroxide 369
Maleic Acid 369
Malic Acid 371
Methyl Alcohol 372

Nickel Chloride 376
Nitric Acid 377
Nitric Oxide 397
Nitric Tetraoxide 398
Nitrogen 398
Nitrous Acid 400

Oleic Acid 400
Oxalic Acid 401
Oxygen 402
Ozone 406

Perchloric Acid 406
Petroleum Oils 407
Phenol 410
Phosgene 412

Phosphoric Acid 412
Phosphorus 431
Potassium Bromide 432
Potassium Chloride 434
Potassium Fluoride 436
Potassium Hydroxide 436
Potassium Iodide 441
Potassium Sulfate 442
Potassium Thiocyanate 444
Propionic Acid 444
Pyridine 447

Seawater 448
Sodium 476
Sodium Bicarbonate 477
Sodium Borate 479
Sodium Bromide 480
Sodium Carbonate 481
Sodium Chloride 483
Sodium Fluoride 515
Sodium Hydroxide 516
Sodium Hypochlorite 543
Sodium Nitrate 546
Sodium Nitrite 548
Sodium Perchlorate 549
Sodium Peroxide 550
Sodium Silicate 551
Sodium Sulfate 552
Sodium Sulfide 558
Sodium Sulfite 561
Sodium Thiosulfate 562
Steam 563
Stearic Acid 569
Succinic Acid 570
Sulfur 571
Sulfur Dioxide 576
Sulfur Trioxide 580
Sulfuric Acid 581
Sulfurous Acid 643

Tannic Acid 646
Tartaric Acid 647
Trichlorethylene 650
Trichloroacetic Acid 652

Urea 653

Water 655

References 679

Expanded Contents

A

Acetaldehyde, CH_3CHO, *also* Ethanal, Acetic aldehyde
Acetic acid, CH_3COOH, *also* Ethanoic acid, Vinegar acid
Acetic aldehyde, *see* Acetaldehyde
Acetic anhydride, $(CH_3CO)_2O$, *also* Ethanoric anhydride
Acetone, CH_3COOH_3, *also* 2-propanone, Dimethyl ketone
Activated oxygen, *see* Ozone
Adipic acid, $HOCC(CH_2)_4COOH$, *also* Hexanedioic acid
Air, *see* Atmosphere
Aluminum chloride, $AlCl_3$, Al_2Cl_6
Aluminum fluoride, $AlF_3 \cdot 3\ 1/2H_2O$
Aluminum hydroxide, $Al(OH)_3$, *also* Aluminum trihydroxide, Aluminum trihydrate, Hydrated aluminum, Hydrated aluminum oxide
Aluminum sulfate
Aluminum trihydrate, *see* Aluminum hydroxide
Aluminum trihydroxide, *see* Aluminum hydroxide
Amber acid, *see* Succinic acid
Ammonia, NH_3, *also* Anhydrous ammonia
Ammoniae, *see* Ammonium chloride
Ammonium carbonate, $(NH_4)_2CO_3$
Ammonium chloride, NH_4Cl, *also* Ammoniae, Salmiai, Ammonium nituriate
Ammonium fluoride, NH_4F
Ammonium hydroxide, NH_4OH
Ammonium nitrate, NH_4NO_3
Ammonium nituriate, *see* Ammonium chloride
Ammonium phosphate, $NH_4H_2PO_4$, $(NH_4)_2HPO_4$
Ammonium sulfate, $(NH_4)_2SO_4$
Anhydrous ammonia, *see* Ammonia
Anhydrous hydrogen fluoride, ANF, *see* Hydrofluoric acid
Aqua regia, *also* Nitrohydrochloric acid, Chloroazoatic acid
Aqueous hydrogen fluoride, HF, *see* Hydrofluoric acid
Arcanite, *see* Potassium sulfate
Atmosphere, *also* Air

B

Baking soda, *see* Sodium bicarbonate
Barium carbonate, $BaCo_3$, *also* Witherite
Barium chloride, $BaCl_2$
Barium hydroxide, $Ba(OH)_28H_2O$
Benzene, C_6H_6, *also* Benzol, Phenyl hydride, Phene, Coal naptha, Cyclohexatriene
Benzene carboxylic acid, *see* Benzoic acid
Benzinoform, *see* Carbon tetrachloride
Benzoic acid, C_6H_5COOH, *also* Benzene carboxylic acid, Phenyl formic acid
Benzol, *see* Benzene
Bleach, *see* Calcium hypochlorite
Boracic acid, *see* Boric acid
Boric acid, H_3BO_3, *also* Boracic acid, Orthoboric acid, Sassolite
Bromine, Br
Bucite, *see* Magnesium hydroxide
Butanol, *see* Butyl alcohol
Butyl alcohol, *also* Butanol
Butane, $CH_3(CH_2)_2CH_3$, *also* n-butane, Methyl-ethyl methane
Butane diacid, *see* Succinic acid
Butanedioic acid, *see* Succinic acid

C

Cadmium sulfate, $CdSO_4$

Calcium bromide, $CaBr_2$
Calcium chloride, $CaCl_2$
Calcium fluoride, CaF_2, *also* Fluorite, Feldspar
Calcium hydrate, *see* Calcium hydroxide
Calcium hydroxide, $Ca(OH)_2$, *also* Calcium hydrate, Hydrated lime, Slaked lime
Calcium hypochlorite, $Ca(ClO)_2 \cdot 4H_2O$, *also* Calcium oxychloride, Chlorinated lime, Bleach
Calcium oxychloride, *see* Calcium hypochlorite
Camphor, $C_{10}H_{16}O$, *also* d-2-camphanone, Japan camphor, Laurel camphor, Formosa camphor, Gum camphor
Caprylic acid, $CH_3(CH_2)_6COOH$, *also* Hexylacetic acid, n-octanoic acid, Octylic acid, Octic acid
Carbamide, *see* Urea
Carbolic acid, *see* Phenol
Carbon, C
Carbon dioxide, CO_2, *also* Carbonic anhydride, Carbonic acid gas
Carbon bisulfide, CS_2, *also* Carbon disulfide
Carbon disulfide, *see* Carbon bisulfide
Carbon monoxide
Carbon tetrachloride, CCl_4, *also* Tetrachloromethane, Perchloro methane, Benzinoform
Carbonic acid, H_2CO_2
Carbonic acid gas, *see* Carbon dioxide
Carbonic anhydride, *see* Carbon dioxide
Carbonyl chloride, *see* Phosgene
Caustic potash, *see* Potassium hydroxide
Caustic soda, *see* Sodium hydroxide
Cellulose, *see* Cellulose acetate
Cellulose acetate, *also* Cellulose, Cellulose pentaacetate, Cellulose tetraacetate, Cellulose triacetate
Cellulose pentaacetate, $C_6H_5(OOCCH_3)_5$, *see* Cellulose acetate
Cellulose tetraacetate, $C_6H_6O(OOCCH_3)_4$, *see* Cellulose acetate
Cellulose triacetate, $C_6H_7O_2(OOCCH_3)_3$, *see* Cellulose acetate
Cesium hydrate, *see* Cesium hydroxide
Cesium hydroxide, CsOH, *also* Cesium hydrate
Chile saltpeter, *see* Sodium nitrate
Chlorides
Chlorinated lime, *see* Calcium hypochlorite
Chlorine, Cl
Chlorine dioxide, ClO_2
Chlorine water
Chloroacetic acid, $CH_2ClCOOH$, *also* Monochloroacetic acid
Chloroazoatic acid, *see* Aqua regia
Chloroethane, *see* Ethyl chloride
Chloroform, CCl_3, *also* Trichloromethane, Formyl trichloride, Methenyl trichloride
Chloroformyl chloride, *see* Phosgene
Chloromagnesite, *see* Magnesium chloride
Chlorosulfonic acid, $ClSO_3H$, *also* Chlorosulfuric acid, Sulfuric chlorohydrin
Chlorosulfuric acid, *see* Chlorosulfonic acid
Chromic acid, H_2CrO_4
Citric acid, $(COOH)CH_2C(OH)(COOH)CH_2COOH$, *also* 2-hydroxy-1,2,3-propane tricarboxylic acid
Coal naptha, *see* Benzene
Common salt, *see* Sodium chlorida
Copals
Copper chloride, *see* Cupric chloride
Copper nitrate, *see* Cupric nitrate
Copper sulfate, *see* Cupric sulfate
Cresol, $CH_2C_6H_4OH$, *also* Cresylic acid, Methyl phenol, Cresylol, Tricresol
Cresylic acid, *see* Cresol
Cresylol, *see* Cresol
Cupric chloride, $CuCl_2$, *also* Copper chloride
Cupric nitrate, $Cu(NO_3)_2 \cdot 3H_2O$, *also* Copper nitrate

Cupric sulfate, CuSO₄, *also* Hydrocyanite, Copper sulfate
Cyclohexatriene, *see* Benzene

D

Dextronic acid, *see* Gluconic acid
Dichloroacetic acid, CHCl₂COOH, *also* Dichloroethanoic acid
Dichloroethanoic acid, *see* Dichloroacetic acid
Digallic acid, *see* Tannic acid
Dihydric alcohol, *see* Ethylene glycol
Dimethyl ketone, *see* Acetone
d-2-camphanene, *see* Camphor

E

Elaine oil, *see* Oleic acid
Ethanal, *see* Acetaldehyde
Ethane dioic acid, *see* Oxalic acid
Ethanoic acid, *see* Acetic acid
Ethanoic anhydride, *see* Acetic anhydride
Ethanol, *see* Ethyl alcohol
Ether, (C₂H₅)₂, *also* Ethyl ether
Ethyl alcohol, CH₃CH₂OH, *also* Ethanol, Grain alcohol
Ethyl chloride, CH₃CH₂Cl, *also* Chloroethane, Hydrochloric ether, Muriatic ether
Ethyl ether, *see* Ether
Ethylene alcohol, *see* Ethylene glycol
Ethylene glycol, CH₂OHCH₂OH, *also* Glycol, Ethylene alcohol, Glycol alcohol, Dihydric alcohol

F

Fatty acids, CₙH₂ₙ∝₁COOH
Feldspar, *see* Calcium fluoride
Ferric chloride, FeCl₃
Ferric sulfate, Fe₂(SO₄)₃ · 9H₂O, *also* Iron sulfate Ferrisulpas, *see* Ferrous sulfate
Ferrous chloride, FeCl₂ · 4H₂O, *also* Iron chloride, Iron dichloride
Ferrous sulfate, FeSO₄ · 7H₂O, *also* Ferrisulpas, Green copperas, Green vitriol, Iron sulfate, Melanterite
Fluorine, F
Fluorite, *see* Calcium fluoride
Fluosilicic acid, H₂S₁F₆, *also* Hydrofluorosilic acid
Formaldehyde, HCHO, *also* Methanol, Formol, Methylene oxide
Formic acid, HCOOH, *also* Methanoic acid
Formol, *see* Formaldehyde
Formonitrile, *see* Hydrogen cyanide
Formosa camphor, *see* Camphor
Formyl trichloride, *see* Chloroform
Fraude's reagent, *see* Perchloric acid

G

Gallotannin, *see* Tannic acid
Gelatin, *also* Glutin
Gluconic acid, C₅H₆(OH)₅COOH, *also* Dextronic acid
Glutin, *see* Gelatin
Clycerin, *see* Glycerol
Glycerol, CH₂OHCHOHCH₂OH, *also* Glycerin, Glycyl alcohol
Glycol, *see* Ethylene glycol
Glycol alcohol, *see* Ethylene glycol
Glycolic acid, CH₂OHCOOH, *also* Hydroxacetic acid
Glycyl alcohol, *see* Glycerol
Grain alcohol, *see* Ethyl alcohol
Green copperas, *see* Ferrous sulfate

Green vitriol, *see* Ferrous sulfate
Gum camphor, *see* Camphor

H

Halite, *see* Sodium chloride
Hexanedioic acid, *see* Adipic acid
Hexylacetic acid, *see* Caprylic acid
Hydrated aluminum, *see* Aluminum hydroxide
Hydrated aluminum oxide, *see* Aluminum hydroxide
Hydrated lime, *see* Calcium hydroxide
Hydrobromic acid, HBr
Hydrochloric acid, HCl, *also* Muriatic acid
Hydrochloric ether, *see* Ethyl chloride
Hydrocyanic acid, *see* Hydrogen cyanide
Hydrocyanite, *see* Cupric sulfate
Hydrofluoric acid, *also* Anhydrous hydrogen fluoride, Aqueous hydrogen fluoride
Hydrofluorosilic acid, *see* Fluosilicic acid
Hydrogen, H₂
Hydrogen chloride, HCl
Hydrogen cyanide, HCN, *also* Hydrocyanic acid, Prussic acid, Formonitrile
Hydrogen disulfide, *see* Hydrogen sulfide
Hydrogen peroxide, H₂O₂
Hydrogen sulfide, H₂S, *also* Hydrogen disulfide Hydroiodic acid, HI
Hydroxacetic acid, *see* Glycolic acid
Hydroxysuccinic acid, *see* Malic acid
Hypo, *see* Sodium thiosulfate
Hypochlorites
Hypochlorous acid, HOCl

I

Iodine, I
Iron chloride, *see* Ferrous chloride
Iron dichloride, *see* Ferrous chloride
Iron sulfate, *see* Ferric sulfate, Ferrous sulfate

J

Japan camphor, *see* Camphor

L

Lactic acid, CH₃CHOHCOOH, *also* 2-hydroxy propanoic acid
Laurel camphor, *see* Camphor
Liquid glass, *see* Sodium silicate
Liquid metals, *also* Mercury
Lithium chloride, LiCl
Lye, *see* Potassium hydroxide, Sodium hydroxide

M

Magnesium chloride, MgCl₂, *also* Chloromagnesite
Magnesium hydrate, *see* Magnesium hydroxide
Magnesium hydroxide, Mg(OH)₂, *also* Magnesium hydrate, Bucite
Maleic acid, HOOCCH:CHCOOH, *also* Maleinic acid, Toxilic acid
Maleinic acid, *see* Maleic acid
Malic acid, HOOCCH(OH)CH₂COOH, *also* Hydroxysuccinic acid
Melanterite, *see* Ferrous sulfate
Mercury, Hg, *see* Liquid metals
Methanoic acid, *see* Formic acid
Methanol, *see* Formaldehyde, Methanol
Methenyl trichloride, *see* Chloroform

Methylacetic acid, *see* Propionic acid
Methyl alcohol, CH$_3$OH, *also* Methanol, Wood alcohol
Methylene oxide, *see* Formaldehyde
Methyl-ethyl methane, *see* Butane
Methyl phenol, *see* Cresol
Monochloroacetic acid, *see* Chloroacetic acid
Muriatic acid, *see* Hydrochloric acid
Muriatic ether, *see* Ethyl chloride

N

Nickel chloride, NiCl$_2$
Nitric acid, HNO$_3$
Nitric oxide, NO, *also* Nitrogen oxide, Nitrogen monoxide
Nitric tetraoxide, N$_2$O$_4$, *also* Nitrogen peroxide, Nitrogen dioxide
Nitrogen, N$_2$
Nitrogen dioxide, NO$_2$, *see* Nitric tetraoxide
Nitrogen oxide, *see* Nitric oxide
Nitrogen peroxide, *see* Nitric tetraoxide
Nitrohydrochloric acid, *see* Aqua regia
Nitrous acid, HNO$_2$
n-octanoic acid, *see* Caprylic acid

O

Octadecenoic acid, *see* Oleic acid
Octic acid, *see* Caprylic acid
Octylic acid, *see* Caprylic acid
Oleic acid, C$_{17}$H$_{33}$COOH, *also* Red oil, Elaine oil, Octadecenoic acid
Orthoboric acid, *see* Boric acid
Oxalic acid, HOOCCOOH · 2H$_2$O, *also* Ethane dioic acid
Oxygen, O$_2$
Ozone, O$_3$, *also* Activated oxygen

P

Perchloric acid, AClO$_4$, *also* Fraude's reagent
Perchloro methane, *see* Carbon tetrachloride
Petroleum oils
Phene, *see* Benzene
Phenol, C$_6$H$_5$OH, *also* Carbolic acid, Phenylic acid
Phenyl formic acid, *see* Benzoic acid
Phenyl hydride, *see* Benzene
Phenylic acid, *see* Phenol
Phosgene, COCl$_2$, *also* Carbonyl chloride, Chloroformyl chloride
Phosphoric acid
Phosphorus, P
Potassium bromide, KBr
Potassium chloride, KCl
Potassium fluoride, K
Potassium hydrate, *see* Potassium hydroxide
Potassium hydroxide, KOH, *also* Caustic potash, Lye, Potassium hydrate
Potassium iodide, KI
Potassium rhodanide, *see* Potassium thiocyanate
Potassium sulfate, K$_2$SO$_4$, *also* Salt of Lemery, Arcanite
Potassium sulfocyanate, *see* Potassium thiocyanate
Potassium thiocyanate, KSCN, *also* Potassium sulfocyanate, Potassium rhodanide
Propanoic acid, *see* Propionic acid
Propionic acid, CH$_2$CH$_2$CCOH, *also* Propanoic acid, Methylacetic acid
Prussic acid, *see* Hydrogen cyanide
Pyridine, C$_5$H$_5$N

R

Red oil, *see* Oleic acid

S

Salmiai, *see* Ammonium chloride
Salt cake, *see* Sodium sulfate
Salt of Lemery, *see* Potassium sulfate
Sassolite, *see* Boric acid
Seawater
Slaked lime, *see* Calcium hydroxide
Soda, *see* Sodium carbonate
Soda ash, *see* Sodium carbonate
Soda niter, *see* Sodium nitrate
Sodium, Na
Sodium acid carbonate, *see* Sodium bicarbonate
Sodium bicarbonate, NaHCO$_2$, *also* Sodium acid carbonate, Baking soda
Sodium borate, Na$_2$B$_4$O$_7$ · 10H$_2$O, *also* Sodium tetraborate, Sodium pyroborate
Sodium bromide, NaBr
Sodium carbonate, NaCO$_3$, *also* Soda, Soda ash
Sodium chloride, NaCl, *also* Common salt, Halite
Sodium fluoride, NaF, *also* Villiaumite
Sodium hydrate, *see* Sodium hydroxide
Sodium hydroxide, NaOH, *also* Caustic soda, Sodium hydrate, Lye
Sodium hypochlorite, NaOCl Sodium hyposulfite, *see* Sodium thiosulfate Sodium metasilicate, *see* Sodium silicate
Sodium nitrate, NaNO$_3$, *also* Soda niter, Chile saltpeter
Sodium nitrite, NaNO$_2$
Sodium perchlorate, NaClO$_4$
Sodium peroxide, Na$_2$O$_2$
Sodium pyroborate, *see* Sodium borate
Silicate of soda, *see* Sodium silicate
Sodium silicate, Na$_2$SiO$_3$, *also* Liquid glass, Silicate of soda, Sodium metasilicate, Soluble glass
Sodium subsulfite, *see* Sodium thiosulfate
Sodium sulfate, Na$_2$SO$_4$, *also* Thenardite, Salt cake
Sodium sulfide, Na$_2$S, *also* Sodium sulfuret
Sodium sulfite, Na$_2$SO$_3$
Sodium sulfuret, *see* Sodium sulfide
Sodium tetraborate, *see* Sodium borate
Sodium thiosulfate, NA$_2$S$_2$O$_3$ · SH$_2$O, *also* Sodium hyposulfite, Hypo, Sodium subsulfite
Soluble glass, *see* Sodium silicate
Steam
Stearic acid
Succinic acid, COOH(CH$_2$)$_2$COOH, *also* Butanedioic acid, Butane diacid, Amber acid
Sulfur
Sulfur dioxide
Sulfur trioxide
Sulfuric acid, H$_2$SO$_4$
Sulfuric chlorohydrin, *see* Chlorosulfonic acid Sulfurous acid, H$_2$SO$_3$

T

Tannic acid, C$_{14}$H$_{10}$O$_9$, *also* Digallic acid, Tannin, Gallotannin
Tannin, *see* Tannic acid
Tartaric acid, HCOC(CHCH)$_2$COCH
Tetrachloromethane, *see* Carbon tetrachloride
Thenardite, *see* Sodium sulfate
Toxilic acid, *see* Maleic acid
Trichlorethylene, CHCl:CCl$_2$

Trichloroacetic acid, CCl_3COOH
Trichloromethane, *see* Chloroform
Tricresol, *see* Cresol
2-hydroxy propanoic acid, *see* Lactic acid
2-hydroxy-1,2,3-propane tricarboxylic acid, *see* Citric acid
2-propanone, *see* Acetone

U

Urea, NH_2CONH_2, *also* Carbamide

V

Villiaumite, *see* Sodium fluoride
Vinegar acid, *see* Acetic acid

W

Water, H_2O
Witherite, *see* Barium carbonate
Wood alcohol, *see* Methyl alcohol

Chemical Listing

A

AClo$_4$ Perchloric acid, Fraude's reagent
ANF, Anhydrous hydrogen fluoride, Hydrofluoric acid
AlCl$_3$, Al$_2$Cl$_6$ Aluminum chloride
AlF$_3$· 3 1/2H$_2$O Aluminum fluoride
Al(OH)$_3$ Aluminum hydroxide, Aluminum trihydroxide, Aluminum trihydrate, Hydrated aluminum, Hydrated aluminum oxide

B

BaCl$_2$ Barium chloride
BaCo$_3$ Barium carbonate, Witherite
Ba(OH)$_2$8H$_2$O Barium hydroxide
Br Bromine

C

C Carbon
CCl$_3$ Chloroform, Trichloromethane, Formyl trichloride, Methenyl trichloride
CCl$_3$COOH Trichloroacetic acid
CCl$_4$ Carbon tetrachloride, Tetrachloromethane, Perchloro methane, Benzinoform
(C$_2$H$_5$)$_2$ Ether, Ethyl ether
C$_5$H$_5$N Pyridine
C$_5$H$_6$(OH)$_5$COOH Gluconic acid, Dextronic acid
C$_6$H$_5$COOH Benzoic acid, Benzene carboxylic acid, Phenyl formic acid
C$_6$H$_5$OH Phenol, Carbolic acid, Phenylic acid
C$_6$H$_5$(OOCCH$_3$)$_5$ Cellulose pentaacetate, Celulose acetate
C$_6$H$_6$ Benzene, Benzol, Phenyl hydride, Phene, Coal naptha, Cyclohexatriene
C$_6$H$_6$O(OOCCH$_3$)$_4$ Celulose tetraacetate, Cellulose acetate
C$_6$H$_7$O$_2$(OOCCH$_3$)$_3$ Cellulose triacetate, Cellulose acetate
C$_{10}$H$_{16}$O Camphor, d-2-camphanone, Japan camphor, Laurel camphor, Formosa camphor, Gum camphor
C$_{14}$H$_{10}$O$_9$ Tannic acid, Digallic acid, Tannin, Gallotannin
C$_{17}$H$_{33}$COOH Oleic acid, Red oil, Elaine oil, Octadecenoic acid
C$_{17}$H$_{33}$COONa Sodium oleate
C$_n$H$_{2n}$$\propto_1$COOH Fatty acids
CH$_2$C$_6$H$_4$OH Cresol, Cresylic acid, Methyl phenol, Cresylol, Tricresol
CH$_2$CH$_2$CCOH Propionic acid, Propanoic acid, Methylacetic acid
CH$_2$ClCOOH Chloroacetic acid, Monochloroacetic acid
CH$_2$OHCH$_2$OH Ethylene glycol, Glycol, Ethylene alcohol, Glycol alcohol, Dihydric alcohol
CH$_2$OHCHOHCH$_2$OH Glycerol, Glycerin, Glycyl alcohol
CH$_2$OHCOOH Glycolic acid, Hydroxacetic acid
CH$_3$CH$_2$Cl Ethyl chloride, Chloroethane, Hydrochloric ether, Muriatic ether
CH$_3$CH$_2$OH Ethyl alcohol, Ethanol, Grain alcohol
CH$_3$(CH$_2$)$_2$CH$_3$ Butane, n-butane
CH$_3$(CH$_2$)$_6$COOH Caprylic acid, Hexylaceic acid, n-octanoic acid, Octylic acid, Octic acid
CH$_3$CHO, Acetaldehyde, Ethanal, Acetic aldehyde
CH$_3$CHOHCOOH Lactic acid, 2-hydroxy propanoic acid
(CH$_3$CO)$_2$O Acetic anhydride, Ethanoric anhydride
CH$_3$COOH, Acetic acid, Ethanoic acid, Vinegar acid
CH$_3$COOH$_3$ Acetone, 2-propanone, Dimethyl ketone
CH$_3$OH Methyl alcohol, Methanol, Wood alcohol
CHCl:CCl$_2$ Trichlorethylene
CHCl$_2$COOH Cichloroacetic acid, Dichloroethanoic acid

CO$_2$ Carbon dioxide, Carbonic anhydride, Carbonic acid gas
COCl$_2$ Phosgene, Carbonyl chloride, Chloroformyl chloride
(COOH)CH$_2$C(OH)(COOH)CH$_2$COOH Citric acid, 2-hydroxy-1,2,3-propane tricarboxylic acid
COOH(CH$_2$)$_2$COOH Succinic acid, Butanedioic acid, Butane diacid, Amber acid
CS$_2$ Carbon bisulfide, Carbon disulfide
CaBr$_2$ Calcium bromide
CaCl$_2$ Calcium chloride
CaF$_2$ Calcium fluoride, Fluorite, Feldspar
Ca(OCl)$_2$ · 4H$_2$O Calcium hypochlorite, Calcium oxychloride, Chlorinated lime, Bleach
Ca(OH)$_2$ Calcium hydroxide, Calcium hydrate, Hydrated lime, Slaked lime
CdSO$_4$ Cadmium sulfate
Cl, Chlorine
ClO$_2$ Chlorine dioxide
ClSO$_3$H Chlorosulfonic acid, Chlorosulfuric acid, Sulfuric chlorohydrin
CsOH Cesium hydroxide, Cesium hydrate
CuCl$_2$ Cupric chloride, Copper Chloride
Cu(NO$_3$)$_2$ · 3H$_2$O Cupric nitrate, Copper nitrate
CuSO$_4$ Cupric sulfate, Hydrocyanite, Copper sulfate

F

F Fluorine
FeCl$_2$ · 4H$_2$O, Ferrous chloride, Iron chloride, Iron dichloride
FeCl$_3$ Ferric chloride
FeSO$_4$ · 7H$_2$O Ferrous suflate, Ferrisulpas, Green copperas, Green vitriol, Iron sulfate, Melanterite
Fe$_2$(SO$_4$)$_3$ · 9H$_2$O Ferric sulfate, Iron sulfate

H

H$_2$ Hydrogen
H$_2$CO$_2$ Carbonic acid
H$_2$CrO$_4$ Chromic acid
H$_2$O Water
H$_2$O$_2$ Hydrogen peroxide
H$_2$S Hydrogen sulfide, Hydrogen disulfide
H$_2$S$_1$F$_6$ Fluosilicic acid, Hydrofluorosilic acid
H$_2$SO$_3$ Sulfurous acid
H$_2$SO$_4$ Sulfuric acid
H$_3$BO$_3$ Boric acid, Boracid acid, Orthoboric acid, Sassolite
HBr Hydrobromic acid
HCl Hydrochloric acid, Muriatic acid, Hydrogen chloride
HCHO Formaldehyde, Methanol, Formol, Methylene oxide
HCN Hydrogen cyanide, Hydrocyanic acid, Prussic acid, Formonitrile
HCOC(CHCH)$_2$COCH Tartaric acid
HCOOH Formic acid, Methanoic acid
HF Aqueous hydrogen, Hydrofluoric acid
HI Hydroiodic acid
HNO$_2$ Nitrous acid
HNO$_3$ Nitric acid
HOCl Hypochlorous acid
HOCC(CH$_2$)$_4$COOH Adipic acid, Hexaneodioic acid
HOOCCH:CHCOOH Maleic acid, Maleinic acid, Toxilic acid
HOOCCH(OH)CH$_2$COOH Malic acid, Hydroxysuccinic acid
HOOCCOOH · 2H$_2$O Oxalic acid, Ethane dioic acid
Hg Mercury

I

I Iodine

K

K Potassium fluoride
KBr Potassium bromide
KCl Potassium chloride
KI Potassium iodide
KOH Potassium hydroxide, Caustic potash, Lye, Potassium hydrate
KSCN Potassium thiocyanate, Potassium sulfocyanate, Potassium rhodanide
K_2SO_4 Potassium sulfate, Salt of Lemery, Arcanite

L

LiCl Lithium chloride

M

$MgCl_2$ Magnesium chloride, Chloromagnesite
$Mg(OH)_2$ Magnesium hydroxide, Magnesium hydrate, Bucite

N

N_2 Nitrogen
N_2O_4 Nitric tetraoxide, Nitrogen peroxide, Nitrogen dioxide
NH_2CONH_2 Urea, Carbamide
NH_3 Anhydrous ammonia
NH_4Cl Ammonium chloride, Ammoniae, Salmiai, Ammonium nituriate
NH_4F Ammonium fluoride
$NH_4H_2PO_4$ $(NH_4)_2HPO_4$, Ammonium phosphate
NH_4NO_3 Ammonium nitrate
NH_4OH Ammonium hydroxide
$(NH_4)_2CO_3$ Ammonium carbonate
$(NH_4)_2S$, Ammonium sulfide

$(NH_4)_2SO_4$ Ammonium sulfate
NO Nitric oxide, Nitrogen oxide, Nitrogen monoxide
NO_2 Nitrogen dioxide, Nitric tetraoxide
Na Sodium
NaBr Sodium bromide
NaCl Sodium Chloride, Common salt, Halite
$NaCO_3$ Sodium carbonate, Soda, Soda ash
$NaClO_4$ Sodium perchlorate
NaF Sodium fluoride, Villiaumite
$NaHCO_2$ Sodium bicarbonate, Sodium acid carbonate, Baking soda
$NaNO_2$ Sodium nitrite
$NaNO_3$ Sodium nitrate, Soda niter, Chile saltpeter
NaOCl Sodium hypochlorite
NaOH Sodium hydroxide, Caustic soda, Sodium hydrate, Lye
$Na_2B_4O_7 \cdot 10H_2O$ Sodium borate, Sodium tetraborate, Sodium pyroborate
Na_2S Sodium sulfide, Sodium sulfuret
Na_2O_2 Sodium peroxide
$Na_2S_2O_3 \cdot 5H_2O$ Sodium thiosulfate, Sodium hyposulfite, Hypo, Sodium subsulfite
Na_2SO_3 Sodium sulfite
Na_2SO_4 Sodium sulfate, Thenardite, Salt cake
Na_2SiO_3 Sodium silicate, Liquid glass, Silicate of soda, Sodium metasilicate, Soluble glass
$NiCl_2$ Nickel chloride

O

O_2 Oxygen
O_3 Ozone

P

P Phosphorus

Obtaining Full Text Documents
of the References in This Handbook

The ASM Library has the full text documents of nearly all of the references that appear in the Additional Reading sections of this Handbook. Standard exceptions are patents, NTIS reports, news briefs, and press releases.

The library provides paper copies of all documents except complete books. Copies can be ordered via telephone, telefax, letter, telex, interlibrary loan form, or vendor dial order service. When ordering a document, please refer to the MetAbs number that appears in the reference. Photocopy orders are usually filled within 24 hours of receipt.

Non-reference books may be borrowed for one month only through interlibrary loan, available from your organizational library or your public library.

Reply to:

ASM INTERNATIONAL
Route 87
Materials Park, OH 44073 USA
Telephone (216) 338-5151
Telex 980-619
Facsimile (216) 338-4634

The Institute of Metals
1 Carlton House Terrace
London SW1Y 5DB UK
Telephone 01-839-4071
Telex 881 4813
Facsimile 01-839-2289

Conversion Rates

Relationships among some of the units commonly used for corrosion rates

d is metal density in grams per cubic centimeter (g/cm^3)

Unit	mdd	g/m²/d	μm/yr	mm/yr	mils/yr	in./yr
Milligrams per square decimeter per day (mdd)..................	1	0.1	36.5/d	0.0365/d	1.144/d	0.00144/d
Grams per square meter per day (g/m²/d)................	10	1	365/d	0.365/d	14.4/d	0.0144/d
Microns per year (μm/yr)..........	0.0274d	0.00274d	1	0.001	0.0394	0.0000394
Millimeters per year (mm/yr).......	27.4d	2.74d	1000	1	39.4	0.0394
Mils per year (mils/yr)	0.696d	0.0696d	25.4	0.0254	1	0.001
Inches per year (in./yr)............	696d	69.6d	25 400	25.4	1000	1

Source: G. Wranglén, *An Introduction to Corrosion and Protection of Metals*, Chapman and Hall, 1985, p 238

Part I

Corrosion of Metals and Alloys

Corrosion Concepts

This section is not meant to be a detailed review of corrosion principles, rather it will briefly present corrosion terms that are common convention in the field of corrosion science and engineering. For details on corrosion principles the reader is directed to Fontana[1] and H.H. Uhlig[2].

Corrosion is an electrochemical process that results in the degradation of a metal or alloy. It is a coupled reaction between an anode and at least one cathode. Corrosion (oxidation) occurs at the anode while reduction occurs at the cathode. The various ways (forms) that corrosion manifests itself are myriad but can often be reduced to several basic types.

While certain corrosion terms such as pitting or crevice corrosion are generally recognized nomenclature, the organization of these forms into a general classification scheme has taken several approaches. The most widely accepted categorization of corrosion forms was provided by Fontana[1]. More recently Craig and Pohlman[3] have presented another categorization scheme to help emphasize certain important factors that contribute to a group of corrosion types.

Certainly more important than the categorization scheme, for the use of this book, is the considerable variety of terms used for types of corrosion. The use of so many terms in the literature to define one form of corrosion is the result of several factors. Among these are the complexity of corrosion mechanisms and the tendency for some investigators to invoke new names for established phenomenon simply because of a minor variation in the way corrosion is manifested. Probably the greatest variation comes in the areas of stress corrosion cracking/hydrogen damage. As our understanding of both these corrosion phenomena increases, the complexity also increases. Therefore, much of the corrosion community has lumped together these forms along with other mechanisms that entail cracking (i.e., corrosion fatigue and liquid metal embrittlement) into a more general term: environmentally induced or environmentally assisted cracking. However, certain aspects of stress corrosion cracking and hydrogen damage are quite different. Yet much confusion exists in the literature because some authors carelessly interchange the two. Therefore, it is incumbent on the reader of this book to be familiar with the specific types of corrosion that may be expected in a particular environment or for a certain alloy and the multitude of names by which they may be referenced. Rather than resort to a classification system, some of the more common forms of corrosion are defined below to assist the reader.

Uniform/General Corrosion: A form of attack that produced overall uniform wastage of the metal. Often associated with atmospheric corrosion and some high temperature oxidation or sulfidation attack.

Pitting Corrosion: A high localized attack of the metal creating pits of varying depth, width, and number. Pitting may often lead to complete perforation of the metal with little or no general corrosion of the surface.

Crevice Corrosion: Similar to pitting corrosion in its localized nature but associated with crevices. Stainless steels and some nickel-base alloys are particularly susceptible to this form of corrosion.

Intergranular Attack: The preferential corrosion of grain boundaries in a metal caused by prior thermal treatments and related to specific alloy chemistries.

Dealloying: The selective removal of one element (usually the least noble) from an alloy by the corrosive environment. Also referred to as selective leaching or dezincification, denickelification, etc. designating the element removed.

Corrosion Fatigue: The initiation and extension of cracks by the combined action of an alternating stress and a corrosive environment. The introduction of a corrosive environment often eliminates the fatigue limit of a ferrous alloy creating a finite life regardless of stress level.

Galvanic Corrosion: Accelerated corrosion of the least noble metal when coupled to one or more other metals. The more noble metals are protected from corrosion by this action.

Erosion-Corrosion: Many forms of flow assisted corrosion are often included in this term such as cavitation, impingement, and corrosion-erosion. All of these types of attack are the result of accelerated corrosion due to flow of solids, liquids or gases.

Stress Corrosion Cracking: The initiation and propagation of cracks by the combined action of a corrosive environment and a tensile stress. Generally, susceptibility to cracking increases with increasing temperature. Not every alloy cracks in every environment, however, the list of environment/alloy combinations that produce stress corrosion cracking is continually increasing.

Hydrogen Damage: There are numerous forms of damage associated with hydrogen which are contained under the collective term "hydrogen damage." For hydrogen embrittlement and hydrogen stress cracking, a tensile stress and hydrogen atoms are necessary to cause failure. However, contrary to stress corrosion cracking, susceptibility is greatest near room temperature. Other terms and forms are: hydrogen induced cracking, blistering, sulfide stress cracking, hydrogen stress corrosion cracking, hydriding, hydrogen attack. There are many others too numerous to mention.

Although these forms are presented in the context of aqueous corrosion, many of them are also operative at high temperature. High temperature corrosion by oxidation and sulfidation can take the form of uniform attack, pitting, or dealloying to name a few. It is of utmost importance the reader recognize the difference between high temperature corrosion (oxidation) and aqueous corrosion. The mechanisms are different and therefore, the correct alloy choice for resistance to one environment often is incorrect if applied to another.

For those not familiar with corrosion, it is important to recognize that most corrosion rates are reported as a time averaged weight loss (mils per year, millimeters per year, etc.) that implies a uniform corrosion rate. However, in actual fact, few metals and alloys corrode in a uniform manner rather, highly localized corrosion (pitting, crevice corrosion, etc.) is the rule. Therefore, the corrosion rates reported in this book and most other books are relative and for purposes of comparison between different alloys.

In simple terms, corrosion can be controlled by any of four methods: cathodic protection, coatings, inhibitors and/or alloy changes. While this reference only addresses the last of these, it is important to recognize that the other methods are often used in combination with alloys of lower corrosion resistance to retard or eliminate corrosion. Therefore, simply choosing the most corrosion resistant alloy may not be the most economical choice.

References:

1. M.G. Fontana, *Corrosion Engineering*, McGraw-Hill Book Co., New York, 1986.

2. H.H. Uhlig and R.W. Revie, *Corrosion and Corrosion Control*, J. Wiley and Sons, New York, 1985.

3. *Metals Handbook*, Vol 13, 9th ed., Corrosion, ASM International, Metals Park, OH, 1987, p 79.

Pure Iron

The general corrosion behavior of pure iron is not unlike many other pure metals; that is, in many instances, pure iron has substantially greater corrosion resistance than many of its alloys, including mild steels and unalloyed cast irons. At the same time, pure iron has little or no resistance against attack by such aggressive chemicals as the stronger acids.

Corrosion in Atmospheres

Irons of high purity show a remarkably high resistance to corrosion. They sometimes remain untarnished in laboratory atmospheres for months or even years. Also, pure iron shows a higher resistance to rusting in rural atmospheres as contrasted with its behavior with mild steel. However, in industrial and/or saline atmospheres, uncoated pure iron has very poor resistance to corrosion—perhaps little, if any, more than mild

steels. Therefore, any form of iron that is relatively pure—such as wrought iron—should be coated to ensure acceptable life in most atmospheres.

Corrosion in Aqueous Solutions

Under some conditions, pure iron does show unusually good corrosion performance in various types of waters. The degree of resistance is largely governed by two major factors: oxygen content and the pH level of the water. When the oxygen content of the water is exceptionally low (almost none) and when the pH value is above 5, the corrosion rate is almost nil. However, when the pH values are under 4 to 5, there is a rapid increase in corrosion rate, especially at higher oxygen levels.

Like many other metals, pure iron resists corrosion caused by aqueous solutions much better when the surface is completely and continuously immersed, as occurs in pipes and tanks.

Cast Irons

Cast irons are primarily alloys of iron that contain more than 2% carbon and 1% or more silicon. With proper alloying, the corrosion resistance of cast irons can be greatly improved. Thus, this group of materials finds wide application in corrosion-inducing environments. Such service conditions include water, soils, acids, alkalis, saline solutions, organic compounds, sulfur compounds, and liquid metals. Table 1 gives the chemical resistance of cast iron to various materials.

The generally used alloying elements that enhance corrosion resistance include silicon, nickel, chromium, copper, and molybdenum. Less frequently, titanium and vanadium are also used.

Silicon

Silicon is not considered an alloying element in cast iron until it exceeds a level of 3%. Between 3 and 14%, there is some increment of corrosion resistance. Above the 14%, silicon causes the corrosion resistance factor to increase dramatically,

Table 1 Chemical Resistance of Cast Iron to Various Materials

This table was compiled from data supplied by material manufacturers. Their nomenclature was condensed into key symbols: A, acceptable—excellent resistance, fully resistant, suitable, recommended, excellent compatibility, fully compatible; Q, questionable—good resistance, minor effect, moderate effect, slight effect, slight attack, fair resistance; N, not recommended—severe effect, unsatisfactory, not acceptable, do not use. Temperature conditions are outlined in the footnotes.
Source: Oberdorfer Pump Division, Syracuse, NY

Material	Resistance rating	Material	Resistance rating	Material	Resistance rating
Acetaldehyde(a)	Q	Alcohol, diacetone	A	Butyraldehyde	A
Acetamide	N	Alcohol, ethyl	A	Calcium bisulfate	N
Acetate solvents	N	Alcohol, hexyl	A	Calcium chloride(a)	Q
Acetone(a)(c)	A	Alcohol, isobutyl	Q	Calcium hydroxide (10%)(c)	A
Acetylene(a)	A	Alcohol, isopropyl	Q	Calcium hypochlorite (2%)(a)	N
Acetylene tetrabromide	N	Alcohol, methyl	A	Calcium hypochlorite (20% on plastics)	N
Acid, acetic (50% unaerated)(a)	N	Alcohol, octyl	A	Calcium sulfate(a)	A
Acid, acetic (50% unaerated)(c)	N	Alcohol, propyl	Q	Calgon	N
Acid, acetic (100% unaerated)(a)	N	Aluminum chloride (5%)(a)	N	Cane sugar liquors	A
Acid, acetic (100% unaerated)(c)	N	Aluminum hydroxide (sat.)(a)	A	Carbon dioxide	N
Acid, acetic anhydride(a)	A	Aluminum oxide	N	Carbon disulfide	N
Acid, acetic anhydride(c)	A	Aluminum sulfate (sat.)(a)	N	Carbon monoxide	N
Acid, acetic, vapor	Q	Amines	N	Carbon tetrachloride	Q
Acid, arsenic(c)	N	Ammonia, anhydrous (liquid)(a)	A	Carbonated beverages	N
Acid, benzene sulfonic	N	Ammonia liquors	A	Castor oil	A
Acid, benzoic(a)	N	Ammonia nitrate	A	Catsup	N
Acid, boric(c)	N	Ammonium bicarbonate(b)	Q	Cellulube	A
Acid, butyric(a)	N	Ammonium bifluoride	N	Chlorinated lime	N
Acid, carbolic (phenol)(a)	N	Ammonium carbonate(a)(c)	A	Chlorine (anhydrous liquid)	Q
Acid, carbonic	N	Ammonium chloride (50%)(a)(c)	N	Chloroacetone	N
Acid, chloroacetic(a)	N	Ammonium hydroxide (10%)	A	Chlorobenzene(a)	N
Acid, chlorosulfonic	N	Ammonium hydroxide (46.5%)	A	Chlorobromomethane	N
Acid, chromic (5%)(a)	N	Ammonium nitrate(a)	A	Chlorobutadiene	N
Acid, chromic (10%)(c)	N	Ammonium oxalate(a)	N	Chloroform(a)	N
Acid, chromic (50%)(c)	N	Ammonium persulfate (a)	N	Chlorox (bleach)	N
Acid, citric (15%)(a)	N	Ammonium phosphate	Q	Chocolate syrup	N
Acid, citric (15%)(c)	N	Ammonium sulfate (sat.)(a)(c)	Q	Cider	N
Acid, citric (conc.)(c)	N	Ammonium thio-sulfate	N	Cinnamon oil	N
Acid, cresylic	Q	Amyl acetate	Q	Citric oils	N
Acids, fatty	N	Amyl alcohol	A	Clove oil	N
Acid, fluoroboric	N	Aniline (sat.)(a)	Q	Coconut oil	N
Acid, fluorosilicic	N	Aniline dyes	Q	Cod liver oil	A
Acid, formic(a)(b)	N	Aniline oil	A	Copper chloride	N
Acid, glacial acetic	N	Anise oil	N	Copper cyanide (sat.)(c)	N
Acid, hydrogromic(c)	N	Antifreeze, Dowgard	A	Copper sulfate (5%)(a)	N
Acid, hydrochloric (20%)(a)	N	Antifreeze, Hubbard-Hall	A	Copper sulfate (sat.)(c)	N
Acid, hydrochloric (37%)(a)	N	Antifreeze, Permaguard	A	Corn oil	A
Acid, hydrochloric (all)(b)	N	Antifreeze, Prestone	A	Cottonseed oil	A
Acid, hydrocyanic	N	Antifreeze, Pyro-Permanent	A	Cream	N
Acid, hydrofluoric (up to 50%)	N	Antifreeze, Pyro-Super	A	Creosols	Q
Acid, hydrofluoric (50–100%)	N	Antifreeze, Shell Zone	A	Creosote oil (coal tar)(b)	A
Acid, lactic (5%)(a)	N	Antifreeze, Texaco P.T.	A	Cutting oil (water-soluble)	A
Acid, lactic (5%)(b)	N	Antifreeze, Telar	A	Cutting oil (sulfur-base)	A
Acid, lactic (10%)(b)(c)	N	Antifreeze, Valvolene	A	Cyclohexane	A
Acid, nitric (conc.)(a)	N	Antifreeze, Zerex	A	Developing solutions (hypos)	N
Acid, nitric (fuming)(a)	N	Aromatic hydrocarbons	A	Dibenzyl ether	N
Acid, oleic (5%)(a)	N	Asphalt	A	Dibromochloropropane	N
Acid, oxalic (10%)(a)	Q	ASTM oils No. 1, No. 2, No. 3	A	Dibutyl ether	N
Acid, phosphoric (crude)	N	Automotive gasoline	A	Diesel fuel	A
Acid, phosphoric (1%)(a)	N	Aviation gasoline	A	De-ester synthetic lubricants	A
Acid, phosphoric (10%)(a)	N	Barbecue sauce	N	Diphenyl oxides	A
Acid, phosphoric (50%)	N	Barium chloride (sat.)(a)	Q	Distillery wort	Q
Acid, phosphoric (pure)	N	Barium hydroxide(a)	A	Ether compounds	Q
Acid, picric water solution	A	Barium nitrate(b)	A	Ethyl acetate	A
Acid, stearic (conc.)(c)	Q	Beef extract	N	Ethyl chloride	Q
Acid, sulfuric (5%)(a)	N	Beer	N	Ethyl ether	Q
Acid, sulfuric (5%)(c)	N	Beet sugar syrups	A	Ethylene chloride	Q
Acid, sulfuric (10%)	N	Benzaldehyde	A	Ethylene dichloride	A
Acid, sulfuric (30%)(a)	N	Benzene(a)	A	Ethylene glycol	A
Acid, sulfuric (30%)(c)	N	Benzine (gasoline)	A	Ethylene oxide	N
Acid, sulfuric (75%)	N	Benzol (benzene)(b)	A	Fatty acids	Q
Acid, sulfuric (conc.)(a)	N	Benzyl chloride	N	Ferric chloride	N
Acid, sulfuric (conc.)(c)	N	Borax	A	Ferric sulfate	N
Acid, sulfuric (fuming)(a)	N	Boron fuels	N	Ferrous chloride	N
Acid, sulfurous(b)	N	Brake fluid	A	Ferrous sulfate	N
Acid, tannic (10%)(a)(b)	Q	Brewery slop	A	Fish oil	N
Acid, tartaric(a)(b)	Q	Brine	N	Formaldehyde (Formaline)	Q
Acid, trichloroacetic(50%)	N	Butane	A	Freon 11	Q
Acrylonitrile	Q	Butanol (butyl alcohol)	A	Freon 12	A
Alcohol, amyl(a)	A	Butter	N	Freon 22	Q
Alcohol, benzyl	A	Buttermilk	N	Fruit juices	N
Alcohol, butyl(a)	N	Butyl acetate(a)	A	Furfural	A

Temperature conditions: (a) room ambient, to 100 °F; (b) medium temperature, 100–200 °F; (c) high temperature, >200 °F; if no temperature is listed, use room ambient.

(Continued)

Table 1 (continued)

Material	Resistance rating	Material	Resistance rating	Material	Resistance rating
Gasoline	A	Oil, coconut	A	Sodium bisulfite	N
Gelatin	N	Oil, corn	A	Sodium carbonate	Q
Ginger oil	N	Oil, cottonseed	A	Sodium chloride	A
Glucose	A	Oil, creosote	A	Sodium chromate	A
Glue	A	Oil, diester synthetic lubricating	A	Sodium cyanide	A
Glycerin (glycerol)	A	Oil, Dromus	A	Sodium hydroxide (15%)(a)	A
Gold monocyanide	N	Oil, hydraulic	A	Sodium hydroxide (20%)	A
Grapefruit oil	N	Oil, linseed	A	Sodium hydroxide (50%)(a)	Q
Grape juice	N	Oil, mineral(a)(b)	A	Sodium hypochlorite	N
Grease	A	Oil, olive	A	Sodium metaphosphate	N
Heptane	A	Oil, pale	A	Sodium nitrite	A
Hexane	A	Oil, palm	A	Sodium perborate	Q
Honey	A	Oil, peanut	A	Sodium peroxide(c)	N
Hydraulic fluids	A	Oil, Pella	A	Sodium phosphate mono	N
Hydrazine (water-base)	Q	Oil, pine	Q	Sodium phosphate DI	A
Hydrazine (alcohol-base)	Q	Oil, rapeseed	A	Sodium phosphate TRI	A
Hydrogen peroxide(a)	N	Oil, red	Q	Sodium polyphosphate	A
Hydrogen peroxide(10%)	N	Oil, Royal Triton	A	Sodium silicate	A
Hydrogen sulfide(a)	N	Oil, sesame seed	A	Sodium sulfate (conc.)(a)	A
Ink	N	Oil, Shell Dieselene	A	Sodium sulfide (sat.)(a)	A
Iodine	N	Oil, silicone	A	Sodium sulfite (5%)(a)	A
Isopropyl alcohol	A	Oil, soybean	A	Sodium thiosulfate	Q
Jet fuel (JP1–JP6)	A	Oil, sperm	A	Sodium tripolyphosphate	N
Kerosene	A	Oil, sulfur-base cutting	A	Sorghum	A
Kerosene & naphtha	A	Oil, turbine	A	Soybean oil	A
Lacquers	Q	Oil, vegetable	A	Soy sauce	N
Lard(a)	A	Oil, water-soluble cutting	A	Sperm oil	A
Larvacide	A	Paint (with xylene)	A	Stannic chloride(a)	N
Lime	A	Palm oil	A	Stannic fluoborate	N
Linseed oil	A	Peanut oil	A	Starch	Q
Lithium bromide	A	Perchloroethylene	A	Stoddard solvent	A
Lube oil SAE 10, 20, 30, etc.	A	Phenol (carbolic acid)	N	Sulfate liquors	N
Lubricating oils	A	Photographic developer	N	Sulfur-base cutting oil	A
Magnesium chloride (5%)(a)	N	Pine oil	Q	Sulfur chloride	N
Magnesium hydroxide(a)	A	Pipeline cleaner	A	Sulfur dioxide (dry)	A
Magnesium nitrate	N	Potassium bicarbonate	A	Tetrachloroethane	Q
Magnesium oxide	A	Potassium carbonate(a)	A	Tetraethyl lead	A
Magnesium sulfate (5%)(b)	A	Potassium chloride(a)	A	Thionyl chloride	N
Mayonnaise	N	Potassium chromate	A	Toluene	A
Malamine resins	N	Potassium cyanide	A	Toothpaste	N
Mercuric chloride	N	Potassium dichromate	A	Transformer oil	A
Mercury	A	Potassium hydroxide (5%)(b)	Q	Transmission fluid	A
Methanol	A	Potassium hydroxide (50%)(b)	Q	Trichloroethane	A
Methyl alcohol	A	Potassium hydroxide (50%)(c)	Q	Trichloroethylene	Q
Methyl chloride	A	Potassium permanganate	A	Trichloropane	A
Methylene bromide	A	Potassium phosphate	N	Trichloropropane	A
Methylene chloride	A	Potassium sulfate (5%)(a)	A	Turpentine	A
Milk	N	Potassium sulfate (5%)(b)	A	Urine	A
Mineral oil	A	Propane	A	Varnish	Q
Molasses	A	Propylene glycol	A	Vegetable juices	N
Multicircuit etch	N	Pyridine	A	Vegetable oil	Q
Mustard	N	Rapeseed oil	A	Vinegar(a)	Q
Naphtha	A	Salad dressing	N	Water, tap (to 180 °F)	Q
Naphthalene	A	Sesame seed oil	A	Water, boiling	Q
Nickel chloride(a)	N	Shellac	A	Water, distilled	N
Nickel sulfate(a)	N	Silica gel	A	Water, mine	Q
Nitro benzene	Q	Silicone X527	A	Water, salt(a)	N
Oil, aniline	A	Silver nitrate	N	Whiskey & wines	N
Oil, ASTM No. 1, No. 3	A	Soap solutions(a)	A	White liquor	Q
Oil, bone	A	Soda ash (sodium carbonate)(a)	A	Xylene	A
Oil, castor	A	Sodium arsenite	N	Zinc chloride(a)	N
Oil, Chevron	A	Sodium bicarbonate(b)	Q	Zinc hydrosulfite	N
Oil, citric	N	Sodium bisulfate	N	Zinc sulfate (sat.)	Q

Temperature conditions: (a) room ambient, to 100 °F; (b) medium temperature, 100–200 °F; (c) high temperature, >200 °F; if no temperature is listed, use room ambient.

but at the expense of strength and ductility. A level over 16% makes the alloy brittle and difficult to manufacture.

Alloying with silicon promotes the formation of strongly adherent surface films. However, considerable time may be required to establish these films fully on the castings. Initial corrosion rates may be relatively high for the first few hours, or even days, of exposure. Thereafter, a sharp decline typically occurs until an extremely low, steady-state rate develops. This lasts for the rest of the time the part is exposed to the corrosive environment.

Nickel

Nickel although commonly used to increase the strengthening and hardening qualities of cast irons, also increases corrosion resistance by the formation of protective oxide films on the surfaces of the castings. Up to 4% is added, in combination with chromium, to improve both corrosion resistance and strength. The resulting enhanced hardness improves erosion-corrosion resistance. Resistance to the effects of acids and alkalis is also improved. Generally, the addition of 12% nickel, or greater, is required to optimize the corrosion resistance level.

Chromium

Chromium may be added to cast irons either by itself or in combination with nickel and/or silicon to increase corrosion resistance. Small additions of chromium are used to refine graphite and matrix microstructures. These refinements improve corrosion resistance in seawater and weak acid environments. Chromium additions between 15 and 30% improve this factor against oxidizing acids such as nitric acid (HNO_3).

Additions of chromium to cast irons create the formation of a protective oxide on the surfaces of the castings. The oxides formed resist oxidizing acids, but they will be of little benefit under reducing conditions. As with silicon additions, higher additions of chromium reduce the ductility of cast iron.

Copper

Copper may be added to cast iron in special cases. Copper additions of 0.25 to 1% increase the resistance of cast iron to dilute acetic (CH_3COOOH), sulfuric (H_2SO_4), and hydrochloric (HCl) acids, as well as to acid mine water. Small additions of copper of up to 10% are made to some high-nickel/chromium cast irons to increase corrosion resistance.

Molybdenum

Molybdenum is added to cast irons to increase strength; however, it may also be added to increase corrosion resistance, particularly in high-silicon cast irons. The addition of molybdenum is particularly useful in HCl. As little as 1% is helpful in some high-silicon irons, but for optimum resistance, between 3 and 4% molybdenum is added.

Forms of Corrosion

Cast irons exhibit the same forms of corrosion as other metals and alloys. These include:

- Galvanic corrosion
- Crevice corrosion
- Pitting
- Intergranular corrosion
- Selective leaching
- Erosion-corrosion
- Stress-corrosion
- Corrosion fatigue
- Fretting corrosion

Coatings

Four general categories of coatings are used on cast irons to enhance corrosion resistance. These are metallic, organic, conversion, and enamel coatings. Coatings on cast irons are generally used to enhance the corrosion resistance of unalloyed and low-alloy cast irons. High-alloy cast irons are rarely coated.

Selection

When properly matched for the service environment for which they are intended, cast irons can provide excellent resistance to a wide range of corrosion environments. The basic parameters to consider before selecting an individual type are:

- Concentration of solution components
- Contaminants, even at ppm levels pH of solution
- Temperature range and rate of change
- Degree of aeration
- Percent and type of solids
- Continuous or intermittent operation
- Upset potential: maximum temperature and concentration
- Unusual conditions, such as high velocity and vacuum
- Materials currently used in the system and potential for galvanic corrosion

Carbon Steels

Carbon steel is the most widely used engineering material in the United States. For example, it accounted for approximately 88% of the tonnage in 1984 and 1985. Despite its relatively limited corrosion resistance, very large amounts of carbon steel are used in marine applications, nuclear and fossil fuel power plants, transportation, chemical processing, mining, construction, and metal-processing equipment. All of these areas present unique corrosion problems. Table 2 gives the corrosion resistance of carbon steel to various environments.

Two very valuable generalizations can be made concerning the corrosion of carbon steels. First, when solving a particular corrosion problem, a dramatic change in attack rate can often be achieved by altering the corrosive environment. For example, in the area of aqueous corrosion, deaeration of water and the addition of corrosion inhibitors effect significant changes. Second, when dealing with carbon steels, the alteration of design factors is a very effective means of minimizing corrosion. Both of these techniques are preferable to simply changing the grade of steel.

Definition

The term "carbon steel" is often loosely used and therefore may be misunderstood. It does not necessarily imply that the steel does not contain alloying elements, which it may. There are, however, sharp restrictions on the amounts of alloys that may be used in the material and still have it qualify as a carbon steel. By their nature, carbon steels have a very limited alloy content, usually less than 2 wt% of the total additions. Unfortunately, these levels of alloying additions do not produce any remarkable changes in general corrosion behavior.

For steel to be considered a carbon steel, it is generally agreed that one or more of the following conditions exists:

- No more than 1 wt% carbon can be included.

- No minimum content is specified or required for aluminum (except as related to deoxidation or grain-size control), chromium, cobalt, niobium, molybdenum, nickel, titanium, tungsten, vanadium, zirconium, or any other element added to obtain a desired alloying effect.

- The specified *minimum* copper content does not exceed 0.40 wt%.

- The *maximum* content specified for any of the following elements does not exceed 1.65% manganese, 0.06% silicon, or 0.60% copper.

Boron may be added to improve hardenability without changing the status of a carbon steel. In all carbon steels, small quantities of alloying elements—such as nickel, chromium, and molybdenum—are likely to be present. Their existence is unavoidable, because they are retained from raw materials used in melting. As a rule, these minor amounts have little or no effect on the end use of the material.

Table 2 Corrosion Resistance of Carbon Steel to Various Environments

E, excellent—virtually unattacked under all conditions; G, good—generally acceptable with a few limitations; S, satisfactory—suitable under many conditions, not recommended for the remainder (consult a steel manufacturer for details); P, poor—unsuitable under all conditions
Source: The Duriron Company, Inc., Dayton, OH

Environment	Resistance rating	Environment	Resistance rating	Environment	Resistance rating	Environment	Resistance rating
Acetate solvents	S	Carbon tetrachloride	S	Lead sulfide	P	Sodium bisulfate	P
Acetic acid, all strengths	P	Cellulose acetate	S	Lithophone	S	Sodium bisulfite	S
Acetic anhydride	P	Chloroacetic acid	P	Magnesium chloride	S	Sodium chlorate	P
Alum	P	Chlorinated water	P	Magnesium sulfate	S	Sodium chloride	S
Aluminum chloride	P	Chlorine dioxide	P	Maleic acid	S	Sodium ferricyanide	S
Aluminum sulfate & H_2SO_4	P	Chlorine gas, wet	P	Malic acid	P	Sodium hydroxide	S
Ammonium chloride	P	Chromic acid	P	Manganese chloride	S	Sodium hydroxide, fused	P
Ammonium fluoride	P	Citric acid	P	Mercuric chloride	P	Sodium hypochlorite	P
Ammonium hydroxide	P	Copper nitrate	P	Mercuric nitrate	P	Sodium nitrate	S
Ammonium nitrate	S	Copper silver nitrate	P	Mercuric sulfate	P	Sodium perchlorate	P
Ammonium phosphate	P	Copper sulfate	P	Mercurous sulfate	P	Sodium phosphate	G
Ammonium sulfate	S	Copper sulfate + 10% H_2SO_4	P	Metal plating solutions	P	Sodium sulfate	S
Ammonium sulfate & H_2SO_4	P	Cupric chloride	P	Mine water	P	Sodium sulfide	P
Aniline dyes	S	Cuprous chloride	P	Mixed acid	P	Sodium sulfite	P
Aniline hydrochloride	P	Ethylene dichloride	P	Nickel chloride	P	Sodium thiosulfate	P
Anodizing solutions	P	Fatty acids	S	Nickel ammonium sulfate	P	Stannic chloride	P
Antimony trichloride	P	Ferric chloride	P	Nitric acid, all strengths	P	Stannous chloride	P
Arsenic acid	P	Ferric ferro-cyanide	P	Nitric acid + 3–5% HF	P	Stearic acid	S
Barium chloride	S	Ferric nitrate	P	Nitrobenzene	S	Sulfite liquors	S
Barium nitrate	S	Ferric sulfate	P	Oleic acid	S	Sulfite liquors + H_2SO_4	P
Barium sulfate	S	Ferric sulfate + 10% H_2SO_4	P	Oleum	S	Sulfur	S
Benzoic acid	P	Ferrous sulfate	P	Oxalic acid	P	Sulfur chloride	P
Black liquor	P	Ferrous sulfate + 10% H_2SO_4	P	Phenol	S	Sulfur dioxide	S
Boric acid	P	Formaldehyde	P	Phosphoric acid + 2% H_2SO_4 1% HF	P	Sulfuric acid, sat. with SO_2	P
Brine, acid	P	Formic acid	P	Phosphoric acid, all strengths	P	Sulfuric acid, up to 100 °F	P
Brine, alkaline	G	Glycerin, crude	P	Picric acid	P	Sulfuric acid, 5% to boiling	P
Bromine, dry	P	HCL waste pickel liquor	P	Phthalic acid	P	Sulfuric acid, 60–100% 176 °F	P
Bromine, wet	P	Hydrochloric acid (<150 °F)	P	Potassium bisulfate	P	Sulfurous acid	P
Cadmium sulfate	P	Hydrochloric acid (>150 °F)	P	Potassium chloride	S	Sugar solutions	S
Calcium bisulfate	P	Hydrofluoric acid	P	Potassium hydroxide	S	Tannic acid	P
Calcium bisulfite & H_2SO_4	P	Hydrofluosilicic acid	P	Potassium iodide	S	Tar and ammonia	S
Calcium chloride	S	Hydrogen peroxide	S	Potassium nitrate	S	Tartaric acid	P
Calcium hydroxide (lime)	S	Hypochlorite bleach	P	Potassium sulfate	S	Titanic sulfate	P
Calcium hypochlorite	P	Iodine, dry	S	Pyridine sulfate	S	Toluene	S
Calcium phosphate	S	Lactic acid	P	Sea water	S	Zinc chloride	P
Carbon bisulfide	P	Lead acetate	P	Sodium bicarbonate	S	Zinc sulfate	P
Carbonic acid	P	Lead nitrate	P	Sodium bichromate	G		

Classification

Carbon steels are arbitrarily divided into three groups according to carbon content. The low-carbon group (commonly referred to as "mild" steels) contains 0.08 to 0.28% carbon. The "medium" group usually contains 0.28 to 0.55% carbon. The "high carbon" group contains 0.50 to 1.0% carbon.

Corrosion Service

As a rule, only the low-carbon (mild) steels are in any way considered for resistance to corrosion. They are generally more corrosion resistant than the medium- and high-carbon groups. More importantly, they are more amenable to welding and forming, a common requirement for building structures of a variety of types.

Without some sort of surface protection, carbon steels are hardly worth considering for resisting attack by very aggressive chemicals, simply because this kind of attack is so very rapid. However, carbon steel in vast quantities has been successfully used in conditions of severe atmospheric and water attack, much of it severe.

The two conditions necessary to initiate corrosion of low-carbon steel within natural environments are water and oxygen. After these essentials, there are a number of variables that affect the corrosion process. For example, samples of mild steels that are wholly immersed corrode faster if uninhibited water is moving around them than if the water is stagnant, but less rapidly where velocity is high if an inhibitor is present. Another of the many variables is the process called "cycling." Water pipes and tanks corrode much more slowly if the immersed surface remains completely submerged as opposed to alternating between submersion and partial or total exposure.

Carbon steels perform well in dry, rural atmospheres, but the rate of corrosion increases quickly in high-humidity saline or industrial atmospheres. The useful service life of carbon steels has been recorded for boiler service of up to 25 years where the conditions are controlled. It is thus obvious that stainless steels, copper-base alloys, and other highly corrosion-resistant alloys are not always required for many such applications.

Corrosive Environments. There are a number of major corrosive conditions into which carbon steels can be successfully introduced. These include:

- Atmospheric corrosion, including humidity, and both natural and man-made pollutants

- Soil corrosion, as determined by such factors as moisture content, level of electrical conductivity, acidity level, amount of dissolved salts, and aeration

- Corrosion in concrete, as caused primarily by chloride ions, and most successfully combated by cathodic protection

- Boiler service, which is a specialized form of aqueous corrosion that also involves elevated temperatures

- Liquid-metal corrosion, which may result in either dissolution and saturation of the liquid metal, or in the formation of intermetallic alloys of the steel with the liquid metal

Coatings (usually paint) can make carbon steels highly resistant to the most aggressive environments. Common examples include buildings, bridges, and ships. The types of coatings available range from oiling for low-cost, temporary protection to vapor deposition for long-term corrosion, heat, and wear resistance. For economic reasons, the desired degree of protection must be determined before a specific coating is selected.

Low-Alloy Steels

There is widespread inconsistency regarding the use of the term "alloy steel." The terms "low-alloy steel" and "alloy steel" are often used ambiguously. For the purposes of this Handbook, an alloy steel is defined as a steel containing significant quantities of alloying elements (other than carbon and the commonly accepted amounts of manganese, silicon, sulfur, and phosphorus added to effect changes in the mechanical or physical properties. The definition could, of course, include stainless steels and iron-base superalloys.

The American Iron and Steel Institute, in conjunction with the Society of Automotive Engineers, offers a more detailed and restrictive definition. A steel is considered to be an alloy steel when the maximum of the range given for the content of alloying elements exceeds one or more of the following limits:

(a) 1.65% manganese, (b) 0.60% silicon, and (c) 0.60% copper. It is considered an alloy steel when a definite minimum quantity of any of the following elements is specified or required within the limits of the recognized constructional alloy steels: aluminum, chromium, cobalt, molybdenum, nickel, niobium, titanium, tungsten, vanadium, zirconium, or any other element added to obtain a specific alloying effect. As a rule, the total amount of alloy in the AISI-SAE grades designated as "alloy steels" does not exceed approximately 4.0% over and above that permitted in carbon steels.

Classification

For the present purposes, steels have been divided into low-alloy steels, those steels with approximately 5% or less total alloying, and alloy steels, those steels with more than 5% alloying elements but not sufficient alloying to enter the stainless steel categories. Although this may not be a universally recognized categorization, it does emphasize the importance of low-alloy steels.

Corrosion Service

It is well recognized that the primary purpose of low-alloy steels is to achieve improved mechanical properties and fracture toughness than can be obtained with carbon steels. In general, the small amount of alloying in low-alloy steels is not sufficient to impart any appreciable corrosion resistance. That is, in fairly corrosive or aggressive environments, alloying up to 5% is not adequate to provide substantial corrosion resistance. However, in less severe environments, such as atmospheric corrosion, small additives of copper, phosphorus, chromium and nickel provide significant improvement in atmospheric corrosion resistance compared to carbon steel.

Copper is especially effective. Data have shown that the presence of no more than 0.6% copper greatly extends the service life of steels in industrial atmospheres. In marine atmospheres, where plain, low-carbon steel showed a weight loss of 43 mg/dm^2 in a specific period of time, steels with additions of 1.03% copper and 0.06% chromium reduced the rate to 17.3 mg/dm^2. Furthermore, for steels containing 1.19%

chromium and 0.46% copper, the corrosion rate dropped to 6.3 mg/dm2. It is obvious then that even relatively small amounts of alloying additions can prolong the service life of steel structures in atmospheric exposure.

In aqueous solutions, low-alloy steels behave essentially the same as carbon steels. Thus, their resistance to various forms of corrosion (i.e., pitting, crevice corrosion, etc.) is similar. However, low-alloy steels are frequently used at much higher strength levels than carbon steels, thus the commonly used phrase high-strength low-alloy steels (HSLA). These applications, by virtue of the need for higher strength, have a tendency to create a greater susceptibility of low-alloy steels to hydrogen damage (embrittlement) and stress-corrosion cracking. Likewise, the resistance to corrosion fatigue of high-strength low-alloy steels may be diminished in corrosive environments more so than carbon steels. This sensitivity to environmentally assisted cracking has produced a large number of papers dealing with this problem, and therefore, the literature is especially focused on this issue.

Besides the many standardized low-alloy steels (AISI, ASTM, etc.), there are numerous proprietary and special-purpose low-alloy steels in the marketplace that find wide application.

Alloy Steels

The term "alloy steels" describes those steels with more than 5% alloying elements, but less than the typical 11% chromium level that constitutes the beginning of the stainless steel family of alloys. Prominent among alloy steels are two systems: one that has increasing chromium contents from essentially 5 up to 9% Cr and the other that emphasizes nickel with a range of approximately 4 to 9% Ni. The former group is used primarily for increased resistance to oxidation at elevated temperatures. The latter group is commonly used for improved fracture toughness down to cryogenic temperatures.

Corrosion Service

Although both of these series (Cr and Ni) have been used in aqueous environments in several industries, they have met with

limited success. In fact, alloy steels are not typically considered for corrosion resistance. The limited corrosion resistance gained at the cost of alloying is not easily justified. Therefore, most designers and corrosion engineers prefer to use either low-alloy steels that are protected by coatings or inhibitors, or to significantly increase alloy content to achieve a stainless steel or iron-base superalloy that possesses inherent corrosion resistance. Because of the limited corrosion resistance of these alloys, the literature does not contain a great deal of information; likewise research activity on the corrosion resistance of these alloys is limited.

As with the low-alloy steels, there are numerous proprietary and special-purpose alloy steels that are similar to the standard chromium and nickel steels in their corrosion resistance.

Stainless Steels

Stainless steels are iron-base alloys containing at least 12% chromium. Maximum corrosion protection occurs, generally, with the highest chromium content, which may range up to about 30%. Corrosion resistance of stainless steels is a function

not only of composition, but also of heat treatment, surface condition, and fabrication procedures, all of which may change the thermodynamic activity of the surface and thus dramatically affect the corrosion resistance. Table 3 gives the relative corrosion resistance of AISI stainless steels.

Table 3 Relative Corrosion Resistance of AISI Stainless Steels

The "X" notations indicate that a specific stainless steel type may be considered as resistant to the corrosive environment categories.
Source: Steel Products Manual "Stainless and Heat Resisting Steels," American Iron and Steel Institute, Washington, DC, Dec 1974

Type No.	UNS No.	Mild atmospheric and fresh water	Atmospheric Industrial	Atmospheric Marine	Salt water	Chemical Mild	Chemical Oxidizing	Chemical Reducing
201	S20100	X	X	X		X	X	
202	S20200	X	X	X		X	X	
205	S20500	X	X	X		X	X	
301	S30100	X	X	X		X	X	
302	S30200	X	X	X		X	X	
302B	S30215	X	X	X		X	X	
303	S30300	X	X			X		
303 Se	S30323	X	X			X		
304	S30400	X	X			X		
304L	S30403	X	X	X		X	X	
	S30430	X	X	X		X	X	
304N	S30451	X	X	X		X	X	
305	S30500	X	X	X		X	X	
308	S30800	X	X	X		X	X	
309	S30900	X	X	X		X	X	
309S	S30908	X	X	X		X	X	
310	S31000	X	X	X		X	X	
310S	S31008	X	X	X		X	X	
314	S31400	X	X	X		X	X	
316	S31600	X	X	X		X	X	
316F	S31620	X	X	X	X	X	X	X
316L	S31603	X	X	X	X	X	X	X
316N	S31651	X	X	X	X	X	X	X
317	S31700	X	X	X	X	X	X	X
317L	S31703	X	X	X	X	X	X	X
321	S32100	X	X	X		X	X	
329	S32900	X	X	X		X	X	
330	N08330	X	X	X	X	X	X	X
347	S34700	X	X	X	X	X	X	X
348	S34800	X	X	X		X	X	
384	S38400	X	X	X		X	X	
403	S40300	X				X		
405	S40500	X				X		
409	S40900	X				X		
410	S41000	X				X		
414	S41400	X				X		
416	S41600	X				X		
416 Se	S41623	X						
420	S42000	X						
420F	S42020	X						
422	S42200	X						
429	S42900	X	X			X	X	
430	S43000	X	X			X	X	
430F	S43020	X	X			X		
430F Se	S43023	X	X			X		
431	S43100	X	X	X		X		
434	S43400	X	X	X		X	X	
436	S43600	X	X	X		X	X	
440A	S44002	X				X		
440B	S44003	X						
440C	S44004	X						
442	S44200	X	X			X	X	
446	S44600	X	X	X		X	X	
	S13800	X	X			X	X	
	S15500	X	X	X		X	X	
	S17400	X	X	X		X	X	
	S17700	X	X	X		X	X	

Stainless steels are used in a wide variety of corrosion-resistant applications. Resistance to tarnish has permitted architectural applications and automobile trim use. Stainless is used for its resistance to foodstuffs and is found in cutlery, flatware, pots and pans, and commercial food-handling equipment. The corrosion environment for the latter applications requires excellent resistance to pitting and crevice corrosion. Where resistance to stress-corrosion cracking may be required in heat-transfer applications, such as steam jacketing for cooking or processing vessels, stainless can be successfully applied.

Iron is not normally an inert element; in most atmospheric or aqueous conditions, iron will corrode. Stainless steels are effectively inert to "aqueous" corrosive environments by virtue of the passivity conveyed by the chromium in solution in iron. They are also very resistant to "dry" corrosion in oxidizing conditions.

Although marine environments can be severe, stainless steels often can provide good resistance. In fresh water, stainless steels have provided excellent service for such items as valve parts and fasteners, as well as pump shafts in water and wastewater treatment plants. Obviously, the precise type of stainless for each application will need to be determined from the many available. Many factors enter into the successful use of stainless steel in demanding corrosion conditions; water velocity, aeration, water purity, and temperature are several that must be considered. Stress-corrosion cracking, pitting, and crevice corrosion of stainless steels may be especially temperature sensitive.

Stainless steels have good applicability in mineral acids, but resistance depends on the concentration of the hydrogen ions and the oxidizing capacity of the acid, as well as the usual variables associated with composition and processing history. In general, application of stainless in chemical environments requires consideration of all forms of corrosion, along with impurity levels in the stainless and the impurity and degree of aeration of the environment. When an alloy with sufficient general corrosion resistance has been selected, care must be taken to ensure that the material will not fail by pitting or crevice corrosion or by stress-corrosion cracking.

Organic acids are generally less aggressive than mineral acids, but they can be corrosive to stainless, especially when impurities are present. The presence of oxidizing agents, in the absence of chlorides, can reduce corrosion rates. All stainless steels resist general corrosion by sodium hydroxide at temperatures below about 66 °C (150 °F). Stress-corrosion cracking of some stainless steels can occur at higher temperatures. Stainless steels also are highly resistant to most neutral or alkaline nonhalide salts. Halogen salts are more corrosive to stainless, because of the tendency to cause local film failure and pitting. Pitting is promoted in aerated or mildly acidic oxidizing solutions. Chlorides generally are more aggressive than the other halides in causing pitting.

At lower temperatures, most austenitic stainless steels resist chlorine or fluorine gas if the gas is completely dry. The presence of even small amounts of moisture results in accelerated attack, especially pitting or, possibly, stress-corrosion cracking. At higher temperatures, in air or in strong oxidizing environments, stainless is highly resistant to oxidation. However, increased attack can occur if sulfur vapor or sulfur compounds are present in the gas.

At high temperatures, in gaseous oxidation, stainless steels are protected principally by the chrome oxide film produced by interaction of oxygen with chromium in the substrate. At lower temperatures, the passivity of a stainless steel is explained through the formation of a protective film on the surface of the metal. This film will form naturally in oxidizing environments, but it will not reform if degraded in a reducing environment. Some stainless compositions are better suited for reducing environments than others. In general, the stainless steel behavior described below is associated with wrought alloy products. Stainless steel castings usually exhibit comparable corrosion resistance to their wrought counterparts and will not be discussed separately.

It is not necessary to chemically treat stainless steels to achieve passivity. The passive film forms spontaneously in the presence of oxygen. Most frequently, when steels are treated to improve passivity (passivation treatment), surface contaminants are removed by pickling to allow the passive film to reform in air, which it does almost immediately.

The principal alloying elements that affect the corrosion resistance of stainless are discussed below.

Chromium

The one element essential in forming the passive film or high-temperature, corrosion-resistant chrome oxide is chromium. Other elements can influence the effectiveness of chromium in forming or maintaining the film, but no other element can, by itself, create the stainless characteristics of stainless steel. The passive film is observed at about 10.5% chromium, but it affords only limited atmospheric protection at this point. As chromium content is increased, the corrosion protection increases. When the chromium level reaches the 25 to 30% level, the passivity of the protective film is very high, and the high-temperature oxidation resistance is maximized. Because high chromium content may produce problems in fabricability or alloy stability, it is better to enhance the corrosion resistance of stainless with additional alloying elements.

Nickel

In sufficient quantities, nickel is used to stabilize the austenitic form of iron and so produce austenitic stainless steels. A corrosion benefit is obtained as well, because nickel is effective in promoting repassivation, especially in reducing environments. Nickel is particularly useful in promoting increased resistance to mineral acids. When nickel is increased to about 8 to 10%—a level required to ensure austenitic structures in a stainless which has about 18% chromium-resistance to stress-corrosion cracking is decreased. However, when nickel is increased beyond that level, resistance to stress-corrosion cracking increases with increasing nickel content.

Manganese

An alternative austenite stabilizer is sometimes present in the form of manganese, which in combination with lower amounts of nickel than otherwise required will perform many of the same functions of nickel in solution. The effects of manganese on corrosion are not well documented; it is known that manganese combines with sulfur to form sulfides. The morphology and composition of these sulfides can have substantial effects on the corrosion resistance of stainless steels, especially their resistance to pitting corrosion.

Other Elements

Molybdenum in moderate amounts in combination with chromium is very effective in terms of stabilizing the passive film in the presence of chlorides. Molybdenum is especially effective in enhancing the resistance to pitting and crevice corrosion. Carbon does not seem to play an intrinsic role in the corrosion characteristics of stainless, but it has an important role by virtue of the tendency of carbide formation to cause matrix or grain boundary composition changes that may lead to reduced corrosion resistance. Nitrogen is beneficial to austenitic stainless in that it enhances pitting resistance, retards formation of sigma phase, and may help to reduce the segregation of chromium and molybdenum in duplex stainless steels.

Forms of Corrosion

The various forms of corrosion attack likely to be found in stainless steels are:

- General corrosion

- Galvanic corrosion

- Pitting corrosion

- Crevice corrosion

- Intergranular corrosion

- Stress-corrosion cracking

- Erosion-corrosion

Stainless steels are susceptible to several forms of localized corrosion attack such as intergranular, crevice, or pitting corrosion. The avoidance of this localized attack is the major effort in selecting a steel for a given application, assuming that strength and other properties are acceptable.

Improper heat treatment can produce detrimental results in stainless steels due to changes in the microstructure. The most troublesome problems are caused by carbide precipitation (sensitization) and by the precipitation of intermetallic phases such as sigma. Sensitization can occur when austenitic stainless steels are heated for a period of time in the range 425 to 870 °C (800 to 1600 °F). Time at temperature and the nature of the carbide precipitation greatly affects the corrosion performance. When the carbide precipitation is at the grain boundaries, the reduction in the local chromium content caused by the precipitation of chromium-rich carbides can affect the passivity of the grain boundary area. The effect is called sensitization. Subsequently, in sensitized alloys, dissolution of the low-chromium area or envelope surrounding each grain leads to intergranular corrosion. Sensitization also lowers resistance to other forms of corrosion such as pitting, crevice corrosion, and stress-corrosion cracking.

Sensitization is best avoided by minimizing the time spent in the critical temperature region, because longer times lead to greater degrees of sensitization. Alternate solutions, which generally are more costly, include reduction of carbon content to very low levels to preclude carbide precipitation, increasing the chromium content after carbide precipitation, or addition of strong carbide formers, most notably titanium or niobium, to tie up the carbon so that it will not form chromium carbides. The latter stainless steels are known as "stabilized" stainless.

It should be recognized that sensitization is not only confined to the intergranular corrosion produced in "aqueous" media.

Use of a sensitized stainless at elevated temperatures also may result in grain boundary attack (intergranular oxidation), which can seriously affect alloy performance.

If a steel should be sensitized, annealing is the only way to restore the inherent corrosion resistance of the material. Full dissolution of the chromium carbides at temperature is necessary so that the chromium may be homogeneously redistributed within the matrix where it acts to produce corrosion resistance. Controlled cooling will be needed to ensure that the stainless is not sensitized again on its return to room temperature. This latter point is important, because sensitization problems continue to occur in industry on a regular basis when proper cooling procedures are not followed during heat treatment or other processing operations such as welding.

Sigma phase can form by precipitation during heat treatment or during service exposure. Its formation can render stainless steels susceptible to intergranular corrosion. It generally occurs in higher alloyed stainless steels and forms most rapidly at temperatures of about 650 to 925 °C (1200 to 1700 °F). Time spent in this temperature region can be critical to the formation of sigma phase. As in the case of sensitization, the detrimental effects of sigma phase formation may be negated by annealing. Although limited information is available on other phase precipitation, it should be clear that any precipitate that extracts important corrosion-resisting elements from solution (or produces a phase that is more anodic or cathodic to the matrix) has the potential to reduce the corrosion resistance of a stainless steel.

Duplex stainless steels, so called because of their combined ferritic/austenitic microstructure, are finding wide use in many industries. First-generation duplex stainless steels (AISI 329) were prone to the segregation of chromium and molybdenum between the ferrite and austenitic phases on solidification after welding, often with significant degradation of the corrosion resistance of the alloy. The addition of nitrogen to such steels has resulted in better phase composition balance and minimal chromium and molybdenum segregation during welding. The newer duplex grades, therefore, have high corrosion resistance and good resistance to stress-corrosion cracking.

Ferritic stainless steels are virtually immune to stress-corrosion cracking. However, stress-corrosion cracking has been observed in all categories of stainless steels. The stress-corrosion cracking behavior of stainless can be summarized as follows:

- An incubation period is needed before cracking occurs.

- Dissolved oxygen aggravates the conditions.

- Low pH solutions are more aggressive than high pH solutions.

- A minimum or threshold stress is required.

- Cracking may be transgranular or intergranular.

- Susceptibility to cracking is influenced by nickel.

- Cracking tendency increases with increasing yield strength and temperature.

Selection of Stainless Steels for Corrosion Resistance

The topic of selection of stainless steels for corrosion resistance is too extensive to be covered in these general comments. One point to remember is that stainless steels will cost more than copper-base alloys, yet they should cost less than nickel- or titanium-base alloys and thus may well be cost effective for a desired application.

Austenitic Stainless Steels

As a group, the austenitic stainless steels have greater corrosion resistance than the martensitic, ferritic, or precipitation-hardening groups. At the same time, there is a wide range of variations with respect to corrosion resistance among the austenitic types. For the sake of discussion, the austenitic alloys can be divided into four classes — A, B, C, and D. Although imprecise and somewhat arbitrary, this breakdown can serve as a guide for selection based on corrosion resistance.

Class A. AISI types 301, 302, 303, 303Se, 304, 304L, 304N, 321, 347, and 348 are all contained within class A. If minor modifications are acknowledged, each of the types in this group can be considered a so-called 18-8 stainless.

Within class A, there is no great difference in the general corrosion resistance of the individual types. Those that have a higher alloy content are slightly better than those with a lower alloy content. For example, type 304 is slightly superior to types 301 and 302, although types 304 and 304L were initially developed for fabricability. As a rule, the free-machining grade type 303 is the least corrosion resistant of the types just mentioned, and it is especially susceptible to pitting corrosion.

Types 321, 347, and 348 are carbide stabilized with titanium and/or niobium. Although their general corrosion resistance may be no higher than types 302 or 304, they are essentially immune to sensitization.

Class B. Only two AISI types are contained in class B—305 and 384. These have relatively high nickel contents (12.0 and 15.0) nominally and respectively. While they both have greater corrosion resistance than the 18-8 steels, they were actually designed for extra-deep drawing and cold heading operations, as allowed by the higher nickel content.

Class C. AISI types 302B, 308, 309, 309S, 310, 310S, and 314 make up the class C group within the austenitic stainless steels.

Type 302B is a modified 18-8 and has a silicon addition (2.5%) that increases oxidation resistance at elevated temperature.

Type 314 represents a higher alloy version (25-20) of an 18-8. It has a silicon addition that is more corrosion resisting, especially to sulfuric acid, than type 302B. It also has high resistance to scaling at elevated temperatures.

Types 308, 309, 309S, 310, and 310S are all higher in chromium and nickel, and they are commonly called 20-11 (308), 24-12 (309, 309S), and 25-20 (310-310S). They have a very high resistance to corrosion and oxidation at elevated temperature.

Class D. AISI types 316, 316L, 316F, 316N, 317, and 317L make up the class D grouping. The general corrosion resistance of the "316-317 family" is considered equal to type 310, although there are differences. The 316-317 types are far more resistant to certain specific types of corrosion, notably pitting.

Martensitic Stainless Steels

The AISI types that make up the martensitic stainless group are 403, 410, 414, 416, 416Se, 420, 420F, 431, 440A, 440B, 440C. All of the martensitic group, although they do meet the minimum corrosion-resistant requirement for a stainless steel, do not in fact rate as high as the ferritic or austenitic grades relative to this quality.

Types 403, 410, 416, and 416Se. Known as "turbine quality," type 403 is virtually identical to type 410, except that it is made from specially processed and rigorously inspected ingots, as required by steam turbine blades. Both types contain just enough chromium to maintain "stainlessness" (nominally 12.5%), but there are no significant amounts of other alloying elements.

Types 416 and 416Se are simply 410 with the addition of free-machining additives. Although offering improved machining characteristics, there is a sacrifice in corrosion resistance.

Types 414 and 431. These stainless steels provide better corrosion resistance than type 410, largely because they contain a nominal amount (2.0%) of nickel. These steels have been well known as 12-2 and 16-2, respectively. Type 431, with 16.0% chromium, ranks highest in the martensitic category with respect to corrosion resistance.

Types 420 and 420F. Despite a higher chromium content, type 420 does not have an appreciably higher corrosion resistance level than type 410. Type 420F is almost identical to type 420, except that there is an addition of sulfur to improve machinability. This results in a slight sacrifice of corrosion resistance.

Type 422. This is another "12-chrome" grade, but with additions to improve high-temperature strength, required by the common elevated service temperatures.

Types 440A, 440B, and 440C.

These are all high-carbon stainless steels and are sometimes called "stainless tool steels." These types have the highest chromium range of any of the martensitic types, yet their corrosion resistance levels are among the lowest because of their higher chromium content. There is a gradual decrease in corrosion resistance from the A to C subtypes. This is also due to the increase in carbon content.

Ferritic Stainless Steels

The AISI types that make up the ferritic stainless steel group are 405, 409, 429, 430, 430F, 430SeF, 434, 436, 442, and 446. As a group, the ferritic stainless steel AISI types do not closely approach the austenitic types with respect to corrosion resistance. There are, however, *some* ferritic types that may nearly equal the corrosion resistance levels of the austenitics in *some* environments, but these are exceptions. At the same time, all of the ferritic types meet the minimum requirements for a stainless steel, which is to say that they remain unattacked in an out-of-doors, unprotected, rural atmosphere.

Type 405. While meeting the minimum requirements for a stainless steel, type 405 is actually relatively low in its resistance to corrosion. The carbon level is 0.08% maximum, and it has a nominal chromium content of 12.5%. An addition of 0.10 to 0.30% aluminum (a powerful ferritizer) prevents the formation of any appreciable amount of austenite at any temperature. It is thus the ideal grade for welding. Because of its low cost and good dimensional stability, the alloy is used principally as a lining for pressure vessels.

Type 409. Of all the stainless steels, type 409 is generally considered to have the lowest degree of corrosion resistance. It contains very nearly the minimum amount of chromium to qualify as a stainless steel (10.5 to 11.75%) and is stabilized with titanium.

Type 429. A need for a higher degree of weldability than that provided by type 430 resulted in the development of type 429. Both alloys have the same carbon content; type 429, however, has a lower chromium content (14.0 to 16.0%). This carbon-chromium ratio allows type 429 to retain its ferritic status.

Types 430, 430F, 430FSe, 434, and 436. These three basic grades, plus the two modifications, represent the old and well-known 17-chrome stainless steel grade, which is the original type 430. Type 430 shows a high resistance against attack by practically all types of atmospheres and also by many types of chemicals, notably oxidizing acids. At times, type 430 replaces the more expensive 18-8 austenitic types.

Type 430F is a machinable grade of type 430. The additives contained in it do reduce the corrosion resistance of the basic type 430.

Type 434 has the same chromium content as type 430, but it also has a nominal 1.0% molybdenum content, which adds greatly to its resistance to certain types of corrosion, notably pitting corrosion.

Type 436 is essentially type 434, but it contains up to 0.70% niobium plus tantalum for carbide stabilization. It is, therefore, suited for elevated temperature applications as well as for room-temperature corrosion resistance.

Types 442 and 446. Frequently, types 442 and 446 are called "chrome-irons." They differ in composition only in chromium content 18.0 to 23.0% for type 442 and 23.0 to 27.0% for type 446. Neither is used to any great extent for corrosion resistance at room temperatures.

Their principal uses are in heat processing equipment where resistance to scaling is important, but strength and hardness are less so. Types 442 and 446 are capable of sustained operation at temperatures up to 980 °C (1800 °C) and 1095 °C (2000 °F), respectively, without experiencing destructive scaling.

Precipitation-Hardening Stainless Steels

There are six AISI types that make up the precipitation-hardening group of stainless steels. These are 630, 631, 632, 633, 634, and 660. There may be other compositions, but they are proprietary.

Accurate evaluation of the corrosion resistance of these types is difficult to summarize, partly because they differ widely in composition and in the formed microstructures. Most of the precipitation-hardening grades form semiaustenitic (duplex) structures. Some types, notably type 630, form a martensitic structure.

Corrosion Resistance. It is generally considered that the average corrosion resistance of the precipitation-hardening group approaches that of the 18-8 austenitic grades and that it is usually superior to the corrosion resistance of the martensitic and ferritic types.

Type 630. Copper is the principal hardening agent in type 630. Its corrosion resistance approaches that of types 302 and 304.

Type 631. In the heat treated condition, type 631 has a duplex structure. It has good corrosion resistance along with high strength.

Type 632. With the exception of an addition of molybdenum, type 632 is very much like type 630. There is an improvement in strength and resistance to pitting corrosion.

Type 633 is also a duplex-structure grade, but has a slightly higher alloy content than types 631 and 632. Thus, its corrosion resistance is better.

Type 634 is semiaustenitic (duplex), but it has an alloy content slightly less than type 633. It does, however, contain molybdenum, which promotes general corrosion resistance, specifically pitting corrosion.

Duplex Stainless Steels

The general corrosion resistance of the commercial duplex stainless steels varies according to the chromium, molybdenum, and nitrogen content. In most corrosive mediums the duplex steels are superior to types 304 and 316 steels. Type 7-Mo duplex steel shows a highly favorable rate of corrosion in boiling 65% nitric acid as contrasted with other stainless steels.

Therefore, 7-Mo is used in nitric acid cooling condensers. It is also resistant in reducing mineral-acid mixtures containing nitric acid. It is superior to type 306 in phosphoric acid environments, in stronger organic acids, and in sulfuric acid.

Pitting Corrosion. The resistance of duplex stainless steels to pitting corrosion is also superior to that of type 304 or 316 stainless steels. The higher alloyed duplex stainless steels containing 25% chromium and 3% molybdenum have good corrosion resistance in seawater and even in hot seawater.

Under certain conditions, duplex stainless steels are used in CO_2 piping systems, as well as in certain sour gas down hole tubing in the petroleum industry.

Intergranular Corrosion. The resistance of the duplex steels to intergranular corrosion varies among the commercial alloys primarily as a function of the carbon content and the alpha-gamma phase balance. Alloys with high carbon content and a phase balance in favor of ferrite are susceptible to intergranular corrosion and require annealing after welding.

The large majority of commercial alloys have low carbon contents (>0.03%) and a 50 to 50 gamma-to-alpha ratio. They also have good resistance to intergranular corrosion. It has been reported that AF22 duplex steel (0.03% C, 21 to 23% Cr, 4.5 to 6.5% Ni, 2.5 to 3.5% Mo, 0.08 to 0.2% N) sensitized up to 30 h at 300 to 1000 °C (570 to 1830 °F) indicated no intergranular attack in the Strauss test. In the Huey test (ASTM A262, Practice C), a certain amount of corrosion loss was noticed and ascribed to gamma-phase and chi-phase formation.

The same research noted no intergranular attack in the Strauss or in the Huey test for welded material 5 mm (0.2 in.) thick.

Other research centering on the fabrication of pressure vessels made out of 44LN (0.03% C, 25% Cr, 6% Ni, 1.5% Mo, 0.17% N) duplex steel reported acceptable intergranular corrosion as tested by ASTM A262-79, Practice A and C.

Intergranular corrosion performance of the duplex steels must consider the alloy composition, the welding process, and the environment in which the fabricated equipment is to operate.

Stress-Corrosion Cracking. While duplex steels are susceptible to chloride-induced stress-corrosion cracking, they are clearly superior to the austenitic grades. The behavior is influenced by composition and phase balance; the higher the amount of ferrite, the better the resistance to stress corrosion. The threshold stress for stress corrosion of the duplex steels is superior to that of type 304. Similar to intergranular corrosion behavior, the resistance to stress-corrosion cracking of the duplex steels should take into consideration the composition, the phase balance, the stress level, and the environment.

Cast Steels

Steel casting compositions are, depending on the alloy content and intended service, generally divided into carbon, low-alloy, corrosion-resistant, or heat-resistant categories. Castings are classified as corrosion resistant if they are capable of sustained operation when exposed to attack by corrosive agents at service temperatures below 315 °C (600 °F).

The term "corrosion resistance" is highly subjective in that its meaning depends entirely on the specific environment into which a metal or alloy is subjected. Carbon and most low-alloy steels are considered resistant only to the most mildly corrosive conditions. With the addition of one or more of the various alloying elements—principally chromium, nickel, molybdenum, or copper—general corrosion resistance tends to increase. The rate of increase depends largely on the nature of the environment. Also, even within the most constant of environmental conditions, the rate of increase in corrosion resistance is not, by any means, a straight line. This is clearly illustrated in Table 4:

Table 4 Petroleum corrosion resistance of cast steels

1000-h test in petroleum vapor under 780 N (175 lb) of pressure at 345 °C (650 °F)

Type of material	Weight loss, mg/cm^2
Cast carbon steel	3040
Cast steel, 2Ni–0.75Cr	2370
Seamless tubing, 5% Cr	1540
Cast steel, 5Cr–1W	950
Cast steel, 3Cr–0.5Mo	730
Cast steel, 12% Cr	6.4
Stainless steel, 18Cr–8Ni	2.1

Under specific environmental conditions, as noted above, the rate of corrosion, as measured by weight loss, is extremely high (3040 mg/cm^2) for plain-carbon steel. With the addition of 2.0% nickel and 0.75% chromium, the corrosion rate decreases substantially. With increasing amounts of alloying additions, the rate continues to decrease. When the chromium content is increased to 12.0%, a drastic decrease in the corrosion rate occurs. This is because, at this point, the cast chromium alloy qualifies as a stainless steel. For the higher alloy 18-8 stainless, the corrosion rate shows a further decrease. It becomes obvious that a number of variables directly influence corrosion rate. As the result, it is misleading for a reader to merely consult a list comparative rates of different alloys exposed to the same corroding medium.

Any graphic or tabular data must be considered as guidelines, not as the basis of application selections. Alloy casting users are urged to consult with corrosion and materials specialists when a particular selection is to be made. Data derived from controlled laboratory tests should be cautiously applied to anticipated service conditions. The best source of information is obtained from equipment used under similar operating conditions. Still, exposing samples to actual service conditions also provides valuable data.

Carbon and Low-Alloy Cast Steels

Unless shielded by a protective coating, iron and steel corrodes in the presence of water and oxygen. The rate at which the process proceeds in the atmosphere depends on the corroding medium, the conditions of the particular location in which the material is used, and the steps taken to retard corrosion.

Cast steel and wrought steel of similar composition and heat treating conditions ordinarily exhibit about the same degree of corrosion resistance within the same environments. Plain-carbon steels and some of the low-alloy steels do not ordinarily resist drastic corrosive conditions, such as sulfuric acid (H_2SO_4). To significantly increase corrosion resistance, it is necessary to use extensive alloying additions.

Atmospheric Corrosion

In the most general terms, it can be stated that the corrosion rate of cast steel varies widely, depending on its specific location. For example, an unprotected plain-carbon steel placed outdoors corrodes slowly in the upper Midwest, whereas the same material rusts several times faster in an ocean harbor location where both temperature and humidity are high and where the air is contaminated with industrial fumes and saline fog.

As a rule, plain-carbon cast steels exposed to any kind of atmosphere should be coated—if only with paint—to realize an acceptable service life. However, there are notable cases where the life of a carbon steel with a very small alloy addition, such as 0.6% copper, can be substantially increased within a given atmosphere.

Exposure to Waters

The aggressiveness of waters as related to the service life of a cast steel also varies over a wide range. Carbon steels should not be considered for service in sea or brackish water without some sort of protection. Mine waters are also quite aggressive. However, the material often yields an acceptable service life when exposed to fresh or inhibited waters, as in boiler use. In such cases, the presence of oxygen is a major positive factor. If the steel is covered with water at all times, the rate of attack is minimized.

Soil Corrosion

Cast steel pipe has been tested for various periods up to 14 years in different types of soils. When compared with similar tests performed on wrought steel of like composition, the results of these tests indicated no significant difference in corrosion rate between the two materials. However, the actual rate of corrosion and rate of pitting of the cast pipe varied widely in direct relation to the specific soil and aeration conditions.

Iron-Base Superalloys

Iron-base superalloys are logically an extension of the stainless steel family, and a more complete description of corrosion behavior for these alloys may be gained by reading about those alloys. Most of the iron-base superalloys are high-chromium austenitic stainless steels to which enough titanium and sometimes aluminum have been added to generate a hardening precipitate such as gamma prime or eta phase. Under some circumstances, more significant alloy modifications have been made, particularly in the case of cast alloys.

Typical applications of iron-base superalloys have been as oxidation-resistant materials for steam and gas turbines, automotive applications, furnace structural components, and in the chemical-processing industry. The corrosion behavior of these materials is usually a direct function of their chromium content. Chromium contents frequently range between 20 and 30% for maximum protection, without creating the formation of the deleterious (to strength) sigma phase. Aluminum, when present, contributes to oxidation resistance. Carbon may combine with the chromium to produce carbides and so reduce the effective corrosion resistance of an alloy. Titanium and other stronger carbide formers may act to ensure maximum utilization of the available chromium by tying up carbon. Manganese, in amounts up to 5%, may provide some additional scale retention by reducing the volatility of the oxide at high temperatures. Active elements, including the rare earth elements, tend to promote oxide scale adherence.

The oxidation resistance of iron-base superalloys at temperatures below about 815 °C (1500 °F)—to which they should be restricted anyway for considerations of strength—depends largely upon chromium content. The level of oxidation resistance compares favorably with that of nickel- or cobalt-base superalloys. Use of iron-base alloys at higher temperatures generally results in an unfavorable comparison of them to nickel-base superalloys, because the latter are also usually highly alloyed with aluminum, which produces, at elevated temperatures, aluminum oxide scale, a more protective film than chrome oxide. However, at lower temperatures in aqueous-corrosion conditions, iron-base superalloys offer good corrosion resistance at a more competitive cost than do nickel-base superalloys.

Selection for Corrosion Resistance

The selection of iron-base alloys for corrosion resistance is frequently limited by an obvious fact—it is generally clear that,

as required oxidation resistance increases, so does the required chromium content. There is thus a natural tendency to choose nickel-base superalloys. However, considerations of fabricability, availability, and cost may be more important choice criteria than a prolonged selection program for the best alloy for oxidation resistance.

There are a great number of iron-base superalloys available, although this may not be obvious from the more common technical literature. Many of them are proprietary.

Aluminum and Aluminum Alloys

Aluminum and its alloys resist attack by a wide range of environments and many chemical compounds. Consequently, aluminum (along with stainless steel) is the metal most thought of by the public and engineering community when lower temperature corrosion resistance is considered. The widespread acceptance of aluminum in cookware, the beverage industry, and as home siding testifies to the utility and applicability of alloys of aluminum as a corrosion-resistant material. Table 5 gives comparative corrosion characteristics of aluminum alloys.

Corrosion Resistance

Resistance to corrosion is a relative consideration, because the environment significantly affects the nature of the attack. Aluminum and its alloys generally have excellent corrosion resistance in many different environments. When applying the material, conditions that cause corrosion of aluminum frequently are the exception rather than the rule.

Actually, aluminum, by virtue of its position in the electromtive force series, is a highly reactive metal. Only magnesium, among the common structural metals, is more reactive. Aluminum owes its excellent corrosion resistance to the barrier oxide film that forms on the metal and its alloys almost immediately in a wide variety of environments. Although the oxide film instantaneously formed on a freshly abraded surface of aluminum is thin (1 nm), it is extremely effective in preventing corrosion. On subsequent exposure to normal atmospheres, or when enhanced by artificial growth processes (anodizing), the film becomes much thicker. The oxide film offers reasonable protection to aluminum at elevated temperatures, but it is most effective in making aluminum passive at lower temperatures in atmospheric or aqueous corrosive conditions. The oxide film is virtually transparent, tough, adherent, and nonflaking. Consequently, once formed, it does not thicken or self-destruct with time under ordinary lower temperature exposure conditions. Because the oxide film is self-renewing, accidental abrasion of the surface film is rapidly repaired.

The conditions that promote corrosion of aluminum and its alloys, therefore, must be those that continuously abrade the film mechanically or promote chemical conditions that locally degrade the protective oxide film and minimize the availability of oxygen to rebuild it.

Maximum corrosion resistance is found with pure aluminum; however, its alloys are highly corrosion resistant to many environments as well. As with most materials, the presence of impurities on the surface or within the metal can significantly degrade corrosion resistance. Clean surfaces resist corrosion much more effectively than surfaces on which there are such deposits. Aluminum exposed to aggressive marine or industrial atmospheres last much longer if it is rained upon frequently or cleaned by water rinsing. Water dilutes and/or washes away the detrimental residues of salt, soot, etc., that accumulate with time. In certain organic chemicals, such as phenol, traces of water prevent corrosion that would otherwise occur.

An increase in temperature strongly influences the corrosion of aluminum in aqueous conditions. However, as the temperature increases in water, the rate of pitting attack is reduced. At the same time, in the atmosphere, moderate heat can be beneficial, because it increases the rate of drying, thereby reducing the period of wetness.

Corrodant velocity can also be an important factor in corrosion; increased movement of a corrosive liquid or gas in contact with the metal generally accelerates corrosion. As in many materials, extremely high velocities of liquids may promote cavitation.

The acidity or alkalinity of the immediate environment (chemical, soil, atmospheric, or aqueous) significantly affects the corrosion of aluminum. The Pourbaix diagram for aluminum with a hydrated aluminum oxide film shows immunity or passive behavior in the pH range of about 3 to 8.5. When aluminum is exposed to higher pH (alkaline) conditions, corrosion may occur, and when the oxide film is perforated locally, accelerated attack occurs, because aluminum is attacked more rapidly than its oxide under alkaline conditions. The result is pitting corrosion. In acidic conditions, the oxide is

Table 5 Comparative Corrosion Characteristics of Aluminum Alloys

Source: *Aluminum Standards and Data 1984*, The Aluminum Association, Washington, DC

Alloy and temper	Resistance to corrosion General(a)	Stress-corrosion cracking(b)	Some applications of alloys	Alloy and temper	Resistance to corrosion General(a)	Stress-corrosion cracking(b)	Some applications of alloys
1060-0, H12, H14, H16, H18...	A	A	Chemical equipment, railroad tank cars	5086-0, H111, H116, H32........	A(d)	A(d)	
1100-0, H12, H14, H16, H18...	A	A	Sheet metal work, spun hollowware, fin stock	5086-H34, H36, H38	A(d)	B(d)	
1350-0, H12, H14, H16, H18, H111, H24, H26..........	A	A	Electrical conductors	5154-0, H32, H34, H36, H38......	A(d)	A(d)	Welded structures, storage tanks, pressure vessels, salt water service
2011-T3, T4, T451	D(c)	D	Screw machine products	5252-H24, H25, H28	A	A	Automotive and appliance trim
2011-T8	D	B		5254-0, H32, H34, H36, H38......	A(d)	A(d)	Hydrogen peroxide and chemical storage vessels
2014-T3, T4, T451	D(c)	C	Truck frames, aircraft structures	5454-0, H111, H32, H34.........	A	A	Welded structures, pressure vessels, marine service
2014-T6, T651, T6510, T6511 ..	D	C		5456-0, H116, H321.............	A(d)	B(d)	High-strength welded structures, pressure vessels, marine applications, storage tanks
2017-T4, T451...............	D(c)	C	Screw machine products, fittings	5457-0.........................	A	A	Automotive parts, appliance trim
2024-T4, T3, T351, T3510, T3511, T361	D(c)	C	Truck wheels, screw machine products, aircraft structures	5652-0, H32, H34, H36, H38......	A	A	Hydrogen peroxide and chemical storage vessels
2024-T6, T81, T851, T8510, T8511, T861	D	B		5657-H241, H25, H26, H28	A	A	Anodized auto and appliance trim
2025-T6	D	C	Forgings, aircraft propellers	6053-T6, T61....................	A	A	Wire and rod for rivets
2036-T4	C	...	Auto body panel sheet	6061-0, T6, T651, T652, T6510, T6511	B	A	Heavy-duty structures requiring good corrosion resistance, truck and marine, railroad cars, furniture, pipelines
2117-T4	C	A	Rivets	6061-T4, T451, T4510, T4511	B	B	
2218-T61, T72...............	D	C	Jet engine impellers and rings	6063-T1, T4, T5, T52, T6, T83, T831, T832	A	A	Pipe railing, furniture, architectural extrusions
2219-T31, T351, T3510, T3511, T37	D(c)	C	Structural uses at high temperatures (to 600 °F), high-strength weldments	6066-0.........................	C	A	Forgings and extrusion for welded structures
2219-T81, T851, T8510, T8511, T87	D	B		6066-T4, T4510, T4511, T6, T6510, T6511	C	B	
2618-T61	D	C	Aircraft engines	6070-T4, T4511, T6	B	B	Heavy-duty welded structures, pipelines
3003-0, H12, H14, H16, H18, H25.....................	A	A	Cooking utensils, chemical equipment, pressure vessels, sheet metal work, builder's hardware, storage tanks	6101-T6, T61, T63, T64	A	A	High-strength bus conductors
				6201-T81	A	A	High-strength electric conductor wire
3004-0, H32, H34, H36, H38...	A	A	Sheet metal work, storage tanks	6262-T6, T651, T6510, T6511, T9...	B	A	Screw machine products
3105-0, H12, H14, H16, H18, H25....................	A	A	Residential siding, mobile homes, rain carrying goods, sheet metal work	6463-T1, T5, T6	A	A	Extruded architectural and trim sections
4032-T6	C	B	Pistons	7001-0, T6, T6510, T6511........	C(c)	C	High-strength structures
5005-0, H12, H14, H16, H18, H32, H34, H36, H38.......	A	A	Appliances, utensils, architectural, electrical conductor	7049-T73, T7352.................	C	B	Aircraft forgings
5050-0, H32, H34, H36, H38...	A	A	Builder's hardware, refrigerator trim, coiled tubes	7050-T73510, T73511, T74(e), T7451(e), T74510(e), T74511(e), T7452(e), T7651, T76510, T76511	C	B	Aircraft and other structures
5052-0, H32, H34, H36, H38...	A	A	Sheet metal work, hydraulic tube, appliances				
5056-0, H111, H12, H14, H32, H34....................	A(d)	B(d)	Cable sheathing, rivets for magnesium, screen wire, zippers	7075-T6, T651, T6510, T6511, T652........................	C(c)	C	Aircraft and other structures
5056-H18, H38	A(d)	C(d)		7075-T73, T7351................	C	B	
5056-H192, H392	B(d)	D(d)		7178-T6, T651, T6510, T6511	C(c)	C	Aircraft and other structures
5083-0, H111, H116, H321.....	A(d)	B(d)	Unfired welded pressure vessels, marine, auto aircraft cryogenics, TV towers, drilling rigs, transportation equipment, missile components	8017-H12, H22, H221	A	A	Electrical conductors
				8030-H12, H221.................	A	A	Electrical conductors
				8176-H14, H24	A	A	Electrical conductors
				8177-H13, H221, H23	A	A	Electrical conductors

(a) Ratings A through E are relative ratings in decreasing order of merit, based on exposures to sodium chloride solution by intermittent spraying or immersion, based on exposures to sodium chloride solution by intermittent spraying or immersion. Alloys with A and B ratings can be used in industrial and seacoast atmospheres without protection. Alloys with C, D, and E ratings generally should be protected, at least on faying surfaces.
(b) Stress-corrosion cracking ratings are based on service experience and on laboratory tests of specimens exposed to the 3.5% sodium chloride alternate immersion test. A, no known instance of failure in service or in laboratory tests; B, no known instance of failure in service, limited failures in laboratory tests of short transverse specimens; C, service failures with sustained tension stress acting in short transverse direction relative to grain structure, limited failures in laboratory tests of long transverse specimens; D, limited service failures with sustained longitudinal or long transverse stress.
(c) In relatively thick sections, the rating would be E.
(d) This rating may be different for material held at elevated temperature for long periods.
(e) T74-type tempers, although not previously registered, have appeared in various literature and specifications as T736-type tempers.

more rapidly attacked than aluminum, and more general attack should result.

Effects of Alloying Elements

Generally, the higher the degree of purity of the aluminum or its alloys, the greater the corrosion resistance. Certain elements such as magnesium or manganese, in amounts less than about 1%, can be alloyed with pure aluminum without seriously reducing the corrosion resistance of the pure metal in many environments. Up to 1% magnesium or up to about 1.25% manganese can be added to high-purity aluminum without increasing the pitting probability factor in water. Depending on the precise purity of pure aluminum, pitting may even be reduced.

The principal alloying elements (copper, magnesium, silicon, and zinc) added to aluminum reduce the atmospheric corrosion resistance somewhat. More significantly, they affect other localized corrosion resistance (stress-corrosion cracking and exfoliation corrosion, for example).

Magnesium

Magnesium in nonhardening type alloys (5000 series) makes them especially immune to aqueous corrosion. The magnesium-silicide alloys (6000 series) offer excellent aqueous corrosion resistance in a stronger material. The copper (2000 series) and zinc (7000 series) alloys are generally much less resistant to aqueous corrosion. Cladding techniques, as discussed below, afford protection for many applications.

Magnesium somewhat increases the resistance of aluminum to corrosion in alkaline solutions, but when present in the grain boundaries as an anodic magnesium aluminum compound, it may promote stress-corrosion cracking and intergranular corrosion. Silicon in small amounts (0.1%) has little effect on pitting corrosion of aluminum, yet greater amounts reduce resistance to pitting. Silicon has a detrimental influence on the resistance of aluminum to seawater.

Chromium

Chromium when added to aluminum-magnesium or aluminum-magnesium-zinc alloys, is used in very small amounts (0.1 to 0.3%) and has a beneficial effect on corrosion resistance. Chromium improves resistance to stress-corrosion cracking in high-strength alloys, but in super-purity aluminum it increases the pitting potential in water. Iron, although not an intentional alloy addition, is the main cause of pitting in aluminum alloys. Its effects may be mitigated by other alloying additions.

Copper

Copper reduces the corrosion resistance of aluminum more than any of the common alloying elements. It can lead to a higher rate of uniform corrosion, greater occurrence of pitting, intergranular corrosion, and stress-corrosion cracking. At low levels (about 0.15%) of copper, the pitting resistance of commercial aluminum is decreased, especially in seawater. In higher copper content alloys (2000 series), the effect of the element is related directly to the fabrication process and heat treatment. At higher copper contents, intergranular corrosion or stress-corrosion cracking are areas of concern.

Zinc

Zinc has only a small influence on the corrosion resistance of commercial aluminum. It may reduce the resistance to acidic media, but improve the resistance to alkaline solutions. When zinc is present in higher levels and in combination with magnesium and copper, the influence of zinc is a function of the fabrication and heat treatment of the alloy. The high-zinc alloys may be susceptible to intergranular corrosion, stress-corrosion cracking, and exfoliation corrosion.

Lithium

Lithium additions are now made to some aluminum alloys. Although lithium is a highly reactive element, the addition of up to 3% lithium makes aluminum only slightly more anodic. Little has been published on the corrosion resistance of lithium-containing alloys, however. In an electrochemical comparison of an aluminum-lithium-magnesium alloy to AA-7075 (aluminum-zinc-magnesium), the lithium alloy exhibited more active corrosion and pitting potentials, along with a higher current density for passivation.

Coatings and Surface Treatments

Although aluminum is highly resistant to corrosion, it is possible to enhance its corrosion resistance with coatings or surface treatment. One of the best ways to enhance the corrosion resistance of aluminum alloy plate is to apply a cladding of pure aluminum on one or both sides. This process produces materials known as "Alclad." Alclad is not restricted to the use of pure aluminum on an alloy; it is possible to bond a more corrosion-resistant alloy to a less corrosion-resistant substrate. Pipe also may be Alcladed, but other shapes or forms present fabrication problems. It is possible to clad an alloy by spraying, yet it is not customarily a cost-effective process.

One of the most important characteristics of aluminum is the ease with which the normally protective oxide film can be enhanced. The surface of aluminum can be altered by chemical and electrochemical treatments to thicken the normal oxide film. Proprietary chemical conversion treatments can produce films that may be the basis for subsequent painting (the films greatly improve paint adhesion to aluminum) and are the basis for the coatings applied to house sidings. Such films are not as effective (when unpainted) as anodized films in providing enhanced corrosion protection.

Copper and Copper Alloys

Copper and copper alloys have been widely used for centuries in many applications because of their excellent corrosion resistance and moderate cost. Despite the formation of the common green patina in natural environments, copper and its alloys corrode at negligible rates in unpolluted water or air and in deaerated nonoxidizing acids. For marine applications, it is known that copper shows resistance to biofouling. Copper alloys resist many saline solutions, neutral or slightly alkaline solutions, and organic chemicals. In strongly reducing conditions at temperatures from about 290 to 400 °C (550 to

750 °F), copper alloys are often superior to stainless steels and other stainless alloys.

Copper and its alloys, however, may be susceptible to more rapid attack in oxidizing acids, oxidizing heavy metal salts, as well as sulfur, ammonia, and some of their compounds. Resistance to acid solutions depends on the alloy composition, specific acid, and the severity of oxidizing conditions in the solutions.

In general, copper and its alloys are used at ambient temperatures when exposed to gaseous environments, but some types are used in gaseous environments at moderately elevated temperatures where they operate in oxidizing conditions. Copper alloys are exposed to liquid/gas environments at fairly high temperatures when used as heat exchangers. The nature of the environment, including treatment of the cooling water, velocity of the cooling water, and various other factors all determine the actual susceptibility of copper alloys to corrosion under these conditions. Copper and brasses are susceptible to erosion-corrosion or impingement attack.

Corrosion-resistant applications of copper and its alloys are extensive; they are used in fresh water supply lines and plumbing fixtures and also in seawater supply lines, heat exchangers, and condensers, paper-making belts, as well as architectural elements and decoration. Table 6 gives corrosion ratings of wrought copper alloys in various corrosive media.

Though classed as corrosion resistant, neither copper nor its alloys form the truly passive corrosion-resistant film that characterizes most true corrosion-resistant alloys. In aqueous environments at ambient temperatures, cuprous oxide forms the protective scale. Alloy additions of aluminum, tin, zinc, and nickel are used to dope the corrosion product films to enhance the natural corrosion resistance of copper and to produce the range of corrosion-resistant capability for which copper alloys are noted.

Copper alloys can be quite susceptible to stress-corrosion cracking. The classic example of stress-corrosion cracking is the "season cracking" of cartridge brass (70 copper-30 zinc). While zinc is the principal culprit, small amounts of phosphorus, arsenic, antimony, silicon, aluminum, or nickel have been found to produce stress-corrosion cracking of copper in ammoniacal solutions. As for other elements, corrosion-resistant behavior of copper is best revealed by considering its alloy systems. The basic systems for copper are copper-tin (bronze), copper-zinc (brass), copper-nickel (cupronickels), and variations of the above, including aluminum-bronzes, phosphor-bronzes, and nickel-silvers. A discussion of the role in corrosion resistance of the principal alloy additions that produce these systems follows.

Zinc

Zinc content in copper can range from a few percent to about 40%. The resistance of brasses to corrosion does not change markedly as long as the zinc content is 15%, or less. When the zinc content exceeds 15%, the alloy may be susceptible to dezincification. This is a process involving the leaching of the zinc from the alloy. It results in a porous, reduced ductility, reddish copper matrix. What remains may support a given load until an increase of pressure or weight exceeds the local ductility and causes fracture. Soft, stagnant, or slow moving waters or saline solutions can lead to dezincification of unmodified brasses. The brasses may be more prone to dezincification in stressed regions (for example, in the bent region of a float arm on a water closet fixture) or where a bend exists (as in an elbow in a fresh water supply line).

High zinc content introduces the possibility of stress-corrosion cracking. Very high zinc content, as in Muntz metal, may lead to excessive corrosion attack in seawater due to dezincification. Limited or no data are available on the effects of zinc in brasses on the rate of corrosion; however, the addition of tertiary and quaternary elements is known to enhance the resistance of zinc-containing alloys to certain environments.

Tin

Tin bronzes are essentially solid solutions of tin in copper. Phosphorus is commonly used as a deoxidizer, and the residual phosphorus content gives rise to the term "phosphor bronze." The addition of tin to copper promotes good resistance to fresh and seawaters. Under some conditions, when more than 5% tin is present, the corrosion resistance in marine applications is enhanced. Where the water velocity is high, tin content for marine applications of copper alloys should exceed 5%. Alloys containing between 8 and 10% tin have high resistance to impingement attack.

Tin bronzes tend to have intermediate pitting resistance. When tin is added to some brasses, the corrosion resistance is substantially increased; in fact, 1% tin inhibits dealloying (dezincification) in 70 copper-30 zinc alloys.

Nickel

Nickel and copper are mutually soluble, and in alloys where copper is the dominant element, commercial alloys range from about 54 to over 90% copper. Nickel provides the best general resistance to aqueous corrosion of all the commercially important alloy elements. It promotes resistance to impingement corrosion and to stress-corrosion cracking.

The addition of nickel to copper-zinc alloys produces nickel-silver alloys. Most commonly these have about 18% nickel and 55 to 65% copper. Such alloy additions promote good resistance to corrosion in both fresh and salt waters. The nickel inhibits dezincification. Nickel-silvers are much more corrosion resistant in saline solutions than brasses of similar copper content.

Other elements

Other elements are added to copper alloys in varying amounts to introduce favorable corrosion characteristics. For example, 2% aluminum is added to 76 copper-22 zinc solutions to produce aluminum brass, and a small amount of arsenic (less than 0.10%) is added to the alloy to inhibit dezincification.

Table 6 Corrosion Resistance of Copper and Copper Alloys to Various Environments

A, suitable under most conditions of use; B, good corrosion resistance, may be considered in place of a metal with an A rating when some property other than corrosion resistance governs its use; C, fair corrosion resistance; D, not suitable
Source: Arco Metals Company—American Brass, Rolling Meadows, IL

Column groups: Copper — Electrolytic tough pitch 110, Phosphorized 122; Low-zinc brass — Commercial bronze 220, Red brass 230; High-zinc brass — Cartridge brass 260, Architectural bronze 385, Muntz metal 280; Special brass — Tobin bronze 4641, Arsenical admiralty 443, Ambraloy 687; Phosphor bronze — Phosphor bronze (A) 510, Phosphor bronze (D) 524; Aluminum bronze — Ambraloy 630; Copper-silicon alloys — Everdur 655, Everdur 651; Cupro-nickel — Cupronickel 10% 706, Cupronickel 30% 715; Nickel silver 18% 752

Environment	ETP 110	Phos. 122	Comm. bronze 220	Red brass 230	Cart. brass 260	Arch. bronze 385	Muntz 280	Tobin 4641	Ars. adm. 443	Ambraloy 687	Phos. br. (A) 510	Phos. br. (D) 524	Ambraloy 630	Everdur 655	Everdur 651	CuNi 10% 706	CuNi 30% 715	Ni silver 752
Acetic acid	B	B	B	B	D	D	D	D	C	C	B	B	B	B	B	B	B	B
Acetic anhydride	B	B	B	B	D	D	D	D	C	C	B	B	B	B	B	B	B	B
Acetone	A	A	A	A	A	A	A	A	A	A	A	A	A	A	A	A	A	A
Acetylene(a)	D	D	D	D	A	A	A	A	D	D	D	D	D	D	D	D	D	D
Alcohols	A	A	A	A	A	A	A	A	A	A	A	A	A	A	A	A	A	A
Alum	B	B	B	B	D	D	D	D	B	B	B	B	B	B	B	B	A	B
Alumina	A	A	A	A	A	A	A	A	A	A	A	A	A	A	A	A	A	A
Aluminum chloride	B	B	B	B	D	D	D	D	C	C	B	B	B	B	B	B	B	B
Aluminum hydroxide	A	A	A	A	A	A	A	A	A	A	A	A	A	A	A	A	A	A
Aluminum sulfate	B	B	B	B	D	D	D	D	B	B	B	B	B	B	B	B	A	B
Ammonia, absolutely dry	A	A	A	A	A	A	A	A	A	A	A	A	A	A	A	A	A	A
Ammonia, moist	D	D	D	D	D	D	D	D	D	D	D	D	D	D	D	D	C	D
Ammonium hydroxide	D	D	D	D	D	D	D	D	D	D	D	D	D	D	D	D	C	D
Ammonium chloride	D	D	D	D	D	D	D	D	D	D	D	D	D	D	D	D	C	D
Ammonium nitrate	D	D	D	D	D	D	D	D	D	D	D	D	D	D	D	D	C	D
Ammonium sulfate	C	C	C	C	D	D	D	D	D	D	C	C	C	C	C	C	B	C
Amyl acetate	A	A	A	A	B	B	B	B	A	A	A	A	A	A	A	A	A	A
Amyl alcohol	A	A	A	A	A	A	A	A	A	A	A	A	A	A	A	A	A	A
Aniline	C	C	C	C	C	C	C	C	C	C	C	C	C	C	C	C	C	C
Aniline dyes	C	C	C	C	C	C	C	C	C	C	C	C	C	C	C	C	C	C
Asphalt	A	A	A	A	A	A	A	A	A	A	A	A	A	A	A	A	A	A
Atmosphere, industrial	A	A	A	A	B	B	B	B	A	A	A	A	A	A	A	A	A	A
Atmosphere, marine	A	A	A	A	B	B	B	B	A	A	A	A	A	A	A	A	A	A
Atmosphere, rural	A	A	A	A	A	A	A	A	A	A	A	A	A	A	A	A	A	A
Barium carbonate	A	A	A	A	A	A	A	A	A	A	A	A	A	A	A	A	A	A
Barium chloride	B	B	B	B	D	D	D	D	C	C	B	B	B	B	B	B	B	B
Barium hydroxide	A	A	A	A	B	B	B	B	A	A	A	A	A	A	A	A	A	A
Barium sulfate	A	A	A	A	A	A	A	A	A	A	A	A	A	A	A	A	A	A
Barium sulfide	C	C	C	C	B	B	B	B	B	B	C	C	C	C	C	C	B	B
Beer(b)	A	A	A	A	B	B	B	B	A	A	A	A	A	A	A	A	A	A
Beet sugar syrups	A	A	A	A	A	A	A	A	A	A	A	A	A	A	A	A	A	A
Benzine	A	A	A	A	A	A	A	A	A	A	A	A	A	A	A	A	A	A
Benzoic acid	A	A	A	A	B	B	B	B	A	A	A	A	A	A	A	A	A	A
Benzol	A	A	A	A	A	A	A	A	A	A	A	A	A	A	A	A	A	A
Black liquor, sulfate process	C	C	C	C	D	D	D	D	D	C	C	C	C	C	C	C	B	C
Bleaching powder, wet	B	B	B	B	D	D	D	D	B	B	B	B	B	B	B	B	B	B
Borax	A	A	A	A	A	A	A	A	A	A	A	A	A	A	A	A	A	A
Bordeaux mixture	A	A	A	A	B	B	B	B	A	A	A	A	A	A	A	A	A	A
Boric acid	A	A	A	A	B	B	B	B	A	A	A	A	A	A	A	A	A	A
Brines	B	B	B	B	D	D	D	D	C	B	B	B	B	B	B	B	A	B
Bromine, dry	A	A	A	A	A	A	A	A	A	A	A	A	A	A	A	A	A	A
Bromine, moist	B	B	B	B	D	D	D	D	C	C	B	B	B	B	B	B	B	B
Butane	A	A	A	A	A	A	A	A	A	A	A	A	A	A	A	A	A	A
Butyl alcohol	A	A	A	A	A	A	A	A	A	A	A	A	A	A	A	A	A	A
Butyric acid	A	A	A	A	C	C	C	C	A	A	A	A	A	A	A	A	A	A
Calcium bisulfite	B	B	B	B	D	D	D	D	B	B	B	B	B	B	B	B	B	B
Calcium chloride	B	B	B	B	D	D	D	C	B	B	B	B	B	B	B	B	A	B
Calcium hydroxide	A	A	A	A	B	B	B	B	A	A	A	A	A	A	A	A	A	A
Calcium hypochlorite	B	B	B	B	D	D	D	D	B	B	B	B	B	B	B	B	B	B
Cane sugar syrups	A	A	A	A	B	B	B	B	A	A	A	A	A	A	A	A	A	A
Carbolic acid	B	B	B	B	B	B	B	B	B	B	B	B	B	B	B	B	B	B
Carbon dioxide, dry	A	A	A	A	A	A	A	A	A	A	A	A	A	A	A	A	A	A

(a) Copper and copper alloys are not attacked by dry gases at room temperature or lower. Acetylene forms an explosive compound with copper when moist and alloys containing more than 65% Cu should not be used with the wet gas under pressure. Moist carbon dioxide is corrosive to brasses high in zinc, but may be handled by other copper alloys. Tin coatings are highly resistant to moist carbon dioxide. Moist chlorine gas is corrosive to all copper alloys. Sulfur dioxide and sulfur trioxide in the presence of moisture form sulfurous and sulfuric acid, respectively. Copper, red brass, Everdur, phosphor bronze and cupronickel should be considered for handling these gases when moist.

(b) Copper and its alloys are resistant to corrosion by most foods and beverages. However, consideration must be given to the possibility that such products handled in equipment made of copper or its alloys may dissolve traces of copper in amounts sufficient to discolor the product or alter its taste. In such cases it is recommended that the metal be tin-coated.

(c) Copper alloys are resistant to most organic solvents such as the acetates, alcohols, aldehydes, ketones, petroleum solvents, and ether. Organic acids in aqueous solution may be handled by copper and most copper alloys, but corrosion will be accelerated if air is present. Binary copper-zinc alloys containing more than 15% Zn may be attacked by dezincification corrosion. Copper alloys may be definitely corroded by chloride hydrocarbons, such as carbon tetrachloride and trichloroethylene, at the boiling point in the presence of moisture unless the hydrocarbons are stabilized by a neutralizer. Of the copper alloys, cupronickel, 30% 715 and tin-coated metal offer the best resistance to moist chloride hydrocarbons.

(d) Copper and copper alloys are rapidly corroded by oxidizing acids such as nitric and chromic. Corrosion by other acids is generally dependent on the presence of oxygen or some other oxidizing agent in the solution. Brasses containing not more than 15% Zn, and special brasses, can be used with many acids, but, in general, high-zinc brasses should not be used with acids due to the danger of rapid corrosion by dezincification. Copper, red brass, phosphor bronze, Everdur, aluminum bronze, and cupronickel offer good resistance to corrosion by hot and cold dilute sulfuric acid and to corrosion by cold concentrated sulfuric acid. Intermediate concentrations of sulfuric acid sometimes are less corrosive to copper alloys than either concentrated acid or dilute acid. Concentrated sulfuric acid may be corrosive at elevated temperatures due to breakdown of the acid with the formation of metallic sulfides and sulfur dioxide gas causing localized pitting attack. Tests indicate that the copper alloys may be corroded by pitting attack by 90 to 95% sulfuric acid at about 50 °C (122 °F), by 80% acid at about 71 °C (160 °F), and by 60% acid at about 100 °C (212 °F).

(Continued)

Table 6   (continued)

Environment	Electrolytic tough pitch 110	Phosphorized 122	Commercial bronze 220	Red brass 230	Cartridge brass 260	Architectural bronze 385	Muntz metal 280	Tobin bronze 4641	Arsenical admiralty 443	Ambraloy 687	Phosphor bronze (A) 510	Phosphor bronze (D) 524	Aluminum bronze Ambraloy 630	Everdur 655	Everdur 651	Cupronickel, 10% 706	Cupronickel, 30% 715	Nickel silver, 18% 752
Carbon dioxide, moist	B	B	B	B	C	C	C	C	B	B	B	B	B	B	B	B	B	B
Carbonated water	B	B	B	B	C	C	C	C	B	B	B	B	B	B	B	B	B	B
Carbonated beverages(b)	B	B	B	B	C	C	C	C	B	B	B	B	B	B	B	B	B	B
Carbon disulfide	B	B	B	B	A	A	A	A	A	A	B	B	B	B	B	B	B	B
Carbon tetrachloride, dry	A	A	A	A	A	A	A	A	A	A	A	A	A	A	A	A	A	A
Carbon tetrachloride, moist(c)	B	B	B	B	D	D	D	D	B	B	B	B	B	B	B	B	A	B
Castor oil	A	A	A	A	A	A	A	A	A	A	A	A	A	A	A	A	A	A
Chlorine, dry	A	A	A	A	A	A	A	A	A	A	A	A	A	A	A	A	A	A
Chlorine, moist	C	C	C	C	D	D	D	D	C	C	C	C	C	C	C	C	B	C
Chloracetic acid	B	B	B	B	D	D	D	D	C	C	B	B	B	B	B	B	B	B
Chloroform, dry	A	A	A	A	A	A	A	A	A	A	A	A	A	A	A	A	A	A
Chromic acid	D	D	D	D	D	D	D	D	D	D	D	D	D	D	D	D	D	D
Cider(b)	A	A	A	A	C	C	C	C	A	A	A	A	A	A	A	A	A	A
Citric acid(b)	A	A	A	A	C	C	C	C	A	A	A	A	A	A	A	A	A	A
Coffee(b)	A	A	A	A	A	A	A	A	A	A	A	A	A	A	A	A	A	A
Copper chloride	C	C	C	C	D	D	D	D	C	C	C	C	C	C	C	C	C	C
Copper nitrate	C	C	C	C	D	D	D	D	C	C	C	C	C	C	C	C	C	C
Copper sulfate	B	B	B	B	D	D	D	D	B	B	B	B	B	B	B	B	B	B
Corn oil(b)	A	A	A	A	B	B	B	B	A	A	A	A	A	A	A	A	A	A
Cottonseed oil(b)	A	A	A	A	B	B	B	B	A	A	A	A	A	A	A	A	A	A
Creosote	A	A	A	A	A	A	A	A	A	A	A	A	A	A	A	A	A	A
Crude oil	B	B	B	B	C	C	C	C	B	B	B	B	B	B	B	B	A	B
Ethers	A	A	A	A	A	A	A	A	A	A	A	A	A	A	A	A	A	A
Ethyl acetate	A	A	A	A	B	B	B	B	A	A	A	A	A	A	A	A	A	A
Ethyl alcohol	A	A	A	A	A	A	A	A	A	A	A	A	A	A	A	A	A	A
Ethyl chloride	B	B	B	B	C	C	C	C	B	B	B	B	B	B	B	B	B	B
Ethylene glycol	A	A	A	A	B	B	B	B	A	A	A	A	A	A	A	A	A	A
Ferric chloride	D	D	D	D	D	D	D	D	D	D	D	D	D	D	D	D	D	D
Ferric sulfate	D	D	D	D	D	D	D	D	D	D	D	D	D	D	D	D	D	D
Ferrous chloride	B	B	B	B	D	D	D	D	B	B	B	B	B	B	B	B	B	B
Ferrous sulfate	B	B	B	B	D	D	D	D	B	B	B	B	B	B	B	B	B	B
Formaldehyde	A	A	A	A	C	C	C	C	A	A	A	A	A	A	A	A	A	A
Formic acid	A	A	A	A	C	C	C	C	A	A	A	A	A	A	A	A	A	A
Freon	A	A	A	A	A	A	A	A	A	A	A	A	A	A	A	A	A	A
Fruit juices(b)	B	B	B	B	D	D	D	D	C	C	B	B	B	B	B	B	B	B
Fuel oil	A	A	A	A	B	B	B	B	A	A	A	A	A	A	A	A	A	A
Furfural	A	A	A	A	C	C	C	C	A	A	A	A	A	A	A	A	A	A
Gasoline	A	A	A	A	A	A	A	A	A	A	A	A	A	A	A	A	A	A
Gelatine(b)	A	A	A	A	A	A	A	A	A	A	A	A	A	A	A	A	A	A
Glucose(b)	A	A	A	A	A	A	A	A	A	A	A	A	A	A	A	A	A	A
Glue	A	A	A	A	B	B	B	B	A	A	A	A	A	A	A	A	A	A
Glycerine	A	A	A	A	A	A	A	A	A	A	A	A	A	A	A	A	A	A
Hydrobromic acid	C	C	C	C	D	D	D	D	C	C	C	C	C	C	C	C	C	C
Hydrocarbons, pure	A	A	A	A	A	A	A	A	A	A	A	A	A	A	A	A	A	A
Hydrochloric acid	C	C	C	C	D	D	D	D	C	C	C	C	C	C	C	C	C	C
Hydrocyanic acid	D	D	D	D	D	D	D	D	D	D	D	D	D	D	D	D	D	D
Hydrofluoric acid	C	C	C	C	D	D	D	D	C	C	C	C	C	C	C	C	B	C
Hydrofluosilicic acid	B	B	B	B	D	D	D	D	B	B	B	B	B	B	B	B	B	B
Hydrogen	A	A	A	A	A	A	A	A	A	A	A	A	A	A	A	A	A	A
Hydrogen peroxide	B	B	B	B	C	C	C	C	B	B	B	B	B	B	B	B	B	B
Hydrogen sulfide, dry	A	A	A	A	A	A	A	A	A	A	A	A	A	A	A	A	A	A
Hydrogen sulfide, moist	D	D	D	D	C	C	C	C	C	C	D	D	C	D	D	D	C	C
Kerosene	A	A	A	A	A	A	A	A	A	A	A	A	A	A	A	A	A	A
Lacquers	A	A	A	A	A	A	A	A	A	A	A	A	A	A	A	A	A	A
Lacquer solvents	A	A	A	A	A	A	A	A	A	A	A	A	A	A	A	A	A	A
Lactic acid(b)	A	A	A	A	C	C	C	C	A	A	A	A	A	A	A	A	A	A

(a) Copper and copper alloys are not attacked by dry gases at room temperature or lower. Acetylene forms an explosive compound with copper when moist and alloys containing more than 65% Cu should not be used with the wet gas under pressure. Moist carbon dioxide is corrosive to brasses high in zinc, but may be handled by other copper alloys. Tin coatings are highly resistant to moist carbon dioxide. Moist chlorine gas is corrosive to all copper alloys. Sulfur dioxide and sulfur trioxide in the presence of moisture form sulfurous and sulfuric acid, respectively. Copper, red brass, Everdur, phosphor bronze and cupronickel, 30% 715 should be considered for handling these gases when moist.

(b) Copper and its alloys are resistant to corrosion by most foods and beverages. However, consideration must be given to the possibility that such products handled in equipment made of copper or its alloys may dissolve traces of copper in amounts sufficient to discolor the product or alter its taste. In such cases it is recommended that the metal be tin-coated.

(c) Copper alloys are resistant to most organic solvents such as the acetates, alcohols, aldehydes, ketones, petroleum solvents, and ether. Organic acids in aqueous solution may be handled by copper and most copper alloys, but corrosion will be accelerated if air is present. Binary copper-zinc alloys containing more than 15% Zn may be attacked by dezincification corrosion. Copper alloys may be definitely corroded by chloride hydrocarbons, such as carbon tetrachloride and trichloroethylene, at the boiling point in the presence of moisture unless the hydrocarbons are stabilized by a neutralizer. Of the copper alloys, cupronickel, 30% 715 and tin-coated metal offer the best resistance to corrosion by moist chloride hydrocarbons.

(d) Copper and copper alloys are rapidly corroded by oxidizing acids such as nitric and chromic. Corrosion by other acids is generally dependent on the presence of oxygen or some other oxidizing agent in the solution. Brasses containing not more than 15% Zn, and special brasses, can be used with many acids, but, in general, high-zinc brasses should not be used with acids due to the danger of rapid corrosion by dezincification. Copper, red brass, phosphor bronze, Everdur, aluminum bronze, and cupronickel offer good resistance to corrosion by hot and cold dilute sulfuric acid and to corrosion by cold concentrated sulfuric acid. Intermediate concentrations of sulfuric acid sometimes are less corrosive to copper alloys than either concentrated acid or dilute acid. Concentrated sulfuric acid may be corrosive at elevated temperatures due to breakdown of the acid with the formation of metallic sulfides and sulfur dioxide gas causing localized pitting attack. Tests indicate that the copper alloys may be corroded by pitting attack by 90 to 95% sulfuric acid at about 50 °C (122 °F), by 80% acid at about 71 °C (160 °F), and by 60% acid at about 100 °C (212 °F).

(Continued)

Table 6 (continued)

Environment	ETP 110	Phosphorized 122	Commercial bronze 220	Red brass 230	Cartridge brass 260	Architectural bronze 385	Muntz metal 280	Tobin bronze 4641	Arsenical admiralty 443	Ambraloy 687	Phosphor bronze (A) 510	Phosphor bronze (D) 524	Aluminum bronze Ambraloy 630	Everdur 655	Everdur 651	Cupronickel 10% 706	Cupronickel 30% 715	Nickel silver 18% 752
Lime	A	A	A	A	A	A	A	A	A	A	A	A	A	A	A	A	A	A
Lime-sulfur	C	C	C	C	B	B	B	B	B	B	C	C	C	C	C	C	B	B
Linseed oil	B	B	B	B	B	B	B	B	B	B	B	B	B	B	B	B	B	B
Magnesium chloride	B	B	B	B	D	D	D	D	D	C	C	B	B	B	B	B	B	B
Magnesium hydroxide	A	A	A	A	A	A	A	A	A	A	A	A	A	A	A	A	A	A
Magnesium sulfate	A	A	A	A	C	C	C	C	C	A	A	A	A	A	A	A	A	A
Mercury	D	D	D	D	D	D	D	D	D	D	D	D	D	D	D	D	D	D
Mercury salts	D	D	D	D	D	D	D	D	D	D	D	D	D	D	D	D	D	D
Methyl alcohol	A	A	A	A	A	A	A	A	A	A	A	A	A	A	A	A	A	A
Methyl chloride, dry	A	A	A	A	A	A	A	A	A	A	A	A	A	A	A	A	A	A
Milk(b)	A	A	A	A	B	B	B	B	A	A	A	A	A	A	A	A	A	A
Mine water	C	C	C	C	D	D	D	D	C	C	C	C	C	C	C	C	C	C
Natural gas	B	B	A	A	A	A	A	A	A	A	A	A	A	A	A	A	A	A
Nitric acid	D	D	D	D	D	D	D	D	D	D	D	D	D	D	D	D	D	D
Nitrogen	A	A	A	A	A	A	A	A	A	A	A	A	A	A	A	A	A	A
Oleic acid	A	A	A	A	C	C	C	C	C	A	A	A	A	A	A	A	A	A
Oxalic acid	A	A	A	A	C	C	C	C	C	A	A	A	A	A	A	A	A	A
Oxygen	A	A	A	A	A	A	A	A	A	A	A	A	A	A	A	A	A	A
Palmitic acid	B	B	B	B	C	C	C	C	B	B	B	B	B	B	B	B	B	B
Paraffin	A	A	A	A	A	A	A	A	A	A	A	A	A	A	A	A	A	A
Phosphoric acid	B	B	B	B	D	D	D	D	C	C	B	B	B	B	B	B	B	B
Potassium carbonate	A	A	A	A	B	B	B	B	A	A	A	A	A	A	A	A	A	A
Potassium chloride	B	B	B	B	D	D	D	C	B	B	B	A	B	A	A	A	A	A
Potassium chromate	A	A	A	A	A	A	A	A	A	A	A	A	A	A	A	A	A	A
Potassium cyanide	D	D	D	D	D	D	D	D	D	D	D	D	D	D	D	D	D	D
Potassium dichromate, acid	D	D	D	D	D	D	D	D	D	D	D	D	D	D	D	D	D	D
Potassium hydroxide	B	B	B	B	C	C	C	C	B	B	B	B	B	B	B	A	A	A
Potassium sulfate	A	A	A	A	B	B	B	B	A	A	A	A	A	A	A	A	A	A
Propane	A	A	A	A	A	A	A	A	A	A	A	A	A	A	A	A	A	A
Rosin	A	A	A	A	A	A	A	A	A	A	A	A	A	A	A	A	A	A
Seawater	B	B	B	B	C	C	C	B	A	A	B	A	A	B	A	A	A	A
Sewage	A	A	A	A	C	C	C	B	A	A	A	A	A	A	A	A	A	A
Silver salts	D	D	D	D	D	D	D	D	D	D	D	D	D	D	D	D	D	D
Soap solutions	A	A	A	A	B	B	B	B	A	A	A	A	A	A	A	A	A	A
Sodium bicarbonate	B	B	B	B	C	C	C	B	B	B	B	B	B	B	A	A	A	A
Sodium bisulfate	B	B	B	B	D	D	D	C	B	B	B	B	B	B	A	A	A	A
Sodium bisulfite	B	B	B	B	D	D	D	C	B	B	B	B	B	B	A	A	A	A
Sodium carbonate	A	A	A	A	B	B	B	B	A	A	A	A	A	A	A	A	A	A
Sodium chloride	B	B	B	B	D	D	D	C	B	A	A	A	A	A	A	A	A	A
Sodium chromate	A	A	A	A	A	A	A	A	A	A	A	A	A	A	A	A	A	A
Sodium cyanide	D	D	D	D	D	D	D	D	D	D	D	D	D	D	D	D	D	D
Sodium dichromate, acid	D	D	D	D	D	D	D	D	D	D	D	D	D	D	D	D	D	D
Sodium hydroxide	B	B	B	B	C	C	C	C	B	B	B	B	B	D	B	A	A	A
Sodium hypochlorite	C	C	C	C	D	D	D	D	C	C	C	C	C	C	C	C	B	B
Sodium nitrate	B	B	B	B	C	C	C	C	B	B	B	B	B	B	A	A	A	A
Sodium peroxide	C	C	C	C	D	D	D	D	C	C	C	C	C	C	C	B	B	B
Sodium phosphate	A	A	A	A	B	B	B	B	A	A	A	A	A	A	A	A	A	A
Sodium silicate	A	A	A	A	B	B	B	B	A	A	A	A	A	A	A	A	A	A
Sodium sulfate	A	A	A	A	B	B	B	B	A	A	A	A	A	A	A	A	A	A
Sodium sulfide	C	C	C	C	B	B	B	B	B	B	C	C	C	C	C	B	B	B
Sodium sulfite	B	B	B	B	D	D	D	D	B	B	B	B	B	B	B	B	B	B
Sodium thiosulfate	C	C	C	C	B	B	B	B	B	C	C	C	C	C	C	C	B	B
Steam	A	A	A	A	C	C	C	A	A	A	A	A	A	A	A	B	A	A
Stearic acid	B	B	B	B	C	C	C	C	B	B	B	B	B	B	B	B	B	B
Sugar solutions	A	A	A	A	A	A	A	A	A	A	A	A	A	A	A	A	A	A
Sulfur, dry	B	B	B	B	A	A	A	A	A	B	B	B	A	A	A	B	A	B

(a) Copper and copper alloys are not attacked by dry gases at room temperature or lower. Acetylene forms an explosive compound with copper when moist and alloys containing more than 65% Cu should not be used with the wet gas under pressure. Moist carbon dioxide is corrosive to brasses high in zinc, but may be handled by other copper alloys. Tin coatings are highly resistant to moist carbon dioxide. Moist chlorine gas is corrosive to all copper alloys. Sulfur dioxide and sulfur trioxide in the presence of moisture form sulfurous and sulfuric acid, respectively. Copper, red brass, Everdur, phosphor bronze and cupronickel, 30% 715 should be considered for handling these gases when moist.

(b) Copper and its alloys are resistant to corrosion by most foods and beverages. However, consideration must be given to the possibility that such products handled in equipment made of copper or its alloys may dissolve traces of copper in amounts sufficient to discolor the product or alter its taste. In such cases it is recommended that the metal be tin-coated.

(c) Copper alloys are resistant to most organic solvents such as the acetates, alcohols, aldehydes, ketones, petroleum solvents, and ether. Organic acids in aqueous solution are corrosive to most copper alloys, but corrosion will be accelerated if air is present. Binary copper-zinc alloys containing more than 15% Zn may be attacked by dezincification corrosion. Copper alloys may be definitely corroded by chloride hydrocarbons, such as carbon tetrachloride and trichloroethylene, at the boiling point in the presence of moisture unless the hydrocarbons are stabilized by a neutralizer. Of the copper alloys, cupronickel, 30% 715 and tin-coated metal offer the best resistance to moist chloride hydrocarbons.

(d) Copper and copper alloys are rapidly corroded by oxidizing acids such as nitric and chromic. Corrosion by other acids is generally dependent on the presence of oxygen or some other oxidizing agent in the solution. Brasses containing not more than 15% Zn, and special brasses, can be used with many acids but, in general, high-zinc brasses should not be used with acids due to the danger of rapid corrosion by dezincification. Copper, red brass, phosphor bronze, Everdur, aluminum bronze, and cupronickel offer good resistance to corrosion by hot and cold dilute sulfuric acid and to corrosion by cold concentrated sulfuric acid. Intermediate concentrations of sulfuric acid sometimes are less corrosive to copper alloys than either concentrated acid or dilute acid. Concentrated sulfuric acid may be corrosive at elevated temperatures due to breakdown of the acid with the formation of metallic sulfides and sulfur dioxide gas causing localized pitting attack. Tests indicate that the copper alloys may be corroded by pitting attack by 90 to 95% sulfuric acid at about 50 °C (122 °F), by 80% acid at about 71 °C (160 °F), and by 60% acid at about 100 °C (212 °F).

(Continued)

Table 6   (continued)

Environment	Electrolytic tough pitch 110	Phosphorized 122	Commercial bronze 220	Red brass 230	Cartridge brass 260	Architectural bronze 385	Muntz metal 280	Tobin bronze 4641	Arsenical admiralty 443	Ambraloy 687	Phosphor bronze (A) 510	Phosphor bronze (D) 524	Aluminum bronze Ambraloy 630	Everdur 655	Everdur 651	Cupronickel, 10% 706	Cupronickel, 30% 715	Nickel silver, 18% 752
Sulfur, molten	D	D	D	D	D	D	D	D	D	D	D	D	D	D	D	D	D	D
Sulfur chloride, dry	A	A	A	A	A	A	A	A	A	A	A	A	A	A	A	A	A	A
Sulfur dioxide, dry	A	A	A	A	A	A	A	A	A	A	A	A	A	A	A	A	A	A
Sulfur dioxide, moist	B	B	B	B	D	D	D	D	B	B	B	B	B	B	B	C	C	C
Sulfur trioxide, dry	A	A	A	A	A	A	A	A	A	A	A	A	A	A	A	A	A	A
Sulfuric acid(d)	B	B	B	B	D	D	D	D	C	C	B	B	B	B	B	B	B	B
Sulfurous acid	B	B	B	B	D	D	D	D	B	B	B	B	B	B	B	C	C	C
Tannic acid	A	A	A	A	B	B	B	B	A	A	A	A	A	A	A	A	A	A
Tar	A	A	A	A	B	B	B	B	A	A	A	A	A	A	A	A	A	A
Tartaric acid(b)	A	A	A	A	C	C	C	C	A	A	A	A	A	A	A	A	A	A
Toluene	A	A	A	A	A	A	A	A	A	A	A	A	A	A	A	A	A	A
Trichloracetic acid	B	B	B	B	D	D	D	D	C	C	B	B	B	B	B	B	B	B
Trichloroethylene, dry	A	A	A	A	A	A	A	A	A	A	A	A	A	A	A	A	A	A
Trichloroethylene, moist	B	B	B	B	C	C	C	C	B	B	B	B	B	B	B	B	A	B
Turpentine	A	A	A	A	B	B	B	B	A	A	A	A	A	A	A	A	A	A
Varnish	A	A	A	A	A	A	A	A	A	A	A	A	A	A	A	A	A	A
Vinegar(b)	B	B	B	B	D	D	D	D	C	C	B	B	B	B	B	B	B	B
Water, potable	A	A	A	A	C	C	C	C	A	A	A	A	A	A	A	A	A	A
Zinc chloride	C	C	C	C	D	D	D	D	C	C	C	C	C	C	C	C	C	C
Zinc sulfate	B	B	B	B	D	D	D	D	B	B	B	B	B	B	B	B	B	B

(a) Copper and copper alloys are not attacked by dry gases at room temperature or lower. Acetylene forms an explosive compound with copper when moist and alloys containing more than 65% Cu should not be used with the wet gas under pressure. Moist carbon dioxide is corrosive to brasses high in zinc, but may be handled by other copper alloys. Tin coatings are highly resistant to moist carbon dioxide. Moist chlorine gas is corrosive to all copper alloys. Sulfur dioxide and sulfur trioxide in the presence of moisture form sulfurous and sulfuric acid, respectively. Copper, red brass, Everdur, phosphor bronze and cupronickel, 30% 715 should be considered for handling these gases when moist.
(b) Copper and its alloys are resistant to corrosion by most foods and beverages. However, consideration must be given to the possibility that such products handled in equipment made of copper or its alloys may dissolve traces of copper in amounts sufficient to discolor the product or alter its taste. In such cases it is recommended that the metal be tin-coated.
(c) Copper alloys are resistant to most organic solvents such as the acetates, alcohols, aldehydes, ketones, petroleum solvents, and ether. Organic acids in aqueous solution may be handled by copper and most copper alloys, but corrosion will be accelerated if air is present. Binary copper-zinc alloys containing more than 15% Zn may be subject to dezincification corrosion. Copper alloys may be definitely corroded by chloride hydrocarbons, such as carbon tetrachloride and trichloroethylene, at the boiling point in the presence of moisture unless the hydrocarbons are stabilized by a neutralizer. Of the copper alloys, cupronickel, 30% 715 and tin-coated metal offer the best resistance to moist chloride hydrocarbons.
(d) Copper and copper alloys are rapidly corroded by oxidizing acids such as nitric and chromic. Corrosion by other acids is generally dependent on the presence of oxygen or some other oxidizing agent in the solution. Brasses containing not more than 15% Zn, and special brasses, can be used with many acids, but, in general, high-zinc brasses should not be used with acids due to the danger of rapid corrosion by dezincification. Copper, red brass, phosphor bronze, Everdur, aluminum bronze, and cupronickel offer good resistance to corrosion by hot and cold dilute sulfuric acid and to corrosion by cold concentrated sulfuric acid. Intermediate concentrations of sulfuric acid sometimes are less corrosive to copper alloys than either concentrated acid or dilute acid. Concentrated sulfuric acid may be corrosive at elevated temperatures due to breakdown of the acid with the formation of metallic sulfides and sulfur dioxide gas causing localized pitting attack. Tests indicate that the copper alloys may be corroded by pitting attack by 90 to 95% sulfuric acid at about 50 °C (122 °F), by 80% acid at about 71 °C (160 °F), and by 60% acid at about 100 °C (212 °F).

Significant amounts of aluminum (5 to 12%) are added to the copper-nickel-iron-silicon-tin system to produce the aluminum bronzes. Aluminum bronzes provide a substantial range of corrosion resistance. Environments that should be avoided include nitric acid, some metallic salts (ferric chloride), moist chlorinated hydrocarbons, and moist ammonia. Exposure to the latter medium could trigger stress corrosion.

Coatings

Metallic coatings are not used for corrosion protection as on some materials. One of the distinctive features of copper is its color, especially that of the high-copper alloys. These are prone to tarnish with exposure in the natural environment. Organic coatings (lacquers) were developed to protect the finish of architectural copper. These types of coatings have limited applicability, especially when wear becomes a problem. The more corrosion-resistant copper alloys such as the cupro-nickels and nickel-silver are very tarnish resistant and do not seem to require a coating for protection.

Selection for Corrosion Resistance

Experience has been the best criterion for selecting the most suitable alloy for a given environment. To take advantage of experience, the corrosion curves in this book should be reviewed, manufacturers should be contacted for additional literature, and corrosion ratings compiled by trade/industry associations such as the Copper Development Association should be requested. There is no guaranteed way to determine the acceptability of a material in a given environment without some sort of laboratory or pilot plant trial. Short-term tests may be made to verify the approximate relationships shown by the corrosion data for copper and its alloys in this book. Long-term tests may show a different behavior. It is important to keep in mind that general corrosion data relates to general attack; if you have localized attack, such as pitting or crevice corrosion, published data may be irrelevant. It generally is understood that copper and its alloys provide a high level of corrosion resistance in a variety of media at reasonable costs. When selecting a material for an application, keep in mind that copper or its alloys may offer a lower cost corrosion alternative to stainless steels and nickel-base alloys.

Magnesium and Magnesium Alloys

Magnesium is rarely used for structural purposes in the unalloyed condition. Consequently, only the corrosion resistance of magnesium-base alloys is of principal concern. Magnesium is an active element and ranges at or near the top of the galvanic series when magnesium-base alloys are being considered. Despite its high ranking in electrochemical reactivity, magnesium is successfully used in a wide variety of industrial applications, including tool parts, ladders, gear boxes, etc. Table 7 gives the suitability of testing magnesium in various substances.

Magnesium alloys are resistant to atmospheric corrosion because protective films form in a process similar to the formation of film in the active metal aluminum. When corrosion does occur, it is the result of the breakdown of this protective film.

Magnesium corrosion can be accelerated by galvanic coupling, high levels of certain impurities (especially nickel, copper, and iron), or contamination (especially of castings) by salts. The principal rate-limiting factors in the atmospheric (aqueous) corrosion of magnesium alloys are associated with the breakdown of the magnesium hydroxide film and the rate of its reformation. Magnesium alloys are anodic to all other structural metals and will undergo galvanic attack if coupled to them. The attack is especially severe if the other metal in the couple is passive or inert as, for example, stainless steels or copper-base alloys.

Magnesium is prone to the usual forms of corrosion, but is especially susceptible to pitting. This effect is the logical consequence of the natural breakdown of the protective film in selective locations. It can also be caused by the selective location of impurities either within the alloy or on its surface. Some magnesium alloys are susceptible to stress-corrosion cracking, but this occurs mainly in alloys containing over about 1.5% aluminum. The tendency toward stress-corrosion cracking increases with increasing aluminum content. Under some circumstances, magnesium alloys are attacked by filiform corrosion or crevice corrosion.

At relative humidities below about 90%, magnesium alloys do not show extensive general corrosion by interior atmospheres. However, as humidity approaches 100%, more extensive tarnish films may form. While the thicknesses of such films are only of minor importance from an appearance point of view, they may be very significant to performance of a component such as a computer disk drive made of die cast magnesium alloy. Coatings or surface treatment can reduce the risk of such problems.

Compositions of the corrosion products that form on magnesium alloys in an atmosphere vary from one location to another and from indoor to outdoor exposure. When humidity is high and a magnesium alloy has been coated or clad, local breakdown of the protective cladding/coating or film can promote pitting corrosion instead of general corrosion on the component.

In stagnant distilled water at room temperature, magnesium alloys rapidly form a protective film that prevents further corrosion. However, small amounts of dissolved salts in the water break down the film locally, leading to pitting corrosion. Dissolved oxygen plays no major role in the corrosion of magnesium alloys in fresh water or saline solutions, contrary to its effect in many other alloy systems. When agitation (erosion) destroys or depletes the surface film, corrosion can be significantly increased. The corrosion of magnesium alloys by pure water substantially increases as temperature increases.

Severe corrosion of magnesium alloys may occur in neutral salt solutions of metals such as copper, nickel, and iron. This occurs because salts are deposited on the surface and form active cathodic sites on the anodic magnesium alloy surface. Magnesium is rapidly attacked by all mineral acids, except hydrofluoric acid and chromic acid. However, pitting may occur in hydrofluoric acid solutions.

Organic compounds such as aliphatic and aromatic hydrocarbons, ketones, ethers, glycols, and higher alcohols are not corrosive to magnesium and its alloys. Ethanol causes slight attack, and anhydrous methanol causes severe attack. Water added to the methanol reduces the rate of attack. Pure halogenated organic compounds do not attack magnesium at ambient temperatures, but at elevated temperatures or if water is present, such compounds may cause severe corrosion. Although ethylene glycol solutions produce negligible attack of magnesium at room temperature, when the magnesium is used alone or connected to steel, a significant acceleration of corrosion attack can occur at higher temperatures (such as 115 *C, or 240 *F) unless inhibitors are used. In acidic foodstuffs such as fruit juices and carbonated beverages, attack of magnesium occurs at a slow but measurable rate.

Magnesium and its alloys are used at moderately elevated temperatures with no significant oxidation attack up to the temperatures at which the alloys can be used structurally. Magnesium alloys are usually creep strength, not oxidation, limited. Water vapor in air or in oxygen sharply increases the rates of oxidation of magnesium and its alloys. These rates increase with temperature.

Dry halogens cause little or no corrosion of magnesium at room or moderately elevated temperatures. The presence of moisture causes pronounced attack by chlorine, some attack by iodine and bromine, but no attack by fluorine. Wet chlorine, iodine, or bromine, below the dew point of any aqueous phase, causes severe attack of magnesium.

Dry, gaseous sulfur dioxide causes no attack at ordinary temperatures. If moisture is present, some corrosion may

Table 7   Magnesium Suitability for Testing in Various Substances

Source: Dow Chemical USA, Midland, MI

Chemical	Concentration, %	Service test warranted
Acetaldehyde	Any	No
Acetic acid	Any	No
Acetone	Any	Yes
Acetylene	100	Yes
Alcohol, butyl	100	Yes
Alcohol, ethyl	100	Yes
Alcohol, isopropyl	100	Yes
Alcohol, methyl	100	No
Alcohol, propyl	100	Yes
Ammonia (gas or liquid)	100	Yes
Ammonium salts (most)	Any	No
Ammonium hydroxide	Any	Yes
Aniline	100	Yes
Anthracene	100	Yes
Arsenates (most)	Any	Yes
Benzaldehyde	Any	No
Benzene	100	Yes
Bichromates	Any	Yes
Boric Acid	1–5	No
Brake Fluids (most)	100	Yes
Bromides (most)	Any	No
Bromobenzene	100	Yes
Butter	100	No
Butylphenols	100	Yes
Calcium arsenate	Any	Yes
Calcium carbonate	100	Yes
Calcium chloride	Any	No
Calcium hydroxide	100	Yes
Camphor	100	Yes
Carbon bisulfide	100	Yes
Carbon dioxide (dry)	100	Yes
Carbon monoxide	100	Yes
Carbon tetrachloride	100	Yes
Carbonated water	Any	No
Castor oil	100	Yes
Cellulose	100	Yes
Cement	100	Yes
Chlorides (most)	Any	No
Chlorine	100	No
Chlorobenzenes	100	Yes
Chloroform	100	Yes
Chlorophenols	Any	No
Chlorophenylphenol	100	Yes
Chromates (most)	Any	Yes
Chromic acid	Any	Yes
Citronella oil	100	Yes
Cod liver oil (crude)	...	Yes
Copals	100	Yes
Coumarin	100	Yes
Cresol	100	Yes
Cyanides (most)	Any	Yes
Dichlorohydrin	100	Yes
Dichlorophenol	100	Yes
Dichromates (see bichromates)		
Diethanolamine	100	Yes
Diethyl aniline	100	Yes
Diethyl benzene	100	Yes
Diethylene glycol solutions	Any	Yes, may need inhibitors
Diphenyl	100	Yes
Diphenylamine	100	Yes
Diphenylmethane	100	Yes
Diphenyl oxide	100	Yes
Dipropylene glycol	100	Yes
Divinylbenzene	100	Yes
Dry cleaning fluids	100	Yes
Ethers	100	Yes
Ethanolamine (mono)	100	Yes
Ethyl acetate	100	Yes
Ethyl benzene	100	Yes
Ethyl bromide	100	No
Ethylcellulose	100	Yes
Ethyl chloride	100	Yes
Ethyl salicylate	100	Yes
Ethylene (gas)	100	Yes
Ethylene dibromide	100	Yes
Ethylene glycol solutions	Any	Yes, may need inhibitors
Fats, cooking (acid-free)	100	Yes
Fatty acids	Any	No
Ferric chloride	Any	No
Fluorides (most)	Any	Yes
Fluosilicic acid	Any	No
Formaldehyde	Any	Yes
Fruit juices and acids	Any	No
Fuel oil	100	Yes
Gasohol (10% ethanol)	100	Yes, if inhibited
Gasohol (10% methanol)	100	Yes, if inhibited
Gasoline (lead-free)	100	Yes, if inhibited
Gasoline (leaded)	100	Yes, if inhibited
Gelatine	Any	Yes
Glycerine C.P.	100	Yes
Grease (acid-free)	100	Yes
Heavy metal salts (most)	Any	No
Hexamine	3	Yes
Hydrochloric acid	Any	No
Hydrofluoric acid	5–60	yes
Hydrogen peroxide	Any	No
Hydrogen sulfide	100	Yes
Iodides	Any	No
Iodine crystals (dry)	100	Yes
Isopropyl acetate	100	Yes
Isopropyl benzene	100	Yes
Isopropyl bromide	Any	No
Kerosene	100	Yes
Lanolin	100	Yes
Lard	100	Yes
Lead arsenate	Any	Yes
Lead oxide	Any	No
Linseed oil	100	Yes
Magnesium arsenate	Any	Yes
Magnesium carbonate	100	Yes
Magnesium chloride	Any	No
Mercury salts	Any	No
Methane (gas)	100	Yes
Methyl bromide	Any	No
Methyl cellulose	100	Yes
Methyl chloride	100	Yes
Methylene chloride	100	Yes
Methyl salicylate	100	Yes
Milk (fresh and sour)	100	No
Mineral acids	Any	No
Monobromobenzene	100	Yes
Monochlorobenzene	100	Yes
Naphtha	100	Yes
Naphthalene	100	Yes
Nicotine sulfate	40	Yes
Nitrates (all)	Any	No
Nitrous gases	100	No
Nitric acid	Any	No
Nitroglycerin	Any	No
Oil, animal (acid- and chloride-free)	Any	Yes
Oil, mineral (chloride-free)	100	Yes
Oil, vegetable (chloride-free)	100	Yes
Oleic acid	100	Yes
Olive oil	100	Yes
Organic acids (most)	Any	No
Orthochlorophenol	100	No
Orthodichlorobenzene	100	Yes
Orthophenylphenol	100	Yes
Oxygen	100	Yes
Paraphenylphenol	100	Yes
Paradichlorobenzene	100	Yes
Pentachlorophenol	100	Yes
Perchloroethylene	100	Yes
Permanganates (most)	Any	Yes
Phenol	100	Yes
Phenyl ethyl acetate	100	Yes
Phenylphenols	100	Yes
Phosphates (most)	Any	Yes
Phosphoric acid	Any	No
Polypropylene glycols	100	Yes
Potassium fluoride	Any	Yes
Potassium hydroxide	Any	Yes
Potassium nitrite	Any	No
Potassium permanganate	Any	Yes
Propylene glycol U.S.P.	100	Yes
Propylene oxide	100	Yes, may need inhibitors
Pyridine (acid free)	100	Yes
Pyrogallol	Any	No
Rubber and rubber cements	100	Yes
Seawater	100	No
Sodium bromate	Any	No
Sodium bromide	Any	No
Sodium carbonate	Any	Yes
Sodium chloride	Any	No
Sodium cyanide	Any	Yes
Sodium dichromate	Any	Yes
Sodium fluoride	Any	Yes
Sodium hydroxide	Any	Yes
Sodium phosphate (tribasic)	Any	Yes
Sodium silicate	Any	Yes
Sodium sulfide	3	Yes
Sodium tetraborate	3	Yes
Steam	100	No
Stearic acid (dry)	100	Yes
Styrene polymer	100	Yes
Sugar solutions (acid-free)	Any	Yes
Sulfates (most)	Any	No
Sulfur	100	Yes
Sulfur dioxide (dry)	100	Yes
Sulfur chloride	Any	No
Sulfuric acid	Any	No
Sulfurous acid	Any	No
Tannic acid	3	No
Tanning solutions	Any	No
Tar, crude and its fractions	100	Yes
Tartaric acid	Any	No
Tetrahydronaphthalene	100	Yes
Titanium tetrachloride	100	Yes
Toluene (toluol)	100	Yes
Trichlorbenzene	100	Yes
Trichloroethylene	100	Yes
Trichlorophenol	100	Yes
Tung oil	100	Yes
Turpentine	100	Yes
Urea	100	Yes
Urea in aqueous solution (cold)	Any	Yes
Urea in aqueous solution (warm)	Any	No
Vinegar	Any	No
Vinylidine chloride	100	Yes
Vinyl toluene	100	Yes
Water, boiling	100	No
Water, distilled	100	Yes
Water, rain	100	Yes
Waxes (acid-free)	100	Yes
Xylol	100	Yes

occur. Wet sulfur dioxide gas is severely corrosive to magnesium. Ammonia (wet or dry) causes no attack at ambient temperatures; dry, gaseous sulfur dioxide causes no attack either. Some corrosion by sulfur dioxide may occur if water is present.

Although a great deal is known about the electrochemistry of magnesium and its alloys, very little information has been published concerning the role of alloying elements on corrosion resistance.

Effect of Alloying Elements

A study of the effects of 14 elements on the saltwater corrosion performance of magnesium in binary alloys showed the following trends. Aluminum, manganese, silicon, tin, lead, thorium, zirconium, and cerium had little or no deleterious effect on the basic saltwater corrosion performance of magnesium at levels either up to and exceeding their limits of solubility in magnesium or up to a maximum of 5%. Cadmium, zinc, calcium, and silver had mild-to-moderate accelerating effects on corrosion rates, whereas iron, cobalt, nickel, and copper had extremely deleterious effects on saltwater corrosion. The tolerances for these latter elements is a function of the basic alloy composition and the composition of the corroding medium.

No information is available on the effects of alloy elements on the elevated temperature (dry corrosion) oxidation resistance of magnesium. It seems probable that aluminum will be beneficial, but high-aluminum-content alloys are not preferred for elevated temperature structural applications, simply because other alloys are stronger.

Coatings

It is a common practice to protect the surface of magnesium and its alloys. They are protected by a wide range of chemical and anodic treatments. Proper cleaning and surface preparation are important steps to achieve optimum, lasting protection. Dichromate, chrome manganate, and chrome pickle treatments may be used. These chemical processes generally involve pickling and conversion of the oxide surface compounds by dipping in the appropriate solutions, which clean and passivate the surface through enhanced formation of magnesium hydroxide and a chromium compound. These films have limited protective value, but form a good base on which to subsequently apply organic coatings.

Anodizing by galvanic or applied current provides alternate protection. A hard, abrasion-resistant and corrosion-resistant surface layer is created. The anodized films are porous, just as in anodizing of aluminum; they may be sealed by immersion treatments in an appropriate solution, followed by draining and drying. Organic resins may be applied instead to seal the anodized surface. Epoxy resins are one type of organic used. Magnesium also may be protected by painting or plating.

Selection for Corrosion Resistance

In general, one does not think of selecting magnesium alloys for corrosion resistance in the same way that one thinks of the passive or more noble structural materials—copper, nickel, titanium (and their alloys), as well as stainless steel or aluminum. There is little to offer in the way of advice relative to alloy composition. Environmental avoidance, principally by the use of appropriate coatings, is the best way to ensure optimum corrosion resistance for the particular application. For maximum protection, high-purity alloys as well as inhibitors (if possible) in the environment will complement the selected protective coating.

Lead and Lead Alloys

The widespread and satisfactory use of lead and some lead alloys results from its ability to resist attack by corrosive chemicals, by a variety of atmospheres, and in underground applications either as a protective covering or as a distribution device containing a variety of highly aggressive chemicals. There is evidence of the use of buried lead pipe as early as ancient Egypt. An early corrosion resistance application during more recent times involved the use of lead in containers for sulfuric acid systems. Table 8 gives the corrosion behavior of lead in commonly used chemicals.

Corrosion Resistance

The corrosion resistance of lead is based on its ability to readily form a tenacious coating of a reaction product. This then becomes a protective coating. In principle, this process is similar to the surface protection that naturally forms on stainless steels and on certain aluminum alloys. Protective coatings on lead may form as the result of exposure to sulfates, oxides, carbonates, chromates, or chemical complexes. In aqueous phases, solubility of the corrosion product must be low enough to depress solution of the protective film formed on the lead. Also, where lead is used for transporting or for holding materials, the degree of turbulence within the system should be considered in construction designs so as to reduce the erosive effects on the protective coatings.

Industrial Applications

Beyond the common and expected use of lead as shielding for X-rays and nuclear installations and for storage battery grids, there are applications in which its corrosion resistance qualities

Table 8 Chemical Resistance of Lead to Various Materials

Source: *Lead for Corrosion Resistant Applications: A Guide,* Lead Industries Association, Inc., New York

Material	Behavior	Material	Behavior
Acetic acid	Lead is resistant to cold glacial acetic acid and acetic anhydride and is used as a material for making storage vessels. Lead is not recommended with lower concentrations because of the accelerating effect on corrosion of velocity, temperature and attack at the liquid-air interface	Chlorinated hydrocarbons	Lead can satisfactorily be used if inhibitors are present
Acetone	Lead is resistant and is used in equipment for its manufacture	Chlorinated polyvinyl chloride	Lead used throughout manufacture
Acetophenone	Lead equipment is used in manufacture and storage	Chlorination processes	Lead is slowly corroded at the temperatures normally used, but has satisfactory life and good economy when compared with other common metals
Acetylene	Lead is resistant to acetylene except when the gas is moist and contains hydrogen phosphide	Chlorine	Lead is resistant to dry chlorine and may be used with moist chlorine up to about 38 °C (100 °F)
Acetylene tetrachloride	Lead is satisfactory for lining feed tanks	Chloroacetic acid	Lead has only fair resistance, but is satisfactory for dilute solutions containing carbon tetrachloride
Adipic acid	Lead-lined digesters are used in manufacture	Chlorobenzene	Lead is satisfactory in solutions of chlorobenzene, sulfur dioxide and water
Alcohol, ethyl	No effect on lead	Chlorobromomethane	When dry (less than 0.02% H_2O) practically noncorrosive to lead
Alcohol, methyl	No effect on lead	Chromic acid	Lead may be used at fairly high concentrations. Used as anodes, heating coils, and tank linings for chromium plating installations. Proprietary lead alloys have been developed for better corrosion resistance with high speed plating solutions
Aluminum chloride	Lead is quite resistant to aluminum chloride at concentrations up to 10%. It is not recommended at higher concentrations. It is used to some extent in equipment for the manufacture of aluminum chloride	Coal tar	Lead is used in the refining and recovery of many by-products
Aluminum sulfate or alum	Lead is used satisfactorily in manufacture and handling of liquid alum	Concrete, cement or mortar	When "green," free lime is present and it will attack lead. If calcium chloride has been added, the attack will be accelerated. Applying asphalt coating on lead is recommended to prevent such corrosion. On aging, the free lime is converted to calcium carbonate, at which time corrosion will cease
Ammonia	Lead is resistant to the dry gas and to anhydrous liquid ammonia		
Ammonium azide	No significant effect on lead		
Ammonium bifluoride	Lead can be used satisfactorily		
Ammonium chloride	Lead may be used at ambient temperatures with concentrations up to 10%	Copper sulfate	Lead is used for anodes and tank linings in electrorefining, electroplating, and electroforming equipment and is preferred for acid solutions
Ammonium fluoride	Lead has acceptable resistance to ammonium fluoride at concentrations up to 20%. It is not recommended for use at high temperatures or in the presence of free ammonia	Dibutyl thiodiglycolate	Part of manufacturing process conducted in lead-lined vessels
Ammonium fluosilicate	Lead is sometimes used for valves and fittings	Dihydroxydiphenyl sulfone	Lead cooling coils and bonded lead-lined pressure vessels used in manufacture
Ammonium hydroxide	Lead is satisfactory for use in the liquid or gas phases at virtually all temperatures and concentrations	Electrogalvanizing	Lead equipment is often employed
		Ether	Little or no effect on lead. Lead used in its manufacture
Ammonium hydroxylamine	Lead is satisfactorily used in hydrolysis	Fatty acids	Lead can be used, but it will corrode slowly in presence of oxygen
Ammonium phosphate	Lead is fairly resistant to ammonium phosphate and is used in the manufacture of ammonium phosphate fertilizer	Ferric chloride	Lead is not recommended
		Ferric sulfate	Lead is resistant over a wide range of concentrations and temperatures. Used in its manufacture
Ammonium sulfate	Lead may be satisfactorily employed in the manufacture and handling of ammonium sulfate	Ferrous chloride	Lead is recommended
		Ferrous sulfate	Lead is suitable for tank linings and coils in production and use
Antimony chloride	Lead is corroded but can be used with comparative economy for chlorinating the trichloride to the pentachloride	Fluorolubes	Shipped in lead-lined pails to prevent contamination and discoloration
Arsenic acid	Lead is quite resistant to dilute arsenic acid. Lead salts may form, but pipe life is satisfactory with periodic cleaning	Formaldehyde (and formic acid)	Lead is resistant to formaldehyde of 100% concentration, but is not recommended for lower concentrations. Its reaction is similar to that with acetic acid
Barium sulfide	Lead tanks are used in handling solutions prior to precipitation of barium sulfide	Hexachlorbutadiene	Is highly corrosive to all metals except lead. Lead used throughout manufacture at temperatures up to 205 °C (400 °F)
Benzol	Pure benzol has little or no effect on lead		
Benzyl chloride	Lead is often used for storage equipment	Hexachlorethane	Lead-lined equipment is used for chlorination vessel and crystallizing basins up to 60% concentration and 136 °C (275 °F)
Benzylphenol	Manufactured in lead-lined vessels at temperatures up to 40 °C (104 °F)		
Bleach solution	Lead is satisfactory for an aqueous bleach solution of hydrogen peroxide and trisodium phosphate	Hydrochloric acid	Use of lead is not generally recommended, but it has been used with some corrosion in concentrations up to 30% at ambient temperatures and 20% at 100 °C (212 °F). Antimonial lead shows better resistance than ordinary lead
Boric acid	Lead is used satisfactorily in its manufacture		
Brine	See Sodium chloride		
Bromine	When cold and acid free, lead may be used for shipping containers	Hydrocyanic acid	Lead is used in its manufacture
Cadmium sulfate	Lead is widely employed for lining plating tanks	Hydrofluoric acid	Lead is commonly used and has fair resistance to dilute acid, under 65% strength at room temperature
Calcium acid phosphate	Lead can be used over a wide range of concentrations and temperatures		
Calcium carbonate	Lead is resistant to all concentrations found in natural waters	Hydrogen chloride (anhydrous hydrochloric acid)	Little effect on lead
Calcium disulfide	Lead is satisfactory	Hydrogen peroxide	A 50% by weight, aqueous solution of hydrogen peroxide has been found to cause pitting, with a penetration in excess of 50 mpy. The lead may catalyze the breakdown of hydrogen peroxide
Calcium hydroxide	Lead is not recommended for use in calcium hydroxide. Its presence in "green" cement corrodes lead in presence of moisture and oxygen		
Calcium pyridine sulfonate	If sulfuric acid is present, lead can be used	Magnesium chloride	Lead is fairly resistant to magnesium chloride at concentrations up to 10%. Otherwise, it is not recommended
Carbon dioxide	Lead is used in acid-carbonate systems for generating CO_2		
Carbon tetrachloride	Lead is used at ambient temperatures		
Castor oil in acid	Lead is used for piping and valves		

(Continued)

Table 8 (continued)

Material	Behavior	Material	Behavior
Cellophane spinning bath solutions	Lead equipment is used extensively	Magnesium sulfate	Lead is resistant over a wide range of concentrations and temperatures
Mercuric sulfate	Highly oxidizing, but lead in general has good resistance to most acid sulfate conditions at room temperature	Sodium chloride	Lead satisfactory for dilute solutions at ordinary temperatures. Sea water and brine are commonly handled in lead or antimonial lead
Mixed acids	Lead can be used with some mixtures of sulfuric acid and nitric acid. Lead used for tank linings for matte finishing brass with 50% sulfuric-50% nitric acid solution	Sodium hydrosulfite	Lead may be used satisfactorily
		Sodium hydroxide	Lead can be used with concentrations up to 30% and temperatures to 25 °C (77 °F). Strong solutions attack lead rapidly
Naphthalene	No effect on lead	Sodium hyposulfite	Lead can be used satisfactorily
Nickel sulfate and nickel plating solutions	Lead commonly used for tank linings and heating coils	Sodium silicate	No significant corrosive effect on lead
		Sodium sulfate	Lead can be used satisfactorily with solutions up to 10% concentration at boiling
Nitro-benzol and nitro-chlor-benzol	Corrosive to lead	Sodium sulfide	Lead can be used at temperatures up to 100 °C (212 °F)
Nitrocellulose	Lead widely used in all rayon manufacturing processes	Sodium sulfite	Lead can be used with solutions up to 20% concentration at 25 °C (77 °F). Used in its manufacture
Nitroglycerine	Lead used to handle spent acid from manufacturing process	Sulfur chloride	Has little effect on lead
Nitrosyl-sulfuric acid	Action on lead is least at specific gravity of about 1.5 to 1.6. Close control thus minimizes corrosion	Sulfur dioxide	Has little effect on lead when dry and can be used moist up to about 200 °C (392 °F)
Organic acids	Lead is generally not recommended, although it may be fairly resistant to organic acids if free sulfuric acid is present	Sulfur trioxide	Can be used satisfactorily with lead up to 150 °C (302 °F)
Oxalic-sulfuric acids	Lead is satisfactory with oxalic acid containing 1% free sulfuric acid in all concentrations from 5 to 50% and all temperatures from cold to boiling	Sulfuric acid	Lead is the standard material for handling this acid. It can be used with concentrations up to 96% at room temperature and 85% up to 220 °C (428 °F). It is sometimes used satisfactorily even up to 250 °C (482 °F)
Oxygen	Dry gas merely tarnishes lead		
Pentachlorethane	Lead used in manufacture and storage at temperatures up to 80 °C (176 °F)	Sulfurous acid	Lead is satisfactory up to about 220 °C (428 °F)
Phenol	Lead may be used satisfactorily	Tannic acid	Lead behavior is similar to that for acetic acid
Phosphoric acid	Lead due to the formation of protective films, may be used with concentrations up to 80% below 93 °C (200 °F). Impure acid has even less effect on lead and can be used up to 85% concentration	Tartaric acid	Lead behavior is similar to that for acetic acid
		Tetrachloroethane	Bonded lead reaction tower and other lead-lined equipment used in manufacture
Phosphorus oxychloride	Storage tanks are constructed of lead or bonded lead. Lead piping, coils and receivers also used in its manufacture. Commonly shipped in lead carboys, lead-lined drums, or lead-lined tank trucks	Thionyl chloride	Lead is satisfactory at temperatures up to 150 °C (302 °F)
		Titanium sulfate	Solutions can be handled in lead
		Titanium tetrachloride	Lead gaskets used in pipe flanges
Photographic solutions	Lead is generally satisfactory	Urea	Lead-lined autoclave and stills used in manufacture at temperatures up to 190 °C (374 °F)
Potassium hydroxide	Lead is satisfactory up to 50% concentration and temperatures to 60 °C (140 °F)	Water, distilled	Has no effect in the absence of dissolved CO_2 and oxygen. Not generally recommended for such use
Potassium metabisulphite	The preferred material of construction is lead and lead-lined steel. Evaporated in lead-lined tanks at 71 °C (160 °F)	Water, natural	Usually has no effect on lead because of protective coating formed from dissolved salts. Very soft waters or those of peaty origin may dissolve lead slightly. Such action can be prevented by treatment of the waters with lime or sodium silicate to raise the "hardness"
Potassium permanganate	Attacks lead; not recommended		
Pyridine	Does not affect lead which is used for vacuum distilling equipment		
Silica gel	Lead is used for tank linings, pipes, and valves in the process of washing silica gel	Wood	Most wood has little or no corrosive effect on lead. A few instances of corrosion by wood containing organic acids, such as green oak, have been reported. Wood to be lined with lead should be inspected for presence of borers
Silicates	These form protective films on lead		
Sodium bifluoride	Successfully handled in lead		
Sodium bisulfate	Lead is resistant to sodium bisulfate over a wide range of temperatures and concentrations	Zinc chloride	Lead can be used satisfactorily
Sodium bisulfite	Lead may be used with a wide range of concentrations and temperatures	Zinc hydrosulfite	Manufactured in lead-lined tanks using lead cooling coils
Sodium carbonate	Dilute solutions do not affect lead. Not recommended for solutions over 25% at temperatures above 66 °C (150 °F)	Zinc sulfate	Lead preferred when solution is acid. Employed for its manufacture and use

are of primary importance. Examples include chemical-industry piping, tanks, tank linings, valves, and fittings. Until a generation ago, the construction industry frequently used the material in roofing gutters, plumbing, shower pans, drain pipes, and flashings. Such applications are constantly encountered in older structures. More recently, telephone and power transmission equipment employed lead sheathing on overhead poles and in both underwater and overhead installations. To a large extent, contemporary engineered materials have replaced the metal in most of these applications. However, lead is still used in the electronics industry and in conjunction with certain types of acids.

Corrosion in Acids

Lead is commercially used for resistance to sulfuric, sulfurous, chromic, and phosphoric acids. It has somewhat poorer, although often adequate, corrosion resistance to hydrochloric and hydrofluoric acids. Lead has excellent resistance to neutral solutions in which carbonates help to form the protective surface. It also has fair resistance to most alkaline solutions.

Lead has very little susceptibility to passivation in oxidizing acids. However, it is very stable in those media in which soluble corrosion products of lead can form. This generalization is especially true with solutions containing sulfate ion, such as sulfuric acid or solutions of its salts. By contrast, lead is not stable in nitric and acetic acids, nor in alkalis.

Lead resists sulfurous, cold phosphoric, chromic, and hydrofluoric acids. In hydrofluoric acid, lead is stable only at an acid concentration of 10%, and this is at comparatively low temperatures. In mixtures of sulfuric and hydrochloric acids, lead is much more stable than in hydrochloric acid alone. With the exception of cold nitric acid at high concentrations, the metal does not resist nitric acid. Lead corrodes rapidly in acetic and formic acids.

The corrosion rate in acids increases rapidly in the presence of oxygen and also in oxygen in combination with soft waters, such as rain and distilled water. Corrosion increases at a rate approximately proportional to the oxygen content of the water.

Atmospheric and Underground Corrosion

Lead is highly resistant in atmospheric exposures. It is frequently preferred over such metals as iron, zinc, and nickel in industrial atmospheres strongly contaminated with sulfur compounds such as H_2S, SO_2, or H_2SO_4.

In most of its forms, lead exhibits consistent durability in all types of atmospheres, including rural, industrial, and marine. In rural settings, the only important environmental factors that affect corrosion are the level of humidity and the amounts of rainfall and air flow. Near the sea, saline air exerts a strong effect on the corrosion rate. In industrial atmospheres, sulfur oxides and minerals in solid emissions may change the pattern of corrosion. However, the protective films that form on lead from exposure to industrial and marine atmospheres are so effective that the extent of the corrosion is usually insignificant.

Although some soils are more corrosive than others, severe corrosion of lead in underground service is rare. In general, the rate of corrosion *decreases* in soil according to the following order—muck, cinders, sand, and clay. When either lime or fresh concrete is present in the envelope of soil, water seepage and the presence of oxygen increase the corrosion rate. This is especially true for underground installations, but also for aboveground structures if the soil factor is discounted. To prevent corrosion under these conditions, lead components are frequently coated with asphalt, which provides protection during the curing of the concrete.

Corrosion in Waters

Distilled water that is free of oxygen and CO_2 does not attack lead. Lead steam coils that handle pure water condensate are not severely corroded if all condensate is returned to the boiler with only negligible amounts of makeup water. If appreciable amounts are used, corrosion from dissolved oxygen can become severe.

In general, the corrosion rate of lead in natural waters depends on water hardness, as caused by calcium and magnesium salts. Moderate amounts of these salts form protective films on the lead that adequately protect it against corrosive attack. Silicate salts present in the water increase both the hardness and the protective value of the film. In contrast, nitrate and chloride ions either interfere with the formation of the protective film or penetrate it. Thus, they increase corrosion. Lead also corrodes severely in underground waters containing either organic acids or large amounts of carbonic acid.

Grades of Lead

For corrosion resistance, lead is usually chosen from the ASTM grades known as acid-copper lead. In some instances, lead alloys are chosen (e.g., alloys such as lead with 0.05% tellurium and lead-antinomy alloys). Lead with 6% antinomy is probably the most common. Data show that corrosion rates for these alloys are not significantly different from commercially pure lead. As a rule, these alloys are used to gain strength over that offered by pure lead.

Disadvantages

Despite the overall excellent corrosion-resisting properties of lead, the metal itself presents usage limitations in at least three areas. First, its strength and hardness are very low, as contrasted with that of stainless steel and other corrosion-resisting metals. Second, lead is extremely heavy compared to steel. Consequently, underground applications lend themselves more readily than aerospace. Third, there is the factor of eye appeal. After it gains its protective coating, the metal simply does not have an appearance that is acceptable for applications demanding a degree of attractiveness.

Zinc and Zinc Alloys

Zinc is one of two metals that are used extensively in protective coatings on steel and sometimes on aluminum. Its excellent protective properties, along with its relatively high corrosion resistance in a natural environment, ensure that the metal will have wide industrial application. When used as a coating, it produces an anodic coating that not only protects mechanically by shielding, but also electrochemically. Zinc and its alloys are used extensively as galvanic anodes. Large amounts of zinc are used to produce copper-zinc (brass) alloys. However, zinc-base alloys find few applications. The susceptibility of zinc to passivation is insignificant, although it can be easily passivated in chromate solutions. Table 9 contains corrosion-rate data for zinc in contact with various chemicals.

Atmospheric Corrosion

The resistance of zinc to corrosion in all types of atmospheres is the property most broadly exploited. In wrought zinc products, this attribute is capitalized on throughout service life. On galvanized steel, the initial corrosion resistance of zinc continues well into the service life of the part. When the underlying steel is finally exposed, the ability of zinc to protect sacrificially continues.

Although several factors contribute to the rate at which zinc corrodes in outdoor exposure, two of the principal governing factors are the frequency and duration of moisture contact and the rate of drying in rural atmospheres. Near industrial sites, these conditions are aggravated by pollutants, usually acids. Thus, the rate of attack depends largely on the degree of acidity in the atmosphere. The most harmful atmospheric conditions are those in which frequent wetting of the metal results from dew, rain, and fog, especially if the moisture has a high acidic content.

Aqueous Corrosion

Temperature, gases in waters, and water hardness, singly or collectively, influence the corrosion rate (or corrosion resistance) of zinc. The corrosion rate of zinc increases rapidly between room temperature and approximately 60 °C (140 °F). At this point, there is a distinct turnaround, and the rate decreases markedly at 100 °C (212 °F). Under comparable circumstances, the corrosion rate of zinc in water is less than that of iron. Thus, zinc coatings are widely used in contact with water. As with other common metals, the rate of attack varies greatly with variations in exposure conditions. With zinc, the corrosion rate depends on temperature, pH, and oxygen concentration. It increases with increasing oxygen and carbon dioxide content.

Under conditions where the oxygen content cannot be replaced as quickly as it is consumed by the corrosion process, such as in stagnant water, zinc is attacked rapidly in localized areas, thereby creating pits. As more oxygen is made available, corrosion becomes more uniform. With further increase in oxygen content of the water, the corrosion rate increases. For example, when thin films of moisture condense on a zinc surface, the concurrent rapid supply of oxygen at the corroding surface has a decided accelerating effect on the corrosion rate.

Both this and the stagnant water types of attack can be minimized by the use of chromate films. Experimentation has shown that, with test pieces immersed in water through which oxygen was bubbled, corrosion occurred about eight times as fast as with specimens in water that was boiled to remove gases and then cooled out of contact with air.

Natural Fresh Waters

The corrosion rate of zinc in natural fresh waters depends on the composition of the water, which can vary over a wide range. Water hardness is an important consideration. Hard waters usually deposit protective films on zinc surfaces. Thus, they are less corrosive than soft waters. As an example, weight losses

ranging from 3 $mg^2/dm^2/day$ in hard water to as much as 27 $mg^2/dm^2/day$ in distilled water have been observed with high-grade zinc.

Dissolved Salts, Acids, and Bases

Zinc should not be considered for use in strong acids and alkalis. Even dilute acids accelerate corrosion rates of zinc beyond the limits of usefulness. Alkaline solutions of moderate strength are less corrosive than corresponding concentrations of acids, but are still sufficiently corrosive so as to eliminate zinc as a candidate material.

The addition of iron, nickel, copper, and noble metals, because of their low hydrogen overvoltage, considerably increase corrosion of zinc in acids.

In neutral solutions, zinc corrodes basically by oxygen depolarization, and the impurities in the zinc do not appreciably change its corrosion behavior. Zinc is not resistant to alkalis, because zinc oxide is amphoteric and forms zincates in solution, such as Na_2ZnO_2.

Nonaqueous Liquids and Gases

Many organic liquids that are nearly neutral in pH and substantially free from water do not attack zinc. Because of this, zinc and zinc-coated products are commonly used with gasoline, glycerine, and inhibited trichlorethylene. The presence of free water may cause local corrosion, because of the lack of access to oxygen. With water present, zinc may function as a catalyst in the decomposition of solutions like trichlorethylene, thereby resulting in acid attack. Some organic compounds, such as low-grade glycerine, attack zinc.

Zinc may safely come in contact with most common gases at normal temperatures, provided water is not present. Moisture content stimulates attack. Dry chlorine does not affect zinc, and hydrogen sulfide is also harmless, because insoluble zinc sulfide is formed. On the other hand, sulfur dioxide and chlorides have a corrosive effect because water-soluble and hygroscopic salts are formed.

Food-Processing Applications

Zinc and zinc coatings are regularly avoided by the food-processing industry simply because zinc is not sufficiently stable in these environments. Moreover, zinc salts are toxic.

Corrosion Inhibitors

When zinc is in contact with water in a closed system, inhibitors are commonly used to minimize corrosion. Inhibitors include sodium dichromate, sodium silicate, and borax. For most purposes, the adjustment of pH to the mildly alkaline range and also the addition of sodium dichromate to the system is the preferred technique of corrosion control. An insufficient amount of inhibitor may result in pitting corrosion.

Table 9 Resistance of Zinc and Zinc Coatings to Corrosion in Chemical Environments

Chemicals and simple mixtures are listed alphabetically, with the main chemical of the mixture listed first. Chemical specialty mixtures, which often contain a number of components, have been placed under application headings (e.g., Agricultural chemicals, Building materials). There was little uniformity in test conditions among the various investigations from which these data were compiled. For example, test temperatures ranged from below zero to the boiling point, and time of immersion from a few hours to several months. The test procedures also included exposure to vapors and partial or total immersion in the solutions. The test conditions adopted in each investigation were no doubt dictated by specific objectives, but in comparing results of the tests, the possible influence of the test variables should be taken into account.
Source: *Zinc: Its Corrosion Resistance*, International Lead Zinc Research Organization, Inc., New York, 1983

Corrosion medium	Material	Type of test(a)	Temperature °C	°F	Duration	Aeration	Agitation	Corrosion rate mg/dm²/day(b)	mil/year	Remarks	Ref
Acetic acid											
0.1 g/L in air		(L) In vapors	30	86	8 days	· · ·	· · ·	69.0	14.0		1
0.005 ppm in air over water	99.95%Zn	(L) In vapors	30	86	21 days	· · ·	· · ·	0.91	0.2	100% RH	2
0.05 ppm in air over water	99.95% Zn	(L) In vapors	30	86	21 days	· · ·	· · ·	2.14	0.4	100% RH	2
0.5 ppm in air over water	99.95% Zn	(L) In vapors	30	86	21 days	· · ·	· · ·	25.9	5.2	100% RH	2
2.0 ppm in air over water	99.95% Zn	(L) In vapors	30	86	21 days	· · ·	· · ·	118.0	23.6	100% RH	2
3.5 ppm in air over water	99.95% Zn	(L) In vapors	30	86	21 days	· · ·	· · ·	143.7	28.8	100% RH	2
5.0 ppm in air over water	99.95% Zn	(L) In vapors	30	86	21 days	· · ·	· · ·	193.0	38.6	100% RH	2
20.0 ppm in air over water	99.95% Zn	(L) In vapors	30	86	21 days	· · ·	· · ·	55.2	11.0	100% RH	2
35.0 ppm in air over water	99.95% Zn	(L) In vapors	30	86	21 days	· · ·	· · ·	35.8	7.2	100% RH	2
50.0 ppm in air over water	99.95% Zn	(L) In vapors	30	86	21 days	· · ·	· · ·	38.8	7.7	100% RH	2
500.0 ppm in air over water	99.95% Zn	(L) In vapors	30	86	21 days	· · ·	· · ·	85.6	17.1	100% RH	2
1% in water	99.95% Zn	(L) In vapors	30	86	6 days	· · ·	· · ·	218.1	43.6	100% RH	2
0.5% in sat'd sodium acetate	99.95% Zn	(L) In vapors	30	86	42 days	· · ·	· · ·	5.52	1.1	72% RH	2
Water solution, pH 3.8	Galv.	(L) In vapors	Room		8 days	· · ·	· · ·	8.0	1.6	100% RH	3
2.1% solution	Galv. steel	(L) In vapors	Room		30 days	· · ·	· · ·	26.5(c)	5.4		4
								13.3(d)	2.7		
								5.4(e)	1.1		
								3.0(f)	0.6		
5.1% solution	Galv. steel	(L) In vapors	Room		30 days	· · ·	· · ·	10.1(c)	2.0		4
								4.6(d)	0.9		
								1.2(e)	0.2		
								2.9(f)	0.6		
6% solution		(L) Immersion	30	86	2 days	None	None	3 050.0	610.0		5
6% solution		(L) Immersion	30	86	2 days	15–20 air bubbles per min	· · ·	3 650.0	730.0		5
Acetone											
CP		(L) In vapors	Boiling		1 month	· · ·	· · ·	0.0	0.0		1
CP		(L) Immersion	Room		6 months	None	None	0.004	<0.1		1
CP + formic acid equiv. to 0.10 mg KOH/g	Sheet	(L) Partial immersion	30	86	7 days	None	None	0.1	<0.1		6
CP + 5% water	Sheet	(L) Partial immersion	30	86	7 days	None	None	0.1	<0.1		6
Agricultural chemicals											
Ammonium sulfamate	Sheet	(F) Immersion	15–40	60–100	98 days	· · ·	· · ·	15.0	3.0		1
Blue Amate Brush Killer	Sheet	(F) Immersion	15–40	60–100	112 days	Yes	Yes	4.7	1.0		1
Esteron Brush Killer (2–4D + 2,4,5–T1 gal/100 gal water	Sheet	(F) Immersion	15–32	60–90	119 days	· · ·	· · ·	18.5	4.0		1
Ammonium sulfate	Galv.	(L) Alternate humidity, weekly cycle forced-air circulation 24 h, 100% RH (1), 24 h, dry air (2). Repeat (1) and (2), then 8 h, 100% RH, 64 h dry air	· · ·	· · ·	121 days	· · ·	· · ·	· · ·	10.0	Zinc stripped	7
Nitrolime	Galv.	As above	· · ·	· · ·	121 days	· · ·	· · ·	· · ·	12.0	Zinc stripped	7
300 g/L CuSO₄ · 5H₂O	Galv.	As above	· · ·	· · ·	121 days	· · ·	· · ·	· · ·	3.0	Zinc partly stripped	7
280 g/L CoSO₄ · 5H₂O	Galv.	As above	· · ·	· · ·	121 days	· · ·	· · ·	· · ·	0.0	Zinc penetrated locally	7
Potassium chloride (com.)	Galv.	As above	· · ·	· · ·	121 days	· · ·	· · ·	· · ·	4.0	Zinc partly stripped	7
Superphosphate	Galv.	As above	· · ·	· · ·	121 days	· · ·	· · ·	· · ·	0.0		7
Super compound	Galv.	As above	· · ·	· · ·	121 days	· · ·	· · ·	· · ·	0.0		7
Super compound + small amount of copper sulfate	Galv.	As above	· · ·	· · ·	121 days	· · ·	· · ·	· · ·	0.0	Zinc penetrated locally	7
Super compound + small amount of cobalt sulfate	Galv.	As above	· · ·	· · ·	121 days	· · ·	· · ·	· · ·	0.0		7

(a) (L) laboratory test; (F) field test. (b) Unless otherwise indicated. Some corrosion rates are given in specialized units dictated by the test procedures used by the original investigators. The conversion to inches per year in some of these cases should not be considered representative of continuous immersion results, but should be evaluated in light of the test conditions. (c) Chromium in surface film, 0.02 μg/dm². (d) Chromium in surface film, 1.3 μg/dm². (e) Chromium in surface film, 2.2 μg/dm². (f) Chromium in surface film, 0.1 μg/dm². (g) Chromium in surface film, 0 μg/dm². (h) Chromium in surface film, 0.2 μg/dm²

(Continued)

Table 9 (continued)

Corrosion medium	Material	Type of test(a)	Temperature °C	°F	Duration	Aeration	Agitation	Corrosion rate mg/dm²/day(b)	mil/year	Remarks	Ref
Agricultural lime	Galv.	As above	...	...	121 days	...	...	...	0.0	Zinc not penetrated	7
Burnt lime	Galv.	As above	...	...	121 days	...	...	...	0.0	Zinc not penetrated	7
Basic slag	Galv.	As above	...	...	121 days	...	...	...	0.0	Zinc not penetrated	7
Bone meal	Galv.	As above	...	...	121 days	...	...	...	0.0	Zinc not penetrated	7
Phosphorized Pollard	Galv.	As above	...	...	121 days	...	...	...	0.0	Zinc not penetrated	7

Damp granular fertilizers

Type	Components	Percent water	Material	Type of test(a)	°C	°F	Duration	Aeration	Agitation	mg/dm²/day(b)	mil/year	Remarks	Ref
11–48–0	$NH_4H_2PO_4$, $(NH_4)_2HPO_4$	5.41	Sp.H.G.(1)	(L) Immersed	60	140	33 days	Repacked with fresh water once a week		80.0	16.0		8
11–48–0	$NH_4H_2PO_4$, $(NH_4)H_2PO_4$	5.41	Die-cast AG-40A(2)	(L) Immersed	60	140	33 days			45.9	10.0	Galv. steel, failed in all mixtures	8
12–12–12	11–48–0, $(NH_4)_2SO_4$, KCl	6.18	(1)	(L) Immersed	60	140	33 days			1 005.0	201.0		8
12–12–12	11–48–0, $(NH_4)_2SO_4$, KCl	6.18	(2)	(L) Immersed	60	140	33 days			1 460.0	318.0		8
13–16–10	11–48–0, $(NH_4)_2SO_4$, KCl	6.68	(1)	(L) Immersed	60	140	33 days			50.0	10.0		8
13–16–10	11–48–0, $(NH_4)_2SO_4$, KCl	6.68	(2)	(L) Immersed	60	140	33 days			55.0	12.0		8
16–20–0	11–48–0, $(NH_4)_2SO_4$	4.10	(1)	(L) Immersed	60	140	33 days			35.0	7.0		8
16–20–0	11–48–0, $(NH_4)_2SO_4$	4.10	(2)	(L) Immersed	60	140	33 days			156.0	34.0		8
35.5–0–0	NH_4NO_3	3.54	(1)	(L) Immersed	60	140	33 days			2 290.0	458.0		8
35.5–0–0	NH_4NO_3	3.54	(2)	(L) Immersed	60	140	33 days			788.0	172.0		8
21–0–0	$(NH_4)_2SO_4$	2.50	(1)	(L) Immersed	60	140	33 days			22.0	4.4		8
21–0–0	$(NH_4)_2SO_4$	2.50	(2)	(L) Immersed	60	140	33 days			6.9	1.5		8
(a) 11–48–0		5.4	Sp.H.G.(1)	(L) Immersion	Room		11 days			37.5	7.5	Four changes of moist fertilizer in all tests	8
(a) 11–48–0		5.4	Die-cast AG-40A(2)	(L) Immersion	Room		11 days			19.7	4.3		8
(a) 11–48–0		5.4	(1)	(L) Immersion	60	140	11 days			38.5	7.7		8
(a) 11–48–0		5.4	(2)	(L) Immersion	60	140	11 days			14.2	3.1		8
(b) 16–20–0		4.1	(1)	(L) Immersion	Room		11 days			16.5	3.3		8
(b) 16–20–0		4.1	(2)	(L) Immersion	Room		11 days			14.2	3.1		8
(b) 16–20–0		4.1	(1)	(L) Immersion	60	140	11 days			83.5	16.7		8
(b) 16–20–0		4.1	(2)	(L) Immersion	60	140	11 days			77.5	16.9		8
(c) 33.5–0–0		3.5	(1)	(L) Immersion	Room		11 days			250.0	50.0		8
(b) 33.5–0–0		3.5	(2)	(L) Immersion	Room		11 days			65.7	14.3		8
(b) 33.5–0–0		3.5	(1)	(L) Immersion	60	140	11 days			595.0	119.0		8
(b) 33.5–0–0		3.5	(2)	(L) Immersion	60	140	11 days			168.0	36.7		8
(d) 21–0–0		2.5	(1)	(L) Immersion	Room		11 days			37.0	7.4		8
(d) 21–0–0		2.5	(2)	(L) Immersion	Room		11 days			19.7	4.3		8
(d) 21–0–0		2.5	(1)	(L) Immersion	60	140	11 days			84.5	16.9		8
(d) 21–0–0		2.5	(2)	(L) Immersion	60	140	11 days			47.3	10.3		8
(e) 27–14–0 (a), (b)		4.5	(1)	(L) Immersion	Room		11 days			92.0	18.4		8
(e) 27–14–0 (a), (b)		4.5	(2)	(L) Immersion	Room		11 days			29.8	6.5		8
(e) 27–14–0 (a), (b)		4.5	(1)	(L) Immersion	60	140	11 days			345.0	69.0		8
(e) 27–14–0 (a), (b)		4.5	(2)	(L) Immersion	60	140	11 days			60.5	13.2		8
(f) 8–32–16 (a), (d), KCl		5.0	(1)	(L) Immersion	Room		11 days			92.0	18.4		8
(f) 8–32–16 (a), (d), KCl		5.0	(2)	(L) Immersion	Room		11 days			32.5	7.1		8
(f) 8–32–16 (a), (d), KCl		5.0	(1)	(L) Immersion	60	140	11 days			130.0	26.0		8
(f) 8–32–16 (a), (d), KCl		5.0	(2)	(L) Immersion	60	140	11 days			100.0	22.0		8
(g) 6–24–24 (a), (d), KCl		5.2	(1)	(L) Immersion	Room		11 days			93.0	18.6	Heterogeneous mixture	8
(g) 6–24–24 (a), (d), KCl		5.2	(2)	(L) Immersion	Room		11 days			44.9	9.8	Heterogeneous mixture	8
(g) 6–24–24 (a), (d), KCl		5.2	(1)	(L) Immersion	60	140	11 days			135.0	27.0	Heterogeneous mixture	8
(g) 6–24–24 (a), (d), KCl		5.2	(2)	(L) Immersion	60	140	11 days			67.5	14.7	Heterogeneous mixture	8

Liquid fertilizers

Corrosion medium	Material	Type of test(a)	°C	°F	Duration	Aeration	Agitation	mg/dm²/day(b)	mil/year	Remarks	Ref
27–14–0.25% solution	99.99% Zn	(L) Partial immersion	Room		21 days	None	None	34.0	6.8		8
27–14–0.25% solution	99.99% Zn	(L) Partial immersion	Room		14 days	Oxygen added daily	...	114.5	22.9		8
27–14–0.25% solution	99.99% Zn	(L) Partial immersion	60	140	21 days	None	None	44.5	8.9		8

(a) (L) laboratory test; (F) field test. (b) Unless otherwise indicated. Some corrosion rates are given in specialized units dictated by the test procedures used by the original investigators. The conversion to inches per year in some of these cases should not be considered representative of continuous immersion results, but should be evaluated in light of the test conditions. (c) Chromium in surface film, 0.02 µg/dm². (d) Chromium in surface film, 1.3 µg/dm². (e) Chromium in surface film, 2.2 µg/dm². (f) Chromium in surface film, 0.1 µg/dm². (g) Chromium in surface film, 0 µg/dm². (h) Chromium in surface film, 0.2 µg/dm²

(Continued)

Table 9 (continued)

Corrosion medium	Material	Type of test(a)	Temperature °C	°F	Duration	Aeration	Agitation	Corrosion rate mg/dm²/day(b)	mil/year	Remarks	Ref
27–14–0.25% solution	99.99% Zn	(L) Partial immersion	60	140	14 days	Oxygen added daily	· · ·	105.0	21.0		8
27–14–0.25% solution	99.99% Zn	(L) Total immersion	Room		21 days	None	None	6.5	1.3		8
27–14–0.25% solution	99.99% Zn	(L) Total immersion	Room		14 days	Oxygen added daily	· · ·	33.5	6.7		8
27–14–0.25% solution	99.99% Zn	(L) Total immersion	60	140	21 days	None	None	8.5	1.7		8
27–14–0.25% solution	99.99% Zn	(L) Total immersion	60	140	14 days	Oxygen added daily	· · ·	45.0	9.0		8
6–16–7 liquid fertilizer	99.99% Zn	(L) Immersion	Room		16 days	· · ·	· · ·	23.5	4.7		8
6–16–7 liquid fertilizer	99.99% Zn	(L) Immersion	60	140	8 days	· · ·	· · ·	75.5	15.1		8
6–16–7 liquid fertilizer	99.99% Zn	(L) Partial immersion	Room		16 days	· · ·	· · ·	40.5	8.1		8
6–16–7 liqiud fertilizer	99.99% Zn	(L) Partial immersion	60	140	8 days	· · ·	· · ·	8.5	1.7		8
6–16–7 liqiud fertilizer	99.99% Zn	(L) Alternate immersion	Room		14 days	None	· · ·	18.5	3.7		8
EB-32 fertilizer solution, contains elemental S, and 0.1% Na₂Cr₂O₇	99.99+% Zn	(L) Immersion	60	140	· · ·	None	None	46 500.0	9 300.0		8
8–24–0 fertilizer solution	99.99+% Zn	(L) Immersion	Room		5 h	None	None	515.0	103.0		8
8–24–0 fertilizer solution	99.99+% Zn	(L) Immersion	Room		10 h	None	None	400.0	80.0		8
8–24–0 fertilizer solution	99.99+% Zn	(L) Immersion	Room		100 h	None	None	240.0	48.0		8
Herbicides											
7% zinc sulfamate	Comm. zinc	(L) Immersion	Room		28 days	· · ·	· · ·	6.5	1.3		8
7% zinc sulfamate	Galv. steel	(L) Immersion	Room		28 days	· · ·	· · ·	6.5	1.3		8
40% zinc sulfamate	Comm. zinc	(L) Immersion	Room		28 days	· · ·	· · ·	3.0	0.6		8
40% zinc sulfamate	Galv. steel	(L) Immersion	Room		28 days	· · ·	· · ·	6.5	1.3		8
7% ammonium sulfamate	Comm. zinc	(L) Immersion	Room		28 days	· · ·	· · ·	35.0	7.0		8
7% ammonium sulfamate	Galv. steel	(L) Immersion	Room		28 days	· · ·	· · ·	65.0	13.0		8
40% ammonium sulfamate	Comm. zinc	(L) Immersion	Room		28 days	· · ·	· · ·	45.0	9.0		8
40% ammonium sulfamate	Galv. steel	(L) Immersion	Room		28 days	· · ·	· · ·	75.0	15.0		8
7% guanidine sulfamate	Comm. zinc	(L) Immersion	Room		28 days	· · ·	· · ·	28.0	5.6		8
7% guanidine sulfamate	Galv. steel	(L) Immersion	Room		28 days	· · ·	· · ·	24.0	4.8		8
40% guanidine sulfamate	Comm. zinc	(L) Immersion	Room		28 days	· · ·	· · ·	4.5	0.9		8
40% guanidine sulfamate	Galv. steel	(L) Immersion	Room		28 days	· · ·	· · ·	4.5	0.9		8
7% Du Pont Ammate	Comm. zinc	(L) Immersion	Room		28 days	· · ·	· · ·	11.0	2.2		8
7% Du Pont Ammate	Galv. steel	(L) Immersion	Room		28 days	· · ·	· · ·	41.5	8.3		8
40% Du Pont Ammate	Comm. zinc	(L) Immersion	Room		28 days	· · ·	· · ·	3.5	0.7		8
40% Du Pont Ammate	Galv. steel	(L) Immersion	Room		28 days	· · ·	· · ·	61.5	12.3		8
Urea											
20% solution	99.99% Zn	(L) Immersion	30	86	1 month	· · ·	· · ·	· · ·	Trace	Solutions changed weekly	8
Saturated urea solution	99.99% Zn	(L) Immersion	30	86	1 month	· · ·	· · ·	1.0	0.2	Solutions changed weekly	8
Moist urea salts–3% water	99.99% Zn	(L) Immersion	30	86	1 month	· · ·	· · ·	10.1	2.1	Slight pitting, kept moist daily	8
Aluminum chloride											
26% AlCl₃ · 6H₂O solution	· · ·	(F) Immersion	10	50	21 days	None	None	13 970.0	2 800.0		1
Ammonia (liquid anhydrous)											
Technical grade	Zinc (99.8% pure)	(L) In vapor	Room		1 month	· · ·	· · ·	1.6	0.3		9
					8 months	· · ·	· · ·	0.09	0.2		9
Ammonium chloride											
0.1 N solution	HG zinc	(L) Immersion	35	95	2 days	· · ·	None	38.3	7.7		1
10% solution	Cp zinc	(L) Immersion	20	68	· · ·	· · ·	· · ·	19.0	3.8		10
10% solution	Zn-1Pb	(L) Immersion	20	68	· · ·	· · ·	· · ·	17.0	3.4		10
10% solution	Zn-1Cd	(L) Immersion	20	68	· · ·	· · ·	· · ·	38.0	7.6		10
10% solution	98.5% Zn	(L) Immersion	20	68	· · ·	· · ·	· · ·	30.0	6.0		10
Ammonium hydroxide											
Reagent		(L) Immersion	30	86	2 days	None	· · ·	46.1	9.3		1
Reagent		(L) Immersion	30	86	2 days	Yes	· · ·	75.5	15.0		1
Ammonium hydroxide											
1.8% solution	Galv. steel	(L) In vapor	Room		30 days	· · ·	· · ·	6.2(g)	1.3		4
								0.4(h)	0.08		
								0.1(d)	0.02		
								0.1(e)	0.02		

(a) (L) laboratory test; (F) field test. (b) Unless otherwise indicated. Some corrosion rates are given in specialized units dictated by the test procedures used by the original investigators. The conversion to inches per year in some of these cases should not be considered representative of continuous immersion results, but should be evaluated in light of the test conditions. (c) Chromium in surface film, 0.02 μg/dm². (d) Chromium in surface film, 1.3 μg/dm². (e) Chromium in surface film, 2.2 μg/dm². (f) Chromium in surface film, 0.1 μg/dm². (g) Chromium in surface film, 0 μg/dm². (h) Chromium in surface film, 0.2 μg/dm²

(Continued)

Table 9 (continued)

Corrosion medium	Material	Type of test(a)	Temperature °C	°F	Duration	Aeration	Agitation	Corrosion rate mg/dm²/day(b)	mil/year	Remarks	Ref
3.5% solution (1N)	Comm. zinc	(L) Immersion	30	86	2 days	None	None	58.0	11.6		4
3.5% solution (1N)	Comm. zinc	(L) Immersion	30	86	2 days	15–20 air bubbles per min	⋯	141.0	28.2		4
Ammonium acid fluoride											
5% NH₄F · HF solution	99.9% Zn	(L) Immersion	20	68	1 day	⋯	⋯	189.0	38.0	Corrosion products not removed	10
10% NH₄F · HF solution	99.9% Zn	(L) Immersoin	20	68	1 day	⋯	⋯	381.0	76.0	Corrosion products not removed	10
20% NH₄F · HF solution	99.9% Zn	(L) Immersion	20	68	14 days	⋯	⋯	420.0	84.0	Corrosion products not removed	10
Ammonium sulfate											
10% solution + free ammonia	Galv.	(L) Immersion	⋯	⋯	⋯	⋯	⋯	61.0	12.2		1
Building materials											
Gypsum plaster (0.046% chloride)	Rolled sheet	(L) Partly embedded	Room		82 days	⋯	⋯	⋯	30.0	Perforated, kept damp	11
Gypsum plaster (0.046% chloride)	Rolled sheet	(L) Partly embedded	Room		107 days	⋯	⋯	3.0	0.6	Dried	11
Gypsum plaster (0.046% chloride)	Rolled sheet	(L) Partly embedded	Room		203 days	⋯	⋯	2.1	0.4	Dried	11
Gypsum plaster (0.046% chloride)	Rolled sheet + Cronak	(L) Partly embedded	Room		107 days	⋯	⋯	0.3	<0.1	Kept damp	11
Gypsum plaster (0.046% chloride)	Rolled sheet + Cronak	(L) Partly embedded	Room		203 days	⋯	⋯	0.3	<0.1	Kept damp	11
Gypsum plaster + 1.5% sodium chloride	Die casting (BS1004 Alloy A)	(L) Partly embedded	Room		91 days	⋯	⋯	200.0	⋯	Pitting at air interface, kept damp	11
Gypsum plaster + 1.5% sodium chloride	Die casting (BS1004 Alloy A)	(L) Partly embedded	Room		6 months	⋯	⋯	30.7	⋯	Pitting at air interface, kept damp	11
Gypsum plaster + 1.5% sodium chloride	Die casting (BS1004 Alloy A)	(L) Partly embedded	Room		12 months	⋯	⋯	37.1	⋯	Pitting at air interface, kept damp	11
Gypsum plaster + 1.5% sodium chloride	Die casting (BS1004 Alloy A) + Cronak	(L) Partly embedded	Room		91 days	⋯	⋯	0.0		Kept damp	11
Gypsum plaster + 1.5% sodium chloride	Die casting (BS1004 Alloy A) + Cronak	(L) Partly embedded	Room		6 months	⋯	⋯	0.8	0.2	Kept damp	11
Gypsum plaster + 1.5% sodium chloride	Die casting (BS1004 Alloy A) + Cronak	(L) Partly embedded	Room		12 months	⋯	⋯	0.2	<0.1	Kept damp	11
Gypsum plaster + 1.5% sodium chloride	Die casting (BS1004 Alloy A) + phosphate	(L) Partly embedded	Room		91 days	⋯	⋯	88.7	⋯	Corrosion at interface, kept damp	11
Gypsum plaster + 1.5% sodium chloride	Die casting (BS1004 Alloy A) + phosphate	(L) Partly embedded	Room		6 months	⋯	⋯	44.5	⋯	Corrosion at interface, kept damp	11
Gypsum plaster + 1.5% sodium chloride	Die casting (BS1004 Alloy A) + phosphate	(L) Partly embedded	Room		12 months	⋯	⋯	29.4	⋯	Corrosion at interface, kept damp	11
Gypsum plaster + 1.5% sodium chloride	Die casting (BS1004 Alloy A)	(L) Surface contact	Room		91 days	⋯	⋯	115.0	25.0	Kept damp	11
Gypsum plaster + 1.5% sodium chloride	Die casting (BS1004 Alloy A)	(L) Surface contact	Room		6 months	⋯	⋯	101.7	22.0	Kept damp	11
Gypsum plaster + 1.5% sodium chloride	Die casting (BS1004 Alloy A)	(L) Surface contact	Room		12 months	⋯	⋯	83.8	18.0	Kept damp	11
Gypsum plaster + 1.5% sodium chloride	Die casting (BS1004 Alloy A) + Cronak	(L) Surface contact	Room		91 days	⋯	⋯	0.4	<0.1	Kept damp	11
Building materials											
Gypsum plaster + 1.5% sodium chloride	Die casting (BS1004 Alloy A) + Cronak	(L) Surface contact	Room		6 months	⋯	⋯	1.33	0.3	Kept damp	11
Gypsum plaster + 1.5% sodium chloride	Die casting (BS1004 Alloy A) + Cronak	(L) Surface contact	Room		12 months	⋯	⋯	0.98	0.2	Kept damp	11
Gypsum plaster + 1.5% sodium chloride	Die casting (BS1004 Alloy A) + phosphate	(L) Surface contact	Room		91 days	⋯	⋯	154.5	34.0	Kept damp	11

(a) (L) laboratory test; (F) field test. (b) Unless otherwise indicated. Some corrosion rates are given in specialized units dictated by the test procedures used by the original investigators. The conversion to inches per year in some of these cases should not be considered representative of continuous immersion results, but should be evaluated in light of the test conditions. (c) Chromium in surface film, 0.02 μg/dm². (d) Chromium in surface film, 1.3 μg/dm². (e) Chromium in surface film, 2.2 μg/dm². (f) Chromium in surface film, 0.1 μg/dm². (g) Chromium in surface film, 0 μg/dm². (h) Chromium in surface film, 0.2 μg/dm²

(Continued)

Table 9 (continued)

Corrosion medium	Material	Type of test(a)	Temperature °C	°F	Duration	Aeration	Agitation	Corrosion rate mg/dm²/day(b)	mil/year	Remarks	Ref
Gypsum plaster + 1.5% sodium chloride	Die casting (BS1004 Alloy A) + phosphate	(L) Surface contact	Room		6 months	. . .	. . .	114.2	25.0	Kept damp	11
Gypsum plaster + 1.5% sodium chloride	Die casting (BS1004 Alloy A) + phosphate	(L) Surface contact	Room		12 months	. . .	. . .	84.1	18.0	Kept damp	11
Plaster of paris	Rolled sheet	Specimen partly embedded and immersed in H₂O	Room		32 days	. . .	. . .	1.5	0.3	H₂O content of plaster during test, 28%	12
Plaster of paris	Rolled sheet	Specimen partly embedded and immersed in H₂O	Room		71 days	. . .	. . .	1.3	0.3	H₂O content of plaster during test, 28%	12
Plaster of paris	Electrolytic	Specimen partly embedded and immersed in H₂O	Room		32 days	. . .	. . .	1.4	0.3	H₂O content of plaster during test, 28%	12
Plaster of paris	Electrolytic	Specimen partly embedded and immersed in H₂O	Room		71 days	. . .	. . .	2.1	0.4	H₂O content of plaster during test, 28%	12
Plaster of paris	Rolled sheet	Specimen partly embedded, in desiccator over H₂O	Room		32 days	. . .	. . .	23.7	4.7	Localized pitting, H₂O content of plaster during test, 15%	12
Plaster of paris	Rolled sheet	Specimen partly embedded, in desiccator over H₂O	Room		71 days	. . .	. . .	18.3	3.7	Localized pitting, H₂O content of plaster during test, 15%	12
Plaster of paris	Electrolytic	Specimen partly embedded, in desiccator over H₂O	Room		32 days	. . .	. . .	23.4	4.7	Localized pitting, H₂O content of plaster during test, 15%	12
Plaster of paris	Electrolytic	Specimen partly embedded, in desiccator over H₂O	Room		71 days	. . .	. . .	22.4	4.5	Localized pitting, H₂O content of plaster during test, 15%	12
Plaster of paris	Rolled sheet	Specimen partly embedded	Room		32 days	. . .	. . .	25.3	5.1	Uniform attack, kept damp	12
Plaster of paris	Rolled sheet	Specimen partly embedded	Room		71 days	. . .	. . .	43.4	8.7	Uniform attack, kept damp	12
Plaster of paris	Electrolytic	Specimen partly embedded	Room		32 days	. . .	. . .	29.4	5.9	Uniform attack, kept damp	12
Plaster of paris	Electrolytic	Specimen partly embedded	Room		71 days	. . .	. . .	39.9	8.0	Uniform attack, kept damp	12
Cement	Rolled sheet	Specimen partly embedded, immersed in H₂O	Room		34 days	. . .	. . .	1.68	0.3		12
Cement	Rolled sheet	Specimen partly embedded, immersed in H₂O	Room		62 days	. . .	. . .	1.03	0.2		12
Cement	Electrolytic	Specimen partly embedded, immersed in H₂O	Room		34 days	. . .	. . .	2.0	0.4		12
Cement	Electrolytic	Specimen partly embedded, immersed in H₂O	Room		62 days	. . .	. . .	1.13	0.2		12
Cement	Rolled sheet	Specimen partly embedded, in desiccator over water	Room		34 days	. . .	. . .	1.85	0.4		12
Cement	Rolled sheet	Specimen partly embedded, in desiccator over water	Room		62 days	. . .	. . .	1.37	0.3		12
Cement	Electrolytic	Specimen partly embedded, in desiccator over water	Room		34 days	. . .	. . .	2.12	0.4		12
Cement	Electrolytic	Specimen partly embedded, in desiccator over water	Room		62 days	. . .	. . .	1.53	0.3		12
Wood from linden tree	Rolled sheet	In contact under H₂O	Room		61 days	. . .	. . .	4.88	1.0		12
Wood from linden tree	Electrolytic	In contact under H₂O	Room		61 days	. . .	. . .	3.90	0.8		12
Wood from pine tree	Rolled sheet	In contact under H₂O	Room		61 days	. . .	. . .	2.74	0.5		12
Wood from pine tree	Electrolytic	In contact under H₂O	Room		61 days	. . .	. . .	3.94	0.8		12

(a) (L) laboratory test; (F) field test. (b) Unless otherwise indicated. Some corrosion rates are given in specialized units dictated by the test procedures used by the original investigators. The conversion to inches per year in some of these cases should not be considered representative of continuous immersion results, but should be evaluated in light of the test conditions. (c) Chromium in surface film, 0.02 μg/dm². (d) Chromium in surface film, 1.3 μg/dm². (e) Chromium in surface film, 2.2 μg/dm². (f) Chromium in surface film, 0.1 μg/dm². (g) Chromium in surface film, 0 μg/dm². (h) Chromium in surface film, 0.2 μg/dm²

(Continued)

Table 9 (continued)

Corrosion medium	Material	Type of test(a)	Temperature °C	°F	Duration	Aeration	Agitation	Corrosion rate mg/dm²/day(b)	mil/year	Remarks	Ref
Wood from beech tree	Rolled sheet	In contact under H₂O	Room		61 days	...	...	2.51	0.5		12
Wood from beech tree	Electrolytic	In contact under H₂O	Room		61 days	...	...	2.30	0.5		12
Sulfur-containing clay	Electrogalv. sheet	Contact	19	66	30 days	...	...	0.1	<0.1		10
Quartz sand	Electrogalv. sheet	Contact	19	66	30 days	...	...	0.1	<0.1		10
Fibrolite	Electrogalv. sheet	Contact	19	66	30 days	...	...	0.03	<0.1		10
Asbestos cement	Electrogalv. sheet	Contact	19	66	30 days	...	...	0.03	<0.1		10
White granulated slag	Electrogalv. sheet	Contact	19	66	30 days	...	...	0.3	<0.1		10
Red brick	Electrogalv. sheet	Contact	19	66	30 days	...	...	0.4	<0.1		10
Mineral wood	Electrogalv. sheet	Contact	19	66	30 days	...	...	0.5	0.1		10
Asbestos	Electrogalv. sheet	Contact	19	66	30 days	...	...	0.8	0.16		10
Portland cement/sand mortar	Electrogalv. sheet	Contact	19	66	30 days	...	...	2.1	0.4		10
Gypsum plaster	Electrogalv. sheet	Contact	19	66	30 days	...	...	2.6	0.5		10
Silica brick	Electrogalv. sheet	Contact	19	66	30 days	...	...	7.4	1.5		10
Calcium chlorate											
1.57% ClO₃	Sheet	(L) Immersion	...		10 days	...	...	14.0	2.8		1
Calcium chloride											
1.1% solution	HG zinc	(L) Partial immersion	35	95	2 days	...	None	32.3	6.5		1
20% solution	Sheet	(L) Partial immersion	−5	23	30 days	...	Yes	12.0	2.4	Based on immersed area	1
20% solution	Galv. sheet	(L) Partial immersion	−5	23	30 days	...	Yes	>15.4	>2.8	Based on immersed area	1
20% solution	Sheet	(L) Partial immersion	33	91	10 days	None	None	3.45	0.7		1
20% solution	Galv. sheet	(L) Partial immersion	33	91	10 days	None	None	2.26	0.5		1
20% solution silicate	Sheet	(L) Partial immersion	35	95	10 days	None	None	2.52	0.5		1
20% solution + 0.05% Ca(OH)₂	Sheet	(L) Partial immersion	35	95	10 days	None	None	2.61	0.5		1
20% solution + 0.17% Na₂Cr₂O₇	Sheet	(L) Partial immersion	35	95	10 days	None	None	2.20	0.4		1
Citric acid											
2% solution	Sheet	(L) Immersion	Room		21 days	None	None	...	...	Specimen dissolved	1
m-Cresol											
Pure, dry	Sheet	(L) Contact	25	77	100 days	None	None	0.15	<0.1		1
Pure, dry	Sheet	(L) In vapors			100 days	...	...	Very high	...		1
Pure + 10% water	Sheet	(L) Contact	25	77	100 days	None	None	0.26	<0.1		1
Pure + 10% water	Sheet	(L) In vapors			100 days	...	...	282.0	56.0		1
o-Cresol											
Pure, dry	Sheet	(L) Contact	25	77	100 days	None	None	0.26	<0.1		1
Pure, dry	Sheet	(L) In vapors			100 days	...	...	271.0	54.0		1
Pure + 10% water	Sheet	(L) Contact	25	77	100 days	None	None	0.07	<0.1		1
Pure + 10% water	Sheet	(L) In vapors			100 days	...	...	56.2	11.2		1
Detergents and cleaners											
Calcium chloride 20% solution	Sheet	(L) Partial immersion	33	91	10 days	None	None	3.45	0.7	Dairy cleaning	1
Calcium chloride 20% solution	Galv. sheet	(L) Partial immersion	33	91	10 days	None	None	2.26	0.5	Dairy cleaning	1
Calcium chloride 20% solution + silicate	Sheet	(L) Partial immersion	35	95	10 days	None	None	2.52	0.5	Dairy cleaning	1
Calcium chloride 20% solution + 0.05% Ca(OH)₂	Sheet	(L) Partial immersion	35	95	10 days	None	None	2.61	0.5	Dairy cleaning	1
Calcium chloride 20% solution + 0.17% Na₂Cr₂O₇	Sheet	(L) Partial immersion	35	95	10 days	None	None	2.20	0.4	Dairy cleaning	1
Lime mix: 2 lb/gal of 66.5% calcium hydroxide + 32.5% magnesium oxide	Sheet	(L) Partial immersion	21	70	5 days	None	None	7.34	1.5	Dairy cleaning	1
Sodium carbonate	Sheet	(L) Partial immersion	66	150	5 h	None	None	39.0	7.8	Dairy cleaning	1
Sodium carbonate	Galv. sheet	(L) Partial immersion	66	150	5 h	None	None	37.0	7.4	Dairy cleaning	1
Sodium hydroxide, 0.5% solution	Sheet	(L) Partial immersion	66	150	5 h	None	None	89.0	17.8	Dairy cleaning	1
Sodium hydroxide, 0.5% solution	Sheet	(L) Partial immersion	21	70	5 days	None	None	4.7	0.9	Dairy cleaning	1
Sodium hydroxide, 0.5% solution	Galv. sheet	(L) Partial immersion	66	150	5 h	None	None	204.0	41.0	Dairy cleaning	1
Sodium hydroxide, 0.5% solution	Galv. sheet	(L) Partial immersion	21	70	5 days	None	None	12.0	2.4	Dairy cleaning	1

(a) (L) laboratory test; (F) field test. (b) Unless otherwise indicated. Some corrosion rates are given in specialized units dictated by the test procedures used by the original investigators. The conversion to inches per year in some of these cases should not be considered representative of continuous immersion results, but should be evaluated in light of the test conditions. (c) Chromium in surface film, 0.02 µg/dm². (d) Chromium in surface film, 1.3 µg/dm². (e) Chromium in surface film, 2.2 µg/dm². (f) Chromium in surface film, 0.1 µg/dm². (g) Chromium in surface film, 0 µg/dm². (h) Chromium in surface film, 0.2 µg/dm²

(Continued)

Table 9 (continued)

Corrosion medium	Material	Type of test(a)	Temperature °C	Temperature °F	Duration	Aeration	Agitation	Corrosion rate mg/dm²/day(b)	Corrosion rate mil/year	Remarks	Ref
Sodium hypochlorite, 1 oz/gal, 236 ppm available chlorine	Sheet	(L) Partial immersion	21	70	5 days	None	None	21.6	4.3	Dairy cleaning	1
Sodium hypochlorite, 1 oz/gal, 236 ppm available chlorine	Galv. sheet	(L) Partial immersion	21	70	5 days	None	None	20.6 g/m²	4.1	Dairy cleaning	1
Diversol, 1.1 oz/gal, 236 ppm available chlorine	Sheet	(L) Partial immersion	21	70	5 days	None	None	4.8 g/m²	1.0	Dairy cleaning	1
Diversol, 1.1 oz/gal, 236 ppm available chlorine	Galv. sheet	(L) Partial immersion	21	70	5 days	None	None	Gained weight	⋯	Dairy cleaning	1
Diversol, 0.64 oz/gal, 137 ppm available chlorine	Sheet	(L) Partial immersion	21	70	5 days	None	None	5.9 g/m²	1.2	Dairy cleaning	1
Diversol, 0.64 oz/gal, 137 ppm available chlorine	Galv. sheet	(L) Partial immersion	21	70	5 days	None	None	7.3 g/m²	1.5	Dairy cleaning	1
Chloramine T, 0.1 oz/gal, 222 ppm available chlorine	Sheet	(L) Partial immersion	21	70	5 days	None	None	16.9 g/m²	3.4	Dairy cleaning	1
Chloramine T, 0.1 oz/gal, 222 ppm available chlorine	Galv. sheet	(L) Partial immersion	21	70	5 days	None	None	0	0	Dairy cleaning	1
Trisodium phosphate 0.16% solution	Sheet	(L) Partial immersion	66	150	5 h	None	None	29.0 g/m²	5.8	Dairy cleaning	1
0.16% solution	Galv. sheet	(L) Partial immersion	66	150	5 h	None	None	1.3 g/m²	0.3	Dairy cleaning	1
0.50% solution	Sheet	(L) Partial immersion	66	150	5 h	None	None	24.0 g/m²	4.8	Dairy cleaning	1
0.50% solution	Galv. sheet	(L) Partial immersion	66	150	5 h	None	None	Gained weight	⋯	Dairy cleaning	1
Carbon tetrachloride-benzol, 90%–10% mixture	Sheet	(F) Immersion	Room	Room	40 days	None	None	41.7 g/m²	>4.0	Dry cleaning	1
Carbon tetrachloride-benzol, 90%–10% mixture	Sheet	(F) Immersion	40	287	38 days	None	Boiling			Dry cleaning; specimen destroyed	1
Perchlorethylene	Sheet	(F) In vapor	27	260	64 days	None	None	117.8 g/m²	23.0	Dry cleaning	1
Perchlorethylene	Sheet	(F) Immersion	51	305	64 days	None	Boiling	407.5 g/m²	82.0	Dry cleaning	1
Sodium tripolyphosphate, 0.08%	Hot dip galv.	(L) Immersion	95	203	7 h	None	None	5.50 g/m²	38.0	Individual component of Syndet at concentration present in detergent	13
Tetrasodium pyrophosphate, 0.085%	Hot dip galv.	(L) Immersion	95	203	7 h	None	None	3.88 g/m²	26.8	As above	13
Sodium perborate, 0.064%	Hot dip galv.	(L) Immersion	95	203	7 h	None	None	0.78 g/m²	5.4	Individual components of Syndet at concentration present in detergent	13
Sodium carbonate, 0.18%	Hot dip galv.	(L) Immersion	95	203	7 h	None	None	0.50 g/m²	3.4	As above	13
Sodium sulfate, 0.12%	Hot dip galv.	(L) Immersion	95	203	7 h	None	None	0.20 g/m²	1.4	As above	13
Sodium chloride, 0.004%	Hot dip galv.	(L) Immersion	95	203	7 h	None	None	0.39 g/m²	2.7	As above	13
Sodium metasilicate, 0.045%	Hot dip galv.	(L) Immersion	95	203	7 h	None	None	0.52 g/m²	3.6	As above	13
Lauryl alcohol sulfonate, 0.18%	Hot dip galv.	(L) Immersion	95	203	7 h	None	None	0.43 g/m²	3.0	As above	13
Lauric acid ethanolamide, 0.015%	Hot dip galv.	(L) Immersion	95	203	7 h	None	None	0.15 g/m²	1.0	As above	13
Sodium tripolyphosphate, 0.15%	Hot dip galv.	(L) Immersion	90	194	12 h	None	None	49.8 g/m²	201.0	Solution also contained 0.1% sodium perborate; solution renewed every hour	14
Sodium tripolyphosphate, 0.50%	Hot dip galv.	(L) Immersion	90	194	12 h	None	None	68.0 g/m²	274.0	As above	14
Tetrasodium pyrophosphate, 0.15%	Hot dip galv.	(L) Immersion	90	194	12 h	None	None	44.1 g/m²	177.0	As above	14
Sodium metaphosphate, 0.15%	Hot dip galv.	(L) Immersion	90	194	12 h	None	None	48.7 g/m²	196.0	As above	14
Ordinary soap, 0.3%	Hot dip galv.	(L) Immersion	90	194	12 h	None	None	6.4 g/m²	26.0	As above	14
Lauryl sulfate, 0.05%	Hot dip galv.	(L) Immersion	90	194	12 h	None	None	Gain	⋯	As above	14
Sodium carbonate, tech. calcined, 0.1%	Hot dip galv.	(L) Immersion	90	194	12 h	None	None	3.3 g/m²	13.0	As above	14
Sodium metasilicate · 5H$_2$O, 0.03%	Hot dip galv.	(L) Immersion	90	194	12 h	None	None	0.6 g/m²	2.4	As above	14
Sodium sulfate, cryst., 0.05%	Hot dip galv.	(L) Immersion	90	194	12 h	None	None	6.6 g/m²	27.0	As above	14

(a) (L) laboratory test; (F) field test. (b) Unless otherwise indicated. Some corrosion rates are given in specialized units dictated by the test procedures used by the original investigators. The conversion to inches per year in some of these cases should not be considered representative of continuous immersion results, but should be evaluated in light of the test conditions. (c) Chromium in surface film, 0.02 μg/dm². (d) Chromium in surface film, 1.3 μg/dm². (e) Chromium in surface film, 2.2 μg/dm². (f) Chromium in surface film, 0.1 μg/dm². (g) Chromium in surface film, 0 μg/dm². (h) Chromium in surface film, 0.2 μg/dm²

(Continued)

Table 9 (continued)

Corrosion medium	Material	Type of test(a)	Temperature °C	°F	Duration	Aeration	Agitation	Corrosion rate mg/dm²/day(b)	mil/year	Remarks	Ref
Sodium tripolyphosphate, 0.15%	Hot dip galv.	(L) Immersion	90	194	12 h	None	None	11.3 g/m²	45.5	Perborate-free solutions	14
Sodium carbonate, 0.1%	Hot dip galv.	(L) Immersion	90	194	12 h	None	None	1.4 g/m²	5.6	Perborate-free solutions	14
Sodium metasilicate · 5H₂O, 0.03%	Hot dip galv.	(L) Immersion	90	194	12 h	None	None	Gain	· · ·	Perborate-free solutions	14
Ordinary soap, 0.03%	Hot dip galv.	(L) Immersion	90	194	12 h	None	None	6.5 g/m²	26.0	Perborate-free solutions	14
Tetrasodium pyrophosphate 0.01%	Hot dip galv.	(L) Immersion	95	203	20 min	None	None	0.15 g/m²	22.0	Effect of solution concentration and duration of immersion	13
0.05–2.5%	Hot dip galv.	(L) Immersion	95	203	20 min	None	None	1.03 g/m²	148.0	As above	13
0.1%	Hot dip galv.	(L) Immersion	95	203	20 min	None	None	1.03 g/m²	148.0	As above	13
0.1%	Hot dip galv.	(L) Immersion	95	203	80 min	None	None	1.65 g/m²	60.0	As above	13
0.1%	Hot dip galv.	(L) Immersion	95	203	7 h	None	None	3.88 g/m²	27.0	As above	13
Sodium tripolyphosphate 0.01%	Hot dip galv.	(L) Immersion	95	203	20 min	None	None	0.10 g/m²	15.0	Effect of solution concentration and duration of immersion	13
0.05–1%	Hot dip galv.	(L) Immersion	95	203	20 min	None	None	1.19 g/m²	173.0	As above	13
0.08%	Hot dip galv.	(L) Immersion	95	203	20 min	None	None	1.19 g/m²	73.0	As above	13
0.08%	Hot dip galv.	(L) Immersion	95	203	20 min	None	None	2.18 g/m²	79.0	As above	13
0.08%	Hot dip galv.	(L) Immersion	95	203	7 h	None	None	5.50 g/m²	38.0	As above	13
Tetrasodium pyrophosphate 0.5 g/L in 0 gr water	Sheet	(L) Immersion	Boiling		5 cycles, each 30 min at boiling + 15 min cooling; solution renewed after each cycle	From boiling	From boiling	6.0 g/m²/5 cycles	77.4	g/m²/5 cycles × 12.9 = mil/year	15
0.5 g/L in 21 gr water	Sheet	(L) Immersion	Boiling		As above	From boiling	From boiling	1.2 g/m²/5 cycles	15.4		15
0.5 g/L in 21 gr water + 1 g/L perborate	Sheet	(L) Immersion	Boiling		As above	From boiling	From boiling	1.5 g/m²/5 cycles	19.4		15
1.0 g/L in 0 gr water	Sheet	(L) Immersion	Boiling		As above	From boiling	From boiling	11.2 g/m²/5 cycles	144.3		15
1.0 g/L in 21 gr water	Sheet	(L) Immersion	Boiling		As above	From boiling	From boiling	4.7 g/m²/5 cycles	60.7		15
1.0 g/L in 21 gr water + 1 g/L perborate	Sheet	(L) Immersion	Boiling		As above	From boiling	From boiling	5.1 g/m²/5 cycles	65.7		15
2.0 g/L in 0 gr water	Sheet	(L) Immersion	Boiling		As above	From boiling	From boiling	25.8 g/m²/5 cycles	333.0		15
2.0 g/L in 21 gr water	Sheet	(L) Immersion	Boiling		As above	From boiling	From boiling	19.0 g/m²/5 cycles	254.0		15
2.0 g/L in 21 gr water + 1 g/L perborate	Sheet	(L) Immersion	Boiling		As above	From boiling	From boiling	21.2 g/m²/5 cycles	273.0		15
3.0 g/L in 0 gr water	Sheet	(L) Immersion	Boiling		As above	From boiling	From boiling	34.5 g/m²/5 cycles	445.0		15
3.0 g/L in 21 gr water	Sheet	(L) Immersion	Boiling		As above	From boiling	From boiling	27.2 g/m²/5 cycles	351.0		15
3.0 g/L in 21 gr water + 1 g/L perborate	Sheet	(L) Immersion	Boiling		As above	From boiling	From boiling	32.8 g/m²/5 cycles	423.0		15
Sodium tripolyphosphate 0.5 g/L in 0 gr water	Sheet	(L) Immersion	Boiling		5 cycles, each 30 min at boiling + 15 min cooling; solution renewed after each cycle	From boiling	From boiling	5.4 g/m²/5 cycles	69.7		15
0.5 g/L in 21 gr water	Sheet	(L) Immersion	Boiling		As above	From boiling	From boiling	2.8 g/m²/5 cycles	36.1		15
0.5 g/L in 21 gr water + 1 g/L perborate	Sheet	(L) Immersion	Boiling		As above	From boiling	From boiling	3.7 g/m²/5 cycles	47.7		15
1.0 g/L in 0 gr water	Sheet	(L) Immersion	Boiling		As above	From boiling	From boiling	14.8 g/m²/5 cycles	191.0		15
1.0 g/L in 21 gr water	Sheet	(L) Immersion	Boiling		As above	From boiling	From boiling	8.5 g/m²/5 cycles	110.0		15
1.0 g/L in 21 gr water + 1 g/L perborate	Sheet	(L) Immersion	Boiling		As above	From boiling	From boiling	11.4 g/m²/5 cycles	147.0		15
2.0 g/L in 0 gr water	Sheet	(L) Immersion	Boiling		As above	From boiling	From boiling	36.9 g/m²/5 cycles	476.0		15
2.0 g/L in 21 gr water	Sheet	(L) Immersion	Boiling		As above	From boiling	From boiling	24.9 g/m²/5 cycles	321.0		15
2.0 g/L in 21 gr water + 1 g/L perborate	Sheet	(L) Immersion	Boiling		As above	From boiling	From boiling	29.7 g/m²/5 cycles	383.0		15
3.0 g/L in 0 gr water	Sheet	(L) Immersion	Boiling		As above	From boiling	From boiling	46.2 g/m²/5 cycles	596.0		15
Sodium tripolyphosphate 3.0 g/L in 21 gr water	Sheet	(L) Immersion	Boiling		As above	From boiling	From boiling	32.6 g/m²/5 cycles	421.0		15
3.0 g/L in 21 gr water + 1 g/L perborate	Sheet	(L) Immersion	Boiling		As above	From boiling	From boiling	39.8 g/m²/5 cycles	513.0		15
Sodium metaphosphate 0.5 g/L in 0 gr water	Sheet	(L) Immersion	Boiling		5 cycles, each 30 min at boiling + 15 min cooling; solution renewed after each cycle	From boiling	From boiling	5.9 g/m²/5 cycles	76.1		15

(a) (L) laboratory test; (F) field test. (b) Unless otherwise indicated. Some corrosion rates are given in specialized units dictated by the test procedures used by the original investigators. The conversion to inches per year in some of these cases should not be considered representative of continuous immersion results, but should be evaluated in light of the test conditions. (c) Chromium in surface film, 0.02 μg/dm². (d) Chromium in surface film, 1.3 μg/dm². (e) Chromium in surface film, 2.2 μg/dm². (f) Chromium in surface film, 0.1 μg/dm². (g) Chromium in surface film, 0 μg/dm². (h) Chromium in surface film, 0.2 μg/dm²

(Continued)

Table 9 (continued)

Corrosion medium	Material	Type of test(a)	Temperature °C	°F	Duration	Aeration	Agitation	Corrosion rate mg/dm²/day(b)	mil/year	Remarks	Ref
0.5 g/L in 21 gr water	Sheet	(L) Immersion	Boiling		As above	From boiling	From boiling	3.7 g/m²/5 cycles	47.7		15
0.5 g/L in 21 gr water + 1 g/L perborate	Sheet	(L) Immersion	Boiling		As above	From boiling	From boiling	4.8 g/m²/5 cycles	61.9		15
1.0 g/L in 0 gr water	Sheet	(L) Immersion	Boiling		As above	From boiling	From boiling	17.1 g/m²/5 cycles	221.0		15
1.0 g/L in 21 gr water	Sheet	(L) Immersion	Boiling		As above	From boiling	From boiling	9.9 g/m²/5 cycles	128.0		15
1.0 g/L in 21 gr water + 1 g/L perborate	Sheet	(L) Immersion	Boiling		As above	From boiling	From boiling	15.9 g/m²/5 cycles	205.0		15
2.0 g/L in 0 gr water	Sheet	(L) Immersion	Boiling		As above	From boiling	From boiling	32.9 g/m²/5 cycles	424.0		15
2.0 g/L in 21 gr water	Sheet	(L) Immersion	Boiling		As above	From boiling	From boiling	28.1 g/m²/5 cycles	362.0		15
2.0 g/L in 21 gr water + 1 g/L perborate	Sheet	(L) Immersion	Boiling		As above	From boiling	From boiling	33.1 g/m²/5 cycles	427.0		15
3.0 g/L in 0 gr water	Sheet	(L) Immersion	Boiling		As above	From boiling	From boiling	49.0 g/m²/5 cycles	632.0		15
3.0 g/L in 21 gr water	Sheet	(L) Immersion	Boiling		As above	From boiling	From boiling	37.4 g/m²/5 cycles	482.0		15
3.0 g/L in 21 gr water + 1 g/L perborate	Sheet	(L) Immersion	Boiling		As above	From boiling	From boiling	47.4 g/m²/5 cycles	612.0		15
Tetrasodium pyrophosphate 0.06% solution	Sheet	(L) Immersion	80	176	6 h	None	None	0.63 mg/in.²/h	47.0		16
0.15% solution of mixture: 40% tetrasodium pyrophosphate + 30% trisodium phosphate 12 H₂O + 30% sodium metasilicate · 5H₂O	Sheet	(L) Immersion	80	176	6 h	None	None	0.48 mg/in.²/h	36.0		16
0.15% solution of mixture: 31.2% sodium hexametaphosphate + 24.7% trisodium phosphate 12 H₂O + 39.2% sodium metasilicate 5H₂O + 4.5% sodium carbonate	Sheet	(L) Immersion	80	176	6 h	None	None	0.15 mg/in.²/h	11.0		16
Commercial soaps and Syndets											
Syndet (1)–0.2% solution (Fab)	Sheet	(L) Immersion	Room		1 week	None	None	6.45 mg/in.²/h	1.3		1
Syndet (1)–0.2% solution (Fab)	Sheet	(L) Immersion	60	140	7 h	None	None	0.7 mg/in.²/h	<0.1		1
Syndet (2)–0.2% solution (Mytron)	Sheet	(L) Immersion	Room		1 week	None	None	24.2 mg/in.²/h	4.9		1
Syndet (2)–0.2% solution (Mytron)	Sheet	(L) Immersion	60	140	7 h	None	None	1.63 mg/in.²/h	0.3		1
Syndet (2)–0.2% solution + sodium silicate	Sheet	(L) Immersion	Room		1 week	None	None	33.5 mg/in.²/h	6.7		1
Syndet (3)–0.2% solution (OS)	Sheet	(L) Immersion	Room		1 week	None	None	24.0 mg/in.²/h	4.8		1
Syndet (4)–0.2% solution (Tide)	Sheet	(L) Immersion	Room		1 week	None	None	11.1 mg/in.²/h	2.2		1
Syndet (4)–0.02% solution (Tide)	Sheet	(L) Immersion	60	140	7 h	None	None	1.92 mg/in.²/h	0.4		1
Syndet (5) containing phosphates, 0.5% solution	Hot dip galv.	(L) Immersion	95	203	20 min	None	None	1.96 g/m²	284.0		13
Syndet (5) containing phosphates, 0.5% solution	Hot dip galv.	(L) Immersion	95	203	80 min	None	None	2.56 g/m²	93.0	pH 10.20	13
Syndet (5) containing phosphates, 0.5% solution	Hot dip galv.	(L) Immersion	95	203	4 h	None	None	4.2 mg/in.²/h	51.0		13
Syndet (5) containing phosphates, 1.0% solution	Hot dip galv.	(L) Immersion	95	203	20 min	None	None	3.4 g/m²	493.0		13
Syndet (5) containing phosphates, 0.5% solution	Hot dip galv.	(L) Immersion	95	203	5 consecutive 20 min on same piece	None	None	1.35 g/m²			13
Syndet (5) containing phosphates, 0.5% solution	Hot dip galv.	(L) Immersion	95	203	As above	None	None	1.39 g/m²			13
Syndet (5) containing phosphates, 0.5% solution	Hot dip galv.	(L) Immersion	95	203	As above	None	None	2.06 g/m²			13
Syndet (5) containing phosphates, 0.5% solution	Hot dip galv.	(L) Immersion	95	203	As above	None	None	2.10 g/m²			13
Syndet (5) containing phosphates, 0.5% solution	Hot dip galv.	(L) Immersion	95	203	As above	None	None	2.30 g/m²			13
Syndet (6)–0.4% solution	Hot dip galv.	(L) Immersion	95	203	80 min	None	None	2.08 g/m²	75.0	pH 9.89	13
Soap (1)–0.8% solution pH 10.65	Hot dip galv.	(L) Immersion	95	203	80 min	None	None	0.65 g/m²	24.0		13
Soap (1)–0.8% solution pH 10.65	Hot dip galv.	(L) Immersion	95	203	5 consecutive 20 min on same piece	None	None	0.20 g/m²			13

(a) (L) laboratory test; (F) field test. (b) Unless otherwise indicated. Some corrosion rates are given in specialized units dictated by the test procedures used by the original investigators. The conversion to inches per year in some of these cases should not be considered representative of continuous immersion results, but should be evaluated in light of the test conditions. (c) Chromium in surface film, 0.02 µg/dm². (d) Chromium in surface film, 1.3 µg/dm². (e) Chromium in surface film, 2.2 µg/dm². (f) Chromium in surface film, 0.1 µg/dm². (g) Chromium in surface film, 0 µg/dm². (h) Chromium in surface film, 0.2 µg/dm².

(Continued)

Table 9 (continued)

Corrosion medium	Material	Type of test(a)	Temperature °C	Temperature °F	Duration	Aeration	Agitation	Corrosion rate mg/dm²/day(b)	mil/year	Remarks	Ref
Soap (1)–0.8% solution pH 10.65	Hot dip galv.	(L) Immersion	95	203	As above	None	None	0.13 g/m²			13
Soap (1)–0.8% solution pH 10.65	Hot dip galv.	(L) Immersion	95	203	As above	None	None	0.07 g/m²			13
Soap (1)–0.8% solution pH 10.65	Hot dip galv.	(L) Immersion	95	203	As above	None	None	0.04 g/m²			13
Soap (1)–0.8% solution pH 10.65	Hot dip galv.	(L) Immersion	95	203	As above	None	None	0.02 g/m²			13
Soap (2)–0.08% solution pH 10.73	Hot dip galv.	(L) Immersion	95	203	80 min	None	None	0.22 g/m²	8.0		13
Soap (2)–0.08% solution pH 10.73	Hot dip galv.	(L) Immersion	95	203	4 h	None	None	0.22 g/m²	2.7		13
Soap (2)–0.5% solution	Hot dip galv.	(L) Immersion	95	203	20 min	None	None	0.17 g/m²	25.0		13
Soap (2)–2.0% solution	Hot dip galv.	(L) Immersion	95	203	20 min	None	None	0.24 g/m²	35.0		13
Syndet (7) (USA) in 0 gr water	Sheet	(L) Immersion	Boiling		5 cycles, each 30 min at boiling + 15 min cooling; solution renewed after each cycle	From boiling	From boiling	49.0 g/m²/5 cycles	632.0	g/m²/5 cycles × 12.9 = mil/year	15
Syndet (7) (USA) in 12.5 gr water	Sheet	(L) Immersion	Boiling		As above	From boiling	From boiling	24.8 g/m²/5 cycles	320.0		15
Syndet (8) (German) in 0 gr water	Sheet	(L) Immersion	Boiling		As above	From boiling	From boiling	7.9 g/m²/5 cycles	102.0		15
Syndet (8) (German) in 12.5 gr water	Sheet	(L) Immersion	Boiling		As above	From boiling	From boiling	13.8 g/m²/5 cycles	178.0		15
Syndet (9) (Swiss) in 0 gr water	Sheet	(L) Immersion	Boiling		As above	From boiling	From boiling	7.8 g/m²/5 cycles	100.0		15
Syndet (9) (Swiss) in 12.5 gr water	Sheet	(L) Immersion	Boiling		As above	From boiling	From boiling	14.1 g/m²/5 cycles	182.0		15
Syndet (10) in soft water	Sheet	(L) Immersion	Boiling		As above	From boiling	From boiling	58.9 g/m²/5 cycles	758.0		15
Syndet (10) + 1% acid orthophosphate	Sheet	(L) Immersion	Boiling		As above	From boiling	From boiling	54.2 g/m²/5 cycles	698.0		15
Syndet (10) + 5% acid orthophosphate	Sheet	(L) Immersion	Boiling		As above	From boiling	From boiling	47.8 g/m²/5 cycles	616.0		15
Syndet (10) + 10% acid orthophosphate	Sheet	(L) Immersion	Boiling		As above	From boiling	From boiling	31.0 g/m²/5 cycles	400.0		15
Syndet (11) in soft water	Sheet	(L) Immersion	Boiling		As above	From boiling	From boiling	34.5 g/m²/5 cycles	446.0	Contains silicates	15
Syndet (11) + 1% acid orthophosphate	Sheet	(L) Immersion	Boiling		As above	From boiling	From boiling	28.2 g/m²/5 cycles	364.0		15
Syndet (11) + 5% acid orthophosphate	Sheet	(L) Immersion	Boiling		As above	From boiling	From boiling	17.9 g/m²/5 cycles	231.0		15
Syndet (11) + 10% acid orthophosphate	Sheet	(L) Immersion	Boiling		As above	From boiling	From boiling	8.7 g/m²/5 cycles	112.0		15
Syndet (12) in soft water	Sheet	(L) Immersion	Boiling		As above	From boiling	From boiling	22.4 g/m²/5 cycles	289.0	Does not contain silicates	15
Syndet (12) + 1% acid orthophosphate	Sheet	(L) Immersion	Boiling		As above	From boiling	From boiling	20.4 g/m²/5 cycles	263.0		15
Syndet (12) + 5% acid orthophosphate	Sheet	(L) Immersion	Boiling		As above	From boiling	From boiling	19.6 g/m²/5 cycles	253.0		15
Syndet (12) + 10% acid orthophosphate	Sheet	(L) Immersion	Boiling		As above	From boiling	From boiling	17.3 g/m²/5 cycles	223.0		15
Hard water soap (3) (USA) in 0 gr water	Sheet	(L) Immersion	Boiling		As above	From boiling	From boiling	7.9 g/m²/5 cycles	102.0		15
Hard water soap (3) (USA) in 12.5 gr water	Sheet	(L) Immersion	Boiling		As above	From boiling	From boiling	13.2 g/m²/5 cycles	170.0		15
Hard water soap (4) (Swiss) in 0 gr water	Sheet	(L) Immersion	Boiling		As above	From boiling	From boiling	2.2 g/m²/5 cycles	28.4		15
Hard water soap (4) (Swiss) in 12.5 gr water	Sheet	(L) Immersion	Boiling		As above	From boiling	From boiling	6.6 g/m²/5 cycles	85.0		15

Laboratory-prepared soap mixtures and Syndets

L Syndet I, composition: Sodium tripolyphosphate, 50%											15
Sodium sulfate, 19%											15
Dodecylbenzylsulfonate, 10%											15
Sodium perborate (4H₂O), 8%											15

(a) (L) laboratory test; (F) field test. (b) Unless otherwise indicated. Some corrosion rates are given in specialized units dictated by the test procedures used by the original investigators. The conversion to inches per year in some of these cases should not be considered representative of continuous immersion results, but should be evaluated in light of the test conditions. (c) Chromium in surface film, 0.02 μg/dm². (d) Chromium in surface film, 1.3 μg/dm². (e) Chromium in surface film, 2.2 μg/dm². (f) Chromium in surface film, 0.1 μg/dm². (g) Chromium in surface film, 0 μg/dm². (h) Chromium in surface film, 0.2 μg/dm²

(Continued)

Table 9 (continued)

Corrosion medium	Material	Type of test(a)	Temperature °C	°F	Duration	Aeration	Agitation	Corrosion rate mg/dm²/day(b)	mil/year	Remarks	Ref
Lauryl sulfate, 5%											15
Sodium metasilicate, 5%											15
Sodium chloride, 1%											15
Sodium salt of EDTA, 0.5%											15
Carboxymethyl cellulose, 0.5%											15
Water, 1%											15
L Syndet I, 6 g/L in 0 gr water	Zinc sheet	(L) Immersion	Boiling		5 cycles, each 30 min at boiling + 15 min cooling; solution renewed after each cycle	From boiling	From boiling	40.2 g/m²/5 cycles	518.0		15
L Syndet I, 6 g/L in 21 gr water	Zinc sheet	(L) Immersion	Boiling		As above	From boiling	From boiling	28.5 g/m²/5 cycles	368.0		15
L Syndet I, 6 g/L in 42 gr water	Zinc sheet	(L) Immersion	Boiling		As above	From boiling	From boiling	12.1 g/m²/5 cycles	156.0		15
L Syndet I, 6 g/L + 0.3 g/L sodium metasilicate, 0 gr H_2O	Zinc sheet	(L) Immersion	Boiling		As above	From boiling	From boiling	36.4 g/m²/5 cycles	470.0		15
L Syndet I, 6 g/L +:											
0.3 g/L sodium disilicate, 0 gr H_2O	Zinc sheet	(L) Immersion	Boiling		As above	From boiling	From boiling	32.9 g/m²/5 cycles	425.0		15
0.3 g/L sodium trisilicate, 0 gr H_2O	Zinc sheet	(L) Immersion	Boiling		As above	From boiling	From boiling	27.6 g/m²/5 cycles	356.0		15
1.8 g/L sodium trisilicate, 0 gr H_2O	Zinc sheet	(L) Immersion	Boiling		As above	From boiling	From boiling	18.3 g/m²/5 cycles	236.0		15
0.3 g/L monoammonium phosphate, 0 gr H_2O	Zinc sheet	(L) Immersion	Boiling		As above	From boiling	From boiling	22.2 g/m²/5 cycles	286.0		15
0.3 g/L monoammonium phosphate, 21 gr H_2O	Zinc sheet	(L) Immersion	Boiling		As above	From boiling	From boiling	14.6 g/m²/5 cycles	188.0		15
0.18 g/L sodium nitrate, 0 gr H_2O	Zinc sheet	(L) Immersion	Boiling		As above	From boiling	From boiling	24.1 g/m²/5 cycles	311.0		15
0.3 g/L magnesium lactate, 0 gr H_2O	Zinc sheet	(L) Immersion	Boiling		As above	From boiling	From boiling	19.3 g/m²/5 cycles	249.0		15
0.3 g/L magnesium lactate, 21 gr H_2O	Zinc sheet	(L) Immersion	Boiling		As above	From boiling	From boiling	21.0 g/m²/5 cycles	271.0		15
0.3 g/L calcium chloride, 0 gr H_2O	Zinc sheet	(L) Immersion	Boiling		As above	From boiling	From boiling	16.0 g/m²/5 cycles	206.0		15
0.36 g/L sodium thiosulfate, 0 gr H_2O	Zinc sheet	(L) Immersion	Boiling		As above	From boiling	From boiling	16.8 g/m²/5 cycles	217.0		15
0.3 g/L sodium aluminate, 0 gr H_2O	Zinc sheet	(L) Immersion	Boiling		As above	From boiling	From boiling	21.7 g/m²/5 cycles	280.0		15
0.3 g/L sodium perborate, 0 gr H_2O	Zinc sheet	(L) Immersion	Boiling		As above	From boiling	From boiling	56.2 g/m²/5 cycles	725.0		15
0.3 g/L sodium perborate, 21 gr H_2O	Zinc sheet	(L) Immersion	Boiling		As above	From boiling	From boiling	34.7g/m²/5 cycles	448.0		15
L Syndet I, 6 g/L + magnesium silicate 0.18 g/L +:											
0 g/L perborate—0 gr H_2O	Zinc sheet	(L) Immersion	Boiling		As above	From boiling	From boiling	51.9 g/m²/5 cycles	669.0		15
2 g/L perborate—0 gr H_2O	Zinc sheet	(L) Immersion	Boiling		As above	From boiling	From boiling	55.8 g/m²/5 cycles	720.0		15
4 g/L perborate—0 gr H_2O	Zinc sheet	(L) Immersion	Boiling		As above	From boiling	From boiling	64.8 g/m²/5 cycles	835.0		15
6 g/L perborate—0 gr H_2O	Zinc sheet	(L) Immersion	Boiling		As above	From boiling	From boiling	75.1 g/m²/5 cycles	968.0		15
8 g/L perborate—0 gr H_2O	Zinc sheet	(L) Immersion	Boiling		As above	From boiling	From boiling	79.0 g/m²/5 cycles	1 020.0		15
10 g/L perborate—0 gr H_2O	Zinc sheet	(L) Immersion	Boiling		As above	From boiling	From boiling	81.2 g/m²/5 cycles	1 050.0		15
12 g/L perborate—0 gr H_2O	Zinc sheet	(L) Immersion	Boiling		As above	From boiling	From boiling	82.0 g/m²/5 cycles	1 060.0		15
13 g/L perborate—0 gr H_2O	Zinc sheet	(L) Immersion	Boiling		As above	From boiling	From boiling	81.9 g/m²/5 cycles	1 060.0		15
15 g/L perborate—0 gr H_2O	Zinc sheet	(L) Immersion	Boiling		As above	From boiling	From boiling	80.4 g/m²/5 cycles	1 040.0		15
20 g/L perborate—0 gr H_2O	Zinc sheet	(L) Immersion	Boiling		As above	From boiling	From boiling	63.7 g/m²/5 cycles	821.0		15
L Syndet II, composition:											
Lauryl sulfate, 10%											14
Dodecylbenzylsulfonate, 17%											14
Sodium tripolyphosphate, 30%											14
Tetrasodium pyrophosphate, 5%											14
Waterglass (powder), 6%											14
Magnesium silicate, 2%											14
Carboxymethylcellulose, 1%											14
Sodium sulfate, 13%											14
Sodium perborate, 16%											14
L Syndet II, 6 g/L solution	Hot dip galv.	(L) Immersion	20	68	12 h	None	None	8.0 g/m²	32.0	Solutions renewed every hour	14

(a) (L) laboratory test; (F) field test. (b) Unless otherwise indicated. Some corrosion rates are given in specialized units dictated by the test procedures used by the original investigators. The conversion to inches per year in some of these cases should not be considered representative of continuous immersion results, but should be evaluated in light of the test conditions. (c) Chromium in surface film, 0.02 µg/dm². (d) Chromium in surface film, 1.3 µg/dm². (e) Chromium in surface film, 2.2 µg/dm². (f) Chromium in surface film, 0.1 µg/dm². (g) Chromium in surface film, 0 µg/dm². (h) Chromium in surface film, 0.2 µg/dm²

(Continued)

Table 9 (continued)

Corrosion medium	Material	Type of test(a)	Temperature °C	°F	Duration	Aeration	Agitation	Corrosion rate mg/dm²/day(b)	mil/year	Remarks	Ref
L Syndet II, 6 g/L solution	Hot dip galv.	(L) Immersion	40	104	12 h	None	None	18.0 g/m²	73.0	Solutions renewed every hour	14
L Syndet II, 6 g/L solution	Hot dip galv.	(L) Immersion	65	149	12 h	None	None	38.0 g/m²	153.0	Solutions renewed every hour	14
L Syndet II, 6 g/L solution	Hot dip galv.	(L) Immersion	90	194	12 h	None	None	78.4 g/m²	316.0	Solutions renewed every hour	14
L Syndet II, 6 g/L solution	Hot dip galv.	(L) Immersion	90	194	12 h	Yes	Vigorous	81.4 g/m²	328.0	Solutions renewed every hour	14
L Syndet II, 6 g/L solution	Zinc sheet	(L) Immersion	90	194	12 h	None	None	67.3 g/m²	271.0	Solutions renewed every hour	14
L Syndet II, without perborate, 5 g/L	Hot dip galv.	(L) Immersion	90	194	12 h	None	None	7.3 g/m²	29.0	Solutions renewed every hour	14
L Syndet II, without perborate, 5 g/L	Hot dip galv.	(L) Immersion	90	194	12 h	Yes	Vigorous	18.2 g/m²	73.0	Solutions renewed every hour	14
L Soap detergent I, composition: Ordinary soap, 40%											14
Soda, 25%											14
Trisodium phosphate, 11%											14
Tetrasodium pyrophosphate, 5%											14
Waterglass (powder), 6%											14
Magnesium silicate, 2%											14
Sodium perborate, 11%											14
L Soap detergent I, 9 g/L	Hot dip galv.	(L) Immersion	90	194	12 h	None	None	5.1 g/m²	21.0	Solutions renewed every hour	14
L Soap detergent I, 9 g/L	Zinc sheet	(L) Immersion	90	194	12 h	None	None	1.6 g/m²	6.4	Solutions renewed every hour	14
L Soap detergent I, 8 g/L (without perborate)	Hot dip galv.	(L) Immersion	90	194	12 h	None	None	1.9 g/m²	7.6	Solutions renewed every hour	14
L Soap detergent II for hard water, composition: Ordinary soap, 35%											14
Soda, 21%											14
Trisodium phosphate, 5%											14
Sodium tripolyphosphate, 20%											14
Waterglass (powder), 6%											14
Magnesium silicate, 2%											14
Sodium perborate, 11%											
L Soap Detergent II, 9 g/L	Hot dip galv.	(L) Immersion	90	194	12 h	None	None	17.0 g/m²	68.0	Solutions renewed every hour	14
L Soap Detergent II, 9 g/L	Zinc sheet	(L) Immersion	90	194	12 h	None	None	6.1 g/m²	25.0	Solutions renewed every hour	14
L Soap Detergent II, 8 g/L (without perborate)	Hot dip galv.	(L) Immersion	90	194	12 h	None	None	7.0 g/m²	33.0	Solutions renewed every hour	14
Ethanol											
200 proof	HG zinc	(L) Immersion	Room		13 months	None	None	· · ·	<0.1		17
200 proof, 95 v/o in distilled H₂O	HG zinc	(L) Immersion	Room		13 months	None	None	· · ·	<0.1		17
200 proof, 75 v/o in distilled H₂O	HG zinc	(L) Immersion	Room		13 months	None	None	· · ·	0.7		17
200 proof, 25 v/o in distilled H₂O	HG zinc	(L) Immersion	Room		13 months	None	None	· · ·	0.7		17
190 proof, 45 v/o in tap water	HG zinc	(L) Immersion	Room		8 months	None	None	1.07	0.2		17
190 proof, 45 v/o in tap water	HG zinc	(L) Immersion	Boiling		5 days	None	Boiling	0.22	<0.1	8 h hot, 16 h cold daily	17
190 proof, 45 v/o in tap water	HG zinc	(L) In vapors	Boiling		5 days	· · ·	· · ·	4.38	0.9	8 h hot, 16 h cold daily	17
190 proof, 40 v/o + 5 v/o methanol in tap water	HG zinc	(L) Immersion	Room		8 months	None	None	3.87	0.8		17

(a) (L) laboratory test; (F) field test. (b) Unless otherwise indicated. Some corrosion rates are given in specialized units dictated by the test procedures used by the original investigators. The conversion to inches per year in some of these cases should not be considered representative of continuous immersion results, but should be evaluated in light of the test conditions. (c) Chromium in surface film, 0.02 μg/dm². (d) Chromium in surface film, 1.3 μg/dm². (e) Chromium in surface film, 2.2 μg/dm². (f) Chromium in surface film, 0.1 μg/dm². (g) Chromium in surface film, 0 μg/dm². (h) Chromium in surface film, 0.2 μg/dm²

(Continued)

Table 9 (continued)

Corrosion medium	Material	Type of test(a)	Temperature °C	°F	Duration	Aeration	Agitation	Corrosion rate mg/dm²/day(b)	mil/year	Remarks	Ref
190 proof, 40 v/o + 5 v/o methanol in tap water	HG zinc	(L) In vapors	Boiling		5 days	⋯	⋯	10.35	2.1	8 h hot, 16 h cold daily	17
190 proof, 50 v/o + 50 v/o CP glycerine	HG zinc	(L) Immersion	Room		8 months	None	None	0.84	0.2		17
190 proof + formic acid (eq to 0.10 mg KOH/g)	Sheet	(L) Partial immersion	30	86	1 week	None	None	3.3	0.7		6
190 proof + 5% water	Sheet	(L) Partial immersion	30	86	1 week	None	None	0.0	0.0		6
Ethyl acetate											
+5 v/o water	Sheet	(L) Partial immersion	30	86	1 week	None	None	37.1	7.4		6
+ formic acid (eq to 0.10 mg KOH/g)	Sheet	(L) Partial immersion	30	86	1 week	None	None	0.5	0.1		6
Ethylene glycol											
50 v/o	Galv. steel	(L) Immersion	−23	−10	14 days	Continuous	None	0.4	<0.1		
50 v/o	Galv. steel	(L) Immersion	−7	20	14 days	Continuous	None	1.63	0.3		
50 v/o	Galv. steel	(L) Immersion	24	75	14 days	Continuous	None	3.3	0.7		
50 v/o	Galv. steel	(L) Immersion	77	170	14 days	Continuous	None	37.1	7.4		
50 v/o + 1% borax	Galv. steel	(L) Immersion	−23	−10	14 days	Continuous	None	6.67	1.3		
50 v/o + 1% borax	Galv. steel	(L) Immersion	−7	20	14 days	Continuous	None	16.7	3.3		
50 v/o + 1% borax	Galv. steel	(L) Immersion	24	75	14 days	Continuous	None	7.9	1.6		
50 v/o + 1% borax	Galv. steel	(L) Immersion	77	170	14 days	Continuous	None	⋯	0.1		
50 v/o + 1% sodium nitrite	Galv. steel	(L) Immersion	−7	20	14 days	Continuous	None	0.85	0.2		
50 v/o + 1% sodium carbonate	Galv. steel	(L) Immersion	−7	20	14 days	Continuous	None	0.24	<0.1		
50 v/o + 1% sodium acetate	Galv. steel	(L) Immersion	−7	20	14 days	Continuous	None	2.91	0.6		
50 v/o + 1% sodium benzoate	Galv. steel	(L) Immersion	−7	20	14 days	Continuous	None	4.05	0.8		
Formaldehyde											
0.1 g/L in air, 90% RH	Sheet	(L) In vapors	30	86	8 days	⋯	⋯	5.0	1.0		1
Formic acid											
2.5% solution	Galv. steel	(L) In vapor	Room		30 days	⋯	⋯	23[1] 6.8[2] 4.4[3] 2.3[4]	4.7 1.4 0.9 0.5		4
4.6% solution	Sheet	(L) Immersion	100	212	4 h	None	None	6 000.0	1 200.0		4
0.1 g/L in air, 90% RH	Sheet	(L) In vapors	30	86	8 days	⋯	⋯	840.0	170.0		1
Vapors in air over solution at pH 3.8, 100% RH	Sheet	(L) In vapors	Room		8 days	⋯	⋯	2.12	0.4		3
Fire-extinguishing liquids											
45 g Al (OH)₃, 10 g KHCO₃, 22 g Na₂SO₄, 113 g K₂SO₄, 10 g foaming agent per liter of solution	Zn-4Cu-0.2Al	(L) Partial immersion	60, Cool,	days 140, days night	5 weeks	None	None	30.1	⋯	Weight changes determined without removing corrosion products	18
11 g Al (OH)₃, 8 g KHCO₃, 37 g Na₂SO₄, 88 g K₂SO₄, 175 g glycerin, 45 g glycol, 15 g foaming agent per liter	Zn-4Cu-0.2Al	(L) Partial immersion	60, Cool,	days 140, days night	5 weeks	None	None	15.3	⋯	As above	18
187 g KHCO₃, 34 g NaHCO₃, 15 g foaming agent per liter	Zn-4Cu-O-2Al	(L) Partial immersion	60, Cool,	days 140, days night	5 weeks	None	None	0.3	⋯	As above	18
47 g NaHCO₃, 141 g KHCO₃, 230 g glycerin, 63 g glycol, 15 g foaming agent per liter	Zn-4Cu-O-2Al	(L) Partial immersion	60, Cool,	days 140, days night	5 weeks	None	None	1.3	⋯	As above	18
180 g NaCl + 14 g Na₂CO₃ per liter	Zn-4Cu-O-2Al	(L) Partial immersion	60, Cool,	days 140, days night	5 weeks	None	None	8.8	⋯	As above	18
500 g commercial K₂CO₃ per liter	Zn-4Cu-O-2Al	(L) Partial immersion	60, Cool,	days 140, days night	5 weeks	None	None	3.2	⋯	As above	18
Carbon tetrachloride (water free)	Zn-4Cu-O-2Al	(L) Partial immersion	60, Cool,	days 140, days nigh	5 weeks	None	None	+(1.0)	⋯	As above	18
Carbon tetrachloride (water free)	Zn-4Cu-O-2Al	(L) In vapors	60, Cool,	days 140, days night	5 weeks	None	None	+(0.9)	⋯	As above	18
Carbon tetrachloride + 1 v/o water	Zn-4Cu-O-2Al	(L) Immersion	60, Cool,	days 140, days night	5 weeks	None	None	+(3.9)	⋯	As above	18
Gasoline											
100 cc untreated	HG sheet	(L) Immersion	Room		6 months	None	None	0.85	0.2		17

(a) (L) laboratory test; (F) field test. (b) Unless otherwise indicated. Some corrosion rates are given in specialized units dictated by the test procedures used by the original investigators. The conversion to inches per year in some of these cases should not be considered representative of continuous immersion results, but should be evaluated in light of the test conditions. (c) Chromium in surface film, 0.02 μg/dm². (d) Chromium in surface film, 1.3 μg/dm². (e) Chromium in surface film, 2.2 μg/dm². (f) Chromium in surface film, 0.1 μg/dm². (g) Chromium in surface film, 0 μg/dm². (h) Chromium in surface film, 0.2 μg/dm²

(Continued)

Table 9 (continued)

Corrosion medium	Material	Type of test(a)	Temperature °C	Temperature °F	Duration	Aeration	Agitation	Corrosion rate mg/dm²/day(b)	Corrosion rate mil/year	Remarks	Ref
100 cc + 40 ppm Lecithin	HG sheet	(L) Immersion	Room		6 months	None	None	0.13	<0.1		17
100 cc + 40 ppm Lecithin + 10 cc water	HG sheet	(L) Immersion	Room		6 months	None	None	3.76	0.8	Corroded in water layer	17
100 cc + 10 cc water	HG sheet	(L) Immersion	Room		6 months	None	None	6.73	1.4	Pitted, corroded in water layer	17
Glue											
12.5% solution, pH 5.6	Sheet	(F) Immersion	50	120	69 days	None	Moderate	83.0	17.0		1
Glycerine											
CP 100%	HG sheet	(L) Immersion	Room		8 months	None	None	. . .	<0.1		17
Glycolic acid											
7.6% solution	Sheet	(L) Immersion	100	212	4 hours	. . .	. . .	36 000.0	7 200.0		1
Hydrochloric acid											
3.6% solution (IN)	Comm. zinc	(L) Immersion	30	86	2 days	None	None	7 500.0	1 510.0		5
3.6% solution (IN)	Comm. zinc	(L) Immersion	30	86	2 days	15–20 air bubbles per min	. . .	6 500.0	1 300.0		5
Isobutanol											
+ formic acid (eq. to 0.10 mg KOH/g)	Sheet	(L) Partial immersion	30	86	1 week	None	None	0.4	<0.1		6
+ 5% water	Sheet	(L) Partial immersion	30	86	1 week	None	None	0.0	0.0		6
Lithium chloride											
30% solution	Sheet	(L) Immersion	15	240	40 days	. . .	Boiling	Destroyed			1
30% solution	Sheet	(L) In vapors	15	240	40 days	. . .	. . .	500.0	100.0		1
Magnesium chloride · 6H₂O											
22 °Be, 42.5% solution	Sheet	(L) Immersion	−5	23	30 days	. . .	Yes	8.7–15.3	1.8–3.1	Deep pits	1
1.2% solution	Electrolytic Zn	(L) Alternate immersion	20	68	7 days	. . .	. . .	28.0	5.6		10
1.2% solution	Electrolytic Zn	(L) Alternate immersion	20	68	14 days	. . .	. . .	21.0	4.2		10
Methanol											
CP	Sheet	(L) Immersion	Room		6 months	None	None	. . .	<0.1		19
CP	Sheet	(L) In vapors	Boiling		1 month	. . .	. . .	. . .	<0.1		19
100%	HG sheet	(L) Immersion	Room		8 months	None	None	0.79	0.2		17
35% solution in tap water	HG sheet	(L) Immersion	Room		8 months	None	None	2.76	0.6		17
35% solution in tap water	HG sheet	(L) In vapors	Boiling		5 days	. . .	. . .	1.08	0.2		17
30% solution in tap water	AC-41A die cast	(L) Immersion	Boiling		1 month	. . .	Boiling	192.0	38.4		17
30% solution in tap water	AC-41A die cast	(L) Immersion	Room		1 year	None	None	9.72	1.9		17
+ formic acid (eq. to 0.10 mg/KOH/g)	Sheet	(L) Partial immersion	30	86	1 week	None	None	8.1	1.6		6
+ 5 v/o water	Sheet	(L) Partial immersion	30	86	1 week	None	None	0.0	0.0		6
Methyl ethyl ketone											
+ 0.03 percent acetic acid and 0.2% H₂O	Sheet	(F) Immersion	10	50	128 days	Slight	Slight	5.2	1.0		1
+ trace acetic acid and 0.1% H₂O	Sheet	(F) In vapors	10	50	30 days	. . .	. . .	1.0	0.2		1
+ heptane and trace of acetic acid and water	Sheet	(F) Immersion	24	75	142 days	Moderate	None	0.6	0.1		1
Naphtha											
Naphtha	Sheet	(F) Immersion	55	310	50 days	. . .	. . .	30.8	6.2		1
Naphtha	Sheet	(F) In vapors	55	310	50 days	. . .	. . .	9.5	1.9		1
Oil											
No. 6 fuel	Sheet	(F) Immersion	Room		267 days	None	None	0.37	<0.1		1
Crude, light	Sheet	(F) Immersion	Room		55 days	. . .	None	0.24	<0.1		1
Crude, light	Sheet	(F) In vapors	Room		55 days	. . .	. . .	0.29	<0.1		1
Neutral, light	Sheet	(F) In vapors	Room		55 days	. . .	. . .	1.49	0.3		1
Neutral, light	Sheet	(F) Immersion	Room		55 days	. . .	None	50.3	10.0		1
Perchlorethylene											
Perchlorethylene	Sheet	(F) In vapors	27	260	64 days	None	None	117.8	23.0		1
Perchlorethylene	Sheet	(F) Immersion	51	305	64 days	. . .	Boiling	407.5	82.0		1

(a) (L) laboratory test; (F) field test. (b) Unless otherwise indicated. Some corrosion rates are given in specialized units dictated by the test procedures used by the original investigators. The conversion to inches per year in some of these cases should not be considered representative of continuous immersion results, but should be evaluated in light of the test conditions. (c) Chromium in surface film, 0.02 µg/dm². (d) Chromium in surface film, 1.3 µg/dm². (e) Chromium in surface film, 2.2 µg/dm². (f) Chromium in surface film, 0.1 µg/dm². (g) Chromium in surface film, 0 µg/dm². (h) Chromium in surface film, 0.2 µg/dm²

(Continued)

Table 9 (continued)

Corrosion medium	Material	Type of test(a)	Temperature °C	°F	Duration	Aeration	Agitation	Corrosion rate mg/dm²/day(b)	mil/year	Remarks	Ref
Pesticides											
Bordeaux mixture 1.3 oz gal copper sulfate + 1.3 oz/gal quicklime	AG-40A die casting	(L) Immersion	Room		20 days	None	None	0.14	<0.1	Solutions prepared from commercial products, changed after 3 and 6 days, weight changes as removed from test	17
Copper sulfate, 1.3 oz/gal	AG-40A die casting	(L) Immersion	Room		20 days	None	None	215.0	43.0	As above	17
Dry lime sulfur, 4.8 oz/gal	AG-40A die casting	(L) Immersion	Room		20 days	None	None	4.54	0.9	As above	17
Nicotine sulfate, 1/2 pint of Black Leaf 40 to 50 gal water	AG-40A die casting	(L) Immersion	Room		20 days	None	None	2.41	1.2	As above	17
White Hellebore, 0.33 oz/gal	AG-40A die casting	(L) Immersion	Room		20 days	None	None	7.20	1.4	As above	17
Calcium arsenate	AG-40A die casting	(L) Immersion	Room		20 days	None	None	Gained weight	...	As above	17
Formalin	AG-40A die casting	(L) Immersion	Room		20 days	None	None	Gained weight	...	As above	17
Paris green	AG-40A die casting	(L) Immersion	Room		20 days	None	None	Gained weight	...	As above	17
Pyrethrum	AG-40A die casting	(L) Immersion	Room		20 days	None	None	Gained weight	...	As above	17
Lead arsenate, 0.5 oz/gal	AG-40A die casting	(L) Immersion	Room		20 days	None	None	2.41	0.5	As above	17
Chlordane-water emulsion	Galv. iron	(L) Partial immersion	25	77	8 weeks	None	None	72.0	14.4		20
DDT, 5% in distilled water	Galv. iron	(L) Partial immersion	25	77	8 weeks	None	None	23.0	4.6		20
Potassium fluoride											
DDT in kerosene or fuel oil	Galv. iron	(L) Partial immersion	25	77	8 weeks	None	None	0.30	<0.1		20
Sodium arsenite, 8 oz/gal in distilled H₂O	Galv. iron	(L) Partial immersion	25	77	8 weeks	None	None	54.0	10.8		20
Sodium chloride, 5% in distilled water	Galv. iron	(L) Partial immersion	25	77	8 weeks	None	None	80.0	16.0		20
Sodium chloride, 5% in distilled water + 5% DDT	Galv. iron	(L) Partial immersion	25	77	8 weeks	None	None	41.0	8.2		20
Bordeaux mixture 1.0 oz/gal copper sulfate + 1.3 oz/gal hydrated lime	Sheet	(L) Immersion	Room		6 days	...	Yes	33.2	6.7		1
Lime sulfur, 1 part 32 °Be + 50 parts water	Sheet	(L) Immersion	Room		6 days	...	Yes	5.7	1.1		1
DDT, sulfur, Malathion emulsion	Sheet	(F)	7–32	20–90	277 days	None	Yes	6.3	1.4		1
Manzate, 70% wettable powder	Sheet	(F)	15–32	60–90	62 days	...	Yes	7.5	1.5		1
Phenol											
Pure, dry	Sheet	(L) Contact	25	77	100 days	None	None	0.13	<0.1		21
Pure, dry	Sheet	(L) In vapors	Boiling		100 days	...	...	Very high	...		21
Pure + 10% water	Sheet	(L) Contact	25	77	100 days	None	None	0.17	<0.1		21
Pure + 10% water	Sheet	(L) In vapors	Boiling		100 days	...	...	14.9	3.0		21
0.1 g/L in air, 90% RH	Sheet	(L) In vapors	30	86	8 days	...	...	1.25	0.3		21
Phenol-formalin-water mixture	Sheet	(L) Partial immersion	27	80	184 days	High	None	17.0	3.4		21
Potassium chloride											
0.01 N (0.07% solution)	Pure sheet	(L) Partial immersion	25	77	4 days	None	None	40.0	8.0		22
0.01 N (0.07% solution)	Pure sheet	(L) Partial immersion	25	77	30 days	None	None	35.4	7.0		22
0.1 N (0.75% solution)	Pure sheet	(L) Partial immersion	25	77	4 days	None	None	70.3	14.0		22
0.1 N (0.75% solution)	HG sheet	(L) Partial immersion	35	95	2 days	None	None	96.6	19.0		23
0.25 N (1.86% solution)	HG sheet	(L) Partial immersion	35	95	2 days	None	None	116.0	23.0		23
0.50 N (3.64% solution)	Pure sheet	(L) Partial immersion	25	77	4 days	None	None	94.3	19.0		22
0.50 N (3.64% solution)	Pure sheet	(L) Partial immersion	25	77	30 days	None	None	101.6	20.0		22
1.0 N (7.13% solution)	Pure sheet	(L) Partial immersion	25	77	4 days	None	None	106.3	21.0		22
2.0 N (13.7% solution)	Pure sheet	(L) Partial immersion	25	77	4 days	None	None	120.0	24.0		22
2.0 N (13.7% solution)	Pure sheet	(L) Partial immersion	25	77	30 days	None	None	114.3	23.0		22
3.0 N (19.8% solution)	Pure sheet	(L) Partial immersion	25	77	4 days	None	None	144.5	29.0		22
5–15 g/L solution	98.5% Zn sheet	(L) Immersion	12	54	65 days	None	None	18.2–11.8	3.6–2.4		24
50–300 g/L solution	98.5% Zn sheet	(L) Immersion	12	54	65 days	None	None	1.1–3.4	0.2–0.7		24

(a) (L) laboratory test; (F) field test. (b) Unless otherwise indicated. Some corrosion rates are given in specialized units dictated by the test procedures used by the original investigators. The conversion to inches per year in some of these cases should not be considered representative of continuous immersion results, but should be evaluated in light of the test conditions. (c) Chromium in surface film, 0.02 μg/dm². (d) Chromium in surface film, 1.3 μg/dm². (e) Chromium in surface film, 2.2 μg/dm². (f) Chromium in surface film, 0.1 μg/dm². (g) Chromium in surface film, 0 μg/dm². (h) Chromium in surface film, 0.2 μg/dm²

(Continued)

Table 9 (continued)

Corrosion medium	Material	Type of test(a)	Temperature °C	°F	Duration	Aeration	Agitation	Corrosion rate mg/dm²/day(b)	mil/year	Remarks	Ref
Potassium dichromate											
14.7% solution (1N)	Comm. zinc	(L) Immersion	30	86	2 days	None	None	0.75	0.15		5
14.7% solution (1N)	Comm. zinc	(L) Immersion	30	86	2 days	15–20 air bubbles per min	· · ·	0.40	<0.1		5
Potassium acid fluoride											
5% KF-HF solution	99.9% Zn	(L) Immersion	20	68	28 days	· · ·	· · ·	14.8	3.0	Corrosion products not removed	25
5% KF-HF solution	99.9% Zn	(L) Immersion	80	176	1 day	· · ·	· · ·	90 800.0	18 600.0	As above	25
10% KF-HF solution	99.9% Zn	(L) Immersion	20	68	28 days	· · ·	· · ·	22.3	4.5	As above	25
10% KF-HF solution	99.9% Zn	(L) Immersion	80	176	1 day	· · ·	· · ·	79 000.0	15 800.0	As above	25
20% KF-HF solution	99.9% Zn	(L) Immersion	20	68	28 days	· · ·	· · ·	16.5	3.3	As above	25
20% KF-HF solution	99.9% Zn	(L) Immersion	80	176	1 day	· · ·	· · ·	29 600.0	5 900.0	As above	25
Potassium fluoride											
5% solution	99.9% Zn	(L) Immersion	20	68	28 days	· · ·	· · ·	4.3	0.9	As above	25
5% solution	99.9% Zn	(L) Immersion	80	176	1 day	· · ·	· · ·	Gained	· · ·	As above	25
10% solution	99.9% Zn	(L) Immersion	20	68	28 days	· · ·	· · ·	Gained	· · ·	As above	25
10% solution	99.9% Zn	(L) Immersion	80	176	1 day	· · ·	· · ·	Gained	· · ·	As above	25
20% solution	99.9% Zn	(L) Immersion	20	68	28 days	· · ·	· · ·	0.2	<0.1	As above	25
20% solution	99.9% Zn	(L) Immersion	80	176	1 day	· · ·	· · ·	Gained	· · ·	As above	25
Potassium nitrate											
5 to 100 g/L solutions	98.5% Zn sheet	(L) Immersion	7	46	189 days	None	None	1.2–3.2	0.2–0.6		24
Potassium sulfate											
5 to 50 g/L solutions	98.5% Zn sheet	(L) Immersion	12	54	57 days	None	None	11.0–7.1	2.2–1.4		24
100 g/L solution	98.5% Zn sheet	(L) Immersion	12	54	57 days	None	None	0.54	0.1		24
n-Propanol											
+ 5% water	Sheet	(L) Partial immersion	30	86	1 week	None	None	0.3	<0.1		6
+ formic acid (eq. to 0.10 mg KOH/g)	Sheet	(L) Partial immersion	30	86	1 week	None	None	0.3	<0.1		6
Sodium bromate											
1% solution	Sheet	(L) Immersion	· · ·	· · ·	10 days	· · ·	· · ·	346.0	69.0		10
2% solution	Sheet	(L) Immersion	· · ·	· · ·	10 days	· · ·	· · ·	137.0	27.0		10
3% solution	Sheet	(L) Immersion	· · ·	· · ·	10 days	· · ·	· · ·	430.0	86.0		10
Sodium bromide											
In vapors, 30-45% RH	Sheet	(F) In vapors	24	75	365 days	Full	· · ·	17.89	3.6		1
Sodium carbonate											
0.5% solution	Sheet	(L) Partial immersion	66	150	5 h	None	None	39.0	7.8	Rate calculated on immersed area	1
0.5% solution	Galv. iron	(L) Partial immersion	66	150	5 h	None	None	37.0	7.4		1
Sodium chlorate											
1.57% ClO₃	Sheet	(L) Immersion	· · ·	· · ·	10 days	· · ·	· · ·	13.0	2.6		10
Sodium chloride											
Solution at pH 8.5	Sheet	(F) Immersion	−8	17	90 days	· · ·	· · ·	126.7	25.5		1
Solution at pH 8.5	Sheet	(F) Spray	−8	17	90 days	Spray	· · ·	66.0	13.3	Local, pitting 0.003 in. (75 μm)	1
0.5–3.0% solutions	Sheet	(L) Immersion	12	54	64 days	None	None	18.1–10.2	3.6–2.0		24
0.1 N, 0.58% solution	HG sheet	(L) Partial immersion	35	95	2 days	None	None	91.4	18.0		1
0.25 N 1.45% solution	HG sheet	(L) Partial immersion	35	95	2 days	None	None	116.3	23.0		1
0.5 N, 2.9% solution	Sheet	(L) Partial immersion	25	77	205 h	· · ·	· · ·	65.1	13.0		10
3.0% solution	Sheet	(L) Immersion	· · ·	· · ·	2 days	· · ·	· · ·	95.0	19.0		10
3.0% solution	Sheet	(L) Immersion	· · ·	· · ·	7 days	· · ·	· · ·	137.0	27.0		10
3.0% solution	Sheet	(L) Immersion	· · ·	· · ·	14 days	· · ·	· · ·	142.0	28.0		10
3.0% + 10 g/L Na₂SO₄·10H₂O	Sheet	(L) Immersion	· · ·	· · ·	2 days	· · ·	· · ·	130.0	26.0		10
3.0% + 10 g/L Na₂SO₄·10H₂O	Sheet	(L) Immersion	· · ·	· · ·	7 days	· · ·	· · ·	215.0	43.0		10
3.0% + 10 g/L Na₂SO₄·10H₂O	Sheet	(L) Immersion	· · ·	· · ·	14 days	· · ·	· · ·	225.0	45.0		10
3.0% + 12 g/L MgCl₂·6H₂O	Sheet	(L) Immersion	· · ·	· · ·	2 days	· · ·	· · ·	5.0	1.0		10
3.0% + 12 g/L MgCl₂·6H₂O	Sheet	(L) Immersion	· · ·	· · ·	7 days	· · ·	· · ·	3.0	0.6		10
3.0% + 12 g/L MgCl₂·6H₂O	Sheet	(L) Immersion	· · ·	· · ·	14 days	· · ·	· · ·	3.0	0.6		10
3.5%, pH 7.0	Sheet	(L) Immersion	30	86	21 days	Saturated	16 ft/min	75.0	15.0	Maximum 0.007 in. pits (175 μm)	1

(a) (L) laboratory test; (F) field test. (b) Unless otherwise indicated. Some corrosion rates are given in specialized units dictated by the test procedures used by the original investigators. The conversion to inches per year in some of these cases should not be considered representative of continuous immersion results, but should be evaluated in light of the test conditions. (c) Chromium in surface film, 0.02 μg/dm². (d) Chromium in surface film, 1.3 μg/dm². (e) Chromium in surface film, 2.2 μg/dm². (f) Chromium in surface film, 0.1 μg/dm². (g) Chromium in surface film, 0 μg/dm². (h) Chromium in surface film, 0.2 μg/dm²

(Continued)

Table 9 (continued)

Corrosion medium	Material	Type of test(a)	Temperature °C	°F	Duration	Aeration	Agitation	Corrosion rate mg/dm²/day(b)	mil/year	Remarks	Ref
3.5% pH 7.0	Sheet	(L) Immersion	30	86	42 days	Saturated	16 ft/min	64.0	12.8	Maximum 0.016 in. pits (402 μm)	1
3.5%, pH 7.0	Galv., 0.001 in. Zn	(L) Immersion	30	86	21 days	Saturated	16 ft/min	37.0	7.4		1
3.5%, pH 7.0	Galv., 0.0015 in. Zn	(L) Immersion	30	86	21 days	Saturated	16 ft/min	74.0	14.8	0.001–0.003 in. pits (25–75 μm)	1
3.5%, pH 7.0	Galv., 0.003 in. Zn	(L) Immersion	30	86	21 days	Saturated	16 ft/min	111.0	22.2	0.001 to 0.003 in. pits (25–75 μm)	1
3.5%, pH 7.0	Galv., 0.001 in. Zn	(L) Immersion	30	86	42 days	Saturated	16 ft/min	19.0	3.8		1
3.5%, pH 7.0	Galv., 0.0015 in. Zn	(L) Immersion	30	86	42 days	Saturated	16 ft/min	23.0	4.6		1
3.5%, pH 7.0	Galv., 0.003 in. Zn	(L) Immersion	30	86	42 days	Saturated	16 ft/min	45.0	9.2		1
1 N, 5.6%, pH 7.85	Sheet	(L) Immersion	35	95	31 days	300 cc/min	15 ft/s	9.3	1.9		26
1 N, 5.6%, pH 8.00	Sheet	(L) Immersion	35	95	30 days	300 cc/min	15 ft/s	37.0	7.4	<0.001 in. pits (<25 μm)	1
1 N, 5.6%	Sheet	(L) Immersion	30	86	2 days	15–20 air bubbles per min	None	65.5	13.1		5
1 N, 5.6%	Sheet	(L) Immersion	30	86	2 days	None	None	25.0	5.0		5
20.0% solution	Sheet	(L) Immersion	Room		500 h	None	None	1.62	0.3		1
20.0% solution	Sheet	(L) Spray	35	95	21 days	. . .	. . .	72.0	14.4		1
20.0% solution	Sheet	(L) Spray	35	95	63 days	. . .	. . .	32.0	6.4		1
20.0% solution	Sheet	(L) Spray	35	95	119 days	. . .	. . .	81.0	16.2		1
20.0% solution	Galv. steel	(L) Spray	35	95	21 days	. . .	. . .	74.0	14.8	0.004 in. pits (<100 μm)	1
20.0% solution	Galv. steel	(L) Spray	35	95	63 days	. . .	. . .	20.0	4.0	0.006 in. pits (150 μm)	1
20.0% solution	Galv. steel	(L) Spray	35	95	119 days	. . .	. . .	22.0	4.4	0.019 in. pits (480 μm)	1
22 °Be, 24% solution	Sheet	(L) Partial immersion	−5	23	30 days	. . .	Yes	2.0–8.7	0.4–1.8	Deep pits, rate calculated on immersed area	1
60–400 g/L solutions	98.5% Zn	(L) Immersion	12	54	64 days	None	None	7.5–2.5	1.5–0.5		24
Sodium hydroxide											
0.5% solution	Sheet	(L) Partial immersion	21	70	5 days	None	None	4.7	0.9	Based on immersed area	1
0.5% solution	Galv. iron	(L) Partial immersion	21	70	5 days	None	None	12.0	2.4	Based on immersed area	1
0.5% solution	Sheet	(L) Partial immersion	66	150	5 h	None	None	89.0	17.8	Based on immersed area	1
0.5% solution	Galv. iron	(L) Partial immersion	66	150	5 h	None	None	204.0	40.8	Based on immersed area	1
3.9% solution (1 N)	Comm. zinc	(L) Immersion	30	86	2 days	None	None	87.5	17.5		5
3.9% solution (1 N)	Comm. zinc	(L) Immersion	30	86	2 days	15–20 air bubbles per min	. . .	175.0	35.0		5
50% solution	Sheet	(L) Immersion	30	86	1 day	None	None	5 940.0	1 190.0		5
50% solution	Sheet	(L) Immersion	30	86	1 day	None	None	4 280.0	860.0		5
50% solution	Galv. iron	(L) Immersion	30	86	1 day	None	None	379.0	75.0		5
Sodium sulfate											
5 to 300 g/L $Na_2SO_4 \cdot 10H_2O$	98.5% Zn	(L) Immersion	12	54	60 days	None	None	13 to 2	2.6–0.4		24
10 g/L $Na_2SO_4 \cdot 10H_2O$	Electrolytic zinc	(L) Immersion	. . .	. . .	2 days	. . .	. . .	10.0	2.0		10
10 g/L $Na_2SO_4 \cdot 10H_2O$	Electrolytic zinc	(L) Immersion	. . .	. . .	7 days	. . .	. . .	16.0	3.2		10
10 g/L $Na_2SO_4 \cdot 10H_2O$	Electrolytic zinc	(L) Immersion	. . .	. . .	14 days	. . .	. . .	16.0	3.2		10
Sulfamic acid											
3% solution	Sheet	(L) Immersion	20–25	68–76	48–95 h	. . .	. . .	. . .	2 200.0		1
3% solution	Galv. iron	(L) Immersion	20–25	68–76	48–95 h	. . .	. . .	. . .	2 280.0		1
3% solution	Sheet	(L) Immersion	66	150	4 h	. . .	. . .	. . .	2 340.0		1
6% solution	Sheet	(L) Immersion	20–25	68–76	48–95 h	. . .	. . .	. . .	2 200.0		1
6% solution	Galv. iron	(L) Immersion	20–25	68–76	48–95 h	. . .	. . .	. . .	2 280.0		1
12% solution	Sheet	(L) Immersion	20–25	68–76	48–95 h	. . .	. . .	. . .	7 800.0		1
12% solution	Galv. iron	(L) Immersion	20–25	68–76	48–95 h	. . .	. . .	. . .	1 400.0		1
20% solution	Sheet	(L) Immersion	20–25	68–76	48–95 h	. . .	. . .	. . .	730.0		1
20% solution	Galv. iron	(L) Immersion	20–25	68–76	48–95 h	. . .	. . .	. . .	910.0		1
Sulfur dioxide											
Liquid + 1% H_2O + 0.21% O_2	Sheet	(L) Immersion	20	68	14 days	. . .	. . .	30.0	6.0		27
0.6% vapors in air, 89% RH	99.6% Zn	(L) In vapors	40	104	2 h	. . .	. . .	604.0	121.0		28
0.6% vapors in air, 89% RH	99.6% Zn	(L) In vapors	40	104	4 h	. . .	. . .	465.0	93.0		28
0.6% vapors in air, 89% RH	99.6% Zn	(L) In vapors	40	104	7 h	. . .	. . .	314.0	63.0		28
0.6% vapors in air, 89% RH	99.6% Zn	(L) In vapors	40	104	24 h	. . .	. . .	92.0	18.0		28

(a) (L) laboratory test; (F) field test. (b) Unless otherwise indicated. Some corrosion rates are given in specialized units dictated by the test procedures used by the original investigators. The conversion to inches per year in some of these cases should not be considered representative of continuous immersion results, but should be evaluated in light of the test conditions. (c) Chromium in surface film, 0.02 μg/dm². (d) Chromium in surface film, 1.3 μg/dm². (e) Chromium in surface film, 2.2 μg/dm². (f) Chromium in surface film, 0.1 μg/dm². (g) Chromium in surface film, 0 μg/dm². (h) Chromium in surface film, 0.2 μg/dm²

(Continued)

Table 9 (continued)

Corrosion medium	Material	Type of test(a)	Temperature °C	°F	Duration	Aeration	Agitation	Corrosion rate mg/dm²/day(b)	mil/year	Remarks	Ref
0.6% vapors in air, 89% RH	99.6% Zn	(L) In vapors	40	104	72 h	...	...	34.7	7.0		28
0.6% vapors in air, 89% RH	99.6% Zn	(L) In vapors	40	104	168 h	...	...	18.4	4.0		28
Trichloroethylene											
Trichloroethylene	Sheet	(F) Immersion	...	...	41 h	...	...	289.0	58.0	In storage tank	1
Trichloroethylene vapors in air	Sheet	(F) In vapors	45	113	41 h	...	...	10.4	2.1	In dryer compartment	1
Trichloroethylene vapors in air	Sheet	(F) In vapors	84	183	41 h	...	...	13.6	2.7	In exhaust duct	1
Trichloroethylene vapors in air	Sheet	(F) In vapors	...	...	41 h	...	...	377.0	76.0	In still	1
Trichloroethylene, 100 cc	HG sheet	(L) Immersion	Room		4 months	None	None	Gained	...	Specimens only scrubbed before weighing, zinc attacked in water layer	17
Trichloroethylene, 100 cc	PW sheet	(L) Immersion	Room		4 months	...	...	Gained	...	As above	17
Trichloroethylene, 95 cc + 15 cc distilled H₂O	HG sheet	(L) Immersion	Room		4 months	None	None	3.08	0.6	As above	17
Trichloroethylene, 95 cc + 15 cc distilled H₂O	PW sheet	(L) Immersion	Room		4 months	None	None	4.53	0.9	As above	17
Trichloroethylene, 95 cc + 15 cc distilled H₂O + 0.15 g borax	HG sheet	(L) Immersion	Room		4 months	None	None	1.05	0.2	As above	17
Trichloroethylene, 95 cc + 15 cc distilled H₂O + 0.15 g borax	PW sheet	(L) Immersion	Room		4 months	None	None	0.25	<0.1	As above	17
Trichloroethylene, 95 cc + 15 cc distilled H₂O + 0.015 g K₂Cr₂O₇	HG sheet	(L) Immersion	Room		4 months	None	None	Gained	...	As above	17
Trichloroethylene, 95 cc + 15 cc distilled H₂O + 0.015 g K₂Cr₂O₇	PW sheet	(L) Immersion	Room		4 months	None	None	Gained	...	As above	17

(a) (L) laboratory test; (F) field test. (b) Unless otherwise indicated. Some corrosion rates are given in specialized units dictated by the test procedures used by the original investigators. The conversion to inches per year in some of these cases should not be considered representative of continuous immersion results, but should be evaluated in light of the test conditions. (c) Chromium in surface film, 0.02 µg/dm². (d) Chromium in surface film, 1.3 µg/dm². (e) Chromium in surface film, 2.2 µg/dm². (f) Chromium in surface film, 0.1 µg/dm². (g) Chromium in surface film, 0 µg/dm². (h) Chromium in surface film, 0.2 µg/dm²

References:

1. International Nickel Company

2. S.G. Clarke and E.E. Longhurst, The Corrosion of Metals by Acid Vapors from Wood, *Journal of Applied Chemistry*, Vol 11, 1961, 435-443

3. P.T. Gilbert and S.E. Hadden, Corrosion of Cadmium and Zinc Coatings in Electrical Equipment, *J. Electrodep. Tech. Soc.*, Vol 25, 1950 41-49

4. L.E. Helwig and J.E. Bird, Protection of Galvanized Coatings from Attack by Organic Acid Vapors, *Metal Finishing*, Nov 1973, 45-49

5. T.S. Fuller, Report of ASTM Committee B-3 on Corrosion of Non-ferrous Metals and Alloys, *Proceedings of the American Society for Testing and Materials*, Vol 27-1, 1927, 281-298

6. P. Schlapfer and A. Bukowiecki, Contribution to the Study of the Corrosion of Metals by Motor Fuels, *Metaux (Corrosion-Industries)*, (France), Vol 23, 1948, 267-277, (in French)

7. T. Marshall and L.G. Neubauer, Corrosion of Aircraft Structural Materials by Agricultural Chemicals, *Corrosion*, Vol 11, 1955, 84t-92t

8. The Consolidated Mining and Smelting Company of Canada, Ltd.

9. D.A. Jones and B.E. Wilde, Corrosion Performance of Some Metals and Alloys in Liquid Ammonia, *Corrosion*, Vol 33, Feb 1977, 46-52

10. F. Ritter, *Korrosionstabellen metallischer Werkstoffe*, 4th ed., Springer-Verlag, Vienna, 1958, 290 (in German)

11. L.A.J. Lodder and S. Baumgarten, Corrosion Tests with Zinc Alloy Die Castings in Damp Gypsum Plaster, *Metallurgia*, Vol 43, 1951, 273-279

12. O. Bauer and G. Schikorr, The Corrosion of Electrolytic and Refined Zinc, *Zeit. Metallk.*, Vol 26, 1934, 73-80 (in German)

13. H. Bablik and H. Belohlavy, Modern Detergents and Hot Dip Galvanizing, *Korrosionstabellen metallischer Werkstoffe*, Vol 8, 1957, 742-746 (in German)

14. A. Bukowiecki, Investigation of the Attack on Metals by Detergents, *Schweizer Archiv fuer Angewandte Wissenschaft und Technik*, Vol 24, 1958, 355-370 (in German)

15. H. Stupel and F. Koch, The Corrosion of Zinc by Modern Detergents, *Korrosionstabellen metallischer Werkstoffe* Vol 11, 1960, 33-39 (in German); also translated in *Soap, Perfumery and Cosmetics*, Vol 32, 1959, 1111-1118

16. L.R. Bacon and E.G. Nutting, Jr., Polyphosphate Detergents in Mechanical Dishwashing, *Industrial and Engineering Chemistry*, Vol 44, 1952, 146-150

17. New Jersey Zinc Company

18. R. Beythein, Corrosion of Phosphated Zinc Alloys by Fire Extinguishing Liquid, *Arch. Metallk.*, Vol 1, 1947, 286-288 (in German)

19. H.O. Teeple, Corrosion by Some Organic Acids and Related Compounds, *Corrosion*, Vol 8, 1952, 14-28

20. G.S. Cook and N. Dickinson, Corrosion of Metals by Insecticidal Solutions, *Corrosion*, Vol 6, 1950, 137-139

21. F.H. Rhodes, P.A. Riedel, and V.K. Hendricks, Corrosion of Metals by Phenols, *Industrial and Engineering Chemistry*, Vol 26, 1934, 533-534

22. C.W. Borgmann and U.R. Evans, The Corrosion of Zinc in Chloride Solutions, *Transactions of the Electrochemical Society*, Vol 65, 1934, 249-274

23. C.W. Borgmann, The Initial Corrosion Rate of Mild Steel, *Industrial and Engineering Chemistry*, Vol 29, 1937, 814-821

24. J.N. Friend and J.S. Tidmus, The Relative Corrosion of Zinc and Lead in Solutions of Inorganic Salts, *Journal of the Institute of Metals*, Vol 31, 1924, 177-191

25. W. Kohler, The Chemical Corrosion Behaviour of Non-ferrous Metals Towards Alkali Mono- and Alkali Hydrogen Fluorides, *Korrosionstabellen metallischer Werkstoffe*, Vol 6, 1955, 478-486 (in German)

26. Union Carbide Corporation, Chemicals Division

27. J. Bollinger, Corrosion Resistance of Various Metals in Liquid Sulfur Dioxide, *Schweizer Archiv fuer Angewandte Wissenschaft und Technik*, Vol 18, 1952, 321-342 (in German)

28. B. Sanyal and D.V. Bhadwar, The Corrosion of Metals in Synthetic Atmospheres Containing Sulfur Dioxide, *Journal of Scientific and Industrial Research* (India), Vol 18A, 1959, 69-74

Tin and Tin Alloys

Tin is a soft, brilliant white, low-melting metal that is most widely used in the form of coatings for steel, that is, tinplate. In the molten state, it reacts with and readily wets most of the common metals and their alloys. Because of its low strength, the pure metal is not regarded as a structural material and is rarely used in monolithic form. Tin is also not used in manufactured articles due to its poor mechanical properties. Rather, the metal is frequently used as a coating for other metals and in alloys to impart corrosion resistance, enhance appearance, and improve solderability. It also finds wide use in alloys, especially tin-base soft solders, bearing alloys, and copper-base bronzes.

Allotropic Modification

In its usual form, tin has a specific gravity of 7.31 (white tin), but there is also a lighter metalloid modification with a specific gravity of 5.75, which exists as a gray powder (gray tin). White tin is stable at temperatures above 13 °C (55 °F). Gray tin is stable below 13 °C (55 °F). The maximum rate of transition of white into gray tin has been established at -48 °C (-54 °F). The allotropic transformation of white tin into gray tin is analogous to external corrosion.

In the past, when many domestic wares, munitions, and organ pipes were made of pure tin, such a transformation created much unpleasantness. Because initial transformation or contact with affected tin accelerated the transformation of healthy metal, the phenomenon received the name "tin disease." Pure tin is more susceptible to this deterioration than tin alloys. Tin alloys with 0.5% bismuth or antimony are not susceptible to transformation into gray tin at low temperatures.

Atmospheric Corrosion

In rural atmospheres, tin retains its bright appearance for many days. In one study, a light dulling was observed after 100 days, and a noticeable, faint yellow-gray tarnish film was seen after 150 days. However, it was also reported that the reflectivity of tin remains practically unchanged over long periods when the tin is washed in soap and water. Thus, at ordinary temperatures, the surface oxide film on tin is very thin and exhibits a very slow rate of growth. The rate of oxidation increases with temperature. Above 190 °C (375 °F), a film thickness sufficient to produce interference colors is reportedly produced in a few hours. At 210 °C (410 °F), this film thickness is produced in 20 min.

In marine and industrial environments, tin deteriorates. It does so at increasing rates, which depend on the aggressiveness of the specific environment.

Water Exposure

Tin maintains a high degree of stability in waters, particularly when they are soft or distilled. It is also quite stable in water containing CO_2 and also in solutions of neutral salts, such as chlorides and sulfates. It is very resistant to food materials and to various organic juices. For this reason, and because of its low toxicity and colorless corrosion products, tin is used extensively as a protective coating in food-processing equipment and in the canning industry as a protective coating for sheet iron. In fruit acids, tin has a more negative potential than iron; therefore, in the absence or deficiency of oxygen in sealed cans, rust does not form, despite the fact that the electroplated tin coating has some porosity. In atmospheric exposures, iron has a more electronegative potential than tin, and therefore, open tin cans rust rapidly in humid atmospheres.

Acids and Bases

The normal equilibrium potential of tin is -0.136 V and its static potential in 0.5N NaCl is -0.25 V. Susceptibility of tin to passivation is very low. Tin dissolves rapidly in nitric acid. It is unusable in alkalis. Tin corrodes in sulfuric and hydrochloric acids of medium-to-high concentrations. It is, however, resistant to dilute acids. Resistance to acids decreases as the accessibility of oxygen from air increases. Tin is very resistant to organic acids, although oxygen also promotes corrosive action.

Soft Solders

Most soft solders contain from about 2 to 98% tin; the balance consists mostly of lead. Two features are particularly relevant to the corrosion behavior of solders with regard to their function as a joining material. First, fluxes are usually used. Second, the solder exposure areas are usually smaller than the area of the materials being joined. By nature, fluxes function as oxide removers and may contain hygroscopic products that, if not removed, promote corrosion.

Nickel and Nickel Alloys

Nickel-base alloys generally are extremely effective corrosion-resistant materials in service environments that range from subzero to elevated temperatures. Nickel-base alloys are known for their ability to resist severe operating conditions involving liquid or gaseous environments, high stresses, and combinations of these factors. Nickel itself has good resistance to corrosion in reducing environments and can be used in oxidizing environments that act to promote the formation of a passive, corrosion-resistant oxide film. Nickel is highly resistant to caustic and chloride-ion-induced stress-corrosion cracking, is resistant to halide ions, and is an acceptable material for handling food. On the other hand, nickel is subject to both general and intercrystalline corrosion by compounds and gases that contain sulfur when the application temperature is greater than about 315 to 371 °C (600 to 700 °F). Nickel alloys may be similarly attacked, as for example by hot corrosion, where sulfur-containing compounds frequently promote the corrosive attack.

Nickel and its alloys have good resistance to corrosion in the normal atmosphere, in natural freshwaters, and in deaerated nonoxidizing acids. They also have excellent resistance to corrosion caused by caustic alkalis. Because nickel is a ductile, hardenable matrix, it forms the basis for a wide variety of strong and corrosion-resistant alloys. The most corrosion-resistant alloys for high-temperature applications are the nickel-base superalloys.

The principal elements used in nickel-base alloys are copper (as in the Monels) and chromium plus aluminum (as in superalloys such as the Hastelloy or Inconel/Incoloy materials). Chromium and aluminum provide elevated temperature oxidation resistance, and chromium and titanium provide resistance to hot corrosion. Other elements also are used to enhance oxidation/hot corrosion resistance. Chromium is a prime promoter of corrosion resistance in some liquid media at lower temperatures, but other alloy elements also are quite significant in the enhancement or promotion of corrosion resistance. Notable among the latter are copper, molybdenum, and tungsten. Other alloy elements are used to a considerable degree in nickel-base alloys, although not primarily for corro-sion (or oxidation) resistance. Superalloys, in particular, may contain, intentionally, up to a dozen elements at controlled levels. The role of the major alloy element additions to nickel are summarized below.

Chromium

Chromium additions promote improved resistance of nickel to oxidizing acids such as nitric and chromic. Chromium also improves resistance to high-temperature oxidation in binary alloys, provided the chromium level exceeds about 5%. In practice, when chromium is the element providing oxidation resistance, a level of 20% or greater was found to be desirable for maximum corrosion protection. Some superalloys have been employed with chromium levels as low as about 8%, but these are all superalloys that use aluminum to form a protective aluminum oxide scale as the primary barrier to oxidation. Although alloys have been formulated with chromium levels up to 50%, customarily most corrosion- or oxidation-resistant alloys relying on chromium for primary environmental protection have contained about 15 to 30% chromium.

A principal role of chromium in modern superalloys has been to promote resistance to hot corrosion. Hot corrosion-resistant nickel-base alloys contain no less than about 14% chromium, and the most resistant alloys contain as much as 22%. Unfortunately for the designers of superalloys, enhanced strength is achieved by reducing the level of chromium so as to incorporate more of the hardening elements that contribute to the outstanding high-temperature strength of the nickel-base superalloys.

Copper

Copper has long been a prime alloying element with nickel, because the two elements are mutually soluble in one another. Each has good ductility and good corrosion resistance, along with the ability to be hardened. Additions of copper provide improvement in the resistance of nickel to nonoxidizing acids. In particular, alloys containing 30 to 40% copper offer useful resistance to nonaerated sulfuric acid and offer excellent resistance to all concentrations of nonaerated hydrofluoric acid. The Monel series of alloys are based on the 70% nickel/30% copper composition and are widely used in the marine, chemical, petroleum, and process industries. Monel alloys are actually better suited to reducing than oxidizing conditions.

In addition to its role as a major alloying element, copper has been found to confer improved resistance to hydrochloric acid and phosphoric acid when 2 to 3% copper is added to nickel-chromium-molybdenum-iron alloys.

Molybdenum

Molybdenum in nickel substantially improves resistance to nonoxidizing acids. Commercial alloys for ambient temperature applications have employed up to 28% molybdenum for service in severe nonoxidizing solutions of hydrochloric, phosphoric, and hydrofluoric acids as well as in sulfuric acid. On the other hand, molybdenum, when used for elevated temperature strength, drastically degrades the hot corrosion resistance of nickel-base superalloys. Molybdenum in nickel superalloys rarely exceeds 6%. However, 9% molybdenum has been combined with 21.5% chromium, 3.5% niobium, and minor other elements in nickel to produce Inconel 625, a non-age-hardenable superalloy with outstanding resistance to reducing or oxidizing conditions. Molybdenum is thought to contribute as well, to the excellent resistance to stress-corrosion cracking and virtual immunity from crevice corrosion in chloride ion environments.

Tungsten

Tungsten behaves in a similar way to molybdenum, in that it degrades the hot corrosion resistance of superalloys, but provides improved resistance to nonoxidizing acids and to localized corrosion. Tungsten is not normally used unless absolutely necessary, because it significantly increases the density of alloys and their cost. Additions of tungsten in superalloys have been as high as 12%. Additions of 3 to 4% of the element, in conjunction with 13 to 16% molybdenum, have resulted in alloys with outstanding resistance to local corrosion.

Iron

Iron is not added to nickel to improve corrosion resistance, but rather to reduce costs. However, iron does provide nickel with improved resistance to sulfuric acid at concentrations above 50% sulfuric.

Silicon

Silicon typically is present in minor amounts as a residual element. In general, silicon is restricted to low levels to minimize processing problems and the potential for embrittling reactions in certain alloys. Under some circumstances, silicon has been intentionally added to promote the elevated temperature oxidation resistance of superalloys where it probably promotes scale retention of the protective oxides formed by chromium or aluminum. Silicon has been used as a major alloying element where resistance to hot sulfuric acid is desired. In those circumstances, 9 to 11% silicon has been used. Such materials are invariably processed as castings.

Aluminum

Aluminum is added to nickel-base alloys principally to produce high-temperature strength through the precipitation of the gamma prime phase in the nickel-chromium matrix. An unexpected benefit of the addition of aluminum was the formation of oxidation-resistant aluminum oxide scales on alloys containing greater than about 4% aluminum. One of the principal problems with the use of aluminum to achieve high-temperature oxidation resistance is that aluminum oxide formation is only conveniently achieved at elevated temperatures, probably above about 870 °C (1600 °F). For alloys operating below such temperatures, chromium provides better oxidation resistance, because the oxides are more likely to be self-healing. Pre-oxidation of aluminum-containing alloys will produce the necessary oxidation resistance for lower temperature operation, but if the protective aluminum oxide scale is abraded or removed in any way, the aluminum in the alloy will not produce the optimum oxidation resistance. Aluminum may actually be detrimental in promoting hot corrosion resistance in superalloys, depending on the level of chromium and aluminum in the alloy, as well as the temperature of exposure to hot corrosion-producing environments.

Titanium

Titanium is not added in any significant amounts to nickel alloys for lower temperature applications; if present, it can tie up carbon, nitrogen, or oxygen, which may be beneficial under some conditions of stress-enhanced corrosion. Titanium is found as a constituent of superalloys, where it acts similarly and in concert with aluminum to produce strength through gamma-prime hardening. Titanium appears to be beneficial for improved hot corrosion resistance, but no quantitative information is available. It is universally recognized that a high titanium-to-aluminum ratio is beneficial for improved hot corrosion resistance. However, the titanium benefit may decrease with increased temperature of hot corrosion attack.

Other elements

Other elements have been added or retained in nickel-base alloys to promote improved corrosion resistance. In particular, in nickel-base superalloys, active element additions such as yttrium, lanthanum, and others have been found to promote improved corrosion resistance, perhaps by increasing the scale retention characteristics. Tantalum has been found to promote elevated temperature oxidation resistance.

Additions of several percent tantalum to the alloy B-1900 or the single-crystal alloy PWA 1480 have resulted in several of the most oxidation-resistant superalloys used in commercial gas turbine applications. On the other hand, none of the above elements have had any significant role in the enhancement of lower temperature corrosion resistance of nickel-base alloys.

As with stainless steels, nickel-base alloys are susceptible to precipitation of a variety of phases (e.g., sigma, chi, etc.) and carbides that are detrimental to corrosion resistance. Therefore, processing and fabrication may have a profound impact on corrosion resistance.

Coatings

In general, nickel and nickel-base alloys are not coated for lower temperature corrosion protection. Nickel-base superalloys, on the other hand, are coated with aluminide diffusion coatings or overlay coatings that provide aluminum and chromium for protection against oxidation and hot corrosion. Aluminide coatings are produced by reacting aluminum with the substrate alloy to produce aluminum-rich nickel aluminide compounds on the surface of the alloy. Such coatings are customarily about 3 mils thick. Overlay coatings also rely on diffusion to achieve bonding; however, the coating contains all of the protective elements required for the application. Such coatings customarily are about 5 mils thick. Protectivity of the coatings is a function of the composition, thickness of the coating, and the exact nature of the environment in which the alloy/coating system will have to perform.

Selection for Corrosion Resistance

Selection for corrosion resistance is clearly a function of the intended application. High-temperature corrosion resistance is not the same as lower temperature, aqueous corrosion resistance. A steam turbine loop is not the same as an aircraft gas turbine, nor as the scrubber in a stack. Generally, the application will have to be evaluated in relation to the chemical interactions likely to take place and the cost of preventing corrosion. Corrosion curves will facilitate preliminary selection, but tests will also be necessary. Consultation with the appropriate manufacturer(s) and trade associations may help to finalize selection, but short-term tests will be required for validation of the selection. Long-term tests may be needed eventually. Nickel-base alloys will be more costly than copper alloys and stainless steels for applications, but their corrosion-resistant properties coupled with their other properties could make them cost-effective in the long run. For many applications, as in a gas turbine, no other alternate materials are available.

Cobalt-Base Alloys and Superalloys

The corrosion behavior of cobalt-base alloys, including superalloys, has not been as well documented as the behavior of nickel alloys. The two are similar in behavior, yet cobalt-base alloys possess somewhat less corrosion resistance in many instances. The relative resistance level is a function of the corroding medium, as well as the composition of the different alloy systems.

Cobalt cannot be classed as an oxidation-resistant material, although cobalt-base superalloys are quite resistant to oxidation and hot corrosion. The scaling and oxidation rates of unalloyed cobalt in air are reported to be 25 times those of nickel; in hot corrosion, however, cobalt-base superalloys may be an order of magnitude more resistant than nickel-base superalloys.

In lower temperature "aqueous" corrosion, the differences between cobalt alloys and nickel alloys may not be as significant. Alloy additions produce reversals of the inherent behavior of the basis metals, cobalt and nickel. In fact, cobalt-chromium alloys of the Vitallium type, which are basically cobalt-base superalloys, have been used successfully for many years as orthopedic implant materials under various trade names. It is reported that Vitallium can be repassivated within a few seconds after a scratch has been made in its surface, but that stainless steel, commonly used for short-term surgical procedures, is not repassivated as rapidly. (Testing was done in Hank's solution.)

Cobalt is superior to nickel in deaerated $6N$ hydrochloric acid at ambient temperatures, but the two metals have about the same resistance in aerated $1N$ hydrochloric acid. Nitric acid attacks cobalt more rapidly than it does nickel. Unfortunately, the published documentation on the corrosion resistance of cobalt and its alloys is minimal.

Cobalt alloys with chromium additions were discovered and exploited somewhat before comparable nickel alloys. Cobalt-chromium alloys have become standard materials for many applications, particularly those requiring corrosion resistance with wear resistance which in these alloys is achieved by high carbon content.

The principal alloying additions to cobalt are chromium and nickel, with the almost invariable presence of carbon as carbides to provide strength and wear resistance. Additionally, molybdenum and tungsten frequently are added to improve hot strength. Sometimes small amounts of other elements are added as well. For example, Haynes Alloy 188 contains about 0.15% lanthanum. These other elements include titanium, aluminum, and niobium. Not all of the above elements are intentionally added for the contribution that they make to corrosion resistance of cobalt alloys; all do produce some effect on corrosion resistance, either directly or indirectly.

Other Elements

The role of other alloying elements on the corrosion resistance of cobalt is even less clear than that of chromium. Most of the work reported concerns the effects of alloy additions on high-temperature oxidation resistance. The following effects are to be anticipated. However, interactions, both beneficial and detrimental, may occur when multiple alloy additions are present. Carbon may be deleterious because it ties up chromium. Vanadium, niobium, and molybdenum are harmful. Tungsten is more or less innocuous at temperatures below about 980 °C (1800 °F), but it is harmful at temperatures above this level. Nickel may be slightly harmful, but manganese and iron may tend to be modestly beneficial. Titanium and zirconium have little effect. Active elements such as yttrium and lanthanum (in amounts less than about 0.5%) appear to be very beneficial, because they seem to improve scale adherence. The effects of aluminum have not been documented; it has been suggested that small aluminum additions may range in effect from innocuous to slightly beneficial. Under hot corrosion conditions, the above behavior may change.

Coatings

Protective coatings apparently are not used on cobalt and its alloys in lower temperature applications. In high-temperature applications, aluminide or overlay coatings have been developed, but are not regularly used. Aluminide coatings have been used on less oxidation-resistant alloys to improve oxidation resistance. Under prolonged exposure to oxidation or hot corrosion, coatings may be used to extend life. Corrosion protective coatings are never used in biological applications.

Selection for Corrosion Resistance

The guidelines for nickel-base alloys, noted elsewhere in this book, should be considered as background to this subject. Cobalt-base alloys have certain similarities involving corrosion resistance and other properties. In addition, there are differences, and these are not always apparent. Cobalt-base alloys are comparable to nickel-base alloys in cost, but prices fluctuate and must be reviewed at the appropriate time. Certainly, cobalt-base alloys will exceed the cost of copper-base alloys and stainless steel alloys. However, in many instances, the corrosion resistance and strength of cobalt-base alloys justify their use. Certainly, in biomaterial applications, cobalt-base alloys are substantially superior to stainless steels in performance. It should be recognized that there are far fewer cobalt-base alloys from which to select than there are available in the copper, nickel or stainless steel systems.

Cobalt alloys find use as hardfacing alloys, an application demanding wear resistance, high hardness, and reasonable corrosion resistance. They have been used in the chemical process industry, have been widely used in dentistry, have performed admirably in high-temperature service in piston and gas turbine engines, and have been the preeminent orthopedic implant material for many years.

Cobalt and its alloys probably are susceptible to the usual corrosion processes such as general corrosion and local corrosion, particularly pitting and crevice corrosion. Only a limited number of environments have been reported to cause stress-corrosion cracking in cobalt-base alloys. These include two general classes of environments — acid chlorides and strong alkalis. Moreover, both of these environments produce stress-corrosion cracking only at temperatures exceeding about 150 to 260 °C (300 to 500 °F). In general, the stress-corrosion cracking behavior of cobalt-base alloys is somewhat similar to that of nickel-base alloys.

Relative to the corrosion resistance of cobalt and its alloys, it should be noted that elemental cobalt undergoes an allotropic phase transformation on heating such that the lower temperature hexagonal crystal structure changes to the face-centered cubic structure (austenitic). Some credence has been attached to the fact that the austenitic structure is more resistant to corrosion attack than the hexagonal structure. When nickel is added in sufficient amounts to cobalt-chromium alloys, it stabilizes the austenitic structure. Consequently, any corrosion effects of nickel on cobalt-base alloys may have both chemical and crystallographic origins.

The principal use of cobalt-base alloys intended as corrosion-resistant materials has been the superalloys. These are cobalt-base alloys containing generally 20 to 30% chromium, less than about 0.7% carbon, along with varying amounts of nickel, molybdenum, and tungsten. The high chromium content is the major contributor to the oxidation and hot corrosion resistance of this class of materials.

Chromium

Chromium tends to confer lower temperature corrosion resistance, or high-temperature oxidation/hot corrosion resistance on cobalt by modifying the oxide film (scale). At high temperatures, the scale forms so as to produce a cobalt-chromium oxide spinel. In gaseous oxidizing environments, maximum oxidation resistance may not be reached until about 30% chromium has been added. This level may be contrasted with nickel-base alloys, which reach optimum oxidation resistance (owing to chromium) when the chromium level reaches about 20%. No information appears to be available on the chromium level necessary to produce atmospheric or biological corrosion resistance in cobalt alloys. However, in view of the fact that Vitallium has had over 50 years of successful application in dentistry and over 30 years of successful application in orthopedic surgery, it may be inferred that a minimum chromium level of 18% is needed.

Titanium and Titanium Alloys

Although highly reactive under certain conditions, titanium and titanium alloys are remarkably resistant to corrosion because of the formation of a stable, self-healing, oxide film that insulates the base material from the surrounding environment. As a consequence of its outstanding corrosion resistance at lower temperatures (in conjunction with other attractive properties such as low density and good strength), titanium and its alloys find extensive use in applications ranging from chemical-processing operations to orthopedic implants. In a wide range of conditions, titanium is more resistant to lower temperature corrosion attack than stainless steels and copper alloys. Tables 10 and 11 provide general corrosion data for unalloyed titanium and titanium alloys respectively.

Unalloyed titanium is highly resistant to corrosion normally associated with many natural environments, including seawater, body fluids, and fruit and vegetable juices. Wet chlorine, molten sulfur, many organic compounds, and most oxidizing acids have essentially no effect on this metal. Titanium is used extensively for handling salt solutions, wet chlorine gas, and nitric acid solutions. Titanium and its alloys also resist H_2S and CO_2 gases at temperatures up to 260 °C (500 °F).

On the other hand, hot, concentrated, low-pH chloride salts corrode titanium; warm or concentrated solutions of hydrochloric, phosphoric, and oxalic acids also are damaging. In general, all acidic solutions that are reducing in nature corrode titanium, unless they contain inhibitors. Strong oxidizers, including anhydrous red fuming nitric acid and 90% hydrogen peroxide, also cause attack. Ionizable fluoride compounds, such as sodium fluoride and hydrogen fluoride, activate the surface and can cause rapid corrosion. Dry chlorine gas is especially harmful.

Most acidic solutions (except those containing soluble fluorides) can be inhibited by the presence of even small amounts of oxidizing agents and heavy metal ions. Thus, titanium can be used in certain industrial process solutions (including hydrochloric and sulfuric acids) that otherwise would be corrosive. Attack by red fuming nitric acid and chlorine gas can be inhibited by small amounts of water.

Because titanium metal itself has a high affinity for oxidation, the protective oxide film can reheal itself almost instantly when fresh metal surfaces are exposed to air or water. Anhydrous conditions in the absence of a source of oxygen may cause titanium to corrode, because the protective oxide film may not be able to be regenerated. The exact nature, composition, and thickness of the protective surface oxide films formed on titanium depends on the environmental conditions.

Successful application of titanium and its alloys can be expected in mildly reducing to highly oxidizing environments in which protective oxide films spontaneously form and remain stable. Titanium exhibits excellent resistance to atmospheric corrosion in both marine and industrial environments. Its resistance to seawater and to body fluids is virtually unsurpassed by that of any other structural metal.

Corrosion Resistance

The major corrosion problem with titanium alloys appears to be crevice corrosion, which occurs in locations where the corroding media are virtually stagnant. Pits, if formed, may progress in a similar manner.

Titanium alloys also may be subject to hot salt-induced stress-corrosion cracking or to accelerated crack propagation in seawater. Gaseous chloride ions and the presence of significant residual stress can promote stress-corrosion cracking. Titanium is regularly handled without danger of stress-corrosion cracking, and its use has been demonstrated in seawater, natural waters, and body fluids. However, at times, chlorides associated with fingerprints (in conjunction with subsequent heat, aqueous halides, and organic fluids such as methanol) have produced cracking. In the extreme, an unstressed Ti-5Al-5Sn-5Zr alloy, exposed to salt and placed in a furnace, reportedly cracked into multiple pieces in a short time due to the simultaneous presence of high residual stresses and salt. Most titanium alloys undergo stress-corrosion cracking in only certain specific environments.

Oxidizing chlorine compounds do not attack titanium alloys over the full range of compositions at lower temperatures. Stress-corrosion cracking is a function of microstructure as well as composition. Alpha titanium or high alpha alloys generally exhibit the greatest susceptibility, whereas beta titanium or beta-processed alpha-beta titanium alloys show less susceptibility. Thus the number of alpha, beta, and alpha-plus-beta alloys available display considerable variability in resistance to stress-corrosion cracking. Such alloys should be chosen with care.

Hot salt or aqueous stress-corrosion cracking phenomena are rarely encountered in the commercial application of titanium alloys. When hot salt stress-corrosion cracking occurs, it usually can be traced to improper design or processing.

Some titanium alloys crack under tensile stress when in contact with liquid cadmium, mercury, or silver-base brazing alloys. This liquid metal embrittlement differs from stress-corrosion cracking. Titanium also can be embrittled by contact with certain solid metals (cadmium and silver, for example) when it is under tensile stress. This attack may be similar to that for liquid metal embrittlement. Service failures have occurred in cadmium-plated titanium alloys at temperatures as low as 66 °C (150 °F).

Titanium alloys are not sufficiently strong to operate above about 538 °C (1000 °F), and thus the elevated temperature oxidation resistance of titanium alloys is rarely an issue. However, titanium alloys have limited oxidation resistance in air above about 650 °C (1200 °F). Titanium has a high affinity for the interstitial elements oxygen, nitrogen, and hydrogen; the dissolution of these elements in titanium alloys to any extent almost always results in embrittlement of the material. Newer titanium alloys based on the titanium aluminides may overcome this difficulty, but their commercial application is a decade away. Consequently, the majority of the corrosion data on titanium and its alloys are currently based on liquid media or gaseous atmospheres at ambient temperatures up to a few hundred degrees Fahrenheit.

For many chemical-processing applications, commercially pure titanium is used. When enhanced strength or corrosion resistance (or both) are required, alloy additions are made. In titanium alloy systems, corrosion resistance has not been the primary property of experimental interest; consequently, data on the effects of various alloying element additions on the corrosion resistance of titanium are limited.

Aluminum

In general, major alloy additions to titanium slightly degrade the corrosion resistance of the material. Aluminum is no exception; it is well known that the optimum chemical corrosion resistance is achieved with commercially pure titanium or in alloys with very minor elemental additions. Aluminum is an alpha phase promoter and is generally detrimental to stress-corrosion resistance, especially when the aluminum level exceeds about 6%. High aluminum concentrations may promote enhanced resistance to oxidation or oxygen embrittlement in titanium, but alloys of the titanium aluminide type are not yet commercially available.

Vanadium and Molybdenum

These refractory metals are found in most commercial titanium alloys and may exist in amounts from a fraction of a percent to over 12%. Little information exists to correlate corrosion behavior with the chemical changes produced by these elements. Their principal effect may lie in the changes that take place in the microstructure of titanium when these elements are used in any significant quantities. Because these elements favor the beta phase in titanium, they are not implicated in the stress-corrosion cracking of titanium alloys.

Other Elements

Minor amounts of other elements can affect the corrosion resistance of titanium. For example, the addition of a few tenths of a percent of palladium has been found to greatly improve the corrosion resistance of commercially pure titanium. Platinum and rhodium may provide the same effect, but they do so at a higher cost. The commercial alloy, Ti Code 12, which contains 0.3% molybdenum and 0.8% nickel, combines some of the favorable properties of nickel and molybdenum additions while avoiding the negative aspects. This alloy has excellent resistance to pitting and crevice corrosion in high-temperature brines, which sometimes attack commercially pure titanium. Small additions of molybdenum and nickel improve the resistance in reducing media such as hydrochloric and sulfuric acids, but the alloy additions are not as effective as the palladium additions mentioned above.

Alloys with modest nickel additions of about 2% have been developed and recommended for service in hot brine environments where crevice corrosion is sometimes a problem. Unfortunately, the addition of nickel tends to enhance the susceptibility of titanium to hydrogen embrittlement and also makes titanium difficult to fabricate.

Tin, added in amounts from 2 to 11%, is not intended to specifically enhance the corrosion properties of titanium. Although tin itself, along with manganese and cobalt, may be intrinsically detrimental to stress-corrosion cracking resistance, the ability of tin to replace aluminum may act to produce an overall improvement in stress-corrosion resistance of tin-containing titanium alloys.

In the area of rapidly solidified alloys, rare earth additions are being developed. The effects of such elements on lower temperature corrosion resistance have not been published; the principal applications of such alloys is expected to be at elevated temperatures.

Coatings

Titanium alloys are not coated to improve corrosion resistance. Wear- and abrasion-resistant coatings have been developed for select applications. Some aluminum coatings were developed to protect titanium alloys from hot salt stress-corrosion cracking, but there was little or no use of these coatings in practice.

Selection of Titanium Alloys for Corrosion Service

The selection of titanium or titanium alloys is best accomplished by observing that there are only two categories of titanium alloys—the essentially pure titaniums, which are largely used for lower temperature chemical and processing equipment, and the more highly alloyed titaniums, which are used in structural applications from the space shuttle to gas turbine engines. These latter types of alloys have been developed principally with strength as a primary criteria and corrosion resistance as a secondary or tertiary criteria. Microstructure is controlled to maximize corrosion resistance, especially hot salt corrosion resistance or seawater crack propagation resistance, after a specific composition has been selected.

For biomedical applications such as prosthetic devices, particularly in total hip replacement, selection consists of finding the optimum combination of corrosion resistance, fabricability, and strength. The standard commercial alloy, Ti-6Al-4V, possesses the best combination of these qualities. For other demanding corrosion-resistant applications at lower temperatures, there are only a limited number of titanium alloys available in the ASTM grade series. Moreover, there are a variety of proprietary alloys available from several manufacturers.

References:

1. N.D. Tomashov and P.M. Altovskii, *Corrosion and Protection of Titanium*, Government Scientific-Technical Publication of Machine-Building Literature (Russian translation), 1963

2. L.C. Covington and R.W. Schutz, "Corrosion Resistance of Titanium," TIMET Corporation, 1982

3. R.L. Kane, The Corrosion of Titanium, in *The Corrosion of Light Metals*, Corrosion Monograph Series, John Wiley & Sons, 1967

4. *Corrosion Resistance of Titanium*, Technical Handbook, Imperial Metals Industries (Kynoch) Ltd., Birmingham, UK

5. W.H. Weiman, *Corrosion*, Vol 22, April 1966, 98-106

6. H. Keller and K. Risch, The Corrosion Behavior of Titanium in Nitric Acid at High Temperatures, *Korrosionstabellen metallischer Werkstoffe*, Vol 9, 1964, 741-743

7. R.L. LaQue and H.R. Copson, *Corrosion Resistance of Metals and Alloys*, 2nd ed., ACS Monograph, Reinhold, 1963, 646-661

8. J.D. Jackson and W.K. Boyd, "Corrosion of Titanium," DMIC Memorandum 218, Defense Materials Information Center, Battelle Memorial Institute, Sept 1966

9. R.W. Schutz and J.S. Grauman, Fundamental Corrosion Characterization of High-Strength Titanium Alloys, in *Industrial Applications of Titanium and Zirconium: Fourth Volume*, STP 917, American Society for Testing and Materials, 1986, 130-143

10. F.M. Reinhart, "Corrosion of Materials in Hydrospace, Part III, Titanium and Titanium Alloys," Technical Note N-921, U.S. Naval Civil Engineering Laboratory, Sept 1967

11. R.W. Schutz, J.A. Hall, and T.L. Wardlaw, "TI-CODE 12, An Improved Industrial Alloys," paper presented at the Japan Titanium Society 30th Anniversary International Symposium, Japan Titanium Society, Aug 1982

12. D.E. Thomas *et al.*, Beta-C: An Emerging Titanium Alloy for the Industrial Marketplace, in *Industrial Applications of Titanium and Zirconium: Fourth Volume*, STP 917, American Society for Testing and Materials, 1986, 144-163

Table 10 General Corrosion Data for Unalloyed Titanium

This table is a compilation of general corrosion rate values for unalloyed titanium (ASTM grades 1 to 4). These values were derived from published sources (Ref 1–8) and from unpublished in-house laboratory tests. These data should be used only as a guideline for alloy performance. Rates may vary depending on changes in medium chemistry, temperature, length of exposure, and other factors. Total alloy suitability cannot be assumed from these values alone, because other forms of corrosion, such as localized attack, may be limiting. In complex, variable, and/or dynamic environments, *in situ* testing may provide more reliable data.

Medium	Concentration, %	Temperature, °C	Corrosion rate, mm/yr	Medium	Concentration, %	Temperature, °C	Corrosion rate, mm/yr
Acetaldehyde	75	149	0.001	Ammonium chloride	Saturated	100	<0.013
	100	149	nil	Ammonium chlorate	300 g/L	50	0.003
Acetate, *n*-propyl	...	87	nil	Ammonium fluoride	10	Room	0.102
Acetic acid	5–99.7	124	nil	Ammonium hydroxide	28	Room	0.003
	33–vapor	Boiling	nil		28	100	nil
	99	Boiling	0.003	Ammonium nitrate	28	Boiling	nil
	65	121	0.003	Ammonium nitrate + 1% nitric acid	28	Boiling	nil
	58	130	0.381	Ammonium oxalate	Saturated	Room	nil
	99.7	124	0.003	Ammonium perchlorate	20	88	nil
Acetic acid + 3% acetic anhydride	Glacial	204	1.02	Ammonium sulfate	10	100	nil
Acetic acid + 1.5% acetic anhydride	Glacial	204	0.005	Ammonium sulfate + 1% H_2SO_4	Saturated	Room	0.010
Acetic acid + 109 ppm Cl	31.2	Boiling	0.259	Aniline	100	Room	nil
Acetic acid + 106 ppm Cl	62.0	Boiling	0.272	Aniline + 2% $AlCl_3$	98	158	>1.27
Acetic acid + 5% formic acid	58	Boiling	0.457	Aniline hydrochloride	5	100	nil
Acetic anhydride	100	21	0.025		20	100	nil
	100	150	0.005	Antimony trichloride	27	Room	nil
	99.5	Boiling	0.013	Aqua regia	3:1	Room	nil
Adipic acid + 15–20% glutaric + 2% acetic acid	25	199	nil		3:1	80	0.86
					3:1	Boiling	1.12
Adipic acid	67	240	nil	Arsenous oxide	Saturated	Room	nil
Adipylchloride and chlorobenzene solution	...	...	nil	Barium carbonate	Saturated	Room	nil
				Barium chloride	5	100	nil
Adiponitrile	Vapor	371	0.008		20	100	nil
Aluminum chloride, aerated	10	100	0.002		25	100	nil
	25	100	3.15	Barium hydroxide	Saturated	Room	nil
Aluminum chloride	10	100	0.002	Barium nitrate	10	Room	nil
	10	150	0.03	Barium fluoride	Saturated	Room	nil
	25	60	nil	Benzaldehyde	100	Room	nil
	25	100	6.55	Benzene (traces of HCl)	Vapor and liquid	80	0.005
Aluminum	Molten	677	164.6				
Aluminum fluoride	Saturated	Room	nil		Liquid	50	0.025
Aluminum nitrate	Saturated	Room	nil	Benzene	Liquid	Room	nil
Aluminum sulfate	Saturated	Room	nil	Benzoric acid	Saturated	Room	nil
	10	80	0.05	Bismuth	Molten	816	High
	10	Boiling	0.12	Bismuth/lead	Molten	300	Good resistance
Aluminum sulfate + 1% H_2SO_4	Saturated	Room	nil	Boric acid	Saturated	Room	nil
Ammonium acid phosphate	10	Room	nil		10	Boiling	nil
Ammonium aluminum chloride	Molten	350–380	Very rapid attack	Bromine	Liquid	30	Rapid attack
Ammonia, anhydrous	100	40	<0.127	Bromine, moist	Vapor	30	<0.003
Ammonia, steam, water	...	222	11.2	Bromine gas, dry	...	21	Dissolves rapidly
Ammonium acetate	10	Room	nil				
Ammonium bicarbonate	50	100	nil	Bromine-water solution	...	Room	nil
Ammonium bisulfite, pH 2.05	Spent pulping liquor	71	0.015	Bromine in methyl alcohol	0.05	60	0.03 (cracking possible)
Ammonium carbamate	50	100	nil				

(Continued)

Table 10 (continued)

Medium	Concentration, %	Temperature, °C	Corrosion rate, mm/yr
N-butyric acid	Undiluted	Room	nil
Calcium bisulfite	Cooking liquor	26	0.001
Calcium carbonate	Saturated	Boiling	nil
Calcium chloride	5	100	0.005
	10	100	0.007
	20	100	0.015
	55	104	0.001
	60	149	<0.003
	62	154	0.406
	73	175	0.80
Calcium hydroxide	Saturated	Room	nil
	Saturated	Boiling	nil
Calcium hypochlorite	2	100	0.001
	6	100	0.001
	18	21	nil
	Saturated	21	nil
Carbon dioxide	100	...	Excellent
Carbon tetrachloride	99	Boiling	0.005
	Liquid	Boiling	nil
	Vapor	Boiling	nil
Carbon tetrachloride + 50% H_2O	50	25	0.005
Chlorine gas, wet	>0.7 H_2O	Room	nil
	>0.95 H_2O	140	nil
	>1.5 H_2O	200	nil
Chlorine saturated water	Saturated	97	nil
Chlorine gas, dry	<0.5 H_2O	Room	May react
Chlorine dioxide	5	82	<0.003
Chlorine dioxide + HOCl, H_2O + Cl_2	15	43	nil
Chlorine dioxide in steam	5	99	nil
Chlorine dioxide	10	70	0.03
Chlorine monoxide (moist)	Up to 15	43	nil
Chlorine trifluoride	100	30	Vigorous reaction
Chloracetic acid	30	82	<0.127
	100	Boiling	<0.127
Chlorosulfonic acid	100	Room	0.312
Chloroform	Vapor and liquid	Boiling	0.000
Chloroform + 50% H_2O	50	25	0.000
Chloropicrin	100	95	0.003
Chromic acid	10	Boiling	0.003
	15	24	0.006
	15	82	0.015
	50	24	0.013
	50	82	0.028
Chromic acid + 5% nitric acid	5	21	<0.003
Citric acid	10	100	0.009
	25	100	0.001
	50	60	0.000
	50	Boiling	0.127–1.27
	672	149	Corroded
Citric acid (aerated)	50	100	<0.127
Copper nitrate	Saturated	Room	nil
Copper sulfate	50	Boiling	nil
Copper sulfate + 2% H_2SO_4	Saturated	Room	0.018
Cupric carbonate + cupric hydroxide	Saturated	Ambient	nil
Cupric chloride	20	Boiling	nil
	40	Boiling	0.005
	55	118	0.003
Cupric cyanide	Saturated	Room	nil
Cuprous chloride	50	90	<0.003
Cyclohexylamine	100	Room	nil
Cyclohexane (plus traces of formic acid)	...	150	0.003
Dichloroacetic acid	100	Boiling	0.007
Dichlorobenzene + 4–5% HCl	...	179	0.102
Diethylene triamine	100	Room	nil
Ethyl alcohol	95	Boiling	0.013
	100	Room	nil
Ethylene dichloride	100	Boiling	0.005–0.127
Ethylene dichloride + 50% water	50	25	0.005
Ethylene diamine	100	Room	nil
Ferric chloride	10–20	Room	nil
	1–30	100	0.004
	10–40	Boiling	nil
	1–30	Boiling	nil
	50	150	0.003

Medium	Concentration, %	Temperature, °C	Corrosion rate, mm/yr
Ferric chloride	10	Boiling	0.00
Ferric sulfate	10	Room	nil
Ferrous chloride + 0.5% HCl	30	79	0.006
Ferrous sulfate	Saturated	Room	nil
Fluoboric acid	5–20	Elevated	Rapid attack
Fluorine, commercial	Gas–liquid	Gas-109	0.864
Fluorine, HF free	Liquid	-196	0.011
	Gas	-196	0.011
Fluorosilicic acid	10	Room	47.5
Formaldehyde	37	Boiling	nil
Formamide vapor	...	300	nil
Formic acid, aerated	10	100	0.005
	25	100	0.001
	50	100	0.001
	90	100	0.001
Formic acid, nonaerated	10	100	nil
	25	100	2.44
	50	Boiling	3.20
	90	100	3.00
Formic acid	9	50	<0.127
Furfural	100	Room	nil
Gluconic acid	50	Room	nil
Glycerin	...	Room	nil
Hydrogen chloride, gas	Air mixture	25–100	nil
Hydrochloric acid, aerated	1	60	0.004
	2	60	0.016
	5	60	1.07
	1	100	0.46
	5	35	0.01
	10	35	1.02
	20	35	4.45
Hydrochloric acid	0.1	Boiling	0.10
	1	Boiling	1.8
Hydrochloric acid + 4% $FeCl_3$ + 4% $MgCl_2$	19	82	0.51
Hydrochloric acid + 4% $FeCl_3$ + 4% $MgCl_2$ + Cl_2 saturated	19	82	0.46
Hydrochloric acid, chlorine saturated	5	190	<0.025
	10	190	28.5
Hydrochloric acid, + 200 ppm Cl_2	36	25	0.432
Hydrochloric acid +1% HNO_3	5	40	nil
+1% HNO_3	5	95	0.091
+5% HNO_3	5	40	0.025
+5% HNO_3	5	95	0.030
+10% HNO_3	5	40	nil
+10% HNO_3	5	95	0.183
+3% HNO_3	8.5	80	0.051
+5% HNO_3	1	Boiling	0.074
Hydrochloric acid +2.5% $NaClO_3$	10.2	80	0.009
+5.0% $NaClO_3$	10.2	80	0.006
Hydrochloric acid +0.5% CrO_3	5	38	nil
+0.5% CrO_3	5	95	0.031
+1% CrO_3	5	38	0.018
+1% CrO_3	5	95	0.031
Hydrochloric acid +0.05% $CuSO_4$	5	38	0.040
+0.05% $CuSO_4$	5	93	0.091
+0.5% $CuSO_4$	5	38	0.091
+0.5% $CuSO_4$	5	93	0.061
+1% $CuSO_4$	5	38	0.031
+1% $CuSO_4$	5	93	0.091
+5% $CuSO_4$	5	38	0.020
+5% $CuSO_4$	5	93	0.061
+0.05% $CuSO_4$	5	Boiling	0.064
+0.5% $CuSO_4$	5	Boiling	0.084
Hydrochloric acid +0.05% $CuSO_4$	10	66	0.025
+0.20% $CuSO_4$	10	66	nil
+0.5% $CuSO_4$	10	66	0.023
+1% $CuSO_4$	10	66	0.023
+0.05% $CuSO_4$	10	Boiling	0.295
+0.5% $CuSO_4$	10	Boiling	0.290
Hydrochloric acid + 0.1% $FeCl_3$	5	Boiling	0.01
Hydrochloric acid + 1 g/L Ti^{4+}	10	Boiling	0.000
Hydrochloric acid + 5.8 g/L Ti^{4+}	20	Boiling	0.000

(Continued)

Table 10 (continued)

Medium	Concentration, %	Temperature, °C	Corrosion rate, mm/yr	Medium	Concentration, %	Temperature, °C	Corrosion rate, mm/yr
Hydrochloric acid + 18% H_3PO_4 +				Nitric acid	35	80	0.051–0.102
5% HNO_3	18	77	0.000		70	80	0.025–0.076
Hydrofluoric acid	1	26	127		17	Boiling	0.076–0.102
Hydrofluoric acid, anhydrous	100	Room	0.127–1.27		35	Boiling	0.127–0.508
Hydrofluoric-nitric acid 5 vol%					70	Boiling	0.064–0.900
HF-35 vol% HNO_3	· · ·	25	452	Nitric acid, not refreshed	5–60	35	0.002–0.007
Hydrofluoric-nitric acid 5 vol%					5–60	60	0.01–0.02
HF-35 vol% HNO_3	· · ·	35	571		30–50	100	0.10–0.18
Hydrogen peroxide	3	Room	<0.127		5–20	100	0.02
	6	Room	<0.127		30–60	190	1.5–2.8
	30	Room	<0.305		70	270	1.2
Hydrogen peroxide					20	290	0.4
+ 2% NaOH	1	60	55.9		70	290	1.1
Hydrogen peroxide				Nitric acid, white fuming	Liquid or	Room	nil
pH 4	5	66	0.061		vapor		
pH 1	5	66	0.152		· · ·	82	0.152
pH 1	20	66	0.69		· · ·	122	<0.127
pH 11	0.08	70	0.42		· · ·	160	<0.127
Hydrogen sulfide (water saturated)	· · ·	21	<0.003	Nitric acid, red fuming	<About 2%	Room	Ignition
Hydrogen sulfide, steam,					H_2O		sensitive
and 0.077% mercaptans	7.65	93–110	nil		>About 2%	Room	Not ignition
Hydroxy-acetic acid	· · ·	40	0.003		H_2O		sensitive
Hypochlorous acid + ClO				Nitric acid	40	Boiling	0.63
and Cl_2 gases	17	38	0.000	+0.01% $K_2Cr_2O_7$	40	Boiling	0.01
Iodine, dry or moist gas	· · ·	25	0.1	+0.01% CrO_3	40	Boiling	0.01
Iodine in water + potassium iodide	· · ·	Room	nil	+0.01% $FeCl_3$	40	Boiling	0.68
Iodine in alcohol	Saturated	Room	Pitted	+1% $FeCl_3$	40	Boiling	0.14
Lactic acid	10–85	100	<0.127	+1% $NaClO_3$	40	Boiling	0.31
	10	Boiling	<0.127	+1% $NaClO_3$	40	Boiling	0.02
Lead	· · ·	816	Attacked	+1% $Ce(SO_4)_2$	40	Boiling	0.10
	· · ·	324–593	Good	+0.1% $K_2Cr_2O_7$	40	Boiling	0.016
Lead acetate	Saturated	Room	nil	Nitric acid, saturated with			
Linseed oil, boiled	· · ·	Room	nil	zirconyl nitrate	33–45	118	nil
Lithium, molten	· · ·	316–482	nil	Nitric acid + 15% zirconyl nitrate	65	127	nil
Lithium chloride	50	149	nil	Nitric acid + 179 g/L $NaNO_3$			
Magnesium	Molten	760	Limited	and 32 g/L NaCl	20.8	Boiling	0.127–0.295
			resistance	Nitric acid + 170 g/L $NaNO_3$			
Magnesium chloride	5–20	100	<0.010	and 2.9 g/L NaCl	27.4	Boiling	0.483–2.92
	5–40	Boiling	0.005	Oxalic acid	1	35	0.03
Magnesium hydroxide	Saturated	Room	nil		5	35	0.13
Magnesium sulfate	Saturated	Room	nil		1	Boiling	107
Manganous chloride	5–20	100	nil		25	60	11.9
Maleic acid	18–20	35	0.002		Saturated	Room	0.508
Mercuric chloride	1	100	0.000	Perchloroethylene + 50% H_2O	50	25	nil
	5	100	0.011	Perchloryl fluoride + liquid ClO_3	100	30	0.002
	10	100	0.001	Perchloryl fluoride + 1% H_2O	99	30	Liquid 0.290
	Saturated	100	0.001		· · ·	· · ·	Vapor 0.003
Mercuric cyanide	Saturated	Room	nil	Phenol	Saturated	25	0.102
Mercury	100	Up to 38	Satisfactory		solution		
	100	Room	nil	Phosphoric acid	10–30	Room	0.020–0.051
	· · ·	371	3.03		30–80	Room	0.051–0.762
Methyl alcohol	91	35	nil		5.0	66	0.005
	95	100	<0.01		6.0	66	0.117
Mercury + iron	· · ·	371	0.079		0.5	Boiling	0.094
Mercury + copper	· · ·	371	0.063		1.0	Boiling	0.266
Mercury + zirconium	· · ·	371	0.033		12	25	0.005
Mercury + magnesium	· · ·	371	0.083		20	25	0.076
Monochloracetic acid	30	80	0.02		50	25	0.19
	100	Boiling	0.013		9	52	0.03
Nickel chloride	5	100	0.004		10	52	0.38
	20	100	0.003		5	Boiling	3.5
Nickel nitrate	50	Room	nil		10	80	1.83
Nitric acid, aerated	10	Room	0.005	Phosphoric acid + 3% nitric acid	81	88	0.381
	30	Room	0.004	Phosphorus oxychloride	100	Room	0.004
	40	Room	0.002	Phosphorus trichloride	Saturated	Room	nil
	50	Room	0.002	Photographic emulsions	· · ·	· · ·	<0.127
	60	Room	0.001	Phthalic acid	Saturated	Room	nil
	70	Room	0.005	Potassium bromide	Saturated	Room	nil
	10	40	0.003	Potassium chloride	Saturated	Room	nil
	20	40	0.005		Saturated	60	nil
	30	50	0.015	Potassium dichromate	Saturated	Room	nil
	40	50	0.016	Potassium ethyl xanthate	10	Room	nil
	50	60	0.037	Potassium ferricyanide	Saturated	Room	nil
	60	60	0.040	Potassium hydroxide + 13% potassium			
	70	70	0.040	chloride	13	29	nil
	40	200	0.610	Potassium hydroxide	50	29	0.010
	70	270	1.22		10	Boiling	<0.127
	20	290	0.305		25	Boiling	0.305

(Continued)

Table 10 (continued)

Medium	Concentration, %	Temperature, °C	Corrosion rate, mm/yr	Medium	Concentration, %	Temperature, °C	Corrosion rate, mm/yr
Potassium hydroxide	50	Boiling	2.74	Sulfamic acid			
	50 anhydrous	241–377	1.02–1.52	+ 0.375 g/L FeCl₃	7.5 g/L	Boiling	0.030
Potassium iodide	Saturated	Room	nil	Sulfur, molten	100	240	nil
Potassium permanganate	Saturated	Room	nil	Sulfur monochloride	⋯	202	>1.09
Potassium perchlorate	20	Room	0.003	Sulfur dioxide, dry	⋯	21	nil
	0–30	50	0.003	Sulfur dioxide, water saturated	Near 100	Room	0.003
Potassium sulfate	10	Room	nil	Sulfur dioxide gas + small amount			
Potassium thiosulfate	1	Room	nil	SO₃ and approximately 3% O₂	18	316	0.006
Propionic acid	Vapor	190	Rapid attack	Sulfuric acid, aerated	1	60	0.008
Pyrogallic acid	355 g/L	Room	nil		3	60	0.013
Salicylic acid	Saturated	Room	nil		5	60	4.83
Seawater	⋯	24	nil		10	35	1.27
Seawater, 4¹⁄₂-year test	⋯	Ambient	nil		40	35	8.64
Sebacic acid	⋯	240	0.008		75	35	1.07
Silver nitrate	50	Room	nil		75	Room	10.8
Sodium	100	To 1100 (593)	Good		1	100	0.005
Sodium acetate	Saturated	Room	nil		3	100	23.4
Sodium aluminate	25	Boiling	0.091		Concentrated	Room	1.57
Sodium bifluoride	Saturated	Room	Rapid		Concentrated	Boiling	5.38
Sodium bisulfate	Saturated	Room	nil		1	100	7.16
	10	66	1.83		3	100	21.1
Sodium bisulfite	10	Boiling	nil	Sulfuric acid	1	Boiling	17.8
	25	Boiling	nil		5	Boiling	25.4
Sodium carbonate	25	Boiling	nil	Sulfuric acid + 0.25% CuSO₄	5	95	nil
Sodium chlorate	Saturated	Room	nil		30	38	0.061
Sodium chlorate					30	95	0.088
+ NaCl 80–250 g/L	0–721 g/L	40	0.003	Sulfuric acid + 0.5% CuSO₄	30	38	0.067
Sodium chloride	Saturated	Room	nil		30	95	0.823
pH 7	23	Boiling	nil	Sulfuric acid + 1.0% CuSO₄	30	38	0.020
pH 1.5	23	Boiling	nil		30	95	0.884
pH 1.2	23	Boiling	0.71	Sulfuric acid + 0.5% CrO₃	5	95	nil
pH 1.2, some dissolved chlorine	23	Boiling	nil		30	95	nil
Sodium citrate	Saturated	Room	nil	Sulfuric acid + 1.0% CuSO₄	30	Boiling	1.65
Sodium cyanide	Saturated	Room	nil	Sulfuric acid vapors	96	38	nil
Sodium dichromate	Saturated	Room	nil		96	66	nil
Sodium fluoride	Saturated	Room	0.008		96	200–300	0.013
pH 7	1	Boiling	0.001	Sulfuric acid + 10% HNO₃	90	Room	0.457
pH 10	1	Boiling	0.001	Sulfuric acid + 50% HNO₃	50	Room	0.635
pH 7	1	204	0.000	Sulfuric acid + 70% HNO₃	30	Room	0.102
Sodium hydrosulfide +				Sulfuric acid + 90% HNO₃	10	Room	nil
sodium sulfide and polysulfides	5–12	110	<0.003	Sulfuric acid + 90% HNO₃	10	60	0.011
Sodium hydroxide	5–10	21	0.001	Sulfuric acid + 95% HNO₃	5	60	0.005
	10	Boiling	0.021	Sulfuric acid + 50% HNO₃	50	60	0.399
	28	Room	0.003	Sulfuric acid + 20% HNO₃	80	60	1.59
	40	80	0.127	Sulfuric acid saturated with chlorine	45	24	0.003
	50	57	0.013		62	16	0.002
	50	Boiling	0.051		5, 10	190	<0.025
	73	129	0.178		82	50	>1.19
	50–73	188	>1.09	Sulfuric acid + 4 g/L Ti⁴⁺	40	100	nil
	50	38	0.023	Sulfurous acid	6	Room	nil
Sodium hypochlorite	6	Room	nil	Tannic acid	25	100	nil
Sodium hypochlorite + 15% NaCl +				Tartaric acid	10–50	100	<0.127
1% NaOH	1.5–4	66–93	0.030		10	60	0.003
Sodium nitrate	Saturated	Room	nil		25	60	0.003
Sodium perchlorate	900 g/L	50	0.003		50	60	0.001
Sodium phosphate	Saturated	Room	nil		10	100	0.003
Sodium silicate	25	Boiling	nil		25	100	nil
Sodium sulfate	10–20	Boiling	nil		50	100	0.0121
	Saturated	Room	nil	Terephthalic acid	77	218	nil
Sodium sulfide	10	Boiling	0.027	Tetrachloroethane, liquid and vapor	100	Boiling	0.001
	Saturated	Room	nil	Tetrachloroethylene + H₂O	⋯	Boiling	0.127
Sodium sulfite	Saturated	Boiling	nil	Tetrachloroethylene	100	Boiling	nil
Sodium thiosulfate	25	Boiling	nil	Tetrachloroethylene, liquid and vapor	100	Boiling	0.001
Sodium thiosulfate + 20% acetic acid	20	Room	nil	Titanium tetrachloride	99.8	300	1.57
Soils, corrosive	⋯	Ambient	nil	Trichloroacetic acid	100	Boiling	14.6
Stannic chloride	5	100	0.003	Trichloroethylene	99	Boiling	0.003–0.127
	24	Boiling	0.045	Trichloroethylene + 50% H₂O	50	25	0.001
Stannic chloride, molten	100	66	nil	Uranium chloride	Saturated	21–90	nil
Stannic chloride	100	35	nil	Uranyl ammonium phosphate filtrate +			
	Saturated	Room	nil	25% chloride + 0.5% fluoride +			
Steam + air	⋯	82	nil	1.4% ammonia + 2.4% uranium	20.9	165	<0.003
Steam + 7.65% hydrogen sulfide	⋯	93–110	nil	Uranyl nitrate containing 25.3 g/L			
Stearic acid, molten	100	180	0.003	Fe³⁺, 6.9 g/L Cr³⁺, 2.8 g/L Ni²⁺,			
Succinic acid	100	185	nil	4.0 M HNO₃ + 1.0 M Cl	120 g/L	Boiling	nil
	Saturated	Room	nil	Uranyl sulfate + 3.1 M Li₂SO₄ +			
Sulfanilic acid	Saturated	Room	nil	100–200 ppm O₂	3.1 M	250	<0.020
Sulfamic acid	3.75 g/L	Boiling	nil	Uranyl sulfate + 3.6 M Li₂SO₄,			
	7.5 g/L	Boiling	2.74	50 psi oxygen	3.8 M	350	0.006–0.432

(Continued)

Table 10 (continued)

Medium	Concentration, %	Temperature, °C	Corrosion rate, mm/yr	Medium	Concentration, %	Temperature, °C	Corrosion rate, mm/yr
Urea + 32% ammonia + 20.5% H_2O, 19% CO_2	28	182	0.079	Zinc chloride	5	Boiling	nil
Water, degassed	· · ·	316	nil		20	104	nil
Water, river, saturated with chlorine	· · ·	93	nil		50, 75	150	nil
X-ray developer solution	· · ·	Room	nil		75	150	0.06
					75	200	Rapid pitting
					80	173	2.1
				Zinc sulfate	Saturated	Room	nil

Table 11 General Corrosion Data for Titanium Alloys

This table is a compilation of general corrosion rate values for commercial titanium alloys other than the unalloyed grades. These values were derived from published sources (Ref 2, 4, 7, 9–12) and from unpublished in-house laboratory tests. These data should be used only as a guideline for alloy performance. Rates may vary depending on changes in medium chemistry, temperature, length of exposure, and other factors. Total alloy suitability cannot be assumed from these values alone, because other forms of corrosion, such as localized attack, may be limiting. In complex, variable, and/or dynamic environments, *in situ* testing may provide more reliable data.

Medium	Alloy	Concentration, %	Temperature, °C	Corrosion rate, mm/yr	Medium	Alloy	Concentration, %	Temperature, °C	Corrosion rate, mm/yr
Acetic acid	Grade 9	99.7	Boiling	nil	Hydrochloric acid	Ti-550	0.5	Boiling	0.056
Acetic acid +						Ti-550	1.0	Boiling	0.64
5% formic acid	Grade 12	58	Boiling	nil		Transage 207	0.5	Boiling	0.005
Ammonium hydroxide	Grade 12	30	Boiling	nil		Transage 207	1.0	Boiling	0.025
Aluminum chloride	Grade 12	10	Boiling	nil		Ti-6-2-4-6	0.5	Boiling	nil
	Grade 7	10	100	<0.025		Ti-6-2-4-6	1.0	Boiling	0.03
	Grade 7	25	100	0.025	Hydrochloric acid, aerated	Ti-6-2-4-6	pH 1	Boiling	0.01
Ammonium chloride	Grade 12	10	Boiling	nil	Hydrochloric acid	Ti-10-2-3	0.5	Boiling	1.10
Ammonium hydroxide	Grade 9	8, 28	150	nil		Ti-3-8-6-4-4	0.5	Boiling	0.003
Aqua regia	Grade 7	3:1	Boiling	1.12		Ti-3-8-6-4-4	1.0	Boiling	0.058
	Grade 12	3:1	Boiling	0.61		Ti-3-8-6-4-4	1.5	Boiling	0.26
	Grade 9	3:1	Boiling	1.29	Hydrochloric acid, aerated	Ti-3-8-6-4-4	pH 1	Boiling	nil
	Grade 9	3:1	25	0.015	Hydrochloric acid	Ti-5Ta	0.5	Boiling	0.013
Calcium chloride	Grade 9	62	150	nil		Ti-5Ta	1.5	Boiling	2.10
	Grade 7	73	177	nil		Ti-6-4	1.0	Boiling	2.52
Chlorine, wet	Grade 7	. . .	25	nil	Hydrochloric acid, aerated	Ti-6-4	pH 1	Boiling	0.60
Chromic acid	Grade 7	10	Boiling	nil	Hydrochloric acid	Grade 9	0.5	Boiling	1.08
	Grade 9	10	Boiling	0.008		Grade 9	1	88	0.009
	Grade 9	30	Boiling	0.053		Grade 9	3	88	3.10
	Grade 9	50	Boiling	0.26	Hydrochloric acid, deaerated	Grade 7	3	82	0.013
Citric acid	Grade 7	50	Boiling	0.025		Grade 7	5	82	0.051
	Grade 12	50	Boiling	0.013		Grade 7	10	82	0.419
	Grade 9	50	Boiling	0.38	Hydrochloric acid	Grade 9	1	Boiling	2.79
Ferric chloride	Grade 7	10	Boiling	nil	Hydrochloric acid, aerated	Grade 9	5	35	0.001
	Grade 12	10	Boiling	nil	Hydrochloric acid, nitrogen saturated	Grade 9	5	35	0.185
	Ti-5Ta	10	Boiling	nil	Hydrochloric acid	Ti-6-2-1-.8	0.5	Boiling	0.020
	Grade 7	30	Boiling	nil		Ti-6-2-1-.8	1.0	Boiling	1.07
	Ti-6-4	10	Boiling	nil		Grade 7	0.5	Boiling	nil
	Ti-3-8-6-4-4	10	Boiling	nil		Grade 7	1.0	Boiling	0.008
	Ti-10-2-3	10	Boiling	nil		Grade 7	1.5	Boiling	0.03
	Ti-6-2-4-6	10	Boiling	0.06		Grade 7	5.0	Boiling	0.23
	Transage 207	10	Boiling	0.19		Grade 12	0.5	Boiling	nil
	Ti-550	10	Boiling	nil		Grade 12	1.0	Boiling	0.04
	Grade 9	10	Boiling	nil		Grade 12	1.5	Boiling	0.25
	Ti-6-2-1-.8	10	Boiling	nil	Hydrochloric acid, hydrogen saturated	Grade 7	1–15	25	<0.025
Formic acid	Grade 9	25	88	<0.13		Grade 7	20	25	0.102
Formic acid, nitrogen-sparged	Grade 9	25	35	<0.13		Grade 7	5	70	0.076
						Grade 7	10	70	0.178
Formic acid	Grade 9	50	Boiling	5.08		Grade 7	15	70	0.33
	Grade 7	45	Boiling	nil		Grade 7	3	190	0.025
	Grade 12	45, 50	Boiling	nil		Grade 7	5	190	0.102
	Grade 7	50	Boiling	0.01		Grade 7	10	190	8.9
	Ti-6-4	50	Boiling	7.92	Hydrochloric acid, oxygen saturated	Grade 7	3, 5	190	0.127
	Transage 207	50	Boiling	0.90		Grade 7	10	190	9.3
	Ti-6-2-4-6	50	Boiling	0.62	Hydrochloric acid, chlorine saturated	Grade 7	3, 5	190	<0.03
	Ti-3-8-6-4-4	50	Boiling	0.98		Grade 7	10	190	29.0
	Ti-5Ta	50	Boiling	3.16					
	Ti-550	50	Boiling	0.02					
	Grade 12	90	Boiling	0.56					
	Grade 7	90	Boiling	0.056					

(Continued)

Table 11 (continued)

Medium	Alloy	Concentration, %	Temperature, °C	Corrosion rate, mm/yr	Medium	Alloy	Concentration, %	Temperature, °C	Corrosion rate, mm/yr
Hydrochloric acid, aerated	Grade 7	1, 5	70	<0.03	Sodium fluoride				
	Grade 7	10	70	0.05	pH 7 .... Grade 12		1	Boiling	0.001
	Grade 7	15	70	0.15	pH 7 .... Grade 7		1	Boiling	0.002
Hydrochloric acid +					Sodium hydroxide .... Grade 9		50	150	0.49
4% FeCl₃ + 4% MgCl₂ ...... Grade 7		19	82	0.49	Sodium sulfate, pH 1 .... Grade 7		10	Boiling	nil
Hydrochloric acid +					Sulfamic acid .... Grade 12		10	Boiling	11.6
4% FeCl₃ + 4% MgCl₂,						Grade 7	10	Boiling	0.37
chlorine saturated .... Grade 7		19	82	0.46	Sulfuric acid,				
Hydrochloric acid					naturally aerated	Grade 12	9	24	0.003
+5 g/L FeCl₃ .... Grade 7		10	Boiling	0.279		Grade 12	9.5	24	0.006
+16 g/L FeCl₃ .... Grade 7		10	Boiling	0.076		Grade 12	10	24	0.38
+16 g/L CuCl₂ .... Grade 7		10	Boiling	0.127		Grade 12	3.5	52	0.013
Hydrochloric acid						Grade 12	3.75	52	1.73
+2 g/L FeCl₃ .... Grade 12		4.2	91	0.058		Grade 12	2.75	66	0.015
+0.2% FeCl₃............... Grade 9		1	Boiling	0.005		Grade 12	3.0	66	1.65
+0.2% FeCl₃............... Grade 9		5	Boiling	0.033		Grade 12	0.75	Boiling	0.003
+0.2% FeCl₃............... Grade 9		10	Boiling	0.305		Grade 12	1.0	Boiling	0.91
+0.1% FeCl₃............... Grade 9		5	Boiling	0.008		Grade 7	1.0	204	0.005
+0.1% FeCl₃............... Ti-550		5	Boiling	0.393		Grade 7	2.0	204	nil
+0.1% FeCl₃............... Transage 207		5	Boiling	0.048		Grade 12	1.0	204	0.91
+0.1% FeCl₃............... Ti-6-2-4-6		5	Boiling	0.068		Grade 9	0.5	Boiling	8.48
+0.1% FeCl₃............... Ti-10-2-3		5	Boiling	0.008	Sulfuric acid,				
+0.1% FeCl₃............... Ti-3-8-6-4-4		5	Boiling	0.018	nitrogen saturated .... Grade 7		5	70	0.15
+0.1% FeCl₃............... Ti-5Ta		5	Boiling	0.020		Grade 7	10	70	9.25
+0.1% FeCl₃............... Ti-6-4		5	Boiling	0.015		Grade 7	1, 5	190	0.13
+0.1% FeCl₃............... Ti-6-2-1.-.8		5	Boiling	0.051		Grade 7	10	190	1.50
+0.1% FeCl₃............... Grade 7		5	Boiling	0.013	Sulfuric acid,				
+0.1% FeCl₃............... Grade 12		5	Boiling	0.020	oxygen saturated .... Grade 7		1–10	190	0.13
Hydrochloric acid +					Sulfuric acid,				
18% H₃PO₄ + 5% HNO₃ .... Grade 7		18	77	nil	chlorine saturated .... Grade 7		10	190	0.051
Hydrogen peroxide						Grade 7	20	190	0.38
pH 1 .... Grade 7		5	23	0.062	Sulfuric acid,				
pH 4 .... Grade 7		5	23	0.010	nitrogen saturated .... Grade 7		10	25	0.025
pH 1 .... Grade 7		5	66	0.127		Grade 7	40	25	0.23
pH 4 .... Grade 7		5	66	0.046	Sulfuric acid, aerated .... Grade 9		5	35	0.025
+500 ppm Ca²⁺, pH 1 ...... Grade 7		5	66	nil	Sulfuric acid,				
+500 ppm Ca²⁺, pH 1 ...... Grade 7		20	66	0.76	nitrogen saturated .... Grade 9		5	35	0.405
Hydrogen peroxide,					Sulfuric acid,				
pH 1 + 5% NaCl........... Grade 7		20	66	0.008	naturally aerated Ti-3-8-6-4-4		1	Boiling	nil
Magnesium chloride .... Grade 7		Saturated	Boiling	nil		Ti-3-8-6-4-4	5	Boiling	1.85
Methyl alcohol .... Grade 9		99	Boiling	nil	Sulfuric acid, aerated .... Grade 7		10	70	0.10
Oxalic acid .... Grade 7		1	Boiling	1.14		Grade 7	40	70	0.94
Nitric acid .... Grade 9		10	Boiling	0.084					
	Grade 9	30	Boiling	0.497	Sulfuric acid +				
Phosphoric acid,					5 g/L Fe₂(SO₄)₃............ Grade 7		10	Boiling	0.178
naturally aerated .... Grade 12		25	25	0.019	Sulfuric acid +				
	Grade 12	30	25	0.056	16 g/L Fe₂(SO₄)₃........... Grade 7		10	Boiling	<0.03
	Grade 12	45	25	0.157	Sulfuric acid +				
	Grade 12	8	52	0.02	16 g/L Fe₂(SO₄)₃........... Grade 7		20	Boiling	0.15
	Grade 12	13	52	0.066	Sulfuric acid +				
	Grade 12	15	52	0.52	15% CuSO₄ .... Grade 7		15	Boiling	0.64
	Grade 12	5	66	0.038	Sulfuric acid +				
	Grade 12	7	66	0.15	3% Fe₂(SO₄)₃ Ti-3-8-6-4-4		50	Boiling	<0.03
	Grade 12	0.5	Boiling	0.071	Sulfuric acid +				
	Grade 12	1.0	Boiling	0.14	1 g/L FeCl₃ Ti-3-8-6-4-4		10	Boiling	0.15
	Grade 7	40	25	0.008	Sulfuric acid +				
	Grade 7	60	25	0.07	50 g/L FeCl₃ Ti-3-8-6-4-4		10	Boiling	0.05
	Grade 7	15	52	0.036	Sulfuric acid +				
	Grade 7	23	52	0.15	1% CuSO₄ .... Grade 7		30	Boiling	1.75
	Grade 7	8	66	0.076	Sulfuric acid +				
	Grade 7	15	66	0.104	100 ppm Cu²⁺ +				
	Grade 7	0.5	Boiling	0.050	1% thiourea (deaerated) .... Grade 7		1	100	nil
	Grade 7	1.0	Boiling	0.107	Sulfuric acid +				
	Grade 7	5.0	Boiling	0.228	100 ppm Cu²⁺ +				
Potassium hydroxide.......... Grade 9		50	150	9.21	1% thiourea (deaerated) ..... Grade 12		1	100	0.23
Seawater .... Grade 9		. . .	Boiling	nil	Sulfuric acid +				
Sodium chloride, pH 1 .... Grade 9		Saturated	93	nil	1000 ppm Cl⁻ .... Grade 7		15	49	0.015

Zirconium

Zirconium is a reactive metal and has a high affinity for oxygen. When it is exposed to an oxygen-containing environment, an adherent, protective oxide film forms on its surface. This film occurs spontaneously in air or water at ambient temperature and below. Moreover, the film is self-healing and protects the base metal from chemical and mechanical attack at temperatures up to 300 °C (570 °F). Consequently, zirconium is very resistant to corrosive attack in most mineral and organic acids, strong alkalis, saline solutions, and some molten salts. Zirconium is not attacked by oxidizing media unless halides are present. The corrosion properties are unaffected as long as this thin layer is not penetrated by reactants at increasing temperatures. Table 12 gives the corrosion resistance of zirconium alloys in various media.

Water

Zirconium does not experience any appreciable attack by water at ordinary temperatures. However, its resistance to both water and steam is markedly affected by impurities such as nitrogen, aluminum, and titanium. Dissolved ferric and cupric chlorides, even in small concentrations, increase the attack.

In high-temperature water, zirconium and many of its alloys show a period of decreasing corrosion followed by a transition to a more rapid linear rate. The time to transition, along with the subsequent rate of attack, varies with purity and with temperature. The corrosion is extremely sensitive to dissolved nitrogen. More than 40 ppm causes a rapid transition to a high rate of corrosion. In like fashion, even small amounts of titanium and aluminum cause deleterious effects. Alloys such as Zircaloy 2 and Zircaloy 4, which contain small amounts of tin, iron, and chromium, rate much better in high-temperature water with respect to corrosion resistance.

Salt Water

Zirconium has excellent resistance to seawater, brackish water, and polluted water. The corrosion properties of Zr702 in natural seawater have been tested. All welded and nonwelded specimens exhibited negligible corrosion rates. Although marine befouling was observed, no corrosion was found beneath the marine organisms. Alloys Zr702 and Zr704, after extensive laboratory and sea testing, demonstrated resistance to general, pitting, and crevice corrosion.

Acids

Zirconium is very resistant to corrosive attack in most mineral and organic acids, strong alkalines, saline solutions, and some molten salts. Most important, historically speaking, it has excellent corrosion-resistant qualities in the presence of hydrochloric acid. There is some evidence of an increment in corrosion due to intergranular penetration when zirconium is exposed to HCl at 200 °C (390 °F) under pressure. However, zirconium is totally resistant to attack in all concentrations of HCl to temperatures well above boiling.

Zirconium has excellent corrosion resistance to HNO_3. This extends from below boiling at 98% HNO_3 up to 250 °C (480 °F) with a 70% concentration.

There are, however, a few media that will attack zirconium. Among them are hydrofluoric acid (HF), ferric chloride ($FeCl_3$), cupric chloride ($CuCl_2$), aqua regia, concentrated sulfuric acid (H_2SO_4), and wet chlorine gas. Zirconium resists attack by H_2SO_4 at all concentrations up to 70% and to temperatures to boiling and above, although the level of resistance depends strongly on temperature.

Organic Media

Zirconium resists corrosion over a wide range of organic compounds, including acetic acid, acetic anhydride, formic acid, urea, ethylene dichloride, formaldehyde, citric acid, lactic acid, tannic acid, and trichloroethylene.

Hafnium

Hafnium occurs naturally in zirconium, and the two are considered "sister" elements. It shares many common properties with zirconium, especially its high corrosion resistance to many media. Hafnium has chemical and metallurgical properties similar to those of zirconium, although its nuclear properties are markedly different. Hafnium has a high thermal neutron absorption cross section in contrast to the very low absorption cross section of zirconium. This quality has made it a primary material for nuclear reactor rods.

Nuclear Grades

As the result of this essential difference between zirconium and hafnium, there are both nuclear and non-nuclear grades of zirconium and zirconium alloys. The nuclear grades are essentially hafnium free; the non-nuclear (i.e., industrial application) grades may contain up to 4.5% hafnium. Nuclear grades also have improved corrosion resistance in waters above 290 °C (550 °F).

Zircaloy, Zr-2.5Nb, and Zr-1Nb are nuclear grade materials. Of the well-known Zircaloy group of alloys now generally used in nuclear reactors, Zircaloy 2 and Zircaloy 4 contain small amounts of tin, iron, and chromium. They therefore have improved corrosion resistance in waters above 290 °C (554 °F).

ASTM specifications for non-nuclear grades list UNS R60704 as the alloy corresponding closely to Zircaloy 4, and UNS R60705 and R60706 as the alloys corresponding closely to Zr-2.5Nb. Alloys known by ASTM grades 702 and 705 are the most important for industrial applications.

In aqueous solutions, hafnium is soluble in hydrofluoric acid (HF) and concentrated H_2SO_4. It is resistant to dilute HCl and H_2SO_4 and is unaffected by HNO_3 in all concentrations. Aqua regia dissolves hafnium, and with the addition of small amounts of soluble fluoride salts, the reaction with other acids is appreciably increased. Hafnium is also very resistant to alkalis.

Corrosion Testing

Because the behavior of zirconium is often negatively influenced by impurities in corrosive environments, corrosion testing prior to use should be carried out in actual plant liquors rather than in purer synthetic solutions created in the laboratory.

Table 12 Corrosion Resistance of Zirconium Alloys in Various Media

Medium	Concentration, %	Temperature °C	°F	Zr702 mm/yr	mils/yr	Zr704 mm/yr	mils/yr	Zr705 mm/yr	mils/yr	Remarks
Acetaldehyde	100	Boiling		<0.05	<2	...	...	...	...	...
Acetic acid	5–99.5	35	95 to boiling	<0.025	<1	...	...	<0.025	<1	...
Acetic acid anhydride	99	Room-boiling		<0.025	<1	...	...	<0.025	<1	...
Acetic acid (glacial)	99.7	Boiling		<0.13	<5	...	...	...	...	...
Acetic acid	100	160	320	<0.025	<1	...	...	...	...	...
Acetic acid + 50 ppm I^-	100	160,200	320,390	<0.025	<1	...	...	...	...	...
Acetic acid + 1% I^- + 100 ppm Fe^{3+}	99	200	390	<0.025	<1	...	...	<0.025	<1	...
Acetic acid + 2% HI	80	100	212	<0.025	<1	...	...	<0.025	<1	...
Acetic acid + 2% HI + 1000 ppm iron added as powder	80	100	212	<0.025	<1					...
Acetic acid + 2% HI, 1% methanol, 500 ppm formic acid, 100 ppm Cu	80	150	300	<0.025	<1	...	...	<0.025	<1	...
Acetic acid + 2% HI, 1% methanol, 500 ppm formic acid, 100 ppm Fe	80	150	300	<0.025	<1	...	...	<0.025	<1	...
Acetic acid + 2% HI	98	150	300	<0.025	<1	...	...	<0.025	<1	...
Acetic acid + 2% HI + 200 ppm Cl^-	80	100	212	<0.025	<1	...	...	<0.025	<1	...
Acetic acid + 2% HI + 200 ppm Fe^{3+}	80	100	212	<0.025	<1	...	...	<0.025	<1	...
Acetic acid + 2% I^-	98	150	300	<0.025	<1	...	...	<0.025	<1	...
Acetic acid + 2% HI + 1% CH_3OH + 500 ppm formic acid	80	150	300	<0.025	<1	...	...	<0.025	<1	...
Acetic acid + 2% HI + 200 ppm Cl^-	80	100	212	<0.025	<1	...	...	<0.025	<1	...
Acetic acid + 50% acetic anhydride	50	Boiling		<0.025	<1	...	...	<0.025	<1	...
Acetic acid + 50% 48% HBr	50	115	240	<0.025	<1	...	...	<0.025	<1	...
Acetic acid + saturated gaseous HCl and Cl_2	100	Boiling		>5	>200	...	...	>5	>200	...
Acetic acid + saturated, gaseous HCl and Cl_2	100	40	100	<0.025	<1					...
Acetic acid + 10% CH_3OH	90	200	390	<0.025	<1	...	...	...	...	...
Aluminum chlorate	30	100	212	<0.05	<2	...	...	...	...	...
Aluminum chloride	5, 10, 25	35–100	95–212	<0.025	<1	...	...	...	...	...
	25	Boiling		<0.025	<1	...	...	<0.025	<1	...
	40	100	212	<0.05	<2	...	...	...	...	...
Aluminum chloride (aerated)	5, 10	60	140	<0.05	<2	...	...	...	...	...
Aluminum fluoride	20	Room		>1.3	>50	...	...	...	...	...
Aluminum potassium sulfate	10	Boiling		nil		...	...	...	...	pH 3.2
Aluminum sulfate	25	Boiling		nil		...	...	nil		pH 3.2
	60	100	212	<0.05	<2	...	...	nil		...
Ammonia (wet)	+H_2O	38	100	<0.13	<5	...	...	...	...	...
Ammonium carbamate		193	380	<0.025	<1	...	...	...	...	58.4% urea, 16.8% ammonia, 14.8% CO_2, 9.9% H_2O at 22–24 MPa (3200–3500 psi)
Ammonium chloride	1, 10, saturated	35–100	95–212	<0.025	<1	...	...	...	...	...
Ammonium hydroxide	28	Room to 100	212	<0.025	<1	...	...	...	...	...
Ammonium fluoride	20	28	80	>1.3	>50	...	...	...	...	pH 8
	20	98	210	>1.3	>50	...	...	...	...	pH 8
Ammonium oxalate	100	100	212	<0.05	<2	...	...	...	...	...
Ammonium sulfate	5, 10	100	212	<0.13	<5	...	...	...	...	...
Aniline hydrochloride	5, 20	35–100	95–212	<0.025	<1	...	...	...	...	...
	5, 20	100	212	<0.05	<2	...	...	...	...	...
Aqua regia	3:1	Room		>1.3	>50	...	...	...	...	3 parts HCl/1 part HNO_3
Barium chloride	5.20	35–100	95–212	<0.025	<1	...	...	...	...	...
	25	Boiling		0.13–0.25	5–10	...	...	...	...	...

(Continued)

Table 12 (continued)

Medium	Concentration, %	Temperature °C	°F	Zr702 mm/yr	Zr702 mils/yr	Zr704 mm/yr	Zr704 mils/yr	Zr705 mm/yr	Zr705 mils/yr	Remarks
Bromine	100-liquid	20	70	<0.25	<10	...	...	0.5–1.3	20–50	Pitting
	vapor	20	70	...	...	...	...	>1.3	>50	Pitting
Bromochloromethane	100	100	212	<0.05	<2	...	...	...	...	...
Cadmium chloride	100	Room		<0.05	<2	...	...	...	...	...
Calcium bromide	100	100	212	<0.05	<2	...	...	...	...	...
Calcium chloride	5, 10, 25	35–100	95–212	<0.025	<1	...	...	...	...	
	70	Boiling		<0.025	<1	...	...	<0.025	<1	B.P. = 162 °C (324 °F)
	75	Boiling		<0.13	<5	...	...	...	...	
	Mixture	79	175	<0.025	<1	...	...	...	...	14% CaCl, 8% NaCl, 0.2% Ca(OH)$_2$
Calcium fluoride	Saturated	28	80	nil		...	...	...	...	pH 5
	Saturated	90	195	nil		...	...	...	...	pH 5
Calcium hypochlorite	2, 6, 20	100	212	<0.13	<5	...	...	...	...	...
Carbonic acid	Saturated	100	212	<0.13	<5	...	...	...	...	...
Carbon tetrachloride	0–100	Room to 100	212	<0.13	<5	...	...	...	...	...
Chlorine (water saturated)		Room		>1.3	>50	...	...	...	...	...
		75	165	>1.3	>50	...	...	...	...	...
Chlorine gas (more than 0.13% H$_2$O)	100	94	200	>1.3	>50	...	...	...	...	...
Chlorine gas (dry)	100	Room		<0.13	<5	...	...	...	...	...
Chlorinated water	...	100	212	<0.05	<2	...	...	...	...	...
Chloroacetic acid	100	Boiling		<0.025	<1	...	...	...	...	...
Chromic acid	10–50	Boiling		<0.025	<1	...	...	...	...	...
Citric acid	10–50	35–100	95–212	<0.025	<1	...	...	...	...	...
	10, 25, 50	100	212	<0.025	<1	...	...	...	...	...
	50	Boiling		<0.13	<5	...	...	...	...	...
Chromium plating solution		66	150	>1.3	>50	...	...	>1.3	>50	M + T chemicals CR-100
Cupric chloride	5, 10, 20	35–100	95–212	>1.3	>50	>1.3	>50	>1.3	>50	...
	20, 40, 50	Boiling		>1.3	>50	>1.3	>50	>1.3	>50	...
Cupric cyanide	Saturated	Room		>1.3	>50	...	...	...	...	B.P. = 115 °C (239 °F)
Cupric nitrate	40	Boiling		Weight gain		...	...	Weight gain		...
Dichloroacetic acid	100	Boiling		<0.5	<20	...	...	...	...	...
Ethylene dichloride	100	Boiling		<0.13	<5	...	...	...	...	...
Ferric chloride	0–50	Room to 100	212	>1.3	>50	>1.3	>50	>1.3	>50	...
	0–50	Boiling		>1.3	>50	>1.3	>50	>1.3	>50	...
Ferric sulfate	10	0–100	32–212	<0.05	<2	...	...	...	...	...
		Boiling		<0.025	<1	...	...	<0.025	<1	...
Formaldehyde	6–37	Room to 100	212	<0.05	<2	...	...	...	...	...
Fluoboric acid	0–70	Elevated		>1.3	>50	...	...	...	...	...
	5–20	Room		>1.3	>50	...	...	...	...	...
Fluosilicic acid	10			>1.3	>50	...	...	...	...	...
Formic acid	10–90	35	95 to boiling	<0.13	<5	...	...	...	...	...
Formic acid (aerated)	10–90	Room to 100	212	<0.13	<5	...	...	...	...	...
Hydrazine	Mixture	109	230	<0.025	<1	...	...	...	...	2% hydrazine + saturated NaCl + 6% NaOH
	Mixture	130	265	nil		...	...	...	...	2% hydrazine + saturated NaCl + 6% NaOH
Hydrobromic acid	48	Boiling		<0.13	<5	...	...	<0.13	<5	B.P. = 125 °C (257 °F); shallow pits
	Mixture	Boiling		<0.025	<1	...	...	<0.025	<1	24% HBr + 50% acetic acid (glacial)
Hydrochloric acid	2	225	435	<0.025	<1	...	...	<0.025	<1	...
	5	Room		<0.025	<1	...	...	...	...	...
	10	35	95	<0.025	<1	...	...	...	...	...
	20	35	95	<0.025	<1	...	...	...	...	...
	32	30	85	<0.025	<1	...	...	...	...	...
	32	82	180	<0.025	<1	...	...	...	...	...
20% HCl + Cl$_2$ gas	...	58	135	0.13–0.25	5–10	...	...	...	...	Pitting
37% HCl + Cl$_2$ gas	...	58	135	<0.13	<5	...	...	...	...	...
10% HCl + 100 ppm FeCl$_3$	...	30	85	<0.025	<1	<0.05	<2	<0.025	<1	SCC observed
10% HCl + 100 ppm FeCl$_3$	...	105	220	<0.13	<5	...	...	...	...	Pitting rate
20% HCl + 100 ppm FeCl$_3$	...	105	220	<0.13	<5	...	...	...	...	...
37% HCl + 100 ppm FeCl$_3$	...	53	125	0.13–0.25	5–10	...	...	...	...	SCC observed
Hydrochloric acid	Mixture	Room		Dissolved		...	...	...	...	20% HCl + 20% HNO$_3$
	Mixture	Room		Dissolved		...	...	...	...	10% HCl + 10% HNO$_3$
Hydrofluoric acid	0–100	Room		>1.3	>50	...	...	...	...	...
Hydrogen peroxide	50	100	212	<0.05	<2	...	...	...	...	...
Hydroxyacetic acid		40	104	<0.13	<5	...	...	...	...	...
Lactic acid	10–100	148	298	<0.025	<1	...	...	...	...	...
	10–85	35	95 to boiling	<0.025	<1	...	...	...	...	...
Magnesium chloride	5–40	Room to 100	212	<0.05	<2	...	...	...	...	...
	47	Boiling		nil		...	...	nil		...
Manganese chloride	5, 20	Room to 100	212	<0.025	<1	...	...	...	...	...
Mercuric chloride	1-saturated	35–100	95–212	<0.025	<1	...	...	...	...	...
	Saturated	Boiling		<0.025	<1	...	...	<0.025	<1	...

(Continued)

Table 12 (continued)

Medium	Concentration, %	Temperature °C	°F	Zr702 mm/yr	mils/yr	Zr704 mm/yr	mils/yr	Zr705 mm/yr	mils/yr	Remarks
Nickel chloride	5, 20	35–100	95–212	<0.025	<1	...	...	...	...	...
	5–20	100	212	<0.025	<1	...	...	...	...	...
	30	Boiling		nil		...	...	nil		...
Nitric acid	20	103	215	<0.025	<1	<0.025	<1	<0.025	<1	...
	70	121	250	<0.025	<1	<0.025	<1	<0.025	<1	...
	10–70	Room to 260	500	<0.025	<1	...	...	...	...	...
	70–98	Room-boiling		<0.025	<1	...	...	...	...	SCC observed
Nitric acid + 1% Fe	65	120	248	<0.025	<1	...	...	...	...	...
Nitric acid + 1% Fe	65	204	400	<0.025	<1	...	...	...	...	...
Nitric acid + 1.45% 304 stainless steel	65	204	400	nil		...	...	...	...	...
Nitric acid + 1% Cl⁻	70	120	248	nil		...	...	...	...	...
Nitric acid + 1% seawater	70	120	248	nil		...	...	...	...	...
Nitric acid + 1% FeCl₃	70	120	248	nil		...	...	...	...	...
Oxalic acid	0–100	100	212	<0.025	<1	...	...	...	...	...
Perchloric acid	70	100	212	<0.05	<2	...	...	...	...	...
Sodium sulfate	0–20	Room to 100	212	<0.05	<2	...	...	...	...	...
Sodium sulfide	33	Boiling		nil		...	...	nil		...
Stannic chloride	5	100	212	<0.025	<1	...	...	...	...	...
	24	Boiling		<0.025	<1	...	...	...	...	...
Succinic acid	0–50	100	212	<0.05	<2	...	...	...	...	...
	100	150	300	<0.05	<2	...	...	...	...	...
Sulfuric acid	0–75	20	70	<0.025	<1	<0.025	<1	<0.025	<1	...
	80	20	70	<0.13	<5	>1.3	>50			...
	80	30	85	0.5–1.3	20–50	>1.3	>50	>1.3	>50	...
	77.5	60	140	0.25–0.5	10–20	...	...	<0.25	<10	...
	75	50	120	<0.025	<1	...	...	...	...	...
	77	50	120	0.13–0.25	5–10	>1.3	>50			...
	80	50	120	>1.3	>50	>1.3	>50	>1.3	>50	...
	75	80	125	<0.13	<5	...	...	<0.13	<5	...
	65	100	212	...	...	<0.025	<1	<0.13	<5	...
	70	100	212	<0.05	<2	...	...	<0.13	<5	...
	75	100	212	<0.13	<5	...	...	<0.13	<5	...
	76	100	212	<0.25	<10	...	...	...	...	...
	77	100	212	<0.5	<20	...	...	...	...	...
	77.5	100	212	>1.3	>50	>1.3	>50	>1.3	>50	...
	60	130	265	...	...	...	...	<0.13	<5	...
	65	130	265	<0.025	<1	...	...	...	...	...
	70	140	285	<0.13	<5	...	...	<0.25	<10	...
	58	Boiling		...	...	<0.025	<1	<0.13	<5	B.P. = 140 °C (284 °F)
	62	Boiling		<0.13	<5	...	...	0.5–1.3	10–20	B.P. = 146 °C (295 °F)
	64	Boiling		<0.13	<5	...	...	0.5–1.3	20–50	B.P. = 152 °C (306 °F)
	68	Boiling		<0.13	<5	...	...	...	...	B.P. = 165 °C (329 °F)
	69	Boiling		<0.13	<5	...	...	...	...	B.P. = 167 °C (333 °F)
	71	Boiling		<0.13	<5	...	...	...	...	B.P. = 171 °C (340 °F)
	72–74	Boiling		0.13–0.25	5–10	>1.3	>50	...	...	...
	75	Boiling		0.25–0.5	10–20	>1.3	>50	...	...	B.P. = 189 °C (372 °F)
Sulfuric acid + 1000 ppm Fe³⁺	60	Boiling		<0.025	<1	...	...	...	...	B.P. = 138–142 °C (280–288 °F)
+ 10 000 ppm Fe³⁺	60	Boiling		<0.13	<5	...	...	...	...	Added as Fe₂(SO₄)₃
Sulfuric acid +200–1000 ppm Fe³⁺	65	Boiling		<0.13	<5	...	...	...	...	B.P. = 152–155 °C (306–311 °F)
+ 10 000 ppm Fe³⁺	65	Boiling		0.13–0.25	5–10	...	...	...	...	Added as Fe₂(SO₄)₃
Sulfuric acid + 14 ppm–141 ppm Fe³⁺	70	Boiling		0.13–0.25	5–10	...	...	...	...	B.P. = 167–171 °C (333–340 °F)
+200 ppm Fe³⁺	70	Boiling		0.25–0.5	10–20	...	...	...	...	Added as Fe₂(SO₄)₃
+1410 ppm–10 000 ppm Fe³⁺	70	Boiling		>1.3	>50	...	...	...	...	...
Sulfuric acid +1000 ppm FeCl₃	60	Boiling		<0.13	<5	<0.13	<5	<0.5	<20	B.P. = 138–142 °C (280–288 °F)
+ 10 000 ppm FeCl₃	60	Boiling		<0.13	<5	<0.5	<20	0.5–1.3	20–50	...
+ 20 000 ppm FeCl₃	60	Boiling		0.5–1.3	20–50	0.5–1.3	20–50	>1.3	>50	...
Sulfuric acid +200 ppm FeCl₃	65	Boiling		<0.13	<5	<0.13	<5	<0.5	<20	B.P. = 152–155 °C (306–311 °F)
+1000 ppm FeCl₃	65	Boiling		<0.13	<5	<0.13	<5	<0.5	<20	...
+ 10 000 ppm FeCl₃	65	Boiling		<0.13	<5	<0.13	<5	<0.5	<20	...
Sulfuric acid + 10 ppm FeCl₃	70	Boiling		<0.5	<20	<0.5	<20	>1.3	>50	B.P. = 167–171 °C (333–340 °F)
+100 ppm FeCl₃	70	Boiling		<0.5	<20	<0.5	<20	>1.3	>50	...
+200 ppm FeCl₃	70	Boiling		<0.5	<20	<0.5	<20	>1.3	>50	...
+1000 ppm FeCl₃	70	Boiling		<0.5	<20	<0.5	<20	>1.3	>50	...
+ 10 000 ppm FeCl₃	70	Boiling		0.5–1.3	20–50	>1.3	>50	>1.3	>50	...
Sulfuric acid +200 ppm Cu²⁺	60	Boiling		<0.13	<5	...	...	...	...	Added as CuSO₄
+1000–10 000 ppm Cu²⁺	60	Boiling		<0.025	<1	...	...	...	...	...

(Continued)

Table 12 (continued)

Medium	Concentration, %	Temperature °C	°F	Zr702 mm/yr	Zr702 mils/yr	Zr704 mm/yr	Zr704 mils/yr	Zr705 mm/yr	Zr705 mils/yr	Remarks
Sulfuric acid										
+200–10 000 ppm Cu^{2+} 65		Boiling		<0.13	<5	...	...	...	...	Added as $CuSO_4$
Sulfuric acid										
+3 ppm Cu^{2+} 70		Boiling		0.13–0.25	5–10	...	...	...	...	Added as $CuSO_4$
+27–226 ppm Cu^{2+} 70		Boiling		>1.3	>50	...	...	...	...	...
Sulfuric acid										
+1000–10 000 ppm NO_3^- 60		Boiling		<0.13	<5	...	...	...	...	Added as $NaNO_3$
+50 000 ppm NO_3^-.................60		Boiling		>1.3	>50	...	...	...	...	...
Sulfuric acid										
+200–1000 ppm NO_3^- 65		Boiling		<0.13	<5	...	...	...	...	Added as $NaNO_3$
+10 000 ppm NO_3^-.................65		Boiling		0.25–0.5	10–20	...	...	...	...	...
+50 000 ppm NO_3^-.................65		Boiling		>1.3	>50	...	...	...	...	...
Sulfuric acid										
+200 ppm NO_3^- 70		Boiling		0.13–0.25	5–10	...	...	...	...	Added as $NaNO_3$
+6000 ppm NO_3^- 70		Boiling		0.5–1.3	20–50	...	...	...	...	...
Sulfuric acid										
+1000 ppm NO_3^- 60		Boiling		<0.13	<5	...	...	...	...	Added as HNO_3
+10 000 ppm NO_3^-.................60		Boiling		0.25–0.5	10–20	...	...	...	...	...
+50 000 ppm NO_3^-.................60		Boiling		>1.3	>50	...	...	...	...	...
Sulfuric acid										
+1000 ppm NO_3^- 65		Boiling		<0.13	<5	...	...	...	...	Added as HNO_3
+10 000–50 000 ppm NO_3^- 65		Boiling		>1.3	>50	...	...	...	...	...
Sulfuric acid	Mixture	Room to 100	212	<0.025	<1	...	...	...	...	1% H_2SO_4, 99% HNO_3
	Mixture	Room to 100	212	nil		...	...	...	...	10% H_2SO_4, 90% HNO_3
	Mixture	Boiling		<0.025	<1	...	...	...	...	14% H_2SO_4, 14% HNO_3
	Mixture	100	212	>1.3	>50	>1.3	>50	>1.3	>50	25% H_2SO_4, 75% HNO_3
	Mixture	Room		<0.025	<1	...	...	...	...	50% H_2SO_4, 50% HNO_3
	Mixture	Boiling		>1.3	>50	>1.3	>50	>1.3	>50	68% H_2SO_4, 5% HNO_3
	Mixture	Boiling to 135	275	0.25–0.5	10–20	0.25–0.5	10–20	>1.3	>50	68% H_2SO_4, 1% HNO_3
	Mixture	Room		>1.3	>50	>1.3	>50	>1.3	>50	75% H_2SO_4, 25% HNO_3
	Mixture	Boiling		<0.025	<1	...	...	...	...	7.5% H_2SO_4, 19% HCl
	Mixture	Boiling		<0.025	<1	...	...	...	...	34% H_2SO_4, 17% HCl
	Mixture	Boiling		<0.025	<1	...	...	...	...	40% H_2SO_4, 14% HCl
	Mixture	Boiling		0.025–0.13	1–5	...	...	...	...	56% H_2SO_4, 10% HCl
	Mixture	Boiling		<0.025	<1	...	...	...	...	60% H_2SO_4, 1.5% HCl
	Mixture	Boiling		<0.13	<5	...	...	...	...	69% H_2SO_4, 1.5% HCl
	Mixture	Boiling		0.25–0.5	10–20	...	...	...	...	69% H_2SO_4, 4% HCl
	Mixture	Boiling		<0.5	<20	...	...	...	...	72% H_2SO_4, 1.5% HCl
	Mixture	Boiling		>1.3	>50	...	...	>1.3	>50	20% H_2SO_4, 7% HCl with 50 ppm F^- impurities
Sulfurous acid.........................6		Room		<0.13	<5	...	...	...	...	...
	Saturated	192	380	0.13–1.3	5–50	...	...	...	...	...
Sulfamic acid 10		Boiling		nil		...	...	nil		B.P. = 101 °C (214 °F)
Tannic acid 25		35–100	95–212	<0.025	<1	...	...	...	...	...
Tartaric acid 10–50		35–100	95–212	<0.025	<1	...	...	...	...	...
Trichloroacetic acid.................10–40		Room		<0.05	<2	...	...	...	...	...
	100	Boiling		>1.3	>50	...	...	...	...	...
	100	100	212	>1.3	>50	...	...	...	...	B.P. = 195 °C (383 °F)
Tetrachloroethane 100		Boiling		<0.13	<5	...	...	...	...	B.P. = 146 °C (295 °F) symmetrical B.P. = 129 °C (264 °F) unsymmetrical
Trichloroethylene......................99		Boiling		<0.13	<5	...	...	...	...	B.P. = 87 °C (189 °F)
Trisodium phosphate................5–20		100	212	<0.13	<5	...	...	...	...	...
Urea reactor mixture..............	Mixture	193	380	0.025	<1	...	...	...	...	58% urea, 17% NH_3, 15% CO_2, 10% H_2O
Zinc chloride........................70		Boiling		nil		...	...	nil		...
	5–20	35	95 to boiling	<0.025	<1	...	...	...	...	...
	40	180	355	<0.025	<1	...	...	<0.025	<1	...

Tantalum and Tantalum Alloys

Tantalum is an exceptionally versatile corrosion-resistant metal. It combines the inertness of glass with the strength and ductility of low-carbon steel. Although expensive, recent fabrication techniques, in which thin linings of tantalum are used in chemical-processing equipment, have resulted in equipment that has the acid corrosion resistance provided by tantalum but at a much lower cost than an all-tantalum construction. In other cases, the long life and reliability of tantalum equipment in severe corrosion applications often more than offsets the higher initial cost. Table 13 gives the effects of acids on tantalum, Table 14 the effects of salts; and Table 15 the effects of miscellaneous corrosive reagents.

The outstanding corrosion resistance and inertness result from a very thin, impervious, protective oxide film that forms upon exposure of the metal to slightly anodic or oxidizing conditions. Although tantalum pentoxide (Ta_2O_5) is the usual oxide form, suboxides may also exist in transition between the base metal and the outer film. It is only when these oxide films react with, or are penetrated by, a chemical reagent that attack occurs on the underlying metal substrate.

The oxide film adheres well, and it appears to be free from porosity. There have, however, been some reports concerning the suboxides, which are stable up to 425 °C (800 °F). When tantalum is heated above this level, only the stable pentoxide exists. Thus, internal stress set up by the metal during oxide conversion causes the protective oxide film to flake and spall.

Tantalum occupies a position toward the electropositive end of the electromotive force (emf) series, and thus it tends to become cathodic in the galvanic cell circuit formed by contact with almost all other metals. Because of this cathodic behavior, atomic hydrogen, which may be liberated, can be absorbed by the tantalum and result in hydrogen embrittlement. Stray voltages can also cause this undesired effect. Therefore, when used in chemical-processing equipment, tantalum must be protected from becoming cathodic so that the material will not become embrittled.

Because of the wide ranges of type, concentration, and temperature of the media to which it exhibits excellent corrosion resistance, tantalum has found primary application in the chemical-processing industry.

Water

Tantalum is not attacked by fresh water, mine waters (which are usually acidic), or seawater, either cold or hot. It shows no sign of corrosion in deionized water at 40 °C (100 °F). For tantalum equipment exposed to boiler waters and condensates, the alkalinity must be controlled. The pH should be less than 9 and preferably no more than 8. No failures caused by exposure of tantalum to steam condensate have ever been recorded. Tantalum is used in many cases at saturated steam pressures above 1035 kPa (150 psi) at temperatures of 185 °C (365 °F) and is considered resistant to saturated steam below 250 °C (480 °F) at a pressure of 3.9 MPa (560 psi).

Acids

The chemical properties of tantalum are similar to those of glass. Thus, tantalum is immune to attack by almost all acids except HF. Tantalum is *not* attacked by such agents as sulfuric acid (H_2SO_4), nitric acid (HNO_3), hydrochloric acid (HCl), aqua regia, perchloric acid ($HClO_4$), chlorine, bromide, hydrobromic acid (HBr), or any of the bromides, phosphoric acid (H_3PO_4) when free of the F- ion, nitric oxides, chlorine

oxides, hypochlorous acid (HClO), organic acids, and hydrogen peroxide (H_2O_2) at ordinary temperatures. Tantalum is attacked, even at room temperature, by strong alkalis, HF, and free sulfur trioxide (SO_3), as in fuming H_2SO_4.

Salts

Tantalum is not attacked by dry salts or by salt solutions at any concentration or temperature unless HF is liberated when the salt dissolves or unless a strong alkali is present. Salts that form acidic solutions have no effect on tantalum. However, fused sodium hydrosulfate ($NaHSO_4$) or $KHSO_4$ dissolves tantalum.

Alkalis

Sodium hydroxide (NaOH) and potassium hydroxide (KOH) solutions do not dissolve tantalum, but they do tend to destroy the metal by formation of successive layers of surface scale. The rate of the destruction increases with concentration and temperature. Damage to tantalum equipment has been experienced unexpectedly when strong alkaline solutions are used during cleaning and maintenance.

Tantalum *is* attacked, even at room temperature, by concentrated alkaline solutions. It is dissolved by molten alkalis. However, tantalum is fairly resistant to dilute alkaline solutions. In a long-term exposure test in a paper mill, tantalum suffered no attack in a solution with a pH of 10.

Organic Compounds

In general, tantalum is completely resistant to organic compounds. It is used in heat exchangers, spargers, and reaction vessels in several important organic reactions, particularly when corrosive inorganics are involved.

Most organic salts, gases, alcohols, ketones, alkaloids, and esters have no effect on tantalum. Specific exceptions, however, should be made for reagents that may hydrolyze to HF or contain free SO_3 or strong alkalis.

Gases

Tantalum and all of its known alloys react with hydrogen, nitrogen, and oxygen at temperatures above 300 °C (570 °F). Hydrogen is dissolved in the pure metal above 350 °C (660 °F); it is evolved at higher temperatures. Little hydrogen remains at 800 °C (1470 °F). An oxide film may inhibit the reaction until higher temperatures are reached.

Nitrides among other phases form at the surface, but at higher temperatures these decompose. At 2100 °C (3800 °F), all the nitrogen is liberated.

Of these reactions, the most important is the reaction with oxygen. Tantalum tends to form oxides when heated in air. Reaction starts above 300 °C (570 °F). It becomes rapid above 600 °C (1100 °F). The scale is not adherent at this point. If the oxidized material is heated above 1000 °C (1830 °F), oxygen diffuses into the material and embrittles it.

Tantalum is attacked by carbon dioxide at 500 °C (930 °F). It is attacked by carbon monoxide above 1100 °C (2000 °F). In either instance, oxide is formed; at higher temperatures, tantalum carbide is also formed.

Table 13 Effects of Acids on Tantalum

Acid	Concentration, %	Temperature, °C (°F)	Code(a)	Acid	Concentration, %	Temperature, °C (°F)	Code(a)
Acetic acid	5–99.5	Room to boiling	E	Nitric acid	5	Room	E
Acetic acid, glacial	99.7	Room to boiling	E		10–40	Room to 100 (212)	E
Acetic acid vapor	0–100	Room to boiling	E		50–65	Room to boiling	E
Acetic anhydride	99	Room	E		69.5	Room to 100 (212)	E
Aqua regia	3 HCl, 1 HNO₃	Room to 77 (170)	E	Nitric acid (white fuming)	90	Room to 82 (180)	E
Arsenic acid	90	Room	E	Nitric acid	95	Room	E
				Nitric acid	Concentrated	Room to boiling	E
Benzoic acid	5	Room	E	Nitric acid	Fuming	Room	E
	Saturated	Room	E	Nitrous acid	5	Room	E
Boric acid	5	Room to boiling	E				
	10	Room to boiling	E	Oleic acid	...	Room	E
	Saturated	Room	E	Oxalic acid	1	Room to 38 (100)	E
Butyric acid	5	Room	E		5	Room to 35 (95)	E
					10	Room to boiling	E
Carbolic acid	Saturated	Room	E		0.5–25	Room to 60 (140)	E
	...	...	E		Saturated	Room to 93 (200)	E
Chloroacetic acid	30	Room to 82 (180)	E				
	100	Room to boiling	E	Perchloric acid	0–100	Room to 150 (300)	E
Chloric acid	...	Room	E	Phenol (carbolic acid)	Saturated	Room	E
Chlorosulfonic acid	10	...	E	Phosphoric acid	1	Room	E
Chromic acid	5–50	Room to boiling	E	Phosphoric acid	5	Room to 100 (212)	E
Citric acid	5	Room	E	Phosphoric acid (still)	10	Room to 175 (350)	E
	10–25	Room to boiling	E	Phosphoric acid (agitated)	10	Room	E
Citric acid (nonaerated)	50	Room to 100 (212)	E	Phosphoric acid (aerated)	10	Room	E
Citric acid (aerated)	50	Room to 100 (212)	E	Phosphoric acid	5–30	Room	E
Citric acid	Concentrated	Room to boiling	E	Phosphoric acid	35–85	Room	E
				Phosphoric acid	85	Room to 38 (100)	E
Dichloroacetic acid	100	Room to 100 (212)	E	Phosphoric-sulfuric + CuSO₄	15H₃PO₄-10H₂SO₄	Room to 66 (150)	E
	100	Room to boiling	E	Picric acid	Concentrated	...	E
				Propionic acid vapor	...	190 (375)	E
Fatty acids	...	...	E	Pyrogallic acid	...	...	E
Fluoboric acid	5–20	Elevated	NR				
Fluorosilicic acid	10	Room	NR	Salicylic acid	...	Room	E
Formic acid (still)	5	Room to 66 (150)	E	Stearic acid	Concentrated	Room to 93 (200)	E
Formic acid (nonaerated)	10–50	Room to boiling	E	Succinic acid	...	Molten	E
Formic acid (aerated)	10–90	Room to 100 (212)	E	Sulfuric acid	1–5	Room to 60 (140)	E
					5	Room to 60 (140)	E
Gallic acid	5	Room to boiling	E		10	Room to boiling	E
					15	Room	E
Hydrobromic acid	0–100	Room to boiling	E		50	Room to boiling	E
Hydrochloric acid (nonaerated)	5–20	Room to 35 (95)	E		Concentrated	Room to 150 (300)	E
Hydrochloric acid (aerated)	5–20	Room to 35 (95)	E		Concentrated	Boiling	NR
Hydrochloric acid	All	Room to 71 (160)	E		Fuming	Room	NR
Hydrochloric acid fumes	Concentrated	Room to 38 (100)	E	Sulfuric acid vapors	96	Room to 150 (300)	E
Hydrocyanic acid	...	...	E	Sulfuric anhydride	Dry	Room	NR
Hydrofluoric acid	5–48	Room	NR	Sulfuric-nitric acid	90–10	Room	E
Hydrofluoric acid (anhydrous)	100	Room	NR		70–30	Room	E
Hydrofluoric acid vapors	...	Room	NR		50–50	Room to 60 (140)	E
Hydrofluoric-nitric acid	1 HF:15 HNO₃	Room	NR		30–70	Room	E
Hydrofluosilicic acid	5	Room	V		10–90	Room to 60 (140)	E
Hydrofluosilicic acid vapors	...	100 (212)	NR	Sulfurous acid	6	Room	E
Hydroxyacetic acid	...	Room to 40 (105)	E		Saturated	Room to 190 (375)	E
				Sulfurous spray	...	Room	E
Lactic acid	5	Room to 66 (150)	E				
	10–100	Room to boiling	E	Tannic acid	10	Room to 66 (150)	E
					25	Room to 100 (212)	E
Malic acid	...	Room and hot	E	Tartaric acid	10	Room to 100 (212)	E
Methyl-sulfuric acid	0–100	Room to 150 (300)	E		25	Room to 100 (212)	E
Molybdic acid	5	Room	E		50	Room to 100 (212)	E
Muriatic acid	...	Room	E				

(a) E, no attack; V, variable depending on temperature and concentration; NR, not resistant

Table 14 Effects of Salts on Tantalum

Salt	Concentration, %	Temperature, °C (°F)	Code(a)
Aluminum acetate	Saturated	Room	E
Aluminum chloride	5	Room	E
Aluminum chloride (aerated)	5–10	Room to 60 (140)	E
Aluminum chloride	25	Room to 100 (212)	E
Aluminum fluoride	5	Room	NR
	Saturated	Room	NR
Aluminum hydroxide	Saturated	...	E
Aluminum potassium sulfate (alum)	2	Room	E
	10	Room to boiling	E
Aluminum sulfate	10–saturated	Room to boiling	E
Ammonium acid phosphate	10	Room	E
Ammonium alum	...	...	E
Ammonium alum (slightly ammoniacal)	...	...	E
Ammonium bicarbonate	50	Room to 100 (212)	E
Ammonium bromide	5	Room	E
Ammonium carbonate	50	Room to 100 (212)	E
Ammonium carbonate (aqueous)	50	Room to boiling	E
Ammonium carbonate	All	Room to hot	E
Ammonium chloride	1	Room	E
	10–50	Room to boiling	E
Ammonium fluoride	10	Room	NR
Ammonium hydroxide	...	...	V
Ammonium monosulfate	...	...	E
Ammonium nitrate	0–100	Room to 150 (300)	E
Ammonium oxalate	5	Room	E
Ammonium persulfate	5	Room	E
Ammonium phosphate	5	Room	E
Ammonium sulfate (aerated)	1	Room	E
	5	Room to 100 (212)	E
Ammonium sulfate	10	Room to 100 (212)	E
Ammonium sulfate	Saturated	Room to boiling	E
Ammonium sulfite	Saturated	Room to boiling	E
Amyl acetate	...	...	E
Aniline hydrochloride	5	Room	E
	20	Room to 38 (100)	E
Antimony trichloride	...	Room	E
Barium carbonate	Saturated	Room	E
Barium chloride	5 to saturated	Room	E
	5	Room to 100 (212)	E
	20	Room to 100 (212)	E
	25	Room to boiling	E
Barium hydroxide	Saturated	...	E E
Barium hydroxide·8H2O	Saturated	Room	E
Barium nitrate	Aqueous solution	Room to hot	E
Barium sulfate	...	Room	E
Butyl acetate	...	Room	E
Calcium bisulfite	...	Room	E
Calcium carbonate	Saturated	Room to boiling	E
Calcium chlorate	Dilute	Room to hot	E
Calcium chloride	5–20	Room to 100 (212)	E
	28	Room to boiling	E
	Concentrated	Room	E
Calcium hydroxide	10–saturated	Room to boiling	E
Calcium hypochlorite	2–saturated	Room to boiling	E
Calcium sulfate	Saturated	Room	E
Copper acetate	Saturated	Room	E
Copper carbonate	Saturated	...	E
Copper chloride (agitated, aerated)	1	Room	E
Copper chloride (agitated)	5	Room	E
Copper chloride (aerated)	5	Room	E
Copper cyanide (electroplating solution)	...	Room	E
Copper cyanide	Saturated	Room to boiling	E
Copper nitrate	1–saturated	Room	E
Copper sulfate	5	Room	E
	Saturated	Room to boiling	E
Cupric carbonate-cupric hydroxide	Saturated	Room	E
Cupric chloride	20–50	Room to boiling	E
Cupric cyanide	Saturated	Room	E
Cupric nitrate	...	Room to 40 (105)	E
Cuprous chloride	50	Room to 90 (195)	E

Salt	Concentration, %	Temperature, °C (°F)	Code(a)
Ferric chloride (still)	1–50	Room to boiling	E
Ferric chloride (agitated)	5	Room	E
Ferric chloride (aerated)	5	Room	E
Ferric hydroxide	...	Room	E
Ferric nitrate	1–5	Room	E
Ferric sulfate	1–saturated	Room	E
Ferrous chloride	...	Room	E
Ferrous sulfate	Dilute	Room	E
Ferrous ammonium citrate	...	...	E
Fluoride salts	Variable	Variable	V
Hydrogen bromide	...	...	E
Hydrogen peroxide	3–30	Room	E
	...	Room to boiling	E
Hydrogen iodide	...	...	E
Hydrogen sulfide	Dry	Room	E
	Saturated H2O	Room	E
Hyposulfite soda (hypo)	...	...	E
Lactic acid salts	...	Room	E
Lead acetate	Saturated	Room	E
Magnesium carbonate	...	...	E
Magnesium chloride (still)	1–5	Room to hot	E
Magnesium chloride	5–40	Room to boiling	E
Magnesium hydroxide	Saturated	Room	E
	Thick suspension	Room	E
Magnesium nitrate	...	...	E
Magnesium sulfate	5	Room to hot	E
	Saturated	Room	E
Manganese carbonate	...	...	E
Manganese chloride	10–50 (Aqueous)	Room to boiling	E
Manganous chloride	5–20	Room to 100 (212)	E
Mercuric bichloride	0.07	Room	E
Mercuric chloride	1–saturated	Room to 100 (212)	E
Mercuric cyanide	Saturated	...	E
Mercurous nitrate	...	...	E
Nickel chloride	5–20	Room to 100 (212)	E
Nickel nitrate	10	Room	E
Nickel nitrate plus 6% H2O	50	Room	E
Nickel sulfate	10	Room	E
Phosphoric anhydride	Dry	Room	E
Phosphorus trichloride	...	...	...
	Saturated	Room	E
Phthalic anhydride	...	...	E
Potassium bichromatic (neutral)	...	Room	E
Potassium bromide	5–saturated	Room	E
Potassium carbonate	1	Room	E
Potassium chlorate	...	...	E
Potassium chloride	1–36	Room to boiling	E
	Saturated	Room	E
Potassium cyanide	...	...	E
Potassium dichromate (neutral)	...	...	E
Potassium ferricyanide	5–saturated	Room	E
Potassium ferricyanide plus 5% NaCl	0.5	Room	E
Potassium ferrocyanide	5	Room	E
Potassium hydrate	...	...	E
Potassium hydroxide	5	Room	E
	27–50	Boiling	NR
Potassium iodide	Saturated	Room	E
Potassium iodide—iodine	...	...	E
Potassium iodide plus 0.1% Na2CO3	Saturated	Room	E
Potassium nitrate	5	Room	E
Potassium oxalate	...	...	E
Potassium permanganate (neutral)	...	...	E
Potassium pyrosulfate	...	Molten	NR
Potassium sulfate	1–5	Room to hot	E
	10	Room	E
Potassium sulfide	...	...	E
Potassium thiosulfate	1	Room	E
Silver bromide	...	...	E

(a) E, no attack; V, variable, depending on temperature and concentration; NR, not resistant

(Continued)

Table 14 (continued)

Salt	Concentration, %	Temperature, °C (°F)	Code(a)	Salt	Concentration, %	Temperature, °C (°F)	Code(a)
Silver chloride	...	...	E	Sodium hyposulfite	Dilute	Room	E
Silver cyanide	...	...	E	Sodium lactate	...	...	E
Silver nitrate	50	Room	E	Sodium nitrate	All	Room	E
Sodium acetate (moist)	5	Room	E	Sodium nitrite	...	...	E
Sodium acetate	Saturated	Room	E		Saturated	Room	E
Sodium aluminate	25	Room to boiling	E	Sodium peroxide	...	100 (212)	V
Sodium benzoate	...	...	E	Sodium phosphate	5–saturated	Room	E
Sodium bicarbonate	All	Room to 66 (150)	E	Sodium pyrosulfate	...	Molten	NR
Sodium bichromate (neutral)	...	...	E	Sodium silicate	...	...	E
Sodium bisulfate	Solution	...	E		25	Room to boiling	E
	10–25	Room to boiling	E	Sodium sulfate (still)	5	Room	E
	Saturated	Room	E		10–20	Room to boiling	E
	...	Molten	NR	Sodium sulfate	Saturated	Room	E
Sodium borate	...	...	E	Sodium sulfide	10	Room to boiling	E
Sodium bromide	5	Room	E		Saturated	Room	E
Sodium carbonate	10–25	Room to boiling	E	Sodium sulfite	5	Room	E
	All	Room	E		10–saturated	Room to boiling	E
Sodium chlorate	10–25	Room	E	Sodium thiosulfate	10–25	Room to boiling	E
	Saturated	Room	E	Sodium thiosulfate—acetic acid	20	Room	E
Sodium chloride (still)	5	Room to 40 (105)	E	Stannic chloride	5	Room to 100 (212)	E
Sodium chloride (aerated)	20	Room	E		24	Room to boiling	E
Sodium chloride	29	Room to boiling	E		100	Molten	E
	Saturated	Room to boiling	E	Stannous chloride	5–saturated	Room	E
Sodium citrate	Saturated	Room	E	Sulfur chloride	Dry	...	E
Sodium cyanide	Saturated	Room	E	Sulfuryl chloride	...	...	E
Sodium dichromate	Saturated	Room	E	Thionyl chloride	...	...	E
Sodium ferricyanide	...	...	E	Tin salts	...	...	E
Sodium ferrocyanide	...	...	E	Titanium tetrachloride	...	...	E
Sodium fluoride	5–saturated	Room	NR	Zinc chloride (still)	5	Room to boiling	E
Sodium hydrosulfite	...	...	E	Zinc chloride	10	Room to boiling	E
Sodium hydroxide	10–saturated	Room	NR		20	Room to 100 (212)	E
	10	Boiling	NR		Saturated	Room	E
	25	Room to boiling	NR	Zinc sulfate	5–saturated	Room	E
	40	80 (175)	NR		25	Room to boiling	E
Sodium hypochlorite	6	Room	E				

(a) E, no attack; V, variable, depending on temperature and concentration; NR, not resistant

Table 15 Effects of Miscellaneous Corrosive Reagents on Tantalum

Medium	Concentration, %	Temperature, °C (°F)	Code(a)	Medium	Concentration, %	Temperature, °C (°F)	Code(a)
Acetone	...	Boiling	E	Chloroform	...	Room	E
Air	...	Below 300 (570)	E	Chromium plating bath	...	Room	E
	...	Above 300 (570)	NR	Cider	...	Room	E
Amines	...	...	E		...	Boiling	E
Aniline	Concentrated	Room	E	Coffee	...	...	E
				Copal varnish	...	...	E
Baking oven gases	...	...	E	Cream of tartar	...	...	E
Beer	...	...	E	Creosote (coal tar)	...	Hot	E
Benzene	...	Room	E	Crude oil	...	...	E
Benzol	...	Hot	E				
Bleaching powder	Solution	Hot	V	Developing solutions	...	Room	E
Blood (meat juices)	...	Cold	E	Distillery wort	...	...	E
Body fluids	...	...	E	Dyewood, liquor	...	Room	E
Borax	...	Fused	NR				
Bromine	Dry	Below 300 (570)	E	Ether	...	Room	E
	Wet	...	E	Ethyl acetate	...	...	E
Bromine water	...	Room	E	Ethyl chloride	5	Room	E
Buttermilk	...	Room	E	Ethyl sulfate	...	...	E
				Ethylene chloride	...	Room	E
Carbon bisulfide	...	Room	E	Ethylene dibromide	...	...	E
Carbon tetrachloride	99	Boiling	E	Ethylene dichloride	100	Boiling	E
	Liquid	Boiling	E				
	Pure	Room	E	Flue gases	...	...	E
	5–10 aqueous solution	Room	E	Fluorine	...	Room	NR
Chlorinated brine	...	...	E	Food pastes	...	...	E
Chlorinated hydrocarbons	...	...	E	Formaldehyde	...	Room	E
Chlorinated water	Saturated	Room	E	Formaldehyde plus			
Chlorine dioxide	...	180 (355)	E	2.5% H_2SO_4	50	158 (315)	E
Chlorine gas	Dry	Up to 250 (480)	E	Fuel oil	...	Hot	E
	Moist (1.5% H_2O)	Up to 375 (705)	E	Fuel oil (containing H_2SO_4)	...	Hot	E
	Moist (30% H_2O)	Up to 400 (750)	E	Fruit juices	...	Room	E
				Furfural	...	...	E

(a) E, no attack; V, variable, depending on temperature and concentration; NR, not resistant

(Continued)

Table 15 (continued)

Medium	Concentration, %	Temperature, °C (°F)	Code(a)	Medium	Concentration, %	Temperature, °C (°F)	Code(a)
Gasoline	...	...	E	Petroleum ether	...	...	E
Glauber's salt	Solution	Hot	E	Phenol	...	...	E
Glue, dry	...	Room	E	Phenolic resins	...	...	E
Glue, solution acid	...	Hot	E	Pine tar oil	...	...	E
Glycerine	...	Room	E	Potash	Solution	Hot	NR
Gypsum	...	...	E				
				Quinine bisulfate (dry)	...	...	E
Hydrocarbons	...	...	E	Quinine sulfate (dry)	...	...	E
Hydrogen	...	Up to 300 (570)	E				
				Rosin	...	Molten	E
Ink	...	...	E				
Iodine	...	Up to 300 (570)	E	Sal ammoniac	20	Boiling	E
Idoform	...	...	E	Salt	Saturated	Room	E
Kerosene	...	Room	E	Salt brine	Saturated	Hot	E
Ketchup	...	Room	E	Salt water	...	...	E
				Sewage	...	...	E
Lard	...	Room	E	Soaps	...	Room	E
Linseed oil	...	...	E	Soy bean oil	...	...	E
Lye (caustic)	34	110 (230)	NR	Starch	Solution	...	E
Lysol	...	100 (212)	E	Steam	...	...	E
				Sugar juice	...	...	E
Mayonnaise	...	Hot and cold	E	Sulfur, dry	...	Molten	E
Meats (unsalted)	...	Room	E	Sulfur, wet	...	...	E
Mash	...	Hot	E	Sulfur dioxide	Dry	Room	E
Methylene chloride	40	Room to boiling	E		Moist	Room	E
Milk	Fresh or sour	Hot or cold	E	Sulfur trioxide	Dry	Room	NR
Mine water, acid	...	...	E				
Molasses	...	...	E	Tomato juice	...	Room	E
Mustard	...	Room	E	Turpentine oil	...	...	E
				Tung oil	...	...	E
Naphtha	...	...	E				
Nitre cake	...	Fused	NR	Varnish	...	...	E
Nitric oxides	...	...	E	Vegetable juices	...	...	E
Nitrosyl chloride	...	...	E	Vegetable oil	...	Hot and cold	E
Nitrous oxide	Dry	...	E	Vinegar	Still	Room	E
					Agitated	Room	E
Oils, crude	...	Hot and cold	E		Aerated	Room	E
Oils, mineral, vegetable	...	Hot and cold	E		Fumes	...	E
Organic chlorides	...	...	E	Vinegar and salt	...	...	E
Oxygen	...	Up to 300 (570)	E				
				Water	...	...	E
Paraffin	...	Molten	E		...	Hot	E
Paraffin	...	Molten	E		Salt	...	E
Paregoric compound	...	...	E		Sea	...	E
				Whiskey	...	...	E

Niobium and Niobium Alloys

Niobium and niobium alloys are used principally in several corrosion-resistant applications. These involve rocket and jet engines, nuclear reactors, sodium vapor highway lighting equipment, and chemical-processing equipment. Niobium has many of the same properties as tantalum, its "sister" metal. One common property is the interaction with the reactive elements hydrogen, oxygen, nitrogen, and carbon at temperatures above 300 °C (570 °F). These reactions cause severe embrittlement. Consequently, at elevated temperatures, the metal must be protectively coated or used in vacuum or inert atmospheres.

Niobium resists a wide variety of corrosive environments, including concentrated mineral acids, organic acids, liquid metals (particularly sodium and lithium), metal vapors, and molten salts. Table 16 gives the corrosion rates of niobium in aqueous media.

Like other reactive metals, niobium derives its corrosion resistance from a readily formed, adherent, passive oxide film. Its corrosion properties are similar to those of tantalum, but niobium is less resistant in aggressive mediums such as hot, concentrated mineral acids.

Niobium is susceptible to hydrogen embrittlement if cathodically polarized by either galvanic coupling or by impressed potential. In addition to being very stable, the anodic niobium oxide film has a high dielectric constant and a high breakdown potential.

Acid Solutions

Niobium is resistant to most organic acids and mineral acids, except hydrofluoric acid (HF), at all concentrations and temperatures below 100 °C (212 °F). These acids include the halogen acids hydrochloric (HCl), hydroiodic (HI), and hydrobromic (HBr); nitric acid (HNO_3); sulfuric acid (H_2SO_4); and phosphoric acid (H_3PO_4). Niobium is especially resistant under oxidizing conditions. At room temperature, niobium is resistant to H_2SO_4 at all concentrations up to 95%. The corrosion rate increases rapidly with temperature and concentration.

Niobium is completely resistant to dilute sulfurous acid (H_2SO_3) at 100 °C (212 °F). In concentrated acid at the same temperature, it has a corrosion rate of 0.25 mm/yr (10 mils/yr). Niobium is completely resistant to HNO_3, having a corrosion rate of 0.025 mm/yr (1 mil/yr) in 70% HNO_3 at 250 °C (480 °F).

Niobium is inert in mixtures of HNO_3 and HCl. It has a corrosion rate of less than 0.025 mm/yr (1 mil/yr) in aqua regia at 55 °C (130 °F). In boiling 40 and 50% H_3PO_4 with small amounts of F- impurity (5 ppm), niobium has a corrosion rate of 0.25 mm/yr (10 mils/yr). In mixtures of HNO_3 10 and H_2SO_4, niobium can dissolve readily.

Alkaline Solutions

In ambient aqueous alkaline solutions, niobium has corrosion rates of less than 0.025 mm/yr (1 mil/yr). At higher temperatures, even though the corrosion rate does not seem excessive, niobium is embrittled even at low concentrations (5%) of sodium hydroxide (NaOH) and potassium hydroxide (KOH). Like tantalum, niobium is embrittled in salts that hydrolyze to form alkaline solutions. These salts include sodium and potassium carbonates and phosphates.

Salt Solutions

Niobium has excellent corrosion resistance to salt solutions, except those that hydrolyze to form alkalis. It is resistant to chloride solutions even in the presence of oxidizing agents. It does not corrode in 10% ferric chloride ($FeCl_3$) at room temperature, and it is resistant to attack in seawater.

Gases

Niobium is easily oxidized. It will oxidize in air above 200 °C (390 °F). The reaction, however, does not become rapid until above red heat (about 500 °C, or 930 °F). At 980 °C (1795 °F), the oxidation rate is 430 mm/yr (17 in./yr). In pure oxygen, the attack is catastrophic at 390 °C (735 °F). Oxygen diffuses freely through the metal; this causes embrittlement.

Niobium reacts with nitrogen above 350 °C (660 °F), with water vapor above 300 °C (570 °F), with chlorine above 200 °C (390 °F), and with carbon dioxide, carbon monoxide, and hydrogen above 250 °C (480 °F).

At a temperature of 100 °C (212 °F), niobium is inert in most common gases, for example, bromine, chlorine, nitrogen, hydrogen, oxygen, carbon dioxide, argon monoxide, and sulfur dioxide (wet or dry).

Table 16   Corrosion of Niobium in Aqueous Media

Source: Teledyne Wah Chang Albany, Albany, OR, 1986

Medium	Concentration, %	Temperature, °C (°F)	Corrosion rate mm/yr	mils/yr
Mineral acids				
Hydrochloric acid	1	Boiling	nil	
Hydrochloric acid (aerated)	15	Room-60 (140)	nil	
Hydrochloric acid (aerated)	15	100 (212)	0.025	1.0
Hydrochloric acid (aerated)	30	35 (95)	0.025	1.0
Hydrochloric acid (aerated)	30	60 (140)	0.05	2.0
Hydrochloric acid (aerated)	30	100 (212)	0.125	5.0
Hydrochloric acid	37	Room	0.025	1.0
Hydrochloric acid	37	60 (140)	0.25	10
Hydrochloric acid	37% with Cl_2	60 (140)	0.5	20
Hydrochloric acid	10% with 0.1% $FeCl_3$	Boiling	0.025	1.0
Hydrochloric acid	10% with 0.6% $FeCl_3$	Boiling	0.125	5.0
Hydrochloric acid	10% with 35% $FeCl_2$ and 2% $FeCl_3$	Boiling	0.05	2.0
Nitric acid	65	Room	nil	
Nitric acid	70	250 (480)	0.025	1.0
Phosphoric acid	60	Boiling	0.5	20
Phosphoric acid	85	Room	0.0025	0.1
Phosphoric acid	85	88 (190)	0.05	2.0
Phosphoric acid	85	100 (212)	0.125	5.0
Phosphoric acid	85	Boiling	3.75	150
Phosphoric acid	85% with 4% HNO_3	88 (190)	0.025	1.0
Phosphoric acid	40–50% with 5 ppm F-	Boiling	0.25	10
Sulfuric acid	5–40	Room	nil	
Sulfuric acid	98	Room	Embrittlement	
Sulfuric acid	10	Boiling	0.125	5.0
Sulfuric acid	25	Boiling	0.25	10
Sulfuric acid	40	Boiling	0.5	20
Sulfuric acid	40% with 2% $FeCl_3$	Boiling	0.25	10

(Continued)

Table 16 (continued)

Medium	Concentration, %	Temperature, °C (°F)	Corrosion rate mm/yr	mils/yr
Sulfuric acid	60	Boiling	1.25	50
Sulfuric acid	60% with 0.1–1% $FeCl_3$	Boiling	0.5	20
Sulfuric acid	20% with 7% HCl and 100 ppm F^-	Boiling	0.25	10
Sulfuric acid	50% with 20% HNO_3	50–80 (120–175)	nil	
Sulfuric acid	50% with 20% HNO_3	Boiling	0.25	10
Sulfuric acid	72% + 3% CrO_3	100 (212)	0.025	1.0
Sulfuric acid	72% + 3% CrO_3	125 (255)	0.125	5.0
Sulfuric acid	72% + 3% CrO_3	Boiling	3.75	150
Organic acids				
Acetic acid	5–99.7	Boiling	nil	
Citric acid	10	Boiling	0.025	1.0
Formaldehyde	37	Boiling	0.0025	0.1
Formic acid	10	Boiling	nil	
Lactic acid	10–85	Boiling	0.025	1.0
Oxalic acid	10	Boiling	1.25	50
Tartaric acid	20	Room-boiling	nil	
Trichloroacetic acid	50	Boiling	nil	
Trichloroethylene	99	Boiling	nil	
Alkalies				
NaOH	1–40	Room	0.125	5.0
NaOH	1–10	98 (208)	Embrittlement	
KOH	5–40	Room	Embrittlement	
KOH	1–5	98 (208)	Embrittlement	
NH_4OH	...	Room	nil	
Salts				
$AlCl_3$	25	Boiling	0.005	0.2
$Al_2(SO_4)_3$	25	Boiling	nil	
$AlK(SO_4)_2$	10	Boiling	nil	
$CaCl_2$	70	Boiling	nil	
$Cu(NO_3)_2$	40	Boiling	nil	
$FeCl_3$	10	Room-boiling	nil	
$HgCl_2$	Saturated	Boiling	0.0025	0.1
K_2CO_3	1–10	Room	0.025	1.0
K_2CO_3	10–20	98 (208)	Embrittlement	
K_3PO_4	10	Room	0.025	1.0
$MgCl_2$	47	Boiling	0.025	1.0
NaCl	Saturated; pH = 1	Boiling	0.025	1.0
Na_2CO_3	10	Room	0.025	1.0
Na_2CO_3	10	Boiling	0.5	20
Na_2HSO_4	40	Boiling	0.125	5.0
NaOCl	6	50 (120)	1.25	50
Na_3PO_4	5–10	Room	0.025	1.0
Na_3PO_4	2.5	98 (208)	Embrittlement	
NH_2SO_3H	10	Boiling	0.025	1.0
$NiCl_3$	30	Boiling	nil	
$ZnCl_2$	40–70	Boiling	nil	
Miscellaneous				
Bromine	Liquid	20 (70)	nil	
Bromine	Vapor	20 (70)	0.025	1.0
Chromium plating solution	25% CrO_3, 12% H_2SO_4, H_2O	92 (198)	0.125	5.0
Chromium plating solution	17% CrO_3, 2% Na_5SiF_6, trace H_2SO_4, H_2O	92 (198)	0.125	5.0
H_2O_2	30	Room	0.025	1.0
H_2O_2	30	Boiling	0.5	20

Noble Metals and Alloys

The technical definition of a noble metal is a metal whose potential is highly positive relative to the hydrogen electrode. However, a more practical and simpler description is a metal having a marked resistance to chemical reaction, particularly to oxidation and to attack by organic acids. Because of their high cost, the terms "noble metals" and "precious metals" are more or less synonymous in general usage.

At least eight metals are considered to be noble metals—gold, silver, platinum, palladium, rhodium, ruthenium, osmium, and iridium. Of these, only the first four are considered to be commercially important. For the most part, they offer resistance that is unmatched in base metals and their alloys.

In general, more data are available for the more abundant, more easily fabricated elements. Silver and platinum have been evaluated in more environments than the other noble metals. Conversely, very little data are available for the intractable elements, osmium and ruthenium. Tables 17 to 23 provide corrosion rates for silver, gold, and platinum in various environments.

Silver

Atmospheric Corrosion. Silver resists attack by dry and moist air in ordinary temperatures. At levels higher than room temperature, f up to 50% at the boiling point. However, hot mixtures of HNO_3O and H_2SO_4 will rapidly attack gold, as well as aqua regia and hydrogen cyanide (with oxygen present). Mixtures of HCl, HBr, and HI with HNO_3 are extremely corrosive to gold. Mixtures of HF and HNO_3 are not corrosive gold. Gold resists most other acids.

Chemicals. Because of its softness and lack of resistance to the use of gold in chemical applications is somewhat

Table 17 Corrosion of Silver in Acids

Acid	Temperature, °C (°F)	Corrosion rate mm/yr	Corrosion rate mils/yr
Acetic, all concentrations	Boiling	<0.05	2
Acetylsalicylic, all concentrations	Boiling	<0.05	2
Aqua regia	Room	Potential dissolution(a)	
Arsenic	Room	Dissolution	
Ascorbic, all concentrations	Room	<0.05	2
Benzoic, all concentrations	130 (265)	<0.05	2
Boric, salt	Boiling	<0.05	2
Butyric	Boiling	<0.05	2
Carbonic, all concentrations	Room	<0.05	2
Chloric, all concentrations	Room	Attacked	
Chlorotoluene-sulfonic	Room	<0.05	2
Chromic, all concentrations	100 (212)	<0.05	2
Citric, to 30% concentration	Boiling	<0.05	2
Crotonic	Boiling	<0.05	2
Fatty acids	400 (750)	<0.05	2
Fluorosilicic	65 (150)	<0.05	2
Formic, pure	Boiling	<0.05	2
Gluconic, all concentrations	Boiling	<0.05	2
Glycerophosphoric, to 50%	Boiling	<0.05	2
Hydrogen selenide	Room	Attacked	
Hydrogen sulfide	Room	Attacked	
Hydrobromic, below 14%	Room	<0.05	2
Hydrochloric		—See Table 2—	
Hydrofluoric, below 50%	Boiling	<0.05	2
Hydroiodic, dilute	Room	<0.25	10
Hypochlorous	Room	Attacked	
Isovaleric, all concentrations	Boiling	<0.05	2
Lactic	Boiling	<0.05	2
Laevulinic, all concentrations	Boiling	<0.05	2
Monochloroacetic, all concentrations	Boiling	<0.05	2
Nitric	Room	Rapid dissolution	
Nitrous	Room	Dissolution	
Oxalic	Boiling	<0.05	2
Phenylacetic, all concentrations	Boiling	<0.05	2
Phosphoric, %			
5	102 (215)	0.003	0.12
45	60 (14)	nil	
45	110 (230)	0.007	0.28
67	60 (140)	0.004	0.16
67	125 (255)	0.02	0.8
85	60 (140)	0.002	0.08
85	140 (285)	0.048	1.9
85	160 (320)	0.306	12
Phthalic, pure	Boiling	<0.05	2
Picric, pure	125 (255)	<0.05	2
Propionic	Boiling	<0.05	2
Pyridine-carboxylic, pure	Room	<0.05	2
Salicylic, all concentrations	Boiling	<0.05	2
Stearic, pure	160 (320)	<0.05	2
Sulfuric, %			
10	Boiling	0.003	0.12
50	Boiling	0.034	1.3
60	Boiling	0.88	34.6
95	Room	0.14	5.5
Sulfurous, all concentrations	90 (195)	<0.05	2
Tartaric, all concentrations(b)	100 (212)	<0.05	2

(a) Attack will occur whenever silver chloride film is ruptured. (b) Oxygen increases attack in dilute tartaric acid at room temperature.

Table 18 Corrosion of Silver in Salts and Other Environments

Environment	Temperature, °C (°F)	Corrosion rate mm/yr	Corrosion rate mils/yr
Alum, all concentrations	Boiling	<0.05	2
Aluminum chloride, all concentrations(a)	Boiling	<0.05	2
Aluminum fluoride, all concentrations	Boiling	<0.05	2
Aluminum sulfate, all concentrations	Boiling	<0.05	2
Ammonium chloride, all concentrations	Boiling	<0.05	2
Ammonium hydroxide(b)	Room	<0.05	2
Ammonium nitrate, <20%	Room	<0.05	2
Ammonium phosphate, all concentrations	Boiling	<0.05	2
Ammonium sulfate, all concentrations	Boiling	<0.05	2
Ammonium thiocyanate, pure	100 (212)	<0.05	2
Antimony pentachloride, pure	90 (195)	<0.05	2
Barium chloride, all concentrations	Boiling	<0.05	2
Barium chloride, all concentrations	Room	<0.05	2
Barium peroxide, all concentrations	Room	Attacked	
Bismuth oxide, all concentrations	Room	Slight attack	
Calcium bisulfite, pure	Boiling	<0.05	2
Calcium carbonate, all concentrations	Room	Slight attack	
Calcium chloride, all concentrations	100 (212)	<0.05	2
Calcium hydroxide, all concentrations	100 (212)	<0.05	2
Calcium sulfate, all concentrations	100 (212)	<0.05	2
Calcium sulfide, all concentrations	Room	Blackens	
Cesium hydroxide, all concentrations	500 (930)	<0.05	2
Cupric chloride, all concentrations	100 (212)	Attacked	
Cupric nitrate, all concentrations	Room	<0.05	2
Cupric sulfate, all concentrations	Room-boiling	<0.05	2
Cupric sulfate in sodium chloride	100 (212)	Attacked	
Cuprous chloride, all concentrations	100 (212)	Attacked	
Cuprous nitrate, all concentrations	100 (212)	Attacked	
Cuprous sulfate, all concentrations	100 (212)	Attacked	
Dyes, acid chromium	Boiling	<0.05	2
Ferric alum, all concentrations	100 (212)	Attacked	
Ferric chloride, <5%	Room	<0.05	2
Ferrous sulfate, all concentrations(c)	Room	<0.05	2
Fluorosilicate, all concentrations	100 (212)	<0.05	2
Hydrogen peroxide, all concentrations	Room	Peroxide decomposed	
Hydrogen sulfide, all concentrations	Room	Blackened	
Lithium chloride, all concentrations	Boiling	<0.05	2
Magnesium chloride, all concentrations	120 (250)	<0.05	2
Magnesium chloride, melt	710 (1310)	Attacked	
Mercuric chloride, all concentrations	Room	Not recommended	
Nitrosyl chloride, dry	Room	<0.05	2
Phosphorus chlorides, pure	Boiling	<0.05	2
Potassium bisulfate, all concentrations	Boiling	<0.05	2
Potassium bromide, all concentrations	200–400 (390–750)	<0.05	2
Potassium carbonate, all concentrations	Boiling	<0.05	2
Potassium chlorate, all concentrations	Boiling	<0.05	2
Potassium cyanide, concentrated, in air	Room	Attacked	
Potassium dichromate, all concentrations	Boiling	<0.05	2
Potassium ferrocyanide, all concentrations	Room	Attacked	
Potassium hydroxide, all concentrations(b)	300 (570)	<0.05	2
Potassium hydroxide, melt(b)	350 (680)	<0.05	2
Potassium nitrate, all concentrations	Boiling	<0.05	2
Potassium nitrate, melt	335 (635)	Attacked	
Potassium perborate, all concentrations(d)	50 (120)	<0.05	2
Potassium permanganate, all concentrations	Boiling	Attacked	
Potassium peroxide, melt	100 (212) above melting point	Attacked	
Potassium persulfate, all concentrations	Room	Attacked	
Potassium sulfate, all concentrations	Boiling	<0.05	2
Sodium bisulfate, melt	400 (750)	Attacked	
Sodium bisulfites, all concentrations	100 (212)	<0.05	2
Sodium carbonate	Boiling	<0.05	2
Sodium chloride, all concentrations	Boiling	<0.05	2
Sodium chromate, all concentrations	Boiling	<0.05	2
Sodium cyanide, all concentrations	Room	Attacked	
Sodium fluorosilicate, pure	100 (212)	<0.05	2
Sodium hydroxide, <95%	Boiling	<0.05	2
Sodium hydroxide, melt(b)(e)	500 (930)	<0.05	2
Sodium hypochlorite, all concentrations	Room	<0.05	2
Sodium hypochlorite plus sodium chloride, saturated solution	Room	<0.05	2
Sodium nitrate, all concentrations	Boiling	<0.05	2
Sodium perborate, all concentrations	50 (120)	<0.05	2
Sodium perchlorate, all concentrations	Boiling	<0.05	2
Sodium perchlorate, melt	480 (900)	Attacked	
Sodium peroxide, melt	400 (750)	Attacked	
Sodium phosphates, all concentrations	Boiling	<0.05	2
Sodium silicates, all concentrations	Boiling	<0.05	2
Sodium sulfate, all concentrations	Boiling	<0.05	2
Sodium sulfide, all concentrations	Room	Slight attack	
Sodium thiosulfate, all concentrations	Room	<0.05	2
Stannic ammonium chloride, all concentrations	Boiling	<0.05	2
Stannic chloride, all concentrations	Boiling	<0.05	2
Sulfuryl chloride, dry and wet	300 (570)	<0.05	2
Thionyl chloride, dry or wet	Boiling	<0.05	2
Uranyl nitrate, all concentrations	Boiling	<0.05	2
Zinc chloride, all concentrations	Boiling	<0.05	2

(a) Provided oxidizing agents are not present. (b) Air must be excluded. (c) Attacked upon heating. (d) Causes deterioration of potassium perborate. (e) Mass transfer possible above 600 °C (1110 °F)

limited. Gold is resistant to nonoxidizing H_3PO_4 and therefore, it is used for lining autoclaves handling phosphate mixtures up to 500 °C (939 °F). In the production of zirconium by the iodide process, gold closure gaskets are used to handle dry iodine vapors at 500 °C (939 °F). The use of gold-lined equipment to perform hydroclorinations and hydrofluorinations of organic compounds in the chemical industry is well established.

Chemical Corrosion. Silver has been used for years in the production of a number of chemical and food products where it has a high degree of corrosion resistance, or where very high purity of product is required.

Silver shows a higher degree of resistance to high-temperature caustic alkalis than most other metals. It is used for evaporating pans in the concentration of sodium hydroxide to the anhydrous melt in the production of chemically pure grades of caustic soda.

Silver has a high degree of resistance to hot, concentrated organic acids such as acetic, formic, citric, lactic, fumaric, phthalic, and benzoic acids, fatty acids, and phenol.

The metal is also used extensively in cases where halogens or halogen acids are involved. One of the most important of these is in handling wet chlorine gas in water-purification installations. It is also used in service with aqueous hydrochloric acid, particularly when the acid is associated with organic hydrocarbon liquids in pressure vessels and process equipment. Resistance of silver to dilute hydrofluoric acid conditions usually is best where there is only a slight possibility for removal of the protective chloride films.

Silver shows a high degree of resistance to boiling hydrofluoric acid solutions of all concentrations when these solutions do not contain any sulfur compounds or sulfuric acid. Silver-tubed condensers are used for condensing 70% hydrofluoric acid from the hot HF vapors formed in the hydrofluorination of uranium compounds.

Table 19 Corrosion of Silver in Organic Compounds

Environment	Temperature, °C (°F)	Corrosion rate mm/yr	mils/yr	Environment	Temperature, °C (°F)	Corrosion rate mm/yr	mils/yr
Acetaldehyde, pure	200–400 (390–750)	<0.05	2	Guinolines, pure	Boiling	<0.05	2
Acetic anhydride, all concentrations	Boiling	<0.05	2	Guinone, inorganic solvent and pure	100 (212)	<0.05	2
Acetone, pure	Boiling	<0.05	2	Hexachloroethane, dry and moist	187 (369)	<0.05	2
Acetylene dichloride, wet and acid	Boiling	<0.05	2	Hexamethylene tetramine, all concentrations(b)	Room	<0.05	2
Ethyl alcohol, all concentrations	Boiling	<0.05	2	Hydrazine, pure	Room	Not recommended	
Amyl acetate, pure	Boiling	<0.05	2	Hydroguinone, pure	Boiling	<0.05	2
Amyl alcohol, pure	Boiling	<0.05	2	Isoborneol acetate, pure	Boiling	<0.05	2
Aniline, pure	Boiling	<0.05	2	Isobutyl chloride, dry and wet	Boiling	<0.05	2
Benzaldehyde, pure and aqueous	Boiling	<0.05	2	Limonene, pure	Boiling	<0.05	2
Benzene, pure	Boiling	<0.05	2	Methyl alcohol, pure	Boiling	<0.05	2
Benzotrifluoride, pure	Boiling	<0.05	2	Methylamines, aqueous	Room	Attacked	
Benzyl chloride, pure	180 (355)	<0.05	2	Methyl chloride, dry and wet	300 (570)	<0.05	2
-bromoisovaleryl bromide, pure	100 (212)	<0.05	2	Methylene chloride, dry and wet	Boiling	<0.05	2
-bromoisovaleryl urea, pure	Melting point	<0.05	2	Methylglycol, pure	Boiling	<0.05	2
Butyl acetate, pure	Boiling	<0.05	2	Milk, pure(c)	Boiling	<0.05	2
Butyl alcohol, pure	Boiling	<0.05	2	Nitrobenzene, pure	Boiling	<0.05	2
Carbon tetrachloride, dry and wet	Boiling	<0.05	2	Nitrocellulose, in water or alcohol	Room	<0.05	2
Chlorobenzene, pure	Boiling	<0.05	2	Nitrophenols, pure	Boiling	<0.05	2
Chlorocresols, all concentrations	Boiling	<0.05	2	Nitrotoluenes, pure	Boiling	<0.05	2
Chloroform, dry or wet	Boiling	<0.05	2	Pentachloroethane, wet, dry, and acid	Boiling	<0.05	2
Chlorohydrins, pure	Boiling	<0.05	2	Phenol, all concentrations	Boiling	<0.05	2
Chloronitrobenzenes, pure	Boiling	<0.05	2	Phthalic anhydride, pure	Boiling	<0.05	2
Chlorotoluene, pure	Boiling	<0.05	2	Potassium acetate, all concentrations	Boiling	<0.05	2
Coniferyl alcohol, all concentrations	80 (175)	<0.05	2	Quinine sulfate, all concentrations	70 (160)	<0.05	2
Copals, pure and wet	400 (750)	<0.05	2	Sodium acetate, all concentrations	Boiling	<0.05	2
Copper acetate, neutral solutions	100 (212)	<0.05	2	Sodium acetate, melt	400 (750)	<0.05	2
Copper acetate, ammoniacal solutions	Room	Attacked		Sodium bisulfate, all concentrations	Boiling	<0.05	2
Coumarin, pure	100 (212)	<0.05	2	Sodium formate, all concentrations	Boiling	<0.05	2
Cresols, pure	Boiling	<0.05	2	Sodium isovalerate, all concentrations	Boiling	<0.05	2
Dextrose, all concentrations	Boiling	<0.05	2	Sodium isovalerate, melt with sodium hydroxide	290 (555)	<0.05	2
Dialkyl sulfates, pure	Boiling	<0.05	2	Sodium methylate, all concentrations in alcohol or ether	100 (212)	<0.05	2
Dibutyl phthalate, pure	Boiling	<0.05	2	Sodium pentachlorophenolate, all concentrations	Boiling	<0.05	2
Dimethylaniline, pure	Boiling	<0.05	2	Sodium phenolate, all concentrations	Boiling	<0.05	2
Diphenyl, pure	400 (750)	<0.05	2	Sodium salicylate, all concentrations	Boiling	<0.05	2
Essential oils, pure(a)	Boiling	<0.05	2	Sodium tartrates, all concentrations	Boiling	<0.05	2
Ether, pure	Boiling	<0.05	2	Sorbital, all concentrations	Boiling	<0.05	2
Ethyl acetate, pure	Boiling	<0.05	2	Sorbose, all concentrations	Boiling	<0.05	2
Ethyl benzene, pure	136 (277)	<0.05	2	Toluene, pure	Boiling	<0.05	2
Ethylene dibromide, wet and acid products	Boiling	<0.05	2	Toluenesulfonyl chlorides, pure	Boiling	<0.05	2
Ethylene dichloride, wet and acid products	Boiling	<0.05	2	Triethanolamine, mixture with diethylene glycol	Room	<0.05	2
Fats, pure	300 (570)	<0.05	2	Vinyl chloride, pure	200 (390)	<0.05	2
Fatty acids, pure	400 (750)	<0.05	2				
Formaldehyde, all concentrations	Boiling	<0.05	2				
Furfural, wet and slightly acid	Boiling	<0.05	2				
Gelatin, pure	Boiling	<0.05	2				
Glycerol, pure	Boiling	<0.05	2				
Guanidine nitrate, all concentrations	Room	Not recommended					

(a) Silver may taint the flavor of fats. (b) Solutions must be free of air and ammonia. (c) Silver may impart metallic taste

Silver resists anhydrous hydrogen fluoride gas at considerably elevated temperatures. It resists hydrogen chloride gas up to about 225 °C (435 °F), but is not resistant to chlorine gas above room temperature.

Gold

Oxidation Resistance. Pure gold owes its corrosion resistance to its inherently low chemical affinity for the other elements. Passive film protection usually does not occur. Therefore, gold is impervious to attack by virtually any atmosphere.

Acids. Gold is resistant to H_2SO_4 to 250 °C (480 °F); attack above this temperature may be primarily dependent on available oxygen. Gold is also resistant to concentrated HCl to its boiling point and also to HNO_3 concentrations of up to 50% at the boiling point. However, hot mixtures of HNO_3O and H_2SO_4 will rapidly attack gold, as well as aqua regia and hydrogen cyanide (with oxygen present). Mixtures of HCl, HBr, and HI with HNO_3 are extremely corrosive to gold. Mixtures of HF and HNO_3 are not corrosive to gold. Gold resists most other acids.

Chemicals. Because of its softness and lack of resistance to halogens, the use of gold in chemical applications is somewhat limited. Gold is resistant to nonoxidizing H_3PO_4 and phosphates; therefore, it is used for lining autoclaves handling phosphate mixtures up to 500 °C (939 °F). In the production of zirconium by the iodide process, gold closure gaskets are used to handle dry iodine vapors at 500 °C (939 °F). The use of gold-lined equipment to perform hydroclorinations and hydrofluorinations of organic compounds in the chemical industry is well established.

Platinum

Atmospheric Corrosion. The exceptional resistance of platinum is well known. It is one of the few metals unaffected

Table 20 Corrosion of Gold in Acids

Acid	Temperature, °C (°F)	Corrosion rate	
		mm/yr	mils/yr
Acetic, glacial	100 (212)	<0.05	2
Aqua regia	Room	Rapid dissolution	
Arsenic, all concentrations	Room	<0.05	2
Chlorosulfonic, all concentrations	Boiling	<0.05	2
Chlorotoluene-sulfonic, all concentrations	Boiling	<0.05	2
Citric, 20%	Boiling	<0.05	2
Citric, 30%	Boiling	<0.05	2
Crotonic, all concentrations	Boiling	<0.05	2
Fatty acids, pure	Boiling	<0.05	2
Glycerophosphoric, 1 to 50%	Boiling	<0.05	2
Hydrobromic, specific gravity 1.7	Room	<0.05	2
Hydrochloric, 36%	Room-100 (212)	<0.05	2
Hydrofluoric, 40%	Room	<0.05	2
Hydrogen sulfide, moist	Room	<0.05	2
Hydroiodic, specific gravity 1.75	Room	<0.05	2
Isovaleric, all concentrations	Boiling	<0.05	2
Lactic, all concentrations	Boiling	<0.05	2
Laevulinic, all concentrations	Boiling	<0.05	2
Nitric, %			
1–50	Boiling	<0.05	2
70	Room	>0.05	2
70	Boiling	0.15	6
Oxalic, all concentrations	Boiling	<0.05	2
Phenol-2,4-disulfonic, all concentrations	100 (212)	<0.05	2
Phthalic, pure	Boiling	<0.05	2
Picric, pure	125 (255)	<0.05	2
Propionic, all concentrations	Boiling	<0.05	2
Pyridine, all concentrations	Boiling	<0.05	2
Pyridine-carboxylic, all concentrations	150 (300)	<0.05	2
Salicylic, all concentrations	Boiling	<0.05	2
Stearic, pure	Boiling	<0.05	2
Sulfuric, all concentrations	250 (480)	<0.05	2
Sulfurous, all concentrations	100 (212)	<0.05	2
Tartaric, all concentrations	Boiling	<0.05	2

by atmospheric exposure, in virtually any atmosphere including severe industrial and saline environments.

Chemical Corrosion. Platinum is resistant to corrosion by single acids, alkalis, aqueous solutions of common salts, and organic materials. The potential pH diagram for the metal as defined by Pourbaix shows that platinum at 25 °C (75 °F) is immune to attack at all but the lowest pH levels and high redox potentials. Even at elevated temperatures, platinum is resistant to dry hydrogen chloride and sulfurous gases. Platinum is resistant to most halogen gases at room temperature, with dry and moist bromine being the exception. Platinum is also essentially inert to many molten salts, and it resists the action of fused glasses if oxidizing conditions are maintained.

Aqua regia and mixtures of HCl and oxidizing agents will attack platinum, as will free halogens and selenic acid to some degree at elevated temperatures.

Alloying Effects on Corrosion Resistance. Alloys containing up to 25% palladium have essentially the same corrosion resistance as platinum, and they are not discolored by heating in air. The corrosion resistance of the entire binary series of rhodium-platinum alloys is excellent, with corrosion resistance tending to improve with higher rhodium content.

All alloys of the gold-platinum binary system remain quite corrosion resistant. Alloys containing more than 60% gold are rapidly attacked by HNO_3 and $FeCl_3$ and are tarnished by exposure to industrial atmospheres.

Palladium

Applications. Palladium applications are limited. Alloyed with rhodium, gold, or platinum, it is used for nonoxidizing electrical contacts and thermocouples. Alloyed with platinum, it is used for contact screens in the ammonia oxidation process and for laboratory ware. In dental prosthesis, medical techniques, and also in jewelry making, palladium-base alloys are often used.

Atmospheric Corrosion. In many respects, palladium resembles platinum and gold, and many comparisons can be drawn regarding physical properties and behavior. Palladium resists attack in virtually all atmospheres including industrial and saline; this remains true even in the presence of hydrogen. In general, however, palladium is less resistant to corrosion than platinum, especially in atmospheres that are strongly oxidizing.

Chemical Corrosion. Palladium is generally resistant to corrosion by most single acids, alkalis, and aqueous solutions of many common salts. It is not attacked at room temperature by H_2SO_4, HCl, HF, acetic, or oxalic acids, although it may experience the effects of such attack at 100 °C (212 °F), or when air is present. Nitric and hot H_2SO_4 attack palladium, as do FeCl and hypochlorite solutions, chlorine, bromine, and, to a negligible extent, iodine.

Table 21 Corrosion of Gold in Salts

Salt	Temperature, °C (°F)	Corrosion rate	
		mm/yr	mils/yr
Aluminum sulfate, 10%	100 (212)	<0.05	2
Ferric chloride in HCl solutions	Room	<0.25	10
Magnesium chloride, all concentrations	Boiling	<0.05	2
Mercuric chloride, 10%	100 (212)	50.0	2000
Nitrosyl chloride, dry	Room	<0.05	2
Potassium bisulfate, all concentrations	Boiling	<0.05	2
Potassium bromide, all concentrations	Boiling	<0.05	2
Potassium carbonate, all concentrations	Boiling	<0.05	2
Potassium chlorate, all concentrations	Boiling	<0.05	2
Potassium dichromate, all concentrations	Boiling	<0.05	2
Potassium hydroxide, all concentrations	300 (570)	<0.05	2
Potassium hydroxide, melt	360 (680)	<0.05	2
Potassium iodide, with iodine	Room	Attacked	
Potassium nitrate, all concentrations	Boiling	<0.05	2
Potassium permanganate, all concentrations	Boiling	<0.05	2
Potassium peroxide, melt	380 (715)	Attacked	
Potassium sulfate, all concentrations	Boiling	<0.05	2
Sodium bisulfate, all concentrations	Boiling	<0.05	2
Sodium bisulfate, melt	400 (750)	<0.05	2
Sodium bisulfites, all concentrations	100 (212)	<0.05	2
Sodium carbonate, all concentrations	Boiling	<0.05	2
Sodium chloride, all concentrations	Boiling	<0.05	2
Sodium chromate, all concentrations	Boiling	<0.05	2
Sodium cyanide, all concentrations	Room	Attacked	
Sodium hydroxide, <90%	Boiling	<0.05	2
Sodium nitrate, all concentrations	Boiling	<0.05	2
Sodium perborate, all concentrations	50 (120)	<0.05	2
Sodium phosphates, all concentrations	Boiling	<0.05	2
Sodium silicates, all concentrations	Boiling	<0.05	2
Sodium sulfate, all concentrations	Boiling	<0.05	2
Sodium sulfide, all concentrations	Boiling	<0.05	2
Sodium sulfite, all concentrations	Boiling	<0.05	2
Stannic ammonium chloride, all concentrations	Boiling	<0.05	2
Stannic chloride, all concentrations	Boiling		
Strontium nitrate, all concentrations	Boiling	<0.05	2
Sulfur monochloride, pure	Boiling	<0.05	2
Sulfuryl chloride, dry and wet	300 (570)	<0.05	2
Thionyl chloride, dry or wet	Boiling	<0.05	2
Uranyl nitrate, all concentrations	Boiling	<0.05	2
Zinc sulfate, 10%	100 (212)	<0.05	2

Table 22 Corrosion of Platinum in Acids

Acid	Temperature, °C (°F)	Corrosion rate	
		mm/yr	mils/yr
Acetic, all concentrations	Boiling	<0.05	2
Acetylsalicylic, all concentrations	Boiling	<0.05	2
Aqua regia	Room	Rapid dissolution	
Ascorbic, all concentrations	Boiling	<0.05	2
Benzoic, all concentrations	130 (265)	<0.05	2
Benzene sulfonic, pure	Room	<0.05	2
Boric, saturated	Boiling	<0.05	2
Butyric, all concentrations	Boiling	<0.05	2
Carbonic, pure	1400 (2550)	<0.05	2
Chloric, all concentrations	Room	<0.05	2
Chlorosulfonic, all concentrations	Boiling	<0.05	2
Chlorotoluene-sulfonic, all concentrations	Boiling	<0.05	2
Citric, <20% concentrations	Boiling	<0.05	2
Citric, 30% concentrations	Boiling	<0.05	2
Crotonic, all concentrations	Boiling	<0.05	2
Fatty, pure	400 (750)	<0.05	2
Fluorosilicic (10% hydrofluoric, 5% fluorosilicic)	Boiling	<0.05	2
Formic, pure	Boiling	<0.05	2
Gluconic, all concentrations	Boiling	<0.05	2
Glycerophosphoric, 1–50% solution	Boiling	<0.05	2
Hydrobromic, fuming	Room	<0.25	10
	100 (212)	4.8	189
Hydrochloric, 36%	Room	nil	
	100 (212)	<0.25	10
Hydrofluoric, 40%	Room	nil	
Hydrogen sulfide, pure	1000 (1830)	<0.05	2
Hydroiodic, specific gravity 1.75	Room	<0.25	10
	100 (212)	13.7	539
Isovaleric, all concentrations	Boiling	<0.05	2
Lactic, all concentrations	Boiling	<0.05	2

(Continued)

Table 22 (continued)

Acid	Temperature, °C (°F)	Corrosion rate mm/yr	mils/yr
Laevolinic, all concentrations	Boiling	<0.05	2
Monochloroacetic, all concentrations	Boiling	<0.05	2
Nitric, 70%	Room	<0.25	10
Nitric, 95%	Room-100 (212)	nil	
Nitrosyl-sulfuric, pure	100 (212)	<0.05	2
Oxalic, all concentrations	Boiling	<0.05	2
Phenol-2,4-disulfonic, all concentrations	100 (212)	<0.05	2
Phenylacetic, all concentrations	Boiling	<0.05	2
Phosphoric, 100 g/L	100 (212)	nil	
Phthalic, pure	Boiling	<0.05	2
Picric, pure	125 (255)	<0.05	2
Propionic, all concentrations	Boiling	<0.05	2
Pyridine, all concentrations	Boiling	<0.05	2
Pyridine-carboxylic, all concentrations	150 (300)	<0.05	2
Salicylic, all concentrations	Boiling	<0.05	2
Stearic, pure	Boiling	<0.05	2
Sulfuric	Room-100 (212)	nil	
Sulfurous, all concentrations	100 (212)	<0.05	2
Tartaric, all concentrations	Boiling	<0.05	2

Table 23 Corrosion of Platinum in Salts

Salt	Temperature, °C (°F)	Corrosion rate mm/yr	mils/yr	Salt	Temperature, °C (°F)	Corrosion rate mm/yr	mils/yr
Alum, all concentrations	Boiling	<0.05	2	Potassium permanganate, all concentrations	Boiling	<0.05	2
Aluminum chloride, all concentrations	Boiling	<0.05	2	Potassium peroxide, all concentrations	100 (212)	<0.05	2
Aluminum fluoride, all concentrations	Boiling	<0.05	2	Potassium peroxide, melt	380 (715)	Attacked	
Aluminum sulfate, 100 g/L	Room-100 (212)	nil		Potassium persulfate, all concentrations	60 (140)	Attacked	
Aluminum sulfate, all concentrations	Boiling	<0.05	2	Potassium sulfate, all concentrations(c)	Boiling	<0.05	2
Ammonium chloride, all concentrations	Boiling	<0.05	2	Potassium sulfate, melt	Melting point	<0.05	2
Ammonium nitrate, all concentrations	Boiling	<0.05	2	Sodium bisulfate, all concentrations	Boiling	<0.05	2
Ammonium persulfate, all concentrations	60 (140)	<0.05	2	Sodium bisulfate, melt	400 (750)	<0.05	2
Ammonium phosphate, all concentrations	Boiling	<0.05	2	Sodium bisulfites, all concentrations	100 (212)	<0.05	2
Ammonium sulfate, all concentrations	Boiling	<0.05	2	Sodium carbonate, all concentrations	Boiling	<0.05	2
Ammonium thiocyanate, pure	Boiling	<0.05	2	Sodium carbonate, melt	860 (1580)	<0.05	2
Antimony pentachloride, pure	100 (212)	<0.05	2	Sodium chloride, all concentrations	Boiling	<0.05	2
Barium chloride, all concentrations	Boiling	<0.05	2	Sodium chloride, melt(d)	800 (1470)	<0.05	2
Calcium hypochlorite, all concentrations	Room	<0.05	2	Sodium chromate, all concentrations	Boiling	<0.05	2
Calcium bisulfite, pure	Boiling	<0.05	2	Sodium cyanide, all concentrations	Room	<0.05	2
Calcium chloride, all concentrations	100 (212)	<0.05	2	Sodium formaldehyde sulfoxylate, all concentrations	90 (195)	<0.05	2
Calcium sulfate, pure	To red heat	<0.05	2	Sodium formate, all concentrations	Boiling	<0.05	2
Calcium sulfide, all concentrations	100 (212)	<0.05	2	Sodium formate, melt	260 (500)	<0.05	2
Calcium tungstate, pure	800 (1470)	<0.05	2	Sodium fluorosilicate, all concentrations	100 (212)	<0.05	2
Calcium tungstate, all concentrations	Boiling	<0.05	2	Sodium hydroxide, <90% pure	Boiling	<0.05	2
Carnallite, pure	500 (930)	<0.05	2	Sodium hydroxide, melt	350 (660)	<0.05	2
Carnallite, all concentrations	Boiling	<0.05	2	Sodium hypochlorite, all concentrations	100 (212)	<0.05	2
Carnallite, saturated solution	Boiling	<0.05	2	Sodium hypochlorite + sodium chloride, saturated solution	100 (212)	<0.25	10
Cupric chloride, 100 g/L	Room	nil		Sodium nitrate, all concentrations	Boiling	<0.05	2
Cupric sulfate, 100 g/L	100 (212)	nil		Sodium perborate, all concentrations	50 (120)	<0.05	2
Ferric chloride, 100 g/L	Room	<0.25	10	Sodium percarbonate, all concentrations	50 (120)	<0.05	2
	100 (212)	16.7	657	Sodium perchlorate, all concentrations	Boiling	<0.05	2
Ferrous sulfate, all concentrations	Room	<0.05	2	Sodium perchlorate, melt	480 (900)	Attacked	
Fluorosilicate, all concentrations	100 (212)	<0.05	2	Sodium peroxide, all concentrations	Boiling	<0.05	2
Lithium chloride, all concentrations	Boiling	<0.05	2	Sodium peroxide, melt	400 (750)	<0.05	2
Magnesium chloride, all concentrations	Boiling	<0.05	2	Sodium phosphates, all concentrations	Boiling	<0.05	2
Magnesium sulfate, all concentrations	100 (212)	<0.05	2	Sodium silicates, all concentrations	Boiling	<0.05	2
Mercury chloride, all concentrations	Boiling	<0.05	2	Sodium sulfate, all concentrations	Boiling	<0.05	2
Nitrosyl chloride, dry	Room	<0.05	2	Sodium sulfide, all concentrations	Boiling	<0.05	2
Phosphorus chlorides, pure	Boiling	<0.05	2	Sodium sulfide, melt	700 (1290)	<0.05	2
Potassium bisulfate, all concentrations	Boiling	<0.05	2	Sodium sulfite, all concentrations	Boiling	<0.05	2
Potassium bisulfate, melt	200–400 (390–750)	<0.05	2	Sodium thiocyanate, all concentrations	Boiling	<0.05	2
Potassium bromide, all concentrations	Boiling	<0.05	2	Sodium thiocyanate, melt	300 (570)	<0.05	2
Potassium bromide, melt	760 (1400)	<0.05	2	Sodium thiosulfate, all concentrations	Boiling	<0.05	2
Potassium carbonate, all concentrations	Boiling	<0.05	2	Stannic ammonium chloride, all concentrations	Boiling	<0.05	2
Potassium carbonate, melt(a)	900 (1650)	<0.05	2	Stannic chloride, all concentrations	Boiling	<0.05	2
Potassium chlorate, all concentrations(b)	Boiling	<0.05	2	Strontium nitrate, all concentrations	Boiling	<0.05	2
Potassium cyanide, 50 g/L	Room	<0.25	10	Sulfite cooking liquor, pH 1.3	Boiling	<0.05	2
	100 (212)	1.4	55	Sulfur monochloride, pure	Boiling	<0.05	2
Potassium dichromate, all concentrations	Boiling	<0.05	2	Sulfuryl chloride, dry and wet	300 (570)	<0.05	2
Potassium ferricyanide, all concentrations	Boiling	<0.05	2	Thionyl chloride, dry or wet	Boiling	<0.05	2
Potassium ferrocyanide, all concentrations	Boiling	<0.05	2	Uranyl nitrate, all concentrations	Boiling	<0.05	2
Potassium hydroxide, all concentrations	300 (570)	<0.05	2				
Potassium hydroxide, melt(a)	300 (570)	<0.05	2				
Potassium nitrate, all concentrations	Boiling	<0.05	2				
Potassium nitrate, melt	335 (635)	Attacked					

(a) Platinum is attacked if strong oxidizers are present. (b) Platinum-iridium anodes used to electrolytically manufacture potassium chlorate. (c) Provided reducing agents are not present. (d) Provided no ammonia is present

Uranium

The environments of primary importance involving the corrosion of uranium are those atomic/nuclear conditions that result from contact with the metal at high temperatures during the malfunction of reactors, as for example water, carbon dioxide, carbon monoxide, air, and steam. In each case, corrosion is favored by large free energy and heat terms for the formation of uranium oxides. The major use of uranium in reactors that are cooled by carbon dioxide has resulted in emphasis on the behavior of uranium in this gas and, to a lesser extent, in carbon monoxide and air. At the same time, other basic corrosion studies emphasize the more traditional environments.

Atmospheric Corrosion

In the atmosphere and at room temperature, uranium readily tarnishes. Electropolishing inhibits the tarnishing process; etching in nitric acid activates the surface. Uranium dioxide and hydrated UO_3 are the principal solid products.

This corrosion is enhanced by water vapor, and thus, the process is controlled by humidity levels. However, the presence of oxygen markedly inhibits attack by water vapor. It is thought that the corrosion is electromechanical in nature, with hydrated UO_3 being formed at cathodic areas.

There is a relationship between percent of alloying additions and corrosion response in hot, humid air. In general, decreasing the total amount of alloying additions, irrespective of the alloying element, increases the resistance to corrosion.

Water

Various recent studies center on the relative resistance of numerous uranium alloys to boiling water at 100 °C (212 °F). It has been shown that the corrosion resistance of uranium alloys to boiling water is inversely proportional to the percentage of alpha uranium present in the particular composition. An increase in the corrosion resistance with alloying is due to the formation of the gamma phase. The most promising alloying additives (molybdenum, niobium, and zirconium) have been extensively studied.

Dilute Salt Solutions

Because the corrosion resistance of uranium alloys in hot, moist air and in boiling water has been found to be proportional to the total alloying content, it is expected that this proportionality also holds true for corrosion in dilute salt solutions. Electrochemical measurements have indicated that this should be the case. In one study, standard or corrosion potentials of various uranium alloys were measures in a $0.0001 M$ potassium chloride (KCl) solution against a saturated calomel electrode. Although the measured potentials versus the total alloying content of the alloys do not produce a strictly linear relationship, the two are directly related. Kinetic data on the corrosion rates of uranium alloys in dilute salt solutions are scarce, but those that have been published confirm this relationship.

Seawater

As with the preceding corrosion environments, the corrosion susceptibility of uranium alloys in seawater is expected to decrease with increasing alloy content. In one investigation, the corrosion potentials of a number of uranium alloys were measured in artificial seawater. The observed trend of decreasing corrosion potential with increasing alloying content is very similar to that discussed previously for dilute salt solutions. Thermodynamics predict a decreasing corrosion rate with increased alloy content. The kinetics of the uranium alloy/seawater reaction were measured galvimetrically; the results showed a logarithmic relationship between the corrosion rate and the total alloy content.

Acids and Bases

An indication of the possible anodic reactions can be obtained by examining a typical Pourbaix diagram for uranium. In the potential range from -1.8 to 1.2 V at low pH (0 to 2.0), uranium forms primarily soluble species. The uranium ion U^{3+} forms the active region near the corrosion potential, and the uranyl ion forms in the transpassive region. In the passive region, UO_2 undoubtedly forms. Anodic polarization techniques can be used to study the ease of transition from the active to the passive state, as well as the dissolution behavior of the metal and its alloys. The transition from the active to the passive state is accompanied by a decrease in corrosion rate on the order of 10^4 to 10^6, which is extremely significant for many applications.

Anodic polarization techniques have been used to study the effects of alloying constituent, temperature, solution composition, solution concentration, pH, and the presence of chloride on the corrosion response of uranium alloys. One of the figures here shows an example of the effect of alloying on anodic polarization; the passive current densities vary inversely with alloying content. Another of the figures shows an example of the effect of solution composition, particularly the addition of chloride, on the anodic polarization behavior. The uranium-molybdenum alloy passivates more easily in sodium sulfate (Na_2SO_4) than in sulfuric acid (H_2SO_4), and the addition of chloride prevents passivation entirely.

Additional conclusions have been reached based on this work, as follows. Uranium binary alloys exhibit active-passive behavior in sodium hydroxide, ammonium hydroxide, sodium nitrate, sodium chromate, and ammonium chromate. The critical current densities for passivity were inversely proportional to the H_2SO_4 concentration. Unlike those of most metals, the dissolution rates of uranium alloys decrease with increasing acid concentration. Chloride additions as small as $0.005 M$ affect the anodic polarization curve, but chromates, sulfates, and nitrates inhibit pitting at this low chloride concentration. The uranium-titanium alloys were found to be more resistant to basic solutions than uranium-molybdenum alloys.

Cemented Carbides

The corrosion of cemented carbides is based on the solubility of the key ingredients used in the various compositions. Although some alloying occurs, the solubility of the tungsten carbide-cobalt (WC-Co) and titanium carbide (TiC) in cobalt or nickel is very limited. The main alloying in the WC-Co compositions is primarily based on the addition of TiC, TaC, and NbC, which form cubic phase solid solutions with WC.

Corrosion of cemented carbides is generally based on the surface depletion of the binder phase such that at the surface region only a carbide skeleton remains. Because the applications are invariably for wear or abrasion, this skeleton is rapidly worn away. At low binder phase contents, the rate of attack is diminished, and in conditions in which the corrosion is not too severe, the reduced binder content will be beneficial. In more severe corrosion, however, the use of a cobalt binder is prohibited, and the WC-Co grade is simply not resistant enough. In these cases, certain corrosion-resistant grades should be used. Table 24 provides data on the corrosion resistance of cemented carbides in various media.

The most common of the corrosion-resistant grades are WC with nickel alloy binders and $TiC-Ni-Mo_2C$-base cemented carbide. Various data indicate that the corrosion rate as a function of pH for these grades tested in buffered solutions. These data show that straight WC-Co grades are resistant down to pH 7. This is also valid for WC-Co grades containing cubic carbides such as TiC, TaC, and NbC. The highest corrosion resistance is obtained for certain alloyed TiC-Ni grades, which are resistant down to about pH 1. When compared, however, with straight WC-Co grades, they are less tough and have lower thermal conductivity. They also have several other disadvantages.

In many corrosion-wear conditions, the proper choice is specially alloyed WC-Ni grades, which are resistant down to pH 2 to 3. Even in certain solutions with pH values less than 2, they have proved to be resistant to corrosion.

Although the pH value is one of the most important parameters when determining the corrosivity of a medium, there are other factors of great influence. These include temperature and electrical conductivity. This latter is dependent on the ion concentration, that is, the amount of dissolved salts in the solution. Thus, a simple definition of corrosivity in a given medium cannot be given. Accordingly, no general rules are valid in all situations.

Acids

In general, it can be stated that the corrosion of cemented WC is fair to good in a limited way in all acids except HNO_3. The corrosion resistance of cemented TiC is excellent in phosphoric acid (H_3PO_4), boric acid, and picric acid. It is somewhat better than cemented WC in HCl or sulfuric acid (H_2SO_4). Cemented TiC exhibits poor corrosion resistance in HNO_3. As expected, increasing the cobalt content to increase strength significantly decreases the corrosion resistance. The same situation exists in virtually all corrosive environments.

Special Grades

To obtain corrosion resistance above and beyond that available with regular WC-Co and TiC-Ni grades, the special corrosion-resistant grades are used. Although they introduce disadvantages, these grades do offer resistance in many media.

Warm Acids and Bases

The straight WC-Co compositions show rapid attack in dilute H_2SO_4 and HNO_3, and little attack in those concentrated acids. Although the corrosion rate is lower in HCl, it is obvious that these compositions are not suitable for use in warm or hot acid solutions. The TiC-6.5Mo composition is quite good in H_2SO_4, moderately good in HCl, and very poor in HNO_3. Several of the binderless compositions and the TaC-base cemented carbide show very acceptable corrosion resistance in these warm acids. These results are to be expected, because the cobalt and nickel binders are completely soluble in these acids.

The corrosion rates of various cemented carbides in basic solutions at 50 °C (120 °F) are an entirely different matter. Although corrosion does proceed, it is slow enough to demonstrate the utility of even the WC-Co compositions in such applications as seal rings in these basic solutions.

Table 24 Corrosion Resistance of Cemented Carbides in Various Media

Data for two AISI austenitic stainless steels are included for comparison.

Medium	Chemical designation	Concentration, %	Temperature, °C (°F)	pH	WC-Co	TiC-NiMo	WC-Ni	WC-CoCr	WC-TaC-Co	Type 302	Type 316
Acetic acid, unaerated	CH₃COOH	4	Room	...	C	B	B	B	A	...	...
Acetic acid (glacial), unaerated	CH₃COOH	99.8	Room	...	C	C	B	A	A	A	A
Acetone	(CH₃)₂CO	...	Room	...	A	A	A	A	A	...	...
Alcohols	...	...	Room	...	A	A	A	A	A	...	...
Ammonia, anhydrous	NH₃	...	...	...	B	B	B	B	A	...	...
Argon gas	Ar	...	...	...	A	A	A	A	A	...	...
Benzene, liquid	C₆H₆	...	Room	...	A	A	A	A	A	...	...
Carbon tetrachloride	CCl₄	Pure	Room	...	A	A	A	A	A	...	...
Chlorine gas, dry	Cl	...	Room	...	C	C	C	C	B	...	...
Chlorine gas, wet	Cl·H₂O	...	Room	...	D	C	C	D	B	...	...
Citric acid	C₃H₄(OH)(COOH)₃	5	Room	1.7	C	A	A	...	...	A	A
Citric acid	C₃H₄(OH)(COOH)₃	5	60 (140)	1.7	D	A	B	...	...	A	A
Copper sulfate solution	CuSO₄	0.01	Room	6	C	A	A	...	...	A-C	A-C
Copper sulfate solution	CuSO₄	0.01	70 (160)	6	D	A	A	...	...	A-C	A-C
Digester liquor, black	...	...	66 (150)	...	B	B	B	B	A	...	...
Esters	...	...	Room	...	A	A	A	A	A	A	A
Ethanol	C₂H₅OH	96	Room	...	A	A	A	...	...	A	A
Ethylene glycol	C₂H₆O₂	...	Room	...	A	A	A	A	A	...	...
Ferrous sulfide	FeS	Slurry in water	Room	...	C	C	C	C	A	...	...
Fluorine, liquid	F	...	−188 (−305)	...		B					
50% formaldehyde, 50% alcohol	...	...	Room	...	C	Uncoupled B Coupled C(c)	C	C	A	...	...
Formic acid	HCOOH	5	Room	...	C	A	C	...	...	A	A
Formic acid	HCOOH	5	60 (140)	1.8	D	A	...	...	...	B	A
Freon gas	C₂Cl₃F₃/CH₂Cl₃	...	Room	...	A	A	A	A	A	...	...
Gasoline	...	...	Room	...	A	A	A	A	A	...	...
Helium, liquid	He	...	−269 (−450)	...	A	A	A	A	A	...	...
Hydrochloric acid	HCl	0.5	Room	1	D	C	C	...	...	C	A
Hydrochloric acid	HCl	0.5	60 (140)	1	D	C	C	...	...	D	A
Hydrochloric acid	HCl	10	Room	...	D	D	D	...	...	D	C
Hydrochloric acid	HCl	37	Room	...	D	D	D	D	A	...	...
Hydrochloric acid	HCl	37	100 (212)	...	D	D	D	D	B	...	...
Hydrofluoric acid, anhydrous	HF	...	Room	...	B	B	B	B	A	...	...
Hydrofluoric acid	HF	1–60	Room	...	D	D	D	D	D	...	...
Hydrogen, liquid	H	...	253 (488)	...	A	A	A	A	A	...	...
Kerosene	...	...	Room	...	A	A	A	A	A	...	...
Magnesium bisulfite digester liquor	MgHSO₃	...	Room	...	B	B	B	B	A	...	...
Methane, liquid	CH₄	...	162 (324)	...	A	A	A	A	A	...	...
Methanol, anhydrous	CH₃OH	...	Room	...	A	A	A	A	A	...	...
Methanol, 20% water	CH₃OH/H₂O	...	Room	...	A	A	A	A	A	...	...
Nitric acid	HNO₃	0.5	Room	1.1	D	C	A	...	...	A	A
Nitric acid	HNO₃	5	Room	...	D	D	D	D	B	...	...
Nitric acid	HNO₃	...	100 (212)	...	D	D	D	D	B	...	...
Nitric acid	HNO₃	10	Room	...	D	B	C	...	...	A	A
Nitrogen, liquid	N	...	196 (385)	...	A	A	A	A	A	...	...
Oil, crude (Sand, salt water, high in sulfur)	...	...	Room	...	C	C	C	C	A	...	...
Oxalic acid	(COOH)₂·2H₂O	5	Room	1	A-B	A	A	...	...	A	A
Oxalic acid	(COOH)₂·2H₂O	5	60 (140)	1	B-C	A	...	...	...	B	A
Oxygen, liquid	O	...	183 (361)	...	A	A	A	A	A	...	...
Perchloric acid	HClO₄	0.5	Room	1.3	C-D	A	C	...	...	D	...
Perchloric acid	HClO₄	0.5	60 (140)	1.3	D	A	D	...	...	D	D
Phosphoric acid	H₃PO₄	5	Room	1.2	D	B	C	...	...	A	A
Phosphoric acid	H₃PO₄	85	Room	...	D	C	C	D	A	...	...
Crude phthalic acid and anhydride	C₆H₄-1,2 (COOH)₂/ C₆H₄-1,2 (CO)₂O	...	250–280 (480–535)	...	C	C	B	C	A	...	...
Sodium carbonate	Na₂CO₃	5	Room	12	A	A	A	...	...	A	A
Sodium carbonate	Na₂CO₃	5	60 (140)	12	A	A	A	...	...	A	A
Sodium chloride	NaCl	3	Room	7	A-B	A	A	...	...	A	A
Sodium chloride	NaCl	3	60 (140)	7	A-B	A	A	...	...	A	A
Sodium cyanide	NaCN	10	Room	...	D	D	D	D	A	...	...
Sodium hydrogen sulfate	NaHSO₄	5	Room	1.2	C-D	A	A-B	...	...	D	A
Sodium hydrogen sulfate	NaHSO₄	5	60 (140)	1.2	D	C	C-D	...	...	D	A
Sodium hydroxide	NaOH	5	Room	14	A	A	A	...	...	A	A
Sodium hydroxide	NaOH	5	60 (140)	14	B	A	A	...	...	A	A
Sodium hydroxide	NaOH	40	Room	16	A	A	A	...	...	A	A
Sodium hydroxide	NaOH	40	60 (140)	16	A	A	A	...	...	A	A
Steam, superheated	H₂O	...	600 (1110)	...	A	A	A	A	A	...	...
Sulfuric acid	H₂SO₄	0.5	Room	1.2	C-D	A	B-C	...	...	C	A
Sulfuric acid	H₂SO₄	0.5	60 (140)	1.2	D	D	D	...	...	D	A

(a) A, highly resistant, negligible attack; B, resistant, light attack; C, poor resistance, medium attack; D, not resistant, not suitable. This table should be used only as a guide. Many factors, such as temperature variations, changes in chemical environment, purity of solutions, and stress or loading conditions, may invalidate these recommendations. Tests under operating conditions should be made. (b) Results were obtained under laboratory conditions in pure solutions and are classified with reference to corrosion resistance only. (c) Coupled to brass.

(Continued)

Table 24 (continued)

| Medium | Chemical designation | Concentration, % | Temperature, °C (°F) | pH | Type of cemented carbide/corrosion resistance(a) | | | | | AISI stainless steels(b) | |
					WC-Co	TiC-NiMo	WC-Ni	WC-CoCr	WC-TaC-Co	Type 302	Type 316
Sulfuric acid ....H$_2$SO$_4$		5	Room	...	C	B	C	C	A	...	...
Sulfuric acid ....H$_2$SO$_4$		5	100 (212)	...	D	C	C	D	A	...	...
Sulfuric acid ....H$_2$SO$_4$		10	Room	0	D	D	B	...	...	...	...
Sulfuric acid ....H$_2$SO$_4$		10	60 (140)	0	D	D	...	...	...	D	A
Sulfur, liquid.......................S		100	130 (265)	...	A	A	...	...	...	D	D
Water, boiler feed ....H$_2$O		...	66 (150)	...	B	C	A	...	...	...	A
Water, fresh, distilled, purified.......H$_2$O		...	Room	...	A	A	A	A	A	...	...
Water, tap.........................H$_2$O		...	Room	...	B	A	B	B	A	...	...
Water, sea.........................	...	...	Room	...	B	B	B	...	A	...	...

(a) A, highly resistant, negligible attack; B, resistant, light attack; C, poor resistance, medium attack; D, not resistant, not suitable. This table should be used only as a guide. Many factors, such as temperature variations, changes in chemical environment, purity of solutions, and stress or loading conditions, may invalidate these recommendations. Tests under operating conditions should be made. (b) Results were obtained under laboratory conditions in pure solutions and are classified with reference to corrosion resistance only. (c) Coupled to brass.

Metallic Glasses

Frequently called amorphous metals and glassy metal systems, metallic glasses have recently been studied extensively for their corrosion resistance, along with a number of other qualities. They are also interesting as a tool for exploring the influence of atomic structure and chemical composition on the corrosion process. They contain none of the classic crystalline or chemical defects found in crystalline solids, such as grain boundaries and second-phase particles, and they are structurally homogeneous.

Although the temperature decrease required by metallic glasses for quenching from the liquid to the solid state is not large, the rate of heat extraction is very high and requires at least one dimension of the resulting alloy to be very thin. Because of this requirement, glassy metals produced by liquid quenching are typically in the form of ribbons, wire, and filaments. Obvious and potential areas of application would seem to be corrosion-resistant coatings and barriers. In certain applications, a thin, highly corrosion-resistant coating may be sufficient, thereby permitting the use of less expensive base materials.

Corrosion Resistance

Some glassy metals exhibit extremely good corrosion resistance due to several factors. Metallic glasses are free from such defects as grain boundaries and second-phase particles that are present in crystalline metals. Corrosion often occurs preferentially at such sites; therefore, glassy metals may be expected to exhibit better corrosion resistance than crystalline alloys. The galvanic corrosion associated with chemical inhomogeneities, such as second-phase particles, is also impossible in glassy metals. In addition, the passive films responsible for corrosion resistance in crystalline alloys also play a role in glassy metal corrosion. Thus, the effect of the amorphous structure, chemical homogeneity, and unique chemical composition on the formation and stability of the passive film must also be considered.

Early research into metallic glasses tended to concentrate on iron-base metal-metalloid glasses, but recently the range of

study has widened to include many alloy systems. Results with nickel-, titanium-, copper-, and cobalt-base alloy systems, among others, have been reported in the literature. The effect of metalloid additions on corrosion behavior is reasonably well characterized, and theories have been proposed to explain the beneficial effect of phosphorus on corrosion. The influence on corrosion behavior on a wide variety of elemental additions has been evaluated, and many such additions increase corrosion resistance. Those with the strongest effect are the classic film formers such as chromium, titanium, and molybdenum.

Corrosion Behavior

Glassy alloys can be grouped into two major categories with intrinsically different corrosion behaviors. The first group includes the transition metal/metal binary alloy systems, such as Cu-Zr, Ni-Ti, W-Si, and Ni-Nb. The second class consists of transition metal/metalloid alloys. These alloys are usually iron-, nickel-, or cobalt-base systems. They may contain film formers, and they normally contain approximately 20 at.% phosphorus, bismuth, silicon, and/or carbon as the metalloid component. For the most part, descriptions of these two types of corrosion behavior are detailed laboratory results and have little direct relationship with actual corrosion conditions.

Localized Behavior

The ability to resist localized corrosion is one of the most percent of chromium very effectively resist pitting in chloride-containing solutions. Polarization curves of glassy alloys obtained in 1N NaCl do not show a characteristic pitting potential, rather they exhibit stable passivity until the onset of transpassivity. In addition, results of a study with Fe$_{25}$Ni$_{40}$Cr$_{15}$-P$_{16}$B$_4$ showed that the passive range of 1N H$_2$SO$_4$ plus 0.1N NaCl is not interrupted by pitting, but extends to transpassivity.

In another study, increasing the chromium content from 0 to 16 at.% in a series of Fe-Ni-Cr-P-B alloy systems facilitated passivation in acidified 1N NaCl, but pitting was not observed on any alloy polarized below the transpassivity potential region. Polarization at transpassive potentials caused numerous pits to form that penetrated the filament and were noncrystallographic in shape.

Chromium

Chromium was shown to be very effective in conferring pitting resistance, such as for the glassy alloys $Fe-Cr_x-B_{13}-C_7$ and $Fe-Cr_x-B_{13}-Si_7$ in 3% NaCl. With chromium levels of 2 and 5 at.%, both alloy types pitted at potentials slightly anodic to the free corrosion potential of about -0.6 V (saturated calomel electrode, SCE). The addition of 8 at.% Cr extended the pitting resistance to about 1 V(SCE), which is an extremely aggressive condition for alloys containing such a low level of chromium. By contrast, type 304 stainless steel contains about 18 wt.% Cr, yet its pitting potential is several hundred millivolts less positive than that of these glassy alloys.

Molybdenum

Molybdenum benefits the pitting resistance of glassy alloys and crystalline steels. The addition of molybdenum to glassy $Fe-Mo_xP_{13}C_7$ alloys suppressed pitting and decreased the critical current density for passivation and the passive current density. As little as 4 at.% Mo prevented pitting in $1N$ HCl, and small additions of molybdenum were more effective than chromium in decreasing corrosion rates. Molybdenum has been shown to facilitate the formation of a passive hydrated chromium or iron oxy-hydroxide film through its enrichment in the corrosion product layer during active dissolution. The enrichment assists the accumulation of the passivating species in the film by lowering the dissolution rate of the species; the molybdenum-rich product subsequently dissolves and thus leaves little molybdenum behind in the film.

Other Alloying Elements

Titanium, tantalum, molybdenum, and tungsten were incorporated by high-rate sputter deposition into alloys of the general composition T_1-T_2, where T_1 = titanium, tantalum, molybdenum, or tungsten, and T_2 = rhenium, iron, cobalt, nickel, or copper. Tungsten-iron and titanium-copper resisted pitting corrosion up to 2.5 V(SCE) in chloride solutions of pH 1 and 7. Addition of tungsten to $Fe-W_xP_{13}C_7$ increased the critical pitting potential to above 2 V(SCE) at x = 6 at.%, but x = 10 at.% caused transpassive dissolution at 1 V(SCE).

Stress-Corrosion Cracking/ Hydrogen Embrittlement

The environmentally induced fracture of glassy alloys, namely stress-corrosion cracking and hydrogen embrittlement in relation to metallic glasses, are beyond the scope of this brief introduction. These topics are detailed in *Metals Handbook*, Vol 13, 9th edition, p 868-869.

Source Journals in Corrosion Science and Engineering

ACCOM
Avesta Corrosion Management
Avesta AB
S-77401 Avesta
Sweden
(in English)

Acta Metallurgica
Pergamon Press, Inc.
Maxwell House
Fairview Park
Elmsford NY 10523

Advanced Materials and Processes
ASM International
Metals Park OH 44073

Aluminum
Aluminium-Verlag GmbH
Konigsallee 30
Postfach 1207
Dusseldorf D-4000
Federal Republic of Germany

Anti-Corrosion Methods and Materials
Sawell Publications, Ltd.
127 Stanstead Road
London SE23 1JE
United Kingdom

Applications of Surface Science
Elsevier Science Publishing
P.O. Box 1663
Grand Central Station
New York NY 10163

Australian Journal of Chemistry
Commonwealth Scientific and Industrial Research
314 Albert Street
East Melbourne
Victoria 3002
Australia

British Corrosion Journal
The Institute of Metals
1 Carlton House Terrace
London SW1 Y5DB
United Kingdom

Canadian Metallurgical Quarterly
Pergamon of Canada, Ltd.
150 Consumers Road, Suite 104
Willowdale, Ontario M2J 1P9 Canada

Chemical Engineering
1221 Avenue of the Americas
New York NY 10020

Corrosion
P.O. Box 218340
Houston TX 77218

Corrosion Prevention and Control
Scientific Surveys, Ltd.
P.O. Box 21
Beaconsfield Bucks HP9 1NS9
United Kingdom

Corrosion Science
Pergamon Press, Ltd.
Headington Hill Hall
Oxford OX3 0BW
United Kingdom

Durability of Building Materials
Elsevier Science Publishers, B.V.
P.O. Box 211
1000 AE Amsterdam
The Netherlands

Engineering Fracture Materials
Pergamon Press, Ltd.
Headington Hill Hall
Oxford OX3 0BW
United Kingdom

Fatigue and Fracture of Engineering Materials and Structures
Pergamon Press, Ltd.
Headington Hill Hall
Oxford OX3 0BW
United Kingdom

Fusion Technology
55 N. Kensington Avenue
La Grange Park IL 60525

High-Temperature Technology
Butterworth Scientific, Ltd.
Westbury House
P.O. Box 63, Guildford
Surrey GU2 5BH
United Kingdom

High Temperatures—High Pressures
Pion, Ltd.
207 Brondesbury Park
London NW2 5JN
United Kingdom

Industrial and Chemical Engineering, Product Research and Development
American Chemical Society
1155 16th Street NW
Washington DC 20036

Iron and Steel International
Industrial Press, Ltd.
Quadrant House
The Quadrant, Sutton
Surrey SM2 5AS
United Kingdom

Journal of Engineering for Gas Turbines
American Society of Mechanical Engineers
United Engineering Center
345 East 47th Street
New York NY 10017

Journal of Engineering Materials and Technology
American Society of Mechanical Engineers
United Engineering Center
345 East 47th Street
New York NY 10017

Journal of Materials for Energy Systems
ASM International
Metals Park OH 44073

Journal of Material Science Letters
Associated Book Publishers, Ltd.
Norway
Andover, Hampshire
United Kingdom

Journal of Metals
420 Commonwealth Drive
Warrendale PA 15086

Journal of Nuclear Materials
North-Holland Publishing Co.
P.O. Box 103
Amsterdam 1000AC
The Netherlands

Journal of Nuclear Science and Technology
Atomic Energy Society of Japan
No. 1-1-13 Shimbashi
Minato-ku
Tokyo 105
Japan

Journal of Pressure Vessel Technology
American Society of Mechanical Engineers
United Engineering Center
345 East 47th Street
New York NY 10017

Journal of the Electrochemical Society
10 South Main Street
Pennington NJ 08534

Journal of the Electrochemical Society of India
Electrochemical Society of India
Indian Institute of Sciences
Bangalore 560 012
India

Journal of the Less-Common Metals
Elsevier Sequoia S-A
Box 851
Lausanne CH-1001
Switzerland 1

Journal of Tribology
American Society of Mechanical Engineers
United Engineering Center
345 East 47th Street
New York NY 10017

Material Science and Engineering
Elsevier Sequoia S-A
Box 851
Lausanne CH-1001
Switzerland 1

Materials Performance
1440 South Creek
P.O. Box 218340
Houston TX 77084

Metal Finishing
One University Plaza
Hackensack NJ 07601

Metallography
Elsevier Applied Science Publishers
52 Vanderbilt Avenue
New York NY 10017

Metallurgical Transactions A
ASM International
Metals Park OH 44073

Nuclear Engineering and Design
Elsevier Sequoia S-A
Box 851
Lausanne CH-1001
Switzerland 1

Oxidation of Metals
Plenum Publishing Corporation
233 Spring Street
New York NY 10013

Plating and Surface Finishing
12644 Research Parkway
Orlando FL 32826

Scripta Metallurgica
Pergamon Press, Inc.
Maxwell House
Fairview Park
Elmsford NY 10523

Surface and Coatings Technology
Journal Information Center
Elsevier Science Publishers
52 Vanderbilt Avenue
New York NY 10017

Transactions of the Iron and Steel Institute of Japan
Iron and Steel Institute
Keidanren Kaiken 9-4
Otemachi-1-chome, Chiyoda-ku
Tokyo 100
Japan

Wear
Editorial Office
Elsevier Sequoia
Mayfield House
256 Banbury Road
Oxford OX2 7DH
United Kingdom

Welding Journal
P.O. Box 3520
Miami FL 33135

Werkstoffe und Korrosion
Verlag Chemie GmbH
Postfach 1260/1280
Weinheim D-6940
Federal Republic of Germany

Zeitschrift fur Metallkunde
Riederer Dr. Verlag GmbH
Gutbrodstr. 9 Postfach 447
Stuttgart D-7000
Federal Republic of Germany

Bibliography

General Interest

Advances in Corrosion Science and Technology, Vol 3, M.G. Fontana, R.W. Staehle, Eds., Plenum Press, New York, 1973

Annual Book of ASTM Standards, American Society for Testing and Materials, Philadelphia, 1988. (All volumes of interest, but especially Vol 03.02, *Wear and Erosion; Metal Corrosion*.)

Atmospheric Corrosion, W.H. Ailor, Ed., John Wiley & Sons, New York, 1982

J.F. Bosich, *Corrosion Prevention for Practicing Engineers*, Barnes & Noble, Inc., New York, 1974

S.C. Britton, *Tin Versus Corrosion*, International Tin Research Institute, (Pub. No. 510), Greenford, England, 1975. (A very practical approach plus an extensive section on specifications and test methods.)

Corrosion; Corrosion Control, Vol 2, 2nd ed., L.L. Shreir, Ed., Newnes-Butterworths, London, 1976

Corrosion Data Survey; Metals Section, 6th ed., National Association of Corrosion Engineers, Houston, 1985

Corrosion/Erosion of Coal Conversion Systems, A.V. Levy, Ed., National Association of Corrosion Engineers, Houston, 1979

Corrosion-Erosion-Wear of Materials in Emerging Fossil Systems, A.V. Levy, Ed., National Association of Corrosion Engineers, 1982

Corrosion Fatigue: Chemistry, Mechanics, and Microstructure, National Association of Corrosion Engineers, 1972

Corrosion; Metal/Environment Reactions, Vol 1, 2nd ed., L.L. Shreir, Ed., Newnes-Butterworths, London, 1976

Corrosion of Metals in the Atmosphere, (MCIC-74-23), Metals and Ceramics Information Center (Battelle), Columbus, 1974

Corrosion Resistant Materials Handbook, 4th ed., D.J. DeRenzo, Ed., Noyes Data Corp., Park Ridge, NJ, 1985

M.G. Fontana, *Corrosion Engineering*, 3rd ed., McGraw-Hill Book Co., New York, 1986

Handbook of Corrosion Resistant Coatings, D.J. DeRenzo, Ed., Noyes Data Corp., Park Ridge, NJ, 1986

Handbook of Corrosion Testing and Evaluation, W.H. Ailor, Ed., John Wiley & Sons, New York, 1971

C.E. Jaske, J.H. Payer, *et al.*, *Corrosion Fatigue of Metals in Marine Environments*, Battelle Press, Columbus, 1981

Manual of Industrial Corrosion Standards and Control, (Pub 534), F.H. Cocks, Ed., American Society for Testing and Materials, Philadelphia, 1973

Metallic Corrosion; Proceedings of the 8th International Congress on Metallic Corrosion, 1981, Vol I, *Deutsche Gesellschaft fur Chemisches Apparatewesen e.V.*, Frankfurt am Main, 1981 (in English)

Metals Handbook, 9th ed., Vol 13, Corrosion, ASM International, Metals Park, OH, 1987. (An encompassing approach for both the basic student and the advanced engineer.)

NACE Corrosion Engineer's Reference Book, R.S. Treseder, Ed., National Association of Corrosion Engineers, Houston, 1980. (A pocket-size book filled with highly practical data.)

Oxidation of Metals and Associated Mass Transport, M.A. Dayanada, S.J. Rothman, Eds., The Metallurgical Society, Warrendale, PA, 1987

J.P. Polar, *A Guide to Corrosion Resistance*, Climax Molybdenum Co., New York, 1978. (An exhaustive guide to corrosion media, test conditions, and corrosion rates for 304, 316, 317, "20," and "Ni-o-nel.")

M. Pourbaix, *Atlas of Electrochemical Equilibria in Aqueous Solutions*, Pergamon Press, Oxford, 1966. (An exhaustive treatment of the subject that includes potential-pH equilibrium diagrams for the majority of the common elements.)

Process Industries Corrosion: The Theory and Practice, B.J. Moniz, W.I. Pollack, Eds., National Association of Corrosion Engineers. Houston, 1986

E. Rabald, *Corrosion Guide*, Elsvier Publishing Co., Inc., New York, 1951. (Approximately 600 pages of corrosion tables organized according to corroding agents and materials.)

Refractory Metals and their Industrial Applications, (STP 849), R.E. Smallwood, Ed., American Society for Testing and Materials, Philadelphia, 1984

P.A. Schweitzer, *Corrosion Resistance Tables; Metals, Plastics, Nonmetallics, and Rubbers*, 2nd ed., Marcel Dekker, Inc., New York, 1986. (An approach that alphabetizes hundreds of corrodents and then lists the corrosion rates of a number of common materials in relation to them and according to mils penetration/year at given temperatures.)

Seawater Corrosion Handbook, M. Schumacher, Ed., Noyes Data Corp., Park Ridge, NJ, 1979

The Corrosion Handbook, H.H. Uhlig, Ed., John Wiley & Sons, New York, 1948. (Although old, still listed in Books in Print. Much valuable information.)

Treatise on Materials Science and Technology; Corrosion: Aqueous Processes and Passive Films, J.C. Scully, Ed., Vol 23, Academic Press, New York, 1983

J.M. West, *Basic Corrosion and Oxidation*, 2nd ed., Ellis Horwood Ltd., Chichester, England, 1986. (Highly academic and theoretical, but an excellent textbook for an advanced student.)

G. Wranglen, *An Introduction to Corrosion and Protection of Metals*, Chapman and Hall, London, 1985. (For advanced student.)

Alloy Steels

J.F. Bosich, *Corrosion Prevention for Practicing Engineers*, Barnes & Noble, Inc., New York, 1974, 214

B.F. Brown, "High Strength Steels," in *The Theory of Stress Corrosion Cracking in Alloys*, J.C. Scully, Ed., North Atlantic Treaty Organization, Brussels, 1971

C.E. Jaske, J.H. Payer, *et al., Corrosion Fatigue of Metals in Marine Environments*, Battelle Press, Columbus, 1981

A. Levy, Y-F. Man, "Elevated Temperature Erosion-Corrosion of 9Cr- 1Mo Steel," *Wear*, Vol 2, Sept 1986, 135-159

A.U. Malik, "High-Temperature Oxidation of Transition Metal, Carbide-Dispersed Iron-Base Alloys," *Oxidation of Metals*, Vol 24, Dec 1985, 233-263

A. McMinn, F.F. Lyle, *et al.*, "Stress Corrosion Crack Growth in NiCrMoV Turbine Disc Steels," *Corrosion*, Vol 41, Sept 1985, 493-503

Y. Nakai, K. Tanaka, *et al.*, "Short-Crack Growth in Corrosion Fatigue for a High Strength Steel," *Engineering Fracture Mechanics*, Vol 24, Oct 1986, 433-444

J. Payer, W. Berry, "Application of Slow Strain-Rate Technique to Stress Corrosion Cracking of Pipeline Steel," in *Stress Corrosion Cracking; The Slow Strain-Rate Technique*, (STP 665), G.M. Ugiansky, J. Payer, Eds., American Society for Testing and Materials, Philadelphia, 1979, 222-234

A.C.C. Tseung, T. Sriskandarajah, *et al.*, "A Method for the Inhibition of Sulphide Stress Corrosion Cracking in Steel - I; Electrochemical Aspects," *Corrosion Science*, Vol 25, June 1985, 383- 393

Aluminum and Aluminum Alloys

B.A. Abd-El-Nabey, N. Khalil, *et al.*, "The Acid Corrosion of Aluminium in Water-Organic Solvent Mixtures," *Corrosion Science*, Vol 25, May 1985, 225-232

D.R. Arnott, N.E. Ryan, *et al.*, "Auger and XPS Studies of Cerium Corrosion Inhibition on 7075 Aluminum Alloys," *Applications of Surface Science*, Vol 22-23, May 1985, 236-251

A.M. Beccaria, G. Poggi, "Aluminum Corrosion in Slightly Alkaline Sodium Sulfate Solutions at Different Hydrocaustic Pressures," *Corrosion*, Vol 43, Mar 1987, 153-158

A.M. Beccaria, G. Poggi, "Influence of Hydrostatic Pressure and Salt Concentration of Aluminum Corrosion in NaCl Solutions," *Corrosion*, Vol 42, Aug 1986, 470-475

G.R. Chanani, "Investigation of Effects of Saltwater on Retardation Behavior of Aluminum Alloys," in *Corrosion and Fatigue Technology*, (STP 642), H.L. Craig, Jr., T.W. Crooker, *et al.*, Eds., American Society for Testing and Materials, Philadelphia, 1976, 51-71

H.P. Chu, J.G. Macco, "Corrosion Fatigue of 5456-H117 Aluminum Alloy in Saltwater," in *Corrosion and Fatigue Technology*, (STP 642), H.L. Craig, Jr., T.W. Crooker, *et al.*, Eds., American Society for Testing and Materials, Philadelphia, 1976, 223-239

E.L. Colvin, G.L. Cahen, Jr., *et al.*, "Effect of Germanium Additions on the Corrosion Behavior of an AlLi Alloy," *Corrosion*, Vol 42, July 1986, 416-421

D.L. Crews, "Interpretation of Pitting Corrosion Data from Statistical Prediction Interval Calculations," in *Galvanic and Pitting Corrosion; Field and Laboratory Studies*, (STP 576), R. Baboian, W.D. France, Eds., American Society for Testing and Materials, Philadelphia, 1976

T.W. Crooker, F.D. Bogar, *et al.*, "Effects of Flowing Natural Seawater and Electrochemical Potential on Fatigue-Crack Growth in Several High-Strength Marine Alloys," in *Corrosion and Fatigue Technology*, (STP 642), American Society for Testing and Materials, H.L. Craig, Jr., T.W. Crooker, Eds., American Society for Testing and Materials, Philadelphia, 1976, 189-201

F.W. Fink, W.K. Boyd, *The Corrosion of Metals in Marine Environments*, (DMIC Report 245), Defense Metals Information Center (Battelle), Columbus, OH, 1970

M.G. Fontana, *Corrosion Engineering*, 3rd ed., McGraw-Hill Book Co., New York, 1986

J.R. Galvele, "Pitting Corrosion," in *Treatise on Materials Science and Technology*, Vol 23, J.C. Scully, Ed., Academic Press, New York, 1983, 1-57

Handbook of Aluminum, 3rd. ed., Alcoa Aluminum Corporation, Cleveland, OH, 1970

K.R. Hasse, R.C. Dorward, "Long-Term Marine Atmospheric Stress Corrosion Tests on High-Strength AlZnMgCu Alloys," *Corrosion*, Vol 42, Nov 1986, 663-669

J.A. Kapp, D. Duquette, *et al.*, "Crack Growth Behavior of Aluminum Alloys Tested in Liquid Mercury," *Journal of Engineering Materials and Technology*, Vol 108, Jan 1986, 37-43

F. King, *Aluminium and Its Alloys*, Ellis Horwood, Ltd., Chichester, England, 1987

J. Larsen-Basse, "Performance of OTEC Heat Exchanger Materials in Tropical Seawaters," *Journal of Metals*, Vol 37, Mar 1985, 24-27

H. Meissner, "Meerwasser-Naturversuche mit Aluminiumwerkstoffen im Arabischen Golf," *Aluminium*, Vol 61, Feb 1985, 91-93

M.P. Mueller, A.W. Thompson, *et al.*, "Stress Corrosion Behavior of 7075 Aluminum in 1N Aluminum Chloride Solutions," *Corrosion*, Vol 41, Mar 1985, 127-136

K. Nisancioglu, O. Lunder, "Improving the Corrosion Resistance of Aluminum Alloys by Cathodic Polarization in Aqueous Media," *Corrosion*, Vol 41, May 1985, 247-257

"Nonferrous Metals," *Materials Engineering*, Penton Publishing, Inc., Dec 1987

M.C. Reboul, D. Dubost, *et al.*, "The Stress Corrosion Susceptibility of Aluminium Alloy 7020 Welded Sheets," *Corrosion Science*, Vol 25, Sept 1983, 999-1018

T.M.H. Saber, M.M. Badran, *et al.*, "A Comparative Study of the Galvanic Corrosion of Stainless Steel-Al and Cu-Al Systems in Aqueous Solutions-Combating Galvanic *Corrosion*," *Corrosion Prevention and Control*, Vol 33, April 1986, 41-46

W.J.D. Shaw, "Corrosion Behavior of the IN-9021 Aluminum Alloy," *Corrosion*, Vol 42, Sept 1986, 554-556

W.J.D. Shaw, "Stress Corrosion Cracking Behavior in IN-9021 Aluminum Alloy," *Metallography*, Vol 19, May 1986, 227-233

D.W. Simm, H.E. Button, "The Corrosion Behaviour of Certain Metals in CCA-Treated Timber; Environmental Tests at 100% Relative Humidity," *Corrosion Prevention and Control*, Vol 32, April 1985, 25-35

M.O. Speidel, "Current Understanding of Stress Corrosion Crack Growth in Aluminum Alloys," in *The Theory of Stress Corrosion Cracking in Alloys*, J.C. Scully, Ed., North Atlantic Treaty Organization, Brussels, 1971

K. Tohma, N. Takahashi, *et al.*, "Compound Effects of Additional Zn, Cu, and Mn on the Electrochemical Properties and Corrosion Resistance of Aluminium," *Aluminium*, Vol 61, April 1985, 277-279

D. Tromans, "Effect of Organic Adsorbants on the Aqueous Stress Corrosion Cracking of AA 7075-T651 Aluminum Alloy," *Corrosion*, Vol 42, Oct 1986, 601-608

K. Videm, "Pitting Corrosion of Aluminum in Contact with Stainless Steel," in *Corrosion of Reactor Materials*, Vol 1, International Atomic Energy Agency, Vienna, 1962, 391-415

Carbon Steels

S.M. Abd El-Haleem, S.S. Abd El Rehim, *et al.*, "Anodic Behavior and Pitting Corrosion of Plain Carbon Steel in NaOH Solutions Containing Chlorine@⅛[- Ion," *Surface and Coatings Technology*, Vol 27, Feb 1986, 167-173

B. Abd-El-Nabey, A. El-Toukhy, *et al.*, "4-Amino-3-Substituted-5-Mercapto-1,2,4-Triazolines as Inhibitors for the

Acid Corrosion of Steel," *Surface and Coatings Technology*, Vol 27, April 1986, 325-334

A.P. Akolzin, P. Ghosh, *et al.*, "Application and Peculiarity of $Ca(OH)_2$ as Inhibitor in Presence of Corrosion Activators," *British Corrosion Journal*, Vol 20, Jan 1985, 32-35

F. Altmayer, "Choosing an Accelerated Corrosion Test," *Metal Finishing*, Vol 83, Oct 1985, 57-60

J.F. Bosich, *Corrosion Prevention for Practicing Engineers*, Barnes & Noble, Inc., New York, 1970

J. Congleton, I. Hussian, *et al.*, "Effect of Applied Potential on Corrosion Fatigue of Wire Ropes in Sea Water," *British Corrosion Journal*, Vol 20, Jan 1985, 5-18

Corrosion Data Survey; Metals Section, 6th ed., National Association of Corrosion Engineers, Houston, 1985

D.L. Crews, "Interpretation of Pitting Corrosion Data from Statistical Prediction Interval Calculations," in *Galvanic and Pitting Corrosion; Field and Laboratory Studies*, (STP 576), R. Baboian, W.D. France, Eds., American Society for Testing and Materials, Philadelphia, 1976

D. DeFlippo, A. Rossi, *et al.*, "Rubber Cure: Accelerating Agents as Inhibitors of Steel Corrosion," *Corrosion Science*, Vol 25, July 1985, 217-221

F.W. Fink, W.K. Boyd, *The Corrosion of Metals in Marine Environments*, (DMIC Report 245), Defense Metals Information Center (Battelle), Columbus, OH, 1970

M.G. Fontana, N.D. Greene, *Corrosion Engineering*, McGraw-Hill Book Co., New York, 1967

Z.A. Foroulis, R.J. Franco, "High Temperature Internal Corrosion of an Acetone Plant Furnace Outlet Tube: Failure Analysis and Laboratory Simulation," *Materials Performance*, Vol 25, Oct 1985, 51-56

L.E. Helwig, "Temporary Rust-Preventive Compounds for Steel Sheet," *Materials Performance*, Vol 25, May 1986, 26-31

J. Hickling, "Strain-Induced Corrosion Cracking of Low-Alloy Steels in LWR Systems; Case Histories and Identification of Conditions Leading to Susceptibility," *Nuclear Engineering and Design*, Vol 91, Feb 1986, 305-330

L. Igetoft, "Reactions on Painted Steel Under the Influence of Sulfur Dioxide, Sodium Chloride, and Combinations Thereof," *Industrial and Engineering Chemistry, Product Research and Development*, Vol 24, Sept 1985, 375-378

R. Jasinski, "Corrosion of N80-type Steel by CO_2/Water Mixture," *Corrosion*, Vol 43, April 1987, 214-218

V. Kucera, E. Mattsson, "Atmospheric Corrosion," in *Corrosion Mechanisms*, F. Mansfeld, Ed., Marcel Dekker, Inc., New York, 1987, 221-284

M. McKenzie, P.R. Vassie, "Use of Weight Loss Coupons and Electrical Resistance Probes in Atmospheric Corrosion Tests," *British Corrosion Journal*, Vol 20, April 1985, 117-124

R.D. Merrick, "Design of Pressure Vessels and Tanks to Minimize Corrosion," *Materials Performance*, Vol 26, Jan 1987, 29-37

R. Narayan, A. Kumar, *et al.*, "The Anodic Polarization and Stress Corrosion Cracking of Eutectoid Steel," *Corrosion Science*, Vol 25, Mar 1985, 449-460

S. Narain, S. Assad, *et al.*, "Case Histories of Corrosion Problems in a Wastewater Treatment Plant," *Materials Performance*, Vol 24, Sept 1985, 23-27

T. Okada, S. Hattori, "Relation Between Concentration of Salt Water and Corrosion Fatigue Strength on 0.37 Percent Carbon Structural Steel," *Journal of Engineering Materials and Technology*, Vol 107, July 1985, 235-239

R.N. Parkins, "Stress Corrosion Cracking of Low-Strength Ferritic Steels," in *The Theory of Stress Corrosion Cracking in Alloys*, J.C. Scully, Ed., North Atlantic Treaty Organization, Brussels, 1971

J. Payer, W. Berry, "Application of Slow Strain-Rate Technique to Stress Corrosion Cracking of Pipeline Steel," in *Stress Corrosion Cracking; The Slow Strain-Rate Technique*, (STP 665), G.M. Ugiansky, J. Payer, Eds., American Society for Testing and Materials, Philadelphia, 1979, 222-234

J. Postlethwaite, M.H. Dubbin, *et al.*, "The Role of Oxygen Mass Transfer in the Erosion-Corrosion of Slurry Pipelines," *Corrosion*, Vol 42, Sept 1986, 514-521

W. Prues, E.S. Lee, *et al.*, "Chemical Mitigation of Corrosion by Chloride Dioxide in Oilfield Waterfloods," *Materials Performance*, Vol 24, May 1985, 45-50

V.S. Sastri, R. Beauprie, *et al.*, "Molybdate as a Pipeline Corrosion Inhibitor for Coal-Water Slurry Systems," *Materials Performance*, Vol 25, June 1986, 45-47

G. Schmitt, K. Bedbur, "Investigations on Structural and Electronic Effects in Acid Inhibitors by AC Impedance," *Werkstoffe und Korrosion*, Vol 36, June 1985, 273-276

J.R. Scully, K.J. Bundy, "Electrochemical Methods for Measurement of Steel Pipe Corrosion Rates in Soil," *Materials Performance*, Vol 24, April 1985, 18-25

I. Sekine, Y. Hirakawa, "Effect of 1-Hydorxyethylidene-1, 1-Diphosphonic Acid on the Corrosion of SS 41 Steel in 0.3% Sodium Chloride Solution," *Corrosion*, Vol 42, May 1986, 272-277

R. Sriram, D. Tromans, "Stress Corrosion Cracking of Carbon Steel in Caustic Aluminate Solutions; Slow Strain Rate Studies," *Corrosion*, Vol 41, July 1985, 381-385

N.C. Subramanyam, S.M. Mayanna, "Azoles as Corrosion Inhibitors for Mild Steel in Alkaline Mine Water," *Corrosion Science*, Vol 25, July 1985, 163-169

A.C. Tonce, "The Relationship of Coatings and Cathodic Protection for Underground Corrosion Control," in *Underground Corrosion*, (STP 741), E. Escalante, Ed., American Society for Testing and Materials, Philadelphia, 1981, 166-181

D. Tromans, E.B. Hawbolt, *et al.*, "Stress Corrosion Cracking of ASTM A516 Steel in Hot Caustic Sulfide Solutions; Potential and Weld Effects," *Corrosion*, Vol 42, Feb 1986, 65-70

H.H. Uhlig, *Corrosion and Corrosion Control; An Introduction to Corrosion Science and Engineering*, 1st ed., John Wiley & Sons, Inc. New York, 1963

H.H. Uhlig, "Iron and Steel," in *The Corrosion Handbook*, H.H. Uhlig, Ed., John Wiley & Sons, New York, 1948

H.H. Uhlig, R.W. Revie, *Corrosion and Corrosion Engineering; An Introduction to Corrosion Science and Engineering*, 3rd ed., John Wiley & Sons, New York, 1985

M.S. Vukasovich, J.P.G. Farr, "Molybdate in Corrosion Inhibition; A Review," *Materials Performance*, Vol 25, May 1986, 9-18

T.R. Weber, M.A. Stranick, *et al.*, "Molybdate Corrosion Inhibition in Deaerated and Low-Oxygen Waters," *Corrosion*, Vol 42, Sept 1986, 542-545

G. Wranglen, *An Introduction to Corrosion and Protection of Metals*, Chapman and Hall, New York, 1985

Cast Irons

H. T. Angus, *Cast Iron: Physical and Engineering Properties*, 2nd ed., Butterworths, London, 1976

D.L. Crews, "Interpretation of Pitting Corrosion Data from Statistical Prediction Interval Calculations," in *Galvanic and Pitting Corrosion; Field and Laboratory Studies*, (STP 576), R. Baboian, W.D. France, Eds., American Society for Testing and Materials, Philadelphia, 1976

M.G. Fontana, N.D. Greene, *Corrosion Engineering*, McGraw-Hill Book Co., New York, 1967

C. McCaul, S. Goldspiel, "Atmospheric Corrosion of Malleable and Cast Irons and Steels," in *Atmospheric Corrosion*, W.H. Ailor, Ed., John Wiley & Sons, New York, 1982

"Physical and Corrosion Properties," in *Source Book on Ductile Iron*, A.H. Rauch, Ed., American Society for Metals, Metals Park, OH, 1977

D.L. Piron, R. Desjardins, "Corrosion Rate of Cast Iron and Copper Pipe by Drinking Water," in *Corrosion Monitoring in Industrial Plants Using Nondestructive Testing and Electrochemical Methods*, (STP 908), G.C. Moran, P. Labine, Eds., American Society for Testing and Materials, Philadelphia, 1986

H.H. Uhlig, *Corrosion and Corrosion Engineering; An Introduction to Corrosion Science and Engineering*, 1st ed., John Wiley & Sons, New York, 1963

H.H. Uhlig, R.W. Revie, *Corrosion and Corrosion Engineering; An Introduction to Corrosion Science and Engineering*, 3rd ed., John Wiley & Sons, New York, 1985

Y. Yahagi, Y. Mizutani, "Corrosive Wear of Cast Iron in Sulphuric Acid," *Journal of Tribology*, Vol 109, April 1987, 238-242

Cast Steel

C. McCaul, S. Goldspiel, "Atmospheric Corrosion of Malleable and Cast Irons and Steels," in *Atmospheric Corrosion*, W.H. Ailor, Ed., John Wiley & Sons, New York, 1982

Cemented Carbides

D.K. Shetty, I.G. Wright, *et al.*, "Effects of Composition and Microstructure on the Slurry Erosion of WC-Co Wear," *Wear*, Vol 114, Jan 1987, 1-18

Cobalt and Cobalt Alloys

W. Betteridge, **Cobalt and Its Alloys**, Ellis Horwood Ltd., Chichester, UK, 1982

R.L. Jones, C.E. Williams, "Mixed $MgSO_4$-Na_2SO_4 Effects in the 973K Hot Corrosion of CoCrAlY," *Journal of the Electrochemical Society*, Vol 133, Jan 1986, 217-233

K.L. Luthra, "Kinetics of the Low Temperature Hot Corrosion of Co-Cr-Al Alloys," *Journal of the Electrochemical Society*, Vol 132, June 1985, 1293-1298

I.G. Wright, V. Nagarajan, *et al.*, "Observations on the Role of Oxide Scales in High-Temperature Erosion-Corrosion of Alloys," *Oxidation of Metals*, Vol 25, April 1986, 175-199

R.S. Young, *Cobalt; Its Chemistry, Metallurgy, and Uses*, Reinhold Publishing Co., New York, 1960

Copper and Copper Alloy

J. Andrew, J. Heron, "Some Comparisons of the Slow Strain-Rate Method with the Constant Strain and Constant Load Methods of Stress Corrosion Testing," in *Stress Corrosion Cracking; The Slow Strain-Rate Technique*, (STP 665), G.M. Ugiansky, J. Payer, Eds., American Society for Testing and Materials, Philadelphia, 1979, 362-372

V.E. Carter, "Atmospheric Corrosion of Non-Ferrous Metals," in *Corrosion Processes*, R. Parkins, Ed., Allied Science Publishers, London, 1982, 77-113

A. Cohen, "Copper Alloys in Marine Environments," in *Source Book on Copper and Copper Alloys*, American Society for Metals, Metals Park, OH, 1979

R. Francis, "Effect of Pollutants on Corrosion of Copper Alloys in Sea Water" *British Corrosion Journal*, Vol 20, June and July 1985, 167-174, 175-182

L.M. Gassa, J.R. Vilche, "Electrochemical Study of the Corrosion Fatigue of Copper and Alpha Brass in Ammoniacal Copper Sulphate Solutions," *Corrosion Science*, Vol 25, May 1985, 145-157

B.Y. Gregory, C. Farrington, *et al.*, "Fatigue Life Behavior of Monocrystalline Copper in 0.1 M Perchloric Acid," *Fatigue and Fracture of Engineering Materials and Structure*, Vol 8, Mar 1985, 259-276

A. Hall, A.J.M. Baker, "Settlement and Growth of Copper-Tolerant Ectocarpus Siliculosus (Dillw) Lyngbye on Different Copper-Based Antifouling Surfaces Under Laboratory Conditions," *Journal of Materials Science*, Vol 21, April 1986, 1210-1252

D.P. Harvey, T.S. Sudarshan, *et al.*, "Corrosion Fatigue Behavior of 90/10 Copper-Nickel Cladding for Marine Structures," *Journal of Materials for Energy Systems*, Vol 7, Dec 1985, 269-275

O. Hollander, R.C. May "The Chemistry of Azole Copper Corrosion Inhibitors in Cooling Water," *Corrosion*, Vol 41, Jan 1985, 35-45

C.H. Huang, "Corrosion Protection of Copper with Benzotriazole," *Plating and Surface Finishing*, Vol 73, June 1986, 96-100

A.A. Ishmail, N.A. Khanem, *et al.*, "A Corrosion Map of Cairo and the Coastal Area of Egypt," *Corrosion Prevention and Control*, Vol 32, Aug 1985, 75-77

C.E. Jaske, A.P. Castillo, "Corrosion Fatigue of Cast Suction-Roll Alloys in Simulated Paper-Making Environments," Materials Performance, Vol 26, April 1987, 37-43

A. Kawashima, A. Agrawal, *et al.*, "Effect of Oxyanions and Chloride Ion on the Stress Corrosion Cracking Susceptibility of Admiralty Brass in Nonammoniacal Aqueous Solutions," in *Stress Corrosion Cracking; The Slow Strain-Rate Technique*, (STP 665), G.M. Ugiansky, J. Payer, Eds., American Society for Testing and Materials, Philadelphia, 1979, 266-278

I.R. Kramer, B. Wu, *et al.*, "Dislocation Distribution in TransgranularStress Corrosion Cracking of Naval Brass," *Materials Science and Engineering*, Vol 82, Sept 1986, 141-150

V. Kucera, E. Mattsson, "Atmospheric *Corrosion*," in *Corrosion Mechanisms*, F. Mansfeld, Ed., Marcel Dekker, Inc., New York, 1987, 221-284

H. Leidheiser, Jr., *The Corrosion of Copper, Tin, and Their Alloys*, John Wiley & Sons, New York, 1971

"Light-Wall Copper-Nickel Condenser Tube," in *Source Book on Copper Alloys*, American Society for Metals, Metals Park, OH, 1979

E. Mattisson, "Focus on Copper in Modern Corrosion Research," *Materials Performance*, Vol 26, April 1987, 9-16

B.B. Moreton, "Copper Alloys in Marine Environments Today and Tomorrow—Part I," *Corrosion Prevention and Control*, Vol 32, Dec 1985, 122-126

S. Motojima, H. Kosaki, "Resistivities Against Seawater Corrosion and Sea-Sands Abrasion of TiB_2-Coated Copper Plate," *Journal of Materials Science Letters*, Vol 4, Nov 1985, 1350-1352

T.O. Ntukogu, I.B. Cadoff, "Effect of Palladium on the Tarnishing of Cu-Ag-Au Alloys," *Journal of the Less-Common Metals*, Vol 125, Nov 1986, 197-205

A.V. Reddy, G. Sundararajan, "Erosion Behaviour of Ductile Materials with Spherical Non-Friable Erodent," *Wear*, Vol 3, Sept 1986, 313-323

G.P. Sheldon, N.W. Polan, "Field Testing of Power Utility CondensorTube Alloys," *Journal of Materials for Energy Systems*, Vol 6, Mar 1986, 313-319

P. Singh, L. Bahadur, "Electrochemical Behavior of Brass (CuZr 63:37) in Binary Mixtures of N, N-Dimethyiformamide and Water," *Corrosion*, Vol 42, Nov 1986, 640-645

G. Wranglen, *An Introduction to Corrosion and Protection of Metals*, Chapman and Hall, New York, 1985

Iron

T. Ohtsuka, K. Kubo, N. Sato, "Raman Spectroscopy of Thin Corrosion Films on Iron at 100 to 150 °C in Air," *Corrosion*, Vol 42, Aug 1986, 476-481

J.P. Orcharo, D.J. Young, "Gas-Phase Composition Effects on the Iron Sulfide Scaling Reaction," *Journal of the Electrochemical Society*, Vol 133, Aug, 1986, 1734-1741

B.G. Pound, G.A. Wright, *et al.*, "Electrochemical Phase Diagrams for the Fe/S/H_2O System Under Geothermal Conditions," *Australian Journal of Chemistry*, Vol 38, Dec 1985, 643-657

N.D. Tomashov, *Theory of Corrosion and Protection of Metals*, B. Tytell, I. Geld, *et al.*, Eds., The McMillan Co., New York, 1966

G. Wranglen, *An Introduction to Corrosion and Protection of Metals*, Chapman and Hall, New York, 1985

Iron-Base Alloys

N. Bandyopadhay, C.L. Briant, "Caustic Stress Corrosion Cracking of Low Alloy Iron Base Materials," *Corrosion*, Vol 41, May 1985, 274- 280

M.G. Nicholas, "Interaction of Fecralloy with Sodium Disilicate Glass," *Journal of Materials Science*, Vol 21, Sept 1986, 3292-3296

J.M. Oh, M.J. McNallan, *et al.*, "Microstructural Development in the Surface Region During Oxidation of Iron-Maganese-Nickel-Silicon Alloys," *Journal of the Electrochemical Society*, Vol 133, May 1986, 1042-1048

P. Papaiacovou, H.J. Grabke, *et al.*, "High Temperature Corrosion of Fe-Cr-Mn Alloys in H_2H_2S and H_2H_2O-H_2S Gas Mixtures," *Werkstoffe und Korrosion*, Vol 36, July 1985, 320-324

P.C. Patnaik, W.W. Smeltzer, "Sulfidation Properties of Fe-Al Alloys (6-28 a/o Al) at 1173 K in Sulfur Vapor at P_{S2} '1.45 x 10^{-3} Pa," *Journal of the Electrochemical Society*, Vol 132, May 1985, 1226-1232

P.C. Patnaik, W.W. Smeltzer, "Sulfidation Properties of Fe-Al Alloys at 1173 K in H_2S-H_2 Atmospheres," *Oxidation of Metals*, Vol 23, Feb-May 1985, 53-75

M. Perez, J.P. Larpin, "Sulfidation Properties of Austenitic Fe-Mn and Fe-Mn-Al Alloys Under Low Sulfur Vapor Pressure (8 Pa) in the Temperature Range 873-1173 K," *Oxidation of Metals*, Vol 24, Aug 1985, 29-45

N.S. Quan, D.J. Young, "Sulfidation Behavior of an Aluminum- Manganese Steel," *Oxidation of Metals*, Vol 25, Feb 1986, 107-119

A. Rahmel, M. Schorr, *et al.*, "Transition from Oxidation to Sulfidation of Fe-Cr Alloys in Gases with Low Oxygen and High Sulfur Pressures," *Oxidation of Metals*, Vol 27, April 1987, 199-220

T.A. Ramanarayanan, D.J. Srolovitz, "Carburization Mechanisms of High Chromium Alloys," *Journal of the Electrochemical Society*, Vol 132, Sept 1985, 2268-2274

W.W. Smeltzer, P.C. Patnaik, "Transition from Internal Sulfidation to External Scale Growth of Fe-Al at 1173 K," *Journal of the Electrochemical Society*, Vol 132, May 1985, 1233-1236

S.C. Tjong, C.S. Wu, "The Microstructure and Stress Corrosion Cracking Behaviour of Precipitation-Hardened Fe-8.7Al-29.7Mn-1.04C Alloy in 20% NaCl Solution," *Materials Science and Engineering*, Vol 80, July 1986, 203-211

Iron-Base Superalloy

R.W. Bradshaw, "Thermal Convection Loop Study of the Corrosion of Incoloy 800 in Molten $NaNO_3$/KNO_3," *Corrosion*, Vol 43, Mar 1987, 173-178

J.H. Kort, T. Fransen, *et al.*, "The Effect of Yttrium Iron Implantation on the Sulphidation of Incoloy 800H," *Applications of Surface Science*, Vol 25, Feb-Mar 1986, 237-240

G.Y. Lai, "High Temperature Corrosion Problems in the Process Industries," *Journal of Metals*, Vol 37, July 1985, 14-19

F.D. Lemkey, J.G. Smeggil, *et al.*, "High Temperature Oxidation and Corrosion of Iron-Based Superalloys," *High Temperatures - High Pressures*, Vol 18, April 1986, 283-291

G. Palumbo, P.J. King, *et al.*, "Pitting Corrosion Behavior of Alloy 800 in Chloride-Sulfate Media," *Corrosion*, Vol 43, Jan 1987, 37-45

Lead

H. Grafen, D. Kuron, "Development of High Corrosion Resistance Lead Alloys Containing Palladium," in *Lead 71; Proceedings, Fourth International Conference on Lead*, European Lead Development Committee, London, 1971, 134-150

G.O. Hiers, "Lead and Lead Alloys," in *The Corrosion Handbook*, H.H. Uhlig, Ed., John Wiley & Sons, New York, 1948

W. Hofmann, *Lead and Lead Alloys; Properties and Technology*, G. Vibrans, Ed., Springer-Verlag, New York, 1970

D. Kelly, P. Niessen, *et al.*, "The Influence of Composition and Microstructure on the Corrosion Behavior of Pb-Ca-Sn Alloys in Sulfuric Acid Solutions," *Journal of the Electrochemical Society*, Vol 132, Nov 1985, 2533-2538

N.D. Tomashov, *Theory of Corrosion and Protection of Metals*, B. Tytell, I. Geld, *et al.*, Eds., The McMillan Co., New York, 1966

Low-Alloy Steel

A. Chavane, M. Habashi, *et al.*, "High-Strength Steels with Improved Sulfide Stress Cracking Resistance," *Corrosion*, Vol 42, Jan 1986, 54-61

C. Duran, E. Treiss, *et al.*, "The Resistance of High Frequency Inductive Welded Pipe to Grooving Corrosion in Salt Water," *Materials Performance*, Vol 25, Sept 1986, 41-48

R. Garber, T. Wada, *et al.*, "Sulfide Stress Cracking Resistant Steels for Heavy Section Wellhead Components," *Journal of Materials for Energy Systems*, Vol 7, Sept 1985, 91-103

P.D. Hicks, F.P.A. Robinson, "Fatigue Crack Growth Rates in a Pressure Vessel Steel Under Various Conditions of Loading and the Environment," *Metallurgical Transactions A*, Vol 17, Oct 1986, 1837-1849

H. Howarth, "The Oxidation Resistance of Low-Alloy Steels," in *Corrosion; Metal/Environment Reactions*, Vol 1, 2nd ed., L.L. Shreir, Ed., Newnes-Butterworths, London, 1976

J. Jaberi, "Effects of Anodic Inhibitors on Stress Corrosion Cracking of a High Strength Steel in Aqueous Environments," *British Corrosion Journal*, Vol 20, 1985, 133-138

J. Kuniya, I. Masaoka, *et al.*, "Stress Corrosion Cracking Susceptibility of Low Alloy Steels Used for Reactor Pressure Vessel in High Temperature Oxygenated Water," *Journal of Pressure Vessel Technology*, Vol 107, Nov 1985, 430-435

R. Padmanabhan, W.E. Wood, "Stress Corrosion Cracking Behavior of 300M Steel Under Different Heat Treated Conditions," *Corrosion*, Vol 41, Dec 1985, 688-699

J.H. Payer, S.P. Pedneker, *et al.*, "Sulfide Stress Cracking Susceptibility of Nickel Containing Steels," *Metallurgical Transactions A*, Vol 17, Sept 1986, 1601-1610

J. Stringer, "Performance Limitations in Electric Power Generating Systems Imposed by High-Temperature Corrosion," *High-Temperature Technology*, Vol 3, Aug 1985, 119-141

S. Tosto, O. DiTollo, *et al.*, "Corrosion Kinetics of HSLA and Low C Steels in the Presence of Cl^- Ion," *Corrosion*, Vol 41, Aug 1985, 458-465

H.H. Uhlig, *Corrosion and Corrosion Engineering; An Introduction to Corrosion Science and Engineering*, 1st ed., John Wiley & Sons, New York, 1963

P.R. Vassie, M. McKenzie, "Electrode Potentials for On-Site Monitoring of Atmospheric Corrosion of Steel," *Corrosion Science*, Vol 25, Aug 1985, 1-13

Y. Yoshino, Y. Minozaki, "Sulfide Stress Cracking Resistance of Low-Alloy Nickel Steels," *Corrosion*, Vol 42, April 1986, 222-233

Magnesium

K.G. Adamson, "Magnesium and Magnesium Alloys," in *Corrosion*, Vol 1, *Metal/Environment Reactions*, L.L. Shreir, Ed., Newnes-Butterworths, London, 1976

K.H.G. Ashby, L.R. Cornwell, "The Role of Water Crystallization in the Swelling of Corrosion Products," *Scripta Metallurgica*, Vol 20, May 1986, 605-608

Robert S. Busk, *Magnesium Products Design*, Marcel Dekker, Inc., New York, 1987

E.F. Emley, *Principles of Magnesium Technology*, Permagon Press, Oxford, 1966

J.T. Evans, "Fracture and Subcritical Crack Growth in Alumina-Fibre/Magnesium Composites," *Acta Metallurgica*, Vol 34, Oct 1986, 2075-2083

A. Froats, T. Kr, *et al.*, "Corrosion of Magnesium and Magnesium Alloys," in *Metals Handbook*, 9th ed., Vol 13, Corrosion, ASM International, Metals Park, OH, 1987

H.P. Godard, M.R. Bothwell, *et al.*, *The Corrosion of Light Metals*, John Wiley & Sons, Inc., New York, 1967

E. Groshart, "Magnesium—The Metal," *Metal Finishing*, Vol 23, Oct 1985, 17-20

H.L. Logan, *The Stress Corrosion of Metals*, John Wiley & Sons, Inc., New York, 1966

P.P. Trzaskoma, "Corrosion Behavior of a Graphite Fiber/Magnesium Metal Matrix Composite in Aqueous Chloride Solution," *Corrosion*, Vol 42, Oct 1986, 609-613

H.H. Uhlig, *Corrosion and Corrosion Control; An Introduction to Corrosion Science and Engineering*, John Wiley & Sons, Inc., New York, 1963

G. Wranglen, *An Introduction to Corrosion and Protection of Metals*, Chapman and Hall, New York, 1985

Maraging Steels

T. Alp, Z. Husain, *et al.*, "Corrosion Fatigue Crack Initiation and Growth in 18 Ni Maraging Steel," *Journal of Materials Science*, Vol 21, Sept 1986, 3263-3268

Metallic Glasses

M.D. Archer, R.J. McKim, "The Stress Corrosion Behavior of Glassy Fe-40Ni-20B Alloy in Aqueous Acidic Media," *Corrosion*, Vol 39, Mar 1983, 91-98

H. Bala, S. Szymura, "Corrosion Behaviour of the $Ti_{75}Ni_{20}Si_5(Ge_5)$ Metallic Glasses," *Journal of Materials Science Letters*, Vol 5, Nov 1986, 1087-1088

R.S. Khairnar, P.P. Karve, *et al.*, "Surface Oxidation of $Fe_{40}B_{20}$ Metallic Glass," *Journal of Materials Science Letters*, Vol 4, Oct 1985, 1282-1284

M. Naka, M. Miyaka, *et al.*, "High Corrosion Resistance of Amorphous Co-Cr-Mo-Zr Alloys," *Scripta Metallurgica*, Vol 17, Nov 1983, 1293-1297

R.F. Sandenbergh, R.M. Latanision, "The Stress Corrosion Cracking of a Glassy $Fe_{32}Ni_{36}Cr_{14}P_{12}B_6$ Alloy," *Corrosion*, Vol 41, July 1985, 369-374

R. Wang, M.D. Merz, "Corrosion Resistance of Amorphous FeNiCrW Alloys," *Corrosion*, Vol 40, June 1984, 272-280

Molybdenum

R.S. Archer, "Molybdenum," in *Rare Metals Handbook*, 2nd ed., C.A. Hampel, Ed., Reinhold Publishing Corp., New York, 1961

Nickel

A.P. Brown, J.E. Battles, "Corrosion of Nickel-200 and AISI-1008 Steel in Sodium Polysulfides and Sulfur at 350 °C,"

Journal of the Electrochemical Society, Vol 133, July 1986, 1321-1325

J.R. Cru, W.G. Lipscomb, "Performance of Nickel 200 and E-Brite 26-1 in First Effect Caustic Environments," *Materials Performance*, Vol 25, April 1986, 9-12

G.A. DiBari, F.X. Carlin, "Decorative Nickel/Chromium Electrodeposits on Steel; 15 Years of Performance Data," *Plating and Surface Finishing*, Vol 72, May 1985, 128-136

R.N. Duncan, "Corrosion Resistance of High-Phosphorous Electroless Nickel Coatings," *Plating and Surface Finishing*, Vol 73, July 1986, 52-57

W.Z. Friend, *Corrosion of Nickel and Nickel-Base Alloys*, John Wiley & Sons, New York, 1980

R.H. Jones, M.J. Danielson, *et al.*, "Role of Segregated P and S in Intergranular Stress Corrosion Cracking of Ni," *Journal of Materials for Energy Systems*, Vol 8, Sept 1986, 185-196

Nickel-Base Alloys

R. Bandy, D. Vanrooyan, "Mechanisms of Stress Corrosion Cracking and Intergranular Attack in Alloy 600 in High Temperature Caustic and Pure Water," *Journal of Materials for Energy Systems*, Vol 7, Dec 1985, 237-245

D.F. Bickford, R.A. Corbett, "Material Selection for the Defense Waste Processing Facility," in *Corrosion of Nickel-Base Alloys*, American Society for Metals, Metals Park, OH, 1985

D.N. Braski, P.D. Goodell, *et al.*, "Effect of Y_2O_3 Dispersoids in 80Ni-20Cr Alloy on the Early Stages of Oxidation at Low-Oxygen Potential," *Oxidation of Metals*, Vol 25, Feb 1986, 29-50

J.R. Crum, W.G. Lipscomb, "Performance of Nickel 200 and E-Brite 26-1 in First Effect Caustic Environments," *Materials Performance*, Vol 25, April 1986, 9-12

T.F. Degnan, "The Effect of Process and Environmental Changes on Corrosion," *Materials Performance*, Vol 26, Jan 1987, 11-15

M.G. Fontana, N.D. Greene, *Corrosion Engineering*, McGraw-Hill Book Co., New York, 1967

W.Z. Friend, *Corrosion of Nickel and Nickel-base Alloys*, John Wiley & Sons, New York, 1980

K. Hattori, M. Tsubota, *et al.*, "Effect of Chloride on the Stress Corrosion Cracking Susceptibility of Inconel X-750 in High-Temperature Water," *Corrosion*, Vol 42, Sept 1986, 531-532

F.G. Hodge, "Nickel and High Nickel Alloys," in *Corrosion and Corrosion Protection Handbook*, P.A. Schweitzer, Ed., Marcel Dekker, Inc., New York, 1983

R.M. Kruger, S.F. Claeys, *et al.*, "The Electrochemical Behavior of P- and C-Doped Ni-16Cr-9Fe," *Corrosion*, Vol 41, Sept 1985, 504-512

G.Y. Lai, "High Temperature Corrosion Problems in the Process Industries," *Journal of Metals*, Vol 37, July 1985, 14-19

R.M. Latanision, "Physical Metallurgy of Nickel-Base Alloys as It Relates to Corrosion," in *Corrosion of Nickel-Base Alloys*, American Society for Metals, Metals Park, OH, 1985

R.A. Page, "Stress Corrosion of I-182 Weld Metal in High Temperature Water; The Effect of a Carbon Steel Couple," *Corrosion*, Vol 41, June 1985, 338-340

J.W. Slusser, J.B. Tircomb, *et al.*, "Corrosion in Molten Nitrate- Nitrite Salts," *Journal of Metals*, Vol 37, July 1985, 24-27

W.J. Tomlinson, S.A. Campbell, "Passivity, Pitting and Corrosion of Anodically Polarized Fe-Ni Alloys in O.5M H_2SO_4 Containing Cl^-," *Journal of Materials Science,*, Vol 21, July 1986, 2590-2596

H.S. Tong, "The Corrosion Behavior of a Ni Based Amorphous Alloy; The Effect of Devitrification," *Corrosion*, Vol 41, Jan 1985, 10-12

I.G. Wright, V. Nagarajan, *et al.*, "Observations on the Role of Oxide Scales in High-Temperature Erosion-Corrosion of Alloys," *Oxidation of Metals*, April 1986, 175-199

Nickel-Base Superalloys

F. Abe, H Araki, *et al.*, "Corrosion Behavior of Nickel Base Heat Resisting Alloys for Nuclear Steelmaking System in High-Temperature Steam," *Transactions of the Iron and Steel Institute of Japan*, Vol 25, May 1985, 424-432

F. Abe, H. Yoshida, "Corrosion Behaviours of Heat Resisting Alloys in Steam at 800 °C and 40 atm Pressure," *Zeitschrift fur Metallkunde*, Vol 76, Mar 1985, 219-225

R. Bandy, R. Roberge, *et al.*, "Intergranular Failures of Alloy 600 in High Temperature Caustic Environments," *Corrosion*, Vol 41, Mar 1985, 142-150

R. Baver, K. Schneider, *et al.*, "Experience with Platinum Aluminide Coatings in Land-Based Gas Turbines," High-Temperature Technology, Vol 3, May 1985, 59-64

C.R. Bergen, "Sodium Silicates; Stress Corrosion Cracking Cracking Agents for Alloys 600 and 690 at 315 °C," *Corrosion*, Vol 41, Feb 1985, 85-88

P.D.W. Bottomley, J.L. Dawson, *et al.*, "Semi-immersed Galvanic Series in Na_2SO_4—NaCl Melts and a Comparison with Full-Immersion Potentials," *High-Temperature Technology*, Vol 4, Feb 1986, 37-45

C. Briant, S. O'Toole, *et al.*, "The Effect of Microstructure on the Corrosion and Stress Corrosion Cracking of Alloy 600 in Acidic and Neutral Environments," *Corrosion*, Vol 42, Jan 1986, 15-27

J.R. Crum, W.G. Lipscomb, "Performance of Nickel 200 and E-Brite 26-1 in First Effect Caustic Environments," *Materials Performance*, Vol 25, April 1986, 9-12

T. Fransen, P.J. Gellings, "Protection of Stainless Steels Against Corrosion in Sulphidizing Environments by Ce Oxide Coatings: X-Ray Absorption and Thermogravimetric Studies," *Applications of Surface Science*, Vol 20, Jan 1985, 257-266

W.Z. Friend, *Corrosion of Nickel and Nickel-Base Alloys*, John Wiley & Sons, New York, 1980

D.F. Hasson, C. Zanis, *et al.*, "Corrosion and Corrosion-Fatigue Behavior of IN625 Weld Surfaced 3.25 Nickel Steel," *Journal of Materials for Energy Systems*, Vol 7, Dec 1985, 256-264

E.L. Hibner, "Modification of Critical Crevice Temperature TestProcedures for Nickel-Alloys in a Ferritic Chloride Environment,"*Materials Performance*, Vol 26, Mar 1987, 37-40

Y. Kurata, T. Kondo, "Effect of Heating Rate on Corrosion Behavior of Ni-base Heat Resisting Alloys," *Transactions of the Iron and Steel Institute of Japan*, Vol 25, Jan 1985, B-27

F.L. LaQue, *Marine Corrosion; Causes and Prevention*, John Wiley & Sons, New York, 1975

K.H. Lee, G. Cragnolino, *et al.*, "Effect of Heat Treatment Applied Potential on the Caustic Stress Corrosion Cracking of Inconel 600," *Corrosion*, Vol 41, Sept 1985, 540-553

X. Liu, J. Shao, *et al.*, "Selective Grain-Boundary Dissolution of Alloy 600 in a Concentrated Caustic Solution at 140 °C," *Journal of Materials for Energy Systems*, Vol 7, Dec 1985, 223-236

A.K. Miskra, "Corrosion of Metals and Alloys in Sulfate Melts at 750 °C," *Oxidation of Metals*, Vol 25, June 1986, 373-396

A.K. Miskra, "Studies on the Hot Corrosion of a Nickel-Base Superalloy, Udimet 700," *Oxidation of Metals*, Vol 25, April 1986, 129-161

J.D. Rubio, R.R. Hart, *et al.*, "Effects of BF_2^+ Ion Implantation on the Corrosion Resistance of Inconel 600," *Corrosion*, Vol 42, Sept 1986,557-558

Y. Sakai, T. Shikama, *et al.*, "Corrosion Behaviour of Inconel 617 Coated with SiO_2 Film of Various Thicknesses in Impure Helium," *Transactions of the Iron and Steel Institute of Japan*, Vol 25, Jan 1985, B-28

J.W. Slusser, J.B. Tircomb, *et al.*, "Corrosion in Molten Nitrate-Nitrite Salts," *Journal of Metals*, Vol 37, July 1985, 24-27

D.J. Stephenson, J.R. Nicholls, *et al.*, "Particle-Surface Interactions During Erosion of a Gas Turbine Material (MarM002) by Pyrolytic Carbon Particles," *Wear*, Vol 1, Aug 1986, 15-29

N. Totsuka, E. Lunarska, *et al.*, "A Sensitive Technique forEvaluating Susceptibility to IGSCC of Alloy 600 in High Temperature Water," *Scripta Metallurgica*, Vol 20, July 1986, 1035-1040

L.B. Traylor, C.E. Price, "A Comparison of Hydrogen and Mercury Embrittlement in Monel at Room Temperature," Journal of Engineering Materials and Technology, Vol 108, Jan 1986, 31-36

E.J. Vineberg, D.L. Douglas, "Effect of Yttrium on the Sulfidation Behavior of Ni-Cr-Al Alloys at 700 °C," *Oxidation of Metals*, Vol 25, Feb 1986, 1-28

Niobium

R.W. Balliett, M. Coscia, *et al.*, "Niobium and Tantalum in Materials Selection," *Journal of Metals*, Vol 38, Sept 1986, 25-27

R.H. Burns, F.S. Shuker, *et al.*, "Industrial Applications of Corrosion-Resistant Tantalum, Niobium, and Their Alloys," in *Refractory Metals and Their Industrial Applications*, (STP 849), R.E. Smallwood, Ed., American Society for Testing and Materials, Philadelphia, 1984, 50-69

R.T. Webster, "The Applications of Zirconium and Niobium," in *Second Symposium on Shell and Tube Heat Exchangers*, W.R. Apblett, Jr., Ed., American Society for Metals, Metals Park, OH, 1982

Noble Metals

J.P. Franey, G.W. Kammlott, *et al.*, "The Corrosion of Silver by Atmospheric Sulfurous Gases," *Corrosion Science*, Vol 25, July 1985, 133-143

M. Marek, "The Corrosion of Dental Materials," in *Treatise on Materials Science and Technology*, Vol 23, J.C. Scully, Ed., Academic Press, New York, 1983, 331-394

M. Rubel, M. Pszonicka, "Oxygen Interaction with Pt - Pd -Rh Catalytic Alloys," *Journal of Materials Science*, Vol 21, Jan 1986, 241-245

N.R. Sorenson, "The Environmentally Assisted Failure of Cusil in Mattsson's Solution," *Corrosion*, Vol 42, May 1986, 299-306 (silver)

G.W. Walkiden, "The Noble Metals," in *Corrosion; Metal/Environment Reactions*, Vol 1, 2nd ed., L.L. Shreir, Ed., Newnes-Butterworths, London, 1976, 6:1-6:23

E.M. Wise, "Gold and Gold Alloys," in *The Corrosion Handbook*, H.H. Uhlig, Ed., John Wiley & Sons, New York, 1948

Powder Metallurgy Metals

P.C. Searson, R.M. Latanision, "The Corrosion and Oxidation Resistance of Iron- and Aluminum-Based Powder Metallurgical Alloys," *Corrosion Science*, Vol 25, 1985, 947-968

Stainless Steels: General

E.A. Baker, T.S. Lee, "Long-Term Atmospheric Corrosion Behavior of Various Grades of Stainless Steel," *Degradation of Metals in the Atmosphere*, (STP 965), S.W. Dean, T.S. Lee, Eds., American Society for Testing and Materials, Philadelphia, 1987, 52-67

D. Cubicciotti, L. Ljungberg, "The Pourbaix Diagram for Cr with Fe and the Stress Corrosion Cracking of Stainless Steel," *Journal of theElectrochemical Society*, Vol 132, April 1985, 987-988

F.L. LaQue, Marine Corrosion; Causes and Prevention, John Wiley & Sons, New York, 1975

Stainless Steels: Austenitic

S. Ahmad, M.L. Mehta, et al., "Electrochemical Studies of Stress Corrosion Cracking of Sensitized AISI 304 Stainless Steel in PolythionicAcids," Corrosion, Vol 41, June 1985, 363-367

M. Asawa, "Stress Corrosion Cracking Regions on Contour Maps of Dissolution Rates for AISI 304 Stainless Steel in Sulfuric Acid Solutions with Chloride, Bromide, or Iodide," Corrosion, Vol 43, April 1987, 198-203

S. Bernhardsson, R. Mellstrom, et al., "Performance of a High AlloyedStainless Steel in Marine Environments," Anti-Corrosion Methods and Materials, Vol 32, April 1985, 7-11

S. Bernhardsson, P. Norberg, et al., "Stainless Steels in the Petrochemical Industries," Iron and Steel International, Vol 58, Feb 1987, 7-9

R.J. Brigham, "The Initiation of Crevice Corrosion on Stainless Steels," Materials Performance, Vol 24, Dec 1985, 44-48

H.E. Chandler, "Ferritic Stainless Steel Combats Chloride Corrosion," Metal Progress, Vol 128, Oct 1985, 63-66.

K. Chopra, D.L. Smith, "Corrosion of Ferrous Alloys in a Flowing Lithium Environment," Journal of Nuclear Materials, Vol 133-134, Aug 1985, 861-866

O.K. Chopra, D.L. Smith, et al., "Liquid-Metal Corrosion," Fusion Technology, Vol 8, Sept 1985, 1956-1969

P.C. Chung, G. Gragnolino, et al., "Instrumented Loading Devices for Monitoring Environmentally Assisted Crack Growth in High Temperature Aqueous Systems," Corrosion, Vol 41, Mar 1985, 179-183

V. Cihal, Intergranular Corrosion of Steels and Alloys, Elesvier Science Publishers, New York, 1984

R.L. Cowan II, C.S. Tedmon, Jr., "Intergranular Corrosion of Iron-Nickel-Chromium Alloys," in Advances in Corrosion Science and Technology, Vol 3, M. Fontana, R. Staehle, Eds., Plenum Press, New York, 1973, 293-400

G. Daufin, J. Pagetti, et al., "Pitting Initiation on Stainless Steels: Electrochemical and Micrographic Aspects," Corrosion, Vol 41, Sept 1985, 533-539

G.O. Davis, J. Kolts, et al., "Polarization Effects in Galvanic Corrosion," Corrosion, Vol 42, June 1986, 329-336

A. Dhirandra, S. Gupta, et al., "'Water Line' and 'Above Water Line' Corrosion of Stainless Steel (ANSI 321) in H_2SO_4 and Its Inhibition," Corrosion Prevention and Control, Vol 34, April 1987, 58-59

A.T. El-Mallah, M.E. Abou Hassan, et al., "Some Aspects of Corrosion Inhibition of Potable Water," Corrosion Prevention and Control, Vol 32, Oct 1985, 100-105

M.G. Fontana, N.D. Greene, Corrosion Engineering, McGraw-Hill Book Co., New York, 1967

A. Garner, "How Stainless Steel Welds Corrode," Metal Progress, Vol 27, April 1985, 31-36

S. Gupta, M. Vajpeyi, et al., "Determination of Corrosion of Stainless Steel (AISI 304) by Mixed Vapours of HCl and HNO_3," Corrosion Prevention and Control, Vol 33, April 1986, 47-50

D.A. Hale, "The Effect of BWR Startup Environments on Crack Growth in Structural Alloys," Journal of Engineering Materials and Technology, Vol 108, Jan 1986, 44-49

D.J. Hall, M.K. Hossain, et al., "Factors Affecting Carburization Behavior of Cast Austenitic Steels," Materials Performance, Vol 24, Jan 1985, 25-31

E.C. Hoxie, "The Application of Austenitic Stainless Steels and High Nickel Alloys for Shell and Tube Heat Exchangers," in Second Symposium on Shell and Tube Heat Exchangers, W.R. Apblett, Jr., Ed., American Society for Metals, Metals Park, OH, 1982

W.M.M. Huijbregts, "Oxygen and Corrosion Potential Effects on Chloride Stress Corrosion Cracking," Corrosion, Vol 42, Aug 1986, 456-462

M.E. Indig, J.E. Weber, "Effects of H_2 Additions on Stress Corrosion Cracking in a Boiling Water Reactor," Corrosion, Vol 41, Jan 1985, 19-30

K.J.L. Iyer, S. Ramakrishna Iyer, et al., "Role of Sodium in Hot Stress Corrosion of AISI 304 Stainless Steel," Corrosion, Vol 41, June 1985, 333-338

H. Kajimura, H. Morikawa, et al., "Effect of Alloying Elements on the Corrosion Resistance of Stainless Steels in Nitric Acid, (Corrosion Resistance of Stainless Steels in Nitric Acid - II)," Transactions of the Iron and Steel Institute of Japan, Vol 25, April 1985, B-131

T. Kawakubo, M. Hishida, "Elastic-Plastic Fracture Mechanics Analysis on Environmentally Accelerated Cracking of Stainless Steel in High Temperature Water," Journal of Engineering Materials and Technology, Vol 107, July 1985, 240-245

R.R. Kirchheiner, F. Hofmann, et al., "A Silicon-Alloyed Stainless Steel for Highly Oxidizing Conditions," Materials Performance, Vol 26, Jan 1987, 49-56

H.H. Krause, P.A. Ireland, et al., "Cyclic Reheat Materials Evaluation," Materials Performance, Vol 26, April 1987, 44-54

Y. Kusaka, T. Masuda, "The Compatibility of Metal Electrodes in the Oil Fired MHD Environment," Journal of Materials for Energy Systems, Vol 8, June 1986, 58-69

A. Levy, Y-F Man, "Surface Degradation of Ductile Metals in Elevated Temperature Gas-Particle Streams," Wear, Vol 2, Sept 1986, 173-186

R.C. Lobb, H.E. Evans, "The Oxidation of Chromium-Depleted Stainless Steels in a CO_2-Based Gas of Low Sulfur Activity," Corrosion Science, Vol 25, Feb 1985, 503-518

I.A. Maier, C. Manfredi, et al., "The Stress Corrosion Cracking of an Austenitic Stainless Steel in HCl⅞NaCl Solutions at Room Temperature," Corrosion Science, Vol 25, May 1985, 15-34

A.U. Malik, S. Ahmad, "Oxidation Behaviour of Silicate-Chromate and Oxide Coated 303 Steel in Presence of Ionic Salts Over Temperature Range of 400 - 1000 *C," *British Corrosion Journal*, Vol 20, Oct 1985, 71-83

F. Mancia, A. Tamba, "Slow Strain Rate Stress Corrosion Cracking of AISI 304 Stainless Steel in NaCl Solution and Its Prevention by Controlled Cathodic Protection," *Corrosion*, Vol 42, June 1986, 362-367

I.Maya, F. Montgomery, *et al.*, "Activation Product Release from Fusion Structural Materials in Helium," *Journal of Nuclear Materials*, Vol 133-134,Aug 1985, 912-916

C.T. Morrison, R.O. Scattergood, "Erosion of 304 Stainless Steel," *Wear*, Vol 1, Aug 1986, 1-13

T.A. Mozhi, K. Nishimoto, *et al.*, "The Effect of Nitrogen on Stress Corrosion Cracking of AISI 304 Stainless Steel in High-Temperature Sulfate Solution," *Corrosion*, Vol 42, April 1986, 197-203

T. Nagoya, T. Yoshii, *et al.*, "Effect of Various Factors on Corrosion Resistance of 20Cr-25Ni-6Mo Stainless Steel for Seawater," *Transactions of the Iron and Steel Institute of Japan*, Vol 25, Jan 1985, B-32

T. Nakayama, M. Takano, "Stress Corrosion Behavior of AISI 304 Stainless in a Boiling 42% $MgCl_2$ Solution Under Cyclic Slow Strain Rate Technique," *Corrosion*, Vol 41, Oct 1985, 592-597

J.Y. Park, W.E. Ruther, *et al.*, "Stress Corrosion Crack Growth Rates in Type 304 Stainless Steel in Simulated BWR Environments," *Journal of Engineering and Materials and Technology*, Vol 108, Jan 1986, 20-25

B.S. Phull, T.S. Lee, "Localized Corrosion of Stainless Steels and Nickel Alloys in Flue Gas Desulfurization Environments," *Materials Performance*, Vol 25, Aug 1986, 30-35

F.P.A. Robinson, P.V. Biljon, "The Substitution of Molybdenum with Vanadium in Cast Austenitic Stainless Steel Alloys," *Corrosion*, Vol 41, April 1985, 220-228

J-I. Sakai, M. Hondu, *et al.*, "Critical Contents of Nickel and Chromium Required for SCC Resistance of High Alloy Oil Country Tubular Goods," *Corrosion*, Vol 41, Feb 1985, 80-84

A.J. Sedriks, "Effects of Alloy Composition and Microstructure on the Passivity of Stainless Steels," *Corrosion*, Vol 42, July 1986, 376-389

P.G. Smith, J.E. Truman, "The Stress Corrosion Resistance of Nonmagnetic Stainless Steel Used in Oil Exploration," *Journal of Materials for Energy Systems*, Vol 6, Mar 1985, 300-312

H.D. Solomon, "Influence of Prior Deformation and Composition on Continuous Cooling Sensitization of AISI 304 Stainless Steel," *Corrosion*, Vol 41, Sept 1985, 512-517

M. Studnicki, "Syntheses of Derivatives of Alkylarylamines and Their Properties as Pickling Inhibitors of Carbon Steels and Stainless Steels," *Industrial and Engineering Chemistry, Product Research and Development*, Vol 25, Mar 1986, 96-102

T. Suzuki, I. Mutoh, *et al.*, "Sodium Corrosion Behavior of Austenitic Alloys and Selective Dissolution of Chromium and Nickel," Journal of Nuclear Materials, Vol 139, June 1985, 97-105

K. Tanno, Y. Yuasa, *et al.*, "Stress Corrosion Cracking of Sensitized AISI 304 Stainless Steel in Oxygenated Na_2SO_4 Solution at High Temperature," *Corrosion*, Vol 43, April 1987, 248-250

H. Tomari, K. Fujiwar, *et al.*, "Intergranular Corrosion and Its Prevention of Boron-Alloyed Austenitic Stainless Steel," *Transactions of the Iron and Steel Institute of Japan*, Vol 25, April 1985, B-132

H.H. Uhlig, R.W. Revie, *Corrosion and Corrosion Control; An Introduction to Corrosion Science and Engineering*, 3rd ed., John Wiley & Sons, New York, 1985

M. Vajpeyi, S. Gupta, *et al.*, "Corrosion of Stainless Steel (AISI 304) in H_2SO_4 Contaminated with HCl and HNO_3," *Corrosion Prevention and Control*, Vol 32, Oct 1985, 102-104

B.E. Wilde, "Influence of Silicon on the Intergranular Stress Corrosion Cracking Resistance of 18Cr-8Ni Base Stainless Steel," *Corrosion*, Vol 42, Nov 1986, 678-681

B.E. Wilde, "The Influence of Silicon on the Pitting Corrosion Resistance of an 18Cr-8Ni Stainless Steel," *Corrosion*, Vol 42, Mar 1986, 147-151

G.L. Wire, E.J. Vesely, *et al.*, "Erosion-Corrosion of Metals in Coal Gasification Atmospheres," *Journal of Materials for Energy Systems*, Vol 8, Sept 1986, 150-167

M. Yasuda, S. Tokunaga, *et al.*, "Corrosion Behavior of 18-8 Stainless Steels in Hot Concentrated Caustic Soda Solutions Under Heat-Transfer Conditions," *Corrosion*, Vol 41, Dec 1985, 720-727

A. Zingales, G. Quartarone, *et al.*, "Sigma Phase Intergranular Corrosion Effects in Austenitic Welds Containing Ferrite," *Corrosion*, Vol 41, Mar 1985, 136-141

Stainless Steels: Duplex

R.M. Davison, J.D. Redmond, "The Application of Ferritic and Duplex Stainless Steels," in *Second Symposium on Shell and Tube Heat Exchangers*, W.R. Apblett, Jr., Ed., American Society for Metals, Metals Park, OH, 1982

Duplex Stainless Steels, R.A. Lula, Ed., American Society for Metals, Metals Park, OH, 1983

G. Herbsleb, P. Schwaab, "Precipitation of Intermetallic Compounds, Nitrides and Carbides in AF 22 Duplex Steel and Their Influence on Corrosion Behavior in Acids," in *Duplex Stainless Steels*, R.A. Lula,Ed., American Society for Metals, Metals Park, OH, 1983

A. Ikeda, S. Mukai, "Corrosion Behavior of 9 to 25% Cr Steels in Wet CO_2 Environments," *Corrosion*, Vol 41, April 1985, 163-169

H. Miyuki, T. Kudo, "25% Cr Containing Duplex Phase Stainless Steel for Hot Sea Water Application," in *Duplex Stainless Steels*, R.A. Lula, Ed., American Society for Metals, Metals Park, OH, 1983

H. Miyuki, J. Murayama, *et al.*, "Localized Corrosion of Duplex Stainless Steels in CO_2-H_2-S-Cl^- Environments at Elevated Temperatures," Paper No. 293 of Corrosion 84 Forum, National Association of Corrosion Engineers, Houston, 1984

M. Onoyama, N. Hayashi, "Evaluation of Corrosion Resistance of a Duplex Stainless Steel in H_2S-CO_2-Chloride Environments," in *Duplex Stainless Steels*, R.A. Lula, Ed., American Society for Metals, Metals Park, OH, 1983

A. John Sedricks, *Corrosion of Stainless Steels*, John Wiley & Sons, New York, 1979

N. Sridhar, J. Kolts, *et al.*, "A Duplex Stainless Steel for Chloride Environments," *Journal of Metals*, Vol 37, Mar 1985, 31-35

N. Sridhar, J. Kolts, "Effects of Nitrogen on the Selective Dissolution of Duplex Stainless Steel," *Corrosion*, Vol 43, Nov 1987, 646-650

Stainless Steels, R.A. Lula, Editor, American Society for Metals, Metals Park, OH

"Steels for the Salt Solution," *Iron and Steel International*, Vol 58, Feb 1985, 9-13

J.E. Truman, K.R. Pirt, "Properties of a Duplex (Austenitic-Ferritic) Stainless Steel and Effects of Thermal History," in *Duplex Stainless Steels*, R.A. Lula, Ed., American Society for Metals, Metals Park, OH, 1983

S.M. Wilhelm, R.D. Kane, "Effect of Heat Treatment and Microstructure on the Corrosion and SCC of Duplex Stainless Steels in H_2S/Cl^- Environments," *Corrosion*, Vol 40, Aug 1984, 431-440

Y.-H. Yau, M.A. Streicher, "Galvanic Corrosion of Duplex FeCr-10%Ni Alloys in Reducing Acids," *Corrosion*, Vol 43, June 1987, 336-372

Stainless Steels: Ferritic

R.M. Davison, J.D. Redmond, "The Application of Ferritic and Duplex Stainless Steels," in *Second Symposium on Shell and Tube Heat Exchangers*, W.R. Apblett, Jr., Ed., American Society for Metals, Metals Park, OH, 1982

H.E. Deverell, "Stabilization of AISI 439 (S43035) Stainless Steel," *Materials Performance*, Vol 24, Feb 1985, 47-50

J.B. Lee, J.F. Smith, *et al.*, "An Analytical Electron Microscope Examination of Sensitized AISI 430 Stainless Steel," *Corrosion*, Vol 41, Feb 1985, 76-77

I.E. Locci, H.K. Kwon, *et al.*, "Stress Corrosion Cracking Initiation in Ferratic Stainless Steels in a Chloride Environment," *Corrosion*, Vol 43, Aug 1987, 465-469

S.K. Mukherjee, G.S. Upadhyaya, "Corrosion Behaviour of Sintered 434L Ferritic Stainless Steel, Al_2O_3 Composites Containing Phosphorus," *Corrosion Science*, Vol 25, Sept 1985, 463-470

T.J. Nichol, J.A. Davis, "Intergranular Corrosion Testing and Sensitization of Two High-Chromium Ferritic Stainless Steels," in *Intergranular Corrosion of Stainless Alloys*, (STP 656), R.F. Steigerwald, Ed., American Society for Testing and Materials, Philadelphia, 1978

Stainless Steels: Martensitic

A.K. Agrawal, W.N. Stiegelmeyer, "Corrosion and Cracking Behaviour of a Martensitic 12Cr-3.5Ni-Fe Alloy in Simulated Sour Gas Environments," *Materials Performance*, Vol 26, Mar 1987, 24-29

A. Atrens, "Environmental Conditions Leading to Pitting/Crevice Corrosion of a Typical 12% Chromium Stainless Steel at 80 °C," *Corrosion*, Vol 39, Dec 1983, 483-487

T. Kurisu, M. Kimura, *et al.*, "Corrosion Resistance of Low C-Ni-13Cr Stainless Steels in CO_2/H_2O Environments," *Transactions of the Iron and Steel Institute of Japan*, Vol 25, April 1985, B-133

H. Kurahashi, T. Kurisu, *et al.*, "Stress Corrosion Cracking of 13Cr Steels in CO_2-H_2-S-C^- Environments," *Corrosion*, Vol 41, April 1985, 211-218

R. Mathis, "Initiation and Early Growth Mechanisms of Corrosion Fatigue Cracks in Stainless Steels," *Journal of Materials Science*, Vol 22, Mar 1987, 907-914

H.M. Shalaby, V.K. Gouda, "Effect of Chloride Concentration and pH on Fatigue Crack Initiation Morphology of Type 403 Stainless Steel," *British Corrosion Journal*, Vol 20, June 1985, 125-132

C.J. Thomas, R.G.J. Edyvean, *et al.*, "Environmentally Assisted Crack Growth in a Martensitic Stainless Steel," *Materials Science and Engineering*, Vol 78, Feb 1986, 55-63

Y. Yoshino, "Stress Corrosion Cracking of CrNi Martensitic Stainless Steel in Concentrated $MgCl_2$ Solutions," *Corrosion*, Vol 42, Oct 1986, 592-600

Y. Yoshino, A. Ikegaya, "Pitting and Stress Cracking of 12Cr-Ni-Mo Martensitic Stainless Steels in Chloride and Sulfide Environments," *Corrosion*, Vol 41, Feb 1985, 105-113

Stainless Steels: Precipitation Hardening

R.R. Gaugh, "Stress Corrosion Cracking of Precipitation-Hardening Stainless Steels," *Materials Performance*, Vol 26, Feb 1987, 29-34

Tantalum and Tantalum Alloys

R.W. Balliett, M. Coscia, *et al.*, "Niobium and Tantalum in Materials Selection," *Journal of Metals*, Vol 38, Sept 1986, 25-27

R.H. Burns, F.S. Shuker, Jr., *et al.*, "Industrial Applications of Corrosion-Resistant Tantalum, Niobium, and Their Alloys," in *Refractory Metals and Their Industrial Applications*, (STP 849), R.E. Smallwood, Ed., American Society for Testing and Materials, Philadelphia, 1984, 50-69

C.A. Hampel, "Tantalum," in Rare *Metals Handbook*, 2nd ed., C.A. Hampel, Ed., Reinhold Publishing Corp., New York, 1961

P.A. Schweitzer, "Tantalum," in *Corrosion and Corrosion Protection Handbook*, P.A. Schweitzer, Ed., Marcel Dekker, Inc., New York, 1983

M. Stern, C. Bishop, "Corrosion and Electrochemical Behavior," in *Columbium and Tantalum*, F. Sisco, E. Epremian, Eds., John Wiley & Sons, Inc., New York, 1963, 304-346

I. Uehara, T. Sakai, *et al.*, "The Corrosion Behavior of Tantalum and Niobium in Hydrobromic Acid Solutions," *Corrosion*, Vol 42, Aug 1986, 492-499

Tin and Tin Alloys

S.S. Abd El Rehim, A.A. Samahi, *et al.*, "Breakdown of Tin Passivity in Aqueous Sodium Stannate Solution," *British Corrosion Journal*, Vol 20, Aug 1985, 196-200

S.C. Britton, *Tin Versus Corrosion*, (Pub. No. 510), International Tin Research Institute, Greenford, England, 1975

R.M. Burns, W.W. Bradley, *Protective Coatings for Metals*, 3rd ed., Reinhold Publishing Corp., New York, 1967

H. Leidheiser, Jr., *The Corrosion of Copper, Tin, and Their Alloys*, John Wiley & Sons, New York, 1971

F.A. Lowenheim, R.A. Woofter, *et al.*, "Tin and Tin Plate," in *Corrosion Resistance of Metals and Alloys*, 2nd ed., F.L. LaQue, H.R. Copson, Eds., Reinhold Publishing Corp., New York, 1963

M.E. Warwick, *Atmospheric Corrosion of Tin and Tin Alloys*, International Tin Research Institute, Greenford, England, no date

M.E. Warwick, W.B. Hampshire, "Atmospheric Corrosion on Tin and Tin Alloys," in A*tmospheric Corrosion*, W.H. Ailor, Ed., John Wiley & Sons, New York, 1982

Titanium

M. Blackburn, J. Feeney, "Stress-Corrosion Cracking of Titanium Alloys," in *Advances in Corrosion Science and Technology*, Vol 3, M. Fontana, R. Staehle, Eds., Plenum Press, New York, 1973, 67-292

H. Jain, T.M. Ahn, *et al.*, "Stress Corrosion of ASTM Grade-2 and Grade-12 Titanium in Simulated Rock Salt Brines at 83 °C," *Corrosion*, Vol 41, July 1985, 375-380

Y.J. Kim, R.A. Oriani, "Brine Radiolysis and Its Effects on the Corrosion of Grade 12 Titanium," *Corrosion*, Vol 43, Feb 1987, 92-97

Y.J. Kim, R.A. Oriani, "Corrosion Properties of the Oxide Film Formed on Grade 12 Titanium in Brine Under Gamma Radiation," *Corrosion*, Vol 43, Feb 1987, 85-91

F.L. LaQue, Marine Corrosion; Causes and Prevention, John Wiley & Sons, New York, 1975

P. McKay, D.B. Mitton, "An Electrochemical Investigation of Localized Corrosion on Titanium in Chloride Environments," *Corrosion*, Vol 41, Jan 1985, 52-62

Uranium

J.H. Gittus, *Uranium*, Butterworths, Washington, 1963

G.L. Powell, W.G. Northcutt, Jr., "Internal Hydrogen Embrittlement of Uranium-5.7 Niobium Alloy," *Journal of Nuclear Materials*, Vol 132, May 1985, 47-51

W.D. Wilkenson, *Uranium Metallurgy; Uranium Corrosion and Alloys*, Vol II, John Wiley & Sons, New York, 1962

Zinc

J. Banas, K.G. Schutze, *et al.*, "Corrosion Studies on Zinc in a Menthonal/Water/Lithium/Chloride/Oxygen System," *Journal of the Electrochemical Society*, Vol 133, Feb 1986, 253-259

R.M. Burns, W.W. Bradley, Protective Coatings for Metals, 3rd ed., Reinhold Publishing Corp., New York, 1967

V. Kucera, E. Mattsson, "Atmospheric Corrosion," in *Corrosion Mechanisms*, F. Mansfeld, Ed., Marcel Dekker, Inc., New York, 1987, 221-284

A.E.B. Mostafa, S.M. Abdel-Wahaab, "The Corrosion Behaviour of Zinc Metal in Acidic Solutions of Polyvinyl-pyrrolidones and Polyvinylpyridines," *Surface and Coatings Technology*, Vol 27, April1 986, 317-324

O.E. Okarafor, "Corrosion Under Sheltered and Unsheltered Sites in Awka, Nigeria," *Corrosion Prevention and Control*, Vol 33, June 1986, 64-67

C.J. Slunder, W.K. Boyd, *Zinc: Its Corrosion Resistance*, 2nd ed., T.K. Christman, J. Payer, Eds., International Lead Zinc Research Organization, New York, 1983

N.D. Tomashov, *Theory of Corrosion and Protection of Metals*, B.Tytell, I. Geld, *et al.*, Eds., The McMillan Co., New York, 1966

Zirconium, Hafnium

ASTM Manual on Zirconium and Hafnium, (STP 639), J.H. Schemel, Ed., American Society for Testing and Materials, Philadelphia, 1977

D. Charquet, E. Steinberg, *et al.*, "Influence of Variations in Early Fabrication Steps on *Corrosion*, Mechanical Properties, and Structure of Zircaloy-4 Products," in *Zirconium in the Nuclear Industry*, (STP 939), Ronald B. Adamson, Leo F.P. Van Swam, Eds., American Society for Testing and Materials, Philadelphia, 1987

J.S. Chen, A. Bronson, *et al.*, "Pitting Corrosion on Zirconium in KCl and KCl-H$_2$SO$_4$ Solutions," *Corrosion*, Vol 41, Aug 1985, 438-445

B. Cheng, R.B. Adamson, "Mechanistic Studies of Zircaloy Nodular Corrosion," in *Zirconium in the Nuclear Industry*, (STP 939), Ronald B. Adamson, Leo F.P. Van Swam, Eds., American Society for Testing and Materials, Philadelphia, 1987

B. Cheng, H.A. Levin, *et al.*, "Development of a Sensitive and Reproducible Steam Test for Zircaloy Nodular Corrosion," in

Zirconium in the Nuclear Industry, (STP 939), Ronald B. Adamson, Leo F.P. VanSwam, Eds., American Society for Testing and Materials, Philadelphia, 1987

Corrosion and Corrosion Protection Handbook, Philip Schweitzer, Ed.,Marcel Decker, Inc., New York, 1983

J.B. Cotton, "Titanium and Zirconium," in *Corrosion; Metal/Environment Reactions*, Vol 1, 2nd ed., L.L. Shreir, Ed., Newnes-Butterworths, London, 1976

B. Cox, R. Hadded, "Methyl Iodide as a Promoter of the SCC of Zirconium Alloys in Iodine Vapour," *Journal of Nuclear Materials*, Vol 137, Jan 1986, 115-123

B. Cox, B.A. Surette, *et al.*, "Stress Corrosion Cracking of Zircaloysin Unirradiated and Irradiated CsI," *Journal of Nuclear Materials*, Vol 138, Mar 1986, 89-98

Edward Hillner, "Corrosion of Zirconium-Base Alloys—An Overview,"in *Zirconium in the Nuclear Industry*, (STP 633), A.L. Lowe, Jr., G.W. Parry, Eds., American Society for Testing and Materials, Philadelphia, 1977

P.Hofmann, J. Spino, "Conditions Under Which CsI Can Cause SCC Failure of Zircaloy Tubing," *Journal of Nuclear Materials*, Vol 127, Jan 1985, 205-220

K.-Y. Huang, C.-H. Tsai, "The Effect of Heat Treatment on the Microstructure and the Corrosion Resistance of Zircaloy-4 in 450 °C Steam," *Journal of Nuclear Materials*, Vol 136, Oct 1985, 16-29

A.B. Johnson, Jr., "Corrosion and Failure Characteristics of Zirconium in High-Pressure Steam in the Temperature Range of 400 to 500 °C," in *Applications-Related Phenomena in Zirconium and Its Alloys*, (STP 458), American Society for Testing and Materials, Philadelphia, 1969

S. Kass, "The Development of the Zircaloys," in *Corrosion of Zirconium Alloys*, (STP 368), American for Testing and Materials, Philadelphia, 1964

T. Kubo, T. Motomiya, *et al.*, "Low-Cycle Corrosion Fatigue of Zircaloy-2 in Iodine Atmospheres," *Journal of Nuclear Materials*, Vol 140, Sept 1986, 185-196

T. Kubo, Y. Wakashima, *et al.*, "Distribution of Intermetallic Particles and Its Effects on SCC of Zirconium Alloys," *Journal of Nuclear Materials*, Vol 138, April 1986, 256-267

T. Kubo, Y. Wakashima, *et al.*, "Effects of Intermetallic Particles on the SCC Initiation of Zirconium Alloys," *Journal of Nuclear Materials*, Vol 132, June 1985, 126-136

R. Kuwae, K. Sato, *et al.*, "Influence of Some Factors on Nodular Corrosion Behavior of Zircaloy-2," *Journal of Nuclear Science and Technology*, Vol 23, July 1986, pp 661-663

J.E. LeSurf, "The Corrosion Behavior of 2.5Nb Zirconium Alloy," in *Applications-Related Phenomena in Zirconium and Its Alloys*, (STP 458), American Society for Testing and Materials, Philadelphia, 1969

B. Lustman, "Corrosion of Zirconium and Its Alloys," in *Metallurgy of Zirconium*, B. Lustman, F. Kerze, Eds., McGraw-Hill Book Co., New York, 1955, 553-686

M. Maguire, "The Pitting Susceptibility of Zirconium in Aqueous Cl^-, Br^-, and I^- Solutions," in *Industrial Applications of Titanium and Zirconium*, (STP 830), R.T. Webster, C.S. Young, Eds., American Society for Testing and Materials, Philadelphia, 1983

G. Marx, A. Bestanpouri, *et al.*, "Investigation of the Corrosion of Valve Metals and Alloys Under the Influence of Plutonium," *Journal of the Less-Common Metals*, Vol 121, July 1986, 507-513

P. Mayer, A.V. Manolescu, "Corrosion of Zirconium Alloys in Alternating pH Environment," *Canadian Metallurgical Quarterly*, Vol 24, July-Sept 1985, 197-206

B.J. Moniz, "Corrosion Resistance of Zirconium in Chemical Processing Equipment," in *Industrial Applications of Titanium and Zirconium*, (STP 830), R.T. Webster, C.S. Young, Eds., American Society for Testing and Materials, Philadelphia, 1983

M. Nagai, S. Shimada, *et al.*, "Evaluation of SCC Crack Behavior in Zirconium and Zircaloy-2 Using Nonlinear Fracture Mechanics Parameters," *Nuclear Engineering and Design*, Vol 88, Oct 1985, 319-326

G.C. Palit, H.S. Gadiyar, "Pitting Corrosion of Zirconium in Chloride Solution," *Corrosion*, Vol 43, Mar 1987, 140-148

M. Paljevic, "Interaction of Zr_2Al with Oxygen at High Temperatures," *Journal of the Less-Common Metals*, Vol 120, June 1986, 293-299

V.F. Urbanic, B. Cox, "Long-Term Corrosion and Deuteriding Behaviuor of Zircaloy-2 Under Irradiation," *Canadian Metallurgical Quarterly*, Vol 24, July-Sept 1985, 189-196

J. Vehlow, "Corrosion of Zircaloy-4 in H_2SO_4-NaF and Its Application for Measuring the Distribution Pattern of Fission Products in Zircaloy-4 Fuel Hulls," *Werkstoffe und Korrosion*, Vol 36, May 1985,195-202

R.T. Webster, "The Applications of Zirconium and Niobium," in *Second Symposium on Shell and Tube Heat Exchangers*, W.R. Apblett, Jr., Ed., American Society for Metals, Metals Park, OH, 1982

R.E. Williford, "Chemically Assisted Crack Nucleation in Zircaloy," in *Journal of Nuclear Materials*, Vol 132, May 1985, 52-61

T.L. Yau, R.T. Webster, "Corrosion of Zirconium and Hafnium," in *Metals Handbook*, 9th ed., Vol 13, *Corrosion*, ASM International, Metals Park, OH, 1987

N.A. Zreiba, D.O. Northwood, "The Corrosion/Hydriding Behavior of Zr-2.5 wt.% Nb Nuclear Reactor Pressure Tubing in Pressurized Lithiated Water (pH 12.3) at 300 °C," *Journal of Materials for Energy Systems*, Vol 7, Sept 1985, 104-122

Comparisons

R.W. Balliett, M. Coscia, *et al.*, "Niobium and Tantalum in Materials Selection," *Journal of Metals*, Vol 38, Sept 1986, 25-27

O.K. Chopra, J.A. Shearer, *et al.*, "Effect of Sulfation Accelerators on the Corrosion Behavior of Materials in Fluidized-Bed Environments,"in *Corrosion-Erosion Behavior of Materials*, K. Natesan, Ed., The Metallurgical Society of AIME, 1980

D.R. Flinn, S.D. Cramer, *et al.*, "Field Exposure Study for Determining the Effects of Acid Deposition on the Corrosion and Deterioration of Materials; Description of the Program and Preliminary Results," Durability of Building Materials, Vol 3, Nov 1985, 147-175

H.P. Hack, J.R. Scully, "Galvanic Corrosion Prediction Using Long-and Short-term Polarization Curves," *Corrosion*, Vol 42, Feb 1986, 79-90

G.N. Kirby, "Selecting Alloys for Chloride Service," *Chemical Engineering*, Vol 92, Feb 1985, 81-83

G.H. Koch, N.G. Thompson, "Localized Attack of Nickel-Containing Alloys in SO_2 Scrubber Environments,"*Journal of Materials for Energy Systems*, Vol 8, Sept 1986, 179-210

E.I. Meletis, "Materials Performance in Coal Gasification Environments," *Journal of Materials for Energy Systems*, Vol 8, Mar 1987, 371-384

J.Y.P. Mui, "Corrosion Mechanism of Metals and Alloys in the Silicon-Hydrogen-Chlorosilane System at 500 °C," *Corrosion*, Vol 41, Feb 1985, 63-69

A. Raman, G. Nnaike, *et al.*, "Corrosion Characteristics of Plasma-Sprayed TiN and TiC Coatings on Steel in Salt Water," *Corrosion Science*, Vol 25,Aug 1985, 107-115

P.V. Rao, D.H. Buckley, "Characterization of Solid Particle Erosion Resistance of Ductile Metals Based in Their Properties," *Journal of Engineering for Gas Turbines and Power*, Vol 107, July 1985, 669-678H.H. Uhlig, *Corrosion and Corrosion Engineering; An Introduction to Corrosion Science and Engineering*, 1st ed., John Wiley & Sons, New York, 1963

Environments

D.J. Astley, J.C. Rowlands, "Modelling of Bimetallic Corrosion in Sea Water Systems," *British Corrosion Journal*, Vol 20, Mar 1985, 90-94

V. Chaker, "Simplified Method for the Electrical Soil Resistivity Measurement," in *Underground Corrosion*, (STP 741), E. Escalante, Ed., American Society for Testing and Materials, Philadelphia, 1981, 61-91

F.A. Champion, *Corrosion Testing Procedures*, 2nd ed., JohnWiley & Sons, Inc., New York, 1965

R.L. Cowan II, C.S. Tedmon, Jr., "Intergranular Corrosion of Iron-Nickel-Chromium Alloys," in *Advances in Corrosion Science and Technology*, Vol 3, M. Fontana, R. Staehle, Eds., Plenum Press, New York, 1973, 293-400

A. Garner, "Corrosion of Weldments in Pulp Bleach Plants," *Welding Journal*, Vol 65, Sept 1985, 39-44

F.E. Goodwin, "Corrosion Resistance of Lead Alloys Under Nuclear Waste Repository Conditions," *Corrosion Prevention and Control*, Vol 32, April 1985, 21-24

O.Hollander, R.C. May "The Chemistry of Azole Copper Corrosion Inhibitors in Cooling Water," *Corrosion*, Vol 41, Jan 1985, 35-45

D. Jones, "Localized Corrosion," in *Corrosion Processes*, R.Parkins, Ed., Allied Science Publishers, London, 1982, 161-207

G.H. Koch, N.G. Thompson, "Localized Attack of Nickel-Containing Alloys in SO_2 Scrubber Environments,"*Journal of Materials for Energy Systems*, Vol 8, Sept 1986, 179-210

J. Larsen-Basse, "Performance of OTEC Heat Exchanger Materials in Tropical Waters," *Journal of Metals*, Vol 37, Mar 1985, 25 N.D. Tomashov, *Theory of Corrosion and Protection of Metals*, B. Tytell, I. Geld, *et al.*, Eds., The McMillan Co., New York, 1966

L. Tomlinson, A.M. Pritchard, "Effects of Heat Flux on Corrosion on High Pressure Boilers," *British Corrosion Journal*, Vol 20, Nov 1985, 187-195

Part II

Corrosion Media

Acetaldehyde

Acetaldehyde, CH_3CHO, also known as ethanal or acetic aldehyde, is a colorless flammable liquid that boils at 21 °C. Although used in the manufacturing of dyes and plastics, it is mainly used to manufacture acetic acid. Acetaldehyde is produced commercially by the hydration of acetylene and by the catalytic oxidation of ethyl alcohol.

Material Summaries

The following material summaries were compiled from a survey of the available literature. Inclusion of a material description under a given environment does not imply that it is the most appropriate material for corrosion service in that environment. Likewise, exclusion of a given material does not imply that it is not suitable for corrosion service applications in that environment.

Aluminum. In laboratory tests, aluminum alloy 1100 was resistant to aqueous solutions of 0.1 to 100% acetaldehyde. Aluminum alloy tubing, heat exchangers, stills, tankage, and shipping drums have been used for the production and storage of acetaldehyde.

Corrosion Behavior of Various Metals and Alloys in Acetaldehyde

Material	Condition, other factors, comments	Concen-tration, %	Temperature, °C (°F)	Duration	Corrosion rate, mm/yr (mils/yr) or other	Ref
Magnesium	...	All	...	...	Unsuitable	119
Platinum	...	Pure	200-400 (390-750)	...	<0.05 (<2)	6
Silver	...	Pure	200-400 (390-750)	...	<0.05 (<2)	10
Titanium	...	75	149 (300)	...	0.001 (0.04)	90
	...	100	149 (300)	...	nil	90
Type AM-363 stainless steel	...	Pure	Room	...	Unattacked	120
Type 304 stainless steel	Rayon processing; field or pilot plant test; no aeration; rapid agitation	100	61 (142)	414 d	0.0001 in./yr	89
Type 316 stainless steel	Rayon processing; field or pilot plant test; no aeration; rapid agitation	100	61 (142)	414 d	0.0001 in./yr	89
Type 316 stainless steel	Rayon processing; field or pilot plant test; no aeration; slight to moderate agitation. Water remainder	97-98	66 (150)	294 d	nil	89
Type 316 stainless steel	Chemical processing; field or pilot plant test; slight to moderate aeration; rapid agitation. Plus 14.5% acetic acid, 15% water, 0.5% formic acid	70	99-102 (210-215)	84.5 d	0.0001 in./yr	89
Type 316 stainless steel	Chemical processing; field or pilot plant test; slight to moderate aeration; rapid agitation. Plus 14.3% acetic acid, 0.3% formic acid, water remainder. Slight pitting (maximum depth of pits from incipient to 0.005 in.)	70	118 (245)	169 d	0.0046 in./yr	89
Type 316 stainless steel	Chemical processing; field or pilot plant test; no aeration; slight to moderate agitation. Plus 8% acetic acid, 3% low boilers, water remainder	70	104 (220)	100 d	nil	89
Type 316 stainless steel	Chemical processing; field or pilot plant test; no aeration; slight to moderate agitation. Plus 12% acetic acid, 3% low boilers, water remainder	50	92 (198)	246 d	nil	89
Type 316 stainless steel	Chemical processing; field or pilot plant test; no aeration; slight to moderate agitation. Plus 10% acetic acid, 3% low boilers, water remainder	50	92 (198)	81 d	<0.0001 in./yr	89
Type 317 stainless steel	Rayon processing; field or pilot plant test; no aeration; slight to moderate agitation. Water remainder	97-98	66 (150)	294 d	<0.0001 in./yr	89
Type 317 stainless steel	Chemical processing; field or pilot plant test; no aeration; slight to moderate agitation. Plus 10% acetic acid, 3% low boilers, water remainder	50	92 (198)	81 d	nil	89
Type 317 stainless steel	Chemical processing; field or pilot plant test; no aeration; slight to moderate agitation. Plus 12% acetic acid, 3% low boilers, water remainder	50	92 (198)	246 d	nil	89
Type 317 stainless steel	Chemical processing; field or pilot plant test; no aeration; slight to moderate agitation. Plus 8% acetic acid, 3% low boilers, water remainder	70	104 (220)	100 d	0.0001 in./yr	89
Type 317 stainless steel	Chemical processing; field or pilot plant test; slight to moderate aeration; rapid agitation. Plus 14.3% acetic acid, 0.3% formic acid, water remainder	70	118 (245)	169 d	0.0007 in./yr	89
Zr702	...	100	Boiling	...	<0.05 (<2)	15

Acetic Acid

Acetic acid, CH_3COOH, also known as ethanoic acid or vinegar acid, is a clear, colorless liquid or crystalline mass with a pungent odor, a melting point of 16.7 °C, and a boiling point of 118.1 °C. It is miscible with water, alcohol, and ether, and it crystallizes in deliquescent needles.

Acetic acid, as well as its derivatives, is produced in large quantities. It is the most important organic acid and is frequently encountered as a contaminant in other organic chemical processes. Acetic acid is classified as a weak acid, but the effective acidity in aqueous streams increases rapidly with concentration.

In addition to being the active ingredient in vinegar, acetic acid is required in the production of synthetic resins and fibers, pharmaceuticals, photographic chemicals, flavorants, and bleaching and etching compounds. It is used as an active raw and intermediate material for various organic syntheses and as a solvent for organic substances.

Material Summaries

The following material summaries were compiled from a survey of the available literature. Inclusion of a material description under a given environment does not imply that it is the most appropriate material for corrosion service in that environment. Likewise, exclusion of a given material does not imply that it is not suitable for corrosion service applications in that environment.

Aluminum exhibits good resistance to nearly all concentrations of acetic acid at room temperature and has been used extensively for storage and shipment. It is fairly resistant to 97 to 99% CH_3COOH to the boiling point, but is attacked very rapidly in concentrations near 100% or containing excess $(CH_3CO)_2O$. Aluminum again becomes resistant to pure $(CH_3CO)_2O$, although it causes contamination of the anhydride due to formation of a white crystalline solid, aluminum triacetate, $Al(C_2H_3O_2)_3$, which precipitates in the liquid.

The corrosion resistance of aluminum in acetic acid is strongly affected by contaminants. Aluminum can corrode in almost any concentration of CH_3COOH at any temperature if the acid is contaminated with the proper species.

Cast Irons. Unalloyed cast iron can be used to handle concentrated acetic acid, but it is attacked by more dilute solutions. Austenitic nickel cast irons and high-chromium cast irons exhibit adequate resistance to CH_3COOH. High-silicon cast irons show excellent resistance to most organic acids in all temperature and concentration ranges.

Carbon and Alloy Steels. Steel is attacked quite rapidly by all concentrations of acetic acid, even at room temperature. Glacial CH_3COOH at room temperature is less aggressive than aqueous solutions of the acid, but still gives a rate of attack of 0.8 to 1.3 mm/yr (30 to 50 mils/yr). Therefore, steel is normally unacceptable for use in CH_3COOH service.

Stainless Steels. The chromium stainless steels of the 400 series occasionally exhibit low corrosion rates in laboratory tests in dilute acetic acid. However, because field experience with these materials indicates high corrosion rates and pitting attack, they are rarely used for CH_3COOH production equipment. Type 304 stainless steel is the lowest grade commonly used. Exceptions include the high-purity ferritic stainless steels, which show good resistance.

Type 304 stainless steel finds wide application in dilute CH_3COOH and in the shipment and storage of concentrated CH_3COOH. Data show that glacial CH_3COOH can be handled in type 304 stainless steel to a temperature of about 80 °C (175 °F) and that type 304 has been satisfactory for lower concentrations to the boiling point of the acid. At temperatures above 60 °C (140 °F), use of the low-carbon type 340L is advisable for welded construction to prevent intergranular attack of heat-affected zones.

Type 316 stainless steel is the alloy most commonly used in CH_3COOH processing equipment. It will resist glacial acid to temperatures above the atmospheric boiling point. As with type 304 stainless steel, the low-carbon grade (type 316L) is required for the higher temperature application. Higher alloys, such as 20Cb-3 and Incoloy 825, show better resistance to CH_3COOH than type 316 stainless steel.

Acetic anhydride was produced as a coproduct in the old acetaldehyde oxidation process for acetic acid and is found in other acid streams. When CH_3COOH is truly anhydrous or contains small quantities of $(CH_3CO)_2O$, the rate of attack on type 316 stainless steel increases dramatically. Experience has shown that the introduction of a few tenths of a percent of water will reduce the corrosion.

Impurities present in the manufacture of acetic acid, such as acetaldehyde, formic acid, chlorides, and propionic acid, are expected to increase the attack of stainless steels. Contamination with chloride can cause pitting, rapid stress-corrosion cracking, and accelerated corrosion of type 316 stainless steel. Up to 20 ppm of chloride can be tolerated, but higher concentrations are likely to cause rapid equipment failure.

Transferring heat through a metal wall, as in heat exchangers, can drastically alter the corrosion characteristics of the metal.

Cemented Carbides. Many cemented carbide compositions can be used in acetic acid with little corrosion.

Copper and its alloys, except those with high zinc contents (>15% Zn), show good resistance to all concentrations of acetic acid up to and even above the atmospheric boiling temperature in the absence of oxygen or other oxidants. Copper was used almost exclusively to handle CH_3COOH until the advent of the stainless steels, but type 316 stainless steel and higher alloys are currently used.

Copper and copper alloys are used successfully in commercial processes involving exposure to CH_3COOH and related chemical compounds or in the manufacture of this acid. One plant kept records concerning the corrosion rate of C11000 used in two different CH_3COOH still systems. One still operated at 115 to 140 °C (240 to 285 °F) and handled a solution containing 50% CH_3COOH and about 50% $(CH_3CO)_2O$, with some esters also present. After operating for 663 h, the kettle showed an average penetration rate of 210 μm/yr (8.4 mils/yr). The rate was lower (60 μm/yr, or 2.4 mils/yr) for the bottom column and was lower yet (30 μm/yr, or 1.2 mils/yr) for the middle and top columns. A second still operating at 60 to 140 °C (140 to 285 °F) contained a 70% solution of CH_3COOH, the remainder being anhydride, esters, and ketones. After 1464 h, the kettle showed a corrosion rate of 120 μm/yr (4.8 mils/yr). The rate was only 30 μm/yr (1.2 mils/yr) for the middle and top columns.

In another field test, C11000 and C65500 coupons were placed in an acetic acid storage tank at ambient temperature. The stored solution contained 27% CH_3COOH, 1% butyl acetate, 70% H_2O, and small amounts of acetates, aldehydes, and other acids. During the 3984-h exposure, the specimens were immersed in the liquid phase 80% of the time and were in the vapor phase 20% of the time. The C11000 specimens showed a corrosion rate of 38 to 53 μm/yr (1.5 to 2.1 mils/yr); the C65500 specimens, 30 to 45 μm/yr (1.2 to 1.8 mils/yr).

In laboratory tests at room temperature, C61300 and C62300 exhibited typical corrosion rates of 65 to 80 μm/yr (2.5 to 3.2 mils/yr) in 10 to 40% CH_3COOH. The copper-aluminum alloys are suitable for use in CH_3COOH and the range of aliphatic and aromatic organic acids. The addition of chlorine atoms to the organic molecule will not increase the tendency toward pitting or crevice corrosion. Alloy C61300 is extensively used for pressure and valve castings.

The absence of oxidizing agents is essential for copper to resist attack by CH_3COOH and other organic acids. Copper is nearly immune to attack by pure, uncontaminated CH_3COOH, yet slight contamination with air through storage under an air atmosphere or by entry of air through a pump seal can increase the rate of attack in a copper column to hundreds of mils per year. One set of laboratory tests at room temperature in 50% CH_3COOH showed corrosion rats of 1.8 mm/yr (71.5 mils/yr) when the solution was sparged with oxygen, but only 0.08 mm/yr (3.1 mils/yr) when the solution was nitrogen sparged.

The addition of nickel to copper moderates the effect of oxidants. Tests in boiling 50% acetic acid sparged with air for 120 h gave rates of 7.9 mm/yr (310 mils/yr) for copper, 4.8 mm/yr (188 mils/yr) for copper alloy C71500 (copper-nickel, 30%), and 2.1 mm/yr (84 mils/yr) for copper containing 67% Ni. Similar reductions with increasing nickel content were noted when Fe^{3+} ion was added to the solution; however, rates still remained quite high.

Aluminum bronzes are generally suitable for service in CH_3COOH.

Lead has very limited resistance to acetic acid. It has been used to store glacial CH_3COOH where temperature, degree of aeration, and velocity are low, but dilute CH_3COOH, even at room temperature, attacks lead at rates exceeding 1.3 mm/yr (50 mils/yr). These rates increase rapidly with increasing aeration and velocity. However, although acetic acid rapidly attacks lead when dilute, it has little effect at strengths of 52 to 70%.

Nickel. Tests have shown that aeration and oxidizing ions have detrimental effects on the resistance of Nickel 200 and Monel 400 to corrosion by acetic acid, especially in dilute concentrations. No deliberate aeration or deaeration was done in these tests. The corrosion rates of all the alloys are quite low in these environments. Even though pure acetic acid is not very aggressive, the addition of contaminants can increase the corrosion rates.

Hastelloy alloys C-276 and B resist acetic acid solutions at all concentrations and normal temperatures. These materials are sometimes used where the acid is used in conjunction with inorganic acids and salts that limit the use of stainless steels or copper alloys. Hastelloy B is used under reducing conditions, such as with combinations of CH_3COOH and H_2SO_4, whereas Hastelloy C-276 is commonly used in highly oxidizing CH_3COOH solutions.

Silver has been frequently used in Europe to handle acetic acid, and it is quite resistant to all concentrations at normal temperatures. Because of cost, silver has been used very little in the United States.

Tin. Even small additions of lead to tin impair the retention of its bright reflective surface in common atmospheres. With increasing lead content, the appearance of soldered joints becomes increasingly dull, like that of lead. However, destructive corrosion (except effects from flux residues) is highly unusual.

On rare occasions, within enclosed spaces, condensed pure water may extract lead, but more common causes of trouble are volatile organic acids. Acetic acid vapors from wood or insulating materials, and formic acid (HCOOH) or other acids that may come from insulating materials, may attack lead-containing solders to produce a white incrustation and cause serious destruction of metal.

Titanium resists all concentrations of acetic acid up to the atmospheric boiling point. Electrochemical studies in CH_3COOH solutions suggest that it is possible to attack titanium in anhydrous acetic acid, but titanium has been used very successfully. The high-strength titanium alloys should not be used, because of their susceptibility to stress-corrosion cracking.

Zirconium resists corrosion in acetic acid and acetic anhydride.

Additional Reading

J.R. Pickens, D. Venables, and J.A.S. Green, "The Delayed Fracture of Aluminum Alloys," Report No. AD-A085137, Martin Marietta Laboratories, May 1980. MetAbs No. 81-350519. **Abstract:** The stress corrosion cracking of high-purity Al-Zn-Mg alloys has been studied in terms of the effects of bulk chemistry, bulk microstructure, oxide film chemistry and oxide film morphology.

A.I. Onuchukwu and F.K. Oppong-Boachie, The Corrosion Behavior of Aluminum Alloy AA1060 in p- Quinone and Acetic Acid Media, *Corros. Sci.*, 21(11), 919-926, 1986. MetAbs No. 87-350971. **Abstract:** The corrosion characteristics of 1060 Al alloy in different concentrations of p-quinone and acetic acid in 6.5% KNO_3 as supporting electrolyte have been studied by a potentiostatic polarization technique.

I. Sekine, S. Hatakeyama, and Y. Nakazawa, Corrosion Behavior of Type 430 Stainless Steel in Formic and Acetic Acids, *Corros. Sci.*, 27(3), 275-288, 1987. MetAbs No. 87-351485. **Abstract:** The corrosion behavior of Type 430 stainless steel in formic and acetic acid solutions was investigated by measuring the corrosion weight loss, the polarization curve, the corrosion potential variation with time and the impedance at the steel-solution interface.

I. Sekine, S. Hatakeyama, and Y. Nakazawa, Effect of Water Content on the Corrosion Behavior of Type 430 Stainless Steel in Formic and Acetic Acids, *Electrochim. Acta,* 32(6), 915-920, 1987. MetAbs No. 87-352343. **Abstract:** Corrosion of Type 430 stainless steel was studied in the formic acid-water and in the acetic acid-water systems. Weight-loss measurements were made at ambient temperature and at the solution boiling points.

T.-L. Yau, Zirconium Resists Corrosion in a Wide Range of Acetic Acid and Anhydride Environments, *Outlook,* 8(3), 2-5, 1987. MetAbs No. 87-352523. **Abstract:** Superior corrosion resistance makes Zr the first structural material choice for acetic acid and anhydride operations. Comparisons with alternatives (304 and 316 Stainless Steel, 20Cb3, Alloy 600, Alloy 400) report effects of concentration, temperature, impurities, oxygen and heat transfer conditions. Conditions promoting attack on Zr are listed.

S. Jayakrishnan, M. Pushpavanam, and S.R. Natarajan, Dissolution Behavior of Electrodeposited Bright Nickel-Iron Alloys, *Trans. SAEST,* 21(4), 207-212, 1986. MetAbs No. 87-352807. **Abstract:** Studies on the extent to which corrosion resistance of Ni is altered by the addition of Fe as an alloying element in Ni-Fe alloys to replace the Ni layer in Ni-Cr protective systems are discussed.

I. Sekine, A. Masuko, and K. Senoo, Corrosion Behavior of AISI 316 Stainless Steel in Formic and Acetic Acid Solutions, *Corrosion*, 43(9), 553-560, 1987. MetAbs No. 88-350052. **Abstract:** The corrosion behavior of AISI 316 stainless steel in formic and acetic acids was investigated by measuring the corrosion weight loss, the polarization curve, the impedance at the steel/solution interface, and the variation of natural electrode potential with time.

G.B. Elder, Materials of Construction for Organic Acids, in *Process Industries Corrosion — The Theory and Practice*, National Association of Corrosion Engineers, Houston, 287-296, 1986. MetAbs No. 88-350337.

Abstract: The organic acids constitute an important group of chemicals that are handled industrially in large volume. The corrosion characteristics and materials (Al 1100 and 5086, Cu-Ni, steel and Ti) used to manufacture and store formic, acetic and propionic acid are presented in detail.

Corrosion Behavior of Various Metals and Alloys in Acetic Acid

Material	Condition, other factors, comments	Concen-tration, %	Temperature, °C (°F)	Duration	Corrosion rate, mm/yr (mils/yr) or other	Ref
Stainless steels						
Carpenter Pyromet Alloy 102	Annealed. Glacial	...	...	48 h	0.076 (3.04)	30
Carpenter Pyromet Alloy 102	Glacial. Stress relieved at 843 °C (1550 °F) for ½ h, furnace cooled	...	...	48 h	0.025 (1)	30
Carpenter Pyromet Alloy 102	Plus acetic anhydride (1:1). Annealed	...	...	48 h	0.686 (27.44)	30
Carpenter Pyromet Alloy 102	Plus acetic anhydride (1:1). Stress relieved at 843 °C (1550 °F) for ½ h, furnace cooled	...	...	48 h	0.711 (28.44)	30
Carpenter Pyromet Alloy 102	Plus 2% formic acid. Annealed	10	...	48 h	0.152 (6.08)	30
Carpenter Pyromet Alloy 102	Plus 2% formic acid. Stress relieved at 843 °C (1550 °F) for ½ h, furnace cooled	10	...	48 h	0.102 (4.08)	30
Jessop JS700	...	60	Boiling	48 h	<0.051 (<0.002 in./yr)	97
Jessop JS700	Anhydride (1:1)	...	Boiling	48 h	0.025 (0.001 in./yr)	97
Type 20 stainless steel	(a)	10	106 (223)	51 d	0.102 (4.0)	66
Type 20 stainless steel	(a)	24	110 (230)	51 d	0.102 (4.0)	66
Type 20 stainless steel	(a)	83	116 (241)	51 d	0.127 (5.0)	66
Type 20 stainless steel	(a)	87	122 (252)	51 d	0.203 (8.0)	66
Type 20 stainless steel	(a)	98	128 (262)	51 d	0.05 (2.0)	66
Type 20 stainless steel	(a)	99.5	130 (266)	51 d	0.013 (0.5)	66
Type 304 stainless steel	Test conducted in three 48-h periods	50 wt%	Boiling	48 h	0.275 (11)	47
Type 304 stainless steel	...	20	Boiling	...	0.76 (30)	55
Type 304 stainless steel	...	Conc	Boiling	...	0.081 (3.2)	55
Type 304 stainless steel	Plus 220 ppm Cl⁻	Conc	Boiling	...	6.86 (270)	55
Type 304 stainless steel	(a)	83	116 (241)	51 d	1.68 (66)	66
Type 304 stainless steel	(a)	87	122 (252)	51 d	1.07 (42)	66
Type 304 stainless steel	(a)	98	128 (262)	51 d	0.18 (7.0)	66
Type 304 stainless steel	No activation	20	Boiling	24 h	0.75 (30)	52
Type 304 stainless steel	No activation	80	Boiling	24 h	...	52
Type 304 stainless steel	Plus 2-10% HCOOH. Completely corroded	30-50	106 (223)	...	...	55
Type 304 stainless steel	Aerated	5	21 (70)	...	Very good	121
Type 304 stainless steel	Aerated	10	21 (70)	...	Very good	121
Type 304 stainless steel	...	10	Boiling	...	Very good	121
Type 304 stainless steel	...	60	15 (60)	...	Very good	121
Type 304 stainless steel	...	60	Boiling	...	Good	121
Type 304 stainless steel	...	100	21 (70)	...	Very good	121
Type 304 stainless steel	...	100	Boiling	...	Good	121
Type 316 stainless steel	...	10	Boiling	...	0.0025 (0.1)	51
Type 316 stainless steel	...	20	Boiling	...	0.0076 (0.3)	55
Type 316 stainless steel	...	Conc	Boiling	...	0.013 (0.5)	55
Type 316 stainless steel	Plus 220 ppm Cl⁻	Conc	Boiling	...	4.57 (180)	55
Type 316 stainless steel	(a)	10	106 (223)	51 d	0.05 (2.0)	66
Type 316 stainless steel	(a)	24	110 (230)	51 d	0.069 (2.7)	66
Type 316 stainless steel	(a)	83	116 (241)	51 d	0.023 (9.0)	66
Type 316 stainless steel	(a)	87	122 (252)	51 d	0.406 (16.0)	66
Type 316 stainless steel	(a)	98	128 (262)	51 d	0.05 (2.0)	66
Type 316 stainless steel	(a)	99.5	130 (266)	51 d	0.0076 (0.3)	66
Type 316 stainless steel	All specimens sensitized at 650 °C (1200 °F); attacked intergranularly. (a)	10	106 (223)	51 d	0.102 (4.0)	66
Type 316 stainless steel	All specimens sensitized at 650 °C (1200 °F); attacked intergranularly. (a)	83	116 (241)	51 d	0.56 (22)	66
Type 316 stainless steel	All specimens sensitized at 650 °C (1200 °F); attacked intergranularly. (a)	98	128 (262)	51 d	0.102 (4.0)	66
Type 316 stainless steel	No activation	20	Boiling	24 h	0.0075 (0.3)	52

(Continued)

Corrosion Behavior of Various Metals and Alloys in Acetic Acid (Continued)

Material	Condition, other factors, comments	Concentration, %	Temperature, °C (°F)	Duration	Corrosion rate, mm/yr (mils/yr) or other	Ref
Type 316 stainless steel	No activation	80	Boiling	24 h	...	52
Type 316 stainless steel	Plus 2-10% HCOOH	30-50	106 (223)	...	76-500 μm/yr (3-20)	55
Type 316 stainless steel	Glacial	...	93-110 (200-230)	...	<38 μm/yr (<1.5)	55
Type 316 stainless steel	Glacial. Plus 4% HCOOH	...	93-110 (200-230)	...	84 μm/yr (3.3)	55
Type 316 stainless steel	Plus 1.25% HCOOH	25	104 (220)	...	38 μm/yr (1.5)	55
Type 316 stainless steel	Plus 4% HCOOH	25	104 (220)	...	76 μm/yr (3.0)	55
Type 316 stainless steel	Aerated	5	21 (70)	...	Very good	121
Type 316 stainless steel	Aerated	10	21 (70)	...	Very good	121
Type 316 stainless steel	...	10	Boiling	...	Very good	121
Type 316 stainless steel	...	60	15 (60)	...	Very good	121
Type 316 stainless steel	...	60	Boiling	...	Good	121
Type 316 stainless steel	...	100	21 (70)	...	Very good	121
Type 316 stainless steel	...	100	Boiling	...	Good	121
Type 316L stainless steel	Mill annealed. Based on four 24-h tests	10	Boiling	24 h	0.015-0.018 (0.58-0.72)	50
Type 317 stainless steel	(a)	10	106 (223)	51 d	0.0076 (0.3)	66
Type 317 stainless steel	(a)	24	110 (230)	51 d	0.069 (2.7)	66
Type 317 stainless steel	(a)	83	116 (241)	51 d	0.102 (4.0)	66
Type 317 stainless steel	(a)	87	122 (252)	51 d	0.025 (1.0)	66
Type 317 stainless steel	(a)	98	128 (262)	51 d	0.025 (1.0)	66
Type 317 stainless steel	(a)	99.5	130 (266)	51 d	0.01 (0.4)	66
Type 317 stainless steel	Plus 2-10% HCOOH	30-50	106 (223)	...	50-280 μm/yr (2-11)	55
Type 317 stainless steel	Plus 1.25% HCOOH	25	104 (220)	...	<25 μm/yr (<1.0)	55
Type 317 stainless steel	Plus 4% HCOOH	25	104 (220)	...	50 μm/yr (2.0)	55
Type 317L stainless steel	...	60	Boiling	48 h	<0.051 (<0.002 in./yr)	97
Type 321 stainless steel	Plus 4% HCOOH. Completely corroded	25	104 (220)	...	...	55
Type 347 stainless steel	Plus 2-10% HCOOH. Completely corroded	30-50	106 (223)	...	...	55
Type 347 stainless steel	Plus 4% HCOOH. Completely corroded	25	104 (220)	...	...	55
Type 410 stainless steel	...	33	Room	...	Attacked	121
Type 410 stainless steel	...	10	Room	...	Unattacked	121
Type 410 stainless steel	Vapor	100	Room	...	Attacked	121
Type 410 stainless steel	Vapor	33	Room	...	Attacked	121
Type 410 stainless steel	Aerated	5	21 (70)	...	Good	121
Type 410 stainless steel	Aerated	10	21 (70)	...	Poor	121
Type 410 stainless steel	...	10	Boiling	...	Poor	121
Type 410 stainless steel	...	60	15 (60)	...	Poor	121
Type 410 stainless steel	...	60	Boiling	...	Poor	121
Type 410 stainless steel	...	100	21 (70)	...	Poor	121
Type 410 stainless steel	...	100	Boiling	...	Poor	121
Type 410 stainless steel	...	100	Room	...	Unattacked	121
Type 430 stainless steel	Aerated	5	21 (70)	...	Very good	121
Type 430 stainless steel	Aerated	10	21 (70)	...	Good	121
Type 430 stainless steel	...	10	Boiling	...	Good	121
Type 430 stainless steel	...	60	15 (60)	...	Fair	121
Type 430 stainless steel	...	60	Boiling	...	Fair	121
Type 430 stainless steel	...	100	21 (70)	...	Fair	121
Type 430 stainless steel	...	100	Boiling	...	Fair	121
Type 444 stainless steel	No activation	20	Boiling	24 h	0.005 (0.2)	52
Type 444 stainless steel	No activation	80	Boiling	24 h	0.005 (0.2)	52
Type AM-363 stainless steel	...	...	Room	...	Attacked	120
Aluminum						
Aluminum (>99.5%)	0-100% solution	...	0-118 (32-244)	...	Restricted applications	92
Aluminum-manganese alloys	0-100% solution	...	0-118 (32-244)	...	Restricted applications	92

(Continued)

Corrosion Behavior of Various Metals and Alloys in Acetic Acid (Continued)

Material	Condition, other factors, comments	Concentration, %	Temperature, °C (°F)	Duration	Corrosion rate, mm/yr (mils/yr) or other	Ref
Coppers						
70-30 cupronickel	(b)	...	...	...	Good	93
90-10 cupronickel		...	...	...	Good	93
Admiralty brass	...	...	...	...	Fair	93
Aluminum bronze	(b)	...	...	...	Good	93
Ampco 8, aluminum bronze	Generally suitable, crude	...	...	...	<0.05 (<2)	96
Ampco 8, aluminum bronze	Generally suitable. Conditions such as aeration or temperature could restrict use. Vapors	...	...	...	<0.5 (<20)	96
Architectural bronze	...	...	...	...	Not suitable	93
Brass	...	...	...	...	Fair	93
C11000	Annealed; test specimens were exposed in cycle feed lines	90	30-50 (86-122)	672 h	0.06 (2.4)	69
C11000	Annealed; test specimens were exposed in cycle feed lines	90	30-50 (86-122)	816 h	0.03 (1.2)	69
C11000	Cold worked; test specimens were exposed in cycle feed lines	90	30-50 (86-122)	672 h	0.09 (3.6)	69
C11000	Cold worked; test specimens were exposed in cycle feed lines	90	30-50 (86-122)	792 h	0.09 (3.6)	69
C11000	Test specimens were exposed in the acetic acid recovery column, where concentration of the acetic acid was 45% max	45	...	1038 h	0.03 max (1.2 max)	69
C11000	Test specimens were exposed to crude by-product acetic acid (approximately 25% concentration) in pump suction line from storage tank	25	...	432 h	0.274 (10.8)	69
C11000	Test specimens were exposed to crude by-product acetic acid (approximately 25% concentration) in pump suction line from storage tank	25		792 h	0.152 (6.0)	69
C11000	Plus an acetic anhydride acetone mixture	...	110-140 (230-285)	1115 h	0.483 (19.0)	70
C11000	Plus an acetic anhydride acetone mixture	...	110-140 (230-285)	2952 h	0.066-0.07 (2.6-2.8)	70
C11000	With an equal part acetic anhydride	...	130-145 (265-295)	1115 h	0.12-0.533 (4.7-21.0)	70
C11000	With 5% acetic anhydride, liquid phase	95	120 (250)	865 h	0.097-0.116 (3.8-4.4)	70
C11000	With 5% acetic anhydride, vapor phase	95	120 (250)	865 h	0.102-0.104 (4.0-4.1)	70
C11000	With 50% acetic anhydride	50	150 (300)	2448 h	0.084-0.090 (3.3-3.6)	70
C11000	...	Pure	...	2448 h	0.005 (0.2)	70
C11000 coupled to type 316 stainless steel	With 5% acetic anhydride, liquid phase	95	120 (250)	865 h	0.102-0.216 (4.0-8.5)	70
C11000 coupled to type 316 stainless steel	With 5% acetic anhydride, vapor phase	95	120 (250)	865 h	0.094-0.213 (3.7-8.4)	70
C65500	Test specimens were exposed in the acetic acid recovery column, where concentration of the acetic acid was 45% max	45	...	1038 h	0.03 max (1.2 max)	69
C65500	Plus an acetic anhydride acetone mixture	...	110-140 (230-285)	1115 h	0.213 (8.4)	70
C65500	Plus an acetic anhydride acetone mixture	...	110-140 (230-285)	2952 h	0.07-0.09 (2.7-3.6)	70
C65500	With an equal part acetic anhydride	...	130-145 (265-295)	1115 h	0.116-0.236 (4.6-9.3)	70
Cartridge brass	...	...	...	...	Not suitable	93
Commercial bronze	(b)	...	...	...	Good	93
Copper joint	Test specimens were exposed in cycle feed lines. Joint brazed with BCuP-5 filler metal	90	...	1512 h	0.183 (7.2)	69
Copper joint	Test specimens were exposed in cycle feed lines. Joint brazed with BCuP-5 filler metal	90	...	4000 h	0.12 (4.8)	69
Copper joint	Test specimens were exposed in cycle feed lines. BAg filler metal	90	...	1512 h	0.183 (7.2)	69
Copper joint	Test specimens were exposed in cycle feed lines. BAg filler metal	90	...	4000 h	0.12 (4.8)	69
Copper joint	Test specimens were exposed in the acetic acid recovery column, where concentration of the acetic acid was 45% max. BAg filler metal	45	...	1038 h	0.03 max (1.2 max)	69
Electrolytic copper	(b)	...	...	...	Good	93
Free-cutting brass	...	...	...	...	Not suitable	93
Muntz metal	...	...	...	...	Not suitable	93
Naval brass	...	...	...	...	Not suitable	93

(Continued)

Corrosion Behavior of Various Metals and Alloys in Acetic Acid (Continued)

Material	Condition, other factors, comments	Concentration, %	Temperature, °C (°F)	Duration	Corrosion rate, mm/yr (mils/yr) or other	Ref
Nickel silver	(b)	18	...	...	Good	93
Phosphor bronze	5% Sn. (b)	...	...	...	Good	93
Phosphor bronze	8% Sn. (b)	...	...	...	Good	93
Phosphor copper	(b)	...	...	...	Good	93
Red brass	(b)	...	...	...	Good	93
Silicon bronze	Low. (b)	...	...	...	Good	93
Silicon bronze	High. (b)	...	...	...	Good	93
Titanium						
Ti-3Al-2.5V	ASTM Grade 9	100	Boiling	...	nil	91
Titanium	Grade 9	99.7	Boiling	...	nil	33
Titanium	...	5-99.7	124 (255)	...	nil	90
Titanium	...	33-vapor	Boiling	...	nil	90
Titanium	...	99	Boiling	...	0.003 (0.12)	90
Titanium	...	65	121 (250)	...	0.003 (0.12)	90
Titanium	...	58	130 (266)	...	0.381 (15.24)	90
Titanium	...	99.7	124 (255)	...	0.003 (0.12)	90
Titanium	Plus 3% $(CH_3CO)_2O$	Glacial	204 (399)	...	1.02 (40.8)	90
Titanium	Plus 1.5% $(CH_3CO)_2O$	Glacial	204 (399)	...	0.005 (0.2)	90
Titanium	Plus 109 ppm Cl	31.2	Boiling	...	0.259 (10.36)	90
Titanium	Plus 106 ppm Cl	62.0	Boiling	...	0.272 (10.88)	90
Titanium	Plus 5% (HCOOH)	58	Boiling	...	0.457 (18.28)	90
Titanium	Grade 12. Plus 5% formic acid	58	Boiling	...	nil	33
Titanium	...	100	Boiling	...	nil	91
Heat- and corrosion-resistant alloys						
18Cr-2Mo	...	20	Boiling	...	0.005 (0.2)	55
18Cr-2Mo	...	80	Boiling	...	0.005 (0.2)	55
26Cr-1Mo	Plus 220 ppm Cl⁻	Conc	Boiling	...	0.5 (20)	55
26Cr-1Mo	...	20	Boiling	...	0.0	55
26Cr-1Mo	...	Conc	Boiling	...	0.013 (0.5)	55
29Cr-4Mo	...	20	Boiling	...	0.0	55
44Co-31Cr-13W	(c)	10	Boiling	...	0.1 (4)	53
44Co-31Cr-13W	(c)	99	Boiling	...	0.007 (0.3)	53
44Co-31Cr-13W	(d)	10	Boiling	...	0.002 (0.1)	53
44Co-31Cr-13W	(d)	99	Boiling	...	nil	53
50Co-20Cr-15W-10Ni	...	10	Boiling	...	0.002 (0.1)	53
50Co-20Cr-15W-10Ni	...	99	Boiling	...	nil	53
50Co-20Cr-15W-10Ni	(d)	10	Boiling	...	0.002 (0.1)	53
50Co-20Cr-15W-10Ni	(d)	99	Boiling	...	nil	53
53Co-30Cr-4.5W	(c)	10	Boiling	...	0.007 (0.3)	53
53Co-30Cr-4.5W	(c)	99	Boiling	...	0.01 (0.4)	53
53Co-30Cr-4.5W	(d)	10	Boiling	...	0.007 (0.3)	53
53Co-30Cr-4.5W	(d)	99	Boiling	...	0.007 (0.3)	53
18Cr-2Ni-12Mn	Test conducted in three 48-h periods	50 wt%	Boiling	48 h	0.005 (0.2)	47
Cabot alloy No. 625	Average of four 24-h periods	10	Boiling	...	<0.02 (<0.6)	67
Cabot alloy No. 625	Average of four 24-h periods	99	Boiling	...	0.01 (0.4)	
Ferralium	...	10	Boiling	...	0.01 (0.4)	51
Hastelloy alloy B-2	Glacial. (e)	99	Boiling	...	<0.01 (<0.3)	63
Hastelloy alloy B-2	(e)	10	Boiling	...	<0.02 (<0.5)	63
Hastelloy alloy B-2	(e)	30	Boiling	...	0.01 (0.4)	63
Hastelloy alloy B-2	(e)	50	Boiling	...	0.01 (0.4)	63
Hastelloy alloy B-2	(e)	70	Boiling	...	<0.01 (<0.3)	63
Haynes alloy 21	...	99	Boiling	...	0.017 (0.67)	23
Haynes alloy No. 25	(f)	10	Room	24 h	nil	68
Haynes alloy No. 25	(f)	50	Room	24 h	nil	68
Haynes alloy No. 25	(f)	99	Room	24 h	nil	68

(Continued)

Corrosion Behavior of Various Metals and Alloys in Acetic Acid (Continued)

Material	Condition, other factors, comments	Concentration, %	Temperature, °C (°F)	Duration	Corrosion rate, mm/yr (mils/yr) or other	Ref
Haynes alloy No. 25	(f)	10	66 (150)	24 h	nil	68
Haynes alloy No. 25	(f)	50	66 (150)	24 h	nil	68
Haynes alloy No. 25	(f)	99	66 (150)	24 h	nil	68
Haynes alloy No. 25	(f)	10	Boiling	24 h	<0.01 (<0.1)	68
Haynes alloy No. 25	(f)	50	Boiling	24 h	<0.01 (<0.1)	68
Haynes alloy No. 25	(f)	99	Boiling	24 h	nil	68
Haynes alloy 25	...	99	Boiling	...	0.0056 (0.22)	23
Haynes alloy 188	...	99	Boiling	...	0.005 (0.20)	23
Haynes alloy 556	...	99	Boiling	...	0.005 (0.20)	23
Haynes alloy 6B	...	99	Boiling	...	0.0008 (0.03)	23
Inconel alloy 601	Plus 0.5% H_2SO_4. Average of two tests	10	80 (176)	7 d	1.161 (45.7)	64
Inconel alloy 601	...	10	80 (176)	7 d	<0.002 (<0.1)	64
Inconel alloy 601	Plus 0.5% NaCl. Average of two tests	10	80 (176)	30 d	0.554 (21.8)	64
Inconel alloy 690	...	10	80 (176)	...	<0.03 (<1)	57
Inconel alloy 690	Plus 0.5% H_2SO_4	10	80 (176)	...	<0.03 (<1)	57
Incoloy alloy 800	Plus 0.5 % H_2SO_4. No pitting. (g)	10	80 (176)	7 d	<0.003 (<0.1)	44
Incoloy alloy 800	Plus 0.5 % NaCl. Incipient pits after 42 d. (g)	10	80 (176)	42 d	<0.003 (<0.1)	44
Incoloy alloy 800	No pitting. (g)	10	80 (176)	7 d	<0.003 (<0.1)	44
Incoloy alloy 825	Less than 0.1% water in still	99.9	107 (225)	40 d	0.005 (0.2)	43
Incoloy alloy 825	1% formic acid, 5% high boiling esters	94	127 (260)	465 d	0.018 (0.7)	43
Incoloy alloy 825	1.5% formic acid, 1 to 1.5% water	96.5-98	124 (255)	262 d	0.152 (6.0)	43
Incoloy alloy 825	2.5% formic acid, 6.0% water	91.5	110-127 (230-260)	55 d	0.079 (3.1)	43
Incoloy alloy 825	1.5 to 3.0% formic acid, 0.5% potassium permanganate, balance water	95	110-143 (230-290)	55 d	0.038 (1.5)	43
Incoloy alloy 825	Vapors of 85% acetic acid, 10% acetic anhydride, 5% water, plus some acetone, acetonitrile, in vapor line just before condenser	85	116-135 (240-275)	875 d	0.008 (0.3)	43
Incoloy alloy 825	6% propionic acid, 20% butane, 5% pentane, 8% ethyl acetate, 5% methyl ethyl ketone, plus other esters and ketones	40	174 (345)	217 d	0.051 (2.0)	43
MP35N	...	99	Boiling	...	0.015 (0.6)	23
Multimet	(f)	10	Room	24 h	nil	68
Multimet	(f)	50	Room	24 h	nil	68
Multimet	(f)	99	Room	24 h	nil	68
Multimet	(f)	10	66 (150)	24 h	nil	68
Multimet	(f)	50	66 (150)	24 h	nil	68
Multimet	(f)	99	66 (150)	24 h	nil	68
Multimet	(f)	10	Boiling	24 h	<0.01 (<0.1)	68
Multimet	(f)	50	Boiling	24 h	<0.01 (<0.1)	68
Multimet	(f)	99	Boiling	24 h	<0.01 (<0.1)	68
Nickel 200	Unaerated	5	116 (240)	...	0.007 (0.28)	21
Nickel 200	Unaerated	10	30 (86)	...	0.0025 (0.1)	21
Nickel 200	Unaerated	50	30 (86)	...	0.006 (0.25)	21
Nickel 200	Unaerated	99.9	30 (86)	...	0.003 (0.13)	21
Nickel 200	Aerated	30	30 (86)	...	0.084 (3.3)	21
Nickel 200	Aerated	50	30 (86)	...	0.11 (4.3)	21
Nickel 200	Aerated	99.9	116 (240)	...	0.009 (0.36)	21
Nickel 200	(h)	99	Boiling	24 h	0.11 (4.5)	50
Nickel 200	No air	100	Boiling	...	0.036 (1.4)	50
Nickel 200	No air	50	Boiling	...	0.076 (3)	50
Nickel 200	Air sparge	100	Boiling	...	0.025 (1)	50
Nickel 200	Air sparge	50	Boiling	...	1.6 (63)	50
Nickel 200	3200 ppm Cu^{2+} added as acetate	100	Boiling	...	0.81 (32)	65
Nickel 200	3200 ppm Cu^{2+} added as acetate	50	Boiling	...	0.71 (28)	65
Nickel 200	Air saturated	0.10	Room	...	0.25 (10)	44
Nickel 200	Air saturated	5	Room	...	1 (40)	44
Nickel 200	Air saturated	85	Room	...	10 (400)	44

(Continued)

Corrosion Behavior of Various Metals and Alloys in Acetic Acid (Continued)

Material	Condition, other factors, comments	Concentration, %	Temperature, °C (°F)	Duration	Corrosion rate, mm/yr (mils/yr) or other	Ref
Nickel 400	Unaerated	2	30 (86)	...	0.0008 (0.03)	21
Nickel 400	Unaerated	50	30 (86)	...	0.0025 (0.1)	21
Nickel 400	Unaerated	5	116 (240)	...	0.0008 (0.03)	21
Nickel 400	Unaerated	10	30 (86)	...	0.002 (0.08)	21
Nickel 400	Unaerated	25	30 (86)	...	0.002 (0.08)	21
Nickel 400	Unaerated	75	30 (86)	...	0.0013 (0.05)	21
Nickel 400	Unaerated	99.9	30 (86)	...	0.002 (0.08)	21
Nickel 400	Aerated	10	30 (86)	...	0.008 (0.33)	21
Nickel 400	Aerated	25	30 (86)	...	0.01 (0.41)	21
Nickel 400	Aerated	50	30 (86)	...	0.019 (0.74)	21
Nickel 400	Aerated	75	30 (86)	...	0.009 (0.36)	21
Nickel 400	Aerated	99.9	30 (86)	...	0.006 (0.23)	21
Nickel 400	Aerated	99.9	116 (240)	...	0.004 (0.15)	21
Nickel 400	No air	100	Boiling	...	0.0025 (0.1)	50
Nickel 400	No air	50	Boiling	...	0.025 (1)	50
Nickel 400	Air sparge	100	Boiling	...	0.05 (2)	50
Nickel 400	Air sparge	50	Boiling	...	2.1 (84)	50
Nickel 400	3200 ppm Cu^{2+} added as acetate	100	Boiling	...	2.97 (117)	65
Nickel 400	3200 ppm Cu^{2+} added as acetate	50	Boiling	...	0.9 (36)	65
Nickel 400	(h)	99	Boiling	24 h	0.015 (0.6)	50
Nickel 600	Unaerated	2	30 (86)	...	0.0013 (0.05)	21
Nickel 600	Unaerated	5	116 (240)	...	0.002 (0.08)	21
Nickel 600	Unaerated	10	30 (86)	...	0.0005 (0.02)	21
Nickel 625	(h)	10	Boiling	24 h	0.01-0.019	50
Nickel 625	(h)	99	Boiling	24 h	(0.39-0.77)	50
Nickel 825	(h)	10	Boiling	24 h	0.01 (0.4)	50
Nickel B-2	(h)	99	Boiling	24 h	0.0152-0.016 (0.60-0.63)	50
Nickel B-2	(h)	10	Boiling	24 h	0.03 (1.2)	50
Nickel C-4	(h)	99	Boiling	24 h	0.0112-0.013 (0.44-0.50)	50
Nickel C-276	(h)	99	Boiling	24 h	0.0005 (0.02)	50
Nickel C-276	(h)	10	Boiling	24 h	0.0076 (0.3)	50
Nickel G	(h)	99	Boiling	24 h	0.011-0.0114 (0.41-0.45)	50
Nickel G	(h)	10	Boiling	24 h	0.03 (1.2)	50
Nickel G-2	(h)	99	Boiling	24 h	0.011-0.014 (0.43-0.54)	50
Nickel G-3	(h)	99	Boiling	24 h	0.005 (0.2)	50
					0.015 (0.6)	50
Zirconium						
Zr702	Plus saturated gaseous HCl and Cl_2	100	Boiling	...	>5 (>200)	15
Zr702	Plus saturated gaseous HCl and Cl_2	100	40 (100)	...	<0.025 (<1)	15
Zr702	Plus 10% CH_3OH	90	200 (390)	...	<0.025 (<1)	15
Zr702	...	5-99.5	35 (95 to boiling)	...	<0.025 (<1)	15
Zr702	...	100	160 (320)	...	<0.025 (<1)	15
Zr702	Glacial	99.7	Boiling	...	<0.13 (<5)	15
Zr702	Plus 50 ppm I^-	100	160 (320)	...	<0.025 (<1)	15
Zr702	Plus 50 ppm I^-	100	200 (390)	...	<0.025 (<1)	15
Zr702	Plus 1% I^- + 100 ppm Fe^{3+}	99	200 (390)	...	<0.025 (<1)	15
Zr702	Plus 2% HI	80	100 (212)	...	<0.025 (<1)	15
Zr702	Plus 2% HI	98	150 (300)	...	<0.025 (<1)	15
Zr702	Plus 2% HI + 1000 ppm Fe added as powder	80	100 (212)	...	<0.025 (<1)	15
Zr702	Plus 2% HI, 1% CH_3OH, 500 ppm (HCOOH), 100 ppm Cu	80	150 (300)	...	<0.025 (<1)	15
Zr702	Plus 2% HI, 1% CH_3OH, 500 ppm (HCOOH), 100 ppm Fe	80	150 (300)	...	<0.025 (<1)	15
Zr702	Plus 2% HI + 200 ppm Cl^-	80	100 (212)	...	<0.025 (<1)	15
Zr702	Plus 2% HI + 200 ppm Fe^{3+}	80	100 (212)	...	<0.025 (<1)	15
Zr702	Plus 2% I^-	98	150 (300)	...	<0.025 (<1)	15

(Continued)

Corrosion Behavior of Various Metals and Alloys in Acetic Acid (Continued)

Material	Condition, other factors, comments	Concentration, %	Temperature, °C (°F)	Duration	Corrosion rate, mm/yr (mils/yr) or other	Ref
Zr702	Plus 2% HI + 1% CH$_3$OH + 500 ppm (HCOOH)	80	150 (300)	...	<0.025 (<1)	15
Zr702	Plus 50% (CH$_3$·CO)$_2$O	50	Boiling	...	<0.025 (<1)	15
Zr705	Plus saturated gaseous HCl and Cl$_2$	100	Boiling	...	>5 (>200)	15
Zr705	...	5-99.5	35 (95 to boiling)	...	<0.025 (<1)	15
Zr705	Plus 1% I$^-$ + 100 ppm Fe^{3+}	99	200 (390)	...	<0.025 (<1)	15
Zr705	Plus 2% HI	80	100 (212)	...	<0.025 (<1)	15
Zr705	Plus 2% HI	98	150 (300)	...	<0.025 (<1)	15
Zr705	Plus 2% HI, 1% CH$_3$OH, 500 ppm (HCOOH), 100 ppm Cu	80	150 (300)	...	<0.025 (<1)	15
Zr705	Plus 2% HI, 1% CH$_3$OH, 500 ppm (HCOOH), 100 ppm Fe	80	150 (300)	...	<0.025 (<1)	15
Zr705	Plus 2% HI + 200 ppm Cl$^-$	80	100 (212)	...	<0.025 (<1)	15
Zr705	Plus 2% HI + 200 ppm Fe^{3+}	80	100 (212)	...	<0.025 (<1)	15
Zr705	Plus 2% I$^-$	98	150 (300)	...	<0.025 (<1)	15
Zr705	Plus 2% HI + 1% CH$_3$OH + 500 ppm (HCOOH)	80	150 (300)	...	<0.025 (<1)	15
Zr705	Plus 2% HI + 200 ppm Cl$^-$	80	100 (212)	...	<0.025 (<1)	15
Zr705	Plus 50% (CH$_3$·CO)$_2$O	50	Boiling	...	<0.025 (<1)	15
Lead, tin, and zinc						
Lead	Glacial. Practically resistant; Pb recommended for use	...	24 (75)	...	<500 μm/yr (<20)	95
Lead	Glacial	...	Room	...	<0.25 (<10)	17
Tin	Hydrogen	6	...	...	15 mg/dm^2/d	59
Tin	Oxygen	6	...	...	2300 mg/dm^2/d	59
Tin	...	10	20 (68)	...	Resistant	94
Tin	...	10	60 (140)	...	Unsuitable	94
Tin	...	10	100 (212)	...	Unsuitable	94
Tin	Glacial	...	20 (68)	...	Unsuitable	94
Tin	Glacial	...	60 (140)	...	Unsuitable	94
Tin	Glacial	...	100 (212)	...	Unsuitable	94
Noble metals						
Gold	Glacial	...	100 (212)	...	<0.05 (<2)	8
Iridium	Glacial	...	100 (212)	...	nil	29
Rhodium	Glacial	...	100 (212)	...	nil	29
Silver	...	All	Boiling	...	<0.05 (<2)	4
Others						
Cobalt	Static	5	25 (77)	...	0.05 (2)	54
Havar	...	99	Boiling	...	0.078 (3.1)	23
Magnesium	...	All	...	...	Unsuitable	119
Niobium	...	5- 99.7	Boiling	...	nil	2
Tantalum	...		100 (212)	...	nil	42

(a) Data were obtained during processing of acetic acid containing ionized halogens; concentration of halide ions varied during period of observation; estimated range of concentration, 5 to 10 ppm. (b) May be considered in place of a copper metal when some property, other than corrosion resistance, governs its use. (c) Heat treated 4 h at 899 °C (1650 °F), furnace cooled; cast specimen 38 mm x 25 mm x 6 mm (1.5 in. x 1 in. x 0.25 in.), 120-grit abrasive finish. Average of five 24-h periods. (d) Cast specimen 38 mm x 25 mm x 6 mm (1.5 in. x 1 in. x 0.25 in.), 120-grit abrasive finish. Average of five 24-h periods. (e) Determined in laboratory tests. It is recommended that samples be tested under actual plant conditions. All test specimens were heat-treated at 1066 °C (1950 °F), water quenched. (f) All data are steady-state as calculated from a minimum of five 24-h test periods. All data were obtained using corrosion specimens prepared from 12-gage, solution heat-treated sheet. (g) Solutions were prepared with reagent-grade chemicals. Test specimens were cold-rolled, annealed sheet, 2.84 mm (0.112 in.) thick. (h) Mill annealed. Based on four 24-h tests.

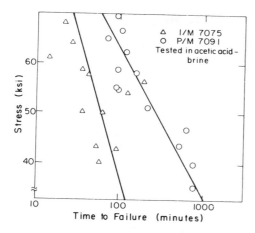

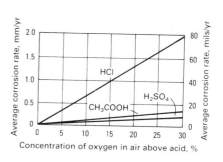

Iron- and aluminum-base P/M alloys. Stress vs. time to failure. Curves for unnotched specimens of conventional alloy 7075 and powder alloy 7091 at the same stress level in acetic acid brine. Source: P.C. Searson and R.M. Latanison, "The Corrosion and Oxidation Resistance of Iron- and Aluminum-Based Powder Metallurgical Alloys," *Corrosion Science,* Vol 25, 1985, 958.

Copper. Effect of oxygen on corrosion rates for copper in 1.2*N* solutions of nonoxidizing acids. Specimens are immersed for 24 h at 24 °C (75 °F). Oxygen content of the solutions varied from test to test, depending on the concentration of oxygen in the atmosphere above the solutions. Source: *Metals Handbook*, 9th ed., Vol 13, Corrosion, ASM International, Metals Park, OH, 1987, 627.

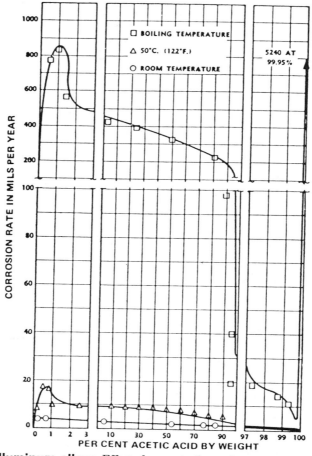

Alluminum alloys. Effect of concentration and temperature on the resistance of alloy 1100 in acetic acid. Source: *Guidlines for the Use of Aluminum with Food and Chemicals; Compatibility Data on Aluminum in the Food and Chemical Process Industries*, 5th ed., The Aluminum Association, Washington, DC, 1984, 11.

Acetic Anhydride

Acetic anhydride, $(CH_3CO)_2O$, also known as ethanoric anhydride, is a liquid with a pungent odor that boils at 140 °C (284 °F). It is used for acetyration, because it forms acetic acid when combined with water.

Material Summaries

The following material summaries were compiled from a survey of the available literature. Inclusion of a material description under a given environment does not imply that it is the most appropriate material for corrosion service in that environment. Likewise, exclusion of a given material does not imply that it is not suitable for corrosion service applications in that environment.

Aluminum. In limited laboratory tests, aluminum alloy 3003 showed moderate (13 mils/yr) attack by acetic anhydride at 100 °C (212 °F). Mild attack at ambient temperature and at 50 °C (122 °F) was observed in other tests on aluminum alloy 1100. Acetic anhydride at the boiling point had mild action (~5 mils/yr). Acetic anhydride has been produced and handled in aluminum and aluminum alloy reaction vessels, piping, storage tanks, heat exchangers, drums, and tank cars. Valves made of aluminum alloy A356.0 have also been used.

Additional Reading

T.-L. Yau, Zirconium Resists Corrosion in a Wide Range of Acetic Acid and Anhydride Environments, *Outlook,* 8(3), 2-5, 1987. MetAbs No. 87-352523. **Abstract:** Corrosion resistance of Zr is compared with the alternatives–304 SS, 316 SS, 20Cb3, Alloy 600, and Alloy 400. The effects of concentration, temperature, impurities, oxygen and heat transfer conditions are reported. Conditions promoting attack on Zr are listed.

Corrosion Behavior of Various Metals and Alloys in Acetic Anhydride

Material	Condition, other factors, comments	Concentration, %	Temperature, °C (°F)	Duration	Corrosion rate, mm/yr (mils/yr) or other	Ref
Stainless steels						
AM-363 stainless steel	...	Pure	Room	...	Slightly attacked	120
Type 304 stainless steel	Anhydride	90	21 (70)	...	Good	121
	...	90	Boiling	...	Poor	121
Type 304 stainless steel	Chemical processing; field or pilot plant test; no aeration; slight to moderate agitation	100	137 (277)	571 d	0.012 in./yr	89
Type 304 stainless steel	Chemical processing; field or pilot plant test; slight to moderate agitation. Plus 40% ethylidene diacetate, 5% acetic acid, 5% solids	50	150 (302)	150 d	0.0003 in./yr	89
Type 304 stainless steel	Chemical processing; field or pilot plant test; no aeration; slight to moderate agitation. Plus 20% acetic acid	80	131 (268)	571 d	0.009 in./yr	89
Type 304 stainless steel	Chemical processing; field or pilot plant test; no aeration; rapid agitation. Plus 30% acetic acid	70	134-138 (273-280)	718 d	0.004 in./yr	89
Type 304 stainless steel	Chemical processing; field or pilot plant test; no aeration; rapid agitation. Plus 40% acetic acid. Moderate pitting: maximum depth of pits from 0.005 to 0.010 in.	60	130-136 (266-277)	718 d	0.005 in./yr	89
Type 304 stainless steel	Chemical processing; field or pilot plant test; no aeration; rapid agitation. Plus 50% acetic acid	50	128-139 (262-282)	718 d	0.007 in./yr	89
Type 316 stainless steel	Chemical processing; field or pilot plant test; no aeration; rapid agitation. Plus 50% acetic acid	50	128-139 (262-282)	718 d	0.001 in./yr	89
Type 316 stainless steel	Chemical processing; field or pilot plant test; no aeration; rapid agitation. Plus 40% acetic acid	60	130-136 (266-277)	718 d	0.0008 in./yr	89
Type 316 stainless steel	Chemical processing; field or pilot plant test; no aeration; rapid agitation. Plus 30% acetic acid	70	134-138 (273-280)	718 d	0.0008 in./yr	89
Type 316 stainless steel	Chemical processing; field or pilot plant test; no aeration; slight to moderate agitation. Plus 20% acetic acid	80	131 (268)	571 d	0.0006 in./yr	89
Type 316 stainless steel	Chemical processing; field or pilot plant test; slight to moderate agitation. Plus 40% ethylidene diacetate, 5% acetic acid, 5% solid	50	150 (302)	150 d	0.0002 in./yr	89
Type 316 stainless steel	Rayon processing; field or pilot plant test; no aeration; rapid agitation	100	134 (273)	287 d	0.0001 in./yr	89
Type 316 stainless steel	Chemical processing; field or pilot plant test; no aeration; slight to moderate agitation	100	137 (277)	571 d	0.005 in./yr	89
Type 316 stainless steel	Anhydride	90	21 (70)	...	Good	121
	...	90	Boiling	...	Good	121

(Continued)

Corrosion Behavior of Various Metals and Alloys in Acetic Anhydride (Continued)

Material	Condition, other factors, comments	Concen-tration, %	Temperature, °C (°F)	Duration	Corrosion rate, mm/yr (mils/yr) or other	Ref
Type 317 stainless steel	Chemical processing; field or pilot plant test; no aeration; rapid agitation. Plus 50% acetic acid	50	128-139 (262-282)	718 d	0.0007 in./yr	89
Type 317 stainless steel	Chemical processing; field or pilot plant test; no aeration; rapid agitation. Plus 40% acetic acid	60	130-136 (266-277)	718 d	0.0006 in./yr	89
Type 317 stainless steel	Chemical processing; field or pilot plant test; no aeration; rapid agitation. Plus 30% acetic acid	70	134-138 (273-280)	718 d	0.0005 in./yr	89
Type 317 stainless steel	Chemical processing; field or pilot plant test; no aeration; slight to moderate agitation. Plus 20% acetic acid	80	131 (268)	571 d	0.0004 in./yr	89
Type 317 stainless steel	Chemical processing; field or pilot plant test; slight to moderate agitation. Plus 40% ethylidene diacetate, 5% acetic acid, 5% solids	50	150 (302)	150 d	0.0001 in./yr	89
Type 317 stainless steel	Chemical processing; field or pilot plant test; no aeration; slight to moderate agitation	100	137 (277)	571 d	0.003 in./yr	89
Type 410 stainless steel	Anhydride	90	21 (70)	...	Fair	121
	...	90	Boiling	...	Poor	121
		100	Room	...	Slightly attacked	121
Type 430 stainless steel	Anhydride	90	21 (70)	...	Fair	121
	...	90	Boiling	...	Poor	121
Aluminum						
Aluminum (99.0-99.5%)	...	Pure	...	...	Satisfactory	92
Aluminum-manganese alloys	...	Pure	...	...	Satisfactory	92
Aluminum-silicon alloys	...	Pure	...	...	Satisfactory	92
Coppers						
70-30 cupronickel	(a)	...	...	...	Good	93
90-10 cupronickel	(a)	...	...	...	Good	93
Admiralty brass	...	...	...	...	Fair	93
Aluminum bronze	(a)	...	...	...	Good	93
Ampco 8, aluminum bronze	Generally suitable. Conditions such as aeration or temperature could restrict use	...	...	...	<0.5 (<20)	96
Architectural bronze	...	...	...	...	Not suitable	93
Brass	...	...	...	...	Fair	93
Cartridge brass	...	...	...	...	Not suitable	93
Commercial bronze	(a)	...	...	...	Good	93
C11000	Test specimens were exposed in stills separating acetic acid from acetic anhydride. Top of column	...	...	2448 h	0.06 (2.4)	69
	Test specimens were exposed in stills separating acetic acid from acetic anhydride. Kettle	...	...	2448 h	0.9-1.08 (36.0-43.2)	69
C65500	Test specimens were exposed in stills separating acetic acid from acetic anhydride. Top of column	...	...	2448 h	0.06 (2.4)	69
	Test specimens were exposed in stills separating acetic acid from acetic anhydride. Kettle	...	...	2448 h	0.487-0.731 (19.2-28.8)	69
Electrolytic copper	(a)	...	...	...	Good	93
Free-cutting brass	...	...	...	...	Not suitable	93
Muntz metal	...	...	...	...	Not suitable	93
Naval brass	...	...	...	...	Not suitable	93
Nickel silver	(a)	18	...	...	Good	93
Phosphor copper	(a)	...	...	...	Good	93
Phosphor bronze	5% Sn. (a)	...	...	...	Good	93
	8% Sn. (a)	...	...	...	Good	93
Red brass	(a)	...	...	...	Good	93
Silicon bronze	Low. (a)	...	...	...	Good	93
	High. (a)	...	...	...	Good	93
Titanium						
Titanium	...	99-99.5	20 to boiling (70 to boiling)	...	<0.13 (<5)	20
Titanium	...	100	21 (70)	...	0.025 (1)	90
	...	100	150 (302)	...	0.005 (0.2)	90
	...	99.5	Boiling	...	0.013 (0.52)	90

(Continued)

Corrosion Behavior of Various Metals and Alloys in Acetic Anhydride (Continued)

Material	Condition, other factors, comments	Concentration, %	Temperature, °C (°F)	Duration	Corrosion rate, mm/yr (mils/yr) or other	Ref
Heat- and corrosion-resistant alloys						
Alloy 825	Rayon processing; field or pilot plant test; no aeration; rapid agitation	100	134 (273)	287 d	0.0001 in./yr.	89
Carpenter 20	Rayon processing; field or pilot plant test; no aeration; rapid agitation	100	134 (273)	287 d	0.0001 in./yr.	89
Nickel 200	Plus 1% acetic acid in a still	99	154 (310)	...	0.005 (0.2)	44
Nickel 200	Plus 40% acetic acid in a still	60	140 (284)	...	0.015 (0.6)	44
Lead, tin, and zinc						
Lead	Negligible corrosion; Pb recommended for use	...	24 (75)	...	<50 μm/yr (<2)	95
Noble metals						
Platinum	Pt-Au alloys perform better than pure Pt	All	Boiling	...	<0.05 (<2)	6
Silver	...	All	Boiling	...	<0.05 (<2)	10
Zirconium						
Zr702	...	99	Room to boiling	...	<0.025 (<1)	15
Zr705	...	99	Room to boiling	...	<0.025 (<1)	15

(a) May be considered in place of a copper metal when some property, other than corrosion resistance, governs its use.

Acetone

Acetone, CH_3COCH_3, also known as 2-propanone and dimethyl ketone, is a colorless, volatile, flammable liquid that boils at 56 °C (133 °F). It is miscible with water and is often used as a solvent in the manufacture of lacquers and paints.

Material Summaries

The following material summaries were compiled from a survey of the available literature. Inclusion of a material description under a given environment does not imply that it is the most appropriate material for corrosion service in that environment. Likewise, exclusion of a given material does not imply that it is not suitable for corrosion service applications in that environment.

Aluminum. In laboratory tests, aluminum and aluminum-magnesium alloys have shown resistance to acetone at all temperatures. Aluminum pipes, stills, heat exchangers, and storage tanks have been used to handle acetone. Redistilled acetone was reported to have caused mild corrosion in an aluminum storage tank. Valves made of aluminum alloy 356.0 have been used in handling acetone.

Additional Reading

Z.A. Foroulis, and R.J. Franco, High Temperature Internal Corrosion of an Acetone Plant Furnace Outlet Tube: Failure Analysis and Laboratory Simulation, *Mater. Perform., 25*(10), 51-56, 1986. MetAbs No. 87-350139. **Abstract:** The results of an investigation of the causes and mechanism of failure of a carbon steel furnace outlet tube in an acetone plant are summarized. The failure analysis was supplemented with a laboratory program undertaken to study the cause of failure and to screen alternative construction materials.

Corrosion Behavior of Various Metals and Alloys in Acetone

Material	Condition, other factors, comments	Concentration, %	Temperature, °C (°F)	Duration	Corrosion rate, mm/yr (mils/yr) or other	Ref
Irons and steels						
Carbon steel	Laboratory corrosion rate	...	482 (900)	...	1.0 (40)	71
Carbon steel	Laboratory corrosion rate; tube metal temperature near the point of failure was estimated based on oxide thickness measurements on the outside diameter	...	621 (1150)	...	4.8 (190)	71
Carbon steel	Laboratory corrosion rate; tube metal temperature near the point of failure was estimated based on oxide thickness measurements on the outside diameter	...	565 (1050)	...	2.2 (85)	71

(Continued)

Corrosion Behavior of Various Metals and Alloys in Acetone (Continued)

Material	Condition, other factors, comments	Concen-tration, %	Temperature, °C (°F)	Duration	Corrosion rate, mm/yr (mils/yr) or other	Ref
Carbon steel	Laboratory corrosion rate; tube metal tempera-ture near the point of failure was estimated based on oxide thickness measurements on the outside diameter	...	593 (1100)	...	3.2 (125)	71
Carbon steel	Field corrosion rate, based on tube thickness measurements near the return bend and the ther-mocouple, away from the area of failure	...	482 (900)	...	0.76-1.3 (30-50)	71
Carbon steel	Field corrosion rate, based on metal loss on the inside tube diameter near the rupture. Tube metal temperature near the point of failure was estimated based on oxide thickness measure-ments on the outside diameter	...	593 (1100)	...	4.3 (170)	71
Stainless steels						
AM-363 stainless steel	...	Pure	Room	...	Unattacked	120
Type 304 stainless steel	Rayon processing; field test; no aeration; rapid agitation. Plus mesityl oxide, dibutyl alcohol, and water	98	58 (137)	181 d	0.00011 in./yr	89
Type 304 stainless steel	Soap (solvent recovery) processing; field test; no aeration; slight to moderate agitation; with car-bon over the standard maximum. Plus oleic lino-leic acid remainder (still half immersed)	90	63 (145)	6 d	nil	89
Type 304 stainless steel	Soap (solvent recovery) processing; field test; no aeration; slight to moderate agitation. Plus oleic linoleic acid remainder (still half immersed)	90	63 (145)	6 d	0.0001 in./yr	89
Type 304 stainless steel	Chemical processing; no aeration; slight to mod-erate agitation. Plus 30% methyl acetate, 10% acetaldehyde, pH 5.0-6.0	60	80 (176)	210 d	0.0003 in./yr	89
Type 304 stainless steel	Plastic (distillation) processing; field test; no aer-ation; slight to moderate agitation. Plus 60% water (column, in bottom pump discharge line)	40	63 (145)	59 d	<0.0001 in./yr	89
Type 304 stainless steel	Chemical processing; field test; slight to moder-ate aeration; rapid agitation. Plus 38% methanol, 15% methyl acetate, 2% water, and 0.1% acetic acid	45	57 (135)	210 d	nil	89
Type 304 stainless steel	Rayon processing; no aeration; rapid agitation. Plus 16% metanol, 12% methyl acetate, 3% ace-taldehyde, 1% ethyl acetate, 1% ethanol, and methyl-ethyl ketone	16	92 (198)	294 d	<0.0001 in./yr	89
Type 316 stainless steel	Rayon processing; no aeration; rapid agitation. Plus 16% metanol, 12% methyl acetate, 3% ace-taldehyde, 1% ethyl acetate, 1% ethanol, and methyl-ethyl ketone	16	92 (198)	294 d	<0.0001 in./yr	89
Type 316 stainless steel	Chemical processing; field test; slight to moder-ate aeration; rapid agitation. Plus 38% methanol, 15% methyl acetate, 2% water, and 0.1% acetic acid	45	57 (135)	210 d	nil	89
Type 316 stainless steel	Plastic (distillation) processing; field test; no aer-ation, slight to moderate agitation. Plus 60% water (column, in bottom pump discharge line)	40	63 (145)	59 d	<0.0001 in./yr	89
Type 316 stainless steel	Chemical processing; no aeration; slight to mod-erate agitation. Plus 30% methyl acetate, 10% acetaldehyde, pH 5.0-6.0	60	80 (176)	210 d	0.00038 in./yr	89
Type 316 stainless steel	Soap (solvent recovery) processing; field test; no aeration; slight agitation. Plus oleic linoleic acid remainder (still half immersed)	90	63 (145)	6 d	0.0001 in./yr	89
Type 316 stainless steel	Rayon processing; field test; no aeration; rapid agitation. Plus mesityl oxide, dibutyl alcohol, and water	98	58 (137)	181 d	<0.0001 in./yr	89
Type 410 stainless steel	...	Pure	Room	...	Slightly attacked	121
Copper						
70-30 cupronickel	...	...	...	...	Suitable	93
90-10 cupronickel	...	...	...	...	Suitable	93
Admiralty brass	...	...	...	...	Suitable	93
Aluminum bronze	...	...	...	...	Suitable	93
Ampco 8, aluminum bronze	Generally suitable	...	...	...	<0.05 (<2)	96

(Continued)

Corrosion Behavior of Various Metals and Alloys in Acetone (Continued)

Material	Condition, other factors, comments	Concentration, %	Temperature, °C (°F)	Duration	Corrosion rate, mm/yr (mils/yr) or other	Ref
Architectural bronze	...	...	...	...	Suitable	93
Brass	...	...	...	...	Suitable	93
Cartridge brass	...	...	...	...	Suitable	93
Commercial bronze	...	...	...	...	Suitable	93
Electrolytic copper	...	...	...	...	Suitable	93
Free-cutting brass	...	...	...	...	Suitable	93
Muntz metal	...	...	...	...	Suitable	93
Naval brass	...	...	...	...	Suitable	93
Nickel silver	...	18	...	...	Suitable	93
Phosphor copper	...	...	...	...	Suitable	93
Phosphor bronze	5% Sn	...	...	...	Suitable	93
Phosphor bronze	8% Sn	...	...	...	Suitable	93
Red brass	...	...	...	...	Suitable	93
Silicon bronze	Low	...	...	...	Suitable	93
Silicon bronze	High	...	...	...	Suitable	93
Lead, tin, and zinc						
Lead	Negligible corrosion; Pb recommended for use	10-90	24-100 (75-212)	...	<50 μm/yr (<2)	95
Noble metals						
Platinum	...	Pure	Boiling	...	<0.05 (<2)	6
Silver	...	Pure	Boiling	...	<0.05 (<2)	10
Others						
Magnesium	...	All	Room	...	Resistant	119

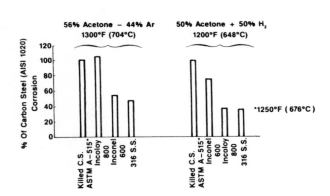

Carbon steel. Comparison of corrosion rates of various alloys in acetone-argon and acetone-hydrogen mixtures with carbon steel. Specimens were exposed for 3 h. Source: Z.A. Foroulis and R.J. Franco, "High Temperature Internal Corrosion of an Acetone Plant Furnace Outlet Tube: Failure Analysis and Laboratory Simulation," *Materials Performance*, Vol 25, Oct, 1985, 55.

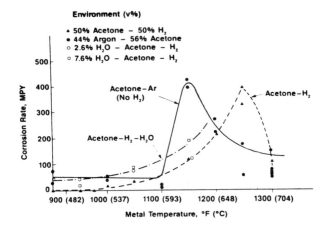

Carbon steel. Effect of temperature on corrosion of carbon steel in acetone vapors. Specimens were exposed for 3 h. Source: Z.A. Foroulis and R.J. Franco, "High Temperature Internal Corrosion of an Acetone Plant Furnace Outlet Tube: Failure Analysis and Laboratory Simulation," *Materials Performance*, Vol 25, Oct, 1985, 53.

Adipic Acid

Adipic acid, HOCC(CH₂)₄COOH, also known as hexanedioic acid and 1,4-butanedicarboxylic acid, is a colorless crystalline dicarboxylic acid. It is slightly soluble in water and has a melting point of 152 °C. It is used in the manufacture of nylon and urethane rubber.

Material Summaries

The following material summaries were compiled from a survey of the available literature. Inclusion of a material description under a given environment does not imply that it is the most appropriate material for corrosion service in that environment. Likewise, exclusion of a given material does not imply that it is not suitable for corrosion service applications in that environment.

Aluminum. Aluminum alloy 3003 was mildly attacked by acid in concentrations of 20 and 50%. Aluminum is used in piping, shipping, and storing of adipic acid and its salts.

Corrosion Behavior of Various Metals and Alloys in Adipic Acid

Material	Condition, other factors, comments	Concentration, %	Temperature, °C (°F)	Duration	Corrosion rate, mm/yr (mils/yr) or other	Ref
AM-363 stainless steel	...	Pure	Room	...	Unattacked	120
Titanium	...	0-67	204 (400)	...	<0.05 (<2)	20
Titanium	Plus 20% glutaric acid, 5% acetic acid	25	200 (390)	...	nil	20
Titanium	Plus 15-20% glutaric acid + CH₃·COOH	25	199 (390)	...	nil	90
Titanium	...	67	240 (464)	...	nil	90

Aluminum Chloride

Aluminum chloride, AlCl₃ or Al₂Cl₆, is a deliquescent compound found in white to colorless hexagonal crystals. Aluminum chloride reacts vigorously with water and fumes in air. It is used as a catalyst in cracking petroleum and in organic synthesis.

Material Summaries

The following material summaries were compiled from a survey of the available literature. Inclusion of a material description under a given environment does not imply that it is the most appropriate material for corrosion service in that environment. Likewise, exclusion of a given material does not imply that it is not suitable for corrosion service applications in that environment.

Aluminum. Aluminum alloy containers have been used to store and transport anhydrous aluminum chloride. Aluminum alloys are corroded by moist aluminum chloride and aluminum chloride solutions. The degree of corrosion depends on the temperature and the amount of free hydrochloric acid produced by hydrolysis.

Additional Reading

M.P. Mueller, A.W. Thompson, and I.M. Bernstein, Stress Corrosion Behavior of 7075 Aluminum in 1*N* Aluminum Chloride Solutions, *Corrosion*, *41*(3), 127-136, 1985. MetAbs No. 85-351099. **Abstract:** Stress corrosion cracking tests were conducted in 1*N* AlCl₃ solution on 7075 Al in three tempers: T6, T73, and an underaged temper (UT) approximately equal in strength to T73. Tests were conducted both in mode I (tension) and in mode III (torsion).

Corrosion Behavior of Various Metals and Alloys in Aluminum Chloride

Material	Condition, other factors, comments	Concentration, %	Temperature, °C (°F)	Duration	Corrosion rate, mm/yr (mils/yr) or other	Ref
Stainless steels						
Type 304 stainless steel	...	5	21 (70)	...	Poor	121
Type 304 stainless steel	...	25	21 (70)	...	Poor	121
Type 304 stainless steel	Chemical processing; field or pilot plant test; no aeration; rapid agitation. Aluminum chloride, water, oil	...	45-91 (113-195)	30 d	0.011 in./yr	89
Type 304 stainless steel	Chemical processing; field or pilot plant test; strong aeration; rapid agitation. With carbon over the standard maximum. Aluminum chloride, dust, solvent fumes (mainly benzene). Moderate pitting (maximum depth of pits from 0.005 to 0.010 in.)	5	Room	30 d	0.0007 in./yr	89

(Continued)

Corrosion Behavior of Various Metals and Alloys in Aluminum Chloride (Continued)

Material	Condition, other factors, comments	Concentration, %	Temperature, °C (°F)	Duration	Corrosion rate, mm/yr (mils/yr) or other	Ref
Type 304 stainless steel	Chemical processing; field or pilot plant test; strong aeration; rapid agitation. Aluminum chloride, dust, solvent fumes (mainly benzene). Moderate pitting (maximum depth of pits from 0.005 to 0.010 in.)	5	Room	30 d	0.0006 in./yr	89
Type 316 stainless steel	Chemical processing; field or pilot plant test; strong aeration; rapid agitation. Aluminum chloride, dust, solvent fumes (mainly benzene). Moderate pitting (maximum depth of pits from 0.005 to 0.010 in.)	5	Room	30 d	0.0004 in./yr	89
Type 316 stainless steel	Chemical processing; field or pilot plant test; strong aeration; rapid agitation. Plus 5% ammonium chloride, pH 2. Slight pitting (maximum depth of pits from incipient to 0.005 in.)	5	26 (78)	88 d	0.00015 in./yr	89
Type 316 stainless steel	Chemical processing; field or pilot plant test; no aeration; rapid agitation. Aluminum chloride, water, oil	...	45-91 (113-195)	30 d	0.004 in./yr	89
Type 316 stainless steel	...	5	21 (70)	...	Fair	121
Type 316 stainless steel	...	25	21 (70)	...	Fair	121
Type 317 stainless steel	Chemical processing; field or pilot plant test; strong aeration; rapid agitation. Plus 5% ammonium chloride, pH 2. Severe pitting (maximum depth of pits from 0.005 to 0.010 in.)	5	26 (78)	88 d	0.00024 in./yr	89
Type 410 stainless steel	...	5	21 (70)	...	Poor	121
Type 410 stainless steel	...	25	21 (70)	...	Poor	121
Type 410 stainless steel	...	...	Room	...	Attacked	121
Type 430 stainless steel	...	5	21 (70)	...	Poor	121
Type 430 stainless steel	...	25	21 (70)	...	Poor	121
Aluminum						
Aluminum (99.0-99.5%)	Anhydrous	...	20 (68)	...	Satisfactory	92
Aluminum alloys	Anhydrous	...	20 (68)	...	Satisfactory	92
Coppers						
70-30 cupronickel	(a)	...	...	...	Good	93
90-10 cupronickel	(a)	...	...	...	Good	93
Admiralty brass	...	...	...	...	Fair	93
Aluminum bronze	(a)	...	...	...	Good	93
Architectural bronze	...	...	...	...	Not suitable	93
Brass	...	...	...	...	Fair	93
Cartridge brass	...	...	...	...	Not suitable	93
Commercial bronze	(a)	...	...	...	Good	93
Electrolytic copper	(a)	...	...	...	Good	93
Free-cutting brass	...	...	...	...	Not suitable	93
Muntz metal	...	...	...	...	Not suitable	93
Naval brass	...	...	...	...	Not suitable	93
Nickel-silver	(a)	18	...	...	Good	93
Phosphor bronze	5% Sn. (a)	...	...	...	Good	93
Phosphor bronze	8% Sn. (a)	...	...	...	Good	93
Phosphor copper	(a)	...	...	...	Good	93
Red brass	(a)	...	...	...	Good	93
Silicon bronze	Low. (a)	...	...	...	Good	93
Silicon bronze	High. (a)	...	...	...	Good	93
Titanium						
Titanium	Grade 12	10	Boiling	...	nil	33
Titanium	Grade 7	10	100 (212)	...	<0.025 (<1)	33
Titanium	Grade 7	25	100 (212)	...	0.025 (1)	33
Titanium	Aerated	10	100 (212)	...	0.002 (0.08)	90
Titanium	Aerated	25	100 (212)	...	3.15 (126)	90
Titanium	...	10	100 (212)	...	0.002 (0.08)	90
Titanium	...	10	150 (302)	...	0.03 (1.2)	90
Titanium	...	25	60 (140)	...	nil	90
Titanium	...	25	100 (212)	...	6.55 (262)	90

(Continued)

Corrosion Behavior of Various Metals and Alloys in Aluminum Chloride (Continued)

Material	Condition, other factors, comments	Concentration, %	Temperature, °C (°F)	Duration	Corrosion rate, mm/yr (mils/yr) or other	Ref
Heat- and corrosion resistant alloys						
Carpenter 20	Chemical processing; field or pilot plant test; no aeration; rapid agitation. Aluminum chloride, water, oil	...	45-91 (113-195)	30 d	0.005 in./yr	89
Zirconium						
Zr702	...	5, 10, 25	35-100 (95-212)	...	<0.025 (<1)	15
Zr702	...	25	Boiling	...	<0.025 (<1)	15
Zr702	...	40	100 (212)	...	<0.05 (<2)	15
Zr702	Aerated	5, 10	60 (140)	...	<0.05 (<2)	15
Zr705	...	25	Boiling	...	<0.025 (<1)	15
Lead, tin, and zinc						
Lead	Practically resistant; Pb recommended for use	0-10	24 (75)	...	<500 μm/yr (<20)	95
Tin	Pitting possible in stagnant solutions	...	20 (68)	...	Resistant	94
Tin	...	...	60 (140)	...	Unsuitable	94
Tin	...	...	100 (212)	...	Unsuitable	94
Tantalum						
Tantalum	...	10	100 (212)	...	nil	42
Noble metals						
Platinum	...	All	Boiling	...	<0.05 (2)	5
Silver	Provided oxidizing agents are not present	All	Boiling	...	<0.05 (2)	9
Others						
Niobium	...	25	Boiling	...	0.005 (0.2)	2

(a) May be considered in place of a copper metal when some property, other than corrosion resistance, governs its use.

Aluminum Fluoride

Aluminum fluoride, AlF_3, is an anhydrous crystalline powder with a melting point of 1291 °C. Aluminum fluoride (hydrated), $AlF_3 \cdot 3\frac{1}{2}H_2O$, is a white crystalline powder that is insoluble in water.

Material Summaries

The following material summaries were compiled from a survey of the available literature. Inclusion of a material description under a given environment does not imply that it is the most appropriate material for corrosion service in that environment. Likewise, exclusion of a given material does not imply that it is not suitable for corrosion service applications in that environment.

Aluminum. Aluminum alloys 3003 and 5154 are resistant to solid aluminum fluoride at ambient temperature and 100% relative humidity in laboratory tests. Aluminum is corroded by aluminum fluoride solutions.

Corrosion Behavior of Various Metals and Alloys in Aluminum Fluoride

Material	Condition, other factors, comments	Concentration, %	Temperature, °C (°F)	Duration	Corrosion rate, mm/yr (mils/yr) or other	Ref
Stainless steels						
Type 304 stainless steel	...	5	21 (70)	...	Poor	121
Type 316 stainless steel	...	5	21 (70)	...	Poor	121
Type 410 stainless steel	...	5	21 (70)	...	Poor	121
Type 410 stainless steel	...	...	Room	...	Attacked	121
Type 430 stainless steel	...	5	21 (70)	...	Poor	121
Titanium						
Titanium	...	Saturated	Room	...	nil	90
Noble metals						
Platinum	...	All	Boiling	...	<0.05 (<2)	5
Silver	...	All	Boiling	...	<0.05 (<2)	9
Zirconium						
Zr702	pH 3.2	20	Room	...	>1.3 (>50)	15

Aluminum Hydroxide

Aluminum hydroxide, Al(OH)$_3$, also known as aluminum trihydroxide, aluminum trihydrate, aluminum hydrate, hydrated alumina, and hydrated aluminum oxide, is a white to whitish-yellow water-insoluble powder with a specific gravity of 2.42. It has a melting point of 155 °C. Aluminum hydroxide is used as a base for pigments, as a water repellent in textile coatings, and as an antacid in medicine. Aluminum hydroxide is soluble in hydrochloric or sulfuric acids or in sodium hydroxide.

Additional Reading

R. Sriram and D. Tromans, The Anodic Polarization Behaviour of Carbon Steel in Hot Caustic Aluminate Solutions, *Corros. Sci.*, *25*(2), 79-91, 1985. MetAbs No. 85-351703. **Abstract:** The anodic polarization behaviour of 0.18% C steel in hot (92 °C) caustic aluminate solutions was investigated by potentiodynamic polarization and cyclic voltammetry techniques.

Corrosion Behavior of Various Metals and Alloys in Aluminum Hydroxide

Material	Condition, other factors, comments	Concentration, %	Temperature, °C (°F)	Duration	Corrosion rate, mm/yr (mils/yr) or other	Ref
Coppers						
70-30 cupronickel	...	...	...	...	Suitable	93
90-10 cupronickel	...	...	...	...	Suitable	93
Admiralty brass	...	...	...	...	Suitable	93
Aluminum bronze	...	...	...	...	Suitable	93
Ampco 8, aluminum bronze	Generally suitable	...	...	...	<0.05 (<2)	96
Architectural bronze	...	...	...	...	Suitable	93
Brass	...	...	...	...	Suitable	93
Cartridge brass	...	...	...	...	Suitable	93
Commercial bronze	...	...	...	...	Suitable	93
Electrolytic copper	...	...	...	...	Suitable	93
Free-cutting brass	...	...	...	...	Suitable	93
Muntz metal	...	...	...	...	Suitable	93
Naval brass	...	...	...	...	Suitable	93
Nickel silver	...	18	...	...	Suitable	93
Phosphor bronze	5% Sn	...	...	...	Suitable	93
Phosphor bronze	8% Sn	...	...	...	Suitable	93
Phosphor copper	...	...	...	...	Suitable	93
Red brass	...	...	...	...	Suitable	93
Silicon bronze	High	...	...	...	Suitable	93
Silicon bronze	Low	...	...	...	Suitable	93
Stainless steels						
AM-363 stainless steel	...	...	Room	...	Unattacked	120

Aluminum Sulfate

Aluminum sulfate, Al$_2$(SO$_4$)$_3$, is a colorless salt composed of monoclinic crystals with a specific gravity of 2.71. It is used in manufacturing dyes, paint, and varnish removers. It decomposes with the application of heat and it is water soluble.

Material Summaries

The following material summaries were compiled from a survey of the available literature. Inclusion of a material description under a given environment does not imply that it is the most appropriate material for corrosion service in that environment. Likewise, exclusion of a given material does not imply that it is not suitable for corrosion service applications in that environment.

Aluminum. Aluminum alloys 3003 and 5154 under laboratory conditions of ambient temperature and 100% relative humidity were resistant to solid aluminum sulfate. Aqueous solutions of 0.1 to 25% aluminum sulfate showed a mild attack on aluminum alloy 1100 during laboratory tests. The paper industry has used aluminum piping for aluminum sulfate solutions. Valves of aluminum alloy 356.0 have also been used for aluminum sulfate solutions.

Corrosion Behavior in Various Metals and Alloys in Aluminum Sulfate

Material	Condition, other factors, comments	Concen-tration, %	Temperature, °C (°F)	Duration	Corrosion rate, mm/yr (mils/yr) or other	Ref
Stainless steels						
AM-363 stainless steel	...	...	Room	...	Slightly attacked	120
Type 304 stainless steel	...	10	21 (70)	...	Very good	121
Type 304 stainless steel	Chemical processing; field or pilot plant test; no aeration; rapid agitation	20-60	118 (244)	36 d	0.03 in./yr	89
Type 304 stainless steel	Chemical processing; field or pilot plant test; strong aeration; no agitation	20-60	118 (244)	36 d	0.009 in./yr	89
Type 304 stainless steel	Chemical processing; field or pilot plant test; no aeration; rapid agitation. pH 2-3. Severe pitting: maximum depth of pits over 0.010 in.	50-55	107-113 (225-235)	8 d	0.634 in./yr	89
Type 304 stainless steel	Research; laboratory test; no aeration; slight to moderate agitation	40-50	88 (190)	>6 d	0.058 in./yr	89
Type 304 stainless steel	Research; laboratory test. With carbon over the standard minimum	30-40	79 (175)	>6 d	nil	89
Type 316 stainless steel	...	10	21 (70)	...	Very good	121
Type 316 stainless steel	Chemical processing; field or pilot plant test; no aeration; rapid agitation. pH 2-3	50-55	107-113 (225-235)	8 d	0.196 in./yr	89
Type 316 stainless steel	Chemical processing; field or pilot plant test; no aeration; rapid agitation	20-60	118 (244)	36 d	0.009 in./yr	89
Type 316 stainless steel	Chemical processing; field or pilot plant test; strong aeration; no agitation	20-60	118 (244)	36 d	0.004 in./yr	89
Type 316 stainless steel	Research; laboratory test; no aeration; slight to moderate agitation	40-50	88 (190)	>6 d	0.0003 in./yr	89
Type 316 stainless steel	Research; laboratory test	30-40	79 (175)	>6 d	0.0002 in./yr	89
Type 317 stainless steel	Chemical processing; field or pilot plant test; no aeration; rapid agitation. pH 2-3	50-55	107-113 (225-235)	8 d	0.09 in./yr	89
Type 410 stainless steel	...	10	21 (70)	...	Poor	121
Type 410 stainless steel	...	...	Room	...	Slightly attacked	121
Type 410 stainless steel	Plus 1.0% H_2SO_4	Saturated	Room	...	Attacked	121
Type 410 stainless steel	Plus 1.0% soluble carbonate	Saturated	Room	...	Attacked	121
Type 430 stainless steel	...	10	21 (70)	...	Unattacked	121
Aluminum						
Aluminum (>99.5%)	Solution	...	...	...	Restricted applications	92
Coppers						
70-30 cupronickel	..	...	...	...	Suitable	93
90-10 cupronickel	(a)	...	...	...	Good	93
Admiralty brass	(a)	...	...	...	Good	93
Aluminum bronze	(a)	...	...	...	Good	93
Ampco 8, aluminum bronze	Generally suitable	...	...	...	<0.05 (<2)	96
Architectural bronze	...	...	...	...	Not suitable	93
Brass	(a)	...	...	...	Good	93
Cartridge brass	...	...	...	...	Not suitable	93
Commercial bronze	(a)	...	...	...	Good	93
Electrolytic copper	(a)	...	...	...	Good	93
Free-cutting brass	...	...	...	...	Not suitable	93
Muntz metal	...	...	...	...	Not suitable	93
Naval brass	...	...	...	...	Not suitable	93
Nickel silver	(a)	18	...	...	Good	93
Phosphor bronze	5% Sn. (a)	...	...	...	Good	93
Phosphor bronze	5% Sn. (a)	...	...	...	Good	93
Phosphor copper	(a)	...	...	...	Good	93
Red brass	(a)	...	...	...	Good	93
Silicon bronze	Low. (a)	...	...	...	Good	93
Silicon bronze	High. (a)	...	...	...	Good	93
Titanium						
Titanium	...	Saturated	Room	...	nil	90
Titanium	...	10	80 (176)	...	0.05 (2)	90
Titanium	...	10	Boiling	...	0.12 (4.8)	90

(Continued)

Corrosion Behavior in Various Metals and Alloys in Aluminum Sulfate (Continued)

Material	Condition, other factors, comments	Concentration, %	Temperature, °C (°F)	Duration	Corrosion rate, mm/yr (mils/yr) or other	Ref
Titanium	Plus 1% H$_2$SO$_4$	Saturated	Room	...	nil	90
Heat- and corrosion-resistant alloys						
Carpenter 20	Research; laboratory test	30-40	79 (175)	>6 d	0.0006 in.\yr	89
Incoloy 800	Solutions were prepared with reagent-grade chemicals. Test specimens were cold-rolled, annealed sheet, 2.84 mm (0.112 in.) thick. No pitting	5	80 (176)	7 d	<0.003 (<0.1)	44
Inconel 690	...	5	80 (176)	...	<0.03 (<1)	57
Inconel 601	...	5	80 (176)	7 d	<0.002 (<0.1)	64
Monel 400	Quiet immersion in storage tank	25	35 (95)	112 d	0.04 (1.6)	79
Monel 400	In evaporator concentrating solution	To 57	115 (240)	44 d	0.408 (16.3)	79
Nickel 200	Quiet immersion in storage tank	25	35 (95)	...	0.015 (0.6)	44
Nickel 200	In evaporator concentrating solution	To 57	115 (240)	...	1.5 (59)	44
Nickel 200	Quiet immersion in storage tank	25	35 (95)	112 d	0.015 (0.6)	79
Nickel 200	In evaporator concentrating solution	To 57	115 (240)	44 d	1.475 (59)	79
Zirconium						
Zr702	...	25	Boiling	...	Weight gain	62
Zr702	...	25	Boiling	...	nil	15
Zr702	...	60	100 (212)	...	<0.05 (<2)	15
Zr705	...	25	Boiling	...	Weight gain	62
Zr705	...	25	Boiling	...	nil	15
Noble metals						
Iridium	...	100 g/L	100 (212)	...	nil	18
Palladium	...	100 g/L	Room	...	nil	17
Palladium	...	100 g/L	100 (212)	...	nil	17
Platinum	...	100 g/L	Room-100 (212)	...	nil	5
Platinum	...	All	Boiling	...	<0.05 (<2)	5
Rhodium	...	100 g/L	100 (212)	...	nil	29
Ruthenium	...	100 g/L	100 (212)	...	nil	18
Ruthenium	...	100 g/L	100 (212)	...	nil	18
Silver	...	All	Boiling	...	<0.05 (<2)	9
Others						
Hafnium	...	25	...	10 d	nil	11
Hafnium	...	25	...	10 d	nil	11
Magnesium alloy AZ61A	Specimen size, 75 x 25 x 1.5 mm (3 x 1 x 0.06 in.); surface preparation, HNO$_3$ pickling; volume of testing solution, 100 ml. Specimens were alternately immersed 30 s in solution and held 2 min in air	3	35 (95)	7 d	11.2 g/m^2/d	12
Niobium	...	25	Boiling	...	nil	2

(a) May be considered in place of a copper metal when some property, other than corrosion resistance, governs its use.

Ammonia

Ammonia, NH$_3$, is a colorless gaseous alkaline compound with a melting point of -77.7 °C and a boiling point of -33.35 °C. It is very soluble in water, has a highly characteristic pungent odor, is lighter than air, and is formed as a result of the decomposition of most nitrogenous organic materials. Anhydrous ammonia, a major commercial chemical, is used in the manufacture of fertilizers, HNO$_3$, acrylonitrile, and other products, and as an electrolytic solvent.

Material Summaries

The following material summaries were compiled from a survey of the available literature. Inclusion of a material description under a given environment does not imply that it is the most appropriate material for corrosion service in that environment. Likewise, exclusion of a given material does not imply that it is not suitable for corrosion service applications in that environment.

Carbon Steels. Except for a sensitivity to stress-corrosion cracking, carbon steel is fully acceptable in ammonia service. In most cases, the developing cracks have been detected by inspection before leakage or rupture. However, there have been a few catastrophic failures. For example, in France in 1968, a tanker ruptured, killing 5 people. A second case was in South Africa, where a large tank failed in 1973 with 22 fatalities. The primary causes of the cracking are high stresses and air contamination. Nitrogen and carbon dioxide were suggested by separate investigators as promoting stress-corrosion cracking. Cracking is accelerated by the use of high-strength steels, the presence of hard welds, and air contamination. The cracking mechanism can be inhibited by water above about 0.1%. Thermal stress relief, if done properly, reduces stress below the critical level.

Alloy Steels. Low-alloy steel storage tanks have been used for many years for storage of ammonia. Stress-corrosion cracking has been the primary corrosion problem in vessels used for ammonia storage. It has been shown in several investigations that high stresses and oxygen (air) contamination are the primary causes of such cracking and that the addition of 0.1 to 0.2% water inhibits stress-corrosion cracking in alloy steel storage vessels.

Stainless Steels. In ammonia and ammonium hydroxide (NH_4OH), stainless steels have shown good resistance at all concentrations up to the boiling point.

Aluminum. In laboratory tests, 1100, 3003 and other copper-free aluminum alloys have been found to be resistant to dry, gaseous ammonia even at elevated temperatures. Alloys 1100 and 3003 were also resistant to pure anhydrous liquid ammonia, but contaminants can result in pitting of the metal. In dilute ammonia solutions (up to ~10%), the initial rate of attack is controlled by diffusion of OH^- ions to the aluminum surface and is a function of pH. Passivation of the aluminum surface occurs when a critical amount of corrosion product builds up at the aluminum surface, forming a protective film. If solution saturation of soluble corrosion product is relieved before passivation, film formation may not occur. A careful analysis of exposure conditions is required in using aluminum alloys in dilute ammonia. Aluminum alloys have been used in refrigeration systems handling liquid ammonia containing up to 5% water and in producing synthetic ammonia. Aluminum alloy compressors, heat exchangers, evaporators, condensers, and piping have been used in producing ammonia. Aluminum alloy pressure vessels have been used for storing and transporting ammonia. Carbon dioxide and hydrogen sulfide have been used to inhibit corrosion under condensing conditions.

Copper. Ammonia and ammonium compounds are the corrosive substances most often associated with stress-corrosion cracking of copper alloys. All copper-base alloys can be made to crack in ammonia vapor, ammonia solutions, ammonium ion solutions, and environments in which ammonia is a reaction product. These compounds are sometimes present in the atmosphere; in other cases, they are in cleaning compounds or in chemicals used to treat boiler water.

Both oxygen and moisture must be present for ammonia to be corrosive to copper alloys; other compounds, such as CO_2, are thought to accelerate stress-corrosion cracking in ammonia atmospheres. Moisture films on metal surfaces will dissolve significant quantities of ammonia, even from atmospheres with low ammonia concentrations. The rate at which cracks develop is critically dependent on many variables, including stress level, specific alloy, oxygen concentration in the liquid, pH or ammonia concentration, copper ions concentration, and potential.

Stress-corrosion cracking occurs in a great variety of brasses that differ widely in composition, degree of purity, and microstructure. The behavior of a copper alloy subjected to the combined effect of tensile stress and ammonia is an index of susceptibility to stress-corrosion cracking. Susceptibility to stress-corrosion cracking diminishes as the copper content of the brass is increased.

Protracted heating of 70Cu-30Zn brass at 100 °C (212 °F) does not develop cracks and does not reduce the internal stress appreciably. Surface defects that localize stresses do not appear to contribute to the development of cracks in the absence of an essential corroding agent, such as ammonia.

Severe corrosion and pitting do not of themselves lead to cracking. Cracks often follow an intercrystalline path.

Traces of ammonia in the environment are an important agent in inducting stress-corrosion cracking in atmospheric exposure. Ammonia has a specific and selective action on the material in the grain boundaries of brass. Cracking always begins in surface layers that are under tension.

Copper and its alloys are suitable for handling anhydrous ammonia if the ammonia remains anhydrous and if not contaminated with water and oxygen. In one test conducted for 1200 h, C11200 and C26000 each showed an average penetration of 5 μm/yr (0.2 mil/yr) in contact with anhydrous ammonia at atmospheric temperature and pressure. Tests showed the rates of corrosion to be low in the presence of small amounts of water, but oxygen was probably excluded. Aluminum bronzes should be avoided for service in moist ammonia.

Magnesium. Ammonia, wet or dry, causes no attack on magnesium at ordinary temperatures. Some corrosion may occur if water vapor is present.

Tin is not reactive with dry ammonia, and saturated ammonia solutions do not attack tin. More dilute solutions, however, behave like other alkaline solutions of comparable pH.

Titanium. The oxide film on titanium alloys provides an effective barrier to attack by most gases in wet or dry conditions, including ammonia. This protection extends to temperatures in excess of 150 °C (300 °F).

Zirconium is stable in ammonia at temperatures up to about 1000 °C (1830 °F).

Additional Reading

C.F. Schrieber, W.D. Grimes, and W.F. McIlhenny, Study of the Corrosive Effect on Aluminum and CP Titanium of Mixtures of Ammonia and Sea Water That May Be Encountered in OTEC Heat Exchangers, Report No. ANL/OTEC-BCM-004, Dow Chemical, 1979. MetAbs No. 82-350407. **Abstract:** The design most favored for an offshore thermal energy conversion power plant would use an ammonia cycle energy system powered by the small thermal differences existing between warm surface and deep ocean waters. A possibility exists for ammonia or seawater leakage within the evaporator or condenser. The extent to which small concentrations of seawater would affect corrosion of Al and CP Ti by ammonia and the extent to which small concentrations of ammonia might affect the same alloys by seawater are assessed.

S. Erzurum and H.C. Yeh, The Effect of Environment, Cold Work and Crystallography on the Stress Corrosion Cracking of C36000 Alloy, *Corrosion, 39*(5), 161-166, 1983. MetAbs No. 83-351592. **Abstract:** Stress corrosion cracking of C36000 brass, a multiphase Cu-Zn alloy, in two ammoniacal environments—aqueous and vapor—was examined.

R.C. Newman and G.T. Burstein, Early Stages of Film Growth on Alpha Brass Immersed in Ammoniacal Copper (II) Solutions, *Corrosion, 40*(5), 201-204, 1984. MetAbs No. 84-351904. **Abstract:** Films formed on 64-36 brass surfaces in a solution containing 1.0M ($NH_3 + NH_4^+$) + 0.05M Cu(II), pH 7.25, have been analyzed after short immersion times and after mechanical scraping during immersion.

U. Bertocci, F.I. Thomas, and E.N. Pugh, Stress Corrosion Cracking of Brass in Aqueous Ammonia in the Absence of Detectable Anodic Dissolution, *Corrosion, 40*(8), 439-440, 1984. MetAbs No. 84-352704. **Abstract:** Results of experiments designed to examine stress corrosion cracking of alpha brass Cu-30Zn in aqueous ammonia are reported.

A.W. Loginow, A Review of Stress Corrosion Cracking of Steel in Liquefied Ammonia Service, *Mater. Perform., 25*(12), 18-22, 1986. MetAbs No. 87-350788. **Abstract:** Stress corrosion cracking of steel (A517 high-strength steel) in liquefied ammonia (fertilizer) is traced from its early recognition in the 1950s, through agricultural and industrial experiences, to the NACE recommended Department of Transportation regulations to prevent damage, and to extensive laboratory studies of many detrimental and beneficial factors. Based on the studies and various practical experiences, several control measures are discussed, such as control of air contamination, inhibition by water addition, postweld heat treatments, the influence of the strength of the steels used and the applied stress, and periodic inspection techniques.

K.M. Patel and B.N. Oza, Influence of Some Coloring Additives on the Corrosion Behavior of Brass in Ammonia Solution, *J. Electrochem. Soc. India, 35*(4), 257-259, 1986. MetAbs No. 87-351506. **Abstract:** Dyestuffs with fused benzene rings and containing functional groups having atoms like nitrogen, oxygen, and sulfur, which possess a lone pair of electrons, can be used as effective inhibitors in ammonia environment. However, greater solubility of a particular corrosion product with specific compound reduces its effectiveness to a considerable extent when used in high ammonia.

C.A. Farina and U. Grassini, Stress Corrosion Cracking in Non-Aqueous Media, *Electrochim. Acta, 32*(6), 977-980, 1987. MetAbs No. 87-351506.

Abstract: Results concerning stress corrosion cracking in non-aqueous solvents—methanol, ethanol, 2-propanol, dimethylformamide, acetonitrile and liquid ammonia—are reported and discussed.

L. Lunde and R. Nyborg, Stress Corrosion Cracking of Some Metallic Materials in Ammonia at Ambient and Low Temperature, *Ind. Corros., 5*(3), 1987. MetAbs No. 87-352374. **Abstract:** The stress corrosion cracking susceptibility of three carbon-manganese steels and two nickel steels in ammonia has been studied at ambient and low temperature.

P. Kapranos and R. Priestner, Overview of Metallic Materials for Heat Exchangers for Ocean Thermal Energy Conversion Systems, *J. Mater. Sci., 22*(4), 1141-1149, 1987. MetAbs No. 87-610468. **Abstract:** Candidate materials for use in ocean thermal energy conversion system heat exchangers include Al, Cu-Ni, stainless steel and Ti alloys. These are considered and their advantages and disadvantages are discussed.

L. Lunde and R. Nyborg, Stress Corrosion Cracking of Different Steels in Liquid and Vaporous Ammonia, *Corrosion, 43*(11), 680-686, 1987. MetAbs No. 88-350474. **Abstract:** The combined effect of water and oxygen on stress corrosion cracking of C-Mn steel and 9Ni steel in liquid and vaporous ammonia has been studied.

A. Parthasarathi and N.W. Polan, Stress Corrosion Cracking of Copper Alloys: The Effects of Corrosion Potential and Tarnishing Characteristics, *Corrosion, 43*(12), 747-755, 1987. MetAbs No. 88-350655. **Abstract:** The stress corrosion cracking characteristics of a variety of Cu-base alloys has been investigated in four different ammoniacal solutions at 4-14 pH. Failure times were correlated to free corrosion potentials and tarnishing behavior.

Corrosion Behavior of Various Metals and Alloys in Ammonia

Material	Condition, other factors, comments	Concentration, %	Temperature, °C (°F)	Duration	Corrosion rate, mm/yr (mils/yr) or other	Ref
Stainless steels						
Type 304 stainless steel	...	...	21 (70)	...	Very good	121
Type 304 stainless steel	Plastic processing; field or pilot plant test; no aeration; no agitation. Plus hydrogen cyanide, carbon dioxide, and water. Severe pitting: maximum depth of pits over 0.010 in.	90	105 (221)	30 d	0.0001 in./yr	89
Type 304 stainless steel	Metal (distillation) processing; field or pilot plant test; slight to moderate aeration; rapid agitation. Plus 14% carbon dioxide, remainder water (still overhead line)	26	82 (180)	65 d	<0.0001 in./yr	89
Type 304 stainless steel	Petrochemical processing (synthetic urea manufacture); field or pilot plant test; no aeration; slight to moderate agitation. Plus 71% water, 7% carbon dioxide, trace ammonium nitrate, pressure 29 psig (ammonia surge vessel, bottom)	22	65 (150)	300 d	0.0003 in./yr	89
Type 304 stainless steel	Petrochemical processing (synthetic urea manufacture); field or pilot plant test; slight to moderate aeration; slight to moderate agitation. Plus water, low carbon dioxide (ammonia desorber, vapors below liquid trapout tray	20	102 (215)	250 d	0.0033 in./yr	89
Type 304 stainless steel	Chemical processing (urea manufacture); field or pilot plant test; no aeration; rapid agitation. Plus 7% carbon dioxide, remainder water (half immersed)	12	29 (85)	16 d	0.078 in./yr	89
Type 304 stainless steel	Metal processing; field or pilot plant test; slight to moderate aeration; rapid agitation. Plus 14% oxygen, saturated with water vapor, remainder nitrogen (leach autoclave, vapors)	9	76-82 (170-180)	111 d	<0.0001 in./yr	89
Type 304 stainless steel	Metal processing; field or pilot plant test; no aeration; rapid agitation. Plus nickel, cobalt, copper and ammonium sulfates, water solution, solids as 2% copper sulfide, 4-5% vapors of ammonia and water vapor (copper boil reboiler)	8.4	101-107 (215-225)	95 d	<0.0001 in./yr	89

(Continued)

Corrosion Behavior of Various Metals and Alloys in Ammonia (Continued)

Material	Condition, other factors, comments	Concen-tration, %	Temperature, °C (°F)	Duration	Corrosion rate, mm/yr (mils/yr) or other	Ref
Type 316 stainless steel	Metal processing; field or pilot plant test; no aeration; rapid agitation. Plus nickel, cobalt, copper and ammonium sulfates, water solution, solids as 2% copper sulfide, 4-5% vapors of ammonia and water vapor (copper boil reboiler)	8.4	101-107 (215-225)	95 d	<0.0001 in./yr	89
Type 316 stainless steel	Metal processing; field or pilot plant test; slight to moderate aeration; rapid agitation. Plus 14% oxygen, saturated with water vapor, remainder nitrogen (leach autoclave, vapors)	9	76-82 (170-180)	111 d	<0.0001 in./yr	89
Type 316 stainless steel	Chemical processing (urea manufacture); field or pilot plant test; no aeration; rapid agitation. Plus 7% carbon dioxide, remainder water (half immersed)	12	29 (85)	16 d	0.019 in./yr	89
Type 316 stainless steel	Petrochemical processing (synthetic urea manufacture); field or pilot plant test; slight to moderate aeration; slight to moderate agitation. Plus water, low carbon dioxide (ammonia desorber, vapors below liquid trapout tray	20	102 (215)	250 d	0.0006 in./yr	89
Type 316 stainless steel	Petrochemical processing (synthetic urea manufacture); field or pilot plant test; no aeration; slight to moderate agitation. Plus 71% water, 7% carbon dioxide, ammonium nitrate trace, pressure 29 psig (ammonia surge vessel, bottom)	22	65 (150)	300 d	<0.0001 in./yr	89
Type 316 stainless steel	Metal (distillation) processing; field or pilot plant test; slight to moderate aeration; rapid agitation. Plus 14% carbon dioxide, remainder water (still overhead line)	26	82 (180)	65 d	<0.0001 in./yr	89
Type 316 stainless steel	Plastic processing; field or pilot plant test; no aeration; no agitation. Plus hydrogen cyanide, carbon dioxide, and water	90	105 (221)	30 d	0.0001 in./yr	89
Type 316 stainless steel	...	...	21 (70)	...	Very good	121
Type 410 stainless steel	...	...	21 (70)	...	Very good	121
Type 430 stainless steel	...	...	21 (70)	...	Very good	121
Aluminum						
Aluminum (99.0-99.5%)	Moist gas	...	...	...	Satisfactory	92
Aluminum (99.0-99.5%)	Solution	...	...	...	Satisfactory	92
Aluminum-magnesium alloys	Moist gas	...	...	...	Satisfactory	92
Coppers						
Ampco 8, aluminum bronze	Dry. Generally suitable. Conditions such as aeration or temperature could restrict use	...	...	...	<0.5 (<20)	96
Ampco 8, aluminum bronze	Wet. Generally not suitable	...	...	...	>0.5 (>20)	96
C11000	Liquid plus 1% water. (a)	...	...	1600 h	<0.002 (<0.1)	72
C11000	Vapor plus 1% water. (a)	...	...	1600 h	<0.002 (<0.1)	72
C11000	Liquid. (b)	...	...	1600 h	0.002 (0.1)	72
C11000	Vapor. (b)	...	...	1600 h	<0.002 (<0.1)	72
C11000	Liquid plus 2% water. (a)	...	...	1600 h	0.002 (0.1)	72
C11000	Vapor plus 2% water. (a)	...	...	1600 h	0.002 (0.1)	72
C26000	Liquid with 2% water. (a)	...	...	1600 h	0.005 (0.2)	72
C26000	Vapor with 2% water. (a)	...	...	1600 h	0.002 (0.1)	72
C26000	Liquid. (b)	...	...	1600 h	<0.002 (<0.1)	72
C26000	Vapor. (b)	...	...	1600 h	<0.002 (<0.1)	72
C26000	Liquid plus 1% water. (a)	...	...	1600 h	0.002 (0.1)	72
C26000	Vapor plus 1% water. (a)	...	...	1600 h	<0.002 (<0.1)	72
Nickel silver	Absolutely dry	18	...	...	Suitable	93
Nickel silver	Moist	18	...	...	Not suitable	93
Phosphor bronze	8% Sn. Moist				Not suitable	93
Phosphor copper	Absolutely dry	...	...	...	Suitable	93
Phosphor copper	Moist	...	...	...	Not suitable	93
Red brass	Absolutely dry	...	...	...	Suitable	93
Red brass	Moist	...	...	...	Not suitable	93

(Continued)

Corrosion Behavior of Various Metals and Alloys in Ammonia (Continued)

Material	Condition, other factors, comments	Concentration, %	Temperature, °C (°F)	Duration	Corrosion rate, mm/yr (mils/yr) or other	Ref
Silicon bronze	Low. Absolutely dry	...	...	...	Suitable	93
Silicon bronze	High. Absolutely dry	...	...	...	Suitable	93
Silicon bronze	Low. Moist	...	...	...	Not suitable	93
Silicon bronze	High. Moist	...	...	...	Not suitable	93
Titanium						
Titanium	Anhydrous	100	40 (104)	...	<0.127 (<5.08)	90
Titanium	Plus steam + water	...	222 (432)	...	11.2 (448)	90
Heat- and corrosion-resistant alloys						
Alloy 825	Chemical processing (urea manufacture); field or pilot plant test; no aeration; rapid agitation. Plus 7% carbon dioxide, remainder water (half immersed)	12	29 (85)	16 d	0.015 in./yr	89
Alloy 825	Petrochemical processing (synthetic urea manufacture); field or pilot plant test; no aeration; slight to moderate agitation. Plus 71% water, 7% carbon dioxide, trace ammonium nitrate, pressure 29 psig (ammonia surge vessel, bottom)	22	65 (150)	300 d	<0.0001 in./yr	89
Alloy 825	Metal (distillation) processing; field or pilot plant test; slight to moderate aeration; rapid agitation. Plus 14% carbon dioxide, remainder water (still overhead line)	26	82 (180)	65 d	<0.0001 in./yr	89
Alloy 825	Petrochemical processing (synthetic urea manufacture); field or pilot plant test; slight to moderate aeration; slight to moderate agitation. Plus water, low carbon dioxide (ammonia desorber, vapors below liquid trapout tray	20	102 (215)	250 d	0.0002 in./yr	89
Alloy 825	Plastic processing; field or pilot plant test; no aeration; no agitation. Plus hydrogen cyanide, carbon dioxide, and water	90	105 (221)	30 d	0.0001 in./yr	89
Carpenter 20	Petrochemical processing (synthetic urea manufacture); field or pilot plant test; slight to moderate aeration; slight to moderate agitation. Plus water, low carbon dioxide (ammonia desorber, vapors below liquid trapout tray	20	102 (215)	250 d	0.0002 in./yr	89
Carpenter 20	Plastic processing; field or pilot plant test; no aeration; no agitation. Plus hydrogen cyanide, carbon dioxide, and water	90	105 (221)	30 d	0.0001 in./yr	89
Carpenter 20	Petrochemical processing (synthetic urea manufacture); field or pilot plant test; no aeration; slight to moderate agitation. Plus 71% water, 7% carbon dioxide, trace ammonium nitrate, pressure 29 psig (ammonia surge vessel, bottom)	22	65 (150)	300 d	0.0004 in./yr	89
Zirconium						
Zr702	Wet. Plus H$_2$O	...	38 (100)	...	<0.13 (<5)	15
Lead, tin, and zinc						
Lead	Practically resistant; Pb recommended for use	10-30	24-100 (75-212)	...	<500 μm/yr (<20)	95
Tin	...	...	20 (68)	...	Resistant	94
Tin	...	...	60 (140)	...	Unsuitable	94
Tin	...	...	100 (212)	...	Unsuitable	94
Noble metals						
Platinum	With oxidant. Use of Pt-Rh alloys is preferred for ammonia oxidation (loss is <250 mg of Pt/ton of HNO$_3$)	...	950 (1740)	...	<0.05 (<2)	6
Platinum	...	Pure	Elevated	...	Nitridation	6
Silver	...	Pure	190 (375)	...	<0.05 (<2)	8
Others						
Magnesium	Gas or liquid	100	Room	...	Resistant	119

(a) Any air present was probably depleted during initial stages of test. Atmospheric temperature and pressure of 345 to 1035 kPa (50 to 150 psi). Specimens were placed at the top and bottom of 2-L bombs that were charged with ammonia. Pressure varied throughout the test, depending on temperature. Water was added to two of the bombs before charging with ammonia.
(b) Atmospheric temperature and pressure of 345 to 1035 kPa (50 to 150 psi). Specimens were placed at the top and bottom of 2-L bombs that were charged with ammonia. Pressure varied throughout the test, depending on temperature. Water was added to two of the bombs before charging with ammonia.

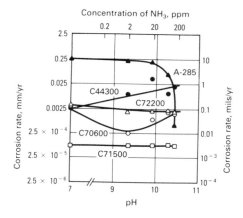

Copper alloys. Corrosion rates of copper alloys in aerated NH_3 solutions. Test duration: 1000 h. Source: *Metals Handbook*, 9th ed., Vol 13, Corrosion, ASM International, Metals Park, OH, 1987, 622.

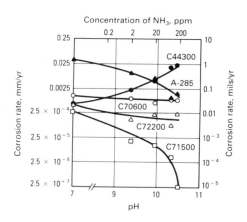

Copper alloys. Corrosion rates of copper alloys in deaerated NH_3 solutions. Test duration: 1000 h. Source: *Metals Handbook*, 9th ed., Vol 13, Corrosion, ASM International, Metals Park, OH, 1987, 622.

Ammonium Carbonate

Ammonium carbonate, $(NH_4)_2CO_3$, is a white water-soluble, volatile solid prepared by reaction of NH_4OH and CO_2 and crystallizing from dilute alcohol. Ammonium carbonate loses NH_3, CO_2, and H_2O at ordinary temperatures, and rapidly at 58 °C.

Material Summaries

The following material summaries were compiled from a survey of the available literature. Inclusion of a material description under a given environment does not imply that it is the most appropriate material for corrosion service in that environment. Likewise, exclusion of a given material does not imply that it is not suitable for corrosion service applications in that environment.

Aluminum. In laboratory tests under conditions of 100% relative humidity and ambient temperature, aluminum alloy 3003 showed resistance, whereas aluminum alloy 5154 was mildly attacked by solid ammonium carbonate. Aluminum alloy 3003 showed resistance in other tests to aqueous solutions of 1, 5, and 50% ammonium carbonate. Piping and storage tanks of aluminum alloys have been used to handle ammonium carbonate.

Iridium. Iridium is resistant to anodic corrosion in aqueous electrolytes, but may be attacked in ammonium carbonate solutions under the action of an alternating current.

Additional Reading

J.W. Lee, K. Osseo-Asare, and H.W. Pickering, Anodic Dissolution of Iron in Ammoniacal Ammonium Carbonate Solution, *J. Electrochem. Soc.*, *132*(3), 550-555, 1985. MetAbs No. 85-350863. **Abstract:** The electrochemical behavior of Fe (99.7% pure) has been characterized in aqueous ammoniacal ammonium carbonate solution.

Corrosion Behavior of Various Metals and Alloys in Ammonium Carbonate

Material	Condition, other factors, comments	Concentration, %	Temperature, °C (°F)	Duration	Corrosion rate, mm/yr (mils/yr) or other	Ref
Stainless steels						
Type 304 stainless steel	Chemical processing; field or pilot plant test; slight to moderate aeration; slight to moderate agitation. With carbon over the standard maximum. Plus ammonia, pH 9-10	...	29-46 (85-115)	41 d	0.0001 in./yr	89
Type 316 stainless steel	Chemical processing; field or pilot plant test; slight to moderate aeration; slight to moderate agitation. Plus ammonia, pH 9-10	...	29-46 (85-115)	41 d	0.0001 in./yr	89
Type 410 stainless steel	...	1	21 (70)	...	Good	121
Type 410 stainless steel	...	5	21 (70)	...	Good	121
Type 410 stainless steel	...	...	Room	...	Unattacked	121
Type 430 stainless steel	...	1	21 (70)	...	Good	121
Type 430 stainless steel	...	5	21 (70)	...	Good	121
Aluminum						
Aluminum (>99.5%)	Solution	...	20-70 (68-158)	...	Satisfactory	92

Ammonium Chloride

Ammonium chloride, NH4Cl, also known as ammoniae, salmiai, and ammonium nituriate, is a white crystalline solid. It is soluble in water, aqueous solutions of ammonia, and is slightly soluble in methyl alcohol. Ammonium chloride is found in nature as a sublimation product of volcanic activity, or is produced by neutralizing HCl (either in liquid or gaseous phase) with NH3 gas or liquid NH4OH then evaporating the excess H2O. The salt decomposes at 350 °C and sublimes under controlled conditions at 520 °C. Ammonium chloride is used as an electrolyte in dry cell batteries, as a flux for soldering, tinning and galvanizing, and as a processing ingredient in textile printing and hide tanning. Use as a source of nitrogen for fertilizers is limited because of the possible build-up of damaging chloride residuals in the soil.

Material Summaries

The following material summaries were compiled from a survey of the available literature. Inclusion of a material description under a given environment does not imply that it is the most appropriate material for corrosion service in that environment. Likewise, exclusion of a given material does not imply that it is not suitable for corrosion service applications in that environment.

Aluminum. In laboratory tests at 100% relative humidity and ambient temperature, aluminum alloy 3003 suffered moderate attack (~6 mils/yr) by solid ammonium chloride. Aqueous solutions (up to 20%) of ammonium chloride caused mild attack (~3 mils/yr) but localized pitting at all concentrations on aluminum alloy 1100 at ambient temperature. At the boiling point, concentrated solutions of ammonium chloride are very corrosive.

Additional Reading

S.H. Sanad, H. Abbas, A.A. Ismail, and K.M. El-Sobki, Benzotriazole as a Corrosion Inhibitor for Brass, *Surf. Technol.,* 25(1), 39-48, 1985. MetAbs No. 85-352057. **Abstract:** The effect of benzotriazole on the corrosion of 67/33, 70/30, and 90/10 brasses in 0.1N HCl, 0.1N H2SO4 and 0.1N NH4Cl was studied by means of immersion tests and galvanostatic measurements.

Corrosion Behavior of Various Metals and Alloys in Ammonium Chloride

Material	Condition, other factors, comments	Concentration, %	Temperature, °C (°F)	Duration	Corrosion rate, mm/yr (mils/yr) or other	Ref
Stainless steels(a)						
Type 304 stainless steel	...	10	Boiling	...	Poor	121
Type 304 stainless steel	Chemical processing; field or pilot plant test; slight to moderate aeration; slight to moderate agitation. Plus isopropanol, water, sodium chloride, pH 6.5-8.5. Severe pitting (maximum depth of pits over 0.010 in.)	75	49 (120)	183 d	0.0006 in./yr	89
Type 304 stainless steel	Chemical processing; field or pilot plant test; slight to moderate aeration; slight to moderate agitation. Sensitized specimens. Plus isopropanol, water, sodium chloride, pH 6.5-8.5. Moderate pitting (maximum depth of pits from 0.005 to 0.010 in.)	75	49 (120)	183 d	0.0008 in./yr	89
Type 304 stainless steel	Laboratory test; no aeration; no agitation. Plus 33% zinc chloride, 34% water. Severe pitting (maximum depth of pits over 0.010 in.)	33	60 (140)	33 d	0.0013 in./yr	89
Type 304 stainless steel	Chemical processing; field or pilot plant test; slight to moderate aeration; slight to moderate agitation. Plus isopropanol, water, sodium chloride, pH 6.5-8.5 (transfer line)	75	49 (120)	12 d	0.0003 in./yr	89
Type 304 stainless steel	Chemical processing; field or pilot plant test; slight to moderate aeration; slight to moderate agitation. Sensitized specimens. Plus isopropanol, water, sodium chloride, pH 6.5-8.5 (transfer line)	75	49 (120)	12 d	0.0007 in./yr	89
Type 304 stainless steel	Chemical processing; field or pilot plant test; no aeration; slight to moderate agitation. Plus water (tubular gas cooler), 2% ammonia, 3% carbon dioxide, 8% sodium chloride	18	30-80 (86-176)	68 d	<0.0001 in./yr	89
Type 316 stainless steel	Chemical processing; field or pilot plant test; slight to moderate aeration; slight to moderate agitation. Plus isopropanol, water, sodium chloride, pH 6.5-8.5. Moderate pitting (maximum depth of pits from 0.005 to 0.010 in.)	75	49 (120)	183 d	<0.0001 in./yr	89
Type 316 stainless steel	Chemical processing; field or pilot plant test; no aeration; slight to moderate agitation. Plus water (tubular gas cooler), 2% ammonia, 3% carbon dioxide, 8% sodium chloride	18	30-80 (86-176)	68 d	<0.0001 in./yr	89

(Continued)

Corrosion Behavior of Various Metals and Alloys in Ammonium Chloride (Continued)

Material	Condition, other factors, comments	Concentration, %	Temperature, °C (°F)	Duration	Corrosion rate, mm/yr (mils/yr) or other	Ref
Type 316 stainless steel	Laboratory test; no aeration; no agitation. Plus 33% zinc chloride, 34% water. Severe pitting (maximum depth of pits over 0.010 in.)	33	60 (140)	33 d	0.0001 in./yr	89
Type 316 stainless steel	Chemical processing; field or pilot plant test; slight to moderate aeration; slight to moderate agitation. Plus isopropanol, water, sodium chloride, pH 6.5-8.5 (transfer line)	75	49 (120)	12 d	0.0002 in./yr	89
Type 316 stainless steel	Chemical processing; field or pilot plant test; slight to moderate aeration; slight to moderate agitation. Sensitized specimens. Plus isopropanol, water, sodium chloride, pH 6.5-8.5 (transfer line)	75	49 (120)	12 d	0.0004 in./yr	89
Type 316 stainless steel	Chemical processing; field or pilot plant test; slight to moderate aeration; slight to moderate agitation. Sensitized specimens. Plus isopropanol, water, sodium chloride, pH 6.5-8.5. Slight pitting (maximum depth of pits from incipient to 0.005 in.)	75	49 (120)	183 d	0.0005 in./yr	89
Type 316 stainless steel	Annealed. All solutions from CP chemicals. Tests made in the laboratory	10	Boiling	...	<0.025 (<1)	19
Type 316 stainless steel	...	10	Boiling	...	Good	121
Type 317 stainless steel	Chemical processing; field or pilot plant test; slight to moderate aeration; slight to moderate agitation. Plus isopropanol, water, sodium chloride, pH 6.5-8.5 (transfer line)	75	49 (120)	12 d	0.0003 in./yr	89
Type 317 stainless steel	Chemical processing; field or pilot plant test; slight to moderate aeration; slight to moderate agitation. Plus isopropanol, water, sodium chloride, pH 6.5-8.5. Severe pitting (maximum depth of pits over 0.010 in.)	75	49 (120)	183 d	<0.0001 in./yr	89
Type 410 stainless steel	...	...	Room	...	Slightly attacked	121
Type 410 stainless steel	...	10	Boiling	...	Poor	121
Type 430 stainless steel	...	10	Boiling	...	Poor	121
AM-363 stainless steel	...	...	Room	...	Attacked	120
Aluminum						
Aluminum-manganese alloys	Solution	...	20-70 (68-158)	...	Satisfactory	92
Aluminum (>99.5%)	Solution	...	20-70 (68-1158)	...	Satisfactory	92
Coppers						
70-30 cupronickel	...	...	...	...	Fair	93
90-10 cupronickel	...	...	...	...	Not suitable	93
Admiralty brass	...	...	...	...	Not suitable	93
Aluminum bronze	...	...	...	...	Not suitable	93
Ampco 8, aluminum bronze	Generally not suitable	...	...	...	>0.5 (>20)	96
Architectural bronze	...	...	...	...	Not suitable	93
Brass	...	...	...	...	Not suitable	93
Cartridge brass	...	...	...	...	Not suitable	93
Commercial bronze	...	...	...	...	Not suitable	93
Electrolytic copper	...	...	...	...	Not suitable	93
Free-cutting brass	...	...	...	...	Not suitable	93
Muntz metal	...	...	...	...	Not suitable	93
Naval brass	...	...	...	...	Not suitable	93
Nickel silver	...	18	...	...	Not suitable	93
Phosphor bronze	5% Sn	...	...	...	Not suitable	93
Phosphor bronze	8% Sn	...	...	...	Not suitable	93
Phosphor copper	...	...	...	...	Not suitable	93
Red brass	...	...	...	...	Not suitable	93
Silicon bronze	Low	...	...	...	Not suitable	93
Silicon bronze	High	...	...	...	Not suitable	93

(Continued)

Corrosion Behavior of Various Metals and Alloys in Ammonium Chloride (Continued)

Material	Condition, other factors, comments	Concentration, %	Temperature, °C (°F)	Duration	Corrosion rate, mm/yr (mils/yr) or other	Ref
Titanium						
Titanium	Grade 12	10	Boiling	...	nil	33
Titanium	...	Saturated	100 (212)	...	<0.013 (<0.52)	90
Heat- and corrosion-resistant alloys						
Alloy 825	Chemical processing; field or pilot plant test; slight to moderate aeration; slight to moderate agitation. Plus isopropanol, water, sodium chloride, pH 6.5-8.5 (transfer line)	75	49 (120)	12 d	0.0001 in./yr	89
Alloy 825	Chemical processing; field or pilot plant test; slight to moderate aeration; slight to moderate agitation. Plus isopropanol, water, sodium chloride, pH 6.5-8.5. Moderate pitting (maximum depth of pits from 0.005 to 0.010 in.) Crevice attack (tendency to concentration-cell corrosion)	75	49 (120)	183 d	<0.0001 in./yr	89
Carpenter 20	Chemical processing; field or pilot plant test; slight to moderate aeration; slight to moderate agitation. Plus isopropanol, water, sodium chloride, pH 6.5-8.5 (transfer line)	75	49 (120)	12 d	0.0002 in./yr	89
Carpenter 20	Chemical processing; field or pilot plant test; slight to moderate aeration; slight to moderate agitation. Plus isopropanol, water, sodium chloride, pH 6.5-8.5. Moderate pitting (maximum depth of pits from 0.005 to 0.010 in.) Crevice attack (tendency to concentration-cell corrosion)	75	49 (120)	183 d	<0.0001 in./yr	89
Incoloy 800	Solutions were prepared with reagent-grade chemicals. Test specimens were cold-rolled, annealed sheet, 2.84 mm (0.112 in.) thick. Pitting after 42 d	5	80 (176)	42 d	<0.003 (<0.1)	44
Inconel 601	Pitting attack	5	80 (176)	30 d	0.002 (0.1)	64
Monel 400	In evaporator concentrating solution	28-40	102 (216)	32 d	0.3 (12.0)	79
Nickel 200	In evaporator concentrating solution	28-40	102 (216)	...	0.21 (8.4)	44
Nickel 200	In evaporator concentrating solution	28-40	102 (216)	32 d	0.21 (8.4)	79
Zirconium						
Zr702	...	40	Boiling	...	Weight gain	62
Zr702	...	1, 10, saturated	35-100 (95-212)	...	<0.025 (<1)	15
Zr705	...	40	Boiling	...	Weight gain	62
Lead, tin, and zinc						
Lead	Practically resistant; Pb recommended for use	0-10	24 (75)	...	<500 μm/yr (<20)	95
Tin	...	...	20 (68)	...	Resistant	94
Tin	...	...	60 (140)	...	Unsuitable	94
Tin	...	...	100 (212)	...	Unsuitable	94
Tantalum						
Tantalum	...	10	100 (212)	...	nil	42
Noble metals						
Platinum	...	All	Boiling	...	<0.05 (<2)	5
Silver	...	All	Boiling	...	<0.05 (<2)	9
Silver	Vapor	...	200 (390)	...	Attacked	8

(a) Stainless steel is susceptible to pitting and stress-corrosion cracking even though its general corrosion rate is low.

Ammonium Fluoride

Ammonium fluoride, NH_4F, is a white crystalline salt that is soluble in cold water. It is unstable and emits a strong odor of ammonia. Ammonium fluoride is used in etching glass, preserving wood, and in the textile industry as a mordant.

Material Summaries

The following material summaries were compiled from a survey of the available literature. Inclusion of a material description under a given environment does not imply that it is the most appropriate material for corrosion service in that environment. Likewise, exclusion of a given material does not imply that it is not suitable for corrosion service applications in that environment.

Aluminum. Solid ammonium fluoride caused mild attack (~3 mils/yr) of aluminum alloy 3003 under laboratory conditions of 100% relative humidity and ambient temperature. Other tests proved aluminum alloy 1100 resistant to solutions of 10 to 25% ammonium fluoride at ambient temperature. However, solutions of 50% concentration were very corrosive to aluminum alloy 3003 at 93 °C (200 °F).

Additional Reading

T. Hurlen and K.H. Johansen, Effects of Fluoride Ions on the Corrosion and Passive Behavior of Aluminium, *Acta Chem. Scand., A39*(8), 545-551, 1985. MetAbs No. 86-350584. **Abstract:** Stationary and transient polarization measurements were used to study high-purity Al electrodes in deoxygenated solutions of 1M ammonium acetate (pH 7.2) with ammonium fluoride additions of 0 to 5 mM at 25 °C.

Corrosion Behavior of Various Metals and Alloys in Ammonium Fluoride

Material	Condition, other factors, comments	Concentration, %	Temperature, °C (°F)	Duration	Corrosion rate, mm/yr (mils/yr) or other	Ref
Stainless steels						
Type 304 stainless steel	Glass processing; field or pilot plant test; no aeration; no agitation. With carbon over the standard maximum. Glass-etching solution, total hydrofluoric acid, 30%, 24.8% free hydrofluoric acid, 12.5% combined ammonia, 11.5% sodium fluorosilicate	34.5	16 (60)	30 d	0.165 in./yr	89
Type 304 stainless steel	Glass processing; field or pilot plant test; no aeration; no agitation. Glass-etching solution, total hydrofluoric acid, 30%, 24.8% free hydrofluoric acid, 12.5% combined ammonia, 11.5% sodium fluorosilicate	34.5	16 (60)	30 d	0.177 in./yr	89
Type 304 stainless steel	Field or pilot plant test; slight to moderate aeration; no agitation. Water solution	10	25 (77)	61 d	0.011 in./yr	89
Type 304 stainless steel	Research; laboratory test; no aeration; slight to moderate agitation. Water solution	6	93 (200)	>6 d	0.150 in./yr	89
Type 304 stainless steel	Chemical processing; laboratory test; no aeration; rapid agitation. Ammonium hydroxide excess, pH moderately basic	15	51 (125)	94 d	<0.0001 in./yr	89
Type 316 stainless steel	Chemical processing; laboratory test; no aeration; rapid agitation. Ammonium hydroxide excess, pH moderately basic	15	51 (125)	94 d	<0.0001 in./yr	89
Type 316 stainless steel	Glass processing; field or pilot plant test; no aeration; no agitation. With carbon over the standard maximum. Glass-etching solution, total hydrofluoric acid, 30%, 24.8% free hydrofluoric acid, 12.5% combined ammonia, 11.5% sodium fluorosilicate	34.5	16 (60)	30 d	0.04 in./yr	89
Type 316 stainless steel	Field or pilot plant test; slight to moderate aeration; no agitation. Water solution	10	25 (77)	61 d	0.0095 in./yr	89
Type 316 stainless steel	Research; laboratory test; no aeration; slight to moderate agitation. Water solution	6	93 (200)	>6 d	0.140 in./yr	89
Heat- and corrosion-resistant alloys						
Alloy 825	Field or pilot plant test; slight to moderate aeration; no agitation. Water solution	10	25 (77)	61 d	0.0005 in./yr	89
Alloy 825	Chemical processing; laboratory test; no aeration; rapid agitation. Ammonium hydroxide excess, pH moderately basic	15	51 (125)	94 d	<0.0001 in./yr	89
Alloy 825	Metal processing; field or pilot plant test; slight to moderate aeration; rapid agitation. 50% to anhydrous ammonium bifluoride, unidentified ore	50	27-199 (80-390)	10 d	0.0071 in./yr	89
Carpenter 20	Field or pilot plant test; slight to moderate aeration; no agitation. Water solution	10	25 (77)	61 d	0.0013 in./yr	89
Carpenter 20	Metal processing; field or pilot plant test; slight to moderate aeration; rapid agitation; cast specimens. 50% to anhydrous ammonium bifluoride, unidentified ore	50	27-199 (80-390)	10 d	0.0096 in./yr	89
Titanium						
Titanium	...	10	Room	...	0.102 (4.08)	90
Zirconium						
Zr702	pH 8	20	28 (80)	...	>1.3 (>50)	15
Zr702	pH 8	20	98 (210)	...	>1.3 (>50)	15

Ammonium Hydroxide

Ammonium hydroxide, NH$_4$OH, is a hydrate of ammonia and exists in crystalline form at -79 °C. Normally, it is only found in an aqueous solution also known as aqua ammonia and ammonia water. It is prepared by dissolving NH$_3$ in H$_2$O. Reagent grade ammonium hydroxide contains from 28 to 30% NH$_3$ at 15.6 °C. Industrial sales specify the concentration of NH$_3$ in solution in terms of specific gravity. Common concentrations are 20 °Be, which would be a concentration of 17.8% NH$_3$ (specific gravity 0.933) and 26 °Be (specific gravity 0.897), or a concentration of 29.4% NH$_3$.

Ammonium hydroxide is an excellent medium for the reaction of NH$_3$ (which becomes the NH$_4$$^+$ radical in solution) with other compounds for the preparation of ammonium salts and other nitrogen-containing chemicals. It is an ingredient in deodorants, etching compounds, and cleaning and bleaching materials. Ammonium hydroxide, as aqua ammonia, finds wide use as a neutralizing agent, because it is inexpensive and strongly alkaline.

Material Summaries

The following material summaries were compiled from a survey of the available literature. Inclusion of a material description under a given environment does not imply that it is the most appropriate material for corrosion service in that environment. Likewise, exclusion of a given material does not imply that it is not suitable for corrosion service applications in that environment.

Aluminum. Aluminum alloys suffer an initial rapid attack by dilute ammonium hydroxide solutions. The attack rate drops as the concentration of ammonium hydroxide and pH increase. In laboratory tests, the rate of attack of dilute ammonium hydroxide on aluminum alloy 1100 dropped from (~6 mils/yr) to less than 1 mil/yr as the concentration reached 10N. The rate was mild (~2 mils/yr) as the solution reached a pH value of 13. The decrease in attack has been attributed to the formation of a film on the aluminum alloy as the solution becomes oversaturated with aluminum precipitate. Processing equipment such as pressure vessels, pipes, storage tanks, and tank cars have used aluminum alloys. Aluminum bronzes are generally suitable for service in anhydrous ammonium hydroxide.

Stainless Steels. In NH$_4$OH, stainless steels have shown good resistance at all concentrations up to the boiling point of ammonium hydroxide.

Copper. Copper and copper alloys suffer rapid attack by concentrated solutions of ammonium hydroxide to form a soluble complex copper-ammonium compound. In some cases, the corrosion of copper exposed to dilute solutions of ammonium hydroxide is low. Copper specimens submerged at room temperature for 1 week in 0.01N ammonium hydroxide solution suffered a weight loss of 3.5 mil/yr.

Copper-zinc alloys are also attacked by ammonium hydroxide solutions. In laboratory tests of 2N ammonium hydroxide solutions at room temperature, copper-zinc alloys corrode at 1.8 to 6.6 mm/yr (70 to 260 mils/yr). Alloys containing more than 15% zinc could suffer stress-corrosion cracking, either from unrelieved residual stresses or applied service loads. Copper-nickel alloys corrode at 0.25 to 0.50 mm/yr (10 to 20 mils/yr) in 2N ammonium hydroxide solutions at room temperature. The corrosion rate for copper-tin alloys in 2N ammonium hydroxide solution is 1.3 to 2.5 mm/yr (50 to 100 mils/yr). Copper-silicon alloys corrode at a rate of 0.75 to 5 mm/yr (30 to 200 mils/yr) in a room-temperature 2N ammonium hydroxide solution.

Nickel. Nickel 200 resists attack by 1% concentrations of ammonium hydroxide, but stronger concentrations can cause rapid attack.

Titanium. Titanium alloys resist corrosion of boiling ammonium hydroxide solutions up to saturation. Titanium alloys may eventually suffer hydrogen embrittlement when temperatures exceed 80 °C and the pH is over 12. The addition of dissolved oxidizing species can extend resistance to hydrogen uptake in hot caustic solutions. Some examples of oxidizing agents are chlorate, hypochlorite, or nitrate compounds.

Additional Reading

T.K.G. Namboodhiri and R.S. Tripathi, The Stress-Assisted Dezincification of 70/30 Brass in Ammonia, *Corros. Sci., 26*(10), 745-756, 1986. MetAbs No. 87-351013. **Abstract:** Zinc and Cu losses from 70/30 brass specimens tensile loaded to various stress levels and exposed to 10N NH$_4$OH were estimated at different time intervals by atomic absorption spectroscopic analysis of the corrodent.

R.S. Tripathi and T.K.G. Namboodhiri, Mechanically Assisted Dezincification and Stress Corrosion Cracking of 60/40 Brass, *J. Electrochem. Soc. India, 35*(3), 183-187, 1986. MetAbs No. 87-351502. **Abstract:** Dezincification studies and slow strain rate tensile testing of annealed and cold rolled 60/40 brass were carried out in 10N NH$_4$OH.

Corrosion Behavior of Various Metals and Alloys in Ammonium Hydroxide

Material	Condition, other factors, comments	Concentration, %	Temperature, °C (°F)	Duration	Corrosion rate, mm/yr (mils/yr) or other	Ref
Stainless steels						
Type 316 stainless steel	...	...	21 (70)	...	Very good	121
Type 410 stainless steel	...	...	Room	...	Unattacked	121
Type 410 stainless steel	...	...	21 (70)	...	Very good	121
Type 430 stainless steel	...	...	21 (70)	...	Very good	121
Coppers						
70-30 cupronickel	...	..	...	...	Fair	93
90-10 cupronickel	...	...	...	...	Not suitable	93

(Continued)

Corrosion Behavior of Various Metals and Alloys in Ammonium Hydroxide (Continued)

Material	Condition, other factors, comments	Concentration, %	Temperature, °C (°F)	Duration	Corrosion rate, mm/yr (mils/yr) or other	Ref
Admiralty brass	...					
Aluminum bronze	...	...	...	...	Not suitable	93
Ampco 8, aluminum bronze	Generally not suitable	...	...	...	Not suitable	93
Architectural bronze	...	..	...	...	>0.5 (>20)	96
Brass	...					
Cartridge brass	...	...	...	...	Not suitable	93
Commercial bronze	...	...	...	...	Not suitable	93
Electrolytic copper	...	...	...	...	Not suitable	93
Free-cutting brass	...	...	...	...	Not suitable	93
Muntz metal	...	...	...	...	Not suitable	93
Naval brass	...	...	...	...	Not suitable	93
Nickel silver	...	...	...	...	Not suitable	93
Phosphor bronze	5% Sn	18	...	...	Not suitable	93
Phosphor bronze	8% Sn	...	...	...	Not suitable	93
Phosphor copper	...	...	...	...	Not suitable	93
Red brass	...	...	...	...	Not suitable	93
Silicon bronze	Low	...	...	...	Not suitable	93
Silicon bronze	High	...	...	...	Not suitable	93
Titanium			...	...	Not suitable	93
Ti-3Al-2.5V	ASTM Grade 9	8	150 (302)	...	nil	91
Ti-3Al-2.5V	ASTM Grade 9	28	150 (302)	...	nil	91
Titanium	...	28	26 (79)	...	0.002 (0.08)	1
Titanium	...	70	Boiling	...	nil	1
Titanium	Grade 12	30	Boiling	...	nil	33
Titanium	...	28	26 (79)	...	0.002 (0.08)	1
Titanium	...	70	Boiling	...	nil	1
Titanium	...	28	Room	...	0.003 (0.12)	90
Titanium	...	28	100 (212)	...	nil	90
Titanium	Grade 9	8, 28	150 (300)	...	nil	33
Titanium	...	8	150 (302)	...	nil	91
Titanium	...	28	150 (302)	...	nil	91
Type 304	...	...	21 (70)	...	Very good	121
Heat- and corrosion-resistant alloys						
Inconel 601	...	5	80 (176)	7 d	nil	64
Inconel 601	...	10	80 (176)	7 d	nil	64
Inconel 690	...	5	80 (176)	...	<0.03 (<1)	57
Inconel 690	...	10	80 (176)	...	<0.03 (<1)	57
Incoloy 800	(a)	5	80 (176)	7 d	<0.003 (<0.1)	44
Incoloy 800	(a)	10	80 (176)	7 d	<0.003 (<0.1)	44
Zirconium						
Zr702	...	28	Room to 100 (room to 212)	...	<0.025 (<1)	15
Lead						
Lead	Negligible corrosion; Pb recommended for use	3.5–40	27 (80)	...	<50 μm/yr (<2)	95
Noble metals						
Silver	Air must be excluded	...	Room	...	<0.05 (<2)	9
Others						
Cobalt	Static	5	25 (77)	...	0.02 (0.8)	54
Magnesium	...	All	Room	...	Suitable	119
Niobium	...	...	Room	...	nil	2

(a) Solutions were prepared with reagent-grade chemicals. Test specimens were cold-rolled, annealed sheet, 2.84 mm (0.112 in.) thick. No pitting occurred.

Ammonium Nitrate

Ammonium nitrate, NH_4NO_3, is a colorless crystalline solid existing in two forms. Between -16 and 32 °C, the crystals are tetragonal; between 32 and 84 °C, the crystals are rhombic. The melting point of NH_4NO_3 is 169.6 °C, and it decomposes above 210 °C. When heated, ammonium nitrate yields nitrous oxide gas. Ammonium nitrate is soluble in water, in acetic acid solutions containing ammonia, is slightly soluble in ethanol, and is moderately soluble in methanol. Ammonium nitrate is a very insensitive and stable high explosive used as a slow-burning propellant for rockets when compounded with burning rate catalysts. Although the major applications of ammonium nitrate are explosives and fertilizers, it is also used in insecticides, rust inhibitors, and pyrotechnics.

Material Summaries

The following material summaries were compiled from a survey of the available literature. Inclusion of a material description under a given environment does not imply that it is the most appropriate material for corrosion service in that environment. Likewise, exclusion of a given material does not imply that it is not suitable for corrosion service applications in that environment.

Stainless steels. Stainless steels are excellent for service in ammonium nitrate.

Aluminum. Aluminum alloy 3003 resisted corrosion of dry ammonium nitrate at ambient temperature and of aqueous solutions of ammonium nitrate at temperatures up to 82 °C (180 °F) in laboratory tests. Aluminum alloys have been used in the production, handling, shipment, and storage of ammonium nitrate solutions prepared for fertilizer applications.

Although concentrations of up to 83% ammonium nitrate at temperatures up to 121 °C (250 °F) were acceptable, corrosion at welds can occur in hot 83% solutions in the presence of free nitric acid. The solution should therefore be maintained by agitation at a uniform pH above 6. Welded aluminum alloy 3003 tank bottoms and piping are more resistant to hot acidic conditions. Avoiding mercury contamination is a serious problem in the handling of ammonium nitrate. Aluminum alloy production and storage equipment have been used for servicing ammoniated ammonium nitrate.

Copper. Copper alloy Cu-23Zn-12Ni telephone wires were observed to suffer stress-corrosion cracking in 2 years. Laboratory tests duplicating the conditions (high humidity, positive potential, a constant load of 386 MPa, and exposure to nitrate salts including ammonium nitrate) gave the same result. Cracking occurred without an applied potential when the concentration of nitrates at the surface was high. Wires of Cu-20Ni did not crack.

Additional Reading

S. Natarajan and V. Sivan, Corrosion Behaviour of Steels Used in Boiler Plants, *J. Electrochem. Soc. India,* 34(4), 250-255, 1985. MetAbs No. 86-350905. **Abstract:** Boiler corrosion is due to many environmental factors such as steam, flue gases, etc. The neutral aqueous medium can cause severe pitting type of corrosion in boiler steels compared to acid and alkaline media. The corrosion behavior of C-Mn (SA515 Grade 70) and Cr-Mo steels (T11, T22, 2.25Cr-1Mo) used in boiler plants in NH_4NO_3 solution at three different temperatures and stress-corrosion behavior of two different Cr-Mo steels exposed to three varied concentrations of caustic solution at room temperature for a period of 30 days, using C-ring method as the test procedure, are discussed.

Corrosion Behavior of Various Metals and Alloys in Ammonium Nitrate

Material	Condition, other factors, comments	Concentration, %	Temperature, °C (°F)	Duration	Corrosion rate, mm/yr (mils/yr) or other	Ref
Stainless steels						
AM-363 stainless steel	...	...	Room	...	Unattacked	120
Type 304 stainless steel	...	All	21 (70)	...	Very good	121
Type 304 stainless steel	Petroleum processing; field or pilot plant test; no aeration; slight to moderate agitation; with carbon over the standard medium. 17% free ammonia, 17% water	66	Room	715 d	<0.0001 in./yr	89
Type 304 stainless steel	Research; laboratory test; slight to moderate agitation. 21.7% free ammonia, 13.3% water	65	53 (128)	14	0.0286 in./yr	89
Type 304 stainless steel	Research; laboratory test; slight to moderate agitation. 21.7% free ammonia, 13.3% water	65	53 (128)	20	0.0127 in./yr	89
Type 304 stainless steel	Petrochemical processing (synthetic urea manufacture); slight to moderate aeration; slight to moderate agitation. Water and carbon dioxide traces, pressure 30 psig (bottom of ammonia desorber, vapors)	20	143 (290)	300 d	<0.0001 in./yr	89
Type 304 stainless steel	Petrochemical processing (synthetic urea manufacture); slight to moderate aeration; slight to moderate agitation; sensitized specimens. Water and carbon dioxide traces, pressure 30 psig (bottom of ammonia desorber, vapors)	20	143 (290)	300 d	<0.0001 in./yr	89
Type 316 stainless steel	Petrochemical processing (synthetic urea manufacture); slight to moderate aeration; slight to moderate agitation. Water and carbon dioxide traces, pressure 30 psig (bottom of ammonia desorber, vapors)	20	143 (290)	300 d	<0.0001 in./yr	89
Type 316 stainless steel	Petrochemical processing (synthetic urea manufacture); slight to moderate aeration; slight to moderate agitation; sensitized specimens. Water and carbon dioxide traces, pressure 30 psig (bottom of ammonia desorber, vapors)	20	143 (290)	300 d	<0.0001 in./yr	89

(Continued)

Corrosion Behavior of Various Metals and Alloys in Ammonium Nitrate (Continued)

Material	Condition, other factors, comments	Concentration, %	Temperature, °C (°F)	Duration	Corrosion rate, mm/yr (mils/yr) or other	Ref
Type 316 stainless steel	...	All	21 (70)	...	Very good	121
Type 316 stainless steel	Petroleum processing; field or pilot plant test; no aeration; slight to moderate agitation. 17% free ammonia, 17% water	66	Room	715 d	<0.0001 in./yr	89
Type 316 stainless steel	Research; laboratory test; slight to moderate agitation. 21.7% free ammonia, 13.3% water	65	53 (128)	14	0.0286 in./yr	89
Type 316 stainless steel	Research; laboratory test; slight to moderate agitation. 21.7% free ammonia, 13.3% water	65	53 (128)	20	nil	89
Type 317 stainless steel	Petroleum processing; field or pilot plant test; no aeration; slight to moderate agitation. 17% free ammonia, 17% water	66	Room	715 d	<0.0001 in./yr	89
Type 410 stainless steel	...	All	21 (70)	...	Good	121
Type 410 stainless steel	...	...	Room	...	Unattacked	121
Type 430 stainless steel	...	All	21 (70)	...	Very good	121
Coppers						
70-30 cupronickel	...	...	...	...	Fair	93
90-10 cupronickel	...	...	...	...	Not suitable	93
Admiralty brass	...	...	...	...	Not suitable	93
Aluminum-magnesium alloys	Solution	...	20 (68)	...	Satisfactory	92
Aluminum bronze	...	...	...	...	Not suitable	93
Ampco 8, aluminum bronze	Generally not suitable	...	...	...	>0.5 (>20)	96
Architectural bronze	...	...	...	...	Not suitable	93
Brass	...	...	...	...	Not suitable	93
Cartridge brass	...	...	...	...	Not suitable	93
Commercial bronze	...	...	...	...	Not suitable	93
Electrolytic copper	...	...	...	...	Not suitable	93
Free-cutting brass	...	...	...	...	Not suitable	93
Muntz metal	...	...	...	...	Not suitable	93
Naval brass	...	...	...	...	Not suitable	93
Nickel silver	...	18	...	...	Not suitable	93
Phosphor bronze	5% Sn	...	...	...	Not suitable	93
Phosphor bronze	8% Sn	...	...	...	Not suitable	93
Phosphor copper	...	...	...	...	Not suitable	93
Red brass	...	...	...	...	Not suitable	93
Silicon bronze	Low	...	...	...	Not suitable	93
Silicon bronze	High	...	...	...	Not suitable	93
Titanium						
Titanium	...	28	Boiling	...	nil	90
Titanium	Plus 1% HNO_3	28	Boiling	...	nil	90
Titanium	...	...	100 (212)	...	Resistant	94
Heat- and corrosion-resistant alloys						
Alloy 825	Petrochemical processing (synthetic urea manufacture); field or pilot plant test; slight to moderate aeration; slight to moderate agitation. Water and carbon dioxide traces, pressure 30 psig (bottom of ammonia desorber, vapors)	20	143 (290)	300 d	<0.0001 in./yr	89
Carpenter 20	Petrochemical processing (synthetic urea manufacture); field or pilot plant test; slight to moderate aeration; slight to moderate agitation. Water and carbon dioxide traces, pressure 30 psig (bottom of ammonia desorber, vapors)	20	143 (290)	300 d	<0.0001 in./yr	89
Lead, tin, and zinc						
Lead	Corrosion rate too high to merit any consideration of Pb	10-30	24-49 (75-120)	...	>1270 µm/yr (>50)	95
Tin	...	...	20 (68)	...	Resistant	94
Tin	...	...	60 (140)	...	Resistant	94
Noble metals						
Platinum	...	All	Boiling	...	<0.05 (<2)	5
Silver	...	<20	Room	...	<0.05 (<2)	9

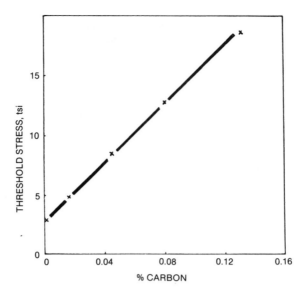

Ferritic steels. The effect of carbon content of annealed mild steels on threshold stress for cracking in boiling 4N NH$_4$NO$_3$. Source: R.N. Parkins, Stress Corrosion Cracking of Low-Strength Ferritic Steels, in *The Theory of Stress Corrosion Cracking in Alloys*, J.C. Scully, Ed., North Atlantic Treaty Organization, Brussels, 1971, p 172.

Ammonium Phosphate

Ammonium phosphate occurs in two forms—the monobasic, NH$_4$H$_2$PO$_4$, and dibasic, (NH$_4$)$_2$HPO$_4$, forms. It is a white crystalline solid that is soluble in water. Ammonium phosphate is a product of the reaction between ammonia and phosphoric acid. Ammonium phosphate is an important fertilizer and is used as a fire retardant.

Material Summaries

The following material summaries were compiled from a survey of the available literature. Inclusion of a material description under a given environment does not imply that it is the most appropriate material for corrosion service in that environment. Likewise, exclusion of a given material does not imply that it is not suitable for corrosion service applications in that environment.

Aluminum. Concentration and temperature affect the corrosion of aluminum by ammonium phosphate. The diammonium salt corrodes aluminum; therefore, the use of aluminum equipment to handle ammonium phosphate solutions should be avoided without the use of inhibitors. The monobasic salt is less corrosive than the dibasic form, and the attack rate decreases with time. In laboratory tests, aluminum alloy 3003 suffered mild attack (~10 mils/yr) in solutions of the monobasic salt with concentrations up to 28%.

Corrosion Behavior of Various Metals and Alloys in Ammonium Phosphate

Material	Condition, other factors, comments	Concentration, %	Temperature, °C (°F)	Duration	Corrosion rate, mm/yr (mils/yr) or other	Ref
Stainless steels						
Type 304 stainless steel	Chemical processing; laboratory test; no aeration; no agitation. Approximate concentration, ammonium monophosphate	40	60 (140)	22 d	<0.0001 in./yr	89
Type 304 stainless steel	Chemical processing; field or pilot plant test; no aeration; no agitation. With carbon over the standard maximum. Ammonium monophosphate, saturated water solution	Saturated	28 (82)	150 d	<0.0001 in./yr	89

(Continued)

Corrosion Behavior of Various Metals and Alloys in Ammonium Phosphate (Continued)

Material	Condition, other factors, comments	Concentration, %	Temperature, °C (°F)	Duration	Corrosion rate, mm/yr (mils/yr) or other	Ref
Type 316 stainless steel	Chemical processing; strong aeration; slight to moderate agitation. Ammonium phosphate traces in steam; ammonia, ammonium sulfate, fluorine compounds and silica traces present (agitator). Slight pitting: maximum depth of pits from incipient to 0.005 in.	...	100-121 (212-250)	12 d	0.031 in./yr	89
Type 316 stainless steel	Chemical processing; field or pilot plant test; strong aeration; slight to moderate agitation. Plus 3% sulfuric acid, ammonium phosphate, water	...	50-70 (122-158)	30 d	0.006 in./yr	89
Type 316 stainless steel	Chemical processing; laboratory test; no aeration; no agitation. Approximate concentration, ammonium monophosphate	40	60 (140)	22 d	<0.0001 in./yr	89
Type 316 stainless steel	Chemical processing; field or pilot plant test; no aeration; no agitation. Ammonium monophosphate, saturated water solution	Saturated	28 (82)	150 d	<0.0001 in./yr	89
Type 317 stainless steel	Chemical processing; field or pilot plant test; no aeration; no agitation. Ammonium monophosphate, saturated water solution	Saturated	28 (82)	150 d	<0.0001 in./yr	89
Type 410 stainless steel	...	...	Room	...	Unattacked	121
Aluminum						
Aluminum-magnesium alloys	Solution	...	20 (68)	...	Satisfactory	92
Copper						
Ampco 8, aluminum bronze	Generally suitable Conditions such as aeration or temperature could restrict use	...	...	...	<0.5 (<20)	96
Titanium						
Titanium	...	10	Room	...	nil	90
Heat- and corrosion-resistant alloys						
Alloy 825	Chemical processing; strong aeration; slight to moderate agitation. Ammonium phosphate traces in steam; ammonia, ammonium sulfate, fluorine compounds and silica traces present (agitator)	...	100-121 (212-250)	12 d	0.001 in./yr	89
Alloy 825	Chemical processing; field or pilot plant test; strong aeration; slight to moderate agitation. Plus 3% sulfuric acid, ammonium phosphate, water	...	50-70 (122-158)	30 d	0.001 in./yr	89
Noble metals						
Platinum	...	All	Boiling	...	<0.05 (<2)	5
Silver	...	All	Boiling	...	<0.05 (<2)	9

Ammonium Sulfate

Ammonium sulfate, $(NH_4)_2SO_4$, is a solid composed of colorless rhombic crystals. It has a melting point of 140 °C and is soluble in water.

Material Summaries

The following material summaries were compiled from a survey of the available literature. Inclusion of a material description under a given environment does not imply that it is the most appropriate material for corrosion service in that environment. Likewise, exclusion of a given material does not imply that it is not suitable for corrosion service applications in that environment.

Aluminum. Aluminum alloy 3003 resists attack by solid ammonium sulfate under laboratory conditions of ambient temperature and 100% relative humidity. In other laboratory tests, aluminum alloy 1100 resisted concentrations of 1 to 45% ammonium sulfate solutions at ambient temperature. Aluminum alloy equipment has been used in the production and shipment of ammonium sulfate.

Corrosion Behavior of Various Metals and Alloys in Ammonium Sulfate

Material	Condition, other factors, comments	Concentration, %	Temperature, °C (°F)	Duration	Corrosion rate, mm/yr (mils/yr) or other	Ref
Stainless steels						
AM-363 stainless steel	...	...	Room	...	Slightly attacked	120
Type 304 stainless steel	Coal by-product processing; field or pilot plant test; no aeration; slight to moderate agitation. Plus 5% sulfuric acid, saturated water solution	...	38-47 (100-116)	33 d	<0.0001 in./yr	89
Type 304 stainless steel	...	10	21 (70)	...	Good	121
Type 304 stainless steel	...	10	Boiling	...	Good	121
Type 304 stainless steel	Mining; field or pilot plant test; no aeration; no agitation. Plus hydrogen sulfide, free ammonia trace (autoclave, vapors). Moderate pitting (maximum depth of pits from 0.005 to 0.010 in.)	approx 40	60-71 (140-160)	1 d	0.03 in./yr	89
Type 304 stainless steel	Mining; field or pilot plant test; no aeration; no agitation. Sensitized specimens. Plus hydrogen sulfide, free ammonia trace (autoclave, vapors). Moderate pitting (maximum depth of pits from 0.005 to 0.010 in.)	approx 40	60-71 (140-160)	1 d	0.24 in./yr	89
Type 304 stainless steel	Chemical processing; field or pilot plant test; slight to moderate aeration; rapid agitation. With carbon over the standard maximum. Plus 20% ammonium sulfide 2 gal/800 gal approximately of reacted solution, 0-75% sulfuric acid, ammonia added with the acid. Severe pitting (maximum depth of pits over 0.010 in.)	approx 38	66-93 (150-200)	6 d	0.339 in./yr	89
Type 304 stainless steel	Chemical processing; field or pilot plant test; slight to moderate aeration; rapid agitation. Plus 20% ammonium sulfide 2 gal/800 gal approximately of reacted solution, 0-75% sulfuric acid, ammonia added with the acid. Severe pitting (maximum depth of pits over 0.010 in.)	approx 38	66-93 (150-200)	6 d	0.75 in./yr	89
Type 304 stainless steel	Chemical processing; slight to moderate aeration; slight to moderate agitation. Plus 0.3% sulfur dioxide, 10% sulfuric acid	36	82 (180)	25 d	0.0014 in./yr	89
Type 316 stainless steel	Mining; field or pilot plant test; no aeration; no agitation. Sensitized specimens. Plus hydrogen sulfide, free ammonia trace (autoclave, vapors). Moderate pitting (maximum depth of pits from 0.005 to 0.010 in.)	approx 40	60-71 (140-160)	1 d	0.03 in./yr	89
Type 316 stainless steel	Chemical processing; field or pilot plant test; slight to moderate aeration; rapid agitation. Plus 20% ammonium sulfide 2 gal/800 gal approximately of reacted solution, 0-75% sulfuric acid, ammonia added with the acid	approx 38	66-93 (150-200)	6 d	0.024 in./yr	89
Type 316 stainless steel	Chemical processing; slight to moderate aeration; slight to moderate agitation. Plus 0.3% sulfur dioxide, 10% sulfuric acid. Severe pitting (maximum depth of pits over 0.010 in.)	36	82 (180)	25 d	0.0075 in./yr	89
Type 316 stainless steel	...	10	21 (70)	...	Good	121
Type 316 stainless steel	...	10	Boiling	...	Good	121
Type 317 stainless steel	Coal by-product processing; field or pilot plant test; no aeration; slight to moderate agitation. Plus 5% sulfuric acid, saturated water solution	...	38-47 (100-116)	33 d	<0.0001 in./yr	89
Type 410 stainless steel	...	10	21 (70)	...	Fair	121
Type 410 stainless steel	...	10	Boiling	...	Poor	121
Type 410 stainless steel	...	...	Room	...	Slightly attacked	121
Type 410 stainless steel	Plus 0.5% H_2SO_4	...	Room	...	Slightly attacked	121
Type 410 stainless steel	Plus 0.5% H_2SO_4	...	Room	...	Attacked	121
Type 410 stainless steel	Plus 5.0% H_2SO_4	...	Room	...	Fair	121
Type 430 stainless steel	...	10	21 (70)	...	Fair	121
Type 430 stainless steel	...	10	Boiling	...	Poor	121
Aluminum						
Aluminum-manganese alloys	Solution	...	20 (68)	...	Satisfactory	92
Aluminum (>99.5%)	Solution	...	20 (68)	...	Satisfactory	92
Coppers						
70-30 cupronickel	May be considered in place of a copper metal when some property, other than corrosion resistance, governs its use	...	...	...	Good	93

(Continued)

Corrosion Behavior of Various Metals and Alloys in Ammonium Sulfate (Continued)

Material	Condition, other factors, comments	Concentration, %	Temperature, °C (°F)	Duration	Corrosion rate, mm/yr (mils/yr) or other	Ref
90-10 cupronickel	...	...	...	...	Fair	93
Admiralty brass	...	...	...	...	Not suitable	93
Aluminum bronze	...	...	...	...	Fair	93
Ampco 8, aluminum bronze	Generally suitable. Conditions such as aeration or temperature could restrict use	...	...	...	<0.5 (<20)	96
Architectural bronze	...	...	...	...	Not suitable	93
Brass	...	...	...	...	Not suitable	93
Cartridge brass	...	...	...	...	Not suitable	93
Commercial bronze	...	...	...	...	Fair	93
Electrolytic copper	...	...	...	...	Fair	93
Free-cutting brass	...	...	...	...	Not suitable	93
Muntz metal	...	...	...	...	Not suitable	93
Naval brass	...	...	...	...	Not suitable	93
Nickel silver	...	...	...	...	Fair	93
Phosphor bronze	5% Sn	...	...	...	Fair	93
Phosphor bronze	8% Sn	...	...	...	Fair	93
Phosphor copper	...	...	...	...	Fair	93
Red brass	...	...	...	...	Fair	93
Silicon bronze	Low	...	...	...	Fair	93
Silicon bronze	High	...	...	...	Fair	93
Titanium						
Titanium	...	10	100 (212)	...	nil	90
Titanium	Plus 1% H_2SO_4	Saturated	Room	...	0.010 (0.4)	90
Heat- and corrosion-resistant alloys						
Incoloy 800	Solutions were prepared with reagent-grade chemicals. Test specimens were cold-rolled, annealed sheet, 2.84 mm (0.112 in.) thick. No pitting	5	80 (176)	7 d	nil	44
Inconel 601	...	5	80 (176)	7 d	0.002 (0.1)	64
Inconel 690	...	5	80 (176)	...	<0.03 (<1)	57
Monel 400	(a)	Saturated	40 (106)	33 d	0.075 (3.0)	79
Nickel 200	(a)	Saturated	41 (106)	...	0.015 (3.0)	44
Nickel 200	(a)	Saturated	40 (106)	33 d	0.075 (3.0)	79
Zirconium						
Zr702	...	5, 10	100 (212)	...	<0.13 (<5)	15
Lead, tin, and zinc						
Lead	During storage of liquid alkyl detergent. Mixing tank and crystallizer-saturated, 5% H_2SO_4 solution	...	47 (116)	...	0.025-0.125 (1-5)	48
Lead	Solution plus 5% H_2SO_4	Saturated	47 (116)	...	0.025 (1)	48
Lead	Solution plus 5% H_2SO_4	Saturated	47 (116)	...	0.125 (5)	48
Lead	Practically resistant; Pb recommended for use	...	24 (75)	...	<500 μm/yr (<20)	95
Noble metals						
Platinum	...	All	Boiling	...	<0.05 (<2)	5
Silver	...	All	Boiling	...	<0.05 (<2)	9

(a) Plus 5% H_2SO_4, in suspension tank during crystallization.

Aqua Regia

Aqua regia, also known as nitrohydrochloric acid and chloroazoatic acid, is a fuming, volatile liquid that is made by mixing three parts concentrated hydrochloric acid with one part concentrated nitric acid. It is very corrosive with a suffocating odor and reacts with all metals. Aqua regia typically reacts by oxidizing the metal to a metallic ion and reducing the nitric acid to nitric oxide. Its reaction with silver produces silver chloride. Aqua regia dissolves the common metallic oxides and hydroxides, the ignited oxides of tin, aluminum, chromium, and iron, and the higher oxides of lead, cobalt, nickel, and manganese. It is used for testing gold and platinum.

Material Summaries

The following material summaries were compiled from a survey of the available literature. Inclusion of a material description under a given environment does not imply that it is the most appropriate material for corrosion service in that environment. Likewise, exclusion of a given material does not imply that it is not suitable for corrosion service applications in that environment.

Aluminum. Laboratory tests show aqua regia to be very corrosive to all aluminum alloys.

Niobium. Niobium has been reported to have a corrosion rate of less than 0.025 mm/yr (1 mil/yr) in aqua regia at 55 °C (130 °F).

Gold. Aqua regia rapidly attacks gold.

Iridium. Iridium resists cold and boiling aqua regia, but may be dissolved by aqua regia under pressure by heating to 250 to 300 °C (480 to 570 °F).

Platinum. Platinum is attacked by aqua regia and mixtures of hydrochloric acid and oxidizing agents.

Rhodium. Rhodium is unattacked by aqua regia at 100 °C (212 °F) in either wrought or cast form.

Ruthenium. Ruthenium is the most chemically resistant of the platinum metals and is not attacked or dissolved by either hot or cold aqua regia.

Tantalum. Tantalum is not attacked by aqua regia at ordinary temperatures.

Zirconium. Aqua regia attacks zirconium.

Hafnium. Hafnium is dissolved by aqua regia, and with the addition of small amounts of soluble fluoride salts, the reaction with other acids is appreciably increased.

Corrosion Behavior of Various Metals and Alloys in Aqua Regia

Material	Condition, other factors, comments	Concentration, %	Temperature, °C (°F)	Duration	Corrosion rate, mm/yr (mils/yr) or other	Ref
Titanium						
Titanium	Grade 7	...	Boiling	...	1.12 (44.8)	33
Titanium	Grade 12	...	Boiling	...	0.61 (24.4)	33
Titanium	Grade 9	...	Boiling	...	1.29 (51.6)	33
Titanium	...	...	Room	...	nil	90
Titanium	...	...	80 (176)	...	0.86 (34.4)	90
Titanium	...	...	Boiling	...	1.12 (44.8)	90
Titanium	Grade 9	...	25 (75)	...	0.015 (0.6)	33
Titanium	...	...	Boiling	...	1.1 (44)	91
Ti-3Al-2.5V	ASTM Grade 9	...	Boiling	...	1.27 (51)	91
Ti-3Al-2.5V	ASTM Grade 9	...	Room	...	0.01 (0.6)	91
Titanium	...	...	Room	...	nil	91
Zirconium						
Zirconium	...	...	Room	...	Dissolved	36
Zr702	3 parts HCl/1 part HNO$_3$	3:1	Room	...	>1.3 (>50)	15
Lead, tin, and zinc						
Tin	...	...	20 (68)	...	Unsuitable	94
Tin	...	...	60 (140)	...	Unsuitable	94
Tin	...	...	100 (212)	...	Unsuitable	94
Tantalum						
Tantalum	...	...	25 (78)	...	nil	42
Noble metals						
Gold	...	...	Room	...	Rapid dissolution	8
Iridium	...	...	Room-boiling	...	nil	29
Osmium	...	...	Boiling	...	Rapid dissolution	17
Palladium	...	...	Room	...	Rapid dissolution	17
Rhodium	...	...	Boiling	...	nil	29
Ruthenium	...	...	100 (212)	...	nil	18
Silver	Attack will occur whenever silver chloride film is ruptured	...	Room	...	Potential dissolution	4
Silver	Potential dissolution. Attack will occur whenever silver chloride film is ruptured.	...	Room	...	...	4

Atmospheric Environments

Atmospheres are often classified as being rural, industrial, or marine in nature, but this is an oversimplification. For example, there are locations along the seacoast that have heavy industrial pollution in the atmosphere, and they are both marine and industrial. Furthermore, two decidedly rural environments can differ widely in average yearly temperature and rainfall and can therefore have considerably different corrosive tendencies. Industrial expansion into formerly rural areas can easily change the aggressiveness of a particular location. Finally, long-term trends in the environment, such as changes in rainfall patterns, mean temperature, and perhaps acid rain, can make extrapolations from past behavior less reliable. Other factors that limit the usefulness of atmospheric exposure data are the general nonlinearity of weight loss due to corrosion with time and the fact that most atmospheric corrosion data are presented as an average over the entire test panel surface. Most atmospheric exposure data for steels show a decrease in the rate of attack with time of exposure so that extrapolations of such data to times longer than those covered by the exposure data can lead to an over design in cross section. Finally, in many cases, the average weight loss per unit area is of less concern than the time to perforation. This factor is more related to localized attack, which can be masked by the averaging of data, as is done in weight loss determinations.

Given these variables, the design engineer is well justified in using atmospheric-corrosion data as more indicative than quantitative. Perhaps most important, it should be remembered that it is impossible to describe either the extent or rate of corrosion under atmospheric conditions with a single parameter, which is what much of the reported corrosion data persist in doing. When the results of a several-year exposure test are condensed to a single value, such as the average loss per year or the total loss for the exposure period, one cannot estimate the values of the kinetic parameters governing the system. Without the values of these parameters, extrapolation of results to longer exposure periods becomes quite unreliable. When good estimates for the kinetic parameters are available, extrapolations to 7- or 8-year performance from 1- to 2-year data have been found to agree within 5% of observed performance.

Rainwater has been recognized as a potential source of corrosive agents that can be inadvertently transported into a protective environment and cause deterioration of susceptible materials.

Inadvertent admission of atmospheric moisture into silos and launch control centers of missile systems has been cited as the cause of most of the general corrosion problems associated with the various metals contained in these structures. Despite the fact that corrosion problems have been encountered in missile silos, the maintenance of a humidity-controlled environment has generally been effective in protecting most components from corrosion. For example, one manufacturer has not found a single case of corrosion of beryllium components in rocket thrusters during periodic examinations of all operational units through years of continued service. These components were maintained under humidity-controlled conditions.

One study demonstrated the noncorroding nature of pure water vapor when the beryllium surface is uncontaminated and free of exposed Be_2C inclusions. Polished, bare specimen coupons were subjected to an atmosphere of 95% relative humidity at 40 °C (100 °F) for 30 days with no apparent corrosive attack. Neither microscopic examination nor weight gain measurements indicated corrosive attack on any of the specimens.

Material Summaries

The following material summaries were compiled from a survey of the available literature. Inclusion of a material description under a given environment does not imply that it is the most appropriate material for corrosion service in that environment. Likewise, exclusion of a given material does not imply that it is not suitable for corrosion service applications in that environment.

Aluminum

Most aluminum alloys have been shown to be resistant to atmospheric corrosion in laboratory tests and have been used widely in structural and architectural applications. The A.O. Smith Building in Milwaukee (completed in 1930) may have been the forerunner of aluminum curtain wall construction. When examined in 1962, a 6.35-mm (250-mil) cast panel from this building showed an average measured depth of attack of 0.053 mm (2.1 mils). Aluminum shingles for residential roofing were first marketed in 1928. One such roof made of 0.508-mm (20-mil) 3003 alloy sheet, when examined after 30 years of exposure to an industrial atmosphere, exhibited an average depth of corrosion attack of 0.076 mm (3.0 mils). Since 1930, aluminum roofing and siding have been used in many applications throughout the world. Alclad aluminum roofing and siding have been employed in a wide variety of industrial atmospheres. In such applications, corrosion is arrested at the cladding/core interface due to cathodic protection by the 1% Zn aluminum alloy cladding. Large quantities of these alclad aluminum sheet products have been used in port facilities throughout the United States in applications such as transit sheds, storage buildings, and the like. Aluminum has been used for electrical power cables since early in this century. One of the first stranded aluminum power cables exhibited an average measured depth of corrosion attack of 0.109 mm (4.3 mils) after 51 years of service near Hartford, Connecticut. Most aluminum alloys have excellent resistance to atmospheric corrosion (often called weathering), and in many outdoor applications, such alloys do not require shelter, protective coatings, or maintenance. Aluminum alloy products that have no external protection and therefore depend critically on this property include electrical conductors, outdoor lighting poles, ladders, and bridge railings. Such products often retain a bright metallic appearance for many years, but their surfaces may become dull, gray, or even black as a result of pollutant accumulation. Corrosion of most aluminum alloys by weathering is restricted to mild surface roughening by shallow pitting, with no general thinning. However, such attack is more severe for alloys with higher copper contents, and such alloys are seldom used in outdoor applications without protection. Corrosivity of the atmosphere to metals varies greatly from one geographic location to another, depending on such weather factors as wind direction, precipitation and temperature changes, amount and type of urban and industrial pollutants, and proximity to natural bodies of water. Service life may also be affected by the design of the structure if weather conditions cause repeated moisture condensation in unsealed crevices or in channels with no provision for drainage. Laboratory exposure tests, such as salt spray, total-immersion tests, provide useful comparative information, but have limited value for predicting actual service performance and sometimes exaggerate differences among alloys that are negligible under atmospheric conditions. Consequently, extensive long-term evaluations of the effects of exposure in different industrial, chemical, seacoast, tropical, and rural environments have been made.

Effect of Exposure Time. A very important characteristic of weathering of aluminum and of corrosion of aluminum under many other environmental conditions is that corrosion rate decreases with time to a relatively low, steady-state rate. This deceleration of corrosion occurs regardless of alloy composition, type of environment, or the parameter by which the corrosion is measured. However, loss in tensile strength, which is influenced somewhat by pit acuity and distribution, but is basically a result of loss of effective cross section, decelerates more gradually than depth of attack.

The decrease in rate of penetration of corrosion is dramatic. In general, rate of attack at discrete locations, which is initially about 0.1 mm/yr (4 mils/yr), decreases to much lower and nearly constant rates within a period of about 6 months to 2 years. For the deepest pits, the maximum rate after about 2 years does not exceed about 0.003 mm/yr (0.11 mil/yr) for severe seacoast locations and may be as low as 0.0008 mm/yr (0.03 mil/yr) in rural or arid climates.

Wrought Alloys. Aluminum alloy sheet was tested in desert, rural, sea-coast, and industrial exposures. Results after 20 years of exposure were as follows. In aggressive (seacoast and industrial) environments, the bare (nonalclad) heat treated alloys—2017-T3 and, to a lesser extent, 6051-T4—exhibited more severe corrosion and greater resulting loss in tensile strength than the non-heat-treatable alloys. Alclad 2017-T3, although as severely corroded as the non-heat-treatable materials, did not show measurable loss in strength; in fact, some specimens of this alloy were 2 to 3% higher in strength after 20 years because of long-term natural aging.

Data from these and other weathering programs demonstrate that differences in resistance to weathering among non-heat-treatable alloys are not great, that alclad products retain their strength well because corrosion penetration is confined to the cladding layer, and that corrosion and resulting strength loss tend to be greater for bare (nonalclad) heat-treatable 2xxx and 7xxx series alloys.

Casting Alloys. The testing program that was the source of the strength change data for wrought alloys also provided weathering data for casting alloys exposed for the same period and at the same sites. Specimens were separately sand-cast and permanent mold cast tensile bars, each with a reduced section 12.7 mm (0.5 in.) in diameter. Alloys with relatively high copper contents, such as 295.0-T6, 208.0-F, 319.0-T6, and 319.0-T61, showed the greatest losses. Alloys of the zinc-containing 7xxx series generally exhibited larger strength losses than alloys having low zinc or copper contents. In all cases, as for wrought materials, severity of corrosion varied widely, depending on environmental conditions.

Cast Irons

Atmospheric corrosion of cast irons is basically of interest only for unalloyed and low-alloy cast irons. Atmospheric corrosion rates are determined by the relative humidity and the presence of various gases and solid particles in the air. The high humidity, sulfur dioxide (SO_2) or similar compounds found in many industrialized areas, and chlorides found in marine atmospheres increase the rate of attack on cast irons.

Cast irons typically exhibit very low corrosion rates in industrial environments—generally under 0.13 mm/yr (5 mils/yr)—and the cast irons are usually found to corrode at lower rates than steel structures in the same environment. White case irons show the lowest rate of corrosion of the unalloyed materials. Pearlitic irons are generally more resistant than ferritic irons to atmospheric corrosion.

In marine atmospheres, unalloyed cast irons also exhibit relatively low rates of corrosion. Low alloy additions are sometimes made to improve corrosion resistance further. Higher alloy additions are even more beneficial, but are rarely warranted. Gray iron offers some added resistance over ductile iron in marine atmospheres.

Carbon Steels

The effects of various atmospheres on the corrosion rates of cold-rolled carbon steels were determined in a series of weight-loss measurements performed after 2 years of exposure. The most startling feature of this study was the extreme range of corrosion rates occurring at the various test sites. For example, Geleta Point Beach, Panama, was found to be more than 450 times as aggressive as a site at Normal Wells, N.W.T., Canada. This difference in corrosion rate is easily greater than any effect that can be produced by small changes in composition of the steel. Again, this underscores the fact that in dealing with the corrosion of carbon steels the alteration of design or environmental factors is usually more effective than changing the grade of steel.

Further examination shows that the marine environments tended to be near the aggressive end of the list and that cold environments were generally less aggressive than warm sites. The average yearly temperature cannot, in general, be isolated from the moisture effect, because most of the more tropical exposure sites are also in regions with high humidity. One exception is arid Phoenix, Arizona.

Because carbon steels are by definition not very highly alloyed, it is not surprising that most grades do not exhibit large differences in atmospheric corrosion rates. Nevertheless, alloying can make changes in the atmospheric corrosion rate of carbon steel. The elements generally found to be most beneficial in this regard are copper, nickel, silicon, chromium, and phosphorus. Of these, the most striking example is that of copper; increases from 0.01 to 0.05% have been shown to decrease the corrosion rate by a factor of two to three. Additions of the above elements in combination are generally more effective than when added singly, although the effects are not additive. The effectiveness of these elements in retarding corrosion also appears to depend on the corrosive environment, with the most benefit appearing in industrial atmospheres.

Alloy Steels

A study of 270 alloy steels was performed in which experimental heats of steel involving systematic combinations of chromium, copper, nickel, silicon, and phosphorus were tested to determine the individual and joint contributions of these elements to corrosion resistance. The data showed that long-term atmospheric corrosion of carbon steels can be reduced by small additions of copper, that additions of nickel are also effective, and that chromium in sufficient amounts is helpful if copper is present. The maximum resistance to corrosion was obtained in this study when alloy contents were raised to their highest levels.

Some of the results obtained in industrial environments were as follows. The corrosion rate for carbon steel becomes constant after about 5 years. The corrosion rate for copper steel levels off to a constant value after about 3 years. High-strength low-alloy steel, which contains several alloying elements, exhibits a constant rate after approximately 2 years, and corrosion of this steel eventually ceases. ASTM low-alloy steels A242, A588, A514, and A517 exhibit significantly better performance than either carbon steel or structural copper steel.

Although the results given above provide good estimates of average corrosion behavior, corrosion rates can increase significantly in severe environments. This study does, however, demonstrate the effectiveness of increased alloy content on corrosion resistance.

Stainless Steels

The atmospheric contaminants most often responsible for the rusting of structural stainless steels are chlorides and metallic iron dust. Chloride contamination may originate from the calcium chloride ($CaCl_2$) used to make concrete or from exposure in marine or industrial locations. Iron contamination may occur during fabrication or erection of the structure. Contamination should be minimized, if possible.

The corrosivity of different atmospheric exposures can vary greatly and can dictate application of different grades of stainless steel. Rural atmospheres, uncontaminated by industrial fumes or coastal salt, are extremely mild in terms of corrosivity for stainless steel, even in areas of high humidity. Industrial or marine environments can be considerably more severe.

Resistance to staining can depend on the specific exposure. For example, several 300-series stainless steels showed no rust after long-term exposures in New York City. On the other hand, staining was observed after much shorter exposures at Niagara Falls in a severe industrial-chemical environment near plants producing chlorine or HCl.

Although marine environments can be severe, stainless steels often provide good resistance. In a study comparing several AISI 300-series stainless steels after a 15-year exposure to a marine atmosphere 250 m (800 ft) from the ocean at Kure Beach, North Carolina, materials containing molybdenum exhibited only extremely slight rust stain, and all grades were easily cleaned to reveal a bright surface. Type 304 stainless steel may provide satisfactory resistance in many marine applications, but more highly alloyed grades are often selected when the stainless is sheltered from washing by the weather and is not cleaned regularly.

Type 302 and 304 stainless steels have had many successful architectural applications. Type 430 stainless steel has been used in many locations, but there have been problems. For example, type 430 stainless steel rusted in sheltered areas after only a few months of exposure in an industrial environment. The type 430 stainless steel was replaced by type 302, which provided satisfactory service. In more aggressive environments, such as marine or severely contaminated atmospheres, type 316 stainless steel is especially useful.

Stress-corrosion cracking is generally not a concern when austenitic or ferritic stainless steels are used in atmospheric exposures. Several austenitic stainless steels were exposed to a marine atmosphere at Kure Beach, North Carolina. Annealed and quarter-hard wrought AISI types, 201, 301, 302, 304, and 316 stainless steels were not susceptible to stress-corrosion cracking. In the as-welded condition, only type 301 stainless steel experienced failure. Following sensitization at 650 °C (1200 °F) for 1.5 h and furnace cooling, failures were obtained only for materials with carbon contents of 0.043% or more.

Stress-corrosion cracking must be considered when quench-hardened martensitic stainless steels or precipitation-hardening grades are used in marine environments or in industrial locations where chlorides are present. Several hardenable stainless grades were exposed as U-bends 25 m (80 ft) from the ocean at Kure Beach, North Carolina. Most samples were cut longitudinally, and two alloys received different heat treatments to produce different hardness or strength levels. The results of the study indicated that Custom 450 stainless and stainless alloy 355 resisted cracking. Stainless alloy 355 failed in this type of test when fully hardened; resistance was imparted by the 540 °C (1000 °F) temper. Precipitation-hardenable grades are expected to exhibit improved corrosion resistance when higher aging temperatures (lower strengths) are used.

Resistance to stress-corrosion cracking is of particular interest in the selection of high-strength stainless steels for fastener applications. Cracking of high-strength fasteners is possible and often results from hydrogen generation due to corrosion or contact with a less noble material, such as aluminum. Resistance to stress-corrosion cracking can be improved by optimizing the heat treatment, as noted above.

Fasteners for atmospheric exposure have been fabricated from a wide variety of alloys. Type 430 and unhardened type 410 stainless steels have been used when moderate corrosion resistance is required in a lower strength material. Better-than-average corrosion resistance has been obtained by using type 305 and Custom Flo 302HQ stainless steels when lower strength is acceptable.

Coppers

Copper and copper alloys are suitable for atmospheric exposure. Copper and copper alloys resist corrosion by industrial, marine, and rural atmospheres, except atmospheres containing NH_3 or certain other agents where stress-corrosion cracking has been observed in high-zinc alloys (>20% Zn). The copper metals most widely used in atmospheric exposure are C11000, C22000, C23000, C385000, and C75200. Alloy C11000 is an effective material for roofing, flashings, gutters, and downspouts. The severity of the corrosion attack in marine atmospheres is somewhat less than that in industrial atmospheres, but greater than that in rural atmospheres. However, these rates decrease with time.

Individual differences in corrosion rates do exist between alloys, but these differences are frequently less than the differences caused by environmental factors. Thus, it becomes possible to classify the corrosion behavior of copper alloys in a marine atmosphere into two general categories: those alloys that corrode at a moderate rate and include high-copper alloys, silicon bronze, and tin bronze; and those alloys that corrode at a lower rate and include brass, aluminum bronze, nickel silver, and copper nickel.

Environmental factors can cause the median thickness loss to vary by as much as 50% or more in a few extreme cases. Those environmental factors that tend to accelerate metal loss include high humidity, high temperatures (either ambient or due to solar radiation), proximity to the ocean, long times of wetness, and the presence of pollutants in the atmosphere. The converse of these conditions would tend to retard metal loss.

Metallurgical factors can also affect metal loss. Within a given alloy family, those with a higher alloy content tend to corrode at a lower rate. Surface finish also plays a role in that a highly polished metal will corrode slower than one with a rougher surface. Finally design details can affect corrosion behavior. For example, designs that allow the collections and stagnations of rainwater will often exhibit wastage rates in the puddle areas that are more typical of those encountered in seawater immersions.

Certain copper alloys are susceptible to various types of localized corrosion that can greatly affect their utility in a marine atmosphere. Brasses and nickel silvers containing more than 15% Zn can suffer from dealloying. The extent of this attack is greater on alloys that contain higher proportions of zinc. In addition, these same alloys are subject to stress-corrosion cracking in the presence of small quantities of NH_3 or other gaseous pollutants. Many natural environments contain pollutants that, in the presence of moisture, may cause stress-corrosion problems. Sulfur dioxide, oxides of nitrogen, and NH_3 are known to induce stress-corrosion cracking of some copper alloys. Chlorides may also cause problems. Inhibited grades of these alloys are available that resist dealloying but are susceptible to stress-corrosion cracking.

Alloys containing large amounts of manganese tend to be somewhat prone to pitting in marine atmospheres, as are the cobalt-containing beryllium-coppers. A tendency toward intergranular corrosion has been observed in silicon bronzes and aluminum brass, but its occurrence is somewhat sporadic.

On the whole, however, even under somewhat adverse conditions, the average thickness losses for copper alloys in a marine atmosphere tend to be very slight, typically under 50 μm. Thus, copper alloys can be safely specified for applications requiring long-term durability in a marine atmosphere. Design considerations for the atmospheric use of copper alloys include allowance for free drainage of structures, the possibility of staining from runoff water, and the use of smooth or polished surfaces.

Copper-Tin Alloys. Early studies were conducted on Cu-6.3Sn-0.08P wire and Cu-6.3Sn-0.08P-0.5Zn sheet in rural, suburban, urban, industrial, and marine environments for 1 year. The bronze samples ranked consistently high among the materials tested.

In a study involving exposure of screen wire cloth at four sites for up to 9 years, Cu-2Sn bronze was found to exhibit the lowest strength losses at all sites from a group of alloys that included brasses, aluminum bronze, and nickel-copper. Outstanding corrosion resistance of a Cu-2Sn bronze exposed to sulfur-bearing gases in railway tunnels was also reported.

Another investigation compared the behavior of five stainless steels and a low-alloy steel with that of a Cu-4.38Sn-0.36P bronze exposed at tropical inland and seacoast sites for 8 years. The coastal site was more aggressive toward the bronze, which showed higher weight losses at both sites than the stainless steels, but the low-alloy steel was more severely attacked. However, the bronze was free of pitting and suffered no loss in strength, which was not the case with some of the stainless steels. These researchers summarized the results of 16-year exposures on three tin-containing alloys (Cu-4.38Sn-0.36P, Cu-39Zn-0.84Sn, and Cu-40Zn-1Fe-0.65Sn) exposed at marine, inland semirural, and two tropical sites. In general, the copper alloys resisted corrosion in the tropical zones, although less so at coastal sites compared to inland sites. The tin-containing alloys were as good as, or slightly superior to, the other alloys.

More recent work by the same investigators included previous data plus additional information on the following cast bronzes: Cu-5Sn-5Pb-5Zn, Cu-6Sn-2Pb-3Zn-1Ni, Cu-9Sn-3Zn-1Ni, and Cu-3Sn-2Zn-6Ni. The conclusions were much the same as before. The later work included a study of the effect of coupling phosphor bronze to equal areas of numerous other metals, and this work indicated that the coastal sites were 4 to 8 times more aggressive than the inland sites. Evaluation of the effect of corrosion on the solderability of a Cu-2Sn-9Ni alloy was reported by workers at Bell Telephone, who found this material to be superior to both nickel silver and an 8% Sn phosphor bronze.

Alloys in the Cu-Sn-Al system were evaluated, and those alloys containing at least 5% each of tin and aluminum were found to have good corrosion resistance in rural, urban, and industrial environments. The most promising material was Cu-5Sn-7Al. Another researcher noted that such alloys could be brittle, but that the addition of 1% Fe and 1% Mn overcame this difficulty without detracting from the corrosion resistance of the alloy.

Iridium

Iridium alloys containing up to 60% Rh have been proposed for high-temperature thermocouples. The couple iridium versus Ir-40Rh is regarded as one of the most satisfactory for use in oxidizing atmospheres at temperatures as high as 2100 °C (3810 °F).

Lead

In most of its forms, lead exhibits consistent durability in all types of atmospheric exposure, including industrial, rural, and marine. These three atmospheric environments are distinct because each involves different factors that promote corrosion. In rural areas, which are relatively free of pollutants, the only important environmental factors influencing corrosion rate are humidity, rainfall, and air flow. However, near or on the sea, chlorides entrained in marine air often exert a strong effect on corrosivity. In industrial environments, sulfur oxide gases and the minerals in solid emissions change the patterns of corrosion behavior con-

siderably. However, the protective films that form on lead and its alloys are so effective that corrosion is insignificant in most natural atmospheres. The extent of this protection is demonstrated by the survival of lead roofing and auxiliary products after hundreds of years of atmospheric exposure. In fact, the metal is preserved permanently if these films are not damaged.

Antimonial lead, such as UNS 52760 (Pb-2.75Sb-0.2Sn-0.18As-0.075Cu), exhibits approximately the same corrosion rate in atmospheric environments as chemical lead (99.9% commercial-purity lead). However, the greater hardness, strength, and resistance to creep of antimonial lead often make it more desirable for use in specific chemical and architectural applications. The ability of some antimonial leads to retain this greater mechanical strength in atmospheric environments has been demonstrated in exposure tests in which sheets containing 4% Sb and smaller amounts of arsenic and tin were placed in semirestricted positions for 3 years. They showed less tendency to buckle than chemical lead, indicating that their greater resistance to creep had been retained.

Magnesium

A clean, unprotected magnesium alloy surface exposed to indoor or outdoor atmospheres free from salt spray will develop a gray film that protects the metal from corrosion while causing only negligible losses in mechanical properties. Chlorides, sulfates, and foreign materials that hold moisture on the surface can promote corrosion and pitting of some alloys unless the metal is protected by properly applied coatings.

The surface film that ordinarily forms on magnesium alloys exposed to the atmosphere gives limited protection from further attack. Unprotected magnesium and magnesium alloy parts are resistant to rural atmospheres and moderately resistant to industrial and mild marine atmospheres, provided they do not contain joints or recesses that entrap water in association with an active galvanic couple.

Corrosion of magnesium alloys increases with relative humidity. At 9.5% humidity, neither pure magnesium nor any of its alloys exhibit evidence of surface corrosion after 18 months. At 30% humidity, only minor corrosion may occur. At 80% humidity, the surface may exhibit considerable corrosion. In marine atmospheres heavily loaded with salt spray, magnesium alloys require protection for prolonged survival.

Indoor Atmospheres. Before the computer age, reaction of magnesium alloys with indoor atmospheres was of concern primarily from the standpoint of appearance, not function. The widespread introduction of magnesium die casting into the computer disk drive environment has imposed strict new standards of surface stability on the metal because of the need to maintain a clean particle-free atmosphere at the disk/head interface. The corrosion of magnesium alloys in indoor atmospheres increases with relative humidity. At relative humidities up to about 90%, corrosion is very minor; as humidity increases beyond this level, heavier tarnish films develop.

Nickel

Nickel and nickel-base alloys have very good resistance to atmospheric corrosion. Corrosion rates are typically less than 0.0025 mm/yr (0.1 mil/yr), with varying degrees of surface discoloration depending on the alloy. Nickel 200 will become dull and acquire a thin adherent corrosion film, which is usually a sulfate. A greater tarnish will result in industrial sulfur-containing atmospheres than in rural or marine atmospheres.

Corrosion of alloy 400 is negligible in all types of atmospheres, although a thin gray-green patina will develop. In sulfurous atmospheres, a brown patina may be produced. Because of its low corrosion rate and pleasing patina, alloy 400 has been used for architectural service, such as roofs, gutter, and flashings, and for outdoor sculpture.

Nickel alloys containing chromium and iron, such as alloys 600 and 800, also have very good atmospheric corrosion resistance, but may develop a slight tarnish after prolonged exposure, especially in industrial atmospheres. Nickel-chromium-molybdenum materials such as alloys 825, 625, G, C-276 and C-22 develop very thin and protective passive oxide films that prevent even significant tarnishing. A mirror finish can be maintained after extended exposure to the atmosphere.

Although alloy 400 has been used for atmospheric service in the past, atmospheric exposures requiring nickel alloys are now relatively infrequent. Less costly low-alloy stainless steels or plated materials are normally used.

Palladium

Palladium alloys containing more than 10% Au are resistant to tarnish by industrial sulfur-bearing environments, and those with more than 20% Au are resistant to HNO_3 and HCl. Palladium alloys with 10% of either rhodium or iridium are untarnished by industrial sulfur-bearing atmospheres.

Platinum

Platinum is one of the few metals that is unaffected by atmospheric exposure, even in sulfur-bearing industrial atmospheres. Alloys containing more than 60% Ag are tarnished by exposures to industrial atmospheres.

Tin

In clean dry air, tin retains a bright appearance for many days. In one study, a light dulling was observed after 100 days, and noticeable, faint yellow-gray tarnish film was seen after 150 days. However, it was also reported that the reflectivity of tin remains practically unchanged over long periods when the tin is washed with soap and water. Thus, at ordinary temperatures, the surface oxide film on tin is very thin and exhibits a very slow rate of growth. The rate of oxidation increases with temperature. Above 190 °C (375 °F), a film thickness sufficient to produce interference colors is reportedly produced in a few hours; at 210 °C (410 °F), a film thickness sufficient to produce interference colors is reportedly produced in a few hours; at 210 °C (410 °F), this film thickness is produced in 20 min.

Pewter. By definition, modern pewter is an alloy that contains 90 to 90% Sn, 1 to 8% Sb, 0.25 to 3% Cu, and a maximum of 0.05% Pb and As. Material that conforms to these standards has about the same degree of corrosion resistance to ordinary atmospheres as pure tin. Alloys within this range are widely used for decorative items, containers, and flatware. Indoors, they retain a bright, white luster in the same manner as pure tin. Because contamination from fabrication residues can deteriorate the protective oxide, care should be exercised in finishing to remove residues from soldering fluxes and cleaning solutions.

In years past, pewter alloys contained lead in sufficient quantities to affect its corrosion resistance significantly, for example, by producing a dark patina during atmospheric exposure. Modern pewter can be chemically treated to reproduce this patina.

Soft Solders. Even small additions of lead to tin impair the retention of its bright reflective surface in common atmospheres. With increasing lead content, the appearance of soldered joints becomes increasingly dull, like that of lead. However, destructive corrosion (except effects from flux residues) is highly unusual. On rare occasions, within enclosed spaces, condensed pure water may extract lead, but more common causes of trouble are volatile organic acids. Acetic acid (CH_3COOH) vapors from wood or insulating materials and formic acid ($HCOOH$) or other acids that may come from insulating materials may attack lead-containing solders to produce a white incrustation and cause serious destruction of metal.

Contact of solder with other metals can impose a serious risk in conditions of exposure to sea spray or where pockets or crevices can trap moisture or flux residues. In most atmospheric conditions, the formation of lead sulfate ($PbSO_4$) protects the solder. However, in chloride pollution conditions, nickel, copper, and their alloys are likely to be cathodic to solder. Zinc tends to be strongly anodic to soft solders, but correctly designed zinc roof coverings appear to suffer no deterioration at the soldered joints.

Zinc

It is generally accepted that the corrosion rate of zinc is low; it ranges from 0.13 μm/yr (0.005 mil/yr) in more moist industrial atmospheres. Zinc is more corrosion resistant than steel in most natural atmospheres, the exceptions being ventilated indoor atmospheres where the corrosion of both steel and zinc is extremely low and certain highly corrosive industrial atmospheres. For example, in seacoast atmospheres, the corrosion rate of zinc is about 1/25 that of steel. For both steel and zinc, corrosion rates vary significantly among different locations and climates.

Indoor Exposure. Zinc corrodes very little in ordinary indoor atmospheres of moderate relative humidity. In general, a tarnish film begins to form at spots where dust particles are present on the surface; the film then develops slowly. This attack may be a function of the percentage of relative humidity at which the particles absorb moisture from the air. However, moisture has little effect on the tarnish formation up to 70% relative humidity. The degree of corrosion is related to the relative humidity at and above this point, because the zinc corrosion products absorb enough moisture to stimulate the attack to a perceptible rate.

Rapid corrosion can occur where the temperature decreases and where visible moisture that condenses on the metal dries slowly. This is related to the ease with which such thin moisture films maintain a high oxygen content because of the small volume of water and large water/air interface area. Considerably accelerated corrosion can then take place with the formation of a film that is too thick. Atmospheres inside industrial buildings can be corrosive, particularly where heated moisture and gases, such as SO_2, condense near a cool room.

Atmospheric Exposure. Several atmospheric exposure programs have been conducted throughout the world to obtain corrosion rate data for zinc exposed to representative natural atmospheres. These programs have provided quantitative evidence of the excellent resistance of zinc over a wide range of atmospheric conditions. Although there is considerable spread in terms of percentage in the corrosion rates observed, the actual corrosion rate rarely exceeded about 8 μm/yr (0.3 mil/yr) in average metal loss, even under the more severe conditions. This is well within all standards of acceptable corrosion performance.

The amount of zinc corrosion with increasing time of exposure depends on the type of atmosphere. In semi-industrial and rural atmospheres, the corrosion rate is approximately constant. On the other hand, the corrosion rate decreases with time in marine atmospheres and increases with time in industrial atmospheres. In all cases, the yearly change in corrosion rate decreases with time and approaches a steady rate. The equilibrium corrosion rate also depends on the environment. The rate in a rural atmosphere is only about one-fifth that in an industrial atmosphere and one-third that in a marine atmosphere.

Although neither iron nor zinc corrodes appreciably in the rural climate of Normal Wells, Northwest Territory (N.W.T.), the atmospheres at the Geleta Point Beach site in the Panama Canal zone appears to be the most corrosive to these metals. Corrosivity can vary appreciably over very short distances. For example, a comparison of the corrosion rates for two Kure Beach, North Carolina, sites shows that the corrosion rate for zinc at the 25-m (80-ft) site is roughly three times that of the 250-m (800-ft) site, although the sites were only 225 m (720 ft) apart.

The corrosion rate data for steel in the same atmosphere show that steel, in general, corrodes at a greater rate than zinc in all atmospheres. The progress of corrosion with time, however, may be quite different for the two metals; therefore, direct comparison of corrosion rates should specify the duration of exposure for which the comparison are made. For example, the corrosion rate of zinc decreases with time in a severe sea-coast environment (Kure Beach: 25-m, or 80-ft, site), but that of steel increases with time. On the other hand, the reverse is true in an industrial environment.

Zinc owes its high degree of resistance to atmospheric corrosion to the formation of insoluble basic carbonate films. Environmental conditions that interfere with the formation of such films may attack zinc quite rapidly. The most important factors that control the rate at which zinc corrodes in atmospheric exposures are:

* The duration and frequency of moisture contact

* The rate at which the surface dries

* The extent of industrial pollution of the atmosphere

The latter is the most important because the formation of basic corrosive films is prevented when the zinc is attacked by acidic moisture. The effect of industrial pollutants is illustrated by considering that in highly industrial environments a 2-oz/ft^2 (610-g/m^2) zinc coating will begin to exhibit rusting after 4 years and may be 80% rusted in 10 years. A similar coating would not be expected to display rusting after 30 to 40 years of exposure in rural atmospheres and after 15 to 25 years in marine environments.

In dry air, zinc is slowly attacked by atmospheric oxygen. A thin, dense layer of oxide is formed on the surface of the zinc, and a porous outer layer then forms on top of it. Although the outer layer breaks away occasionally, the thin under layer remains and protects the metal by restricting its interaction with the oxygen. Under these conditions, which occur in some inland tropical climates, the zinc oxidizes very slowly.

The rate of drying is also an important factor because a thin moisture film with higher oxygen concentration promotes corrosion. For normal exposure conditions, the films dry quite rapidly, and only in sheltered areas are drying times slow enough to accelerate the attack of the zinc significantly.

In coastal districts and industrial areas, the air is contaminated with water containing considerable amounts of dissolved salts. Sodium chloride (NaCl) is of course the main salt present in marine atmospheres, and oxides of sulfur are the most important pollutants in industrial and urban atmospheres. The oxides of sulfur dissolve in water to form sulfuric acid (H_2SO_4), which in turn reacts with the zinc hydroxide or zinc carbonate ($ZnCO_3$) formed on the surface to produce zinc sulfate ($ZnSO_4$). Because this salt is very soluble, it is easily removed by rainwater, and this leaves the zinc surface relatively unprotected. This solubility of the zinc corrosion products is one of the most important factors affecting the rate of corrosion of zinc in industrial atmospheres, and it primarily accounts for the fact that this rate may be as much as four or five times greater than that in rural or marine atmospheres, depending on the amount of sulfur present.

If a fresh zinc surface is allowed to stand with large drops of dew on it, as may easily happen if it is stored in a closed space in which the temperature varies periodically, it will be attacked by the oxygen dissolved in the drops of water. These drops of water conduct electricity slightly, and because the oxygen concentration is greater at the outer edges of the drops than at their centers, some electrochemical action results. Therefore, bulky deposits of porous zinc oxide (ZnO) or $Zn(OH)_2$ form on the surface instead of forming a protective layer all over it. This oxide quickly takes up carbon dioxide (CO_2) to form a basic carbonate, commonly known as wet-storage stain. This may form on any new zinc surface unless care is taken to store the metal in a dry airy place until the protective layer has formed over the entire surface. The formation of wet-storage stain may also be prevented by a simple chromate treatment.

Influence of Atmospheric Variables. Atmospheric corrosion has been defined to include corrosion by air temperatures between -18 and 70 °C (0 and 160 °F) in the open and in enclosed spaces of all kinds. Deterioration in the atmosphere is sometimes called weathering. This definition encompasses a great variety of environments of differing corrosivities. The factors that determine the corrrosivity of an atmosphere include industrial pollution, marine pollution, humidity, temperature (especially the spread between daily highs and lows that influences condensation and evaporation of moisture), and rainfall. The atmosphere, as far as corrosion is concerned, is not a simple invariant environment. The influence of these factors on the corrosion of zinc is related to their effect on the initiation and growth of protective films.

Relative Humidity and Rainfall. In relatively dry air, the initial film formed on zinc surfaces is ZnO from the reaction of the zinc with atmospheric oxygen. This will be converted to a hydroxide in the presence of moisture. These films have a relatively minor protective effect. The $Zn(OH)_2$ reacts further with CO_2 in the atmosphere, which forms a basic $ZnCO_3$. This film is very protective and is mainly responsible for the excellent resistance of zinc to ordinary atmospheres.

The significance of atmospheric humidity in the corrosion of zinc is related to the conditions that may cause condensation of moisture on the metal surface and to the frequency and duration of the moisture contact. If the air temperature drops below the dew point, moisture will be deposited. Similarly, lowering the temperature of a metal surface below the air temperature in a humid atmosphere will cause moisture to condense on the metal. If the water evaporates quickly, corrosion is usually not severe, and a protective film is formed on the surface. On the other hand, water that remains in contact with zinc at high humidities, and particularly under poorly ventilated conditions, may cause severe corrosion.

Rainfall is not considered to be a source of serious corrosion unless it remains in contact with the zinc for some time, particularly if access to air is limited. The weight losses sometimes observed after a heavy rainfall indicate the washing away of soluble corrosion products that formed before the rainfall.

In some short-term tests, zinc kept under a roof, but otherwise exposed to the atmosphere, corroded at about the same rate as completely exposed zinc. Sulfur dioxide (SO_2), not rain, is the significant factor in the corrosive attack. In long-term tests, however, the specimens protected from falling rain corroded at a rate considerably lower than that for completely exposed specimens. This is attributed to the formation of a $ZnSO_4$ film on the samples under the roof that is not washed away by the rain. The surface is more acid and absorbs less SO_2 from the air. The higher corrosion rate in the open is not attributed directly to rainfall, but is attributed indirectly to the washing away of the protective film by the rain.

Results of tests on the effect of atmospheric pollution and rainfall on the corrosion of zinc proved that the pH of the rainwater and the total solids contents of the air have some significance. In highly industrial localities, the rainwater is contaminated by acidic sulfur compounds and becomes acidic enough to interfere with the formation of a protective film. This pH value is very significant because it interferes with the zinc formation of protective coatings of carbonates, sulfates, or oxides.

In acid rain environments, such coatings are never stabilized, because they are in a constant flux of dissolution. The United States and Canadian governments, as well as the Electric Power Research Institute, began investigations in the early 1980s on the acid rain corrosion of zinc and galvanized steel. These studies will provide detailed information on the long-term effects of acid rain on these metals.

Industrial and Marine Pollutants. In industrial or marine locations, condensed dew is likely to be contaminated with impurities that are corrosive to zinc. In such circumstances, the corrosivity of the contaminant may be more important than the degree of moisture condensation. Sulfur dioxide is one of the most harmful pollutants in the atmosphere, and it plays a major part in the corrosion of steel and zinc. Exposure tests showed that the correlation between sulfur pollution and corrosion is high for copper-bearing steel and for zinc, and these tests demonstrated that the SO_2 concentration in the air is the determining factor for the intensity of the corrosion of these metals.

Another series of tests found that even at test sites situated far from industrial towns the corrosion products contained a strong sulfate component derived from atmospheric sulfur compounds. This indicates that the effects of this type of pollution are far reaching.

Zinc Coatings. A zinc-coated surface is much less likely to suffer pitting attack than unprotected steel. In one series of tests, the depth of pits on unprotected steel was found to be up to six times the average loss of metal, whereas for zinc-coated steel the ratio was only two or three.

The behavior of zinc coatings of different thicknesses and applied by different methods was examined in tests under actual outdoor service conditions. Results showed that for a particular exposure condition the life of a zinc coating is approximately proportional to the weight of zinc and is independent of the method by which it is applied.

This is a very important result that should always be kept in mind when protective coatings are specified for a particular service application. If a steel structure or component is expected to have a long service life, it is always more economical to apply a sufficiently heavy zinc coating at the start than to renew the coating later on because the initial zinc coating was of inadequate weight. The amount of surface preparation required is nearly always less with the new structure than with an old one and is the same whether a thick or thin coating is to be applied. On the other hand, there is no point in applying a heavy zinc coating to an article that will be discarded for other reasons after a short period of service under mildly corrosive conditions.

Zinc Die Castings. The corrosion behavior of zinc die castings in various natural atmospheres was investigated in a program extending over a 20-year period. Because mechanical properties have an important effect on the practical applications of die castings, changes in these properties were taken as a measure of corrosion damage rather than weight loss. Specimens of alloys AG41A (1% Cu) and AG40A (copper free) were exposed at several locations, and their mechanical properties were determined after 5, 10, and 20 years of exposure.

Round specimens measuring 6.4 mm (¼ in.) in diameter were used for tensile tests, and 6.4 mm (¼ in.) square bars were used as impact specimens. The percentage changes from the original values are included. As in all previous tests on zinc sheet, the industrial atmospheres appeared to be the most harmful. The differences between the rural and the mild indoor atmospheres were relatively minor.

A rather large decrease in the impact strength of both alloys occurred in the interval between the 10- and 20-year exposures in the industrial atmospheres. This also occurred for alloy AC41A exposed to the indoor atmospheres. Such decreases in mechanical properties are probably caused by intergranular corrosion, to which die casting alloys are often very susceptible. Intergranular attack can reduce cross-sectional areas and create stress-raising notches, but it does not reduce the overall specimen dimensions significantly.

Additional Reading

A. Goldman and R.S. Sigmond, Corona Corrosion of Aluminum in Air, *J. Electrochem. Soc.*, *132*(12), 2842-2853, 1985. MetAbs No. 86-350433. **Abstract:** Aluminum suffers severe pitting corrosion when used as an anode in negative corona discharges in ambient air. A comprehensive account of the electrochemical interaction between a low electric field metal surface, especially aluminum, and the unipolar gaseous electrolyte created by an air corona is given.

A.A. Ismail, N.A. Khanem, A.A. Abdul-Azim, A Corrosion Map of Cairo and the Coastal Area of Egypt, *Corros. Prev. Control*, *32*(4), 75-77, 1985. MetAbs No. 86-350196. **Abstract:** Corrosion decay of Al sheet has been measured in Cairo and in a coastal atmosphere over a period of two years. Corrosion of Al and steel are compared.

A.G.C. Kobussen, Corrosion in Condensing Gas-Fired Central Heating Boilers, in *Dewpoint Corrosion*, Ellis Horwood, West Sussex, 178-190, 1985. MetAbs No. 86-350947. **Abstract:** From the analysis of flue gas condensate samples from 327 Dutch condensing boilers, two factors influencing corrosion have been identified. Corrosion of materials is studied in condensing corrosion rigs with an acceleration factor of 3.5. Special attention is paid to evaporation of condensate and addition of HCl to simulate field conditions.

A.M. Beccarla, E.D. Mor, and G. Poggi, Examination of Aluminium Corrosion Products on Marine or Industrial Marine Atmosphere, *Werkst. Korros.*, *34*(5), 236-240, 1983. MetAbs No. 84-350168. **Abstract:** A method has been developed to characterize the passivation film formed on aluminium in marine atmospheres, whether polluted or not by sulfur oxides and fluorides. The method provides useful quantitative information on the aluminium distribution between the various anions, it is deemed to be a useful tool to study the corrosion kinetics and mechanism.

A.T. Kuhn and J. Wellwood, Aqueous and Atmospheric Corrosion of Cobalt-Nickel Alloys, *Br. Corros. J.*, *21*(4), 228-234, 1986. MetAbs No. 87-351173. **Abstract:** The corrosion of cobalt-nickel alloys at ambient temperatures is reviewed. In the aqueous phase, data for the anodic and cathodic half-cell reactions are reported, as also for free corrosion.

B. Engh, O. Solli, S. Aabo, and A.J. Paauw, The Influence of a Corrosive Environment on the Fatigue Life of Aluminium Weldments, in *Aluminum Weldments III*, Aluminium-Verlag GmbH, Dusseldorf, 1985. MetAbs No. 86-350011. **Abstract:** Tests have been performed for several Al alloys to investigate the influence of seawater and saline atmosphere on the fatigue properties. The results of the tests are discussed.

B. Moniz, Process Industries Corrosion: Materials Awareness Is the Key, *ASTM Stand. News*, *15*(5), 50-52, 1987. MetAbs No. 87-351850. **Abstract:** Process variables that influence corrosiveness were summarized. An effective way of developing materials awareness is recommended.

B.B. Moreton, Copper Alloys in Marine Environments Today and Tomorrow. II, *Corros. Prev. Control*, *33*(1), 17-20, 24-25, 1986. MetAbs No. 86-351363. **Abstract:** The excellent corrosion resistance and biofouling resistance of cupronickel alloys 70/30 and 90/10 have led to their extensive use in a number of areas. Research is ongoing on the exact mechanisms of protective films and biofouling resistance of cupronickel alloys.

B.G. Callaghan, Atmospheric Corrosion Testing in Southern Africa, in *Atmospheric Corrosion*, John Wiley & Sons, Somerset, N.J., 1982, 893-912. MetAbs No. 83-351153. **Abstract:** Recognizing the need for long-term planning and for meeting the immediate needs of the building and construction industries in South Africa, the Council for Scientific and Industrial Research initiated long-term atmospheric corrosion exposure programs throughout Southern Africa.

B.W. Lifka, Corrosion Resistance of Aluminium Alloy Plate in Rural Industrial and Seacoast Atmospheres, *Aluminium, 63*(12), 1256-1261, 1987. MetAbs No. 88-350690. **Abstract:** Stress corrosion and exfoliation corrosion test specimens from aluminium alloy plates have completed five years of a scheduled 20 year exposure program in rural atmosphere at Alco Centre, Pennsylvania, industrial atmosphere at Los Angeles, and seacoast atmosphere at Point Judith, Rhode Island. The materials evaluated were 19 mm and 64 mm thick plates of 2024-T351 and T851, 5456-H116, 6061-T651, 7050-T7651 and T7451, and 7075-T651, T7651 and T7351.

C. Aravindakshan, P. Prabhakaram, and A. Sen Gupta, Studies on Aluminium Diffusion Treated Steel for Heat Exchanger Tubes, *Anti-Corros. Methods Mater., 33*(6), 1986. MetAbs No. 87-350681. **Abstract:** Aluminum diffusion treated steel by pack process using ferroaluminum was studied for its heat exchanger tube applications properties.

C. Vargel, Aluminium and the Sea, *Mater. Tech. (Paris), 74*(5-6), 233-245, 1986. MetAbs No. 87-350195. **Abstract:** The 5000 and 6000 series aluminum alloys perform well in a marine environment. Applications for aluminum alloys used in or near seawater are discussed.

C.E. Jaske, J.H. Payer, and V.S. Balint, *Corrosion Fatigue of Metals in Marine Environments*, Metals and Ceramics Information Center, Battelle Columbus Laboratories, Columbus, Ohio, 1981, p 243. MetAbs No. 82-350416. **Abstract:** Major factors involved in corrosion fatigue of metals in marine environments are investigated, including crack initiation and crack growth of carbon and alloy steels, stainless steels, nickel-base, copper-base, aluminum, and titanium alloys.

D. Simpson, A Study Into Corrosion Effects on Aluminium Using a Scanning Electron Microscope and Energy Dispersive X-Ray Analyzer, in *Environmental Problems in Materials Durability*, Parsons Press, Dublin, Ireland, 1984, 257-267. MetAbs No. 85-350921. **Abstract:** Using a Scanning Electron Microscope (SEM) and Energy Dispersive X-Ray Analyzer (EDXA), the effects of atmospheric corrosion on samples of aluminium are examined.

D.A. Jones and B.E. Wilde, Effect of Alternating Current on the Atmospheric Corrosion of Low-Alloy Weathering Steel in Bolted Lap Joints, *Corrosion, 43*(2), 66-70, 1987. MetAbs No. 87-351299. **Abstract:** The present experimental work demonstrated that stray AC can pass through the internal corrosion product within bolted lap joints of low-alloy steel. Thus, electrolytic reactions within the corrosion products can accelerate corrosion within the joints. Polarization resistance measurements in the present study revealed an increase in corrosion rate within joint segments resulting from AC.

D.C. Agarwal, F.G. Hodge, and I.J. Storey, Combating Dewpoint Corrosion With High-Performance Ni-Cr-Mo-Type Alloys, in *Dewpoint Corrosion*, Ellis Horwood, West Sussex, 125-136, 1985. MetAbs No. 86-350944. **Abstract:** With increasing experience in the liquid scrubbing of gas streams, corrosion conditions are known to exist that preclude the use of standard stainless steels in critical locations. Ni-Cr-Mo alloys such as Hastelloy alloy C-276 have been shown to be a cost-effective and reliable solution in these severe problem areas.

D.E. Patterson, R.B. Husar, and E. Escalante, Bronze, Zinc, Aluminum, and Galvanized Steel: Corrosion Rates as a Function of Space and Time Over the United States, in *Materials Degradation Caused by Acid Rain*, American Chemical Society, Washington, D.C., 1986, 152-162. MetAbs No. 87-350321. **Abstract:** The usefulness of existing long-term exposure metals corrosion data necessitates analysis of data on meteorology and pollutant emissions in conjunction with data interpolation tools. The current status of such an effort at Washington University, and the existing exposure data for evidence of key features which may clarify the likely importance of man-made pollutants in metals corrosion are examined.

D.J. Stephenson, J.R. Nicholls, and P. Hancock, The Interaction Between Corrosion and Erosion During Simulated Sea Salt Compressor Shedding in Marine Gas Turbines, *Corros. Sci., 26*(10), 757-767, 1986. MetAbs No. 87-351014. **Abstract:** The erosion-corrosion behavior of IN738C has been examined under conditions simulating compressor shedding of sea salt particles in a marine gas turbine. The results of the study are discussed.

D.R. Flinn, S.D. Cramer, J.P. Carter, and J.W. Spence, Field Exposure Study for Determining the Effects of Acid Deposition on the Corrosion and Deterioration of Materials-Description of Program and Preliminary Results, *Durability Build. Mater., 3*(2), 147-175, 1985. MetAbs No. 86-350359. **Abstract:** Materials exposure sites, fully instrumented to characterize environmental parameters related to air quality, meteorology, and rain chemistry, have been established at five locations in the eastern, northeastern and midwestern US to study the effects of acid precipitation on atmospheric damage to an aluminum alloy. By means of short-term, seasonal, and long-term exposures, the corrosion behavior of aluminum alloy has been characterized using gravimetric, surface-analytical, and corrosion-film chemistry measurements.

D.R. Flinn, S.D. Cramer, J.P. Carter, D.M. Hurwitz, and P.J. Linstrom, Environmental Effects on Metallic Corrosion Products Formed in Short-Term Atmospheric Exposures, in *Materials Degradation Caused by Acid Rain*, American Chemical Society, Washington, D.C., 1986, 119-151. MetAbs No. 87-350320. **Abstract:** The US Bureau of Mines has measured short- and long-term atmospheric corrosion damage on 3003 aluminum at four sites in the east and northeast US as part of the National Acid Precipitation Assessment Program to evaluate the effects of acid deposition on materials. The composition of the corrosion product is relatively unchanged in one- and three-month exposures over a wide variety of environmental conditions.

E. Lichtenberger-Bajza, The Effect of Alloying Elements and the Surface Oxide Layer on the Corrosion Damage of Aluminium Alloys in Acidic Atmosphere, *Magy. Alum., 23*(3-4), 85-91, 1986. MetAbs No. 86-352530. **Abstract:** Aluminum alloys were corrosion tested in acidic conditions with and without an anodic protective film. The test condition is sulfur dioxide and magnesium chloride added to the atmosphere to simulate environmental conditions.

E. Mattsson, Focus on Copper in Modern Corrosion Research, *Mater. Perform., 26*(4), 9-16, 1987. MetAbs No. 87-351869. **Abstract:** A survey is given of recent development work on the corrosion of copper and its alloys. Corrosion on electronic equipment has been studied with the aid of X-ray photoelectron spectroscopy and the quartz crystal microbalance technique.

E.W. Skerrey, Long-Term Atmospheric Performance of Aluminum and Aluminum Alloys, in *Atmospheric Corrosion*, John Wiley & Sons, Inc., Somerset, N.J., 1982. MetAbs No. 83-351122. **Abstract:** Several case studies of the long-term resistance of Al and Al alloys to atmospheric corrosion are presented. Discussions are included on Al structural components at marsh marine sites, the Al-hulled Diana 11 motor cruiser, an Al alloy test facility raft and Al crane jibs used to unload commercial ships. Aluminum alloys described include 1080A, 3103, 5251, 5056 and 6061.

F. Corvo Perez, Atmospheric Corrosion of Steel in a Humid Tropical Climate-Influence of Pollution, Humidity, Temperature, Solar Radiation and Rainfall, *Corrosion, 40*(4), 170-175, 1984. MetAbs No. 84-351892. **Abstract:** Soviet carbon steel CT-3 plates were exposed in five different places in Havana and the city of Havana (rural, industrial-marine and marine stations). Weight loss was evaluated in periods of 6 and 12 months at different starting times. Salinity and SO_2 concentration in the atmosphere were determined.

F. Gatto and A. Perrone, Atmospheric Corrosion Testing of Aluminum in Italy, in *Atmospheric Corrosion,* John Wiley & Sons, Somerset, N.J., 1982, 827-839. MetAbs No. 83-351151. **Abstract:** Regular atmospheric corrosion testing on Al and its alloys was started in Italy by the Instituto Sperimentale dei Metalli Leggeri (ISML) in the early 1950s.

F. Mansfeld, Atmospheric Corrosion, in *Encyclopedia of Materials Science and Engineering,* Vol 1, Pergamon Press Ltd., Oxford, 1986, 233-235. MetAbs No. 86-351722. **Abstract:** Atmospheric corrosion is characterized as an electrochemical process which occurs in thin layers of electrolyte. Constituents of the atmosphere influencing corrosion include oxygen, which affects the rate of the cathodic process and reduces corrosion rates by the formation of protective layers, and ozone, which increases aging of elastomers and organic coatings. A classification of corrosivity of different atmospheres-corrosion loss for aluminum is provided.

F.W. Fahy, Atmospheric Corrosion of Anodized Aluminium Exposed Over a Twelve Year Period in the Main Centres of New Zealand, *Br. Corros. J., 18*(4), 174-183, 1983. MetAbs No. 84-351251. **Abstract:** The effect of atmospheric corrosion was studied on an architectural grade of Al in the as-received "mill finish" condition and the identical material protected with three different thicknesses of anodic coatings exposed at main center sites plus a rural site for comparison.

F.W. Lipfert, Effects of Acidic Deposition on the Atmospheric Deterioration of Materials, *Mater. Perform., 26*(7), 12-19, 1987. MetAbs No. 87-352508. **Abstract:** Recent interest in materials damage and corrosion has included the effects of acidic precipitation, in addition to the effects of gaseous and particulate air pollution. Assessing the relative importance of these usually additive effects requires damage functions, relating the loss of a given material to specific agents in the atmosphere. Such damage functions have been estimated for aluminum.

G. Haynes and R. Baboian, Effect of Acid Rain on Exterior Anodized Aluminum Automotive Trim, in *Materials Degradation Caused by Acid Rain,* American Chemical Society, Washington, D.C., 1986, 213-215. MetAbs No. 87-350326. **Abstract:** An accelerated MIST test procedure has been developed which duplicates the mechanisms of corrosion of anodized Al trim in automotive environments. Blush and bloom of anodized aluminum automotive trim is more severe in environments with acid precipitation and this effect can be duplicated in an acidified MIST test procedure.

G. Haynes and R. Baboian, Electrochemical Observations as Related to Marine Atmospheric Corrosion of Chrome-Flashed Stainless Steels, *J. Electrochem. Soc., 132*(12), 2967-2969, 1985. MetAbs No. 86-350441. **Abstract:** Chrome-flashed 301 stainless steel and chrome-flashed 434 stainless steel undergo localized corrosion when constantly immersed in

chloride containing environments or extended periods of time. Periodic removal of the chrome-flashed stainless steel from the electrolyte reverses or inhibits these changes so that the mixed potential remains in a region where localized corrosion does not occur.

G. Marton, Corrosion Behavior of Aluminum Building Elements in Various Atmospheres, *Magy. Alum., 21*(2), 41-49, 1984. MetAbs No. 84-352326. **Abstract:** The results of long-term tests have confirmed that Al and its alloys can be used in almost any type of area provided that corresponding specifications are obeyed. Alloys studied were Al99.5, AlMg1, AlMg3, AlMg4, AlMgSi0.5, AlMn1Cu, AlMg5, AlZn5Mg1, AlCu4Mg1 and AlZn4Mg2.

G.B. Munier, L.A. Psota-Kelty, and J.D. Sinclair, Ion Chromatographic Analysis of Contaminants on Zinc and Aluminum Surfaces Exposed to a Range of Urban Indoor Environments, in *Atmospheric Corrosion,* John Wiley & Sons, Somerset, N.J., 1982, 275-283. MetAbs No. 83-230257. **Abstract:** Ionic contaminants and corrosion products that accumulate indoors on Al structural surfaces of telephone switching equipment have been analyzed. The immobile character and moisture sensitivity of telephone switching equipment required the use of the moistened filter paper extraction technique. The high sensitivity of ion chromatography, compared to other techniques used previously, has necessitated the selection of a new filter paper.

H. Ishida and R. Johnson, The Inhibition of Copper Corrosion by Azole Compounds in Humid Environments, *Corros. Sci., 26*(9), 657-667, 1986. MetAbs No. 87-350238. **Abstract:** The ability of azole compounds, benzotriazole, 2-undecylimidazole and poly-N-vinylimidazole to inhibit copper corrosion in humid environments is studied using Fourier transform infrared reflection-absorption spectroscopy (FT-IR-RAS).

H. Sandmann and G. Widmer, The Corrosiveness of Fluoride-Containing Fire Gases on Selected Steels, *Fire Mater., 10*(1), 11-19, 1986. MetAbs No. 86-351515. **Abstract:** Combustion gases were produced from several cable-insulation materials in separate experiments conducted in a model fire chamber. These gases were then allowed to interact with stressed metal specimens, consisting for the most part of various stainless and hardened steels, carbon steel and stainless steel sheet. The samples as exposed were stored in a humid atmosphere.

H.A. El-Sayed, H. El-Didamony, and A.H. Ali, Case Histories of Premature Failures of Concrete Structures Due to Reinforcement Corrosion Under Different Environmental Conditions, *Corros. Prev. Control, 33*(4), 88-92, 1986. MetAbs No. 87-350280. **Abstract:** Factors responsible for the corrosion of steel reinforcement in five structures in Egypt subjected to rural, urban and industrial environments leading to concrete cracking and diminishment of the durability of the structures were investigated. The investigation included chemical analysis of concrete and its surrounding medium (water and/or soil), and X-ray analysis of the concrete.

H.S. Campbell, The Corrosion Factor in Marine Environments, *Met. Mater., 1*(8), 479-483, 1985. MetAbs No. 85-352451. **Abstract:** The various types of corrosion that occur in the four related marine environments identified by the author are reviewed, and the suitability of common corrosion-resistant materials for each situation is discussed.

I.H. Craig and R.N. Parkins, Corrosion Fatigue of Metals in the Atmosphere, in *Atmospheric Corrosion,* John Wiley & Sons, Somerset, N.J., 1982, 969-981. MetAbs No. 83-351156. **Abstract:** Information on atmospheric corrosion fatigue is restricted to normal air, humid or otherwise, but not contaminated in the manner that atmospheres can be close to industrial plant or coastal regions, which are usually special cases of aqueous corrosion fatigue. However, the influence of those specific components of the atmosphere, oxygen, nitrogen and water vapor are considered to enable conclusions to be reached on which components of air are primarily responsible for the observed fatigue properties of metals in the atmosphere.

J. Wood and D.A. Harris, Atmospheric Corrosion Tests on Cast Aluminum Alloys, *Br. Foundryman, 74*(10), 217-221, 1981. MetAbs No. 82-350868. **Abstract:** Results of long-term corrosion tests conducted by the Association of Light Alloy Refiners on as-cast and machined specimens of permanent-mould Al-alloy castings are reported and discussed. The composition ranges included alloys with reputedly good and poor corrosion-resistances, exposed at marine, rural, urban, and industrial sites.

J.D. Sinclair and C.J. Weschler, Effects of Acid Rain on Indoor Zinc and Aluminum Surfaces, in *Materials Degradation Caused by Acid Rain,* American Chemical Society, Washington, D.C., 1986, 216-223. MetAbs No. 87-350327. **Abstract:** If the available information on outdoor, indoor, and surface concentrations of ammonium, sulfate, nitrate, calcium, and other species is considered, an estimate of the loading above the background can be made for all areas where outdoor concentrations are known. The relative degree of hazard for the different environments can be estimated from the developed methodology and, based on previous experience with zinc and aluminum surfaces, provides a framework for qualitative rankings of comparable environments.

J.D. Talati and B.M. Patel, Atmospheric Corrosion of Metals Under Moving Conditions, in *Atmospheric Corrosion*, John Wiley & Sons, Somerset, 1982, 695-703. MetAbs No. 83-351145. **Abstract:** A study was made to determine the corrosion rates of metals under conditions having movement of exposed surfaces through different terrains where they are exposed to different climatic conditions and pollution to ascertain the intensity of corrosion of metal surfaces of vehicles (truck and passenger coach bodies) and frequency of application for protective systems.

J.P. Carter, P.J. Linstrom, D.R. Flinn, and S.D. Cramer, The Effects of Sheltering and Orientation on the Atmospheric Corrosion of Structural Metals, *Mater. Perform., 26*(7), 25-32, 1987. MetAbs No. 87-352510. **Abstract:** The US Bureau of Mines, US Department of the Interior, is conducting atmospheric corrosion tests on 3003 aluminum at five sites as part of the National Acid Precipitation Assessment Program. Tests have been conducted on samples boldly exposed to the atmosphere, sheltered from the atmosphere, and facing skyward and groundward.

J.P. Franey, G.W. Kammlott, and T.E. Graedel, The Corrosion of Silver by Atmospheric Sulfurous Gases. *Corros. Sci., 25*(2), 133-143, 1985. MetAbs No. 85-351708. **Abstract:** The effect of exposure to the atmospheric gases H_2S, OCS, CS_2 and SO_2 in humidified air under carefully controlled laboratory conditions is described.

J.R. Crowder and M.A. Ali, Weathering Performance of Building Materials in the Middle East and UK, *Durability Build. Mater., 3*(2), 115-131, 1985. MetAbs No. 86-350358. **Abstract:** The performance of samples of a number of building materials exposed for three to four years at a weathering site in the hot dry climate of Dubai in the Arabian Gulf is reported. Behavior is related to weather conditions and compared with behavior of the same materials exposed in the UK.

K.P. Thurlow and R.W. Laughton, Anodized Aluminium Sealed by Low Temperature Impregnation. II. Results After Three Years UK Outdoor Exposure, *Lea Manufacturing Trans. Inst. Met. Finish., 65*(4), 140-141, 1987. MetAbs No. 88-350288. **Abstract:** An evaluation is made of the performance of cold sealed anodized aluminium over a range of finishes by comparison with hydrothermal sealing.

K.R. Hasse and R.C. Dorward, "Flaw Growth of 7075, 7475, 7050 and 7049 Aluminum Alloy Plate in Stress Corrosion Environments: 4-Year Marine Atmosphere Results," Kaiser Aluminum and Chemical Corp, N82-11181, Oct 1981. MetAbs No. 82-352157. **Abstract:** Crack growth in SL DCB specimens from 7075, 7475, 7050 and 7049-T7X plate, exposed to a marine atmosphere for 53 months, was investigated.

K.R. Hasse and R.C. Dorward, Long-Term Marine Atmospheric Stress Corrosion Tests on High-Strength Aluminum, Zinc, Magnesium, and Copper Alloys, *Corrosion, 42*(11), 663-669, 1986. MetAbs No. 87-350380. **Abstract:** To compare the stress corrosion resistance of the newer high-strength alloys, 7049 and 7050, with the established 7075 alloy, smooth and pre-cracked specimens from 32- and 76-mm-thick plates of each alloy were subjected to 105 months of exposure in a marine atmosphere. Results of the study are discussed.

L. Schra and J. Faber, "Influence of Environments on Constant Displacement Stress Corrosion Crack Growth in High-Strength Aluminum Alloys, National Aerospace Laboratory, NLR-TR-81138U, Amsterdam, 1981. MetAbs No. 83-351306. **Abstract:** An experimental investigation was carried out into the applicability of various corrosive environments for stress corrosion crack propagation testing of high-strength Al alloys (7075, 7175, AZ74.61) using double cantilever beam specimens. Testing under atmospheric conditions was used as a reference.

M. Doruk, Some Observations on the Corrosion of Aircraft at the Air Force Base in Bandirma, Turkey, AGARD (NATO) (CP-315), 4.1-4.8, Aug 1981. MetAbs No. 82-351553. **Abstract:** The types and the causes of corrosion which have been observed primarily on aircraft of Type F-5A at the Air Force Base in Bandirma, Turkey were studied in terms of the effect of aggressive saltwater environments.

M. Lashermes, A. Guilhaudis, M. Reboul, and G. Trentelivres, Thirty-Year Atmospheric Corrosion of Aluminum Alloys in France, in *Atmospheric Corrosion,* John Wiley & Sons, Somerset, N.J., 1982, 353-364. MetAbs No. 83-351123. **Abstract:** Performance of uncoated Al alloys tested in a marine environment for a period of 20 years is discussed.

M. Pourbaix, "Understanding and Laboratory Prediction of the Atmospheric Corrosion Behavior of Steels and of Non-Ferrous Metals and Alloys," Centre Belge Etude Corrosion, AD-A154 642/3/WMS, Jan 1984. MetAbs No. 87-350604. **Abstract:** Accelerated tests were performed on aluminum-manganese, aluminum-copper-magnesium, aluminum-zinc-copper-magnesium and on 7075-T73 clad with aluminum-zinc, in a typical marine simulated atmosphere and in a typical industrial simulated atmosphere.

M.C. Reboul, B. Dubost, and M. Lashermes, The Stress Corrosion Susceptibility of Aluminium Alloy 7020 Welded Sheets, *Corros. Sci., 25*(11), 999-1018, 1985. MetAbs No. 86-350703. **Abstract:** Welded and artificially aged 7020 sheet are prone to stress corrosion cracking in a damp atmosphere. The cracks initiate at the rootside of the weld in the finely recrystallized weld plate edge and propagate through the grain boundaries until failure. TEM examination near the weld joint area shows that sensitive material is more rapidly cooled than similar densensitized (postweld solutionized and air-quenched and artificially aged) material.

M.D. Samu, "Investigation of Stress Corrosion Behavior of Some Aluminum-Zinc-Magnesium Alloys in Tropical Environment," Indian Institute of Metals, Calcutta, 1985, 630-640. MetAbs No. 86-352216. **Abstract:** Aluminum, zinc, and magnesium alloys in both the welded and unwelded condition were stress corrosion tested in a test environment of $95 \pm 5\%$ relative humidity and spraying of 3.5% NaCl solution twice daily. SEM micrographs of the fracture surfaces and polarization curves are given. It is shown that welding marginally improves the stress corrosion resistance.

M.E. Komp, Atmospheric Corrosion Ratings of Weathering Steels-Calculation and Significance, *Mater. Perform.*, 26(7), 42-44, 1987. MetAbs No. 87-352512. **Abstract:** A review of the calculation methods for atmospheric corrosion ratings of high-strength, low-alloy weathering steels shows that a wide range of "rating numbers" relative to carbon steel (or Cu-bearing steel) can be obtained from the same data set by using different methods. It is recommended that the use of corrosion rating numbers for weathering steels be phased out and that a more meaningful method of rating the performance of these steels be sought.

M.I. Manning, Effects of Air Pollution on Structural Materials, *Central Electricity Research Laboratories Met. Mater.*, 4(4), 213-217, 1988. MetAbs No. 88-351785. **Abstract:** There is renewed emphasis on air pollution effects on materials in the context of the acid rain debate. Variations in corrosivity for metals are revealed by studies of the degradation of components on the electricity transmission system which is subjected to the varying environmental stresses of the regions through which it passes.

M.K. Han, J.A. Beavers, and W. Goins, Stress Corrosion Cracking Failure of Brass Electrical Connectors in an Outdoor Atmospheric Environment, *Mater. Perform.*, 26(7), 20-24, 1987. MetAbs No. 87-352509. **Abstract:** The findings are presented of a failure analysis performed on Cu-30Zn, Cu-20Zn and Cu-38Zn-2.5Pb brass electrical connectors (pins) that had failed during service in outdoor switch yards and the results of laboratory studies performed in conjunction with the failure analysis.

N. Maruyama, S. Horibe, and M. Sumita, Corrosion Fatigue in Simulated Aggressive Marine Environment, *J. Mater. Sci. Lett.*, 5(9), 953-955, 1986. MetAbs No. 86-352459. **Abstract:** The fatigue properties of a commercial high strength steel were investigated in a simulated marine environment. Surface damage exhibited by the specimens was found to depend on environment.

N.J.H. Holroyd and D. Hardie, Strain-Rate Effects in the Environmentally Assisted Fracture of a Commercial High-Strength Aluminium Alloy (7049), *Corros. Sci.*, 21(2), 129-144, 1981. MetAbs No. 82-352186. **Abstract:** Specimens of 7049, cut parallel to the short transverse direction, have been tested at slow strain-rates in the T651 condition using various environments: vacuum, dry air, laboratory air and sea-water, with and without prior exposure to sea-water.

N.S. Berke and H.E. Townsend, Comparison of the Kesternich Sulfur Dioxide Test With Industrial Atmospheric Corrosion Tests of Zinc-, Aluminum-, and Aluminum-Zinc-Coated Steel Sheet, *ASTM J. Test. Eval.*, 13(1), 74-76, 1985. MetAbs No. 85-350636. **Abstract:** Results of the Deutsches Institute fur Normung (DIN) Kesternich sulfur dioxide test (DIN 50018) are compared with those of long-term industrial atmospheric exposure tests of sheet steels coated with zinc, aluminum, and aluminum-zinc alloy coatings.

O.E. Okorafor, Corrosion Under Sheltered and Unsheltered Sites in Awka, Nigeria, *Corros. Prev. Control*, 33(3), 64-67, 1986. MetAbs No. 86-352130. **Abstract:** An investigation has been carried out to determine the effect of exposure time on the corrosion of aluminum under sheltered and unsheltered exposure conditions in Awka, Nigeria after two years of exposure.

P. Lovland, Nickel Alloys Show Benefits on Offshore Platforms, *Metallurgia* 54(2), 67-68, 1987. MetAbs No. 87-351489. **Abstract:** Nickel-containing materials such as cupronickel alloys, stainless steels and nickel-base alloys have been found to provide optimum techno-economic solutions to material selection in marine environments. Reviewed are factors such as corrosion resistance, fabrication ability and cost which determine the selection of marine materials.

P. Tate, Stress Corrosion Cracking of Brass Wall-Ties, *Prakt. Metallogr.*, 22(9), 463-466, 1985. MetAbs No. 86-350377. **Abstract:** A number of cracked brass wall ties were examined metallographically. It was concluded that the ties failed by a mechanism of stress corrosion cracking assisted by dezincification.

P.G.R. Zaya and D.P. Doyle, The Effect of Manufacturing Processes on the Atmospheric Corrosion of Aluminum Conductor Wires, *Mater. Perform.*, 26(5), 50-55, 1987. MetAbs No. 87-351957. **Abstract:** Aluminum wire specimens (1.5, 2.0, and 3.0 mm diam) were exposed on test racks at three aggressive atmospheric test stations and withdrawn for examination after periods of six months and one year. Losses in mechanical properties (ultimate tensile strength, 0.2% yield strength, and elongation) and weight were used to assess the influence of production method and grain size in aggressive outdoor environments.

P.L. Lane, J.A. Gray, and C.J.E. Smith, Comparison of Corrosion Behavior of Lithium-Containing Aluminium Alloys and Conventional Aerospace Alloys, in *Aluminium-Lithium Alloys III,* The Institute of Metals, London, 1986, 273-281. MetAbs No. 86-351561. **Abstract:** Marine exposure and accelerated laboratory corrosion tests have been used to compare the corrosion behavior of some aluminum, lithium, magnesium, and copper alloys with conventional aerospace alloys.

P.R. Vassie, Corrosion of Structural Steelwork in Bridge Enclosures, Box Sections and Anchorage Chambers, *Br. Corros. J.*, 22(1), 37-44, 1987. MetAbs No. 87-351703. **Abstract:** Some designs of highway bridges have structural steelwork exposed to the air within closed spaces such as box sections. Corrosion rates of clean and pre-rusted mild steel were measured using electrical resistance probes.

P.R. Vassie and M. McKenzie, Electrode Potentials for On-Site Monitoring of Atmospheric Corrosion of Steel, *Corros. Sci.*, 25(1), 1-13, 1985. MetAbs No. 85-350964. **Abstract:** Measurement of electrode potential as a method of judging the protective qualities of rusts during atmospheric corrosion, was investigated as a means of assessing the performance of Cor-Ten B weathering steel structures.

P.V. Strekalov, G.Kh. Dzhincharadze, Z.G. Egutidze, and G.G. Penov, Influence of Surface Roughness on Atmospheric Corrosion of Copper and Aluminum Alloys, *Prot. Met. (USSR)*, 21(3), 354-358, 1985. MetAbs No. 86-350796.

R. Summitt and F.T. Fink, The USAF Corrosion Testing Program and a Corrosion Severity Index Algorithm, in *Atmospheric Corrosion*, John Wiley & Sons, Somerset, N.J., 1982, 245-263. MetAbs No. 83-351119. **Abstract:** An environmental Corrosion Severity Classification System was proposed by USAF AFLC personnel at Warner-Robins AFB in 1971. Classifications were to be used for anticipating corrosion-related damage to aircraft and for scheduling appropriate repairs and maintenance actions. Environmental severity ratings have been computed for approx 200 sites.

R.C. Dorward and K.R. Hasse, Stress Corrosion Cracking Behavior of an AlLiCuMg Alloy, *Corrosion*, 43(7), 408-413, 1987. MetAbs No. 87-352749. **Abstract:** Al--2.4Li--1.2Cu--0.6Mg--0.1Zr alloy plates were aged to various temper conditions and subjected to short-transverse stress corrosion tests in laboratory and marine atmosphere environments, using both smooth and pre-cracked specimens.

R.C. Dorward and K.R. Hasse, The Fractography of Long-Transverse Stress Corrosion Cracking in Al-Zn-Mg-Cu Alloys, *Corros. Sci.*, 22(3), 251-257, 1982. MetAbs No. 82-351749. **Abstract:** Precracked TLoriented double cantilever beam specimens from 7075-T7351, 7050-T75651 and 7049-T7351 alloy plates were exposed to a marine atmosphere for over four years. The stress corrosion cracking observed is discussed.

R.E.v.d. Leest, On the Atmospheric Corrosion of Thin Copper Films, *Werkst. Korros.*, 37(12), 629-632, 1986. MetAbs No. 87-351212. **Abstract:** Sputtered and electrodeposited copper specimens were exposed to the laboratory atmosphere for 18 months, after which the corrosion products were analyzed by electrochemical methods and reflectance spectra.

R.F. Littlejohn, D.M. Lloyd, and D.M. Willis, Experience in Coal-Fired Industrial Boilers, in *Dewpoint Corrosion*, Ellis Horwood, West Sussex, 35-49, 1985. MetAbs No. 86-350939. **Abstract:** Although the term industrial boilers covers a wide variety of boiler types and methods of firing, they have several features in common that are relevant to sulfur trioxide formation and acid condensation. Measurements of SO_3 concentration, dewpoints and corrosion on several commercially operating plants have been considered.

R.N. Britton and R.L. Stevens, Materials Requirements for Condensing Boilers, in *Dewpoint Corrosion*, Ellis Horwood, West Sussex, 159-177, 1985. MetAbs No. 86-350946. **Abstract:** Condensing the moisture content of the flue products in a gas boiler offers the prospect of a step change in thermal efficiency and reduced running costs for customers. In order that this be achieved, the condensing heat exchanger must both resist the environment and also be relatively inexpensive to manufacture. The assessment program carried out at Watson House to identify promising materials and to evaluate their corrosion behavior, fabrication routes, etc., is described.

R.R. Gaugh, Stress Corrosion Cracking of Precipitation-Hardening Stainless Steels, *Mater. Perform.*, 26(2), 29-34, 1987. MetAbs No. 87-351144. **Abstract:** Stress corrosion cracking tests were performed on specimens of precipitation-hardening stainless steels UNS S13800, S15500, and S17400 in various heat-treated conditions. Specimens were exposed to a severe seacoast atmosphere for periods up to 18 years.

S. Feliu and M. Morcillo, Atmospheric Corrosion Testing in Spain, in *Atmospheric Corrosion*, John Wiley & Sons, Somerset, N.J., 1982, 913-921. MetAbs No. 83-351154. **Abstract:** Test specimens of Al have been exposed at several sites in Madrid inside louvered boxes and in the open air to compare both behaviors.

S. Feliu and M. Morcillo, Corrosion in Rural Atmospheres in Spain, *Br. Corros. J.*, 22(2), 99-102, 1987. MetAbs No. 87-352388. **Abstract:** The effect of time of wetness, relative humidity, rainfall, and temperature on the corrosion of Al exposed at a large number of rural sites in Spain is studied.

S. Gowri and S. Seshan, Weathering Steel—the Corrosion Resistant HSLA Steel, *Tool Alloy Steels*, 19(4), 103-106, 1985. MetAbs No. 86-350460. **Abstract:** Weathering steels, possess excellent corrosion resistance. The composition, corrosion behavior and probable applications of the weathering steels are briefly described.

S. Ramu, N.S. Rengaswamy, and K.I. Vasu, Corrosion Behavior of HSLA Steels, *Tool Alloy Steels*, 20(12), 403-405, 1986. MetAbs No. 87-352368. **Abstract:** The corrosion behavior of HSLA steels is briefly discussed. Characteristics of the rust products on HSLA and mild steel are compared. The effects of polluted atmospheres, salt spray, relative humidity, the rolling process, and concrete environments are described.

S. Yajima, Y. Togawa, S. Matsushita, and T. Kanbe, Outdoor Exposure and Accelerated Tests of Electroless Nickel Plating, *Plat. Surf. Finish.*, 74(8), 66-71, 1987. MetAbs No. 87-352754. **Abstract:** A cyclic acceler-

ated corrosion test that includes exposure to high humidity, neutral salt spray, and SO_2 was evaluated to simulate the effects of outdoor exposure on electroless nickel.

S.A. Nugent and J.A. Eady, Corrosion Resistance of Architectural Anodized Aluminium Sections. (Retroactive Coverage), *Met. Australas.*, 16(7), 5-7, 1984. MetAbs No. 86-351504. **Abstract:** Factors responsible for corrosion of anodized aluminum are investigated. Aspects studied include alloy composition, microstructure and surface finish, anodizing process parameters, coating properties, fabricating and installation treatments and environmental conditions.

S.B. Lyon, G.E. Thompson, J.B. Johnson, G.C. Wood, and J.M. Ferguson, Accelerated Atmospheric Corrosion Testing Using a Cyclic Wet/Dry Exposure Test: Aluminum, Galvanized Steel, and Steel, UMIST, Central Electricity Research Laboratories, *Corrosion*, 43(12), 719-726, 1987. MetAbs No. 88-350650. **Abstract:** Overhead electrical power transmission conductors, constructed from aluminum wires centrally reinforced by galvanized steel strands, have been found, in a few isolated instances, to suffer from internal corrosion, which is associated with the presence of chloride ion, and external corrosion, which is associated with sulfate ion. A cyclic wet/dry exposure test, with salt spray solutions containing appropriate ratios of sulfate and chloride ion, was used to simulate these observations.

S.C. Byrne and A.C. Miller, "Effect of Atmospheric Pollutant Gases on the Formation of Corrosive Condensate on Aluminum," American Society for Testing and Materials, Philadelphia, 1982, 359-373. MetAbs No. 83-351644. **Abstract:** As part of a program to develop predictive methods to estimate the long-term durability of Al parts, a methodology was developed to calculate the chemical composition of condensates formed on Al (99.99%) exposed to polluted air. It is proposed that the maximum concentrations of ionic species in a condensate must be limited by the equilibrium condition established between the dissolved ions and the gases from which they formed.

S.J. Ketcham and E.J. Jankowsky, "Shipboard Exposure Tests of Aluminum Alloys," Tri-Service Conference on Corrosion, AFWAL-TR-81-4019, Vol 1, Air Force Wright Aeronautical Laboratory, Wright-Patterson AFB, Ohio, 1980. MetAbs No. 82-350485. **Abstract:** A program is underway to determine quantitatively the corrosivity of the aircraft carrier environment by exposing a variety of materials on a carrier deck.

S.K. Doss and G.A. Condas, Atmospheric Corrosion of Magnetic-Film Structures, *Metall. Trans. A*, 18A(1), 158-161, 1987. MetAbs No. 87-350679. **Abstract:** A study of the field (atmospheric) and laboratory corrosion of an all metallic thin-film magnetic recording disk was made. The object was to find the primary atmospheric pollutants and their corrosion mechanisms. The structure of the disk consisted of a machined aluminum-magnesium (AA5086) substrate, 4 μm of polished Haynes alloy 188, 0.035 μm of an iron-cobalt-chromium magnetic film and 0.075 μm of a rhodium overcoat.

S.W. Dean, A New Quantitative Approach to Classifying Atmospheric Corrosion: ISO Breaks New Ground, *ASTM Stand. News*, 15(5), 36-39, 1987. MetAbs No. 87-351848. **Abstract:** An approach to developing calculational methods for estimating corrosion rates using aluminum is discussed. Since none of the ASTM G-1 standards have attempted to provide this type of information, this represents a new direction in standards activity in the US.

S.W. Dean and W.H. Anthony, "Atmospheric Corrosion of Wrought Aluminum Alloys During a Ten-Year Period," STP 965, in *Air Products and Chemicals Degradation of Metals in the Atmosphere*, ASTM, Philadelphia, 1987, 191-205. MetAbs No. 88-351452. **Abstract:** The deterioration in mechanical properties, mass loss, and the appearance of various forms of localized corrosion are documented for the exposure of a representative group of unstressed wrought Al alloys at three test sites over a ten-year period.

T. Hakkarainen and S. Ylasaari, Atmospheric Corrosion Testing in Finland, in *Atmospheric Corrosion*, John Wiley & Sons, Somerset, N.J., 1982, 787-795. MetAbs No. 83-351150. **Abstract:** Al alloys perform well in the Finnish atmosphere. Laboratory experiments show that soot powder on the surface may be detrimental to the corrosion resistance of Al, especially in the presence of high SO_2 concentration in the air.

T. Kan, M. Hiromatsu, and S. Ishioka, Development of Low Carbon-High Phosphorus Steel Plate With Superior Atmospheric Corrosion Resistance, *SEAISI Q.*, *15*(2), 27-35, 1986. MetAbs No. 87-350918. **Abstract:** To save on the maintenance cost of repainting bridges, buildings, etc., atmospheric corrosion-resistant steel plate that can be used for welded structures without painting has been developed with 50-kgf/mm^2 tensile strength; 0.05C-1.3Mn-0.08P-0.3Cu-0.4Cr-0.012Ti composition; corrosion rate 1/3 of plain carbon steel; good resistance to the hot- and cold-cracking; and excellent toughness in heat-affected zone.

T.E. Graedel, Concentrations and Metal Interactions of Atmospheric Trace Gases Involved in Corrosion, in *International Congress on Metallic Corrosion*, Vol 1, National Research Council of Canada, Ottawa, 1984, 396-401. sMetAbs No. 84-352769. **Abstract:** A review of the literature of atmospheric corrosion and of atmospheric chemistry demonstrates that 14 different atmospheric trace gases are known to interact with a variety of metals (including Al). The concentration ranges of these gases in different atmospheric regimes are displayed and discussed.

T.E. Graedel, J.T. Plewes, J.P. Franey, G.W. Kammlott, and R.C. Stoffers, Sulfidation Under Atmospheric Conditions of Cu-Ni, Cu-Sn and Cu-Zn Binary and Cu-Ni-Sn and Cu-Ni-Zn Ternary Systems, *Metall. Trans. A*, *16A*(2), 275-284, 1985. MetAbs No. 85-350456. **Abstract:** The corrosion susceptibility of binary and ternary alloys can be assessed by controlled exposures to corrosive environments of samples selected from different regions of the phase diagram. To conduct such studies, 24 high-purity alloys from the Cu-Ni, Cu-Sn and Cu-Zn binary and Cu-Ni-Sn and Cu-Ni-Zn ternary systems were prepared.

T.S. Humphries and E.E. Nelson, "Sea Coast Stress Corrosion Cracking of Aluminum Alloys," NASA, N81-18164, 29, Jan 1981. MetAbs No. 81-351919. **Abstract:** The stress corrosion cracking resistance of high-strength, wrought Al alloys in a sea coast atmosphere was investigated and the results were compared with those obtained in laboratory tests.

V. Kucera and E. Mattsson, *Atmospheric Corrosion*, Marcel Dekker, New York, 1987. MetAbs No. 87-352578. **Abstract:** The main features of atmospheric corrosion are surveyed for aluminum. Efforts are made to correlate the fundamental corrosion properties with test results and application.

V.A. Callcut, Expanding Markets for 90/10 Copper—Nickel Alloys, *Met. Mater.*, *1*(8), 489-494, 1985. MetAbs No. 85-352452. **Abstract:** The 90/10 copper—nickel alloy has a unique combination of properties in resistance to marine corrosion and biofouling. Some background to the reasons for the increasing utilization of the material is given and applications for the cladding of ships' hulls and offshore structures is described.

W. Bogaerts, A. Van Haute, and D. Schouteden, "Atmospheric Corrosion and Degradation of Construction Materials for Solar Collectors," Commission of the European Communities, Luxembourg, 1984. MetAbs No. 85-350065. **Abstract:** Atmospheric corrosion and degradation of construction materials for solar heat collectors are discussed. Available information on the corrosion behavior and corrosion rate of different metals under a number of environmental conditions are described. An explanatory approach-similar to the one of Mattsson-which is based on simple thermodynamic fundamentals, may provide a comprehensive general image of the influence of different atmospheric components.

W. Bogaerts, A. Van Haute, and P. Weisgerber, "Corrosion Studies on Collector Materials," Commission of the European Communities, Luxembourg, 1985. MetAbs No. 85-351724. **Abstract:** The results of a number of long- and short-term atmospheric corrosion tests on solar absorber plates in various SO_2-polluted atmospheres are given. Results are quantitatively compared for the different collector types and environments.

Y.N. Mikhailovskii, Theoretical and Engineering Principles of Atmospheric Corrosion of Metals, in *Atmospheric Corrosion*, John Wiley & Sons, Somerset, N.J., 1982, 85-105. MetAbs No. 83-351114. **Abstract:** The physical-chemical principles for the atmospheric corrosion of metals are reviewed. Atmospheric metal corrosion under dry, moist and wet conditions is discussed and corrosion mechanisms are considered. A model is proposed for atmospheric corrosion as a function of time and meteorological conditions.

Corrosion Behavior of Various Metals and Alloys in Atmospheres

Materials	Condition, other factors, comments	Concentration, %	Temperature, °C (°F)	Duration	Corrosion rate, mm/yr (mils/yr) or other	Ref
Irons and steels						
ASTM A242 (type 1)	Industrial (Newark, NJ). Average reduction in thickness 0.033 mm (1.3 mils)	...	...	3.5 yr	...	125
ASTM A242 (type 1)	Industrial (Newark, NJ). Average reduction in thickness 0.038 mm (1.5 mils)	...	...	7.5 yr	...	125
ASTM A242 (type 1)	Industrial (Newark, NJ). Average reduction in thickness 0.046 mm (1.8 mils)	...	...	15.5 yr	...	125
ASTM A242 (type 1)	Semi-industrial (Monroeville, PA). Average reduction in thickness 0.028 mm (1.1 mils)	...	...	1.5 yr	...	125
ASTM A242 (type 1)	Semi-industrial (Monroeville, PA). Average reduction in thickness 0.030 mm (1.2 mils)	...	...	3.5 yr	...	125
ASTM A242 (type 1)	Semi-industrial (Monroeville, PA). Average reduction in thickness 0.036 mm (1.4 mils)	...	...	7.5 yr	...	125
ASTM A242 (type 1)	Semi-industrial (Monroeville, PA). Average reduction in thickness 0.046 mm (1.8 mils)	...	...	15.5 yr	...	125

(Continued)

Corrosion Behavior of Various Metals and Alloys in Atmospheres (Continued)

Materials	Condition, other factors, comments	Concen-tration, %	Temperature, °C (°F)	Duration	Corrosion rate, mm/yr (mils/yr) or other	Ref
ASTM A242 (type 1)	Semi-industrial (South Bend, PA). Average reduction in thickness 0.025 mm (1.0 mils)	...	...	1.5 yr	...	125
ASTM A242 (type 1)	Semi-industrial (South Bend, PA). Average reduction in thickness 0.033 mm (1.3 mils)	...	...	3.5 yr	...	125
ASTM A242 (type 1)	Semi-industrial (South Bend, PA). Average reduction in thickness 0.046 mm (1.8 mils)	...	...	7.5 yr	...	125
ASTM A242 (type 1)	Semi-industrial (South Bend, PA). Average reduction in thickness 0.056 mm (2.2 mils)	...	...	15.5 yr	...	125
ASTM A242 (type 1)	Rural (Potter County, PA). Average reduction in thickness 0.020 mm (0.8 mils)	...	...	2.5 yr	...	125
ASTM A242 (type 1)	Rural (Potter County, PA). Average reduction in thickness 0.028 mm (1.1 mils)	...	...	3.5 yr	...	125
ASTM A242 (type 1)	Rural (Potter County, PA). Average reduction in thickness 0.033 mm (1.3 mils)	...	...	7.5 yr	...	125
ASTM A242 (type 1)	Rural (Potter County, PA). Average reduction in thickness 0.036 mm (1.4 mils)	...	...	15.5 yr	...	125
ASTM A242 (type 1)	Moderate marine (Kure Beach, NC, 250 m or 800 ft from ocean). Average reduction in thickness 0.015 mm (0.6 mils)	...	...	0.5 yr	...	125
ASTM A242 (type 1)	Moderate marine (Kure Beach, NC, 250 m or 800 ft from ocean). Average reduction in thickness 0.028 mm (1.1 mils)	...	...	1.5 yr	...	125
ASTM A242 (type 1)	Moderate marine (Kure Beach, NC, 250 m or 800 ft from ocean). Average reduction in thickness 0.046 mm (1.8 mils)	...	...	3.5 yr	...	125
ASTM A242 (type 1)	Moderate marine (Kure Beach, NC, 250 m or 800 ft from ocean). Average reduction in thickness 0.064 mm (2.5 mils)	...	...	7.5 yr	...	125
ASTM A242 (type 1)	Severe marine (Kure Beach, NC, 25 m or 80 ft from ocean). Average reduction in thickness 0.056 mm (2.2 mils)	...	...	0.5 yr	...	125
ASTM A242 (type 1)	Severe marine (Kure Beach, NC, 25 m or 80 ft from ocean). Average reduction in thickness 0.084 mm (3.3 mils)	...	...	2.0 yr	...	125
ASTM A242 (type 1)	Severe marine (Kure Beach, NC, 25 m or 80 ft from ocean). Average reduction in thickness 0.493 mm (19.4 mils)	...	...	5.0 yr	...	125
ASTM A514 (type B) and A517 (grade B)	Industrial (Newark, NJ). Average reduction in thickness 0.036 mm (1.4 mils)	...	...	3.5 yr	...	125
ASTM A514 (type B) and A517 (grade B)	Industrial (Newark, NJ). Average reduction in thickness 0.043 mm (1.7 mils)	...	...	7.5 yr	...	125
ASTM A514 (type B) and A517 (grade B)	Industrial (Newark, NJ). Average reduction in thickness 0.053 mm (2.1 mils)	...	...	15.5 yr	...	125
ASTM A514 (type B) and A517 (grade B)	Semi-industrial (Monroeville, NJ). Average reduction in thickness 0.030 mm (1.2 mils)	...	...	1.5 yr	...	125
ASTM A514 (type B) and A517 (grade B)	Semi-industrial (Monroeville, NJ). Average reduction in thickness 0.036 mm (1.4 mils)	...	...	3.5 yr	...	125
ASTM A514 (type B) and A517 (grade B)	Semi-industrial (Monroeville, NJ). Average reduction in thickness 0.043 mm (1.7 mils)	...	...	7.5 yr	...	125
ASTM A514 (type B) and A517 (grade B)	Semi-industrial (Monroeville, NJ). Average reduction in thickness 0.046 mm (1.8 mils)	...	...	15.5 yr	...	125
ASTM A514 (type B) and A517 (grade B)	Semi-industrial (South Bend, PA). Average reduction in thickness 0.025 mm (1.0 mils)	...	...	1.5 yr	...	125
ASTM A514 (type B) and A517 (grade B)	Semi-industrial (South Bend, PA). Average reduction in thickness 0.038 mm (1.5 mils)	...	...	3.5 yr	...	125
ASTM A514 (type B) and A517 (grade B)	Semi-industrial (South Bend, PA). Average reduction in thickness 0.048 mm (1.9 mils)	...	...	7.5 yr	...	125
ASTM A514 (type B) and A517 (grade B)	Semi-industrial (South Bend, PA). Average reduction in thickness 0.064 mm (2.5 mils)	...	...	15.5 yr	...	125
ASTM A514 (type B) and A517 (grade B)	Rural (Potter County, PA). Average reduction in thickness 0.030 mm (1.2 mils)	...	...	3.5 yr	...	125
ASTM A514 (type B) and A517 (grade B)	Rural (Potter County, PA). Average reduction in thickness 0.038 mm (1.5 mils)	...	...	7.5 yr	...	125
ASTM A514 (type B) and A517 (grade B)	Rural (Potter County, PA). Average reduction in thickness 0.051 mm (2.0 mils)	...	...	15.5 yr	...	125

(Continued)

Corrosion Behavior of Various Metals and Alloys in Atmospheres (Continued)

Materials	Condition, other factors, comments	Concen-tration, %	Temperature, °C (°F)	Duration	Corrosion rate, mm/yr (mils/yr) or other	Ref
ASTM A514 (type B) and A517 (grade B)	Moderate marine (Kure Beach, NC, 250 m or 800 ft from ocean). Average reduction in thickness 0.018 mm (0.7 mils)	...	...	0.5 yr	...	125
ASTM A514 (type B) and A517 (grade B)	Moderate marine (Kure Beach, NC, 250 m or 800 ft from ocean). Average reduction in thickness 0.030 mm (1.2 mils)	...	...	1.5 yr	...	125
ASTM A514 (type B) and A517 (grade B)	Moderate marine (Kure Beach, NC, 250 m or 800 ft from ocean). Average reduction in thickness 0.048 mm (1.9 mils)	...	...	3.5 yr	...	125
ASTM A514 (type B) and A517 (grade B)	Moderate marine (Kure Beach, NC, 250 m or 800 ft from ocean). Average reduction in thickness 0.074 mm (2.9 mils)	...	...	7.5 yr	...	125
ASTM A514 (type B) and A517 (grade B)	Severe marine (Kure Beach, NC, 20 m or 80 ft from ocean). Average reduction in thickness 0.028 mm (1.1 mils)	...	...	0.5 yr	...	125
ASTM A514 (type B) and A517 (grade B)	Severe marine (Kure Beach, NC, 20 m or 80 ft from ocean). Average reduction in thickness 0.099 mm or (3.9 mils)	...	...	3.5 yr	...	125
ASTM A514 (type B) and A517 (grade B)	Severe marine (Kure Beach, NC, 20 m or 80 ft from ocean). Average reduction in thickness 0.127 mm (5.0 mils)	...	...	5.0 yr	...	125
ASTM A514 (type F) and A517 (grade F)	Industrial (Newark, NJ). Average reduction in thickness 0.056 mm (2.2 mils)	...	...	3.5 yr	...	125
ASTM A514 (type F) and A517 (grade F)	Semi-industrial (Monroeville, PA). Average reduction in thickness	...	...	1.5 yr	...	125
ASTM A514 (type F) and A517 (grade F)	Semi-industrial (Monroeville, PA). Average reduction in thickness 0.061 mm (2.4 mils)	...	...	3.5 yr	...	125
ASTM A514 (type F) and A517 (grade F)	Semi-industrial (South Bend, PA). Average reduction in thickness 0.038 mm (1.5 mils)	...	...	1.5 yr	...	125
ASTM A514 (type F) and A517 (grade F)	Semi-industrial (South Bend, PA). Average reduction in thickness 0.061 mm (2.4 mils)	...	...	3.5 yr	...	125
ASTM A514 (type F) and A517 (grade F)	Rural (Potter County, PA). Average reduction in thickness 0.046 mm (1.8 mils)	...	...	3.5 yr	...	125
ASTM A514 (type F) and A517 (grade F)	Moderate marine (Kure Beach, NC, 250 m or 800 ft from ocean). Average reduction in thickness 0.025 mm (1.0 mils)	...	...	0.5 yr	...	125
ASTM A514 (type F) and A517 (grade F)	Moderate marine (Kure Beach, NC, 250 m or 800 ft from ocean). Average reduction in thickness 0.043 mm (1.7 mils)	...	...	1.5 yr	...	125
ASTM A514 (type F) and A517 (grade F)	Moderate marine (Kure Beach, NC, 250 m or 800 ft from ocean). Average reduction in thickness 0.056 mm (2.2 mils)	...	...	3.5 yr	...	125
ASTM A514 (type F) and A517 (grade F)	Severe marine (Kure Beach, NC, 20 m or 80 ft from ocean). Average reduction in thickness 0.018 mm (0.7 mils)	...	...	0.5 yr	...	125
ASTM A514 (type F) and A517 (grade F)	Severe marine (Kure Beach, NC, 20 m or 80 ft from ocean). Average reduction in thickness 0.053 mm (2.1 mils)	...	...	2.0 yr	...	125
ASTM A514 (type F) and A517 (grade F)	Severe marine (Kure Beach, NC, 20 m or 80 ft from ocean). Average reduction in thickness 0.099 mm (3.9 mils)	...	...	3.5 yr	...	125
ASTM A588 (grade A)	Industrial (Newark NJ). Average reduction in thickness 0.046 mm (1.8 mils)	...	...	3.5 yr	...	125
ASTM A588 (grade A)	Industrial (Newark NJ). Average reduction in thickness 0.053 mm (2.1 mils)	...	...	7.5 yr	...	125
ASTM A588 (grade A)	Semi-industrial (Monroeville, PA). Average reduction in thickness 0.036 mm (1.4 mils)	...	...	1.5 yr	...	125
ASTM A588 (grade A)	Semi-industrial (Monroeville, PA). Average reduction in thickness 0.053 mm (2.1 mils)	...	...	3.5 yr	...	125
ASTM A588 (grade A)	Semi-industrial (Monroeville, PA). Average reduction in thickness 0.061 mm (2.4 mils)	...	...	7.5 yr	...	125
ASTM A588 (grade A)	Semi-industrial (South Bend, PA). Average reduction in thickness 0.033 mm (1.3 mils)	...	...	1.5 yr	...	125
ASTM A588 (grade A)	Semi-industrial (South Bend, PA). Average reduction in thickness 0.048 mm (1.9 mils)	...	...	3.5 yr	...	125
ASTM A588 (grade A)	Semi-industrial (South Bend, PA). Average reduction in thickness 0.069 mm (2.7 mils)	...	...	7.5 yr	...	125

(Continued)

Corrosion Behavior of Various Metals and Alloys in Atmospheres (Continued)

Materials	Condition, other factors, comments	Concentration, %	Temperature, °C (°F)	Duration	Corrosion rate, mm/yr (mils/yr) or other	Ref
ASTM A588 (grade A)	Rural (Potter County, PA). Average reduction in thickness 0.030 mm (1.2 mils)	...	...	2.5 yr	...	125
ASTM A588 (grade A)	Rural (Potter County, PA). Average reduction in thickness 0.036 mm (1.4 mils)	...	...	3.5 yr	...	125
ASTM A588 (grade A)	Rural (Potter County, PA). Average reduction in thickness 0.038 mm (1.5 mils)	...	...	7.5 yr	...	125
ASTM A588 (grade A)	Moderate marine (Kure Beach, NC, 250 m or 800 ft from ocean). Average reduction in thickness 0.020 mm (0.8 mils)	...	...	0.5 yr	...	125
ASTM A588 (grade A)	Moderate marine (Kure Beach, NC, 250 m or 800 ft from ocean). Average reduction in thickness 0.043 mm (1.7 mils)	...	...	1.5 yr	...	125
ASTM A588 (grade A)	Moderate marine (Kure Beach, NC, 250 m or 800 ft from ocean). Average reduction in thickness 0.064 mm (2.5 mils)	...	...	3.5 yr	...	125
ASTM A588 (grade A)	Moderate marine (Kure Beach, NC, 250 m or 800 ft from ocean). Average reduction in thickness 0.094 mm (3.7 mils)	...	...	7.5 yr	...	125
ASTM A588 (grade A)	Severe marine (Kure Beach, NC, 20 m or 80 ft from ocean). Average reduction in thickness 0.097 mm (3.8 mils)	...	...	0.5 yr	...	125
ASTM A588 (grade A)	Severe marine (Kure Beach, NC, 20 m or 80 ft from ocean). Average reduction in thickness 0.310 mm (12.2 mils)	...	...	2.0 yr	...	125
ASTM A588 (grade A)	Severe marine (Kure Beach, NC, 20 m or 80 ft from ocean). Average reduction in thickness 0.729 mm (28.7 mils)	...	...	3.5 yr	...	125
ASTM A588 (grade A)	Severe marine (Kure Beach, NC, 20 m or 80 ft from ocean). Average reduction in thickness 0.986 mm (38.8 mils)	...	...	5.0 yr	...	125
Low-carbon steel (0.27% Cu)	Marine; at Kure Beach, NC. 75.4% change in tensile strength	...	...	...	0.150 (5.91)	14
Low-carbon steel (0.27% Cu)	Industrial; at Madison, IL. 11.9% change in tensile strength	...	...	...	0.025 (1.00)	14
Low-carbon steel (0.27% Cu)	Rural; near Midland, MI. 7.5% change in tensile strength	...	...	...	0.015 (0.59)	14
Structural carbon steel	Industrial (Newark, NJ). Average reduction in thickness 0.084 mm (3.3 mils)	...	...	3.5 yr	...	125
Structural carbon steel	Industrial (Newark, NJ). Average reduction in thickness 0.104 mm (4.1 mils)	...	...	7.5 yr	...	125
Structural carbon steel	Industrial (Newark, NJ). Average reduction in thickness 0.135 mm (5.3 mils)	...	...	15.5 yr	...	125
Structural carbon steel	Semi-industrial (Monroeville, PA). Average reduction in thickness 0.056 mm (2.2 mils)	...	...	1.5 yr	...	125
Structural carbon steel	Semi-industrial (Monroeville, PA). Average reduction in thickness 0.094 mm (3.7 mils)	...	...	3.5	...	125
Structural carbon steel	Semi-industrial (Monroeville, PA). Average reduction in thickness 0.130 mm (5.1 mils)	...	...	7.5	...	125
Structural carbon steel	Semi-industrial (Monroeville, PA). Average reduction in thickness 0.185 mm (7.3 mils)	...	...	15.5	...	125
Structural carbon steel	Semi-industrial (South Bend, PA). Average reduction in thickness 0.046 mm (1.8 mils)	...	...	1.5	...	125
Structural carbon steel	Semi-industrial (South Bend, PA). Average reduction in thickness 0.074 mm (2.9 mils)	...	...	3.5	...	125
Structural carbon steel	Semi-industrial (South Bend, PA). Average reduction in thickness 0.117 mm (4.6 mils)	...	...	7.5	...	125
Structural carbon steel	Semi-industrial (South Bend, PA). Average reduction in thickness 0.178 mm (7.0 mils)	...	...	15.5 yr	...	125
Structural carbon steel	Rural (Potter County, PA). Average reduction in thickness 0.051 mm (2.0 mils)	...	...	3.5 yr	...	125
Structural carbon steel	Rural (Potter County, PA). Average reduction in thickness 0.076 mm (3.0 mils)	...	...	7.5	...	125
Structural carbon steel	Rural (Potter County, PA). Average reduction in thickness 0.119 mm (4.7 mils)	...	...	15.5	...	125
Structural carbon steel	Moderate marine (Kure Beach, NC, 250 m or 800 ft from ocean). Average reduction in thickness 0.023 mm (0.9 mils)	...	...	0.5 yr	...	125

(Continued)

Corrosion Behavior of Various Metals and Alloys in Atmospheres (Continued)

Materials	Condition, other factors, comments	Concen-tration, %	Temperature, °C (°F)	Duration	Corrosion rate, mm/yr (mils/yr) or other	Ref
Structural carbon steel	Moderate marine (Kure Beach, NC, 250 m or 800 ft from ocean). Average reduction in thickness 0.058 mm (2.3 mils)	...	...	1.5 yr	...	125
Structural carbon steel	Moderate marine (Kure Beach, NC, 250 m or 800 ft from ocean). Average reduction in thickness 0.124 mm (4.9 mils)	...	...	3.5 yr	...	125
Structural carbon steel	Moderate marine (Kure Beach, NC, 250 m or 800 ft from ocean). Average reduction in thickness 0.142 mm (5.6 mils)	...	...	7.5 yr	...	125
Structural carbon steel	Severe marine (Kure Beach, NC, 25 m or 80 ft from ocean). Average reduction in thickness 0.183 mm (7.2 mils)	...	...	0.5 yr	...	125
Structural carbon steel	Severe marine (Kure Beach, NC, 25 m or 80 ft from ocean). Average reduction in thickness 0.914 mm (36.0 mils)	...	...	2.0 yr	...	125
Structural carbon steel	Severe marine (Kure Beach, NC, 25 m or 80 ft from ocean). Average reduction in thickness 1.448 mm (57.0 mils)	...	...	3.5 yr	...	125
Structural carbon steel	Severe marine (Kure Beach, NC, 25 m or 80 ft from ocean). Specimen corroded completely away	...	...	5.0 yr	...	125
Structural copper steel	Industrial (Newark, NJ). Average reduction in thickness 0.066 mm (2.6 mils)	...	...	3.5 yr	...	125
Structural copper steel	Industrial (Newark, NJ). Average reduction in thickness 0.081 mm (3.2 mils)	...	...	7.5 yr	...	125
Structural copper steel	Industrial (Newark, NJ). Average reduction in thickness 0.102 mm (4.0 mils)	...	...	15.5 yr	...	125
Structural copper steel	Semi-industrial (Monroeville, PA). Average reduction in thickness 0.043 mm (1.7 mils)	...	...	1.5 yr	...	125
Structural copper steel	Semi-industrial (Monroeville, PA). Average reduction in thickness 0.064 mm (2.5 mils)	...	...	3.5 yr	...	125
Structural copper steel	Semi-industrial (Monroeville, PA). Average reduction in thickness 0.081 mm (3.2 mils)	...	...	7.5 yr	...	125
Structural copper steel	Semi-industrial (Monroeville, PA). Average reduction in thickness 0.119 mm (4.7 mils)	...	...	15.5	...	125
Structural copper steel	Semi-industrial (South Bend, PA). Average reduction in thickness 0.036 mm (1.4 mils)	...	...	1.5 yr	...	125
Structural copper steel	Semi-industrial (South Bend, PA). Average reduction in thickness 0.056 mm (2.2 mils)	...	...	3.5 yr	...	125
Structural copper steel	Semi-industrial (South Bend, PA). Average reduction in thickness 0.081 mm (3.2 mils)	...	...	7.5 yr	...	125
Structural copper steel	Semi-industrial (South Bend, PA). Average reduction in thickness 0.122 mm (4.8 mils)	...	...	15.5 yr	...	125
Structural copper steel	Rural (Potter County, PA). Average reduction in thickness 0.033 mm (1.3 mils)	...	...	2.5 yr	...	125
Structural copper steel	Rural (Potter County, PA). Average reduction in thickness 0.043 mm (1.7 mils)	...	...	3.5 yr	...	125
Structural copper steel	Rural (Potter County, PA). Average reduction in thickness 0.064 mm (2.5 mils)	...	...	7.5 yr	...	125
Structural copper steel	Rural (Potter County, PA). Average reduction in thickness 0.097 mm (3.8 mils)	...	...	15.5 yr	...	125
Structural copper steel	Moderate marine (Kure Beach, NC, 250 m or 800 ft from ocean). Average reduction in thickness 0.020 mm (0.8 mils)	...	...	0.5 yr	...	125
Structural copper steel	Moderate marine (Kure Beach, NC, 250 m or 800 ft from ocean). Average reduction in thickness 0.048 mm (1.9 mils)	...	...	1.5 yr	...	125
Structural copper steel	Moderate marine (Kure Beach, NC, 250 m or 800 ft from ocean). Average reduction in thickness 0.084 mm (3.3 mils)	...	...	3.5 yr	...	125
Structural copper steel	Moderate marine (Kure Beach, NC, 250 m or 800 ft from ocean). Average reduction in thickness 0.114 mm (4.5 mils)	...	...	7.5 yr	...	125
Structural copper steel	Severe marine (Kure Beach, NC, 25 m or 80 ft from ocean). Average reduction in thickness 0.109 mm (4.3 mils)	...	...	0.5 yr	...	125

(Continued)

Corrosion Behavior of Various Metals and Alloys in Atmospheres (Continued)

Materials	Condition, other factors, comments	Concentration, %	Temperature, °C (°F)	Duration	Corrosion rate, mm/yr (mils/yr) or other	Ref
Structural copper steel	Severe marine (Kure Beach, NC, 25 m or 80 ft from ocean). Average reduction in thickness 0.483 mm (19.0 mils)	...	...	2.0 yr	...	125
Structural copper steel	Severe marine (Kure Beach, NC, 25 m or 80 ft from ocean). Average reduction in thickness 0.965 mm (38.0 mils)	...	...	3.5 yr	...	125
Structural copper steel	Severe marine (Kure Beach, NC, 25 m or 80 ft from ocean). Specimen completely corroded away	...	...	5.0 yr	...	125
Aluminum						
1100-H14	Maximum depth of attack in 7 yr, 0.07 mm (2.6 mils). Average depth of attack in 7 yr, 0.029 mm (1.1 mils). Loss of tensile strength in 7 yr, 0%. (a)	...	...	7 yr	345 nm/yr (13.6 μin./yr)	127
1135-H14	Maximum depth of attack in 7 yr, 0.08 mm (3.3 mils). Average depth of attack in 7 yr, 0.037 mm (1.5 mils). Loss of tensile strength in 7 yr, 0.4%. (a)	...	...	7 yr	321 nm/yr (12.6 μin./yr)	127
1188-H14	Maximum depth of attack in 7 yr, 0.121 mm (4.8 mils). Average depth of attack in 7 yr, 0.046 mm (1.8 mils). Loss of tensile strength in 7 yr, 0%. (a)	...	...	7 yr	250 nm/yr (9.8 μin./yr)	127
1199-H18	Maximum depth of attack in 7 yr, 0.096 mm (3.8 mils). Average depth of attack in 7 yr, 0.057 mm (2.2 mils). Loss of tensile strength in 7 yr, 3.9%. (a)	...	...	7 yr	205 nm/yr (8.1 μin./yr)	127
2014-T6	Maximum depth of attack in 7 yr, 0.077 mm (3.0 mils). Average depth of attack in 7 yr, 0.050 mm (2.0 mils). Loss of tensile strength in 7 yr, 1.7%. (a)	...	...	7 yr	644 nm/yr (25.4 μin./yr)	127
2024-T3	Maximum depth of attack in 7 yr, 0.076 mm (3.0 mils). Average depth of attack in 7 yr, 0.067 mm (2.6 mils). Loss of tensile strength in 7 yr, 2.0%. (a)	...	...	7 yr	1022 nm/yr (40.2 μin./yr)	127
2024-T81	Maximum depth of attack in 7 yr, 0.097 mm (3.8 mils). Average depth of attack in 7 yr, 0.076 mm (3.0 mils). Loss of tensile strength in 7 yr, 6.0%. (a)	...	...	7 yr	725 nm/yr (28.5 μin./yr)	127
2024-T86	Maximum depth of attack in 7 yr, 0.077 mm (3.0 mils). Average depth of attack in 7 yr, 0.058 mm (2.3 mils). Loss of tensile strength in 7 yr, 6.2%. (a)	...	...	7 yr	806 nm/yr (31.7 μin./yr)	127
3003-H14	Maximum depth of attack in 7 yr, 0.086 mm (3.4 mils). Average depth of attack in 7 yr, 0.052 mm (2.0 mils). Loss of tensile strength in 7 yr, 1.1%. (a)	...	...	7 yr	295 nm/yr (11.6 μin./yr)	127
3004-H34	Maximum depth of attack in 7 yr, 0.119 mm (4.7 mils). Average depth of attack in 7 yr, 0.044 mm (1.7 mils). Loss of tensile strength in 7 yr, 1.1%. (a)	...	...	7 yr	414 nm/yr (16.3 μin./yr)	127
4043-H14	Maximum depth of attack in 7 yr, 0.105 mm (4.1 mils). Average depth of attack in 7 yr, 0.034 mm (1.3 mils). Loss of tensile strength in 7 yr, 2.8%. (a)	...	...	7 yr	335 nm/yr (13.2 μin./yr)	127
5005-H34	Maximum depth of attack in 7 yr, 0.076 mm (3.0 mils). Average depth of attack in 7 yr, 0.027 mm (1.1 mils). Loss of tensile strength in 7 yr, 0.9%. (a)	...	...	7 yr	373 nm/yr (14.7 μin./yr)	127
5050-H34	Maximum depth of attack in 7 yr, 0.107 mm (4.2 mils). Average depth of attack in 7 yr, 0.058 mm (2.3 mils). Loss of tensile strength in 7 yr, 0.5%. (a)	...	...	7 yr	349 nm/yr (13.7 μin./yr)	127
5052-H34	Maximum depth of attack in 7 yr, 0.062 mm (2.4 mils). Average depth of attack in 7 yr, 0.043 mm (1.7 mils). Loss of tensile strength in 7 yr, 0.8%. (a)	...	...	7 yr	362 nm/yr (14.3 μin./yr)	127
5083-H34	Maximum depth of attack in 7 yr, 0.088 mm (3.5 mils). Average depth of attack in 7 yr, 0.056 mm (2.2 mils). Loss of tensile strength in 7 yr, 2.2%. (a)	...	...	7 yr	375 nm/yr (14.8 μin./yr)	127

(Continued)

Corrosion Behavior of Various Metals and Alloys in Atmospheres (Continued)

Materials	Condition, other factors, comments	Concentration, %	Temperature, °C (°F)	Duration	Corrosion rate, mm/yr (mils/yr) or other	Ref
5083-O	Maximum depth of attack in 7 yr, 0.102 mm (4.0 mils). Average depth of attack in 7 yr, 0.052 mm (2.0 mils). Loss of tensile strength in 7 yr, 1.8%. (a)	...	...	7 yr	469 nm/yr (18.5 μin./yr)	127
5086-H34	Maximum depth of attack in 7 yr, 0.105 mm (4.1 mils). Average depth of attack in 7 yr, 0.076 mm (3.0 mils). Loss of tensile strength in 7 yr, 1.9%. (a)	...	...	7 yr	436 nm/yr (17.2 μin./yr)	127
5154-H34	Maximum depth of attack in 7 yr, 0.091 mm (3.6 mils). Average depth of attack in 7 yr, 0.065 mm (2.6 mils). Loss of tensile strength in 7 yr, 0.9%. (a)	...	...	7 yr	326 nm/yr (12.8 μin./yr)	127
5357-H34	Maximum depth of attack in 7 yr, 0.138 mm (5.4 mils). Average depth of attack in 7 yr, 0.102 mm (4.0 mils). Loss of tensile strength in 7 yr, 0.4%. (a)	...	...	7 yr	292 nm/yr (11.5 μin./yr)	127
5454-H34	Maximum depth of attack in 7 yr, 0.105 mm (4.1 mils). Average depth of attack in 7 yr, 0.030 mm (1.2 mils). Loss of tensile strength in 7 yr, 0.5%. (a)	...	...	7 yr	342 nm/yr (13.5 μin./yr)	127
5454-O	Maximum depth of attack in 7 yr, 0.095 mm (3.7 mils). Average depth of attack in 7 yr, 0.041 mm (1.6 mils). Loss of tensile strength in 7 yr, 1.5%. (a)	...	...	7 yr	348 nm/yr (13.7 μin./yr)	127
5456-O	Maximum depth of attack in 7 yr, 0.104 mm (4.1 mils). Average depth of attack in 7 yr, 0.037 mm (1.5 mils). Loss of tensile strength in 7 yr, 0.4%. (a)	...	...	7 yr	381 nm/yr (15.0 μin./yr)	127
6061-T4	Maximum depth of attack in 7 yr, 0.57 mm (2.2 mils). Average depth of attack in 7 yr, 0.038 mm (1.5 mils). Loss of tensile strength in 7 yr, 0.4%. (a)	...	...	7 yr	378 nm/yr (14.9 μin./yr)	127
7075-T6	Maximum depth of attack in 7 yr, 0.098 mm (3.9 mils). Average depth of attack in 7 yr, 0.042 mm (1.7 mils). Loss of tensile strength in 7 yr, 0.7%. (a)	...	...	7 yr	688 nm/yr (27.1 μin./yr)	127
7079-T6	Maximum depth of attack in 7 yr, 0.065 mm (2.6 mils). Average depth of attack in 7 yr, 0.037 mm (1.5 mils). Loss of tensile strength in 7 yr, 0.5%. (a)	...	...	7 yr	635 nm/yr (25.0 μin./yr)	127
Alclad 2014-T6	Maximum depth of attack in 7 yr, 0.043 mm (1.7 mils). Average depth of attack in 7 yr, 0.028 mm (1.1 mils). Loss of tensile strength in 7 yr, 0%. (a)	...	...	7 yr	358 nm/yr (14.1 μin./yr)	127
Alclad 2024-T3	Maximum depth of attack in 7 yr, 0.046 mm (1.8 mils). Average depth of attack in 7 yr, 0.027 mm (1.1 mils). Loss of tensile strength in 7 yr, 0%. (a)	...	...	7 yr	264 nm/yr (10.4 μin./yr)	127
Alclad 3003-H14	Maximum depth of attack in 7 yr, 0.128 mm (5.0 mils). Average depth of attack in 7 yr, 0.117 mm (4.68 mils). Loss of tensile strength in 7 yr, 0%. (a)	...	...	7 yr	345 nm/yr (13.6 μin./yr)	127
Alclad 5155-H34	Maximum depth of attack in 7 yr, 0.053 mm (2.1 mils). Average depth of attack in 7 yr, 0.035 mm (1.4 mils). Loss of tensile strength in 7 yr, 0%. (a)	...	...	7 yr	345 nm/yr (13.6 μin./yr)	127
Alclad 6061-T6	Maximum depth of attack in 7 yr, 0.098 mm (3.9 mils). Average depth of attack in 7 yr, 0.025 mm (1.0 mils). Loss of tensile strength in 7 yr, 0.7%. (a)	...	...	7 yr	356 nm/yr (14.0 μin./yr)	127
Alclad 7075-T6	Maximum depth of attack in 7 yr, 0.053 mm (2.1 mils). Average depth of attack in 7 yr, 0.041 mm (1.6 mils). Loss of tensile strength in 7 yr, 0.1%. (a)	...	...	7 yr	502 nm/yr (19.8 μin./yr)	127
Alclad 7079-T6	Maximum depth of attack in 7 yr, 0.072 mm (2.8 mils). Average depth of attack in 7 yr, 0.036 mm (1.4 mils). Loss of tensile strength in 7 yr, 0%. (a)	...	...	7 yr	324 nm/yr (12.8 μin./yr)	127
Aluminum 2024-T3	Marine; at Kure Beach, NC. 2.5% change in tensile strength	...	...	...	0.002 (0.06)	14
Aluminum 2024-T3	Industrial; at Madison, IL. 1.5% change in tensile strength	...	...	...	0.002 (0.08)	14
Aluminum 2024-T3	Rural; near Midland, MI. 0.4% change in tensile strength	...	...	...	0.0001 (0.005)	14

(Continued)

Corrosion Behavior of Various Metals and Alloys in Atmospheres (Continued)

Materials	Condition, other factors, comments	Concen-tration, %	Temperature, °C (°F)	Duration	Corrosion rate, mm/yr (mils/yr) or other	Ref
Coppers						
70-30 cupronickel	Industrial	...	...	...	Suitable	93
70-30 cupronickel	Marine	...	...	...	Suitable	93
70-30 cupronickel	Rural	...	...	...	Suitable	93
90-10 cupronickel	Industrial	...	...	...	Suitable	93
90-10 cupronickel	Marine	...	...	...	Suitable	93
90-10 cupronickel	Rural	...	...	...	Suitable	93
70Cu-29Ni-1Sn	Industrial (Altoona, PA). (a)	...	...	20 yr	0.00264 (0.104)	25
70Cu-29Ni-1Sn	Industrial marine (New York, NY). (a)	...	...	20 yr	0.00213 (0.084)	25
70Cu-29Ni-1Sn	Tropical rural marine (Key West, FL). (a)	...	...	20 yr	0.00028 (0.011)	25
70Cu-29Ni-1Sn	Humid marine (La Jolla, CA). (a)	...	...	20 yr	0.00036 (0.014)	25
70Cu-29Ni-1Sn	Northern rural (State College, PA). (a)	...	...	20 yr	0.00048 (0.019)	25
70Cu-29Ni-1Sn	Dry rural (Phoenix, AZ). (a)	...	...	20 yr	0.00010 (0.004)	25
Admiralty brass	Industrial	...	...	...	Suitable	93
Admiralty brass	Marine	...	...	...	Suitable	93
Admiralty brass	Rural	...	...	...	Suitable	93
Aluminum bronze	Industrial	...	...	...	Suitable	93
Aluminum bronze	Marine	...	...	...	Suitable	93
Aluminum bronze	Rural	...	...	...	Suitable	93
Architectural bronze	Industrial. (b)	...	...	...	Good	93
Architectural bronze	Marine. (b)	...	...	...	Good	93
Architectural bronze	Rural	...	...	...	Suitable	93
Brass	Industrial	...	...	...	Suitable	93
Brass	Marine	...	...	...	Suitable	93
Brass	Rural	...	...	...	Suitable	93
C11000	Industrial (Altoona, PA)	...	...	20 yr	0.00140 (0.055)	25
C11000	Industrial marine (New York, NY)	...	...	20 yr	0.00138 (0.054)	25
C11000	Tropical rural marine (Key West, FL)	...	...	20 yr	0.00056 (0.022)	25
C11000	Humid marine (La Jolla, CA)	...	...	20 yr	0.00127 (0.050)	25
C11000	Northern rural (State College, PA)	...	...	20 yr	0.00043 (0.017)	25
C11000	Dry rural (Phoenix, AZ)	...	...	20 yr	0.00013 (0.005)	25
C12000	Industrial (Altoona, PA)	...	...	20 yr	0.00132 (0.052)	25
C12000	Industrial marine (New York, NY)	...	...	20 yr	0.00122 (0.048)	25
C12000	Tropical rural marine (Key West, FL)	...	...	20 yr	0.00051 (0.020)	25
C12000	Humid marine (La Jolla, CA)	...	...	20 yr	0.00142 (0.056)	25
C12000	Northern rural (State College, PA)	...	...	20 yr	0.00036 (0.014)	25
C12000	Dry rural (Phoenix, AZ)	...	...	20 yr	0.00008 (0.003)	25
C23000	Industrial (Altoona, PA)	...	...	20 yr	0.00188 (0.074)	25
C23000	Industrial marine (New York, NY)	...	...	20 yr	0.00188 (0.074)	25
C23000	Tropical rural marine (Key West, FL)	...	...	20 yr	0.00056 (0.022)	25
C23000	Humid marine (La Jolla, CA)	...	...	20 yr	0.00033 (0.013)	25
C23000	Northern rural (State College, PA)	...	...	20 yr	0.00046 (0.018)	25
C23000	Dry rural (Phoenix, AZ)	...	...	20 yr	0.00010 (0.004)	25
C26000	Industrial (Altoona, PA)	...	...	20 yr	0.00305 (0.120)	25
C26000	Industrial marine (New York, NY)	...	...	20 yr	0.00241 (0.095)	25
C26000	Tropical rural marine (Key West, FL)	...	...	20 yr	0.00020 (0.008)	25
C26000	Humid marine (La Jolla, CA)	...	...	20 yr	0.00015 (0.006)	25
C26000	Northern rural (State College, PA)	...	...	20 yr	0.00046 (0.018)	25
C26000	Dry rural (Phoenix, AZ)	...	...	20 yr	0.00010 (0.004)	25
C44200	Industrial (Altoona, PA)	...	...	20 yr	0.00213 (0.084)	25
C44200	Industrial marine (New York, NY)	...	...	20 yr	0.00251 (0.099)	25
C44200	Tropical rural marine (Key West, FL)	...	...	20 yr	...	25
C44200	Humid marine (La Jolla, CA)	...	...	20 yr	0.00033 (0.013)	25
C44200	Northern rural (State College, PA)	...	...	20 yr	0.00053 (0.021)	25
C44200	Dry rural (Phoenix, AZ)	...	...	20 yr	0.00010 (0.004)	25
C52100	Industrial (Altoona, PA)	...	...	20 yr	0.00224 (0.088)	25
C52100	Industrial marine (New York, NY)	...	...	20 yr	0.00254 (0.100)	25

(Continued)

Corrosion Behavior of Various Metals and Alloys in Atmospheres (Continued)

Materials	Condition, other factors, comments	Concentration, %	Temperature, °C (°F)	Duration	Corrosion rate, mm/yr (mils/yr) or other	Ref
C52100	Tropical rural marine (Key West, FL)	...	...	20 yr	0.00071 (0.028)	25
C52100	Humid marine (La Jolla, CA)	...	...	20 yr	0.00231 (0.091)	25
C52100	Northern rural (State College, PA)	...	...	20 yr	0.00033 (0.013)	25
C52100	Dry rural (Phoenix, AZ)	...	...	20 yr	0.00013 (0.005)	25
C61000	Industrial (Altoona, PA)	...	...	20 yr	0.00163 (0.064)	25
C61000	Industrial marine (New York, NY)	...	...	20 yr	0.00160 (0.063)	25
C61000	Tropical rural marine (Key West, FL)	...	...	20 yr	0.00010 (0.004)	25
C61000	Humid marine (La Jolla, CA)	...	...	20 yr	0.00015 (0.006)	25
C61000	Northern rural (State College, PA)	...	...	20 yr	0.00025 (0.010)	25
C61000	Dry rural (Phoenix, AZ)	...	...	20 yr	0.00051 (0.002)	25
C65500	Industrial (Altoona, PA)	...	...	20 yr	0.00165 (0.065)	25
C65500	Industrial marine (New York, NY)	...	...	20 yr	0.00173 (0.068)	25
C65500	Tropical rural marine (Key West, FL)	...	...	20 yr	...	25
C65500	Humid marine (La Jolla, CA)	...	...	20 yr	0.00138 (0.054)	25
C65500	Northern rural (State College, PA)	...	...	20 yr	0.00051 (0.020)	25
C65500	Dry rural (Phoenix, AZ)	...	...	20 yr	0.00015 (0.006)	25
Cartridge brass	Industrial. (b)	...	...	...	Good	93
Cartridge brass	Marine. (b)	...	...	...	Good	93
Cartridge brass	Rural	...	...	...	Good	93
Commercial bronze	Industrial	...	...	...	Suitable	93
Commercial bronze	Marine	...	...	...	Suitable	93
Commercial bronze	Rural	...	...	...	Suitable	93
Electrolytic copper	Industrial	...	...	...	Suitable	93
Electrolytic copper	Marine	...	...	...	Suitable	93
Electrolytic copper	Rural	...	...	...	Suitable	93
Free-cutting brass	Industrial. (b)	...	...	...	Good	93
Free-cutting brass	Marine. (b)	...	...	...	Good	93
Free-cutting brass	Rural	...	...	...	Suitable	93
Muntz metal	Industrial. (b)	...	...	...	Good	93
Muntz metal	Marine. (b)	...	...	...	Good	93
Muntz metal	Rural	...	...	...	Suitable	93
Naval brass	Industrial. (b)	...	...	...	Good	93
Naval brass	Marine. (b)	...	...	...	Suitable	93
Naval brass	Rural	...	...	...	Suitable	93
Nickel silver	Industrial	18	...	...	Suitable	93
Nickel silver	Marine	18	...	...	Suitable	93
Nickel silver	Rural	18	...	...	Suitable	93
Phosphor copper	Industrial	...	...	...	Suitable	93
Phosphor bronze	5% Sn. Industrial	...	...	...	Suitable	93
Phosphor bronze	8% Sn. Industrial	...	...	...	Suitable	93
Phosphor copper	Marine	...	...	...	Suitable	93
Phosphor bronze	5% Sn. Marine	...	...	...	Suitable	93
Phosphor bronze	8% Sn. Marine	...	...	...	Suitable	93
Phosphor copper	Rural	...	...	...	Suitable	93
Phosphor bronze	5% Sn. Rural	...	...	...	Suitable	93
Phosphor bronze	8% Sn. Rural	...	...	...	Suitable	93
Red brass	Industrial	...	...	...	Suitable	93
Red brass	Marine	...	...	...	Suitable	93
Red brass	Rural	...	...	...	Suitable	93
Silicon bronze	Low. Industrial	...	...	...	Suitable	93
Silicon bronze	High. Industrial	...	...	...	Suitable	93
Silicon bronze	Low. Marine	...	...	...	Suitable	93
Silicon bronze	High. Marine	...	...	...	Suitable	93
Silicon bronze	Low. Rural	...	...	...	Suitable	93
Silicon bronze	High. Rural	...	...	...	Suitable	93
Lead, tin, and zinc						
Lead	Chemical. Industrial (Altoona, PA)	...	...	10 yr	0.0007 (0.029)	129

(Continued)

Corrosion Behavior of Various Metals and Alloys in Atmospheres (Continued)

Materials	Condition, other factors, comments	Concentration, %	Temperature, °C (°F)	Duration	Corrosion rate, mm/yr (mils/yr) or other	Ref
Lead	1% Sb. Industrial (Altoona, PA)	...	...	10 yr	0.0006 (0.023)	129
Lead	Chemical. Industrial (New York, NY)	...	...	20 yr	0.0004 (0.015)	129
Lead	1% Sb. Industrial (New York, NY)	...	...	20 yr	0.0003 (0.013)	129
Lead	Chemical. Seacoast (Sandy Hook, NJ)	...	...	20 yr	0.0005 (0.021)	129
Lead	1% Sb. Seacoast (Sandy Hook, NJ)	...	...	20 yr	0.0005 (0.020)	129
Lead	Chemical. Seacoast (Key West, FL)	...	...	10 yr	0.0006 (0.023)	129
Lead	1% Sb. Seacoast (Key West, FL)	...	...	10 yr	0.0005 (0.022)	129
Lead	Chemical. Seacoast (La Jolla, CA)	...	...	20 yr	0.0005 (0.021)	129
Lead	1% Sb. Seacoast (La Jolla, CA)	...	...	20 yr	0.0006 (0.023)	129
Lead	Chemical. Rural (State College, PA)	...	...	20 yr	0.0003 (0.013)	129
Lead	1% Sb. Rural (State College, PA)	...	...	20 yr	0.0003 (0.014)	129
Lead	Chemical. Semi-arid (Phoenix, AZ)	...	...	20 yr	0.0001 (0.004)	129
Lead	1% Sb. Semi-arid (Phoenix, AZ)	...	...	20 yr	0.0003 (0.012)	129
Lead	Chemical. East coast, marine (Kure Beach, NC) 80-ft site	...	...	2 yr	0.0013 (0.052)	129
Lead	6% Sb. East coast, marine (Kure Beach, NC) 80-ft site	...	...	2 yr	0.0010 (0.041)	129
Lead	Chemical. Industrial (Newark, NJ)	...	...	2 yr	0.0014 (0.056)	129
Lead	6% Sb. Industrial (Newark, NJ)	...	...	2 yr	0.0010 (0.042)	129
Lead	Chemical. West coast, marine (Point Reyes, CA)	...	...	2 yr	0.0009 (0.036)	129
Lead	6% Sb. West coast, marine (Point Reyes, CA)	...	...	2 yr	0.0006 (0.026)	129
Lead	Chemical. Rural (State College, PA).	...	...	2 yr	0.0014 (0.055)	129
Lead	6% Sb. Rural (State College, PA)	...	...	2 yr	0.0010 (0.039)	129
Lead	Urban (Birmingham, UK)	99.96	...	7 yr	0.0009 (0.037)	129
Lead	1.6% Sb. Urban (Birmingham, UK)	...	...	7 yr	0.0001 (0.004)	129
Lead	Industrial (Wakefield, UK)	99.95	...	1 yr	0.0018 (0.074)	129
Lead	Marine (Southport, UK)	99.95	...	1 yr	0.0017 (0.070)	129
Lead	Suburban (Bourneville, UK)	99.95	...	1 yr	0.0019 (0.077)	129
Lead	Rural (Cardington, UK)	99.95	...	1 yr	0.0014 (0.056)	129
Lead	Chemical. Tropical, marine (Cristobal, CZ)	...	...	8 yr	0.0013 (0.053)	129
Lead	Chemical. Tropical, inland (Miraflores, CZ)	...	...	8 yr	0.0007 (0.030)	129
Tin	Heavy industrial	7.29 g/cm³	...	20 yr	0.0017 (0.067)	128
Tin	Marine heavy industrial	7.29 g/cm³	...	20 yr	0.0013 (0.051)	128
Tin	Marine (New Jersey)	7.29 g/cm³	...	10 yr	0.0019 (0.075)	128
Tin	Marine (Florida)	7.29 g/cm³	...	10 yr	0.0023 (0.09)	128
Tin	Marine (California)	7.29 g/cm³	...	20 yr	0.0029 (0.11)	128
Tin	Semi-arid	7.29 g/cm³	...	20 yr	0.00044 (0.017)	128
Tin	Rural	7.29 g/cm³	...	10 yr	0.00049 (0.019)	128
Magnesium						
AZ31B-H24	Marine; at Kure Beach, NC. 7.4% change in tensile strength	...	...	...	0.018 (0.70)	14
AZ31B-H24	Industrial; at Madison, IL. 11.2% change in tensile strength	...	...	...	0.027 (1.09)	14
AZ31B-H24	Rural; near Midland, MI. 5.9% change in tensile strength	...	...	...	0.013 (0.53)	14

(a) Although obsolete, this alloy indicates the corrosion resistance expected of C71500. (b) May be considered in place of a copper metal when some property, other than corrosion resistance, governs its use.

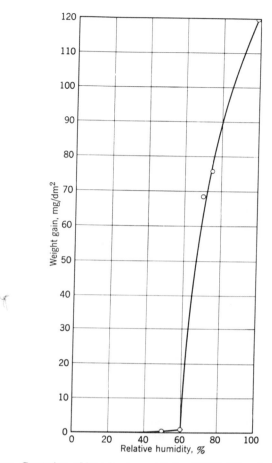

Iron. Corrosion of iron in air containing 0.01% SO_2 after 55 days of exposure, showing critical humidity. Source: H.H. Uhlig, *Corrosion and Corrosion Control: An Introduction to Corrosion Science and Engineering*, John Wiley & Sons, New York, 1963, 147.

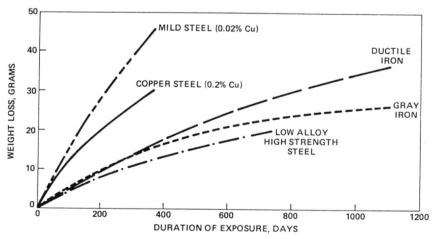

NOTE: SPECIMEN SIZE WAS 4 X 6 INCHES

Steels and cast irons. Results of exposure of steels and cast irons to corrosion by atmosphere at Kure, NC, Beach 80 ft from the ocean. Source: C. McCaul and S. Goldspiel, "Atmospheric Corrosion of Malleable and Cast Irons and Steels," in *Atmospheric Corrosion*, W.H. Ailor, Ed., John Wiley & Sons, New York, 1982, 440.

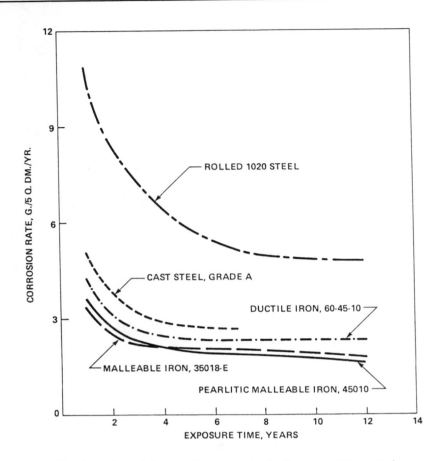

Steel and cast irons. Corrosion rates for ferrous metals exposed 12 years. Source: C. McCaul and S. Goldspiel, "Atmospheric Corrosion of Malleable and Cast Irons and Steels," in *Atmospheric Corrosion*, W.H. Ailor, Ed., John Wiley & Sons, New York, 1982, 439.

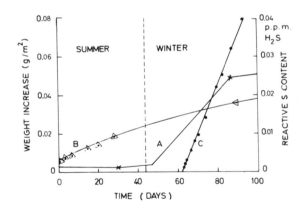

Copper. Effect of initial atmospheric exposure conditions on subsequent corrosion of copper. A = sulfur content of air; B = specimens put out in summer; C = specimens put out in winter. Source: G. Wranglen, *An Introduction to Corrosion and Protection of Metals*, Chapman Hall, New York, 1985, 123.

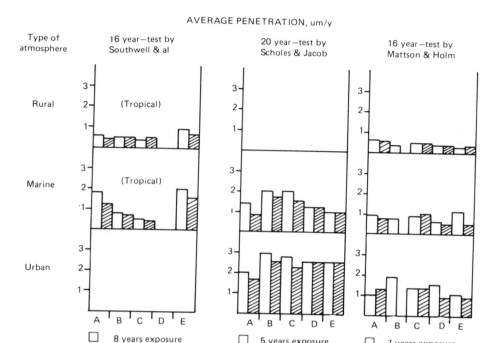

Copper. General corrosion rates for copper and copper alloys in the atmosphere, sloping surfaces. A = low-alloyed copper; B = low-zinc brass; C = high-zinc brass; D = nickel silver; E = tin bronze. Source: V. Kucera and E. Mattson, "Atmospheric Corrosion," in *Corrosion Mechanisms*, F. Mansfeld, Ed., Marcel Dekker, New York, 1987, 274.

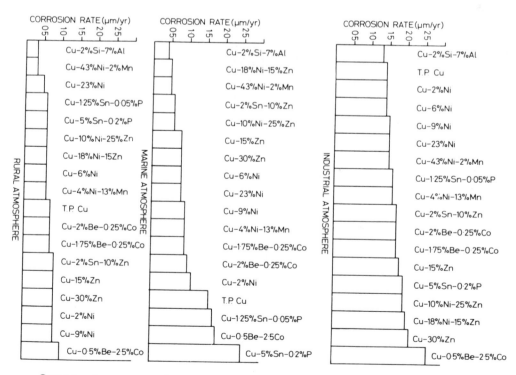

Copper. Average corrosion rates for copper alloys during 7 years of atmospheric exposure. Source: V.E. Carter, "Atmospheric Corrosion of Non-Ferrous Metals," in *Corrosion Processes*, R. Parkins, Ed., Allied Science Publishers, London, 1982, 101.

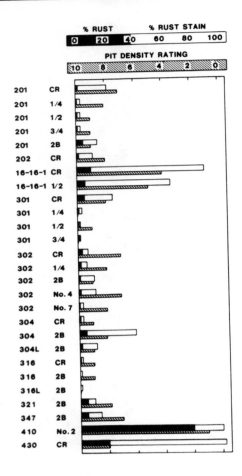

Stainless steel. Relative performance of stainless steels exposed 250 m from the ocean for 26 years. Source: E.A. Baker and T.S. Lee, "Long-Term Atmospheric Corrosion Behavior of Various Grades of Stainless Steel," *Degradation of Metals in the Atmosphere* (STP 965), S.W. Dean and T.S. Lee, Ed., ASTM, Philadelphia, 1987, 63.

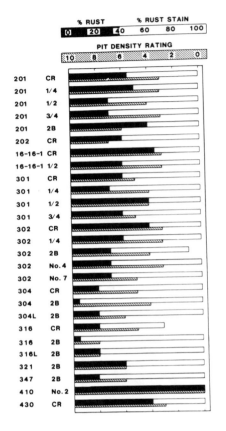

Stainless steel. Relative performance of stainless steels exposed 25 m from the ocean for 26 years. Source: E.A. Baker and T.S. Lee, "Long-Term Atmospheric Corrosion Behavior of Various Grades of Stainless Steel," *Degradation of Metals in the Atmosphere* (STP 965), S.W. Dean and T.S. Lee, Ed., ASTM, Philadelphia, 1987, 62.

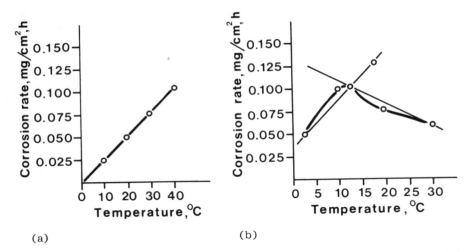

Steels. Influence of air temperature on the atmospheric corrosion rate of carbon steel (a) during rain, and (b) at drying-out of a film of water at a constant relative humidity of 75%. Source: V. Kucera and E. Mattsson, "Atmospheric Corrosion," in *Corrosion Mechanisms*, F. Mansfield, Ed., Marcel Dekker, New York, 1987, 225.

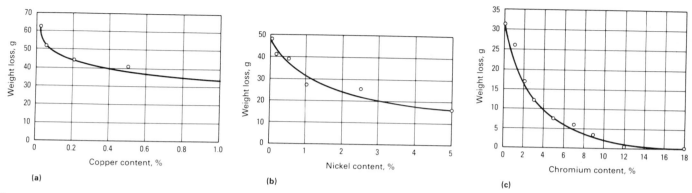

Steels. Effect of alloying additions on the corrosion of steel in a marine atmosphere at Kure Beach, NC (90-month exposure). (a) Effect of copper on 100 by 150 mm specimen. (b) Effect of nickel on 100 by 150 mm specimen. (c) Effect of chromium on 75 by 150 mm specimen. Source: *Metals Handbook,* 9th ed., Vol 13, Corrosion, ASM International, Metals Park, OH, 1987, 540.

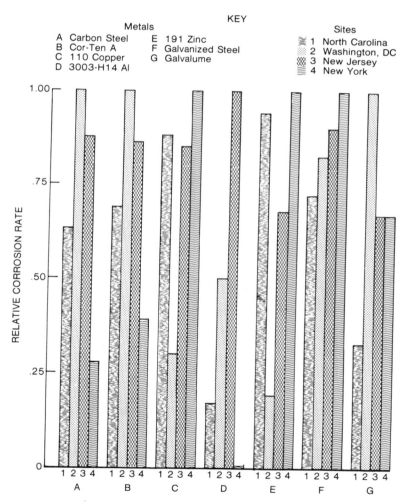

Steels, copper, and zinc. Relative annual average monthly corrosion rates for five metals and two coated steels at four materials exposure sites in 1983. Average monthly corrosion rates for a given metal were normalized by dividing by the maximum annual average measured at the four sites. Source: D.R. Flinn, S.D. Cramer, *et al.,* "Field Exposure Study for Determining the Effects of Acid Deposition on the Corrosion and Deterioration of Materials: Description of the Program and Preliminary Results," *Durability of Building Materials,* Vol 3, 1985, 168.

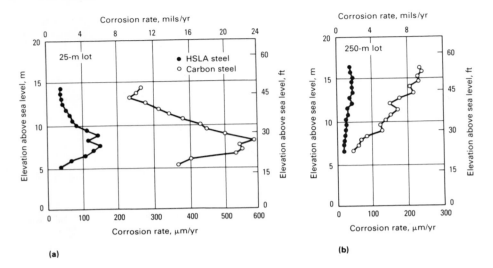

(a)

(b)

High-strength low-alloy steels. Effect of elevation above sea level for carbon and HSLA steels at Kure Beach, NC. (a) 25-m (80-ft) lot. (b) 250-m (800-ft) lot. Source: *Metals Handbook*, 9th ed., Vol 13, Corrosion, ASM International, Metals Park, OH, 1987, 910.

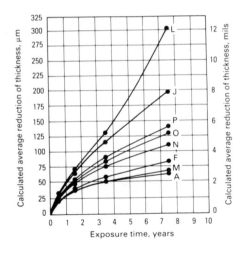

Steel	Composition, %							
	C	Mn	P	S	Si	Cu	Ni	Cr
A(a).........	0.09	0.24	0.15	0.024	0.80	0.43	0.05	1.1
M(a).........	0.06	0.48	0.11	0.030	0.54	0.41	0.51	1.0
F(a).........	0.05	0.36	0.05	0.016	0.008	1.1	2.0	0.01
N(a).........	0.11	0.55	0.08	0.026	0.06	0.55	0.28	0.31
O(a).........	0.16	1.4	0.013	0.021	0.18	0.30	0.50	0.03
P(a).........	0.23	1.5	0.018	0.021	0.19	0.29	0.04	0.08
J(b).........	0.19	0.52	0.008	0.039	0.01	0.29	0.05	0.05
L(b).........	0.16	0.42	0.013	0.021	0.01	0.02	0.02	0.01

(a) High-strength low-alloy steels. (b) Structural carbon and structural copper steels

Steels. Effect of exposure time on corrosion of steels in marine atmosphere at Kure Beach, NC. Source: *Metals Handbook*, 9th ed., Vol 13, Corrosion, ASM International, Metals Park, OH, 1987, 541.

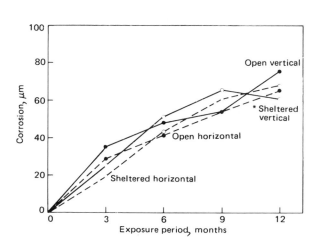

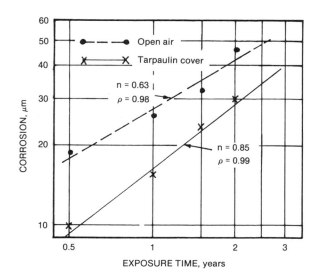

Carbon steels. Corrosion-time curves from Thorney Island specimens; weight loss coupon data; curve marked * shows lower apparent corrosion after 12 months exposure than after 9 months. Source: M. McKenzie and P.R. Vassie, "Use of Weight Loss Coupons and Electrical Resistance Probes in Atmospheric Corrosion Tests," *British Corrosion Journal*, Vol 20, April 1985, 123.

Steels. Relationship between corrosion and exposure time for mild steel under tarpaulin cover and in the open air. Source: O.E. Okarafor, "Corrosion Under Sheltered and Unsheltered Sites in Awka, Nigeria," *Corrosion Prevention and Control*, Vol 33, June 1986, 67.

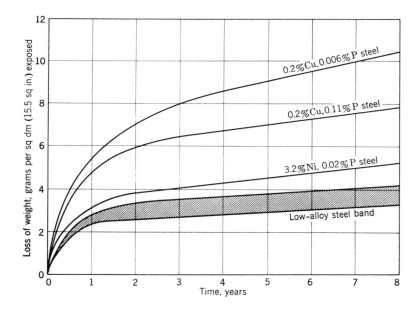

Low-alloy steels. Atmospheric corrosion of steels as a function of time (industrial atmosphere). Source: H.H. Uhlig, *Corrosion and Corrosion Engineering: An Introduction to Corrosion Science and Engineering*, 1st ed., John Wiley & Sons, New York, 1963, 140.

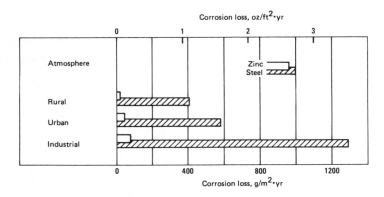

Zinc. Corrosion losses of uncoated steel and zinc in various atmospheres. Source: *Metals Handbook*, 9th ed., Vol 2, Properties and Selection: Nonferrous Alloys and Pure Metals, American Society for Metals, Metals Park, OH, 1979, 646.

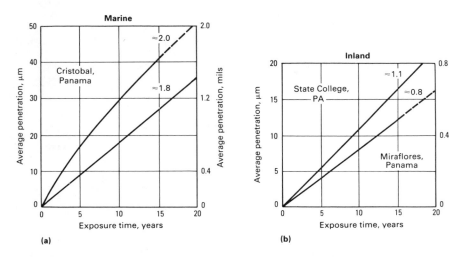

Zinc. Comparison of corrosion rates for zinc at tropical and temperate exposure sites. Numbers on curves are stabilized corrosion rates in microns per year. Source: *Metals Handbook*, 9th ed., Vol 13, Corrosion, ASM International, Metals Park, OH, 1987, 912.

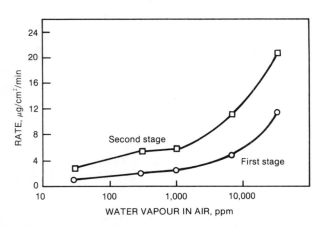

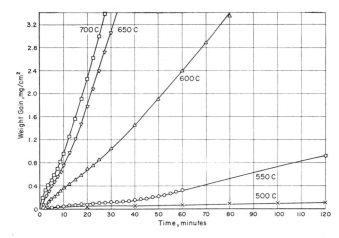

Uranium. Effect of water vapor on reaction of uranium (1-cm cubes) in air at 200 °C. Source: J.H. Gittus, *Uranium*, Butterworths, Washington, 1963, 396.

Tantalum. Reaction of tantalum with air at various temperatures. Source: C.A. Hampel, "Tantalum," in *Rare Metals Handbook*, 2nd ed., C.A. Hampel, Ed., Reinhold Publishing, New York, 1961, 503.

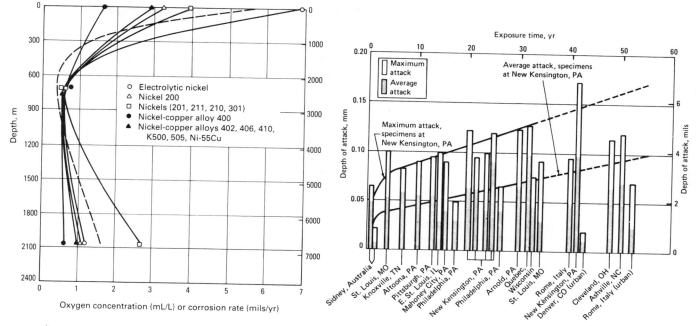

Nickels and nickel coppers. Corrosion of nickels and nickel-copper alloys versus depth after 1 year of exposure compared to the shape of the dissolved oxygen profile (dashed line). Source: *Metals Handbook*, 9th ed., Vol 13, Corrosion, ASM International, Metals Park, OH, 1987, 904.

Aluminum. Correlation of weathering data for specimens of alloys 1100, 3003 and 3004, all in H14 temper, exposed in industrial atmosphere (curves) with service experience with aluminum alloys in various locations (bars). Source: *Metals Handbook*, 9th ed., Vol 2, Properties and Selection: Nonferrous Alloys and Pure Metals, American Society for Metals, Metals Park, OH, 1979, 222.

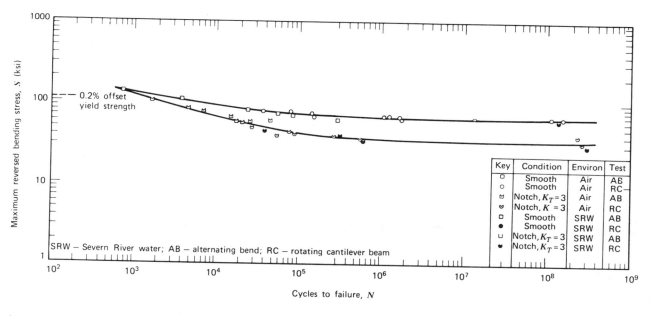

Titanium. Corrosion fatigue for Ti-6Al-4V in Severn River water at the U.S. Navy Marine Engineering Laboratory. Source: F.L. LaQue, *Marine Corrosion: Causes and Prevention*, John Wiley & Sons, New York, 1975, 226.

Barium Carbonate

Barium carbonate, $BaCO_3$, also known as witherite, is a white powder that is soluble in acids, with the exception of sulfuric acid. It has a melting point of 174 °C and is used in television picture tubes, rodenticide, optical glass and ceramic flux.

Material Summaries

The following material summaries were compiled from a survey of the available literature. Inclusion of a material description under a given environment does not imply that it is the most appropriate material for corrosion service in that environment. Likewise, exclusion of a given material does not imply that it is not suitable for corrosion service applications in that environment.

Aluminum. In laboratory conditions of 100% relative humidity and ambient temperature, aluminum alloy 3003 was resistant to solid barium carbonate.

Corrosion Behavior of Various Metals and Alloys in Barium Carbonate

Material	Condition, other factors, comments	Concentration, %	Temperature, °C (°F)	Duration	Corrosion rate, mm/yr (mils/yr) or other	Ref
Stainless steels						
AM-363 stainless steel	...	...	Room	...	Unattacked	120
Coppers						
70-30 cupronickel	...	...	...	...	Suitable	93
90-10 cupronickel	...	...	...	...	Suitable	93
Admiralty brass	...	...	...	...	Suitable	93
Aluminum bronze	...	...	...	...	Suitable	93
Architectural bronze	...	...	...	...	Suitable	93
Brass	...	...	...	...	Suitable	93
Cartridge brass	...	...	...	...	Suitable	93
Commercial bronze	...	...	...	...	Suitable	93
Electrolytic copper	...	...	...	...	Suitable	93
Free-cutting brass	...	...	...	...	Suitable	93
Muntz metal	...	...	...	...	Suitable	93
Naval brass	...	...	...	...	Suitable	93
Nickel silver	...	18	...	...	Suitable	93
Phosphor bronze	5% Sn	...	...	...	Suitable	93
Phosphor bronze	8% Sn	...	...	...	Suitable	93
Phosphor copper	...	...	...	...	Suitable	93
Red brass	...	...	...	...	Suitable	93
Silicon bronze	Low	...	...	...	Suitable	93
Silicon bronze	High	...	...	...	Suitable	93
Titanium						
Titanium	...	Saturated	Room	...	nil	90

Barium Chloride

Barium chloride, $BaCl_2$, is a colorless toxic salt with a melting point of 963 °C. It is soluble in water. Barium chloride is used in metal surface treatment and as a rat poison.

Material Summaries

The following material summaries were compiled from a survey of the available literature. Inclusion of a material description under a given environment does not imply that it is the most appropriate material for corrosion service in that environment. Likewise, exclusion of a given material does not imply that it is not suitable for corrosion service applications in that environment.

Aluminum. In laboratory test conditions of 100% relative humidity and ambient temperature, aluminum alloy 3003 was resistant to solid barium chloride. Aluminum alloy 1100 resisted 0.001 to 0.4N solutions of barium chloride at ambient temperature.

Corrosion Behavior of Various Metals and Alloys in Barium Chloride

Material	Condition, other factors, comments	Concentration, %	Temperature, °C (°F)	Duration	Corrosion rate, mm/yr (mils/yr) or other	Ref
Stainless steels						
Type 304 stainless steel	Chemical processing; laboratory test. With carbon over the standard maximum. Plus saturated water solution	...	Room	2-4 d	<0.0001 in./yr	89
Type 304 stainless steel	Chemical processing; laboratory test. Solution repeatedly evaporated	30	100 (212)	2-4 d	<0.0001 in./yr	89
Type 304 stainless steel	...	10	21 (70)	...	Good	121
Type 304 stainless steel	(a)	...	845 (1550)	30 d	1.9 (75)	73
Type 304 stainless steel	Coal by product processing; field or pilot plant test; no aeration; slight to moderate agitation. Plus trace sulfide, hydrochloric acid excess, pH 2-3. Severe pitting (maximum depth of pits over 0.010 in.)	20	80 (176)	28 d	0.25 in./yr	89
Type 310 stainless steel	(a)	...	845 (1550)	30 d	2.0 (79)	73
Type 316 stainless steel	Coal by-product processing; field or pilot plant test; no aeration; slight to moderate agitation. Plus trace sulfide, hydrochloric acid excess, pH 2-3. Severe pitting (maximum depth of pits over 0.010 in.)	20	80 (176)	28 d	0.16 in./yr	89
Type 316 stainless steel	...	10	21 (70)	...	Good	121
Type 316 stainless steel	Chemical processing; field or pilot plant test; no aeration; rapid agitation. Plus free chlorine, water solution, pH 1. Severe pitting (maximum depth of pits over 0.010 in.)	25	35 (95)	11 d	0.052 in./yr	89
Type 410 stainless steel	...	...	Room	...	Slightly attacked	121
Type 410 stainless steel	...	10	21 (70)	...	Fair	121
Type 430 stainless steel	...	10	21 (70)	...	Good	121
Coppers						
70-30 cupronickel	(b)	...	...	...	Good	93
90-10 cupronickel	(b)	...	...	...	Good	93
Admiralty brass	...	...	...	...	Fair	93
Aluminum bronze	(b)	...	...	...	Good	93
Ampco 8, aluminum bronze	Generally suitable	...	...	...	<0.05 (<2)	96
Architectural bronze	...	...	...	...	Not suitable	93
Brass	...	...	...	...	Fair	93
Cartridge brass	...	...	...	...	Not suitable	93
Commercial bronze	(b)	...	...	...	Good	93
Electrolytic copper	(b)	...	...	...	Good	93
Free-cutting brass	...	...	...	...	Not suitable	93
Muntz metal	...	...	...	...	Not suitable	93
Naval brass	...	...	...	...	Not suitable	93
Nickel silver	(b)	...	...	...	Good	93
Phosphor copper	(b)	...	...	...	Good	93
Phosphor bronze	5% Sn. (b)	...	...	...	Good	93
Phosphor bronze	8% Sn. (b)	...	...	...	Good	93
Red brass	(b)	...	...	...	Good	93
Silicon bronze	Low. (b)	...	...	...	Good	93
Silicon bronze	High. (b)	...	...	...	Good	93
Titanium						
Titanium	...	5	100 (212)	...	nil	90
Titanium	...	20	100 (212)	...	nil	90
Titanium	...	25	100 (212)	...	nil	90
Heat- and corrosion-resistant alloys						
Alloy 825	Coal by-product processing; field or pilot plant test; no aeration; slight to moderate agitation. Plus trace sulfide, hydrochloric acid excess, pH 2-3. Severe pitting (maximum depth of pits over 0.010 in.). Crevice attack (tendency to concentration-cell corrosion)	20	80 (176)	28 d	0.042 in./yr	89

(Continued)

Corrosion Behavior of Various Metals and Alloys in Barium Chloride (Continued)

Material	Condition, other factors, comments	Concentration, %	Temperature, °C (°F)	Duration	Corrosion rate, mm/yr (mils/yr) or other	Ref
Hastelloy alloy S	(a)	...	845 (1550)	30 d	0.1 (40)	73
Hastelloy alloy X	(a)	...	845 (1550)	30 d	0.97 (38)	73
Haynes alloy 188	(a)	...	845 (1550)	30 d	0.69 (27)	73
Haynes alloy 556	(a)	...	845 (1550)	30 d	0.11 (44)	73
Haynes alloy 214	(a)	...	845 (1550)	30 d	1.8 (71)	73
Incoloy 800	Solutions were prepared with reagent-grade chemicals. Test specimens were cold-rolled, annealed sheet, 2.84 mm (0.112 in.) thick. Pitting occurred after 42 d	10	80 (176)	42 d	<0.003 (<0.1)	44
Inconel 601	Pitting attack	10	80 (176)	30 d	0.002 (0.1)	64
Inconel 600	(a)	...	845 (1550)	30 d	2.4 (96)	73
Multimet	(a)	...	845 (1550)	30 d	0.75 (30)	73
Zirconium						
Zr702	...	5, 20	35-100 (95-212)	...	<0.025 (<1)	15
Zr702	...	25	Boiling	...	0.13-0.25 (5-10)	15
Lead, tin, and zinc						
Lead	Practically resistant; Pb recommended for use	10	24-100 (75-212)	...	<500 μm/yr (<20)	95
Noble metals						
Platinum	...	All	Boiling	...	<0.05 (<2)	5
Silver	...	All	Boiling	...	<0.05 (<2)	9
Silver	...	All	Room	...	<0.05 (<2)	9

(a) Plus KCl and NaCl. Average metal affected = metal loss + internal penetration. (b) May be considered in place of a copper metal when some property, other than corrosion resistance, governs its use.

Barium Hydroxide

Barium hydroxide, $Ba(OH)_2 \cdot 8H_2O$, is a colorless solid composed of monoclinic crystals. It has a melting point of 78 °C and is soluble in water and insoluble in acetone. It is used in the fusion of silicates and fat saponification.

Material Summaries

The following material summaries were compiled from a survey of the available literature. Inclusion of a material description under a given environment does not imply that it is the most appropriate material for corrosion service in that environment. Likewise, exclusion of a given material does not imply that it is not suitable for corrosion service applications in that environment.

Aluminum. Aqueous solutions of barium hydroxide are very corrosive to aluminum alloys in laboratory tests. Therefore, aluminum alloys are not used to service barium hydroxide.

Corrosion Behavior of Various Metals and Alloys in Barium Hydroxide

Material	Condition, other factors, comments	Concentration, %	Temperature, °C (°F)	Duration	Corrosion rate, mm/yr (mils/yr) or other	Ref
Aluminum						
Aluminum (>99.5%)	Solution	...	...	...	Restricted applications	92
Coppers						
70-30 cupronickel	...	...	...	...	Suitable	93

(Continued)

Corrosion Behavior of Various Metals and Alloys in Barium Hydroxide (Continued)

Material	Condition, other factors, comments	Concentration, %	Temperature, °C (°F)	Duration	Corrosion rate, mm/yr (mils/yr) or other	Ref
90-10 cupronickel	...	...	...	...	Suitable	93
Admiralty brass	...	...	...	...	Suitable	93
Aluminum bronze	...	...	...	...	Suitable	93
Architectural bronze	(a)	...	...	...	Suitable	93
Brass	...	...	...	...	Good	93
Cartridge brass	(a)	...	...	...	Suitable	93
Commercial bronze	...	...	...	...	Good	93
Electrolytic copper	...	...	...	...	Suitable	93
Free-cutting brass	(a)	...	...	...	Suitable	93
Muntz metal	(a)	...	...	...	Good	93
Naval brass	(a)	...	...	...	Good	93
Nickel silver	...	...	...	...	Good	93
Phosphor bronze	5% Sn	18	...	...	Suitable	93
Phosphor bronze	8% Sn	...	...	...	Suitable	93
Phosphor copper	...	...	...	...	Suitable	93
Red brass	...	...	...	...	Suitable	93
Silicon bronze	Low	...	...	...	Suitable	93
Silicon bronze	High	...	...	...	Suitable	93
Titanium						
Titanium	...	Saturated	Room	...	nil	90

(a) May be considered in place of a copper metal when some property, other than corrosion resistance, governs its use.

Benzene

Benzene, C_6H_6, also known as benzol, phenyl hydride, phene, cyclohexatriene and coal naptha, is a colorless, flammable liquid. It is an aromatic hydrocarbon that boils at 80.1 °C. It is used as a solvent and an intermediate in manufacturing organic compounds such as styrene and phenol.

Material Summaries

The following material summaries were compiled from a survey of the available literature. Inclusion of a material description under a given environment does not imply that it is the most appropriate material for corrosion service in that environment. Likewise, exclusion of a given material does not imply that it is not suitable for corrosion service applications in that environment.

Aluminum. Aluminum alloys 3003, 5052, 5154, and 6061 are resistant to benzene at ambient temperature and at 50 °C (122 °F). Laboratory tests show that the addition of moisture increases the corrosive action of benzene on aluminum alloys. Aluminum equipment such as stills, condensers, heat exchangers, and fractionators have been used in servicing benzene.

Corrosion Behavior of Various Metals and Alloys in Benzene

Material	Condition, other factors, comments	Concentration, %	Temperature, °C (°F)	Duration	Corrosion rate, mm/yr (mils/yr) or other	Ref
Stainless steels						
Type 304 stainless steel	Chemical processing; field or plant test; no aeration; rapid agitation. Plus 0.5% methylaldehyde, <0.5% formaldehyde, <0.5% methyl formate, plus impurities	98.5	93-104 (200-220)	13 d	0.0012 in./yr	89
Type 304 stainless steel	Rayon processing; field or plant test; no aeration; rapid agitation. Plus 1.5% water, 0.04% acetic acid, 0.02% decomposition gases	98.3	77 (170)	275 d	0.0001 in./yr	89
Type 304 stainless steel	Rayon processing; field or plant test; no aeration; rapid agitation. Plus 1.5% water, 0.04% acetic acid, 0.02% decomposition gases	98.3	77 (170)	275 d	0.0001 in./yr	89

(Continued)

Corrosion Behavior of Various Metals and Alloys in Benzene (Continued)

Material	Condition, other factors, comments	Concen-tration, %	Temperature, °C (°F)	Duration	Corrosion rate, mm/yr (mils/yr) or other	Ref
Type 304 stainless steel	Coal by-product processing; field or plant test; slight to moderate aeration; rapid agitation. Plus 4.5% sulfuric acid, impurities from crude benzene (washer). Severe pitting: maximum depth of pits over 0.010 in.; crevice attack (tendency to concentration-cell corrosion)	95	50-60 (122-140)	44 d	0.0668 in./yr	89
Type 304 stainless steel	Pharmaceutical processing; field or plant test; slight to moderate aeration; slight to moderate agitation. Plus water. Slight pitting: maximum depth of pits from incipient to 0.005 in.	...	21 (70)	42 d	<0.0001 in./yr	89
Type 304 stainless steel	Chemical processing; field or plant test; slight to moderate aeration; rapid agitation. Plus oleum, probably some sulfur dioxide and trioxide (vapors during first 12 h)	...	185 (365)	1.5 d	0.47 in./yr	89
Type 304 stainless steel	Chemical processing; field or plant test; slight to moderate aeration; rapid agitation. Plus oleum, probably some sulfur dioxide and trioxide (vapors during first 12 h)	...	185 (365)	1.5 d	0.43 in./yr	89
Type 304 stainless steel	Rayon processing; field or plant test; no aeration; rapid agitation. Plus furnace vapors, water, acetic anhydride, decomposition gases	...	104 (220)	275 d	0.0019 in./yr	89
Type 304 stainless steel	Rayon processing; field or plant test; no aeration; rapid agitation. Plus furnace vapors, water, acetic anhydride, decomposition gases	...	104 (220)	275 d	0.0021 in./yr	89
Type 316 stainless steel	Chemical processing; field or plant test; no aeration; rapid agitation. Plus 0.5% methylaldehyde, <0.5% formaldehyde, <0.5% methyl formate, plus impurities	98.5	93-104 (200-220)	13 d	0.0007 in./yr	89
Type 316 stainless steel	Coal by-product processing; field or plant test; slight to moderate aeration; rapid agitation. Plus 4.5% sulfuric acid, impurities from crude benzene (washer). Severe pitting: maximum depth of pits over 0.010 in.; crevice attack (tendency to concentration-cell corrosion)	95	50-60 (122-140)	44 d	Corrosion	89
Type 316 stainless steel	Chemical processing; field or plant test; slight to moderate aeration; no agitation. Plus 5% hydrochloric acid, 5% water, chlorinated benzene. Severe pitting: maximum depth of pits over 0.010 in.; crevice attack (tendency to concentration-cell corrosion)	90	26 (80)	60 d	0.021 in./yr	89
Type 316 stainless steel	Pharmaceutical processing; field or plant test; slight to moderate aeration; slight to moderate agitation. Plus water. Slight pitting: maximum depth of pits from incipient to 0.005 in.	...	21 (70)	42 d	0.0001 in./yr	89
Type 316 stainless steel	Chemical processing; field or plant test; slight to moderate aeration; no agitation. Plus 40% chlorinated benzene, 5% hydrochloric acid, 5% water	50	26 (80)	60 d	0.051 in./yr	89
Type 317 stainless steel	Chemical processing; field or plant test; slight to moderate aeration; rapid agitation. Plus oleum, probably some sulfur dioxide and trioxide (vapors during first 12 h)	...	185 (365)	1.5 d	0.77 in./yr	89
Type 317 stainless steel	Chemical processing; field or plant test; slight to moderate aeration; rapid agitation. Plus oleum, probably some sulfur dioxide and trioxide (vapors during first 12 h)	...	185 (365)	1.5 d	0.73 in./yr	89
Type 317 stainless steel	Rayon processing; field or plant test; no aeration; rapid agitation. Plus furnace vapors, water, acetic anhydride, decomposition gases	...	104 (220)	275 d	0.0011 in./yr	89
Type 317 stainless steel	Rayon processing; field or plant test; no aeration; rapid agitation. Plus furnace vapors, water, acetic anhydride, decomposition gases	...	104 (220)	275 d	0.001 in./yr	89
Aluminum						
Aluminum (99.0-99.5%)	...	...	...	...	Excellent	92
Aluminum-manganese alloys	...	...	...	...	Excellent	92
Coppers						
70-30 cupronickel	...	...	...	...	Suitable	93
90-10 cupronickel	...	...	...	...	Suitable	93

(Continued)

Corrosion Behavior of Various Metals and Alloys in Benzene (Continued)

Material	Condition, other factors, comments	Concentration, %	Temperature, °C (°F)	Duration	Corrosion rate, mm/yr (mils/yr) or other	Ref
Admiralty brass	...	...	...	...	Suitable	93
Aluminum bronze	...	...	...	...	Suitable	93
Ampco 8, aluminum bronze	Generally suitable	...	...	...	<0.05 (<2)	96
Architectural bronze	...	...	...	...		
Brass	...	...	...	...	Suitable	93
Cartridge brass	...	...	...	...	Suitable	93
Commercial bronze	...	...	...	...	Suitable	93
Electrolytic copper	...	...	...	...	Suitable	93
Free-cutting brass	...	...	...	...	Suitable	93
Muntz metal	...	...	...	...	Suitable	93
Naval brass	...	...	...	...	Suitable	93
Nickel silver	...	...	...	...	Suitable	93
Phosphor bronze	5% Sn	18	...	...	Suitable	93
Phosphor bronze	8% Sn	...	...	...	Suitable	93
Phosphor copper	...	...	...	...	Suitable	93
Platinum	...	...	...	...	Suitable	93
Red brass	...	Pure	Boiling	...	<0.05 (<2)	6
Silicon bronze	Low	...	...	...	Suitable	93
Silicon bronze	High	...	...	...	Suitable	93
Titanium						
Titanium	Plus HCl, NaCl. Vapor and liquid	...	80 (175)	...	0.005 (0.2)	20
Titanium	Traces of HCl	Vapor & liquid	80 (176)	...	0.005 (0.2)	90
Titanium	Traces of HCl	Liquid	50 (122)	...	0.025 (1)	90
Titanium	...	Liquid	Room	...	nil	90
Heat- and corrosion-resistant alloys						
Carpenter 20	Chemical processing; field or plant test; slight to moderate aeration; no agitation. Plus 5% hydrochloric acid, 5% water, chlorinated benzene. Severe pitting: maximum depth of pits over 0.010 in.; crevice attack (tendency to concentration-cell corrosion)	90	26 (80)	60 d	0.014 in./yr	89
Carpenter 20	Chemical processing; field or plant test; slight to moderate aeration; no agitation. Plus 40% chlorinated benzene, 5% hydrochloric acid, 5% water	50	26 (80)	60 d	0.054 in./yr	89
Lead, tin, and zinc						
Lead	Practically resistant; Pb recommended for use	...	24 (75)	...	<500 μm/yr (<20)	95
Noble metals						
Silver	...	Pure	Boiling	...	<0.05 (<2)	10

Benzoic Acid

Benzoic acid, C_6H_5COOH, also known as benzene carboxylic acid and phenyl formic acid, is a colorless, monoclinic crystalline solid that has a melting point of 122.4 °C and sublimes readily at 100 °C. It is an aromatic carboxylic acid that is slightly soluble in water and moderately soluble in alcohol and ether. It is used as a preservative and its derivatives are valuable in medicine, commerce, and industry.

Material Summaries

The following material summaries were compiled from a survey of the available literature. Inclusion of a material description under a given environment does not imply that it is the most appropriate material for corrosion service in that environment. Likewise, exclusion of a given material does not imply that it is not suitable for corrosion service applications in that environment.

Aluminum. Tests under laboratory conditions of ambient temperature and 100% relative humidity showed that aluminum alloys 3003 and 5154 were resistant to solid benzoic acid. The production of benzoic acid has taken place in sublimation equipment, hoppers, and piping made of aluminum alloys.

Corrosion Behavior of Various Metals and Alloys in Benzoic Acid

Material	Condition, other factors, comments	Concentration, %	Temperature, °C (°F)	Duration	Corrosion rate, mm/yr (mils/yr) or other	Ref
Stainless steels						
Type 304 stainless steel	...	90	138 (280)	...	0.38 (15)	22
Type 304 stainless steel	...	10	21 (70)	...	Good	121
Type 316 stainless steel	...	90	138 (280)	...	0.13 (5)	22
Type 316 stainless steel	...	10	21 (70)	...	Good	121
Type 410 stainless steel	...	10	21 (70)	...	Good	121
Type 410 stainless steel	...	...	Room	...	Unattacked	121
Type 430 stainless steel	...	10	21 (70)	...	Good	121
Aluminum						
Aluminum (>99.5%)	Solid	...	...	...	Excellent	92
Aluminum (>99.5%)	Solution	...	...	...	Satisfactory	92
Aluminum-manganese alloys	...	...	...	...	Satisfactory	92
Coppers						
70-30 cupronickel	...	...	...	...	Suitable	93
90-10 cupronickel	...	...	...	...	Suitable	93
Admiralty brass	...	...	...	...	Suitable	93
Aluminum bronze	...	...	...	...	Suitable	93
Architectural bronze	(a)	...	...	...	Good	93
Brass	...	...	...	...	Suitable	93
Cartridge brass	(a)	...	...	...	Good	93
Commercial bronze	...	...	...	...	Suitable	93
Electrolytic copper	...	...	...	...	Suitable	93
Free-cutting brass	(a)	...	...	...	Good	
Muntz metal	(a)	...	...	...	Good	93
Naval brass	(a)	...	...	...	Good	93
Nickel silver	...	18	...	...	Suitable	93
Phosphor copper	...	...	...	...	Suitable	93
Phosphor bronze	5% Sn	...	...	...	Suitable	93
Phosphor bronze	8% Sn	...	...	...	Suitable	93
Red brass	...	...	...	...	Suitable	93
Silicon bronze	Low	...	...	...	Suitable	93
Silicon bronze	High	...	...	...	Suitable	93
Titanium						
Titanium	...	Saturated	Room	...	nil	90
Lead, tin, and zinc						
Lead	Corrosion rate too high to merit any consideration of Pb	...	24 (75)	...	>1270 μm/yr (>50)	95
Tin	...	...	20 (68)	...	Resistant	94
Tin	...	...	60 (140)	...	Unsuitable	94
Tin	...	...	100 (212)	...	Unsuitable	94
Noble metals						
Silver	...	All	130 (265)	...	<0.05 (<2)	4

(a) May be considered in place of a copper metal when some property, other than corrosion resistance, governs its use.

Boric Acid

Boric acid, H_3BO_3, also known as boracic acid, orthoboric acid, and sassolite, is a white solid composed of triclinic crystals with a melting point of 185 °C. It is a derivative of barium oxide and is soluble in water.

Material Summaries

The following material summaries were compiled from a survey of the available literature. Inclusion of a material description under a given environment does not imply that it is the most appropriate material for corrosion service in that environment. Likewise, exclusion of a given

material does not imply that it is not suitable for corrosion service applications in that environment.

Aluminum. Laboratory tests conducted under the conditions of ambient temperature and 100% relative humidity showed that the aluminum alloys 3003 and 5154 resisted attack by solid boric acid. Aqueous solutions of 1 to 15% boric acid at 60 °C (140 °F) did not attack the aluminum alloys 1100, 3003, or 6061 in other tests. Boric acid has been serviced by aluminum alloy equipment such as drying kilns, valves, and tanks.

Cemented Carbides. Corrosion resistance of cemented titanium carbide is excellent in boric acid and somewhat better than cemented tungsten carbide in hydrochloric acid or sulfuric acid.

Titanium. Near nil corrosion rates have been reported for titanium in boric acid service over the full concentration range to temperatures well beyond the boiling point.

Additional Reading

R.C. Newman, R. Roberge, and R. Bandy, Environmental Variables in the Low-Temperature Stress Corrosion Cracking of Inconel 600, *Corrosion, 39*(10), 386-390, 1983. MetAbs No. 84-350292. **Abstract:** The low-temperature stress-corrosion cracking of sensitized Inconel 600 has been examined using aerated 1.3% boric acid solutions with small additions of sodium thiosulfate.

Corrosion Behavior of Various Metals and Alloys in Boric Acid

Material	Condition, other factors, comments	Concentration, %	Temperature, °C (°F)	Duration	Corrosion rate, mm/yr (mils/yr) or other	Ref
Stainless steels						
AM-363 stainless steel	...	...	Room	...	Unattacked	120
Type 304 stainless steel	Chemical processing; laboratory test; no aeration; no agitation	70	150 (302)	1 d	0.245-0.35 in./yr	89
Type 304 stainless steel	Chemical processing; laboratory test; no aeration; no agitation	50	150 (302)	1 d	0.045 in./yr	89
Type 304 stainless steel	Chemical processing; laboratory test; no aeration; no agitation	30	150 (302)	1 d	0.025 in./yr	89
Type 304 stainless steel	Research	~15.7	24 (75)	70 d	<0.0001 in./yr	89
Type 304 stainless steel	Chemical (distillation) processing; field or pilot plant test; no aeration; rapid agitation. Reboiler	2.5	91 (195)	4.5 d	<0.0001 in./yr	89
Type 304 stainless steel	Chemical (distillation) processing; field or pilot plant test; no aeration; rapid agitation. With carbon over the standard maximum. Reboiler	2.5	91 (195)	4.5 d	0.0002 in./yr	89
Type 304 stainless steel	...	10	21 (70)	...	Very good	121
Type 304 stainless steel	...	Saturated	Boiling	...	Good	121
Type 304 stainless steel	Chemical (boric-acid manufacture) processing; field or pilot plant test; slight to moderate aeration; rapid agitation. Plus mixed liquor, sulfates, sulfites, borax, boric acid. Severe pitting (maximum depth of pits over 0.010 in.). Crevice attack (tendency to concentration-cell corrosion)	...	54-104 (130-220)	45 d	0.0048 in./yr	89
Type 304 stainless steel	Chemical (boric-acid manufacture) processing; field or pilot plant test; slight to moderate aeration; rapid agitation. With carbon over the standard maximum. Plus mixed liquor, sulfates, sulfites, borax, boric acid. Moderate pitting (maximum depth of pits from 0.005 to 0.010 in.)	...	54-104 (130-220)	45 d	0.001 in./yr	89
Type 304 stainless steel	Chemical processing; strong aeration; no agitation. Plus solution saturated with sulfur dioxide; boric acid. Crevice attack (tendency to concentration-cell corrosion)	...	60 (140)	31 d	<0.0001 in./yr	89
Type 304 stainless steel	Chemical processing; strong aeration; rapid agitation. Boric acid, sublimed, impurities. Severe pitting (maximum depth of pits over 0.010 in.). Crevice attack (tendency to concentration-cell corrosion)	...	54-104 (130-220)	45 d	0.0047 in./yr	89
Type 304 stainless steel	Chemical processing; strong aeration; rapid agitation. With carbon over the standard maximum. Boric acid, sublimed, impurities. Severe pitting (maximum depth of pits over 0.010 in.). Crevice attack (tendency to concentration-cell corrosion)	...	54-104 (130-220)	45 d	0.002 in./yr	89
Type 316 stainless steel	Chemical processing; strong aeration; rapid agitation. Boric acid, sublimed, impurities. Slight pitting (maximum depth of pits from incipient to 0.005 in.)	...	54-104 (130-220)	45 d	0.0047 in./yr	89
Type 316 stainless steel	Chemical processing; strong aeration; no agitation. Plus solution saturated with sulfur dioxide; boric acid. Crevice attack (tendency to concentration-cell corrosion)	...	60 (140)	31 d	<0.0001 in./yr	89

(Continued)

Corrosion Behavior of Various Metals and Alloys in Boric Acid (Continued)

Material	Condition, other factors, comments	Concentration, %	Temperature, °C (°F)	Duration	Corrosion rate, mm/yr (mils/yr) or other	Ref
Type 316 stainless steel	Chemical (boric-acid manufacture) processing; field or pilot plant test; slight to moderate aeration; rapid agitation. Plus mixed liquor, sulfates, sulfites, borax, boric acid	...	54-104 (130-220)	45 d	0.0001 in./yr	89
Type 316 stainless steel	Chemical (distillation) processing; field or pilot plant test; no aeration; rapid agitation. Reboiler	2.5	91 (195)	4.5 d	0.0001 in./yr	89
Type 316 stainless steel	...	10	21 (70)	...	Very good	121
Type 316 stainless steel	...	Saturated	Boiling	...	Good	121
Type 410 stainless steel	...	10	21 (70)	...	Good	121
Type 410 stainless steel	...	Saturated	Boiling	...	Fair	121
Type 410 stainless steel	...	...	Room	...	Unattacked	121
Type 430 stainless steel	...	10	21 (70)	...	Good	121
Type 430 stainless steel	...	Saturated	Boiling	...	Fair	121
Aluminum						
Aluminum (99.0-99.5%)	Solution	...	...	...	Satisfactory	92
Aluminum-manganese alloys	Solution	...	...	...	Satisfactory	92
Coppers						
70-30 cupronickel	...	...	...	...	Suitable	93
90-10 cupronickel	...	...	...	...	Suitable	93
Admiralty brass	...	...	...	...	Suitable	93
Aluminum bronze	...	...	...	...	Suitable	93
Ampco 8, aluminum bronze	Generally suitable	...	...	...	<0.05 (<2)	96
Architectural bronze	(a)	...	...	...	Good	93
Brass	...	...	...	...	Suitable	93
Cartridge brass	(a)	...	...	...	Good	93
Commercial bronze	...	...	...	...	Suitable	93
Electrolytic copper	...	...	...	...	Suitable	93
Free-cutting brass	(a)	...	...	...	Good	93
Muntz metal	(a)	...	...	...	Good	93
Naval brass	(a)	...	...	...	Good	93
Nickel silver	...	18	...	...	Suitable	93
Phosphor copper	...	...	...	...	Suitable	93
Phosphor bronze	5% Sn	...	...	...	Suitable	93
Phosphor bronze	8% Sn	...	...	...	Suitable	93
Red brass	...	...	...	...	Suitable	93
Silicon bronze	Low	...	...	...	Suitable	93
Silicon bronze	High	...	...	...	Suitable	93
Titanium						
Titanium	...	Saturated	Room	...	nil	90
Titanium	...	10	Boiling	...	nil	90
Lead, tin, and zinc						
Lead	Practically resistant; Pb recommended for use	10-100	24-149 (75-300)	...	<500 μm/yr (<20)	95
Tin	...	...	20 (68)	...	Resistant	94
Tin	...	...	60 (140)	...	Resistant	94
Tin	...	...	100 (212)	...	Resistant	94
Noble metals						
Silver	Salt	...	Boiling	...	<0.05 (<2)	4
Others						
Magnesium	...	1-5	Room	...	Unsuitable	119

(a) May be considered in place of a copper metal when some property, other than corrosion resistance, governs its use.

Bromine

Bromine, Br, is a chemical nonmetallic element. It is a dark red liquid that volatilizes at room temperature into a brown irritating vapor. Bromine is a member of the halogen series and has a boiling point of 58.78 °C. It is chemically reactive, has bleaching action, and is used in plastics, organic synthesis, and to produce dibromide ethylene.

Material Summaries

The following material summaries were compiled from a survey of the available literature. Inclusion of a material description under a given environment does not imply that it is the most appropriate material for corrosion service in that environment. Likewise, exclusion of a given material does not imply that it is not suitable for corrosion service applications in that environment.

Magnesium resists corrosion from dry bromine at room or slightly elevated temperatures. Even if it contains 0.02% water, dry bromine causes no more attack at its boiling point (58 °C, or 136 °F) than at room temperature. Some attack is observed in the presence of a small amount of water. Magnesium is severely attacked by wet bromine below the dew point of any aqueous phase.

Nickel. In laboratory tests at room temperature, bromine commercially dried with sulfuric acid corroded Nickel 200 at a rate of 0.04 mils/yr. The corrosion rate of Nickel 200 increased to 2.5 mils/yr when bromine was saturated with water. Bromine vapor did not affect the material.

Niobium is an excellent material for equipment to handle liquid bromine, because it resists corrosion even when water saturated. Niobium is unaffected by bromine at 100 °C (212 °F).

Platinum is not resistant to either dry or wet bromine.

Palladium is attacked by bromine when air is present.

Ruthenium. Saturated aqueous solutions of bromine attack ruthenium slowly.

Silver is resistant to dry bromine.

Tantalum is not attacked by bromine at ordinary temperatures. It is inert up to 150 °C (300 °F). Bromine does attack tantalum at 300 °C (570 °F). No effect is observed when the bromine is dissolved in solutions of salt or acid.

Tin is readily attacked by bromine at room temperature.

Titanium may be used to handle wet bromine gas environments. Water content is critical because rapid, exothermic, halogenation reactions may occur in a dry environment. The temperature and gas flow rate determine the water content. Due to the low water solubility of liquid bromine, titanium alloys cannot be rendered passive. In bromide solutions, the susceptibility of titanium alloys to crevice corrosion should be considered.

Zirconium is quite resistant to pitting corrosion in bromide solutions.

Corrosion Behavior of Various Metals and Alloys in Bromine

Material	Condition, other factors, comments	Concentration, %	Temperature, °C (°F)	Duration	Corrosion rate, mm/yr (mils/yr) or other	Ref
Coppers						
70-30 cupronickel	Dry	...	...	...	Suitable	93
70-30 cupronickel	Moist. (a)	...	...	...	Good	93
90-10 cupronickel	Dry	...	...	...	Suitable	93
90-10 cupronickel	Moist. (a)	...	...	...	Good	93
Admiralty brass	Dry	...	...	...	Suitable	93
Admiralty brass	Moist	...	...	...	Fair	93
Aluminum bronze	Dry	...	...	...	Suitable	93
Aluminum bronze	Moist. (a)	...	...	...	Good	93
Architectural bronze	Dry	...	...	...	Suitable	93
Architectural bronze	Moist	...	...	...	Not suitable	93
Brass	Dry	...	...	...	Suitable	93
Brass	Moist	...	...	...	Fair	93
Cartridge brass	Dry	...	...	...	Suitable	93
Cartridge brass	Moist	...	...	...	Not suitable	93
Commercial bronze	Dry	...	...	...	Suitable	93
Commercial bronze	Moist. (a)	...	...	...	Good	93
Electrolytic copper	Dry	...	...	...	Suitable	93
Electrolytic copper	Moist. (a)	...	...	...	Good	93
Free-cutting brass	Dry	...	...	...	Suitable	93
Free-cutting brass	Moist	...	...	...	Not suitable	93
Muntz metal	Dry	...	...	...	Suitable	93
Muntz metal	Moist	...	...	...	Not suitable	93
Naval brass	Dry	...	...	...	Suitable	93
Naval brass	Moist	...	...	...	Not suitable	93

(Continued)

Corrosion Behavior of Various Metals and Alloys in Bromine (Continued)

Material	Condition, other factors, comments	Concentration, %	Temperature, °C (°F)	Duration	Corrosion rate, mm/yr (mils/yr) or other	Ref
Nickel silver	Dry	18	...	...	Suitable	93
Nickel silver	Moist. (a)	18	...	...	Good	93
Phosphor bronze	5% Sn. Dry	...	...	...	Suitable	93
Phosphor bronze	8% Sn. Dry	...	...	...	Suitable	93
Phosphor bronze	5% Sn. Moist. (a)	...	...	...	Good	93
Phosphor bronze	8% Sn. Moist. (a)	...	...	...	Good	93
Phosphor copper	Dry	...	...	...	Suitable	93
Phosphor copper	Moist. (a)	...	...	...	Good	93
Red brass	Dry	...	...	..	Suitable	93
Red brass	Moist. (a)	...	...	...	Good	93
Silicon bronze	Low. Dry	...	...	...	Suitable	93
Silicon bronze	High. Dry	...	...	...	Suitable	93
Silicon bronze	Low. Moist. (a)	...	...	...	Good	93
Silicon bronze	High. Moist. (a)	...	...	...	Good	93
Titanium						
Titanium	...	Liquid	30 (86)	...	Rapid attack	90
Titanium	Moist	Vapor	30 (86)	...	<0.003 (<0.12)	90
Titanium	Gas, dry	...	21 (70)	...	Dissolves rapidly	90
Titanium	Water solution	...	Room	...	nil	90
Titanium	In methyl alcohol. Cracking possible	0.05	60 (140)	...	0.03 (1.2)	90
Zirconium						
Zr702	Pitting	100-liquid	20 (70)	...	<0.25 (<10)	15
Zr705	Pitting	100-liquid	20 (70)	...	0.5-1.3 (20-50)	15
Zr705	Pitting	Vapor	20 (70)	...	>1.3 (>50)	15

(a) May be considered in place of a copper metal when some property, other than corrosion resistance, governs its use.

Butyl Alcohol

Butyl alcohol, also known as butanol, exists in three isomeric alcohols that are toxic and soluble in most organic liquids. *n*-butyl alcohol, $CH_3(CH_2)_2CH_2OH$, also known as 1-butanol, propyl carbinol, and *prim*-butyl alcohol, is a colorless liquid with a boiling point of 117.71 °C. It is used in manufacturing perfumes and lacquers. *sec*-butyl alcohol, $CH_3CH_2CHOHCH_3$, also known as 2-butanol, ethyl-methyl carbinol, butylene hydrate, and 2-hydroxy butane, is a colorless liquid with a boiling point of 99.5 °C. It is used in the preparation of fruit essence. *tert*-butyl alcohol, $(CH_3)_3COH$, also known as 2-methyl 2-propanol and trimethyl carbinol, is a colorless liquid with a boiling point of 82.8 °C.

Material Summaries

The following material summaries were compiled from a survey of the available literature. Inclusion of a material description under a given environment does not imply that it is the most appropriate material for corrosion service in that environment. Likewise, exclusion of a given material does not imply that it is not suitable for corrosion service applications in that environment.

Aluminum. A water-cooled tube of aluminum alloy 3003 was found to resist vapors from *n*-butyl alcohol during laboratory tests. In other tests at 204 °C (400 °F), aluminum alloy 3003 was resistant to *n*-butyl alcohol with 5% water, but was corroded by a solution with 1.5% water. At the same temperature, secondary and tertiary butyl alcohols with 0.3% water did not corrode aluminum alloy 3003. Pure butyl alcohol and butyl alcohol-water mixtures have been handled by aluminum alloy equipment such as decanters, tanks, and heat exchangers.

Additional Reading

P.L. De Anna, The Effects of Water and Chloride Ions on the Electrochemical Behaviour of Iron and 304L Stainless Steel in Alcohols, *Corros. Sci.*, 25(1), 43-53, 1985. MetAbs No. 85-350967. **Abstract:** The electrochemical behavior of pure iron and 304L stainless steel in protic organic media has been characterized by determination of current-potential potentiodynamic curves. The media studied were methyl, ethyl, isopropyl, n-butyl and 2-chloroethyl alcohols. The influence of water and chloride ion concentration on the cathodic and anodic electrochemical reactions has been investigated.

V.K. Singh and V.B. Singh, Electrochemical Behavior of AISI 304 Stainless Steel: Corrosion, Passivity, and Pitting in Alcohols + H_2SO_4 Mixtures, *Corrosion*, 43(12), 756-762, 1987. MetAbs No. 88-350656. **Abstract:** The electrochemical behavior of austenitic AISI 304 stainless steel in alcoholic solutions (ethanol, isopropanol, and t-butanol) containing different concentrations of sulfuric acid (0.001 to 1.0M) has been investigated using potentiostatic and potentiodynamic techniques.

Corrosion Behavior of Various Metals and Alloys in Butyl Alcohol

Material	Condition, other factors, comments	Concentration, %	Temperature, °C (°F)	Duration	Corrosion rate, mm/yr (mils/yr) or other	Ref
Stainless steels						
AM-363 stainless steel	...	...	Room	...	Unattacked	120
Type 304 stainless steel	Chemical processing; field or pilot plant test; no aeration; slight to moderate agitation. Plus 95% water	5	90 (195)	39 d	0.0018 in./yr	89
Type 304 stainless steel	Chemical processing; field or pilot plant test; no aeration; slight to moderate agitation. Plus 90% water, 5% methyl and ethyl alcohol	5	90 (195)	39 d	0.00013 in./yr	89
Type 304 stainless steel	Chemical processing; no aeration; rapid agitation. Plus 8% higher alcohols, 0.5% carbonyls	9	129 (265)	243 d	<0.0001 in./yr	89
Type 304 stainless steel	Chemical processing; field or pilot plant test; no aeration; rapid agitation. Plus 8.5-9% water, 8% higher alcohols, 1-1.5% carbonyls	82	121 (250)	243 d	<0.0001 in./yr	89
Type 304 stainless steel	Pharmaceutical processing; strong aeration; no agitation. Plus 3-4% hydrochloric acid. Slight pitting: maximum depth of pits from incipient to 0.005 in.; crevice attack (tendency to concentration-cell corrosion)	96-97	Room	18 d	0.0257 in./yr	89
Type 304 stainless steel	Chemical processing; field or pilot plant test; no aeration; rapid agitation. Plus 0.3% carbonyls, esters, trace of heavy alcohols	99	129 (265)	277 d	0.00035 in./yr	89
Type 316 stainless steel	Chemical processing; field or pilot plant test; no aeration; slight to moderate agitation. Plus 90% water, 5% methyl and ethyl alcohol	5	90 (195)	39 d	<0.0001 in./yr	89
Type 316 stainless steel	Chemical processing; field or pilot plant test; no aeration; slight to moderate agitation. Plus 95% water	5	90 (195)	39 d	0.003 in./yr	89
Type 316 stainless steel	Pharmaceutical processing; strong aeration; no agitation. Plus 3-4% hydrochloric acid. Moderate pitting: maximum depth of pits from 0.005 to 0.010 in.; crevice attack (tendency to concentration-cell corrosion)	96-97	Room	18 d	0.0149 in./yr	89
Type 317 stainless steel	Chemical processing; field or pilot plant test; no aeration; slight to moderate agitation. Plus 90% water, 5% methyl and ethyl alcohol	5	90 (195)	39 d	nil	89
Type 317 stainless steel	Chemical processing; field or pilot plant test; no aeration; slight to moderate agitation. Plus 95% water	5	90 (195)	39 d	0.002 in./yr	89
Aluminum						
Aluminum-manganese alloys	Liquid	...	20-boiling point (68-boiling point)	...	Restricted applications	92
Coppers						
70-30 cupronickel	...	...	...	...	Suitable	93
90-10 cupronickel	...	...	...	...	Suitable	93
Admiralty brass	...	...	...	...	Suitable	93
Aluminum bronze	...	...	...	...	Suitable	93
Architectural bronze	...	...	...	...	Suitable	93
Brass	...	...	...	...	Suitable	93
Cartridge brass	...	...	...	...	Suitable	93
Commercial bronze	...	...	...	...	Suitable	93
Electrolytic copper	...	...	...	...	Suitable	93
Free-cutting brass	...	...	...	...	Suitable	93
Muntz metal	...	...	...	...	Suitable	93
Naval brass	...	...	...	...	Suitable	93
Nickel silver	...	18	...	...	Suitable	93
Phosphor bronze	5% Sn	...	...	...	Suitable	93
Phosphor bronze	8% Sn	...	...	...	Suitable	93
Phosphor copper	...	...	...	...	Suitable	93
Platinum	...	Pure	Boiling	...	<0.05 (<2)	6
Red brass	...	...	...	...	Suitable	93
Silicon bronze	Low	...	...	...	Suitable	93
Silicon bronze	High	...	...	...	Suitable	93

(Continued)

Corrosion Behavior of Various Metals and Alloys in Butyl Alcohol (Continued)

Material	Condition, other factors, comments	Concentration, %	Temperature, °C (°F)	Duration	Corrosion rate, mm/yr (mils/yr) or other	Ref
Noble metals						
Silver	...	Pure	Boiling	...	<0.05 (<2)	10
Others						
Magnesium	...	100	Room	...	Resistant	119

Butane

Butane, $CH_3(CH_2)_2CH_3$, also known as n-butane and methyl-ethyl methane, is a colorless gas that occurs in natural gas and is obtained by cracking petroleum. It is used as a refrigerant and as a fuel.

Material Summaries

The following material summaries were compiled from a survey of the available literature. Inclusion of a material description under a given environment does not imply that it is the most appropriate material for corrosion service in that environment. Likewise, exclusion of a given material does not imply that it is not suitable for corrosion service applications in that environment.

Carbon Steel. Butane is most often transported and stored in carbon steel piping and equipment.

Aluminum. Butane has been successfully piped in aluminum alloy tubing.

Corrosion Behavior of Various Metals and Alloys in Butane

Material	Condition, other factors, comments	Concentration, %	Temperature, °C (°F)	Duration	Corrosion rate, mm/yr (mils/yr) or other	Ref
Stainless steels						
Type 304 stainless steel	Chemical processing; field or pilot plant test; slight to moderate aeration; slight to moderate agitation. Plus 0.5% water, 0.5% acetic acid, 1% isobutane	98	29 (185)	276 d	nil	89
Type 304 stainless steel	Chemical processing; field or pilot plant test; slight to moderate aeration; slight to moderate agitation. Plus 0.5% water, 0.5% acetic acid, 1% isobutane	98	29 (185)	276 d	0.0003 in./yr	89
Type 304 stainless steel	Rayon processing; field or pilot plant test; no aeration; rapid agitation. Plus carbon dioxide, water, esters, ketones, 1% acetic acid	98	30-45 (86-113)	363 d	<0.0001 in./yr	89
Type 304 stainless steel	Chemical processing; field or pilot plant test; slight to moderate aeration; no agitation. Plus 3% water, 22% carbonyls and esters, 10% acetic acid	65	52 (125)	108 d	nil	89
Type 304 stainless steel	Rayon processing; field or pilot plant test; no aeration; slight to moderate agitation. Plus alcohols, ketones, esters, acetone, methyl acetate, methylethyl ketone, ethyl acetate, water	60	55-69 (131-156)	360 d	<0.0001 in./yr	89
Type 304 stainless steel	Rayon processing; field or pilot plant test; no aeration; slight to moderate agitation. Plus alcohols, ketones, esters, acetone, methyl acetate, methylethyl ketone, ethyl acetate, water	60	55-69 (131-156)	360 d	0.0002 in./yr	89
Type 304 stainless steel	Rayon processing; field or pilot plant test; no aeration; slight to moderate agitation. Plus alcohols, ketones, esters, acetone, methyl acetate, methylethyl ketone, ethyl acetate, water	60	55-69 (131-156)	360 d	0.0001 in./yr	89
Type 304 stainless steel	Chemical processing; field or pilot plant test; slight to moderate aeration; slight to moderate agitation. Plus esters and water, mainly acetic acids, 65% nitrogen. Severe pitting (maximum depth of pits over 0.010 in.)	20	171 (340)	108 d	0.003 in./yr	89
Type 304 stainless steel	Chemical processing; field or pilot plant test; slight to moderate aeration; slight to moderate agitation. Plus light hydrocarbons, 0.5% oxygen, 75% nitrogen, acids and esters remainder	20	52 (125)	108 d	nil	89

(Continued)

Corrosion Behavior of Various Metals and Alloys in Butane (Continued)

Material	Condition, other factors, comments	Concen-tration, %	Temperature, °C (°F)	Duration	Corrosion rate, mm/yr (mils/yr) or other	Ref
Type 304 stainless steel	Rayon processing; field or pilot plant test; no aeration; rapid agitation. Plus trace aldehydes, esters, ketones, water, nitrogen and carbon dioxide	98	30-45 (86-113)	363 d	0.0001 in./yr	89
Type 304 stainless steel	Petroleum processing; field or pilot plant test; no aeration; no agitation. Plus trace of water ("DBS" debutanizer bottom), sulfuric acid, dibutyl sulfite, butylene. Moderate pitting (maximum depth of pits over 0.010 in.)	...	121 (250)	52 d	0.006 in./yr	89
Type 316 stainless steel	Chemical processing; field or pilot plant test; slight to moderate aeration; slight to moderate agitation. Plus 0.5% water, 0.5% acetic acid, 1% isobutane	98	29 (185)	276 d	nil	89
Type 316 stainless steel	Chemical processing; field or pilot plant test; slight to moderate aeration; slight to moderate agitation. Plus 0.5% water, 0.5% acetic acid, 1% isobutane	98	29 (185)	276 d	0.00015 in./yr	89
Type 316 stainless steel	Rayon processing; field or pilot plant test; no aeration; rapid agitation. Plus carbon dioxide, water, esters, ketones, 1% acetic acid	98	30-45 (86-113)	363 d	<0.0001 in./yr	89
Type 316 stainless steel	Chemical processing; field or pilot plant test; slight to moderate aeration; no agitation. Plus 3% water, 22% carbonyls and esters, 10% acetic acid	65	52 (125)	108 d	nil	89
Type 316 stainless steel	Chemical processing; field or pilot plant test; slight to moderate aeration; no agitation. Low-carbon grade (0.03% C max). Plus 3% water, 22% carbonyls and esters, 10% acetic acid	65	52 (125)	108 d	nil	89
Type 316 stainless steel	Rayon processing; field or pilot plant test; no aeration; slight to moderate agitation. Plus alcohols, ketones, esters, acetone, methyl acetate, methylethyl ketone, ethyl acetate, water	60	55-69 (131-156)	360 d	<0.0001 in./yr	89
Type 316 stainless steel	Chemical processing; strong aeration; rapid agitation. Plus 1% carbon dioxide, 2% water, 4% acetic acid, 10% nitrogen, 27% various organics	56	175 (347)	210 d	0.0003 in./yr	89
Type 316 stainless steel	Chemical processing; field or pilot plant test; slight to moderate aeration; slight to moderate agitation. Plus esters and water, mainly acetic acids, 65% nitrogen. Slight pitting (maximum depth of pits from incipient to 0.005 in.)	20	171 (340)	108 d	0.0008 in./yr	89
Type 316 stainless steel	Chemical processing; field or pilot plant test; slight to moderate aeration; slight to moderate agitation. Sensitized specimens. Plus esters and water, mainly acetic acids, 65% nitrogen. Moderate pitting (maximum depth of pits from 0.005 to 0.010 in.)	20	171 (340)	108 d	0.003 in./yr	89
Type 316 stainless steel	Chemical processing; field or pilot plant test; slight to moderate aeration; slight to moderate agitation. Plus light hydrocarbons, 0.5% oxygen, 75% nitrogen, acids and esters remainder	20	52 (125)	108 d	nil	89
Type 316 stainless steel	Chemical processing; field or pilot plant test; slight to moderate aeration; slight to moderate agitation. Low-carbon grade (0.03% C max). Plus light hydrocarbons, 0.5% oxygen, 75% nitrogen, acids and esters remainder	20	52 (125)	108 d	nil	89
Type 316 stainless steel	Rayon processing; field or pilot plant test; no aeration; rapid agitation. Plus trace aldehydes, esters, ketones, water, nitrogen and carbon dioxide	98	30-45 (86-113)	363 d	0.0001 in./yr	89
Type 316 stainless steel	Petroleum processing; field or pilot plant test; no aeration; no agitation. Plus trace of water ("DBS" debutanizer bottom), sulfuric acid, dibutyl sulfite, butylene. Slight pitting (maximum depth of pits from incipient to 0.005 in.)	...	121 (250)	52 d	0.002 in./yr	89
Coppers						
70-30 cupronickel	...	...	...	...	Suitable	93
90-10 cupronickel	...	...	...	...	Suitable	93
Admiralty brass	...	...	...	...	Suitable	93
Aluminum bronze	...	...	...	...	Suitable	93

(Continued)

Corrosion Behavior of Various Metals and Alloys in Butane (Continued)

Material	Condition, other factors, comments	Concentration, %	Temperature, °C (°F)	Duration	Corrosion rate, mm/yr (mils/yr) or other	Ref
Ampco 8, aluminum bronze	Generally suitable	...	...	...	<0.05 (<2)	96
Architectural bronze	...	...	...	...	Suitable	93
Brass	...	...	...	...	Suitable	93
Cartridge brass	...	...	...	...	Suitable	93
Commercial bronze	...	...	...	...	Suitable	93
Electrolytic copper	...	...	...	...	Suitable	93
Free-cutting brass	...	...	...	...	Suitable	93
Muntz metal	...	...	...	...	Suitable	93
Naval brass	...	...	...	...	Suitable	93
Nickel silver	...	18	...	...	Suitable	93
Phosphor bronze	5% Sn	...	...	...	Suitable	93
Phosphor bronze	8% Sn	...	...	...	Suitable	93
Phosphor copper	...	...	...	...	Suitable	93
Red brass	...	...	...	...	Suitable	93
Silicon bronze	Low	...	...	...	Suitable	93
Silicon bronze	High	...	...	...	Suitable	93
Heat- and corrosion-resistant alloys						
Alloy 825	Chemical processing; strong aeration; rapid agitation. Plus 1% carbon dioxide, 2% water, 4% acetic acid, 10% nitrogen, 27% various organics	56	175 (347)	210 d	0.0002 in./yr	89
Carpenter 20	Chemical processing; strong aeration; rapid agitation. Plus 1% carbon dioxide, 2% water, 4% acetic acid, 10% nitrogen, 27% various organics	56	175 (347)	210 d	0.0003 in./yr	89

Cadmium Sulfate

Cadmium sulfate, $CdSO_4$, is an efflorescent crystalline solid that is soluble in water. It is used as an antiseptic, in the treatment of venereal diseases and rheumatism, and to detect the presence of hydrogen sulfide.

Material Summaries

The following material summaries were compiled from a survey of the available literature. Inclusion of a material description under a given environment does not imply that it is the most appropriate material for corrosion service in that environment. Likewise, exclusion of a given material does not imply that it is not suitable for corrosion service applications in that environment.

Aluminum. Laboratory tests conducted at 100% relative humidity and ambient temperature showed aluminum alloys 3003 and 5154 to be resistant to solid cadmium sulfate. Aluminum alloy 3003 suffered mild attack by an aqueous solution of 1 to 15% cadmium sulfate at ambient temperature. Cadmium sulfate has been handled in aluminum alloy equipment such as filter press plates, pipes, and tanks.

Corrosion Behavior of Various Metals and Alloys in Cadmium Sulfate

Material	Condition, other factors, comments	Concentration, %	Temperature, °C (°F)	Duration	Corrosion rate, mm/yr (mils/yr) or other	Ref
Lead	Negligible corrosion; Pb recommended for use	10-30	24-100 (75-212)	...	<50 μm/yr (<2)	95
Type 304 stainless steel	Chemical processing; laboratory test; no aeration; no agitation. Alternately immersed	30	100 (212)	1-4 d	0.0005 in./yr	89

Calcium Bromide

Calcium bromide, $CaBr_2$, is a colorless crystalline solid with a melting point of 765 °C. It is deliquescent and is soluble in water and absolute alcohol. Calcium bromide is used in medicine. Calcium bromide (hydrated), $CaBr_2 \cdot 3H_2O$, has a melting point of 80.5 °C.

Corrosion Behavior of Various Metals and Alloys in Calcium Bromide

Material	Condition, other factors, comments	Concentration, %	Temperature, °C (°F)	Duration	Corrosion rate, mm/yr (mils/yr) or other	Ref
Steels						
Carbon steel	Uninhibited brine, 1000 psi pressure. Plus 20 wt% ZnBr2	10 wt%	176 (350)	7 d	3.59 (141.3)	180
Carbon steel	Uninhibited brine, 1000 psi pressure. Plus 30 wt% ZnBr2	10 wt%	176 (350)	7 d	5.14 (202.5)	180
Carbon steel	Uninhibited brine, 1000 psi pressure. Plus 20 wt% ZnBr2	20 wt%	176 (350)	7 d	1.97 (77.6)	180
Carbon steel	Uninhibited brine, 1000 psi pressure. Plus 30 wt% ZnBr2, 5 wt% CaCl2	20	176 (350)	7 d	2.06 (81.4)	180
Carbon steel	Uninhibited brine, 1000 psi pressure. Plus 20 wt% ZnBr2, 5 wt% CaCl2	10	176 (350)	7 d	1.97 (77.7)	180
Carbon steel	Uninhibited brine, 1000 psi pressure. Plus 20 wt% ZnBr2, 5 wt% CaCl2	20	176 (350)	7 d	1.33 (52.4)	180
Carbon steel	Uninhibited brine, 1000 psi pressure. Plus 30 wt% ZnBr2, 5 wt% CaCl2	10	176 (350)	7 d	3.009 (118.5)	180
Carbon steel	Uninhibited brine, 1000 psi pressure. Plus 30 wt% ZnBr2	20 wt%	176 (350)	7 d	2.875 (113.2)	180
Carbon steel	Uninhibited brine, 1000 psi pressure. Plus 30 wt% ZnBr2	10 wt%	176 (350)	14 d	2.908 (114.5)	180
Carbon steel	Uninhibited brine, 1000 psi pressure. Plus 20 wt% ZnBr2	10 wt%	176 (350)	14 d	1.32 (52.0)	180
Carbon steel	Uninhibited brine, 1000 psi pressure. Plus 20 wt% ZnBr2	20 wt%	176 (350)	14 d	1.181 (46.5)	180
Carbon steel	Uninhibited brine, 1000 psi pressure. Plus 30 wt% ZnBr2	20 wt%	176 (350)	14 d	1.49 (58.7)	180
Carbon steel	Uninhibited brine, 1000 psi pressure. Plus 20 wt% ZnBr2, 5 wt% CaCl2	10	176 (350)	14 d	1.087 (42.8)	180
Carbon steel	Uninhibited brine, 1000 psi pressure. Plus 20 wt% ZnBr2, 5 wt% CaCl2	20	176 (350)	14 d	6.55 (25.8)	180
Carbon steel	Uninhibited brine, 1000 psi pressure. Plus 30 wt% ZnBr2, 5 wt% CaCl2	10	176 (350)	14 d	1.73 (68.2)	180
Carbon steel	Uninhibited brine, 1000 psi pressure. Plus 30 wt% ZnBr2, 5 wt% CaCl2	20	176 (350)	14 d	1.13 (44.7)	180
Type 304 stainless steel	Metal processing (air dehumidification); field or pilot plant test; strong aeration; rapid agitation. With carbon over the standard maximum. Plus 41.97% water, 11.53% lithium bromide, 8.58% calcium chloride, specific gravity 1.56 (under spray nozzles). Moderate pitting: maximum depth of pits from 0.005 to 0.010 in.; crevice attack (tendency to concentration-cell corrosion)	37.97	49 (120)	38 d	0.0009 in./yr	89
Type 317 stainless steel	Metal processing (air dehumidification); field or pilot plant test; strong aeration; rapid agitation. With carbon over the standard maximum. Plus 41.97% water, 11.53% lithium bromide, 8.58% calcium chloride, specific gravity 1.56 (under spray nozzles). Severe pitting: maximum depth of pits over 0.010 in.; crevice attack (tendency to concentration-cell corrosion)	37.97	49 (120)	38 d	0.0014 in./yr	89
Zirconium						
Zr702	...	100	100 (212)	...	<0.05 (<2)	15

Corrosion Test Results for Carbon Steel in Different Densities of Calcium Bromide/Zinc Bromide Brines at 21 °C (70 °F)

Density, lb/gal	Corrosion rate, mils/yr				
	1 day	4 days	7 days	14 days	30 days
14.2	0.9	0.7	0.3	0.2	0.3
15.2	2.2	0.6	0.4	0.2	0.1
15.8	0.9	0.5	0.4	0.2	0.1
16.4	2.2	0.6	0.5	0.3	0.1
17.0	2.7	0.6	0.6	0.2	0.1
18.0	2.7	0.5	0.6	0.3	0.1
19.2	2.7	0.7	0.3	0.3	0.1

Note: The 14.2 lb/gal density is $CaBr_2$, and the 19.2 lb/gal density is $ZnBr_2/CaBr_2$. The 19.2 lb/gal brine contained a film-forming amine inhibitor.
Source: Dow Chemical USA

Corrosion Test Results for Carbon Steel in Different Densities of Calcium Bromide/Zinc Bromide Brines at 65 °C (150 °F)

Density, lb/gal	Corrosion rate, mils/yr				
	1 day	4 days	7 days	14 days	30 days
14.2	2.7	2.1	1.7	1.3	1.0
15.2	2.7	0.8	0.5	0.4	0.2
15.8	3.1	0.8	0.7	0.4	0.1
16.4	3.1	0.8	1.1	0.6	0.2
17.0	5.3	0.9	1.0	1.4	0.3
18.0	8.0	1.1	0.8	0.7	0.4
19.2	4.0	1.7	1.7	2.4	1.0

Note: The 14.2 lb/gal density is $CaBr_2$, and the 19.2 lb/gal density is $ZnBr_2/CaBr_2$. The 19.2 lb/gal brine contained a film-forming amine inhibitor.
Source: Dow Chemical USA

Corrosion Test Results for Carbon Steel in Different Densities of Calcium Bromide/Zinc Bromide Brines at 121 °C (250 °F)

Density, lb/gal	Corrosion rate, mils/yr				
	1 day	4 days	7 days	14 days	30 days
14.2	12.0	5.0	2.8	2.3	0.4
15.2	6.7	3.4	7.9	6.4	6.8
15.8	6.2	4.0	4.8	2.8	6.7
16.4	9.8	6.1	9.4	4.2	12.5
17.0	30.2	8.3	8.8	8.3	13.4
18.0	38.7	76.0	...	21.2	50.7
19.2	94.7	102.0	35.0	45.0	66.9

Note: The 14.2 lb/gal density is $CaBr_2$, and the 19.2 lb/gal density is $ZnBr_2/CaBr_2$. The 19.2 lb/gal brine contained a film-forming amine inhibitor.
Source: Dow Chemical USA

Calcium Chloride

Calcium chloride, $CaCl_2$, is colorless deliquescent solid that is soluble in water and ethanol. It is formed from the reaction of calcium carbonate and hydrochloric acid or calcium hydroxide and ammonium chloride. It is used in medicine, as an antifreeze, and as a coagulant.

Material Summaries

The following material summaries were compiled from a survey of the available literature. Inclusion of a material description under a given environment does not imply that it is the most appropriate material for corrosion service in that environment. Likewise, exclusion of a given material does not imply that it is not suitable for corrosion service applications in that environment.

Aluminum. Under laboratory conditions of 100% relative humidity and ambient temperature, solid calcium chloride caused moderate attack (around 6 mils/yr) on aluminum alloys 3003, 5154, and 6061. Aqueous solutions of concentrations up to 45% caused mild attack with evidence of pitting in other tests at ambient temperature. The addition of sodium dichromate can inhibit the corrosive action of calcium chloride. Aluminum alloy equipment has been used to handle inhibited calcium chloride refrigeration brines. Calcium chloride solutions have been controlled with valves of aluminum alloy 356.0.

Additional Reading

C. Andrade and C.L. Page, Pore Solution Chemistry and Corrosion in Hydrated Cement Systems Containing Chloride Salts: A Study of Cation Specific Effects, *Br. Corros. J.*, *21*(1), 49-53, 1986. MetAbs No. 86-351187. **Abstract:** The free chloride and hydroxyl ion concentrations of the pore electrolyte phase present in mature, hydrated cement pastes containing equivalent quantities of chloride ion, introduced into the mix water as NaCl or $CaCl_2$, have been determined for two commercial cements. The corrosion rates of mild steel electrodes embedded in these materials have also been monitored by the method of linear polarization.

H. Farzammehr, Ch. Dehghanian, and C.E. Locke, Study of the Effects of Cations on Chloride Caused Corrosion of Steel in Concrete, *Rev. Tech.*, *10*(1), 33-40, 1987. MetAbs No. 87-352824. **Abstract:** There have been differences observed in chloride ion behavior in concrete, depending on the type of associated cation. An electrochemical study has been combined with a pore solution analysis study to determine the effects of cations on chloride-caused corrosion of steel in concrete.

Corrosion Behavior of Various Metals and Alloys in Calcium Chloride

Material	Condition, other factors, comments	Concen- tration, %	Temperature, °C (°F)	Duration	Corrosion rate, mm/yr (mils/yr) or other	Ref
Stainless steels						
Type 304 stainless steel	Dairy processing; field or pilot plant test; no aeration; slight to moderate agitation. Calcium chloride cooling brine. Slight pitting: maximum depth of pits from incipient to 0.005 in.	...	-12 (10)	372 d	0.0001 in./yr	89
Type 304 stainless steel	Chemical processing (air conditioning and refrigeration); field or pilot plant test; strong aeration; rapid agitation. Calcium and magnesium-chloride brine liquors, 50% total chlorides (evaporator). Slight pitting: maximum depth of pits from incipient to 0.005 in.	...	Boiling	26 d	0.0002 in./yr	89
Type 304 stainless steel	...	10	21 (70)	...	Good	121
Type 304 stainless steel	Food processing (air cooling); field or pilot plant test; strong aeration; rapid agitation. Plus 0.0017% sodium bichromate as inhibitor, pH 7-8.5 (in brine-spray air stream, dehumidifier)	21.5	-15 to -16 (3 to 4)	338 d	<0.0001 in./yr	89
Type 304 stainless steel	Food processing; field or pilot plant test; slight to moderate aeration; no agitation. Plus 0.0017% sodium bichromate as inhibitor, pH 7-8.5 (boiling tank, under spray chamber)	21.5	32-107 (90-225)	337 d	<0.0001 in./yr	89
Type 304 stainless steel	Chemical processing (air conditioning and refrigeration); field or pilot plant test; strong aeration; rapid agitation. Calcium, magnesium and sodium-chloride brine in 28% concentration. Moderate pitting: maximum depth of pits from 0.005 to 0.010 in.; crevice attack (tendency to concentration-cell corrosion)	28	71 (160)	31 d	<0.0001 in./yr	89
Type 304 stainless steel	Chemical processing; field or pilot plant test; no aeration; no agitation. Calcium-magnesium-chloride bittern, 8.69% magnesium chloride, 1.06% sodium chloride, specific gravity 1.38 (alternately immersed). Moderate pitting: maximum depth of pits from 0.005 to 0.010 in.; crevice attack (tendency to concentration-cell corrosion)	28.69	79 (175)	130 d	<0.0001 in./yr	89
Type 304 stainless steel	Dairy processing; field or pilot plant test; no aeration; slight to moderate agitation. Cooling brine. Moderate pitting: maximum depth of pits from 0.005 to 0.010 in.; crevice attack (tendency to concentration-cell corrosion)	~30	-12 (10)	355 d	<0.0001 in./yr	89
Type 304 stainless steel	Chemical processing; field or pilot plant test; no aeration; rapid agitation. Plus 1-1.3% sodium chloride, approximately 0.1% calcium hydroxide (evaporator). Slight pitting: maximum depth of pits from incipient to 0.005 in.	~58	165 (330)	31 d	0.002 in./yr	89
Type 316 stainless steel	Chemical processing (air conditioning and refrigeration); field or pilot plant test; strong aeration; rapid agitation. Calcium and magnesium-chloride brine liquors, 50% total chlorides (evaporator). Slight pitting: maximum depth of pits from incipient to 0.005 in.	...	Boiling	26 d	0.0001 in./yr	89
Type 316 stainless steel	Dairy processing; field or pilot plant test; no aeration; slight to moderate agitation. Calcium chloride cooling brine	...	-12 (10)	372 d	0.0001 in./yr	89
Type 316 stainless steel	...	10	21 (70)	...	Good	121
Type 316 stainless steel	Food processing; field or pilot plant test; slight to moderate aeration; no agitation. Plus 0.0017% sodium bichromate as inhibitor, pH 7-8.5 (boiling tank, under spray chamber)	21.5	32-107 (90-225)	337 d	<0.0001 in./yr	89
Type 316 stainless steel	Food processing (air cooling); field or pilot plant test; strong aeration; rapid agitation. Plus 0.0017% sodium bichromate as inhibitor, pH 7-8.5 (in brine-spray air stream, dehumidifier)	21.5	-15 to -16 (3 to 4)	338 d	<0.0001 in./yr	89
Type 316 stainless steel	Chemical processing (air conditioning and refrigeration); field or pilot plant test; strong aeration; rapid agitation. Calcium, magnesium and sodium-chloride brine. Moderate pitting: maximum depth of pits from 0.005 to 0.010 in.; crevice attack (tendency to concentration-cell corrosion)	28	71 (160)	31 d	<0.0001 in./yr	89

(Continued)

Corrosion Behavior of Various Metals and Alloys in Calcium Chloride (Continued)

Material	Condition, other factors, comments	Concentration, %	Temperature, °C (°F)	Duration	Corrosion rate, mm/yr (mils/yr) or other	Ref
Type 316 stainless steel	Chemical processing; field or pilot plant test; no aeration; no agitation. Calcium-magnesium-chloride bittern, 8.69% magnesium chloride, 1.06% sodium chloride, specific gravity 1.38 (alternately immersed). Moderate pitting: maximum depth of pits from 0.005 to 0.010 in.; crevice attack (tendency to concentration-cell corrosion)	28.69	79 (175)	130 d	<0.0001 in./yr	89
Type 316 stainless steel	Dairy processing; field or pilot plant test; no aeration; slight to moderate agitation. Cooling brine. Moderate pitting: maximum depth of pits from 0.005 to 0.010 in.; crevice attack (tendency to concentration-cell corrosion)	~30	-12 (10)	355 d	<0.0001 in./yr	89
Type 316 stainless steel	Chemical processing; field or pilot plant test; no aeration; rapid agitation. Plus 1-1.3% sodium chloride, approximately 0.1% calcium hydroxide (evaporator). Slight pitting: maximum depth of pits from incipient to 0.005 in.	~58	165 (330)	31 d	0.0017 in./yr	89
Type 410 stainless steel	...	...	Room	...	Attacked	121
Type 430 stainless steel	...	10	21 (70)	...	Fair	121
Coppers						
70-30 cupronickel	...	...	...	...	Suitable	93
90-10 cupronickel	...	...	...	...	Suitable	93
Admiralty brass	(a)	...	...	...	Good	93
Aluminum bronze	(a)	...	...	...	Good	93
Architectural bronze	...	...	...	...	Not suitable	93
Brass	(a)	...	...	...	Good	93
Cartridge brass	...	...	...	...	Not suitable	93
Commercial bronze	(a)	...	...	...	Good	93
Electrolytic copper	(a)	...	...	...	Good	93
Free-cutting brass	...	...	...	...	Not suitable	93
Muntz metal	...	...	...	...	Not suitable	93
Naval brass	...	...	...	...	Fair	93
Nickel silver	...	18	...	...	Suitable	93
Phosphor bronze	5% Sn. (a)	...	...	...	Good	93
Phosphor bronze	8% Sn	...	...	...	Suitable	93
Phosphor copper	(a)	...	...	...	Good	93
Red brass	(a)	...	...	...	Good	93
Silicon bronze	Low. (a)	...	...	...	Good	93
Silicon bronze	High. (a)	...	...	...	Good	93
Titanium						
Titanium	Grade 7	62	150 (300)	...	nil	33
Titanium	...	5	100 (212)	...	0.005 (0.2)	90
Titanium	...	10	100 (212)	...	0.007 (0.28)	90
Titanium	...	20	100 (212)	...	0.015 (0.6)	90
Titanium	...	55	104 (219)	...	0.001 (0.04)	90
Titanium	...	60	149 (300)	...	<0.003 (<0.12)	90
Titanium	...	62	154 (309)	...	0.406 (16.24)	90
Titanium	...	73	175 (347)	...	0.80 (32)	90
Titanium	Grade 7	73	177 (350)	...	nil	33
Heat- and corrosion-resistant alloys						
Incoloy 800	Solutions were prepared with reagent-grade chemicals. Test specimens were cold-rolled, annealed sheet, 2.84 mm (0.112 in.) thick. Pitting occurred after 42 d	5	80 (176)	42 d	<0.003 (<0.1)	44
Inconel 601	Pitting attack	5	80 (176)	30 d	0.002 (0.1)	64
Zirconium						
Zr702	...	70	Boiling	...	0.0005 (0.2)	62
Zr702	...	5, 10, 25	35-100 (95-212)	...	<0.025 (<1)	15
Zr702	BP 162 °C (324 °F)	70	Boiling	...	<0.025 (<1)	15

(Continued)

Corrosion Behavior of Various Metals and Alloys in Calcium Chloride (Continued)

Material	Condition, other factors, comments	Concentration, %	Temperature, °C (°F)	Duration	Corrosion rate, mm/yr (mils/yr) or other	Ref
Zr702	...	75	Boiling	...	<0.13 (<5)	15
Zr702	Plus 8% NaCl, 0.2% Ca(OH)₂	14	79 (175)	...	<0.025 (<1)	15
Zr705	BP 162 °C (324 °F)	70	Boiling	...	<0.025 (<1)	15
Zr705	...	70	Boiling	...	Weight gain	62
Lead, tin, and zinc						
Lead	Negligible corrosion; Pb recommended for use	20	24 (75)	...	<50 µm/yr (<2)	95
Tin	...	...	20 (68)	...	Resistant	94
Tin	...	...	60 (140)	...	Unsuitable	94
Tin	...	...	100 (212)	...	Unsuitable	94
Hafnium						
Hafnium	...	70	...	10 d	nil	11
Hafnium	...	70	...	10 d	nil	11
Noble metals						
Platinum	...	All	100 (212)	...	<0.05 (<2)	5
Silver	...	All	100 (212)	...	<0.05 (<2)	9
Others						
Magnesium	...	All	Room	...	Unsuitable	119
Niobium	...	70	Boiling	...	nil	2

(a) May be considered in place of a copper metal when some property, other than corrosion resistance, governs its use.

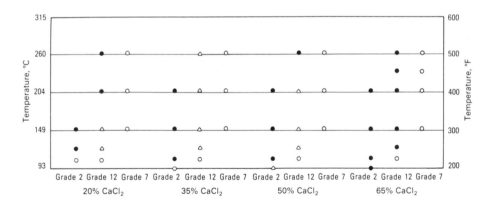

Titanium. Temperature guidelines for avoiding localized attack of grades 2, 7, and 12 titanium in concentrated calcium chloride solutions in the absence of crevices. Closed circle denotes susceptibility to localized attack; open triangle indicates incipient edge attack. Source: *Metals Handbook*, 9th ed., Vol 13, Corrosion, ASM International, Metals Park, OH, 1987, 684.

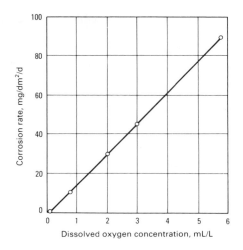

Low-carbon steel. Effect of oxygen concentration on the corrosion of low-carbon steel in slowly moving water containing 165 ppm calcium chloride at 24 °C (75 °F). Source: *Metals Handbook*, 9th ed., Vol 13, Corrosion, ASM International, Metals Park, OH, 1987, 903.

Calcium Fluoride

Calcium fluoride, CaF_2, also known as fluorite and feldspar, is a colorless solid composed of cubic crystals. It has a melting point of 1360 °C. It has a low water solubility, but is readily soluble in ammonium salt solutions. Calcium fluoride is used in the synthesis of hydrofluoric acid and in etching glass.

Corrosion Behavior of Various Metals and Alloys in Calcium Fluoride

Material	Condition, other factors, comments	Concen-tration, %	Temperature, °C (°F)	Duration	Corrosion rate, mm/yr (mils/yr) or other	Ref
Lead	Practically corrosion resistant; Pb recommended for use	...	24-100 (75-212)	...	<500 μm/yr (<20)	95
Zr702	pH 5	Saturated	28 (80)	...	nil	15
Zr702	pH 5	Saturated	90 (195)	...	nil	15

Calcium Hydroxide

Calcium hydroxide, $Ca(OH)_2$, also known as calcium hydrate and hydrated or slaked lime, is a white solid that is slightly soluble in water. It is used in medicine, construction, and agriculture.

Material Summaries

The following material summaries were compiled from a survey of the available literature. Inclusion of a material description under a given environment does not imply that it is the most appropriate material for corrosion service in that environment. Likewise, exclusion of a given material does not imply that it is not suitable for corrosion service applications in that environment.

Aluminum alloys are rapidly etched by calcium hydroxide solutions in laboratory tests. This action subsides as a protective film forms on the aluminum alloy surface.

Titanium alloys are resistant to boiling solutions of calcium hydroxide up to saturation. Although corrosion rates are near nil, titanium alloys under the conditions of temperatures over 80 °C (175 °F) and a pH of 12 or more may experience hydrogen buildup and eventual embrittlement. The addition of dissolved chlorate, hypochlorite, or nitrate compounds in hot caustic solutions can extend resistance to hydrogen uptake to somewhat higher temperatures.

Additional Reading

W.J. Tomlinson and S.A. Brown, Corrosion of Anodically Polarized Zn-Al Alloys in Saturated Ca(OH)$_2$ Containing Cl⁻, *Surf. Coat. Technol.,* *27*(1), 95-100, 1986. MetAbs No. 86-350597. **Abstract:** Cast Zn-Al alloys containing 0, 20, 40, 55, 80 and 100% Al have been anodically polarized in saturated Ca(OH)$_2$ containing Cl⁻, and the conditions for corrosion and pitting with respect to alloy composition, chloride concentration and alloy microstructure have been defined.

A.P. Akolzin, P. Ghosh, and Yu. Ya. Kharitonov, Application of Calcium Hydroxide for Preventing Corrosion of Carbon Steel, *Indian J. Technol.,* *23*(4), 136-140, 1985. MetAbs No. 86-351587. **Abstract:** The corrosion behavior of carbon steel 20 was studied in detail by the polarization resistance method and by the weight loss method in pure Ca(OH)$_2$ solutions as well as Ca(OH)$_2$ solutions containing low concentrations of Cl⁻ and SO$_4^{2-}$ ions. Analogous experiments with equivalent solutions of NaOH were conducted.

Corrosion Behavior of Various Metals and Alloys in Calcium Hydroxide

Material	Condition, other factors, comments	Concentration, %	Temperature, °C (°F)	Duration	Corrosion rate, mm/yr (mils/yr) or other	Ref
Stainless steels						
AM-363 stainless steel	...	...	Room	...	Unattacked	120
Type 304 stainless steel	Chemical processing; field or pilot plant test; slight to moderate aeration; slight to moderate agitation. Calcium hydroxide slurry, some undissolved calcium hydroxide and silica	...	90 (194)	203 d	<0.0001 in./yr	89
Type 304 stainless steel	Tanning; field or pilot plant test. Calcium-hydroxide lime liquors, ammonia fumes, sodium sulfide	...	...	180 d	<0.0001 in./yr	89
Type 304 stainless steel	Pulp and paper processing; field or pilot plant test; slight to moderate aeration; slight to moderate agitation. Plus calcium carbonate, sodium hydroxide, sodium sulfide	...	49 (120)	204 d	<0.0001 in./yr	89
Type 316 stainless steel	Tanning; field or pilot plant test. Calcium-hydroxide lime liquors, ammonia fumes, sodium sulfide	...	...	180 d	<0.0001 in./yr	89
Type 316 stainless steel	Pulp and paper processing; field or pilot plant test; slight to moderate aeration; slight to moderate agitation. Plus calcium carbonate, sodium hydroxide, sodium sulfide	...	49 (120)	204 d	<0.0001 in./yr	89
Type 410 stainless steel	...	...	Room	...	Unattacked	121
Aluminum						
Aluminum-magnesium alloys	Solution	...	20 (68)	...	Satisfactory	92
Aluminum (>99.5%)	Solution	...	20 (68)	...	Satisfactory	92
Coppers						
70-30 cupronickel	...	...	...	...	Suitable	93
90-10 cupronickel	...	...	...	...	Suitable	93
Admiralty brass	...	...	...	...	Suitable	93
Aluminum bronze	...	...	...	...	Suitable	93
Ampco 8, aluminum bronze	Generally suitable. Conditions such as aeration or temperature could restrict use	...	...	...	<0.5 (<20)	96
Architectural bronze	(a)	...	...	...	Good	93
Brass	...	...	...	...	Suitable	93
Cartridge brass	(a)	...	...	...	Good	93
Commercial bronze	...	...	...	...	Suitable	93
Electrolytic copper	...	...	...	...	Suitable	93
Free-cutting brass	(a)	...	...	...	Good	93
Muntz metal	(a)	...	...	...	Good	93
Naval brass	(a)	...	...	...	Good	93
Nickel silver	...	18	...	...	Suitable	93
Phosphor bronze	5% Sn	...	...	...	Suitable	93
Phosphor bronze	8% Sn	...	...	...	Suitable	93
Phosphor copper	...	...	...	...	Suitable	93
Red brass	...	...	...	...	Suitable	93
Silicon bronze	Low	...	...	...	Suitable	93
Silicon bronze	High	...	...	...	Suitable	93

(Continued)

Corrosion Behavior of Various Metals and Alloys in Calcium Hydroxide (Continued)

Material	Condition, other factors, comments	Concen-tration, %	Temperature, °C (°F)	Duration	Corrosion rate, mm/yr (mils/yr) or other	Ref
Titanium						
Titanium	...	Saturated	Room	...	nil	90
Titanium	...	Saturated	Boiling	...	nil	90
Titanium	...	2	100 (212)	...	0.001 (0.04)	90
Titanium	...	6	100 (212)	...	0.001 (0.04)	90
Titanium	...	18	21 (70)	...	nil	90
Titanium	...	Saturated	21 (70)	...	nil	90
Noble metals						
Silver	...	All	100 (212)	...	<0.05 (<2)	9
Others						
Magnesium	...	100	Room	...	Suitable	119

(a) May be considered in place of a copper metal when some property, other than corrosion resistance, governs its use.

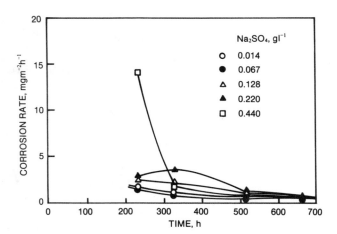

Carbon steel. Variation of corrosion rate with time for carbon steel in 0.43 g/L calcium hydroxide solutions containing various concentrations of sodium sulfate. Source: A.P. Akolzin, P. Ghosh, *et al.*, "Application and Peculiarity of Ca(OH)$_2$ as Inhibitor in Presence of Corrosion Activators," *British Corrosion Journal, 20*, 34, 1985.

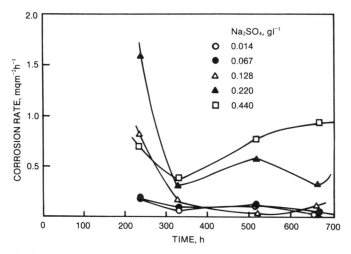

Carbon steel. Variation of corrosion rate with time for carbon steel in 0.76 g/L calcium hydroxide solutions containing various concentrations of sodium sulfate. Source: A.P. Akolzin, P. Ghosh, *et al.*, "Application and Peculiarity of Ca(OH)$_2$ as Inhibitor in Presence of Corrosion Activators," *British Corrosion Journal, 20*, 34, 1985.

Calcium Hypochlorite

Calcium hypochlorite, Ca(OCl)$_2$·4H$_2$O, also known as calcium oxychloride, chlorinated lime, and bleach, is a deliquescent white powder used as a bleaching agent in the textile and pulp industries and as a disinfectant. It contains 60 to 65% available chlorine.

Material Summaries

The following material summaries were compiled from a survey of the available literature. Inclusion of a material description under a given environment does not imply that it is the most appropriate material for corrosion service in that environment. Likewise, exclusion of a given material does not imply that it is not suitable for corrosion service applications in that environment.

Aluminum. In laboratory tests under the conditions of ambient temperature and 100% relative humidity, solid calcium hypochlorite was corrosive (around 27 mils/yr) to aluminum alloy 3003 and caused moderate attack (around 10 mils/yr) to aluminum alloy 5154. Aqueous solutions, except at very low concentrations, attacked aluminum alloy 3003 in other tests at ambient temperature. Calcium hypochlorite is sometimes handled in aluminum baskets and rotary driers. Occasionally, solid calcium hypochlorite is handled in aluminum, because any corrosive residue does not discolor the product.

Corrosion Behavior of Various Metals and Alloys in Calcium Hypochlorite

Material	Condition, other factors, comments	Concen- tration, %	Temperature, °C (°F)	Duration	Corrosion rate, mm/yr (mils/yr) or other	Ref
Stainless steels						
Type 316 stainless steel	Chemical processing; laboratory test	2	60 (140)	...	<0.0001 in./yr	89
Type 316 stainless steel	Chemical processing; laboratory test	2	100 (212)	...	0.0002 in./yr	89
Type 316 stainless steel	Chemical processing; laboratory test	6	36 (97)	...	0.0216 in./yr	89
Type 316 stainless steel	Chemical processing; laboratory test	6	100 (212)	...	0.0005 in./yr	89
Type 316 stainless steel	Chemical processing; field or pilot plant test; slight to moderate aeration; slight to moderate agitation. Bleach slurry, available chlorine 70-100 g/L, lime excess 20-30 g/L. Severe pitting: maximum depth of pits over 0.010 in.; crevice attack (tendency to concentration-cell corrosion)	10	32-38 (90-100)	31 d	0.006 in./yr	89
Type 316 stainless steel	Chemical processing; field or pilot plant test; slight to moderate aeration; slight to moderate agitation. Bleach slurry, available chlorine 70-100 g/L, lime excess 20-30 g/L. Severe pitting: maximum depth of pits over 0.010 in.; crevice attack (tendency to concentration-cell corrosion)	10	32-38 (90-100)	31 d	0.01 in./yr	89
Type 316 stainless steel	Chemical processing; field or pilot plant test; slight to moderate aeration; slight to moderate agitation. Bleach slurry, available chlorine 70-100 g/L, lime excess 20-30 g/L. Severe pitting: maximum depth of pits over 0.010 in.; crevice attack (tendency to concentration-cell corrosion)	10	32-38 (90-100)	31 d	0.006 in./yr	89
Type 316 stainless steel	Chemical processing; field or pilot plant test; slight to moderate aeration; slight to moderate agitation. Bleach. Severe pitting: maximum depth of pits over 0.010 in.; crevice attack (tendency to concentration-cell corrosion)	~15	24 (75)	65 d	0.012 in./yr	89
Type 316 stainless steel	Severe pitting; severe attack under spacer	18-20	20-24 (70-75)	204 d	0.25 (10)	82
Type 317 stainless steel	Chemical processing; field or pilot plant test; slight to moderate aeration; slight to moderate agitation. Bleach slurry, available chlorine 70-100 g/L, lime excess 20-30 g/L. Severe pitting: maximum depth of pits over 0.010 in.; crevice attack (tendency to concentration-cell corrosion)	10	32-38 (90-100)	31 d	0.023 in./yr	89
Type 317 stainless steel	Chemical processing; field or pilot plant test; slight to moderate aeration; slight to moderate agitation. Bleach slurry, available chlorine 70-100 g/L, lime excess 20-30 g/L. Severe pitting: maximum depth of pits over 0.010 in.; crevice attack (tendency to concentration-cell corrosion)	10	32-38 (90-100)	31 d	0.029 in./yr	89
Type 317 stainless steel	Chemical processing; field or pilot plant test; slight to moderate aeration; slight to moderate agitation. Bleach. Severe pitting: maximum depth of pits over 0.010 in.; crevice attack (tendency to concentration-cell corrosion)	~15	24 (75)	65 d	0.0033 in./yr	89
Type 410 stainless steel	...	...	Room	...	Attacked	121
Coppers						
70-30 cupronickel	(a)	...	...	...	Good	93
90-10 cupronickel	(a)	...	...	...	Good	93
Admiralty brass	(a)	...	...	...	Good	93
Aluminum bronze	(a)	...	...	...	Good	93
Ampco 8, aluminum bronze	Generally suitable. Conditions such as aeration or temperature could restrict use	...	...	...	<0.5 (<20)	96
Architectural bronze	...	...	...	...	Not suitable	93
Brass	(a)	...	...	...	Good	93
Cartridge brass	...	...	...	...	Not suitable	93
Commercial bronze	(a)	...	...	...	Good	93
Electrolytic copper	(a)	...	...	...	Good	93
Free-cutting brass	...	...	...	...	Good	93
Muntz metal	...	...	...	...	Not suitable	93
Naval brass	...	...	...	...	Not suitable	93
Nickel silver	(a)	...	...	...	Not suitable	93
Phosphor bronze	5% Sn. (a)	18	...	...	Good	
Phosphor bronze	8% Sn. (a)	...	...	...	Good	93
		...	...	...	Good	93

(Continued)

Corrosion Behavior of Various Metals and Alloys in Calcium Hypochlorite (Continued)

Material	Condition, other factors, comments	Concen-tration, %	Temperature, °C (°F)	Duration	Corrosion rate, mm/yr (mils/yr) or other	Ref
Phosphor copper	(a)	...	...	...	Good	93
Red brass	(a)	...	...	...	Good	93
Silicon bronze	Low. (a)	...	...	...	Good	93
Silicon bronze	High. (a)	...	...	...	Good	93
Titanium						
Titanium	...	2	100 (212)	...	0.001 (0.04)	27
Titanium	...	6	100 (212)	...	0.001 (0.04)	27
Titanium	...	18	25 (77)	...	nil	27
Titanium	No pitting	18-20	20-24 (70-75)	204 d	nil	82
Heat- and corrosion-resistant alloys						
Carpenter 20	Chemical processing; laboratory test	2	60 (140)	...	<0.0001 in./yr	89
Carpenter 20	Chemical processing; laboratory test	2	100 (212)	...	0.0001 in./yr	89
Carpenter 20	Chemical processing; laboratory test	6	36 (97)	...	0.0347 in./yr	89
Carpenter 20	Chemical processing; laboratory test	6	100 (212)	...	0.0004 in./yr	89
Carpenter 20	Chemical processing; field or pilot plant test; slight to moderate aeration; slight to moderate agitation; cast specimens. Bleach. Severe pitting: maximum depth of pits over 0.010 in.; crevice attack (tendency to concentration-cell corrosion)	~15	24 (75)	65 d	0.022 in./yr	89
Chlorimet 3	No pitting	18-20	20-24 (70-75)	204 d	0.025 (1)	82
Hastelloy C	No pitting	18-20	20-24 (70-75)	204 d	<0.0025 (<0.1)	82
Zirconium						
Zirconium	No pitting; severe attack under spacer	18-20	20-24 (70-75)	204 d	0.025 (1)	82
Zr702	...	2, 6, 20	100 (212)	...	<0.13 (<5)	15
Noble metals						
Platinum	...	All	Room	...	<0.05 (<2)	5
Others						
Magnesium alloy AZ61A	Specimen size, 75 x 25 x 1.5 mm (3 x 1 x 0.06 in.); surface preparation, HNO_3 pickling; volume of testing solution, 100 ml. Specimens were alternately immersed 30 s in solution and held 2 min in air	3	35 (95)	7 d	15.5 $g/m^2/d$ (10 $mg/in.^2/d$)	12

(a) May be considered in place of a copper metal when some property, other than corrosion resistance, governs its use.

Camphor

Camphor, $C_{10}H_{16}O$, also known as *d*-2-camphanone, Japan camphor, laurel camphor, Formosa camphor, and gum camphor, is a terpene ketone with a melting point of 175 °C. It is obtained from the wood and bark of the camphor tree and is soluble in water and alcohol. It has two optically active forms (dextro and levo) and an optically inactive mixture (racemic) of these two forms. Camphor is used in pharmaceuticals, in disinfectants, in explosives, and to harden nitrocellulose plastics.

Material Summaries

The following material summaries were compiled from a survey of the available literature. Inclusion of a material description under a given environment does not imply that it is the most appropriate material for corrosion service in that environment. Likewise, exclusion of a given material does not imply that it is not suitable for corrosion service applications in that environment.

Aluminum. Camphor has been handled successfully in aluminum alloy equipment.

Corrosion Behavior of Various Metals and Alloys in Camphor

Material	Condition, other factors, comments	Concen-tration, %	Temperature, °C (°F)	Duration	Corrosion rate, mm/yr (mils/yr) or other	Ref
Stainless steels						
Type 410 stainless steel	...	...	Room	...	Unattacked	121

(Continued)

Corrosion Behavior of Various Metals and Alloys in Camphor (Continued)

Material	Condition, other factors, comments	Concen-tration, %	Temperature, °C (°F)	Duration	Corrosion rate, mm/yr (mils/yr) or other	Ref
Aluminum						
Aluminum (99.0-99.5%)	...	...	20-boiling point (68-boiling point)	...	Satisfactory	92
Aluminum-manganese alloys	...	...	20-boiling point (68-boiling point)	...	Satisfactory	92
Others						
Magnesium	...	100	Room	...	Resistant	119

Caprylic Acid

Caprylic acid, $CH_3(CH_2)_6COOH$, also known as hexylacetic acid, *n*-octanoic acid, octylic acid, and octic acid, is a liquid fatty acid with a melting point of 16 °C. It is found in butter, coconut oil, and other fats. It is used in manufacturing drugs and dyes.

Material Summaries

The following material summaries were compiled from a survey of the available literature. Inclusion of a material description under a given environment does not imply that it is the most appropriate material for corrosion service in that environment. Likewise, exclusion of a given material does not imply that it is not suitable for corrosion service applications in that environment.

Aluminum. Aluminum alloys 3003 and 5052 were resistant to caprylic acid in limited laboratory tests at ambient temperature. Aluminum alloy tank cars have been used to ship caprylic acid.

Corrosion Behavior of Various Metals and Alloys in Caprylic Acid

Material	Condition, other factors, comments	Concen-tration, %	Temperature, °C (°F)	Duration	Corrosion rate, mm/yr (mils/yr) or other	Ref
Coppers						
Copper	...	...	Room	...	<0.02 (<1)	22
Copper	...	...	190 (375)	...	<0.02 (<1)	22
Silicon bronze	...	...	Room	...	<0.02 (<1)	22
Silicon bronze	...	...	190 (375)	...	<0.02 (<1)	22
Steels						
Steel	...	...	Room	...	<0.02 (<1)	22
Steel	...	...	190 (375)	...	0.89 (35)	22
Type 304 stainless steel	...	...	Room	...	<0.02 (<1)	22
Type 304 stainless steel	...	...	190 (375)	...	0.20 (8)	22
Type 316 stainless steel	...	...	Room	...	<0.02 (<1)	22
Type 316 stainless steel	...	...	190 (375)	...	<0.02 (<1)	22

Carbon

Carbon, C, is a nonmetallic element. It is found in nature as graphite (specific gravity 2.25), diamond (specific gravity 3.51), and coal (specific gravity 1.88). Carbon is found in all living things, is insoluble in common solvents, and forms an almost infinite number of organic compounds. A naturally occurring radioactive isotope, ^{14}C, has a half-life of 5780 years and is used in archaeological investigations to date artifacts and ancient documents. Other uses of carbon depend on its form. For example, diamonds for jewels and abrasives, graphite for lubricants, activated carbon to absorb color and gases, and wood carbon for fuel are some common examples.

Material Summaries

The following material summaries were compiled from a survey of the available literature. Inclusion of a material description under a given environment does not imply that it is the most appropriate material for corrosion service in that environment. Likewise, exclusion of a given material does not imply that it is not suitable for corrosion service applications in that environment.

Aluminum. Dry carbon does not attack aluminum alloys in laboratory tests. However, corrosion results when wet carbon contacts aluminum, acts as a cathode, and stimulates galvanic action. Aluminum alloy hopper cars have been used with carbon black.

Tantalum. Carbon reacts directly with tantalum at elevated temperatures to form Ta_2C and TaC. Both TaC and Ta_2C have high melting points, metallic appearance, and high hardness.

Additional Reading

D.J. Stephenson, J.R. Nicholls, and P. Hancock, Particle-Surface Inter-

actions During the Erosion of a Gas Turbine Material (MarM002) by Pyrolytic Carbon Particles, *Wear, 111*(1), 15-29, 1986. MetAbs No. 86-352230. **Abstract:** A single-impact technique was used to study particle-surface interactions during the erosion of a typical turbine blade material, MarM002, by pyrolytic carbon particles. The erosive response of MarM002 was considered at 700, 750, 850 and 950 °C.

M. Svilar and H.D. Ambs, "NOC" Precipitation During the Sintering of Austenitic Stainless Steels and Their Effect on Corrosion, in *SCM Metal Products Progress in Powder Metallurgy 1987*, Vol 43, American Powder Metallurgy Institute, Princeton, 17-20, 1987. MetAbs No. 88-540068. **Abstract:** The corrosion resistance of stainless steel is compromised by nitrogen, oxygen, or carbon when chromium is depleted from the matrix by nitrogen, oxygen, or carbon precipitates. Precipitation can be avoided by either maintaining nitrogen, oxygen or carbon below equilibrium concentration for precipitation, or by cooling rapidly to nonequilibrium metastable structures, or to a kinetically stable structure for carbon and nitrogen.

Corrosion Behavior of Various Metals and Alloys in Carbon

Material	Condition, other factors, comments	Concen-tration, %	Temperature, °C (°F)	Duration	Corrosion rate, mm/yr (mils/yr) or other	Ref
Stainless steels						
AM-363 stainless steel	...	...	Room	...	Unattacked	120
Type 304 stainless steel	Chemical processing. Activated carbon "SXAC-L" adsorbing acetone, trace methylene chloride. Crevice attack (tendency to concentration-cell corrosion)	...	...	57 d	<0.0001 in./yr	89
Type 304 stainless steel	Chemical processing. Activated carbon bed "Norit Sorbonorit III" adsorbing acetone containing trace methylene chloride. Moderate pitting: maximum depth of pits from 0.005 to 0.010 in.; crevice attack (tendency to concentration-cell corrosion); stress-corrosion cracking	...	...	57 d	0.0002 in./yr	89
Type 304 stainless steel	Printing; field or plant test; strong aeration; no agitation. With carbon over the standard maximum. Activated carbon bed "Lactol," petroleum solvent, steam, some unknown chloride source. Severe pitting: maximum depth of pits over 0.010 in.; stress-corrosion cracking	...	Room to 110 (room to 230)	70 d	0.0001 in./yr	89
Type 304 stainless steel	Power processing; field or plant test; strong aeration; slight to moderate agitation. Coal (coal chutes)	...	Room	257 d	0.0047 in./yr	89
Type 304 stainless steel	Carbon black processing; field or plant test; no aeration; rapid agitation. Carbon-black slurry, carbonates, chlorides, sulfates, carbon dioxide and sulfur dioxide from cooling water at pH 7 (bottom of primary cooler)	...	204-482 (400-900)	42 d	0.0011 in./yr	89
Type 304 stainless steel	Chemical processing; field or plant test; strong aeration; strong agitation. Carbon-black slurry and water intermittently, pH 7 approximately (water level of cooler seal, wet and dry, air and slurry. Severe pitting: maximum depth of pits over 0.010 in.; crevice attack (tendency to concentration-cell corrosion)	...	71 (160)	240 d	0.0003 in./yr	89
Type 304 stainless steel	Carbon black processing; field or plant test; strong aeration; strong agitation. Carbon-black slurry, plus sulfuric acid pH 2 (leaching tank)	...	43 (110)	3 d	0.0004 in./yr	89
Type 304 stainless steel	Chemical processing; field or plant test; strong aeration; slight to moderate agitation. Carbon black loose, entrained combustion gases, water vapor, product occasionally on fire. Severe pitting: maximum depth of pits over 0.010 in.	...	49 (120)	324 d	0.0011 in./yr	89
Type 304 stainless steel	Carbon black processing; field or plant test; strong aeration; rapid agitation. Carbon black, hard water (fresh water 52 salt grains/gal), steam (half immersed). Severe pitting: maximum depth of pits over 0.010 in.	...	66 (152)	30 d	0.0001 in./yr	89

(Continued)

Corrosion Behavior of Various Metals and Alloys in Carbon (Continued)

Material	Condition, other factors, comments	Concentration, %	Temperature, °C (°F)	Duration	Corrosion rate, mm/yr (mils/yr) or other	Ref
Type 304 stainless steel	Carbon black processing; field or plant test; slight to moderate aeration; rapid agitation. Carbon black, sulfur, salt and water vapor, oxygen (wet scrubber unit)	...	215 (420)	15 d	0.0002 in./yr	89
Type 304 stainless steel	Petroleum processing; field or plant test; slight to moderate agitation. With carbon over the standard maximum. Plus 80% water (mixer), 20% carbon black paste. Crevice attack (tendency to concentration-cell corrosion)	...	24 (75)	28 d	0.0001 in./yr	89
Type 316 stainless steel	Chemical processing. Activated carbon "SXAC-L" adsorbing acetone, trace methylene chloride. Crevice attack (tendency to concentration-cell corrosion)	...	...	57 d	<0.0001 in./yr	89
Type 316 stainless steel	Chemical processing. Activated carbon bed "Norit Sorbonorit III" adsorbing acetone containing trace methylene chloride. Moderate pitting: maximum depth of pits from 0.005 to 0.010 in.; crevice attack (tendency to concentration-cell corrosion); stress-corrosion cracking	...	...	57 d	0.0001 in./yr	89
Type 316 stainless steel	Printing; field or plant test; strong aeration; no agitation. Activated carbon bed "Lactol," petroleum solvent, steam, some unknown chloride source. Severe pitting: maximum depth of pits over 0.010 in.; stress-corrosion cracking	...	Room to 110 (room to 230)	70 d	0.0001 in./yr	89
Type 316 stainless steel	Power processing; field or plant test; strong aeration; slight to moderate agitation. Coal (coal chutes)	...	Room	257 d	0.0046 in./yr	89
Type 316 stainless steel	Carbon black processing; field or plant test; no aeration; rapid agitation. Carbon-black slurry, carbonates, chlorides, sulfates, carbon dioxide and sulfur dioxide from cooling water at pH 7 (bottom of primary cooler)	...	204-482 (400-900)	42 d	0.001 in./yr	89
Type 316 stainless steel	Chemical processing; field or plant test; strong aeration; strong agitation. Carbon-black slurry and water intermittently, pH 7 approximately (water level of cooler seal, wet and dry, air and slurry	...	71 (160)	240 d	<0.0001 in./yr	89
Type 316 stainless steel	Carbon black processing; field or plant test; strong aeration; strong agitation. Carbon-black slurry, plus sulfuric acid pH 2 (leaching tank)	...	43 (110)	3 d	0.0005 in./yr	89
Type 316 stainless steel	Chemical processing; field or plant test; strong aeration; slight to moderate agitation. Carbon black loose, entrained combustion gases, water vapor, product occasionally on fire. Severe pitting: maximum depth of pits over 0.010 in.	...	49 (120)	324 d	0.0001 in./yr	89
Type 316 stainless steel	Carbon black processing; field or plant test; strong aeration; rapid agitation. Carbon black hard water (fresh water 52 salt grains/gal), steam (half immersed)	...	66 (152)	30 d	0.0001 in./yr	89
Type 316 stainless steel	Carbon black processing; field or plant test; slight to moderate aeration; rapid agitation. Carbon black, sulfur, salt and water vapor, oxygen (wet scrubber unit)	...	215 (420)	15 d	0.0002 in./yr	89
Type 316 stainless steel	Petroleum processing; field or plant test; slight to moderate agitation. With carbon over the standard maximum. Plus 80% water (mixer), 20% carbon black paste	...	24 (75)	28 d	0.0001 in./yr	89
Type 317 stainless steel	Chemical processing. Activated carbon "SXAC-L" adsorbing acetone, trace methylene chloride. Crevice attack (tendency to concentration-cell corrosion)	...	...	57 d	<0.0001 in./yr	89
Type 317 stainless steel	Chemical processing. Activated carbon bed "Norit Sorbonorit III" adsorbing acetone containing trace methylene chloride. Slight pitting: maximum depth of pits from incipient to 0.005 in.	...	...	57 d	0.0001 in./yr	89
Type 317 stainless steel	Carbon black processing; field or plant test; no aeration; rapid agitation. Carbon-black slurry, carbonates, chlorides, sulfates, carbon dioxide and sulfur dioxide from cooling water at pH 7 (bottom of primary cooler)	...	204-482 (400-900)	42 d	0.0007 in./yr	89

(Continued)

Corrosion Behavior of Various Metals and Alloys in Carbon (Continued)

Material	Condition, other factors, comments	Concentration, %	Temperature, °C (°F)	Duration	Corrosion rate, mm/yr (mils/yr) or other	Ref
Type 317 stainless steel	Chemical processing; field or plant test; strong aeration; slight to moderate agitation. Carbon black loose, entrained combustion gases, water vapor, product occasionally on fire. Severe pitting: maximum depth of pits over 0.010 in.	...	49 (120)	324 d	<0.0001 in./yr	89
Type 317 stainless steel	Carbon black processing; field or plant test; strong aeration; rapid agitation. Carbon black hard water (fresh water 52 salt grains/gal), steam (half immersed)	...	66 (152)	30 d	0.0001 in./yr	89
Type 317 stainless steel	Carbon black processing; field or plant test; slight to moderate aeration; rapid agitation. Carbon black, sulfur, salt and water vapor, oxygen (wet scrubber unit)	...	215 (420)	15 d	0.0001 in./yr	89
Aluminum						
Aluminum (99.0-99.5%)	...	...	<650 (<1202)	...	Excellent	92
Heat- and corrosion-resistant alloys						
Alloy 825	Chemical processing. Activated carbon "SXAC-L" adsorbing acetone, trace methylene chloride	...	...	57 d	<0.0001 in./yr	89
Alloy 825	Chemical processing. Activated carbon bed "Norit Sorbonorit III" adsorbing acetone containing trace methylene chloride. Slight pitting: maximum depth of pits from incipient to 0.005 in.	...	...	57 d	0.0001 in./yr	89
Alloy 825	Chemical processing; field or plant test; strong aeration; strong agitation. Carbon-black slurry and water intermittently, pH 7 approximately (water level of cooler seal, wet and dry, air and slurry	...	71 (160)	240 d	<0.0001 in./yr	89
Alloy 825	Chemical processing; field or plant test; strong aeration; slight to moderate agitation. Carbon black loose, entrained combustion gases, water vapor, product occasionally on fire. Slight pitting: maximum depth of pits from incipient to 0.005 in.	...	49 (120)	324 d	0.0004 in./yr	89
Carpenter 20	Chemical processing. Activated carbon "SXAC-L" adsorbing acetone, trace methylene chloride. Slight pitting: maximum depth of pits from incipient to 0.005 in.	...	...	57 d	<0.0001 in./yr	89
Carpenter 20	Chemical processing. Activated carbon bed "Norit Sorbonorit III" adsorbing acetone containing trace methylene chloride. Moderate pitting: maximum depth of pits from 0.005 to 0.010 in.	...	...	57 d	0.0001 in./yr	89
Carpenter 20	Printing; field or plant test; strong aeration; no agitation. Activated carbon bed "Lactol," petroleum solvent, steam, some unknown chloride source. Severe pitting: maximum depth of pits over 0.010 in.	...	Room to 110 (room to 230)	70 d	<0.0001 in./yr	89
Carpenter 20	Chemical processing; field or plant test; strong aeration; strong agitation. Carbon-black slurry and water intermittently, pH 7 approximately (water level of cooler seal, wet and dry, air and slurry	...	71 (160)	240 d	<0.0001 in./yr	89
Carpenter 20	Carbon black processing; field or plant test; strong aeration; strong agitation. Carbon-black slurry, plus sulfuric acid pH 2 (leaching tank)	...	43 (110)	3 d	0.0013 in./yr	89
Carpenter 20	Chemical processing; field or plant test; strong aeration; slight to moderate agitation. Carbon black loose, entrained combustion gases, water vapor, product occasionally on fire. Moderate pitting: maximum depth of pits from 0.005 to 0.010 in.	...	49 (120)	324 d	0.0001 in./yr	89
Carpenter 20	Carbon black processing; field or plant test; strong aeration; rapid agitation. Carbon black hard water (fresh water 52 salt grains/gal), steam (half immersed)	...	66 (152)	30 d	<0.0001 in./yr	89

Carbon Bisulfide

Carbon bisulfide, CS_2, also known as carbon disulfide, is a colorless liquid with a boiling point of 46.3 °C. It is used as a solvent for oils, fats, rubbers, and in paint removers.

Corrosion Behavior of Various Metals and Alloys in Carbon Bisulfide

Material	Condition, other factors, comments	Concentration, %	Temperature, °C (°F)	Duration	Corrosion rate, mm/yr (mils/yr) or other	Ref
Coppers						
70-30 cupronickel	(a)	...	...	...	Good	93
90-10 cupronickel	(a)	...	...	...	Good	93
Admiralty brass	...	...	...	...	Suitable	93
Aluminum bronze	(a)	...	...	...	Good	93
Ampco 8, aluminum bronze	Generally suitable. Conditions such as aeration or temperature could restrict use	...	...	...	<0.5 (<20)	96
Architectural bronze	...	...	...	...	Suitable	93
Brass	...	...	...	...	Suitable	93
Cartridge brass	...	...	...	...	Suitable	93
Commercial bronze	(a)	...	...	...	Good	93
Electrolytic copper	(a)	...	...	...	Good	93
Free-cutting brass	...	...	...	...	Suitable	93
Muntz metal	...	...	...	...	Suitable	93
Naval brass	...	...	...	...	Suitable	93
Nickel silver	(a)	18	...	...	Good	93
Phosphor bronze	5% Sn. (a)	...	...	...	Good	93
Phosphor bronze	8% Sn. (a)	...	...	...	Good	93
Phosphor copper	(a)	...	...	...	Good	93
Red brass	(a)	...	...	...	Good	93
Silicon bronze	Low. (a)	...	...	...	Good	93
Silicon bronze	High. (a)	...	...	...	Good	93
Noble metals						
Platinum	...	Pure	Boiling	...	<0.05 (<2)	6
Others						
Magnesium	...	100	Room	...	Suitable	119

(a) May be considered in place of a copper metal when some property, other than corrosion resistance, governs its use.

Carbon Dioxide

Carbon dioxide, CO_2, also known as carbonic anhydride and carbonic acid gas, is a colorless, odorless gas that liquifies at -65 °C (-86 °F) and solidifies in dry ice at -78.2 °C (-107 °F). It is soluble in water, alcohol, and most alkaline solutions. In a relatively slow reaction, carbon dioxide hydrates in water to become carbonic acid and is corrosive. In petroleum production, the velocity of the carbon dioxide gas can increase the corrosion rate to very high levels, with the presence of salts becoming unimportant. Carbon dioxide is used in preparing carbonated beverages, fire extinguishers, dry ice refrigerants, and as a raw material in the production of sodium carbonate and sodium bicarbonate using the Solvay procedure.

Material Summaries

The following material summaries were compiled from a survey of the available literature. Inclusion of a material description under a given environment does not imply that it is the most appropriate material for corrosion service in that environment. Likewise, exclusion of a given material does not imply that it is not suitable for corrosion service applications in that environment.

Aluminum. Aluminum alloy equipment has been used to handle carbon dioxide in the gaseous, liquid, and solid states.

Carbon and Alloy Steels. In oil and gas production, the use of the carbon dioxide injection method has brought about additional corrosion concerns. This method involves the use of carbon dioxide source wells, which can be highly corrosive due to the reaction of carbon dioxide and water, to form carbonic acid. The addition of chloride and hydrogen sulfide increases the acidic activity. The corrosion rates also change with temperature. At 65 °C (150 °F), the lower alloy steels show an increase in weight loss corrosion with increasing carbon dioxide concentration. However, the corrosion resistance improves above 175 °C (350 °F).

Corrosion resistance at a given concentration level improves as the chromium level of the steel increases. Stainless steels exhibit little or no dependence on either the temperature or the carbon dioxide concentration. However, with the addition of chloride at 65 °C (150 °F), higher alloyed steel corrosion rates begin to increase with the increase in carbon dioxide concentration. The corrosion rate of highly alloyed steels increases as the chloride concentration and the temperature increase. The presence of hydrogen sulfide in the carbon dioxide/brine environment increases the corrosion rate of lower alloy and stainless steels. Carbon steel is corrosion resistant to dry carbon dioxide.

Stainless Steels. Martensitic (AISI 410 and 420), austenitic, and duplex stainless steels have been extensively used to handle wet carbon dioxide gas.

Copper. Copper and copper alloys are usually inert to dry carbon dioxide. Corrosion will occur if moisture is present; the rate is determined by the amount of moisture.

Niobium. Niobium is inert in carbon dioxide at 100 °C (212 °F), but reacts with carbon dioxide above 250 °C (480 °F).

Tantalum. Dry carbon dioxide corrodes tantalum at 810 kPa (8 atm) and 500 °C (930 °F). At 1100 °C (2010 °F), carbon dioxide reacts with tantalum to form Ta_2O_5. A gravimetric balance measured the oxidation rates of tantalum at various partial pressures of carbon dioxide at temperatures ranging from 700 to 950 °C (1290 to 1740 °F). The linear oxidation behavior has been explained by the initial absorption of carbon dioxide followed by the formation of a nonprotective surface layer of Ta_2O_5. Both an equilibrium process and a steady-state reaction have been used to describe the absorption phase.

Tin. Carbon dioxide reacts with molten tin to form carbon monoxide and tin oxide.

Titanium. A protective oxide film allows titanium alloys to resist attack by either wet or dry carbon dioxide at temperatures of 150 °C (300 °F) or above.

Zirconium. Zirconium resists attack by carbon dioxide up to 300 to 400 °C (570 to 750 °F).

Additional Reading

S. Hopson, Amine Inhibitor Copes With Corrosion, *Oil Gas J.*, *83*(26), 44-47, 1985. MetAbs No. 85-352242. **Abstract:** Part of a U.S. oil recovery project is a CO_2 recovery plant designed to produce dry pure CO_2 from the exhaust gas by eliminating other components. When the system was designed, several parts of the plant were upgraded from C steel to stainless steel. This change is discussed in terms of improved corrosion resistance.

A. McMinn, F.F. Lyle Jr., and G.R. Leverant, Stress Corrosion Crack Growth in NiCrMoV Turbine Disc Steels, *Corrosion*, *41*(9), 493-503, 1985. MetAbs No. 85-352342. **Abstract:** A study was made of the effects of metallurgical and environment variables on stress-corrosion cracking propagation rates in NiCrMoV turbine disc steels. Constant displacement tests, using WOL specimens, were performed on steels with yield strengths in the range of 627-1124 MPa. All tests were made at 157 °C in either pure water environments, or environments containing common ionic turbine contaminants (NaCl and NaOH) and gaseous turbine contaminants (air, oxygen, and carbon dioxide).

R.C. Lobb and H.E. Evans, The Oxidation of Chromium-Depleted Stainless Steels in a CO_2-Based Gas of Low Sulphur Activity, *Corros. Sci.*, *25*(7), 503-518, 1985. MetAbs No. 85-352390. **Abstract:** It has been shown that the presence of small quantities of sulfur (in the form carbonyl sulfide) in the oxidant led to extensive breakdown of the "healing" layer at 1123 K in chromium-depleted specimens, allowing continued internal oxidation. The present work examines the effect of CO_2 on the healing condition at various temperatures in the range 973 to 1123 K.

T. Kurisu, M. Kimura, and N. Totsuka, Corrosion Resistance of Low C-Ni-13Cr Stainless Steels in CO_2/H_2O Environments, *Trans. Iron Steel Inst. Jpn.*, *25*(4), B-133, 1985. MetAbs No. 86-350498. **Abstract:** Low C-Ni-13Cr and low C-Ni-Mo-13Cr stainless steel useful for applications such as oil country tubular goods and pipelines in sweet gas environments are discussed in terms of corrosion resistance in CO_2 environments below 150 °C.

G.I. Ogundele and W.E. White, Some Observations on Corrosion of Carbon Steel in Aqueous Environments Containing Carbon Dioxide, *Corrosion*, *42*(2), 71-78, 1986. MetAbs No. 86-350810. **Abstract:** Experimental results and analyses are reported on the corrosion of carbon steel in CO_2-saturated environments that typically represent producing well waters encountered in natural gas reservoirs. Tests were performed at up 95 °C and 700 kPa (100 psig).

B.W. Bradley, CO_2 EOR (Enhanced Oil Recovery) Requires Corrosion Control Program in Gas-Gathering Systems, *Oil Gas J.*, *84*(11), 88-95, 1986. MetAbs No. 86-351557. **Abstract:** The theory of CO_2 corrosion and its control in gas gathering systems of enhanced oil recovery projects involving CO_2 floods are discussed.

L.E. Newton, Jr. and R.H. Hausler, Ed., *CO_2 Corrosion in Oil and Gas Production—Selected Papers, Abstracts and References,* National Association of Corrosion Engineers, Houston, 1984.

R.H. Hausler, Ed., *Advances in CO_2 Corrosion,* Vol I, National Association of Corrosion Engineers, Houston, 1985.

A. Ikeda, S. Mukai, and M. Ueda, CO_2 Corrosion Behavior of Carbon and Chromium Steels, *Sumimo Search*, *31*, 91-102, 1985. MetAbs No. 86-351788. **Abstract:** The influence of environmental and metallurgical factors on CO_2 corrosion of alloy steel is investigated in laboratory tests.

R. Jasinski, Corrosion of N80-Type Steel by $CO_2/Water$ Mixtures, *Corrosion*, *43*(4), 214-218, 1987. MetAbs No. 87-351994. **Abstract:** The initial high corrosion rates of low-alloy carbon steel (N80) in $CO_2/brine$ mixtures are mitigated by the subsequent generation of loosely adherent iron carbide surface films, iron carbonate surface films, and in the case of unbuffered waters, by a significant increase in pH caused by the loss of acid to the corrosion process forming these films. This phenomenon is discussed.

K. Masamura, S. Hashizume, J. Sakai, and I. Matsushima, Polarization Behavior of High-Alloy OCTG in CO_2 Environment as Affected by Chlorides and Sulfides, *Corrosion*, *43*(6), 359-365, 1987. MetAbs No. 87-352498. **Abstract:** Pitting corrosion resistance of high Ni austenitic stainless alloys NIC42, NIC52 and 304 for oil country tubular goods has been examined by electrochemical measurements in a high temperature, high pressure autoclave, simulating well conditions.

J. Rechberger, D. Tromans, and A. Mitchell, Stress Corrosion Cracking of Conventional and Super-Clean 3.5NiCrMoV Rotor Steels in Simulated Condensates, *Corrosion*, *44*(2), 79-87, 1988. MetAbs No. 88-351085. **Abstract:** The stress-corrosion cracking behavior of two bainitic 3.5NiCrMoV low-pressure rotor steels has been studied at 95 °C in environments containing species that are possible contaminants in steam condensates. The environments were 3.5M NaOH, 1M Na$_2$CO$_3$ + 1M NaHCO$_3$ and a saturated CO$_2$/H$_2$O solution. A combination of slow strain rate tensile testing methods and fracture mechanics techniques were used to produce stress-corrosion cracking.

Corrosion Behavior of Various Metals and Alloys in Carbon Dioxide

Material	Condition, other factors, comments	Concentration, %	Temperature, °C (°F)	Duration	Corrosion rate, mm/yr (mils/yr) or other	Ref
Steels						
API N-80 steel	Aqueous solution. (a)	...	Room	2 h	0.508 (200)	24
API N-80 steel	Aqueous solution. (a)	...	Room	24 h	2.28 ± 0.5 (90 ± 22)	24
API N-80 steel	Aqueous solution. (a)	...	Room	24-72 h	≥3 (≥120)	24
API N-80 steel	Aqueous solution plus 4% NaCl. (a)	...	Room	2 h	3.07 ± 0.2 (121 ± 9)	24
API N-80 steel	Aqueous solution plus 4% NaCl. (a)	...	Room	24 h	4.44 (175)	24
API N-80 steel	Aqueous solution plus 4% NaCl. (a)	...	Room	24-72 h	2.44 ± 0.10 (96 ± 4)	24
API N-80 steel	Aqueous solution plus 1 ppt NaHCO$_3$. (a)	...	Room	2 h	3.35 ± 1.67 (132 ± 66)	24
API N-80 steel	Aqueous solution plus 1 ppt NaHCO$_3$. (a)	...	Room	24 h	2.79 ± 0.05 (110 ± 2)	24
API N-80 steel	Aqueous solution plus 1 ppt NaHCO$_3$. (a)	...	Room	24-72 h	2.48 ± 0.05 (98 ± 2)	24
API N-80 steel	Aqueous solution plus 14 ppt NaHCO$_3$. (a)	...	Room	2 h	1.60 ± 0.3 (63 ± 12)	24
API N-80 steel	Aqueous solution plus 14 ppt NaHCO$_3$. (a)	...	Room	24 h	0.43 ± 0.15 (17 ± 6)	24
API N-80 steel	Aqueous solution plus 14 ppt NaHCO$_3$. (a)	...	Room	24-72 h	0.3 ± 0.05 (12 ± 2)	24
API N-80 steel	Aqueous solution. (a)	...	95 (200)	2 h	13.97 (550)	24
API N-80 steel	Aqueous solution. (a)	...	95 (200)	24 h	7.79 ± 0.68 (307 ± 27)	24
API N-80 steel	Aqueous solution. (a)	...	95 (200)	24-72 h	7.11 (280)	24
API N-80 steel	Aqueous solution plus 4% NaOH. (a)	...	95 (200)	2 h	25.4 ± 10.16 (1000 ± 400)	24
API N-80 steel	Aqueous solution plus 4% NaOH. (a)	...	95 (200)	24 h	8.33 ± 0.53 (328 ± 21)	24
API N-80 steel	Aqueous solution plus 4% NaOH. (a)	...	95 (200)	24-72 h	1.27 (50)	24
API N-80 steel	Aqueous solution plus 1 ppt NaHCO$_3$. (a)	...	95 (200)	2 h	5.48 ± 0.20 (216 ± 8)	24
API N-80 steel	Aqueous solution plus 1 ppt NaHCO$_3$. (a)	...	95 (200)	24 h	4.31 ± 0.81 (170 ± 32)	24
API N-80 steel	Aqueous solution plus 1 ppt NaHCO$_3$. (a)	...	95 (200)	24-72 h	2.23 (88)	24
API N-80 steel	Aqueous solution plus 14 ppt NaHCO$_3$. (a)	...	95 (200)	2 h	4.57 (180)	24
API N-80 steel	Aqueous solution plus 14 ppt NaHCO$_3$. (a)	...	95 (200)	24 h	0.66 ± 0.10 (26 ± 4)	24
API N-80 steel	Aqueous solution plus 14 ppt NaHCO$_3$. (a)	...	95 (200)	24-72 h	0.012 (0.5)	24
Type 304 stainless steel	Dry	...	21 (70)	...	Very good	121
Type 304 stainless steel	Food processing; laboratory test. Carbonated water, pressure <5 psig	...	...	5 d	nil	89
Type 304 stainless steel	Mining; field or pilot plant test; strong aeration; rapid agitation. Gas stream, 2% carbon monoxide, 0.25% sulfur dioxide, some oxygen. Slight pitting: maximum depth of pits from incipient to 0.005 in.	10	66 (150)	73 d	<0.0001 in./yr	89
Type 304 stainless steel	Mining; field or pilot plant test; strong aeration; rapid agitation. With carbon over the standard maximum. Gas stream, 2% carbon monoxide, 0.25% sulfur dioxide, some oxygen. Slight pitting: maximum depth of pits from incipient to 0.005 in.	10	66 (150)	73 d	<0.0001 in./yr	89
Type 304 stainless steel	Petroleum; field or pilot plant test; no aeration; rapid agitation. Plus 88% nitrogen, condensed water has 40 ppm iron ions, 3 ppm sulfuric and sulfurous, nitric and nitrous acids (pipe, gas steam)	12	43 (110)	36 d	<0.0001 in./yr	89

(Continued)

Corrosion Behavior of Various Metals and Alloys in Carbon Dioxide (Continued)

Material	Condition, other factors, comments	Concentration, %	Temperature, °C (°F)	Duration	Corrosion rate, mm/yr (mils/yr) or other	Ref
Type 304 stainless steel	Chemical processing; field or pilot plant test; no aeration; rapid agitation. Plus 66.66% water, trace ethanolamine (vapor line of Girdler reactivator)	33.34	113-116 (235-240)	62 d	0.0001 in./yr	89
Type 316 stainless steel	Dry	...	21 (70)	...	Very good	121
Type 316 stainless steel	Petroleum processing; rapid agitation. Plus carbon dioxide and nitrogen, trace chlorine (gaseous mixture). Severe pitting: maximum depth of pits over 0.010 in.; crevice attack (tendency to concentration-cell corrosion)	...	150-200 (302-392)	198 d	0.0022 in./yr	89
Type 316 stainless steel	Mining; field or pilot plant test; strong aeration; rapid agitation. Gas stream, 2% carbon monoxide, 0.25% sulfur dioxide, some oxygen	10	66 (150)	73 d	<0.0001 in./yr	89
Type 316 stainless steel	Petroleum processing; field or pilot plant test; no aeration; rapid agitation. Plus 88% nitrogen, condensed water has 40 ppm iron ions, 10 ppm sulfuric and sulfurous acids, 3 ppm nitric and nitrous acids (pipe, gas steam)	12	43 (110)	36 d	<0.0001 in./yr	89
Type 316 stainless steel	Water purification; rapid agitation. Plus 6% oxygen, 2% carbon monoxide, sulfur dioxide, trace nitrogen. Severe pitting: maximum depth of pits over 0.010 in.	26	40-45 (104-113)	75 d	0.0012 in./yr	89
Type 316 stainless steel	Chemical processing; field or pilot plant test; no aeration; rapid agitation. Plus 66.66% water, trace ethanolamine (vapor line of Girdler reactivator)	33.34	113-116 (235-240)	62 d	0.002 in./yr	89
Type 317 stainless steel	Petroleum processing; rapid agitation. Plus carbon dioxide and nitrogen, trace chlorine (gaseous mixture). Severe pitting: maximum depth of pits over 0.010 in.; crevice attack (tendency to concentration-cell corrosion)	...	150-200 (302-392)	198 d	0.002 in./yr	89
Type 317 stainless steel	Petroleum processing; field or pilot plant test; no aeration; rapid agitation. Plus 88% nitrogen, condensed water has 40 ppm iron ions, 10 ppm sulfuric and sulfurous acids, 3 ppm nitric and nitrous acids (pipe, gas steam)	12	43 (110)	36 d	<0.0001 in./yr	89
Type 317 stainless steel	Chemical processing; field or pilot plant test; no aeration; rapid agitation. Plus 66.66% water, trace ethanolamine (vapor line of Girdler reactivator)	33.34	113-116 (235-240)	62 d	0.0001 in./yr	89
Type 410 stainless steel	Dry	...	21 (70)	...	Very good	121
Type 430 stainless steel	Dry	...	21 (70)	...	Very good	121
Aluminum						
Aluminum (99.0-99.5%)	Solution	...	20 (68)	...	Satisfactory	92
Aluminum (>99.5%)	Solution	...	20 (68)	...	Satisfactory	92
Aluminum-manganese alloys	Solution	...	20 (68)	...	Satisfactory	92
Coppers						
70-30 cupronickel	Dry	...	...	...	Suitable	93
70-30 cupronickel	Moist. (b)	...	...	...	Good	93
90-10 cupronickel	Dry	...	...	...	Suitable	93
90-10 cupronickel	Moist. (b)	...	...	...	Good	93
Admiralty brass	Dry	...	...	...	Suitable	93
Admiralty brass	Moist. (b)	...	...	...	Good	93
Aluminum bronze	Dry	...	...	...	Suitable	93
Aluminum bronze	Moist. (b)	...	...	...	Good	93
Ampco 8, aluminum bronze	Dry. Generally suitable	...	...	...	<0.05 (<2)	96
Ampco 8, aluminum bronze	Wet. Generally suitable. Conditions such as aeration or temperature could restrict use	...	...	...	<0.5 (<20)	96
Architectural bronze	Dry	...	...	...	Suitable	93
Architectural bronze	Moist	...	...	...	Fair	93
Brass	Dry	...	...	...	Suitable	93
Brass	Moist. (b)	...	...	...	Good	93

(Continued)

Corrosion Behavior of Various Metals and Alloys in Carbon Dioxide (Continued)

Material	Condition, other factors, comments	Concentration, %	Temperature, °C (°F)	Duration	Corrosion rate, mm/yr (mils/yr) or other	Ref
Cartridge brass	Dry	...	...	...	Suitable	93
Cartridge brass	Moist	...	...	...	Fair	93
Commercial bronze	Dry	...	...	...	Suitable	93
Commercial bronze	Moist. (b)	...	...	...	Good	93
Electrolytic copper	Dry	...	...	...	Suitable	93
Electrolytic copper	Moist. (b)	...	...	...	Good	93
Free-cutting brass	Dry	...	...	...	Suitable	93
Free-cutting brass	Moist	...	...	...	Fair	93
Muntz metal	Dry	...	...	...	Suitable	93
Muntz metal	Moist	...	...	...	Fair	93
Naval brass	Dry	...	...	...	Suitable	93
Naval brass	Moist	...	...	...	Fair	93
Nickel silver	Dry	18	...	...	Suitable	93
Nickel silver	Moist. (b)	18	...	...	Good	93
Phosphor bronze	5% Sn. Dry	...	...	...	Suitable	93
Phosphor bronze	5% Sn. Moist. (b)	...	...	...	Good	93
Phosphor bronze	8% Sn. Dry	...	...	...	Suitable	93
Phosphor bronze	8% Sn. Moist. (b)	...	...	...	Good	93
Phosphor copper	Moist. (b)	...	...	...	Good	93
Phosphor copper	Dry	...	...	...	Suitable	93
Red brass	Dry	...	...	...	Suitable	93
Red brass	Moist. (b)	...	...	...	Good	93
Silicon bronze	Low. Dry	...	...	...	Suitable	93
Silicon bronze	High. Dry	...	...	...	Suitable	93
Silicon bronze	Low. Moist. (b)	...	...	...	Good	93
Silicon bronze	High. Moist. (b)	...	...	...	Good	93
Titanium						
Titanium	...	100	...	...	Excellent	90
Heat- and corrosion-resistant alloys						
Alloy 825	Petroleum processing; rapid agitation. Plus carbon dioxide and nitrogen, trace chlorine (gaseous mixture). Severe pitting: maximum depth of pits over 0.010 in.; crevice attack (tendency to concentration-cell corrosion)	...	150-200 (302-392)	198 d	0.0013 in./yr	89
Alloy 825	Water purification; rapid agitation. Plus 6% oxygen, 2% carbon monoxide, sulfur dioxide, trace nitrogen. Severe pitting: maximum depth of pits over 0.010 in.	26	40-45 (104-113)	75 d	0.002 in./yr	89
Carpenter 20	Petroleum processing; field or pilot plant test; no aeration; rapid agitation. Plus 88% nitrogen, condensed water has 40 ppm iron ions, 10 ppm sulfuric and sulfurous acids, 3 ppm nitric and nitrous acids (pipe, gas steam)	12	43 (110)	36 d	<0.0001 in./yr	89
Noble metals						
Platinum	No reductant present	...	1400 (2550)	...	<0.05 (<2)	6
Silver	...	Pure	Room	...	<0.05 (<2)	8
Others						
Magnesium	Dry	100	Room	...	Suitable	119

(a) Pressure at 0.83 MPa. (b) May be considered in place of a copper metal when some property, other than corrosion resistance, governs its use.

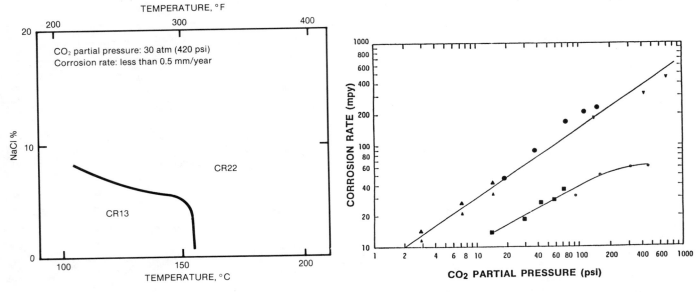

Stainless steel. Relative corrosion resistance of 13% chromium stainless steel and duplex stainless steel (Cr 22) in carbon dioxide as a function of temperature and sodium chloride content. Source: Nippon Kokan K.K.

Steel. Corrosion rate of steel as a function of carbon dioxide partial pressure. Source: D.W. De Berry and W.S. Clark, "Corrosion Due to Use of CO_2 for Enhanced Oil Recovery," U.S. Department of Energy, DOE/MC/08442-T1, 1979.

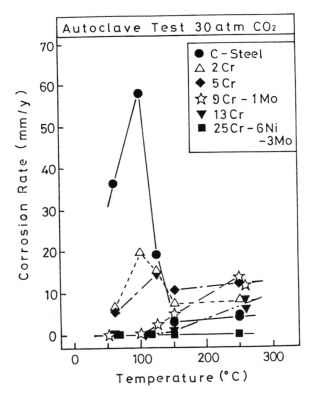

Steels. Corrosion of chromium steels in high-pressure wet carbon dioxide as a function of temperature. Source: A. Ikeda, S. Mukai, and M. Ueda, CO_2 Corrosion Behavior of Carbon and Chromium Steels, *Sumimo Search, 31,* 91-102, 1985.

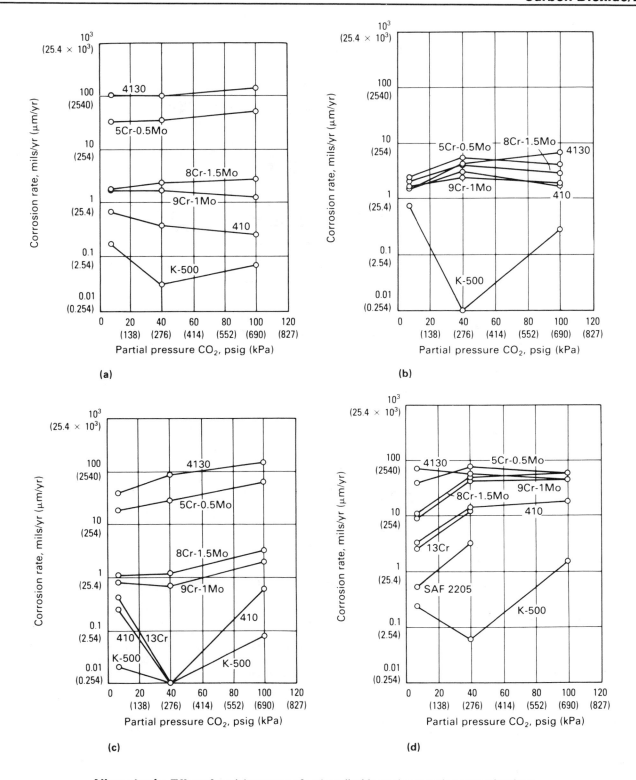

Alloy steels. Effect of partial pressure of carbon dioxide on the corrosion rates of various alloy steels. (a) 0% chlorides at 65 °C (150 °F). (b) 0% chlorides at 175 °C (350 °F). (c) 15.2% chlorides at 65 °C (150 °F). (d) 15.2% chlorides at 175 °C (350 °F). Source: *Metals Handbook*, 9th ed., Vol 13, Corrosion, ASM International, Metals Park, OH, 1987, 536.

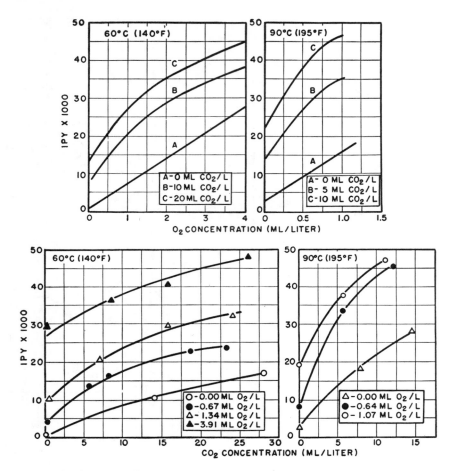

Carbon steel. Corrosion of mild steel (0.15% carbon) as a function of dissolved carbon dioxide and oxygen concentration during a 5-h test; velocity, 45 cm (0.025 ft) per min; specimen size, 6.3 x 2.5 x 0.318 cm (2.5 x 1 x $^1/_8$ in.). Source: H.H. Uhlig, Iron and Steel, in *The Corrosion Handbook*, H.H. Uhlig, Ed., John Wiley & Sons, New York, 1948, 128.

Carbon Monoxide

Carbon monoxide, CO, is a colorless, odorless, toxic gas. It is soluble in alcohol and cupric chloride solutions, but insoluble in water. Carbon monoxide is formed by the incomplete oxidation of carbon. It is found in mines and car exhaust. Carbon monoxide is used in metallurgy as a reducing agent in smelting operations, in the production of carbonyls for the separation of various metals, as an ingredient in the synthesis of phosgene, and as an intermediate in the production of methanol.

Material Summaries

The following material summaries were compiled from a survey of the available literature. Inclusion of a material description under a given environment does not imply that it is the most appropriate material for corrosion service in that environment. Likewise, exclusion of a given material does not imply that it is not suitable for corrosion service applications in that environment.

Copper. Copper and its alloys are inert in dry carbon monoxide. However, corrosion does occur in the presence of moisture; the rate of attack depends on the amount of moisture available. High-pressure equipment made of alloy steels are often lined with copper or copper alloys to protect the alloy steel from carbon monoxide attack.

Niobium. Niobium reacts with carbon monoxide at temperatures above 250 °C (480 °F).

Silver. Silver is not affected by carbon monoxide up to 300 °C (570 °F).

Tantalum. Tantalum reacts with carbon monoxide at 1100 °C (2010 °F) to form tantalum oxide, TaO, which converts to tantalum pentoxide, Ta_2O_5, in the presence of oxygen.

Titanium. Titanium alloys have an oxide film that protects them from attack by either wet or dry carbon monoxide at temperatures up to 150 °C (300 °F).

Zirconium. Zirconium is stable in carbon monoxide at temperatures up to 300 to 400 °C (570 to 750 °F).

Corrosion Behavior of Various Metals and Alloys in Carbon Monoxide

Material	Condition, other factors, comments	Concen-tration, %	Temperature, °C (°F)	Duration	Corrosion rate, mm/yr (mils/yr) or other	Ref
Aluminum (99.0-99.5%)	Gas	...	<500 (<932)	...	Excellent	92
Aluminum alloys	Gas	...	<500 (<932)	...	Excellent	92
Magnesium	...	100	Room	...	Suitable	119
Platinum	No reductant present	...	1400 (2550)	...	<0.05 (<2)	6
Silver	...	Pure	300 (570)	...	<0.05 (<2)	8
Type 304 stainless steel	Chemical processing. Carbon monoxide, high pressure	...	200 (392)	...	Acceptable	89

Carbon Tetrachloride

Carbon tetrachloride, CCl_4, also known as tetrachloromethane, perchloro methane, and benzinoform, is a colorless liquid with a boiling point of 77 °C (170 °F). It is used as a solvent for lacquers, resin, and rubbers, and as a dry cleaning agent.

Material Summaries

The following material summaries were compiled from a survey of the available literature. Inclusion of a material description under a given environment does not imply that it is the most appropriate material for corrosion service in that environment. Likewise, exclusion of a given material does not imply that it is not suitable for corrosion service applications in that environment.

Aluminum. Laboratory tests showed that carbon tetrachloride at ambient temperature did not attack aluminum alloys 3003, 5052, and 5154, but was very corrosive at the boiling point, 77 °C (170 °F). The reaction, evidently electrochemical, produces aluminum chloride, which acts as an accelerator and hexachloroethane. The reaction rate is very dependent on temperature and decreases as the temperature drops from boiling to 50 °C (122 °F). It increases when superheated. The reaction rate increased at lower temperatures when carbon disulfide, water, or oxygen were present, but the same substances decreased the reaction rate at higher temperatures. Stabilizers help control the rate. Aluminum powder that has been in contact with carbon tetrachloride should not be used as a milling medium for comminuting aluminum.

Additional Reading

H.W. White, Study of Corrosion and Corrosion Inhibitor Species on Aluminum Surfaces, in *Tunneling Spectroscopy—Capabilities, Applications and New Techniques*, Plenum Press, New York, 287-309, 1982. MetAbs No. 85-352371. **Abstract:** Applications of tunneling spectroscopy to the provision of fundamental data on the corrosion of Al and Al alloys in chlorinated solvents and acid media are reviewed, the mechanism of surface-reaction inhibition by chemical additives is discussed, and the results are related to the development of improved inhibitors and more resistant alloy compositions. Particular media studied include CCl_4, trichloroethylene, and HCl, and the inhibitors considered comprise formamide, for the CCl_4, and acridine and thiourea for the HCl.

S. Ramesh and V.S. Muralidharan, Studies on the Corrosion of 2S Aluminium in Carbon Tetrachloride, *Trans. SAEST, 21*(2), 119-124, 1986. MetAbs No. 87-350823. **Abstract:** Corrosion of 2S Al was studied as a function of time, temperature and different amounts of water.

Corrosion Behavior of Various Metals and Alloys in Carbon Tetrachloride

Material	Condition, other factors, comments	Concen-tration, %	Temperature, °C (°F)	Duration	Corrosion rate, mm/yr (mils/yr) or other	Ref
Stainless steels						
AM-363 stainless steel	...	...	Room	...	Slightly attacked	120
Type 304 stainless steel	Dry cleaning; field or pilot plant test; no aeration; no agitation. "Kolene" solvent, 10% benzene	90	Room	40 d	<0.0001 in./yr	89
Type 304 stainless steel	Dry cleaning (distillation); field or pilot plant test; no aeration; rapid agitation. With carbon over the standard maximum. "Kolene" solvent, 10% benzene (bottom of still). Slight pitting: maximum depth of pits from incipient to 0.005 in.; crevice attack (tendency to concentration-cell corrosion)	90	142 (287)	38 d	0.0014 in./yr	89

(Continued)

Corrosion Behavior of Various Metals and Alloys in Carbon Tetrachloride (Continued)

Material	Condition, other factors, comments	Concentration, %	Temperature, °C (°F)	Duration	Corrosion rate, mm/yr (mils/yr) or other	
Type 304 stainless steel	Dry cleaning (distillation); field or pilot plant test; no aeration; rapid agitation. "Kolene" solvent, 10% benzene (bottom of still). Slight pitting: maximum depth of pits from incipient to 0.005 in.; crevice attack (tendency to concentration-cell corrosion)	90	142 (287)	38 d	0.0014 in./yr	89
Type 304 stainless steel	Chemical processing; field or pilot plant test; no aeration; slight to moderate agitation. Plus 12% water, 0.4% chlorine, 0.1% hydrochloric acid (vapors). Severe pitting: maximum depth of pits over 0.010 in.; crevice attack (tendency to concentration-cell corrosion)	87.5	60-85 (140-185)	3 d	1.57 in./yr	89
Type 304 stainless steel	Chemical processing (rectification); field or pilot plant test; no aeration; rapid agitation. Crude carbon tetrachloride (column)	...	80 (176)	133 d	<0.0001 in./yr	89
Type 304 stainless steel	Chemical processing (distillation); field or pilot plant test; no aeration; rapid agitation. With carbon over the standard maximum. Plus 75-95% sulfur chlorides (sulfur mono- and dichloride, thiocarbonyl chloride, etc.) (liquid line)	5-25	52-54 (125-130)	35.5 d	0.0001 in./yr	89
Type 316 stainless steel	Dry cleaning; field or pilot plant test; no aeration; no agitation. "Kolene" solvent, 10% benzene	90	Room	40 d	<0.0001 in./yr	89
Type 316 stainless steel	Dry cleaning (distillation); field or pilot plant test; no aeration; rapid agitation. "Kolene" solvent, 10% benzene (bottom of still). Slight pitting: maximum depth of pits from incipient to 0.005 in.; crevice attack (tendency to concentration-cell corrosion)	90	142 (287)	38 d	0.0008 in./yr	89
Type 316 stainless steel	Chemical processing; field or pilot plant test; no aeration; slight to moderate agitation. Plus 12% water, 0.4% chlorine, 0.1% hydrochloric acid (vapors). Severe pitting: maximum depth of pits over 0.010 in.; crevice attack (tendency to concentration-cell corrosion)	87.5	60-85 (140-185)	3 d	1.26 in./yr	89
Type 316 stainless steel	Chemical processing (rectification); field or pilot plant test; no aeration; rapid agitation. Crude carbon tetrachloride (column). Slight pitting: maximum depth of pits from incipient to 0.005 in.; crevice attack (tendency to concentration-cell corrosion)	...	80 (176)	133 d	<0.0001 in./yr	89
Type 316 stainless steel	Chemical processing (distillation); field or pilot plant test; no aeration; rapid agitation. Plus 75-95% sulfur chlorides (sulfur mono- and dichloride, thiocarbonyl chloride, etc.) (liquid line)	5-25	52-54 (125-130)	35.5 d	0.0001 in./yr	89
Type 410 stainless steel	...	...	Room	...	Affected	121
Type 410 stainless steel	Vapors refluxed	...	Room	...	Very slightly affected	121
Aluminum						
Aluminum (99.0-99.5%)	Wet	...	20 (68)	...	Satisfactory	92
Aluminum alloys	Wet	...	20 (68)	...	Satisfactory	92
Coppers						
70-30 cupronickel	Dry	...	...	...	Suitable	93
70-30 cupronickel	Moist	...	...	...	Suitable	93
90-10 cupronickel	Dry	...	...	...	Suitable	93
90-10 cupronickel	Moist. (a)	...	...	...	Good	93
Admiralty brass	Dry	...	...	...	Suitable	93
Admiralty brass	Moist. (a)	...	...	...	Good	93
Aluminum bronze	Dry	...	...	...	Suitable	93
Aluminum bronze	Moist. (a)	...	...	...	Good	93
Ampco 8, aluminum bronze	Generally suitable. Conditions such as aeration or temperature could restrict use	...	...	...	<0.5 (<20)	96
Architectural bronze	Dry	...	...	...	Suitable	93
Architectural bronze	Moist	...	...	...	Not suitable	93
Brass	Dry	...	...	...	Suitable	93

(Continued)

Corrosion Behavior of Various Metals and Alloys in Carbon Tetrachloride (Continued)

Material	Condition, other factors, comments	Concentration, %	Temperature, °C (°F)	Duration	Corrosion rate, mm/yr (mils/yr) or other	Ref
Brass	Moist. (a)	...	...	...	Good	93
Cartridge brass	Dry	...	...	...	Suitable	93
Cartridge brass	Moist	...	...	...	Not suitable	93
Commercial bronze	Dry	...	...	...	Suitable	93
Commercial bronze	Moist. (a)	...	...	...	Good	93
Electrolytic copper	Dry	...	...	...	Suitable	93
Electrolytic copper	Moist. (a)	...	...	...	Good	93
Free-cutting brass	Dry	...	...	...	Suitable	93
Free-cutting brass	Moist	...	...	...	Not suitable	93
Muntz metal	Dry	...	...	...	Suitable	93
Muntz metal	Moist	...	...	...	Not suitable	93
Naval brass	Dry	...	...	...	Suitable	93
Naval brass	Moist	...	...	...	Not suitable	93
Nickel silver	Dry	18	...	...	Suitable	93
Nickel silver	Moist. (a)	18	...	...	Good	93
Phosphor bronze	5% Sn. Dry	...	...	...	Suitable	93
Phosphor bronze	8% Sn. Dry	...	...	...	Suitable	93
Phosphor bronze	5% Sn. Moist. (a)	...	...	...	Good	93
Phosphor bronze	8% Sn. Moist. (a)	...	...	...	Good	93
Phosphor copper	Moist. (a)	...	...	...	Good	93
Phosphor copper	Dry	...	...	...	Suitable	93
Red brass	Dry	...	...	...	Suitable	93
Red brass	Moist. (a)	...	...	...	Good	93
Silicon bronze	Low. Dry	...	...	...	Suitable	93
Silicon bronze	High. Dry	...	...	...	Suitable	93
Silicon bronze	Low. Moist. (a)	...	...	...	Good	93
Silicon bronze	High. Moist. (a)	...	...	...	Good	93
Titanium						
Titanium	...	99	Boiling	...	0.003 (0.12)	20
Titanium	...	100	Boiling	...	0.003 (0.12)	20
Titanium	...	99	Boiling	...	0.005 (0.2)	90
Titanium	...	Liquid	Boiling	...	nil	90
Titanium	...	Vapor	Boiling	...	nil	90
Titanium	Plus 50% H_2O	50	25 °C (77 °F)	...	0.005 (0.2)	90
Zirconium						
Zr702	...	0-100	Room to 100	...	<0.13 (<5)	15
Noble metals						
Platinum	Dry and wet	...	Boiling	...	<0.05 (<2)	6
Silver	Dry and wet	...	Boiling	...	<0.05 (<2)	10
Others						
Magnesium	...	100	Room	...	Suitable	119

(a) May be considered in place of a copper metal when some property, other than corrosion resistance, governs its use.

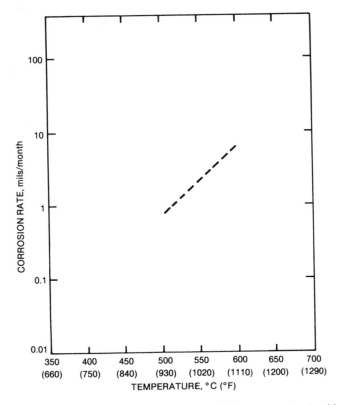

Hastelloy C. Corrosion of Hastelloy alloy C by carbon tetrachloride vapor plus air after 70-h exposure. Source: W.Z. Friend, *Corrosion of Nickel and Nickel-base Alloys*, John Wiley & Sons, New York, 1980, 362.

Carbonic Acid

Carbonic acid, H_2CO_3, exists in solution only. It is prepared by the combination of carbon dioxide and water. For additional information, please see Carbon Dioxide.

Material Summaries

The following material summaries were compiled from a survey of the available literature. Inclusion of a material description under a given environment does not imply that it is the most appropriate material for corrosion service in that environment. Likewise, exclusion of a given material does not imply that it is not suitable for corrosion service applications in that environment.

Aluminum. Aluminum alloy equipment has been used successfully to handle carbonated beverages.

Titanium. Titanium exhibits an almost nil corrosion rate for all concentrations of carbonic acid well beyond its boiling point.

Corrosion Behavior of Various Metals and Alloys in Carbonic Acid

Material	Condition, other factors, comments	Concentration, %	Temperature, °C (°F)	Duration	Corrosion rate, mm/yr (mils/yr) or other	Ref
Stainless steels						
Type 304 stainless steel	...	...	21 (70)	...	Good	121
Type 316 stainless steel	...	...	21 (70)	...	Good	121
Type 410 stainless steel	...	...	21 (70)	...	Good	121
Type 430 stainless steel	...	...	21 (70)	...	Good	121
		(Continued)				

Corrosion Behavior of Various Metals and Alloys in Carbonic Acid (Continued)

Material	Condition, other factors, comments	Concentration, %	Temperature, °C (°F)	Duration	Corrosion rate, mm/yr (mils/yr) or other	Ref
Zirconium						
Zr702	...	Saturated	100 (212)	...	<0.13 (<5)	15
Lead, tin, and zinc						
Lead	Corrosion rate too high to merit any consideration of Pb	...	24 (75)	...	>1270 μm/yr (>50)	95
Noble metals						
Silver	...	All	Room	...	<0.05 (<2)	4
Silver	...	All	Room	...	<0.05 (<2)	4

Cellulose Acetate

Cellulose acetate is the general name for the acetic acid esters of cellulose, cellulose pentaacetate, $C_6H_5(OOCCH_3)_5$, cellulose tetraacetate, $C_6H_6O(OOCCH_3)_4$, and cellulose triacetate, $C_6H_7O_2(OOCCH_3)_3$. Cellulose acetate is a tough, flexible, slow-burning and long-lasting material used in the production of plastic film for food packaging, magnetic tape, and movie film.

Material Summaries

The following material summaries were compiled from a survey of the available literature. Inclusion of a material description under a given environment does not imply that it is the most appropriate material for corrosion service in that environment. Likewise, exclusion of a given material does not imply that it is not suitable for corrosion service applications in that environment.

Aluminum. Cellulose acetate has been prepared and stored successfully in aluminum alloy equipment.

Corrosion Behavior of Various Metals and Alloys in Cellulose Acetate

Material	Condition, other factors, comments	Concentration, %	Temperature, °C (°F)	Duration	Corrosion rate, mm/yr (mils/yr) or other	Ref
Lead	Negligible corrosion; Pb recommended for use	...	24 (75)	...	<50 μm/yr (<2)	95

Cesium Hydroxide

Cesium hydroxide, CsOH, also known as cesium hydrate, is a colorless to yellowish deliquescent solid. It is formed by the vigorous reaction of cesium and water. Cesium hydroxide is the strongest of the alkali metal hydroxides with the lowest lattice energy. It has a melting point of 272.3 °C (522 °F) and is soluble in water. Cesium hydroxide is used as an electrolyte in alkaline batteries at subzero temperatures.

Material Summaries

The following material summaries were compiled from a survey of the available literature. Inclusion of a material description under a given environment does not imply that it is the most appropriate material for corrosion service in that environment. Likewise, exclusion of a given material does not imply that it is not suitable for corrosion service applications in that environment.

Silver. Silver is not attacked by cesium hydroxide at temperatures slightly below 500 °C (930 °F).

Corrosion Behavior of Various Metals and Alloys in Cesium Hydroxide

Material	Condition, other factors, comments	Concentration, %	Temperature, °C (°F)	Duration	Corrosion rate, mm/yr (mils/yr) or other	Ref
Silver	...	All	500 (930)	...	<0.05 (<2)	9

Chlorides

All metallic chlorides, except silver chloride and mercurous chloride, are soluble in water. Lead chloride, cuprous chloride, and thallium chloride are only slightly soluble in water. Alkali chlorides are more volatile than the corresponding alkali oxides, nitrates, or sulfates. Metallic chlorides melt when heated and volatilize or decompose. For example, sodium chloride melts at 804 °C (1480 °F), magnesium chloride crystals decompose to yield magnesium oxide residue and hydrogen chloride, and cupric chloride yields cuprous chloride and chlorine. Sodium, calcium, strontium, and barium metals are produced by electrolyzing the molten metallic chloride.

Material Summaries

The following material summaries were compiled from a survey of the available literature. Inclusion of a material description under a given environment does not imply that it is the most appropriate material for corrosion service in that environment. Likewise, exclusion of a given material does not imply that it is not suitable for corrosion service applications in that environment.

Stainless Steels. Chlorides are generally more aggressive to stainless steels because of the ability of the chloride ion to penetrate the passive film and cause pitting. Pitting is promoted in aerated or mildly acidic oxidizing solutions. Temperature and chloride concentration affect the degree of pitting and the stress-corrosion cracking. At ambient temperature, chloride pitting of 18Cr-8Ni stainless steel may occur, but stress-corrosion cracking is unlikely. At about 65 °C (150 °F) or above, the stress-corrosion cracking of austenitic grades must be considered. Chloride stress-corrosion cracking may be avoided by use of either ferritic grades of stainless steel with a lower nickel content such as 18Cr-2Mo, or duplex alloys such as 7-Mo PLUS, alloy 2205, and Ferralium 255 in elevated temperature chloride environments.

Crevice corrosion of stainless steels in Cl⁻ containing waters is dependent on a number of interrelated factors. Higher Cl⁻ levels in bulk solutions enable the occurrence of attack for a broader range of crevice geometries. Because chlorides concentrate in crevices, even low levels in bulk environments can lead to corrosion for some susceptible stainless steels.

The limited corrosion resistance of sintered stainless steels, particularly in a chloride environment, is commonly thought to derive from the presence of residual pores that give rise to crevice corrosion as a result of oxygen depletion within the pores. There is evidence, however, that factors other than porosity often determine corrosion life. For example, despite similar pore volumes, sizes, and shapes, type 316L stainless steel parts prepared from various powder lots and sintered under varying conditions had corrosion resistances in 5% aqueous sodium chloride solution that varied between 5 and 500 h for a specified degree of corrosion. Furthermore, a comparison of wrought and sintered (85% of theoretical density) type 316L for susceptibility to crevice corrosion in 10% ferric chloride showed that the wrought part was even more severely attacked than the porous P/M part. Lastly, surface analyses of water-atomized stainless steel powders showed the presence of large amounts of oxidized silicon concurrent with a severe depletion of chromium. The surface composition of a sintered part depended on its sintering conditions.

The factors of critical importance for the corrosion resistance of sintered stainless steels include control of iron contamination, carbon, nitrogen, oxygen, and sintered part density. Also, the precautions necessary for maximizing corrosion resistance differ with the sintering atmosphere.

Copper. Copper alloys under cyclic stress have shorter service lives in chloride solutions than in air. Anodically polarizing C26000 and C44300 alloys lowered their fracture stresses in sodium chloride solutions as measured in slow strain experiments.

Magnesium. Chloride solutions are corrosive, because chlorides, even in small amounts, break down the protective film on magnesium.

Amorphous Metals. The stress-corrosion cracking behavior of glassy Fe-Cr-Ni-P-C alloy systems in acidic chloride solutions was investigated with constant extension rate tensile tests. Hydrogen embrittlement occurred at cathodic polarizations up to -300 mV relative to the corrosion potential. In the passive potential region, no cracking occurred in neutral sodium chloride solutions and in acidic solutions at low chloride ion concentrations. Fracture stress decreased only when the specimens were strained in strong acidic solutions containing the chloride ion, and this phenomenon was also attributed to hydrogen embrittlement.

The resistance of Fe-Ni-Cr-P-B glassy alloy filaments to crevice corrosion in acidic solutions containing the chloride ion was attributed to its strong tendency to passivate, which in turn stifled propagation, even under the aggressive conditions of low pH, low dissolved oxygen concentration, and oxidizing potential that prevail within crevices. This resistance to crevice corrosion could be expected to extend to other glassy transition metal-metalloid compositions containing both a film former and phosphorus.

Glassy nickel-phosphorus is another alloy system that has been recently investigated and that appears to resist chloride-induced corrosion. The potentiodynamic polarization curves of both chloride-containing and chloride-free electrolytes are virtually identical. A form of chemical passivity has been proposed to explain the corrosion behavior. Passivation in this system is due to the formation of an ionic barrier layer, not the classic passive oxide film. This barrier layer consists of the hypophosphite ion adsorbed on the nickel-phosphorus surface, which may then be hydrogen bonded to an outer layer of water molecules. This barrier inhibits the transport of water to the surface and thus prevents hydration of nickel, which is the first step in the nickel dissolution process.

Tungsten-iron and titanium-copper alloys prepared by high-rate sputter deposition resisted pitting corrosion up to 2.5 V (SCE) in chloride solutions of pH 1 and 7.

Beryllium. Chloride ions from sources other than tap water can also lead to the pitting attack of beryllium in aqueous baths. Chloride ions may be provided by chlorinated solvents used to clean oils and greases when the solvent is carried into the cleaning bath by an arsenic-machined surface and from plastic piping used in chemical cleaning facilities to avoid metallic contamination.

Nickel. The nickel-chromium-molybdenum alloys, for example alloys C-276, 625, ALLCORR, and C-22, exhibit excellent resistance to pitting in oxidizing chloride media. Pitting resistance is enhanced with the presence of chromium and molybdenum. Nickel alloys are used in pulp and paper mills where conditions are the most corrosive. Alloy 600 has proved to be one of the most resistant alloys to high-temperature chloride salt attack. In fact, alloy 600 along with alloy 800 have been used for over 25 years for digester liquor heater tubing because their high nickel content provides excellent resistance to chloride stress-corrosion cracking. Alloys 601, 617, 690, RA330, and 825 also provide useful resistance.

Tantalum. Over the temperature range commonly used in solution processes, tantalum is inert to phosphorus chlorides.

Tin. The presence of chloride compounds in the paper used for labels and in the materials used in shipping containers may create a serious corrosion problem in tinplate cans during storage. The resistance of tin-silver alloys to chloride attack is considerably better than the resistance of sterling silver. Less discolorization occurred in tin-silver alloys upon heating in air.

Titanium. Titanium alloys generally exhibit superior resistance to crevice corrosion as compared to stainless steel and nickel-base alloys. However, the susceptibility of titanium alloys to crevice corrosion in hot concentrated chloride increases significantly as temperatures increase and pH decreases. Crevice attack of titanium alloys will generally not occur below 70 °C (160 °F) regardless of solution pH or chloride concentration, or when solution pH exceeds 10 regardless of temperature.

Titanium alloy grade 12 provides the most crevice corrosion resistance to hot low-pH salt solutions such as brine with pH between 3 and 11 and at temperatures as high as 300 °C (570 °F). Extensive tests of the crevice corrosion resistance of grade 12 titanium were conducted in concentrated, near-neutral sodium chloride, a mixture of sodium and magnesium chlorides, and ammonium chloride brines at high temperatures. Studies were conducted to assess this alloy for potential applicati... hypersaline geothermal brine, high-level nuclear waste storage, refineries, and salt evaporator brine heaters. In all cases, crevice t... involving Teflon gasket-to-metal and metal-to-metal crevices extended periods revealed no evidence of significant attack to tem... tures as high as 250 °C (480 °F). In saturated ammonium chloride ... tion, no gasket-to-metal or under-salt-deposit attack was noted to 177 °C (350 °F) and at pH 3 to 7. Similar performance is noted for grade 7 titanium under these conditions.

It should be cautioned that deviations from normal crevice corrosion guidelines can be expected in certain acid salts, which when highly concentrated may hydrolyze to form hydrogen chloride at high temperatures. These salts include magnesium, calcium, zinc, and aluminum chlorides. Titanium alloy grade 7 is generally the most resistant in these situations. Teflon gasket-to-metal crevices of various high-strength titanium alloys were also tested in hot sodium chloride brines. Relative alloy crevice corrosion resistance generally parallels alloy resistance in reducing acid media. Titanium alloys containing at least 4 wt% molybdenum exhibit significantly increased crevice corrosion in high-temperature sodium chloride media down to relatively low pH values. Increasing the molybdenum content aided the crevice corrosion resistance, as evidenced in Teflon gasket-to-metal tests performed on Ti-3-8-6-4-4 alloy under conditions simulating those of a deep oil well (downhole). At 300 °C (570 °F) in a pH 3 solution prepared with 250 g/L sodium chloride and 1 g/L sulfur and a 103-kPa (15-psi) hydrogen sulfide, titanium alloy Ti-3-8-6-4-4 showed no susceptibility to crevice attack and revealed superior resistance to grade 12 titanium.

The crevice corrosion resistance in hot sodium chloride brines of grade 9 titanium appears to be essentially the same as that for unalloyed titanium. The increased aluminum content in grade 5 titanium alloy, however, slightly reduces the crevice corrosion resistance in comparison to unalloyed grades. Studies of the effect of chloride concentration on the initiation of crevice corrosion in unalloyed titanium indicate that 0.01% chloride ion at 90 °C (195 °F) and 0.10% chloride ion at 70 °C (160 °F) may be threshold conditions for crevice attack in aerated pH 3 to 5 solutions given tight Teflon gasket-to-metal crevices.

Tests indicate that crevice tightness and type of gasket are critical to crevice corrosion initiation. Teflon gasket-to-metal crevices are generally more susceptible to crack initiation than silicone rubber, neoprene rubber, asbestos and polyvinyl chloride (PVC) gasket-to-metal crevices. Sealants containing chloride salts may significantly increase susceptibility to crevice attack. Metal-to-metal crevices are generally the least susceptible to attack. The addition of impressed anodic potentials or dissolved oxidizing species can lead to shorter incubation time and increased crevice attack in sodium chloride brines.

Zinc. Chlorides have a corrosive action on zinc, because water-soluble and hygroscopic salts are formed.

Zirconium. Zirconium is not subject to crevice attack or pitting corrosion in low-pH chloride solutions or chlorine gas.

Additional Reading

J.R. Keiser and A.R. Olsen, Corrosion Studies in Coal Liquefaction Plants, *Corrosion, Microstructure and Metallography*, Vol. 12, American Society for Metals, 173-186, 1978. MetAbs No. 85-350797. **Abstract:** During the past few years, four direct coal liquefaction pilot plants have been operated in the United States to evaluate several liquefaction processes. Oak Ridge National Laboratory has assisted pilot plant operators by assessing materials performance through supply and examination of corrosion samples, on-site examination of equipment, and analysis of failed pilot plant components in its laboratory.

I.A. Maier, V. Mandredi, and J.R. Galvele, The Stress Corrosion Cracking of an Austenitic Stainless Steel in HCl + NaCl Solutions at Room Temperature, *Corros. Sci.*, 25(1), 15-34, 1985. MetAbs No. 85-350965. **Abstract:** Stress corrosion cracking susceptibility of type AISI 304 stainless steel was studied in mixed HCl + NaCl solutions at room temperature.

A.K. Bairamow, S. Zakipour, and C. Leygraf, An XPS Investigation of Dichromate and Molybdate Inhibitors on Aluminum, *Corros. Sci.*, 25(1), 69-73, 1985. MetAbs No. 85-350969. **Abstract:** In recent years, XPS has been used to study the interaction inhibitors and aluminum. Dichromates and molybdates are frequently used to inhibit the corrosion of aluminum.

Z. Ahmad, Mechanisms of Pitting Initiation in Aluminium and Its Alloys, *Aluminium*, 61(2), 128-129, 1985. MetAbs No. 85-351004. **Abstract:** The role of pitting potential and protection potential on the process leading to initiation and growth of pits in aluminium is described. The physical significance of these potentials is elucidated.

G.N. Kirby, Selecting Alloys for Chloride Service, *Chem. Eng. (NY)*, 92(3), 81-83, 1985. MetAbs No. 85-351021. **Abstract:** Recommendations are presented for the selection of alloys intended for use in chloride environments. Alloy selection depends strongly on pH, temperature, and flow rate of the environment.

G.N. Kirby, Selecting Alloys for Chloride Service. II, *Chem. Eng. (NY)*, 92(5), 99-102, 1985. MetAbs No. 85-351022. **Abstract:** Review is made of the corrosion of Cu alloys (Cu-10Ni, Ni-32Cu) in chloride service. Galvanic protection in the marine industry is discussed.

S. Berhnardsson, P. Norberg, H. Eriksson, and O. Forssell, Stainless Steels in the Petrochemical Industries, *Iron Steel Inst.*, 58(1), 7-9, 1985. MetAbs No. 85-351268. **Abstract:** The corrosion resistance of austenitic and duplex stainless steels is compared. Results of tests in neutral aerated aqueous chloride environments, critical pitting temperature and isocorrosion diagrams in stagnant H_2SO_4 in contact with air are described.

N. Sridhar, J. Kolts, and L.H. Flasche, A Duplex Stainless Steel for Chloride Environments, *J. Met.*, 37(3), 31-35, 1985. MetAbs No. 85-351334. **Abstract:** The effects of microstructural changes on the corrosion, stress corrosion cracking and corrosion fatigue resistance of a duplex stainless steel (Ferralium 255) to chloride environments are examined.

D.V. Moll, R.C. Salvarezza, H.A. Videla, and A.J. Arvia, The Pitting Corrosion of Nickel in Different Electrolyte Solutions Containing Chloride Ions, *J. Electrochem. Soc.*, 132(4), 754-760, 1985. MetAbs No. 85-351341. **Abstract:** The pitting corrosion of 99.99% Ni in different electrolytes containing chloride ions was studied using potentiostatic and potentiodynamic techniques complemented with scanning electron microscopy.

H.P. Lee, K. Nobe, and A.J. Pearlstein, Film Formation and Current Oscillations in the Electrodissolution of Copper in Acidic Chloride Media. I. Experimental Studies, *J. Electrochem. Soc.*, 132(5), 1031-1037, 1985. MetAbs No. 85-351428. **Abstract:** Oscillatory behavior of Cu electrodissolution in various acidic chloride solutions was studied with rotating disk electrodes.

P.G. Smith, J.E. Truman, H.T. Gisborne, and G. Oakes, The Stress Corrosion Resistance of Non-Magnetic Stainless Steels Used in Oil Exploration, *J. Mater. Energy Syst.*, 6(4), 300-312, 1985. MetAbs No. 85-351442. **Abstract:** Austenitic steels of the Cr-Mn-(Ni)-N2 type (304, 304N, Staballoy) are being used in the work hardened condition in substantial section size for some applications, notably as drill collars and stabilizers in the directional drilling of oil wells. Stress-corrosion cracking is discussed.

S. Bernhardsson and R. Mellstrom, Performance of a Highly Alloyed Stainless Steel in Marine Environments, *Anti-Corros. Methods Mater.*, 32(4), 7-11, 1985. MetAbs No. 85-351702. **Abstract:** The report is focused on Sanicro 28, an alloy with 27% Cr, 31% Ni, 3.5% Mo, 1% Cu, and its performance as compared with that of AISI 316. The results of potentiostatic and potentiodynamic measurements in neutral and acid chloride solutions are presented.

A.P. Akolzin, P. Ghosh, and Y.Y. Kharitonov, Application and Peculiarity of Ca(OH)2 as Inhibitor in Presence of Corrosion Activators, *Br. Corros. J.*, 20(1), 32-35, 1985. MetAbs No. 85-351884. **Abstract:** The anticorrosive and protective action of Ca(OH)2 solutions in the presence of corrosion activators (chlorides and sulfates) has been studied for carbon steel.

D.R. Arnott, N.E. Ryan, B.R. Hinton, B.A. Sexton, and A.E. Hugh Auger and XPS Studies of Cerium Corrosion Inhibition on 7 Aluminium Alloy, *Appl. Surf. Sci.*, 22-23(1), 236-251, 1985. MetAbs 85-352046. **Abstract:** Auger and X-ray photoelectron spectroscopy were used to study the oxide film formed on high-strength 7075 Al alloy when immersed in aqueous chloride solutions containing small additions of cerous ions.

M. Fleischmann, I.R. Hill, G. Mengoli, M.M. Musiani, and J. Akhavan, A Comparative Study of the Efficiency of Some Organic Inhibitors for the Corrosion of Copper in Aqueous Chloride Media Using Electrochemical and Surface Enhanced Raman Scattering Techniques, *Electrochim. Acta*, 30(7), 879-888, 1985. MetAbs No. 85-352108. **Abstract:** The efficiency of four corrosion inhibitors (benzimidazole, 1-hydroxybenzotriazole, benzotriazole and 2-mercaptobenzoxazole) for the corrosion inhibition of Cu in aqueous chloride media is investigated using electrochemical and surface enhanced Raman spectroscopic techniques.

R.F. Hehemann, Stress Corrosion Cracking of Stainless Steels, *Metall. Trans. A*, 16(11), 1909-1923, 1985. MetAbs No. 85-352339. **Abstract:** The similarities and differences in the stress corrosion cracking response of ferritic (E-Brite, 26-1S, 29Cr-4Mo, 29Cr-4Mo-2Ni, 26Cr-2Mo) and austenitic (304) stainless steels in chloride solutions are examined.

P. Vassie, Reinforcement Corrosion and the Durability of Concrete Bridges, *Corros. Prev. Control*, 32(3), 43-49, 1985. MetAbs No. 85-352368. **Abstract:** The durability of concrete bridges in the UK is discussed with emphasis on the parts of bridges vulnerable to reinforcement corrosion, the causes of reinforcement corrosion, the detection of reinforcement corrosion, and possible preventive measures.

S. Narain, S. Assad, K.V. Rao, and M.R. Barakat, Case Histories of Corrosion Problems in a Wastewater Treatment Plant, *Mater. Perform.*, 24(9), 23-27, 1985. MetAbs No. 86-350019. **Abstract:** Several failures of carbon steel (API 5L-B) and cast iron equipment in the Ruwais Refinery wastewater treatment plant were encountered within two years of operations. The reasons for corrosion were discussed.

M.A. Streicher, New Stainless Steels for the Process and Power Industries, *Met. Prog.*, 128(5), 29-42, 1985. MetAbs No. 86-350378. **Abstract:** The Ar-O decarburization process and the installation of continuous casters have reduced the cost of producing stainless steels, improved their quality, and have made possible the production of a variety of new types of stainless steel high Ni (25-35%) austenitic stainless steel with 3-6% Mo and approx 20-22% Cr, which provide significant improvements in resistance to chloride stress-corrosion cracking and to chloride pitting and crevice corrosion.

H.E. Chandler, Ferritic Stainless Steel Combats Chloride Corrosion, *Met. Prog.*, 128(5), 63-66, 1985. MetAbs No. 86-350379. **Abstract:** Thyssen Edelstahlwerke AG Research Institute, Krefeld, FRG, has developed Superferrit Remanit 4575, which is highly resistant to corrosion in chloride-containing waters. It is designed for use in hot chloride solutions such as those encountered in seawater desalination plants. Mechanical and physical properties, corrosion behavior, and processing and welding properties of the alloy are described.

M. Cid, A. Penuela, and M.C. Petit, Initiation and Evolution of Corrosion Phenomena on Steel in Neutral Chloride Media, *Mater. Chem. Phys.*, 13(2), 139-152, 1985. MetAbs No. 86-350511. **Abstract:** The influence of initial surface preparation, nature of electrolyte, and hydrodynamic condition on the evolution of both free corrosion potential and limiting diffusion current of oxygen reduction, for two different kinds of steel samples in neutral chloride media is discussed.

D.W. DeBerry and A. Viehbeck, Inhibition of Pitting of Type 304L Stainless Steel by N-Lauroylsarcosine, *J. Electrochem. Soc.*, 133(1), 30-37, 1986. MetAbs No. 86-350553. **Abstract:** The resistance of Type 304L to localized corrosion by aqueous chloride solutions is increased by addition of N-lauroylsarcosine. The effects of N-lauroylsarcosine concentration, chloride concentration, pH, and metal surface prepassivation on the efficiency of pitting inhibition were investigated.

M. Fleischmann, G. Mengoli, M.M. Musiani, and C. Pagura, An Electrochemical and Raman Spectroscopic Investigation of Synergetic Effects in the Corrosion Inhibition of Copper, *Electrochim. Acta*, 30(12), 1591-1602, 1985. MetAbs No. 86-350559. **Abstract:** The synergetic inhibition of copper corrosion by benzotriazole (BTA) and benzylamine (BZA) in chloride and cyanide media is assessed by voltammetric and ac impedance measurements.

J. Banas, K.G. Schutze, and E. Heitz, Corrosion Studies on Zinc in a Methanol/Water/Lithium Chloride/Oxygen System, *J. Electrochem. Soc.*, 133(2), 253-259, 1986. MetAbs No. 86-350878. **Abstract:** The corrosion of zinc (99.999% pure) displays different effects in methanolic and aqueous chloride solutions. Because there is no surface layer formation, corrosion takes place at a higher rate in methanol than in aqueous solutions. An evaluation of the polarization curves gives different kinetic parameters.

P.P. Karve and S.K. Kulkarni, The Effect of Cations Associated With Chloride and Sulfate Ions on the Corrosion of Metallic Glass $Fe_{67}Co_{18}B_{14}Si_1$, *Corros. Sci.*, 25(12), 1091-1102, 1985. MetAbs No. 86-351114. **Abstract:** The electrochemical corrosion behavior of the metallic glass $Fe_{67}Co_{18}B_{14}Si_1$ is studied in 0.05N solutions of alkali metal chlorides and sulfates using a potentiodynamic anodic polarization technique and weight loss measurements. An attempt is made to explain the cation effect as reflected through the changes in pH of the solution, solubilities of the salts and the rest potentials of the sample in these solutions.

W.F. Bogaerts and A.A. Van Haute, Chloride Pitting and Water Chemistry Control in Cooling or Boiler Circuits, *Corros. Sci.*, 25(12), 1149-1161, 1985. MetAbs No. 86-351116. **Abstract:** The effect of different anions (bicarbonate, phosphate, sulfate, hydroxyl) on the pitting corrosion by chloride ions has been investigated for nickel alloys at up to 175 °C.

J.M. Oh, M.J. McNallan, G.Y. Lai, and M.F. Rothman, High Temperature Corrosion of Superalloys in an Environment Containing Both Oxygen and Chlorine, *Metall. Trans. A*, 17A(6), 1087-1094, 1986. MetAbs No. 86-351452. **Abstract:** The corrosion behavior of a series of commercial superalloys in flowing Ar-20O-2Cl at 900 °C has been investigated using thermogravimetric analysis and examination of the condensed corrosion products using X-ray diffraction analysis and optical and scanning electron microscopy.

K.E. Perumal, Solution of Severe Corrosion Problems in Chemical Process Industries With Special Stainless Steels, *Tool Alloy Steels*, 20(2), 53-61, 1986. MetAbs No. 86-352151. **Abstract:** In the application of stainless steels for process equipment in chemical industries, the common stainless steels have some inherent limitations, including poor resistance to general corrosion in reducing and less oxidizing acids and their susceptibility to pitting and stress corrosion cracking in sulfide and chloride-containing solutions. The economical solution to these problems is to upgrade the stainless steel with respect to its corrosion resistance by changing the alloy chemistry: increasing the Ni and Mo contents and adding elements like Cu.

K. Kendell, Corrosion and Cathodic Protection of Reinforcing Steel in Concrete, *Ind. Corros.*, 3(1), 17-18, 1985. MetAbs No. 86-352415. **Abstract:** Reinforcing steel in concrete is protected from corrosion by a passive film produced by the alkaline concrete pore solution. When chloride ions penetrate the concrete cover of the steel surface they destroy this passivity and initiate corrosion. This paper discusses the application of cathodic protection to arrest the corrosion process.

R. Thangappan and S. Chidambaram, Titanium, Tantalum, Zirconium, and Niobium—as Materials of Construction for Equipment in Electrochemical Industry, *Trans. SAEST*, 20(4), 187-189, 1985. MetAbs No. 86-352463. **Abstract:** The resistance of Nb to many acids and mixtures containing chlorides makes them good materials for chemical process equipment where corrosion is a problem. Examples of chemical process equipment applications are given.

K. Hattori, M. Tsubota, and T. Okada, Effect of Chloride on the Stress Corrosion Cracking Susceptibility of Inconel X-750 in High-Temperature Water, *Corrosion*, 42(9), 531-532, 1986. MetAbs No. 86-352577. **Abstract:** The stress corrosion cracking susceptibility of Inconel X-750 and sensitized AISI 304 has been investigated in relation to very low levels of chloride in high-temperature water.

G.K. Chou, Rebar Corrosion and Cathodic Protection, *Wire Ind.*, 52(6), 359-360, 1985. MetAbs No. 86-352729. **Abstract:** Corrosion is the spontaneous tendency for Fe to return to its natural oxidized state. In the normally alkaline concrete environment, a passivating oxide layer initially forms over the steel reinforcement, which prevents the corrosion reaction from proceeding. However, when salt is present in the concrete, this passivating layer is broken down and the reinforcement is unprotected against corrosion.

R. Goetz, B. MacDougall, and M.J. Graham, An AES and SIMS Study of the Influence of Chloride on the Passive Oxide Film on Iron, *Electrochim. Acta*, 31(10), 1299-1303, 1986. MetAbs No. 87-350070. **Abstract:** The kinetics of passivation of Fe in pH 8.4 borate buffer solution at 0 V have been studied in both the presence and absence of $0.5M$ Cl⁻.

R.M. Rieck, A. Atrens, and I.O. Smith, Stress Corrosion Cracking and Hydrogen Embrittlement of Cold Worked AISI Type 304 Austenitic Stainless Steel in Mode I and Mode III, *Mater. Sci. Technol.*, 2(10), 1066-1073, 1986. MetAbs No. 87-350197. **Abstract:** Comparative testing of cold worked AISI type 304 austenitic stainless steel in Mode I and Mode III under conditions of cathodic charging and chloride stress corrosion cracking has been used to assess the role of H in stress-corrosion cracking. The experimental results of these tests and those previously published have been used to deduce the mechanism and rate-controlling step for stress-corrosion cracking.

H. Abd-El-Kader and S.M. El-Raghy, Wear-Corrosion Mechanism of Stainless Steel in Chloride Media, *Corros. Sci.*, 26(8), 647-653, 1986. MetAbs No. 87-350213. **Abstract:** A laboratory technique to study the combined effects of mechanical and electrochemical changes during a wear process in a corroding environment is presented.

H.A. El-Sayed, Corrosion of Steel in Concrete and Its Prevention, *Corros. Prev. Control*, 33(4), 92-99, 1986. MetAbs No. 87-350281. **Abstract:** Instances of reinforcement corrosion in different countries are reviewed. Several examples of reinforced concrete failure are cited. The mechanism of reinforcement and the types of cells proposed for the corrosion process are given.

J.D. Redmond, Selecting Second-Generation Duplex Stainless Steels. I, *Chem. Eng. (NY)*, 93(20), 153-155, 1986. MetAbs No. 87-350309. **Abstract:** Employed initially in oil and gas production, duplex alloys are finding their way into pulp and paper mills, breweries and other chemical-processing plants. Use of the duplexes as an economical alternative to other alloys is discussed.

P.C. Hayfield, Corrosion Prevention in Concrete. The Cathodic Protection of Reinforcing Steel Bars Using Platinized-Type Materials, *Platinum Met. Rev.*, 30(4), 158-166, 1986. MetAbs No. 87-350539. **Abstract:** The cathodic protection of steel reinforcing bars in concrete to prevent their corrosion, brought on principally by deicing salts used on roadways, is at the interesting stage where technology is barely keeping pace with practical demand. Pt and other noble metals, used in conjunction with Ti and Nb, will play a vital role in several of the protection systems that appear to be the forerunners in a rapidly developing industry.

T.K. Vaidyanathan, K.S. Shi, B. Penugonda, and J. Vaidyanathan, Active-Passive Anodic Polarization Behavior of Palladium-Based Binary Alloys, *Can. Metall. Q.*, 25(2), 123-129, 1986. MetAbs No. 87-350672. **Abstract:** The results of a potentiodynamic anodic polarization study of Pd-based binary alloys such as Pd-Cu, Pd-Ag, Pd-Ni and Pd-Co indicate composition dependent polarization behavior in selected chloride media.

J. Charles, P. Soulignac, J.P. Audouard, and D. Catelin, Duplex Stainless Steels Offer Enhanced Mechanical Strength and Corrosion Resistance, *Bull. Cercle Etud. Metaux*, 15(11), 9, 1986. MetAbs No. 87-350686. **Abstract:** The composition of duplex stainless steels can be adapted to the corrosion resistance and mechanical properties required in service conditions. The alpha/gamma structure is able to improve both corrosion resistance and mechanical properties by comparison with monophase stainless steels. The low-alloyed UR 35N duplex stainless steel is discussed.

J. Castel, J.C. Bavay, and P. Bourgain, Advanced Cold Rolled Duplex Stainless Steels as Alternatives for the Chemical Industry, *Bull. Cercle Etud. Metaux*, 15(11), 9, 1986. MetAbs No. 87-350688. **Abstract:** The general and localized corrosion resistance of three N-containing ferritic-austenitic stainless steels has been evaluated by means of electrochemical and gravimetric tests in sulfuric and chloride solutions.

J. Bennett, Corrosion of Reinforcing Steel in Concrete and Its Prevention by Cathodic Protection, *Anti-Corros. Methods Mater.*, 33(11), 12-15, 1986. MetAbs No. 87-350771. **Abstract:** Widespread corrosion of the reinforcing steel in concrete used for the construction of motorway structures has reached serious proportions in the USA. It is caused by excessive and extended use of salt either for clearing snow or ice or the direct and indirect contact on the surface by seawater. Corrosion prevention is discussed.

J.C. Uruchurtu and J.L. Dawson, Noise Analysis of Pure Aluminum Under Different Pitting Conditions, *Corrosion*, 43(1), 19-26, 1987. MetAbs No. 87-350838. **Abstract:** The results presented demonstrate the possibility of using reciprocal frequency electrochemical noise for the detection of pitting corrosion and activation of 99.99% pure aluminum in chloride media. Noise measurements were made in neutral and alkaline solutions with and without chloride ion additions.

G. Palumbo, P.J. King, and K.T. Aust, Pitting Corrosion Behavior of Alloy 800 in Chloride-Sulfate Media, *Corrosion*, 43(1), 37-45, 1987. MetAbs No. 87-350840. **Abstract:** Potentiodynamic polarization techniques were used to determine characteristic pitting potentials for Alloy 800 in chloride and chloride-sulfate media. The effect of chloride concentration in the range of 0.001-1M was investigated.

M.M. Musiani, G. Mengoli, M. Fleischmann, and R.B. Lowry, An Electrochemical and Sers Investigation of the Influence of pH on the Effectiveness of Some Corrosion Inhibitors of Copper, *J. Electroanal. Chem. Interfacial Electrochem.*, 217(1), 187-202, 1987. MetAbs No. 87-350897. **Abstract:** The adsorption on copper of the corrosion inhibitors benzotriazole (BTA), 2-mercaptobenzothiazole, 2-mercaptobenzimidazole and 2-mercaptobenzoxazole has been characterized in both neutral and acid chloride solutions using electrochemical techniques and surface enhanced Raman spectroscopy.

A.A. Mazhar, W.A. Badawy, and M.M. Abou-Romia, Impedance Studies of Corrosion Resistance of Aluminium in Chloride Media, *Surf. Coat. Technol.*, 29(4), 335-345, 1986. MetAbs No. 87-350907. **Abstract:** The electrochemical behavior of aluminum in chloride solutions has been studied using open-circuit impedance measurements.

W.J. Tomlinson and M. Wedgbury, Pitting and Repassivation of Iron in Simulated Concrete Solutions of pH 9.0-14.3 Containing 1M Chloride, *Surf. Coat. Technol.*, 29(4), 357-364, 1986. MetAbs No. 87-350908. **Abstract:** The corrosion potential, pitting and repassivation of pure iron in simulated concrete solutions of saturated $Ca(OH)_2$ containing dissolved oxygen and 1M chloride, of pH 9.0-14.3, have been investigated by potential-time, potentiokinetic and microscopical methods.

J.K. Langalia, P.R. Mehta, and J.R. Sanghavi, Cathodic Protection to Mild Steel in 15% Salt Solution Using Sacrificial Anode, *Bull. Electrochem.*, 2(5), 493-494, 1986. MetAbs No. 87-350966. **Abstract:** A case study is discussed, in which the storage tank of salt solution corroded in 2 months during an experimental run in a textile mill. Laboratory investigations were carried out in 15% salt solution for mild steel plates.

G.P. Marsh, K.J. Taylor, G. Bryan, and S.E. Worthington, The Influence of Radiation on the Corrosion of Stainless Steel, *Corros. Sci.*, 26(11), 971-982, 1986. MetAbs No. 87-350976. **Abstract:** The effect of gamma-radiation on the electrode potential and localized corrosion of type 304L steel in 300 ppm Cl⁻ solution has been studied.

MetAbs No. 87-351060
A. Raharinaivo, P. Brevet, G. Grimaldi, and G. Pannier, Relationships Between Concrete Deterioration and Reinforcing-Steel Corrosion, *Durability Build. Mater.*, 4(2), 97-112, 1986. MetAbs No. 87-351060. **Abstract:** The influence of crack geometry in concrete on carbon steel reinforcement corrosion was studied. Tests were carried out on parallelepipeds of mortar and of concrete.

C.J. Czajkowski, Evaluation of Core Spray Line Cracks From Nine Mile Point Unit No. 1 and Isolation Condenser Cracks at Oyster Creek Unit No. 1, *Int. J. Pressure Vessels Piping*, 27(1), 1-15, 1987. MetAbs No. 87-351148. **Abstract:** Two instances of stress corrosion cracking of stainless steel were investigated at Brookhaven National Laboratory in 1984.

C.B. Thompson and A. Garner, Electrochemical Corrosion Protection of Process Plant Equipment, *Br. Corros. J.*, 21(4), 235-238, 1986. MetAbs No. 87-351174. **Abstract:** Localized corrosion of stainless steels in oxidizing acid chloride environments can be mitigated by electrochemical protection. With this technique, the stainless steel is polarized in the cathodic direction to a potential in the passive zone. In this paper, electrochemical protection systems for bleached pulp washers, vacuum valves and power utility flue gas scrubbers are described.

U. Kamachi Mudali, R.K., Dayal, J.B. Gnanamoorthy, and T.P.S. Gill, Influence of Nitrogen Addition on Microstructure and Pitting Corrosion Resistance of Austenitic Weld Metals, *Werkst. Korros.*, 37(12), 637-643, 1986. MetAbs No. 87-351214. **Abstract:** A study to investigate the role of nitrogen in improving the pitting corrosion resistance of types 316 and 304 stainless steel weld metals has been attempted.

H.G. Wheat and Z. Eliezer, Comments on the Identification of a Chloride Threshold in the Corrosion of Steel in Concrete, *Corrosion*, 43(2), 126-128, 1987. MetAbs No. 87-351306. **Abstract:** Studies have been undertaken to determine the amount of water-soluble chloride remaining on the steel bars themselves, not the amount near the surface. Efforts have been made to initiate the passive/active transition on steel bars in simulated pore solutions to which various amounts of salt have been added.

J.E. Truman and K.B. Lomax, Stress Corrosion Cracking of Non-Magnetic Drill Collars, *Corros. Prev. Control*, 33(6), 135-138, 141, 1986. MetAbs No. 87-351369. **Abstract:** The stress-corrosion cracking of non-magnetic drill collars has proved to be troublesome for on-shore drilling operations. The drill collars are fabricated from 18/8 stainless steel, and experience a service environment of dissolved chlorides and other salts, at temperatures up to 400 °C.

R. Mathis, Initiation and Early Growth Mechanisms of Corrosion Fatigue Cracks in Stainless Steels, *J. Mater. Sci.*, 22(3), 907-914, 1987. MetAbs No. 87-351388. **Abstract:** The mechanism of corrosion fatigue crack initiation in stainless steels was examined in both air and chloride solutions for a duplex steel.

R.F. Sandenbergh, The Stress Corrosion Properties of 3CR12, *Anti-Corros. Methods Mater.*, 34(1), 4-7, 1987. MetAbs No. 87-351424. **Abstract:** The stress corrosion properties of 3CR12 were evaluated in various media by means of potentiodynamic scanning and the slow strain rate techniques.

P.H. Wilmhelmsson, Special Stainless Steels for the Process Industry. I, *Stainless Steel Ind.*, *15*(83), 5-7, 1987. MetAbs No. 87-351455. **Abstract:** The chemical composition, mechanical properties, and stress, chloride and pitting corrosion properties of a proprietary range of duplex and high-alloy stainless steels intended for use in aggressive process environments are briefly reviewed.

T.A. Mozhi, W.A.T. Clark, and B.E. Wilde, The Effect of Nitrogen and Carbon on the Stress Corrosion Cracking Performance of Sensitized AISI 304 Stainless Steel in Chloride and Sulfate Solutions at 250 °C, *Corros. Sci.*, *27*(3), 257-273, 1987. MetAbs No. 87-351484. **Abstract:** Slow strain rate tests were conducted on sensitized AISI 304 stainless steels with varying nitrogen and carbon contents to study their susceptibility to stress-corrosion cracking. The tests were performed in deaerated 0.01M NaCl at 250 °C, at a strain rate of 2×10^{-6} s^{-1} and at various applied potentials in the range -0.4 to 0.1 V(NHE).

P.J. Tate, Failure Analysis—Three Cases of Corrosion Involving Stainless Steels in Chloride Environments, *Prakt. Metallogr.*, *24*(1), 38-42, 1987. MetAbs No. 87-351493. **Abstract:** Three case histories of failures are provided demonstrating improper choice of stainless steel types, including aluminum-base alloy steels, for the service environment.

R.K. Dinnappa and S.M. Mayanna, The Dezincification of Brass and Its Inhibition in Acidic Chloride and Sulfate Solutions, *Corros. Sci.*, *27*(4), 349-361, 1987. MetAbs No. 87-351682. **Abstract:** The dezincification of 60/40 brass has been studied in acidic chloride and sulfate solutions under accelerated experimental conditions using weight loss and potential measurement techniques.

H. Atmani and J.J. Rameau, Stress Corrosion Cracking at Constant Load of 304L Stainless Steel in Molten NaCl-CaCl$_2$ at 570 °C, *Corros. Sci.*, *27*(1), 35-48, 1987. MetAbs No. 87-351711. **Abstract:** The incubation and propagation times of cracks in 304L in molten NaCl-CaCl$_2$ at 570 °C were related to the applied stress value, from creep and creep rate curves. Rest potential versus time curves were recorded simultaneously.

I.M. Palit and H.S. Gadiyar, Pitting Corrosion of Zirconium in Chloride Solution, *Corrosion*, *43*(3), 140-148, 1987. MetAbs No. 87-351813. **Abstract:** Investigations were conducted on the pitting corrosion of Zr in chloride solution under potentiostatic conditions. Both stable and unstable pitting were observed.

T. Hakkarainen, Factors Determining the Dissolution Rate in I Corrosion of Stainless Steels, *Mater. Sci. Forum*, *8*, 81-89, 1986. M No. 87-352146. **Abstract:** The anodic dissolution behavior of aust stainless steel (AISI 304 and AISI 316) in concentrated metal ch solutions, simulating the conditions inside growing corrosion pits studied by electrochemical polarization experiments.

K.G.C. Berkeley, A Negative Approach to Rebar Corrosion, *Chart. Mech. Eng.*, *34*(6), 28-30, 1987. MetAbs No. 87-352418. **Abstract:** This article describes the process of preventing rebar corrosion and outlines new methods of survey and system application which enable electrochemical principles to be adapted to assess the condition of reinforced concrete structures.

E. Reinschmidt, Corrosion Mechanisms in Metallic Bellows, *Chart. Mech. Eng.*, *34*(6), 40-42, 1987. MetAbs No. 87-352420. **Abstract:** Metallic expansion joints are used in a wide variety of applications. They are, therefore, exposed to a very wide range of operating environments and are likely to suffer general corrosion unless steps are taken to prevent attack. Corrosion prevention is discussed.

P. Hancock, Vanadic and Chloride Attack of Superalloys, High-Temperature Corrosion of Superalloys, *Mater. Sci. Technol.*, *3*(7), 536-544, 1987. MetAbs No. 87-352604. **Abstract:** The high-temperature corrosion of superalloys is associated with contaminants. When comparing contaminant conditions, the contaminant flux rate should be considered rather than the contaminant level in the fuel or environment.

H. Satoh, K. Shimogori, and F. Kamikubo, The Crevice Corrosion Resistance of Some Titanium Materials. A Review of the Beneficial Effects of Palladium, *Platinum Met. Rev.*, *31*(3), 115-121, 1987. MetAbs No. 87-352609. **Abstract:** The crevice corrosion that occurs on titanium in chloride solutions at elevated temperatures can constitute a serious problem. The resistance of three titanium materials to this form of corrosion has been evaluated by immersion and electrochemical tests.

M. Keddam, M. Krarti, and C. Pallotta, Some Aspects of the Fluctuations of the Passive Current on Stainless Steel in Presence of Chlorides—Their Relation to the Probablistic Approach of Pitting Corrosion, *Corrosion*, *43*(8), 454-458, 1987. MetAbs No. 87-352838. **Abstract:** The relation between the current fluctuations in the passive range preceding the so-called pitting potential of AISI 304 stainless steel in the presence of chloride ions and the electrochemical behavior of the passive film under potentiodynamic non-steady conditions is presented.

I.E. Locci, H.K. Kwon, R.F. Hehemann, and A.R. Troiano, Stress Corrosion Cracking Initiation in Ferritic Stainless Steels in a Chloride Environment, *Corrosion*, *43*(8), 465-470, 1987. MetAbs No. 87-352840. **Abstract:** The difference in stress-corrosion cracking susceptibility between high and low interstitial ferritic stainless steels (26Cr-1Mo) in chloride solutions is the result of the relation between their corrosion and cracking potentials.

F. Mancia and A. Tamba, Electrochemical Prediction and Control of Localized Corrosion and SCC of Stainless Steels, *Corrosion*, *44*(2), 88-96, 1988. MetAbs No. 88-351086. **Abstract:** The conditions for prevention and control of localized corrosion (pitting, crevice, and stress-corrosion cracking) of AISI 304, 316 stainless steels and superaustenitic 20Cr-25Ni-4.5Mo-1.5Cu stainless steels in chloride-containing waters have been defined using an experimental electrode potential vs. NaCl concentration diagram.

R.M. Kain, A.H. Tuthill, and E.C. Hoxie, The Resistance of Types 304 and 316 Stainless Steels to Crevice Corrosion in Natural Waters, *J. Mater. Energy Syst.*, *5*(4), 205, 1984. **Abstract:** Types 304 and 316 stainless steel are widely and successfully used in piping and equipment to handle fresh waters. However, conditions are encountered that cause localized attack, usually crevice corrosion, in fresh waters of up to 1000 mg/L chloride content. Exposure tests were done to determine the cause of localized attack on these alloys.

R.M. Kain, Crevice Corrosion Behavior of Stainless Steel in Seawater and Related Environments, *Corrosion*, *40*(6), 313-321, 1984. **Abstract:** Numerous metallurgical, environmental, and geometric factors affect crevice corrosion. Mathematical modeling is used to describe the effects of chloride content of the bulk environment and crevice geometry factors on the predicted time to breakdown of passivity for AISI 304 and 316 stainless steels. Results of multiple crevice assembly testing in full strength and diluted seawater environments at 35 °C are also discussed.

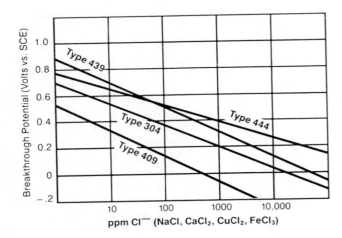

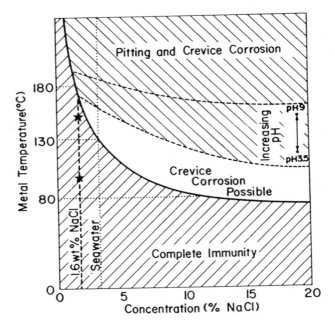

Stainless steels. Effect of chloride concentration on the breakthrough potentials of stainless steels at room temperature. Source: Allegheny Ludlum Corporation, 1985.

Unalloyed titanium. Effect of temperature, chloride concentration, and pH on the localized corrosion of unalloyed titanium. Data on crevice corrosion of grade 2 titanium in 1.6 wt% sodium chloride are included for comparison. Source: P. McKay and D.B. Mitton, "An Electrochemical Investigation of Localized Corrosion on Titanium in Chloride Environments," *Corrosion*, Vol 41, Jan 1985, 61.

How Various Alloys Rate in Tests in Different Types of Chloride Solutions(a)

Successful alloy tests in chloride solutions

Chloride solution	Carbon steel	Duplex 255 SS*	Ferritic 26-1 SS	Alloy 20 (% Ni >30) 2-3% Mo	6-9% Mo	Alloy C-276	Titanium Grade 2
Alkaline	Seawater pH = 8 50° C	Seawater pH = 8 50° C	26% NaCl + Na₂CO₃ pH = 11 boiling	Seawater pH = 8 NR† at 25°C‡	Sat'd. NaCl pH = 8.5-10 120° C	Sat'd. NaCl pH = 8.5-10 120° C	Seawater pH = 8 boiling
Neutral pH	22% NaCl 25° C	26% NaCl 200° C	2/% NaCl 25°C	No data	26% NaCl 200° C	Sat'd. NaCl 125° C	26% NaCl 113° C
Acidic	NR†	4% NaCl + 280 ppm Fe⁺³ pH = 2 35°C	6% FeCl₃ pH = 1 25° C	4% NaCl + 280 ppm Fe⁺³ pH = 2 15°C	4% NaCl + 280 ppm Fe⁺³ pH = 2 25° C	40% MgCl₂ pH = 0.5-1.0 boiling	20% MgCl₂ 100° C
Oxidizing	NR†	6% FeCl₃ 25° C	10% FeCl₃ 38° C	6% FeCl₃ Below −5°C	4% NaCl + 280 ppm Fe⁺³ pH = 2 25°C	15% FeCl₃ 25° C	40% FeCl₃ boiling
Hypochlorite	NR†	No data	5.25% NaOCl 70° C	NR†	10% NaOCl +2% NaOH 30° C	10% NaOCl 25° C	16% NaOCl 25° C

*SS is stainless steel.
†NR is not recommended.
‡Alloy 20Cb-3 pits in seawater at 25°C.

(a) Results of short-term (1 to 10 day) tests. Long-term results may be different.
Source: G.N. Kirby, Selecting Alloys for Chloride Service, *Chemical Engineering, 92,* Feb 1985, p 82.

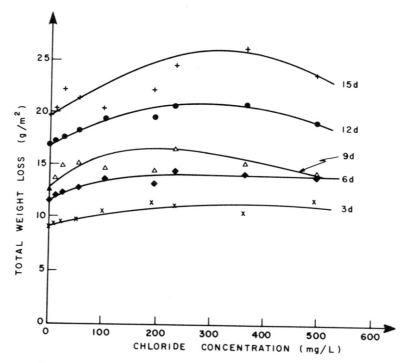

Cast iron. Cumulative weight loss of cast iron as a function of chloride concentration and immersion time. Source: D.L. Piron and R. Desjardins, "Corrosion Rate of Cast Iron and Copper Pipe by Drinking Water," in *Corrosion Monitoring in Industrial Plants Using Nondestructive Testing and Electrochemical Methods* (STP 908), G.C. Moran and P. Labine, Ed., ASTM, Philadelphia, 1986, 369.

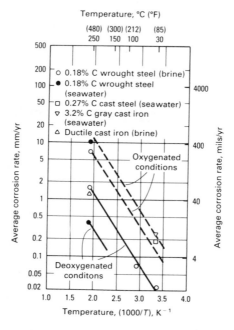

Cast iron. The effect of temperature on the general corrosion rate of cast iron and steel in chloride solutions. Test duration: 2 to 8 weeks. Source: *Metals Handbook*, 9th ed., Vol 13, Corrosion, ASM International, Metals Park, OH, 1987, 978.

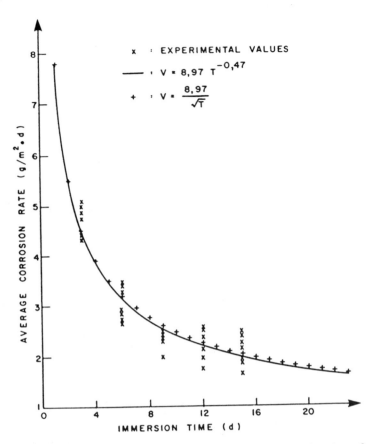

Cast iron. Average corrosion rate of cast iron as a function of immersion time and in the presence of chlorides and nitrates. $(Cl^-) = 157$ mg/L; $(NO_3^-) = 199.0$ mg/L. Source: D.L. Piron and R. Desjardins, "Corrosion Rate of Cast Iron and Copper Pipe by Drinking Water," in *Corrosion Monitoring in Industrial Plants Using Nondestructive Testing and Electrochemical Methods* (STP 908), G.C. Moran and P. Labine, Ed., ASTM, Philadelphia, 1986, 364.

Chlorine

Chlorine (Cl) melts at -101 °C and boils at -34.1 °C. Chlorine gas is about 2½ times heavier than air and is poisonous and irritating to the eyes and throat. Chlorine is used in the manufacturer of PVC, solvents, insecticides, and many non-chlorine-containing compounds. It is also used in bleaching of paper and pulp, in household and commercial bleaches, and in treatment of municipal and industrial water supplies.

Dry chlorine is not corrosive to steels, stainless steels, or nickel alloys at ambient temperature. Steel is usable up to about 150 °C (300 °F) and possibly higher under certain conditions. Stainless steels are usable up to about 300 °C (570 °F), and nickel is commonly used up to about 500 °C (930 °F). However, many industrial chlorine environments contain substantial water, particularly those encountered in the manufacture of chlorine prior to the drying operation. Wet chlorine gas is extremely corrosive at temperatures below the dew point, because the condensate is a very acidic and oxidizing mixture.

Material Summaries

The following material summaries were compiled from a survey of the available literature. Inclusion of a material description under a given environment does not imply that it is the most appropriate material for corrosion service in that environment. Likewise, exclusion of a given material does not imply that it is not suitable for corrosion service applications in that environment.

Aluminum. Aluminum alloy 1100 is more readily attacked by wet than by dry chlorine at room temperature, especially if condensation is present. At temperatures above 130 °C (265 °F), however, the presence of moisture greatly reduces corrosion of aluminum, and data have shown that larger amounts of water have greater effects. Aluminum appears to be usable to 130 °C (265 °F) at 0.06% water, to 200 °C (390 °F) at 1.5% water, and to 545 °C (1015 °F) at 30% water.

In dry chlorine service, care must be taken when evaluating results for aluminum, because the protective aluminum oxide film may delay the onset of corrosion. In one study, there was a 5-h delay before reaction in dry chlorine at 500 °C (930 °F). Aluminum was reported to be usable up to about 120 °C (250 °F).

Steels. Steel is used for handling dry chlorine, and corrosion rates are generally low. Ignition can be a problem, however, and although some studies have indicated a maximum-use temperature of 205 °C (400 °F), the discussion in one of these same studies suggests that a prudent maximum temperature may be nearer 150 °C (300 °F) because of exotherms from reaction with grease-contaminated equipment. For grease-free and properly cleaned equipment, a maximum-use temperature of 200 °C (390 °F) may be acceptable.

In 8-h tests of steel in chlorine service, corrosion rates below 0.0025 mm/yr (0.1 mil/yr) at up to 245 °C (475 °F) were recorded, but ignition occurred at 250 °C (485 °F). A slightly lower ignition temperature was reported for 16- and 20-h tests. Ignition of steel wool (grade 00) occurred at temperatures as low as 185 °C (365 °F).

Refrigerated liquid chlorine can also be handled in steel, but special care should be taken at potential leak sites, such as at valves and non-welded fittings. Because the chlorine is refrigerated, pipelines and associated equipment become encased in ice formed from the moisture in the air. Chlorine from even small leaks is then trapped beneath the ice, forming wet chlorine gas that is corrosive even at low temperatures. Therefore, Alloy 20 materials are often used for valves and other fittings in refrigerated liquid chlorine equipment, and ordinarily nonwetted parts, such as bonnet bolts in valves, are typically made of more resistant alloys.

Dry chlorine is not corrosive to steels, stainless steels, or nickel alloys at ambient temperatures. It is commonly shipped and handled in carbon steel equipment, with higher alloy materials such as nickel, Monel 400, and Hastelloy C usually used for critical parts. Valves are frequently steel with Monel 400 or Hastelloy C trim and stems. Steel is usable up to about 150 °C (300 °F) and possibly higher under certain conditions. Stainless steels are usable up to about 300 °C (570 °F), and nickel is commonly used up to about 500 °C (930 °F). Inconel 600 or low-carbon nickel is often substituted for nickel at temperatures where graphitization may occur. Moisture will greatly accelerate attack of any of these materials, with the additional danger of stress-corrosion cracking of stainless steels.

Tests with various irons and steels in flowing chlorine indicated that ignition occurs at lower temperatures for steels with higher alloy contents, especially for carbon. Ignition at temperatures as low as 220 °C (430 °F) was found for iron containing 0.3% C and 6% other alloy content. This probably accounts for the lower use temperature for cast iron versus steel. Iron alloys with silicon contents in the 10 to 15% range, however, reportedly resisted attack by dry chlorine, but their poor impact properties limit practical applications in such critical service.

Below 250 °C (480 °F), the presence of oxygen and moisture had little effect on iron chlorination rates. Because iron is attacked less rapidly by hydrogen chloride than chlorine, the presence of hydrogen chloride in dry chlorine should have little effect on iron chlorination rates. In practice, however, the use of steel is avoided where moisture may be present.

The temperature limits for many of the alloys correspond to higher corrosion rates than might usually be tolerated for expensive alloys. The rates shown, however, are in most cases higher than those that would occur in prolonged exposures. This is because, for most of the alloys, passivation occurs by the formation of a metal chloride film, after which corrosion decreases rapidly. In many cases, corrosion at higher temperatures is roughly proportional to the vapor pressure of the particular metal chlorides formed.

Stainless Steels. Austenitic stainless steels are significantly more resistant to dry chlorine than steel, aluminum, or copper. Type 304 and type 316 stainless steels may be used at temperatures up to 300 °C (570 °F).

Moisture has a significant effect on corrosion of type 304 and type 316 stainless steels in chlorine. Tests conducted on type 304 in chlorine containing 0.4% water showed rates of approximately 30.5 mm/yr (1200 mils/yr) at 40 °C (105 °F), as opposed to an estimated 0.3 mm/yr (12 mils/yr) at 100 °C (212 °F) in dry chlorine. Corrosion in wet chlorine decreased with increasing temperature until about 370 °C (700 °F), at which point the corrosion was about 4.6 mm/yr (180 mils/yr) and the effect of the moisture disappeared. The detrimental effect of moisture at low temperatures is believed to exist for chromium and austenitic stainless steels in general, including cast stainless steels. The presence of moisture also increases the possibility of stress-corrosion cracking. Chlorinated water in enclosed, poorly ventilated structures (e.g., indoor swimming pools, water treatment facilities, etc.) can promote atmospheric corrosion of stainless steels, as well as other materials.

Copper. Copper and copper alloys have been found to suffer accelerated attack in chlorine gas saturated with water vapor. Copper alloys do not have adequate corrosion resistance for practical use in moist chlorine at temperatures above 200 °C (390 °F). Water vapor at room temperature was shown to accelerate attack on copper and copper alloys. The same effect was reported on copper at temperatures below 200 °C. Above 250 °C (480 °F), however, water vapor and oxygen in chlorine were reported to reduce attack of copper and to increase its ignition temperature from about 300 °C (570 °F) to about 350 °C (660 °F).

In a study on corrosion of copper in dry chlorine, a maximum-use temperature of 205 °C (400 °F) was suggested. In other work, ignition of copper was observed at temperatures from 260 to 300 °C (500 to 570 °F) at high velocities and at temperatures from 290 to 310 °C (555 to 590 °F) at a velocity of 250 ml/min, but did not occur at 40 ml/min.

Lead. Lead has been found to be resistant to corrosion in dry flowing chlorine at temperatures up to 275 °C (525 °F). The average rates reported were 0.06 mm/yr (2.4 mils/yr) at 200 °C (390 °F), 0.13 mm/yr (5.1 mils/yr) at 250 °C (480 °F), 0.14 mm/yr (5.5 mils/yr) at 275 °C (525 °F), 1.5 mm/yr (59 mils/yr) at 295 °C (565 °F), and 2.5 mm/yr (98 mils/yr) at 310 °C (590 °F).

Magnesium. Dry chlorine causes little or no corrosion of magnesium at room or slightly elevated temperatures. The presence of a small amount of water results in pronounced attack by chlorine. Wet chlorine below the dew point of any aqueous phase causes severe attack of magnesium.

In dry chlorine service, magnesium has been found to perform as well as Chromel A and actually better than Monel 400. A maximum-use temperature of 455 °C (850 °F) has been suggested, but use of magnesium in chlorine is not widespread.

Nickel. Nickel 200 and nickel-base alloys show excellent resistance to corrosion in dry chlorine. A temperature of 500 °C (930 °F) appears to be the upper limit for routine use of nickel in dry chlorine service.

Nickel and nickel alloys are adversely affected, however, by the presence of moisture in chlorine at temperatures up to their maximum-use temperatures in dry chlorine. It has been found that 1.5% water vapor can double the reaction rate between chlorine and nickel; 30% water increases the rate from 2 to 20 times. At temperatures above 550 °C (1020 °F), moisture has been reported to have little effect, but the rates at that temperature make the use of nickel marginal even in dry chlorine. Between 425 and 760 °C (795 and 1400 °F), graphitization of Nickel 200 may occur, and a low-carbon version of nickel with a maximum of 0.02% C is normally used. When sulfur compounds are present, Inconel 600 is often substituted for nickel to avoid intergranular attack.

Inconel 600 and Hastelloy B perform nearly as well as nickel in dry chlorine, and Hastelloy C somewhat less well. Chromel A and Monel 400 perform much better than stainless steels, but not as well as the other alloys mentioned above. Monel 400 is commonly used as trim on valves, but it should be used with care in refrigerated systems. Cast ACI alloy CW-12M (Ni-18Cr-18Mo) was reported to corrode in dry chlorine at 0 to 60 °C (32 to 140 °F) at about the same rate as Hastelloy C. Hastelloy C-276 corrodes 2 to 1000 times faster, and Chlorimet 3 corrodes 100 to 1000 times faster in wet chlorine than in dry. Numerous other nickel, nickel-copper, nickel-chromium-iron, and nickel-chromium-molybdenum alloys are also reported to suffer greatly accelerated attack by wet chlorine at temperatures below the dew point.

Niobium. Niobium is resistant to wet chlorine at temperatures up to about 100 °C (212 °F) and to dry chlorine up to approximately 200 °C (390 °F).

Palladium is attacked by chlorine when air is present.

Rhodium is unattacked by chlorine at room temperature, but it may be attacked at elevated temperatures.

Ruthenium is slowly attacked by saturated aqueous solutions of chlorine.

Silver is resistant to both dry and moist chlorine.

Tantalum. Tantalum is not attacked by chlorine or by chlorine oxides at ordinary temperatures. It is inert to wet chlorine at temperatures up to 150 °C (300 °F). Tantalum has been reported to give good service in chlorine plus 1.5% water at temperatures up to 375 °C (705 °F) and in chlorine plus 30% water at up to 400 °C (750 °F), but other studies have indicated less satisfactory performance under these conditions.

In dry chlorine, attack on tantalum has been shown to begin at 250 °C (480 °F), to be violent after 35 min at 450 °C (840 °F), and to be instantaneous at 500 °C (930 °F). Pitting of tantalum in a mixture of dry chlorine and anhydrous methanol at 65 °C (150 °F), presumably caused by the presence of halogenated HCOOH contamination, has been reported.

Tin. Tin is readily attacked by chlorine at room temperature.

Titanium. Titanium is well known for its resistance to corrosion by wet chlorine and is used extensively in various types of chlorine-manufacturing equipment, such as wet chlorine compressors. Titanium is perfectly passive if there is enough water in the chlorine, but it ignites, sometimes at temperatures as low as -18 °C (0 °F), if there is not enough water. With sufficient water, titanium is resistant up to at least 175 °C (345 °F) and probably higher.

The minimum amount of water that is required to maintain the passivity of titanium depends on temperature and other factors. The amount of water required at temperatures between 25 and 175 °C (75 and 350 °F) was found to depend on chlorine pressure, temperature, flow rate, purity, and degree of surface abrasion of the titanium. Crude cell chlorine tested under static conditions required about 0.5% water at 125 °C (255 °F) and 1.2% water at 175 °C (350 °F). Less water was required at flow rates above 0.15 m/s (0.5 ft/s). Pure (99.5%) chlorine requires relatively more water—about 0.93% at room temperature and 1.5% at 200 °C (390 °F) under static conditions.

Although titanium is the preferred metallic material for handling wet chlorine and bromine gas environments, rapid, dangerous, exothermic halogenation reactions may occur with titanium in dry chlorine and bromine gas environments. Mechanical damage to metal surfaces to expose fresh metal facilitates reaction with dry chlorine, but thicker oxide films (thermal oxides) tend to retard initiation of the reaction.

Zinc. Dry chlorine does not affect zinc.

Zirconium. Unalloyed zirconium has been found to corrode in wet chlorine at rates of 2 mm/yr (80 mils/yr) at 15 °C (60 °F) and 4.9 mm/yr (192 mils/yr) at 25 °C (75 °F). Another study reported a corrosion rate of over 1.3 mm/yr (50 mils/yr) in room-temperature chlorine containing 0.3% water. Unalloyed zirconium corrodes at less than 0.13 mm/yr (5 mils/yr) in dry chlorine near room temperature. Stress-corrosion cracking of reactor grade zirconium in 0.01 mg/cm^3 of chlorine gas has been reported at temperatures from 360 to 400 °C (680 to 750 °F). In low-pH chlorine gas, zirconium is not subject to crevice attack.

Additional Reading

Z.A. Foroulis, High Temperature Degradation of Structural Materials in Environments Encountered in the Petroleum and Petrochemical Industries: Some Mechanistic Observations, *Anti-Corros. Methods Mater.*, 32(11), 4-9, 1985. MetAbs No. 86-351179. **Abstract:** Some of the important processes underlying high-temperature degradation of structural materials used in the petroleum and petrochemical industries are reviewed. Particular emphasis is placed on degradation processes involving the interaction of structural metals and alloys with environments containing sulfidizing, carburizing and halogenizing species. The effects of gaseous hydrogen environments at elevated temperatures and pressures on the mechanical properties of steels are discussed.

N.S. Jacobson, M.J. McNallan, and Y.Y. Lee, The Formation of Volatile Corrosion Products During the Mixed Oxidation-Chlorination of Cobalt at 650 °C, *Metall. Trans. A*, 17A(7), 1223-1228, 1986. MetAbs No. 86-351516. **Abstract:** The reaction of cobalt (99.99% pure) with 1% Cl_2 in 1, 10, and 50% O_2/Ar atmospheres has been studied at 650 °C with thermogravimetry and mass spectrometry.

N.R. Sorensen, R.B. Diegle, and S.T. Picraux, The Effects of Phosphorus Implantation on Passivity of Fe-Cr Alloys in Acidic Electrolytes, *J. Mater. Res.*, 1(6), 752-757, 1986. MetAbs No. 87-351081. **Abstract:** The passivation behavior of the phosphorus-implanted alloys in a Cl-containing electrolyte as a function of Cr concentration and P implantation has been investigated.

Corrosion Behavior of Various Metals and Alloys in Chlorine

Material	Condition, other factors, comments	Concentration, %	Temperature, °C (°F)	Duration	Corrosion rate, mm/yr (mils/yr) or other	Ref
Irons and steels						
Carbon steel	Dry	...	120 (250)	...	0.76 (30)	83

(Continued)

Corrosion Behavior of Various Metals and Alloys in Chlorine (Continued)

Material	Condition, other factors, comments	Concentration, %	Temperature, °C (°F)	Duration	Corrosion rate, mm/yr (mils/yr) or other	Ref
Carbon steel	Dry	...	180 (350)	...	1.5 (60)	83
Carbon steel	Dry. Suggested upper temperature limit for continuous use	...	205 (400)	...	3 (120)	83
Carbon steel	Dry	...	230 (450)	...	15 (600)	83
Carbon steel	Dry	...	230 (450)	...	30 (1200)	83
Cast iron	Dry	...	90 (200)	...	0.76 (30)	83
Cast iron	Dry	...	120 (250)	...	1.5 (60)	83
Cast iron	Dry. Suggested upper temperature limit for continuous use	...	180 (350)	...	3 (120)	83
Cast iron	Dry	...	230 (450)	...	15 (600)	83
Cast iron	Dry	...	230 (450)	...	30 (1200)	83
Stainless steels						
Type 304 stainless steel	Dry. Suggested upper temperature limit for continuous use 310 °C (600 °F)	...	290 (550)	...	0.76 (30)	83
Type 304 stainless steel	Dry	...	315 (600)	...	1.5 (60)	83
Type 304 stainless steel	Dry	...	340 (650)	...	3 (120)	83
Type 304 stainless steel	Dry	...	400 (750)	...	15 (600)	83
Type 304 stainless steel	Dry	...	450 (850)	...	30 (1200)	83
Type 316 stainless steel	Dry. Suggested upper temperature limit for continuous use 340 °C (650 °F)	...	310 (600)	...	0.76 (30)	83
Type 316 stainless steel	Dry	...	345 (650)	...	1.5 (60)	83
Type 316 stainless steel	Dry	...	400 (750)	...	3 (120)	83
Type 316 stainless steel	Dry	...	450 (850)	...	15 (600)	83
Type 316 stainless steel	Dry	...	480 (900)	...	30 (1200)	83
Type 316 stainless steel	...	Saturated	25 (75)	56 d	0.008 (0.30)	85
Type 317 stainless steel	Chemical processing; field or pilot plant test; no aeration. Chlorine, hydrochloric acid, naphthalene, naphthalene chloride (vapors)	...	166 (330)	52 d	0.0014 in./yr	89
Type 317 stainless steel	Chemical processing; laboratory test; no aeration; no agitation. Chlorine, hydrochloric acid, propionic acid (chlorinator)	...	20 (68)	2 d	0.28 in./yr	89
Type 317 stainless steel	Chemical processing; laboratory test; no aeration; no agitation. Chlorine, hydrochloric acid, propionic acid	...	20 (68)	1 d	0.0064 in./yr	89
Type 410 stainless steel	Gas, wet and dry	...	Room	...	Attacked	121
Aluminum						
Aluminum alloy 1100	Dry. Suggested upper temperature limit for continuous use	...	120 (250)	...	0.76 (30)	83
Aluminum alloy 1100	Dry	...	150 (300)	...	1.5 (60)	83
Aluminum alloy 1100	Dry	...	150 (300)	...	3 (120)	83
Aluminum alloy 1100	Dry	...	180 (350)	...	15 (600)	83
Aluminum alloy 1100	Dry	...	180 (350)	...	30 (1200)	83
Aluminum alloy 1100	0.06 wt% water in chlorine	...	130 (265)	...	<0.5 (<20)	84
Aluminum alloy 1100	1.5 wt% water in chlorine	...	130 (265)	...	<0.5 (<20)	84
Aluminum alloy 1100	30 wt% water in chlorine	...	140 (285)	...	<0.5 (<20)	84
Aluminum alloy 1100	0.06 wt% water in chlorine	...	170 (340)	...	3.6 (140)	84
Aluminum alloy 1100	30 wt% water in chlorine	...	170 (340)	...	0.53 (21)	84
Aluminum alloy 1100	1.5 wt% water in chlorine	...	200 (390)	...	<0.5 (<20)	84
Aluminum alloy 1100	30 wt% water in chlorine	...	290 (555)	...	1.04 (41)	84
Aluminum alloy 1100	1.5 wt% water in chlorine	...	290 (555)	...	<0.5 (<20)	84
Aluminum alloy 1100	1.5 wt% water in chlorine	...	320 (610)	...	1.04 (41)	84
Aluminum alloy 1100	1.5 wt% water in chlorine	...	350 (660)	...	5.3 m/yr (210 in./yr)	84
Aluminum alloy 1100	1.5 wt% water in chlorine	...	400 (750)	...	21 m/yr (830 in./yr)	84
Aluminum alloy 1100	30 wt% water in chlorine	...	545 (1015)	...	<0.5 (<20)	84
Aluminum alloy 1100	30 wt% water in chlorine	...	615 (1140)	...	5.3 (210)	84
Aluminum alloy 1100	30 wt% water in chlorine	...	630 (1165)	...	7.9 m/yr (311 in./yr)	84
Coppers						
70-30 cupronickel	Dry	...	...	...	Suitable	93

(Continued)

Corrosion Behavior of Various Metals and Alloys in Chlorine (Continued)

Material	Condition, other factors, comments	Concentration, %	Temperature, °C (°F)	Duration	Corrosion rate, mm/yr (mils/yr) or other	Ref
70-30 cupronickel	Moist. May be considered in place of a copper metal when some property, other than corrosion resistance, governs its use	...	...	...	Good	93
90-10 cupronickel	Dry	...	...	...	Suitable	93
90-10 cupronickel	Moist	...	...	...	Fair	93
Admiralty brass	Dry	...	...	...	Suitable	93
Admiralty brass	Moist	...	...	...	Fair	93
Aluminum bronze	Dry	...	...	...	Suitable	93
Aluminum bronze	Moist	...	...	...	Fair	93
Ampco 8, aluminum bronze	Dry. Generally suitable. Conditions such as aeration or temperature could restrict use	...	...	...	<0.5 (<20)	96
Ampco 8, aluminum bronze	Wet. Generally not suitable	...	...	...	>0.5 (>20)	96
Architectural bronze	Dry	...	...	...	Suitable	93
Architectural bronze	Moist	...	...	...	Not suitable	93
Brass	Dry	...	...	...	Suitable	93
Brass	Moist	...	...	...	Fair	93
Cartridge brass	Dry	...	...	...	Suitable	93
Cartridge brass	Moist	...	...	...	Not suitable	93
Commercial bronze	Dry	...	...	...	Suitable	93
Commercial bronze	Moist	...	...	...	Fair	93
Deoxidized copper	Dry. Suggested upper temperature limit for continuous use 205 °C (400 °F)	...	180 (350)	...	0.76 (30)	83
Deoxidized copper	Dry	...	230 (450)	...	1.5 (60)	83
Deoxidized copper	Dry	...	260 (500)	...	3 (120)	83
Deoxidized copper	Dry	...	260 (500)	...	15 (600)	83
Deoxidized copper	Dry	...	290 (550)	...	30 (1200)	83
Electrolytic copper	Dry	...	...	...	Suitable	93
Electrolytic copper	Moist	...	...	...	Fair	93
Free-cutting brass	Dry	...	...	...	Suitable	93
Free-cutting brass	Moist	...	...	...	Not suitable	93
Muntz metal	Dry	...	...	...	Suitable	93
Muntz metal	Moist	...	...	...	Not suitable	93
Naval brass	Dry	...	...	...	Suitable	93
Naval brass	Moist	...	...	...	Not suitable	93
Nickel silver	Dry	18	...	...	Suitable	93
Nickel silver	Moist	18	...	...	Fair	93
Phosphor bronze	5% Sn. Dry	...	...	...	Suitable	93
Phosphor bronze	8% Sn. Dry	...	...	...	Suitable	93
Phosphor bronze	5% Sn. Moist	...	...	...	Fair	93
Phosphor bronze	8% Sn. Moist	...	...	...	Fair	93
Phosphor copper	Moist	...	...	...	Fair	93
Phosphor copper	Dry	...	...	...	Suitable	93
Red brass	Dry	...	...	...	Suitable	93
Red brass	Moist	...	...	...	Fair	93
Silicon bronze	Low. Dry	...	...	...	Suitable	93
Silicon bronze	High. Dry	...	...	...	Suitable	93
Silicon bronze	Low. Moist	...	...	...	Fair	93
Silicon bronze	High. Moist	...	...	...	Fair	93
Titanium						
Titanium	Gas. Wet. Containing >0.7% H_2O	...	Room	...	nil	90
Titanium	Gas. Wet. Containing >0.95% H_2O	...	140 (284)	...	nil	90
Titanium	Gas. Wet. Containing >1.5% H_2O	...	200 (392)	...	nil	90
Titanium	Gas. Dry. Containing <0.5% H_2O	...	Room	...	May react	90
Titanium	Grade 7. Wet	...	25 (75)	...	nil	33
Titanium	Grade 2	Saturated	25 (75)	56 d	0.0005 (0.02)	85

(Continued)

Corrosion Behavior of Various Metals and Alloys in Chlorine (Continued)

Material	Condition, other factors, comments	Concen-tration, %	Temperature, °C (°F)	Duration	Corrosion rate, mm/yr (mils/yr) or other	Ref
Heat- and corrosion-resistant alloys						
20Cb-3	...	Saturated	25 (75)	56 d	0.008 (0.30)	85
44Co-31Cr-13W	As cast, based on five 24-h test periods with cast specimens 38 mm x 25 mm x 6 mm (1.5 in. x 1 in. x 0.25 in.), 120-grit abrasive finish	100	Room	...	4.9 (194)	53
44Co-31Cr-13W	Heat treated 4 h at 899 °C (1650 °F) and furnace cooled; based on five 24-h test periods with cast specimens 38 mm x 25 mm x 6 mm (1.5 in. x 1 in. x 0.25 in.), 120-grit abrasive finish	100	Room	...	6.27 (251)	53
44Co-31Cr-13W	Wet. As-cast specimens 38 mm x 25 mm x 6 mm (1.5 in. x 1 in. x 0.25 in.), 120-grit abrasive finish. Average of five 24-h periods	100	Room	...	4.85 (194)	53
44Co-31Cr-13W	Wet. Heat treated 4 h at 899 °C (1650 °F), furnace cooled; cast specimens 38 mm x 25 mm x 6 mm (1.5 in. x 1 in. x 0.25 in.), 120-grit abrasive finish. Average of five 24-h periods	100	Room	...	6.27 (251)	53
50Co-20Cr-15W-10Ni	...	100	Room	...	0.002 (0.1)	53
50Co-20Cr-15W-10Ni	Wet. Cast specimens 38 mm x 25 mm x 6 mm (1.5 in. x 1 in. x 0.25 in.), 120-grit abrasive finish. Average of five 24-h periods	100	Room	...	0.002 (0.1)	53
53Co-30Cr-4.5W	As cast; based on five 24-h test periods with cast specimens 38 mm x 25 mm x 6 mm (1.5 in. x 1 in. x 0.25 in.), 120-grit abrasive finish	100	Room	...	8.75 (350)	53
53Co-30Cr-4.5W	Heat treated 4 h at 899 °C (1650 °F); based on five 24-h test periods with cast specimens 38 mm x 25 mm x 6 mm (1.5 in. x 1 in. x 0.25 in.), 120-grit abrasive finish	100	Room	...	11.37 (455)	53
53Co-30Cr-4.5W	Wet. As-cast specimens 38 mm x 25 mm x 6 mm (1.5 in. x 1 in. x 0.25 in.), 120-grit abrasive finish. Average of five 24-h periods	100	Room	...	8.75 (350)	53
53Co-30Cr-4.5W	Wet. Heat treated 4 h at 899 °C (1650 °F), furnace cooled; cast specimen 38 mm x 25 mm x 6 mm (1.5 in. x 1 in. x 0.25 in.), 120-grit abrasive finish. Average of five 24-h periods	100	Room	...	11.37 (455)	53
ACI CD-4MCu	Crevice corrosion	Saturated	25 (75)	42 d	0.06 (2.5)	85
ACI CF-8M	Crevice corrosion	Saturated	25 (75)	42 d	0.013 (0.50)	85
ACI CN-7M	Crevice corrosion	Saturated	25 (75)	42 d	0.05 (1.8)	85
ACI CW-12M	...	Saturated	25 (75)	42 d	0.023 (0.90)	85
Cabot alloy No. 625	Wet	...	Room	48 h	<0.003 (0.1)	67
Cabot alloy No. 625	Wet	...	50 (122)	48 h	2.1 (81)	67
Cabot alloy No. 625	Wet	...	70 (158)	48 h	4.7 (186)	67
Hastelloy B	Dry	...	510 (950)	...	0.76 (30)	83
Hastelloy B	Dry. Suggested upper temperature limit for continuous use	...	540 (1000)	...	1.5 (60)	83
Hastelloy B	Dry	...	590 (1100)	...	3 (120)	83
Hastelloy B	Dry	...	650 (1200)	...	15 (600)	83
Hastelloy C	Dry	...	480 (900)	...	0.76 (30)	83
Hastelloy C	Dry. Suggested upper temperature limit for continuous use 510 °C (950 °F)	...	540 (1000)	...	1.5 (60)	83
Hastelloy C	Dry	...	560 (1050)	...	3 (120)	83
Hastelloy C	Dry	...	650 (1200)	...	15 (600)	83
Hastelloy C-276	...	Saturated	25 (75)	56 d	0.0025 (0.10)	85
Hastelloy D	Dry. Suggested upper temperature limit for continuous use	...	205 (400)	...	0.76 (30)	83
Hastelloy D	Dry	...	230 (450)	...	1.5 (60)	83
Hastelloy D	Dry	...	290 (550)	...	3 (120)	83
Haynes No. 25	Wet. Specimens prepared from 12-gage, solution heat-treated sheet	...	Room	24 h	<0.01 (0.1)	68
Inconel 600	Dry	...	510 (950)	...	0.76 (30)	83
Inconel 600	Dry. Suggested upper temperature limit for continuous use	...	540 (1000)	...	1.5 (60)	83
Inconel 600	Dry	...	565 (1050)	...	3 (120)	83
Inconel 600	Dry	...	650 (1200)	...	15 (600)	83

(Continued)

Corrosion Behavior of Various Metals and Alloys in Chlorine (Continued)

Material	Condition, other factors, comments	Concentration, %	Temperature, °C (°F)	Duration	Corrosion rate, mm/yr (mils/yr) or other	Ref
Inconel 600	Dry	...	680 (1250)	...	30 (1200)	83
Monel 400	Dry. Suggested upper temperature limit for continuous use 420 °C (800 °F)	...	400 (750)	...	0.76 (30)	83
Monel 400	Dry	...	450 (850)	...	1.5 (60)	83
Monel 400	Dry	...	480 (900)	...	3 (120)	83
Monel 400	Dry	...	540 (1000)	...	15 (600)	83
Monel 400	Dry	...	540 (1000)	...	30 (1200)	83
Monel 400	...	Saturated	25 (75)	56 d	24 (948)	85
Multimet	Wet. Specimens prepared from 12-gage, solution heat-treated sheet	...	Room	24 h	4.57 (180)	68
Ni-20Cr-1Si	Dry. Suggested upper temperature limit for continuous use 450 °C (850 °F)	...	425 (800)	...	0.76 (30)	83
Ni-20Cr-1Si	Dry	...	480 (900)	...	1.5 (60)	83
Ni-20Cr-1Si	Dry	...	540 (1000)	...	3 (120)	83
Ni-20Cr-1Si	Dry	...	620 (1150)	...	15 (600)	83
Nickel 201	Dry	...	510 (950)	...	0.76 (30)	83
Nickel 201	Dry. Suggested upper temperature limit for continuous use	...	540 (1000)	...	1.5 (60)	83
Nickel 201	Dry	...	590 (1100)	...	3 (120)	83
Nickel 201	Dry	...	650 (1200)	...	15 (600)	83
Nickel 201	Dry	...	680 (1250)	...	30 (1200)	83
Zirconium						
Zr702	In water	Saturated	Room	...	>1.3 (>50)	15
Zr702	In water	Saturated	75 (165)	...	>1.3 (>50)	15
Zr702	Gas (more than 0.13% H$_2$O)	100	94 (200)	...	>1.3 (>50)	15
Zr702	Gas, dry	100	Room	...	<0.13 (<5)	15
Lead, tin, and zinc						
Lead	Practically resistant; Pb recommended for use	...	38 (100)	...	<500 μm/yr (<20)	95
Tantalum and hafnium						
Hf-17.3Zr	...	Saturated	Boiling	2 d	<0.0025 (<0.1)	11
Hf-17.3Zr	...	Saturated	Boiling	4 d	0.005 (0.2)	11
Hf-2.9Zr	...	Saturated	Boiling	2 d	0.015 (0.6)	11
Hf-2.9Zr	...	Saturated	Boiling	4 d	0.005 (0.2)	11
Hf-47.4Zr	...	Saturated	Boiling	2 d	<0.0025 (<0.1)	11
Hf-47.4Zr	...	Saturated	Boiling	4 d	<0.0025 (<0.1)	11
Hf-59.5Zr	...	Saturated	Boiling	2 d	nil	11
Hf-59.5Zr	...	Saturated	Boiling	4 d	<0.0025 (<0.1)	11
Hf-81.4Zr	...	Saturated	Boiling	2 d	<0.0025 (<0.1)	11
Hf-81.4Zr	...	Saturated	Boiling	4 d	<0.0025 (<0.1)	11
Tantalum	Commercial sheet. Average of three 48-h periods	Wet	Room	48 h	<0.025 (<1)	38
Tantalum	High purity. Average of three 48-h periods	Wet	Room	48 h	<0.025 (<1)	38
Tantalum	Wet	...	75 (167)	...	nil	42
Noble metals						
Gold	Dry	...	120 (250)	...	0.76 (30)	83
Gold	Dry	...	150 (300)	...	1.5 (60)	83
Gold	Dry	...	180 (350)	...	3 (120)	83
Gold	Dry	...	200 (400)	...	15 (600)	83
Gold	Dry	...	200 (400)	...	30 (1200)	83
Platinum	Dry. Suggested upper temperature limit for continuous use 260 °C (500 °F)	...	480 (900)	...	0.76 (30)	83
Platinum	Dry	...	510 (950)	...	1.5 (60)	83
Platinum	Dry	...	540 (1000)	...	3 (120)	83
Platinum	Dry	...	560 (1050)	...	15 (600)	83
Platinum	Dry	...	560 (1050)	...	30 (1200)	83
Silver	Dry	...	40 (100)	...	0.76 (30)	83
Silver	Dry	...	65 (150)	...	1.5 (60)	83

(Continued)

Corrosion Behavior of Various Metals and Alloys in Chlorine (Continued)

Material	Condition, other factors, comments	Concentration, %	Temperature, °C (°F)	Duration	Corrosion rate, mm/yr (mils/yr) or other	Ref
Silver	Dry	...	120 (250)	...	3 (120)	
Silver	Dry	...	230 (450)	...	15 (600)	83
Silver	Dry	...	260 (500)	...	30 (1200)	83
Others						83
Cb alloy	Wrought 100% Cb; laboratory button; annealed at 1175 °C (2140 °F) for 30 min. Average of three 48-h periods	Wet	Room	48 h	<0.025 (<1)	38
Cb alloy	Wrought 100% Cb; arc melted; annealed at 1400 °C (2552 °F) for 1 h. Average of three 48-h periods	Wet	Room	48 h	<0.025 (<1)	38
Cb alloy	Wrought 100% Cb; electron-beam melted; annealed at 1400 °C (2552 °F) for 1 h. Average of three 48-h periods	Wet	Room	48 h	<0.025 (<1)	38
Cb alloy	Wrought 0.75% Zr, bal Cb; arc melted; annealed at 1400 °C (2552 °F) for 1 h. Average of three 48-h periods	Wet	Room	48 h	<0.025 (<1)	38
Cb alloy	Wrought 8% Ti, bal Cb; arc melted; annealed at 1400 °C (2552 °F) for 1 h. Average of three 48-h periods	Wet	Room	48 h	<0.025 (<1)	38
Cb alloy	Wrought 50% V, 50% Cb; arc melted. Average of three 48-h periods	Wet	Room	48 h	<0.025 (<1)	38
Magnesium	Dry. Suggested upper temperature limit for continuous use	...	450 (850)	...	0.76 (30)	83
Magnesium	Dry	...	480 (900)	...	1.5 (60)	83
Magnesium	Dry	...	510 (950)	...	3 (120)	83
Magnesium	Dry	...	540 (1000)	...	15 (600)	83
Magnesium	Dry	...	565 (1050)	...	30 (1200)	83
Magnesium	...	100	Room	...	Unsuitable	119

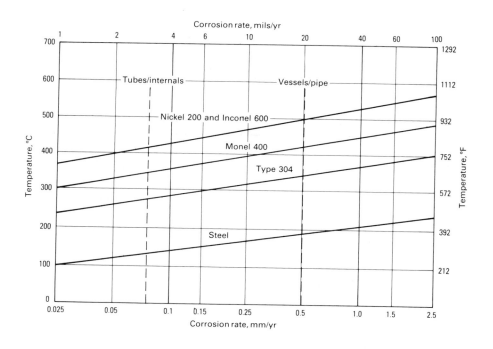

Various alloys. Design guidelines for use in dry chlorine. Source: Chemical Processing Industry.

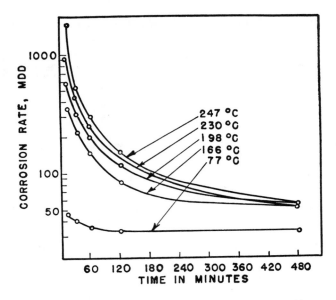

Carbon steel. Rate of corrosion (weight loss) of mild steel in contact with commercial chlorine (0.005% moisture) as a function of time. Source: H.H. Uhlig, "Iron and Steel," in *The Corrosion Handbook*, H.H. Uhlig, Ed., John Wiley & Sons, New York, 1948, 142.

Chlorine Dioxide

Chlorine dioxide, ClO_2, is a yellow-reddish gas. It is a very effective bleaching and water treatment agent. Chlorine dioxide is prepared by the reaction of chlorine and sodium chlorite. It is quite unstable and is commonly prepared immediately before use.

Corrosion Behavior of Various Metals and Alloys in Chlorine Dioxide

Material	Condition, other factors, comments	Concentration, %	Temperature, °C (°F)	Duration	Corrosion rate, mm/yr (mils/yr) or other	Ref
Stainless steels						
Type 304 stainless steel	Pulp and paper processing; field or pilot plant test; strong aeration; rapid agitation. Chlorine dioxide gas and condensed solution	10.8	66 (150)	14.5 d	0.33 in./yr	89
Type 304 stainless steel	Pulp and paper processing; field or pilot plant test; slight to moderate aeration; rapid agitation. Plus methanol, 32% sodium perchlorate, sulfuric acid 60 °Be	...	57 (135)	14.5 d	>0.55 in./yr	89
Type 304 stainless steel	Pulp and paper processing; field or pilot plant test; slight to moderate aeration; rapid agitation. Plus saturated water solution. Severe pitting (maximum depth of pits over 0.010 in.)	~4-5	2 (36)	14.5 d	0.0051 in./yr	89
Type 304 stainless steel	Pulp and paper processing; field or pilot plant test; slight to moderate aeration; slight to moderate agitation. Chlorine dioxide spent liquor, 45% sulfuric acid, 20 g/L sodium chlorate. Severe pitting (maximum depth of pits over 0.010 in.)	...	68 (155)	14.6 d	0.016 in./yr	89

(Continued)

Corrosion Behavior of Various Metals and Alloys in Chlorine Dioxide (Continued)

Material	Condition, other factors, comments	Concentration, %	Temperature, °C (°F)	Duration	Corrosion rate, mm/yr (mils/yr) or other	Ref
Type 316 stainless steel	Pulp and paper processing; field or pilot plant test; slight to moderate aeration; slight to moderate agitation. Chlorine dioxide gas and condensed solution. Severe pitting (maximum depth of pits over 0.010 in.)	10.8	66 (150)	14.5 d	0.29 in./yr	89
Type 316 stainless steel	Pulp and paper processing; field or pilot plant test; slight to moderate aeration; rapid agitation. Plus methanol, 32% sodium perchlorate, sulfuric acid 60 °Be. Severe pitting (maximum depth of pits over 0.010 in.)	...	57 (135)	14.5 d	0.15 in./yr	89
Type 316 stainless steel	Pulp and paper processing; field or pilot plant test; slight to moderate aeration; slight to moderate agitation. Low-carbon grade (0.03% C max). Plus saturated water solution. Severe pitting (maximum depth of pits over 0.010 in.)	~7.2	3 (38)	70 d	0.0052 in./yr	89
Type 316 stainless steel	Pulp and paper processing; field or pilot plant test; slight to moderate aeration; rapid agitation. Plus saturated water solution	~4-5	2 (36)	14.5 d	0.0001 in./yr	89
Type 316 stainless steel	Pulp and paper processing; field or pilot plant test; slight to moderate aeration; slight to moderate agitation. Chlorine dioxide spent liquor, 45% sulfuric acid, 20 g/L sodium chlorate	...	68 (155)	14.6 d	0.0025 in./yr	89
Type 317 stainless steel	Pulp and paper processing; field or pilot plant test; slight to moderate aeration; slight to moderate agitation. Chlorine dioxide gas	...	82 (180)	45 d	Corrosion	89
Type 317 stainless steel	Pulp and paper processing; field or pilot plant test; slight to moderate aeration; slight to moderate agitation. Plus saturated water solution	~7.2	3 (38)	70 d	0.0009 in./yr	89
Titanium						
Titanium	Plus HOCl	15	43 (110)	...	nil	27
Titanium	Plus steam	5	100 (212)	...	0.005 (0.2)	27
Titanium	...	5	82 (180)	...	<0.003 (<0.12)	90
Titanium	Plus HOCl, H_2O + Cl_2	15	43 (110)	...	nil	90
Titanium	...	10	70 (158)	...	0.03 (1.2)	90
Titanium	In steam	5	99 (211)	...	nil	90
Heat- and corrosion-resistant alloys						
Alloy 825	Pulp and paper processing; field or pilot plant test; slight to moderate aeration; slight to moderate agitation. Chlorine dioxide gas	...	82 (180)	45 d	0.056 in./yr	89
Carpenter 20	Pulp and paper processing; field or pilot plant test; slight to moderate aeration; slight to moderate agitation. Plus saturated water solution. Moderate pitting (maximum depth of pits from 0.005 to 0.010 in.)	~7.2	3 (38)	70 d	0.0026 in./yr	89
Carpenter 20	Pulp and paper processing; field or pilot plant test; slight to moderate aeration; rapid agitation. Cast specimens. Plus methanol, 32% sodium perchlorate, sulfuric acid 60 °Be. Severe pitting (maximum depth of pits over 0.010 in.)	...	57 (135)	14.5 d	0.027 in./yr	89
Alloy 825	Pulp and paper processing; field or pilot plant test; slight to moderate aeration; slight to moderate agitation. Plus saturated water solution	~7.2	3 (38)	70 d	0.0032 in./yr	89
Carpenter 20	Pulp and paper processing; field or pilot plant test; slight to moderate aeration; rapid agitation. Cast specimens. Plus saturated water solution	~4-5	2 (36)	14.5 d	0.0007 in./yr	89
Carpenter 20	Pulp and paper processing; field or pilot plant test; slight to moderate aeration; slight to moderate agitation. Cast specimens. Chlorine dioxide spent liquor, 45% sulfuric acid, 20 g/L sodium chlorate	...	68 (155)	14.6 d	0.0011 in./yr	89

Chlorine Water

Chlorine dissolved in water forms a mixture of HCl and hypochlorous acid (HClO). The latter is very oxidizing, which makes the mixture extremely corrosive. Relatively little information is available on corrosion in water containing substantial levels of chlorine, especially near saturation. Aluminum was reported to be unsuitable in HClO and to be attacked with extensive pitting in chlorine-water environments. Zirconium was found to corrode at less than 0.025 mm/yr (1 mil/yr) in chlorine-saturated water.

Corrosion of several alloys in chlorine-saturated water at 25 °C (75 °F) was investigated, and the results show that rates are generally low for the chromium-containing alloys tested and for titanium. Only Monel 400 showed a very high rate (24 mm/yr, or 948 mils/yr), which is to be expected because of its sensitivity to oxidants. No large difference in performance

between cast alloys and their wrought equivalents was found, except for crevice attack on ACI CF-8M, CN-7M, and CD-4MCu.

Related tests were performed in chlorine ice at -20 °C (-4 °F). The results show that corrosion rates for chromium-containing alloys are below 0.0025 mm/yr (0.1 mils/yr), except for ACI CW-12M at 0.0038 mm/yr (0.15 mil/yr). Higher, but not unacceptable, rates were found for steel, N-12M, and M-35. These alloys are sensitive to oxidants in acidic environments, which explains their poorer performance.

Additional Reading

N.R. Sorensen, R.B. Diegle, and S.T. Picraux, The Effects of Phosphorus Implantation on Passivity of Fe-Cr Alloys in Acidic Electrolytes, *J. Mater. Res.*, *1*(6), 752-757, 1986. MetAbs No. 87-351081. **Abstract:** The passivation behavior of the phosphorus-implanted alloys in a Cl-containing electrolyte as a function of Cr concentration and P implantation has been investigated.

Corrosion Behavior of Various Metals and Alloys in Chlorine Water

Material	Condition, other factors, comments	Concentration, %	Temperature, °C (°F)	Duration	Corrosion rate, mm/yr (mils/yr) or other	Ref
Zr702	...	...	100 (212)	...	<0.05 (<2)	15

Chloroacetic Acid

Chloroacetic acid, $CH_2ClCOOH$, also known as monochloroacetic acid, is a colorless solid with a boiling point of 189 °C (372 °F). It is used in manufacturing dyes and in medicine.

Additional Reading

H. Mansour, H.M. Moustafa, A. El-Wafa, and G.A. Noubi, Corrosion of Aluminium in Chloroacetic Acids, *Bull. Electrochem.*, *2*(5), 449-451, 1986. MetAbs No. 87-350962. **Abstract:** The study is concerned with the corrosion of aluminium in mono-, di-, and trichloroacetic acids.

Corrosion Behavior of Various Metals and Alloys in Chloroacetic Acid

Material	Condition, other factors, comments	Concentration, %	Temperature, °C (°F)	Duration	Corrosion rate, mm/yr (mils/yr) or other	Ref
Stainless steels						
Type 304 stainless steel	...	All	21 (70)	...	Poor	121
Type 304 stainless steel	Chemical processing; slight to moderate aeration; slight to moderate aeration. Slight pitting (maximum depth of pits from incipient to 0.005 in.)	100	19-21 (66-70)	3 d	0.013 in./yr	89
Type 304 stainless steel	Chemical processing; field or pilot plant test; no aeration; no agitation. Plus 22% water	78	50-60 (122-140)	17 d	0.0097 in./yr	89
Type 304 stainless steel	Chemical processing; field or pilot plant test; slight to moderate aeration; no agitation. Plus 22% water. Crevice attack (tendency to concentration-cell corrosion)	78	10-25 (50-77)	17 d	0.0001 in./yr	89
Type 316 stainless steel	Chemical processing; field or pilot plant test; no aeration; no agitation. Plus 22% water	78	50-60 (122-140)	17 d	0.0025 in./yr	89
Type 316 stainless steel	Chemical processing; field or pilot plant test; slight to moderate aeration; no agitation. Plus 22% water	78	10-25 (50-77)	17 d	<0.0001 in./yr	89
Type 316 stainless steel	Chemical processing; slight to moderate aeration; slight to moderate aeration	100	19-21 (66-70)	3 d	0.0002 in./yr	89

(Continued)

Corrosion Behavior of Various Metals and Alloys in Chloroacetic Acid (Continued)

Material	Condition, other factors, comments	Concen-tration, %	Temperature, °C (°F)	Duration	Corrosion rate, mm/yr (mils/yr) or other	Ref
Type 316 stainless steel	...	All	21 (70)	...	Poor	121
Type 317 stainless steel	Chemical processing; field or pilot plant test; no aeration; no agitation. Plus 22% water	78	50-60 (122-140)	17 d	0.002 in./yr	89
Type 317 stainless steel	Chemical processing; field or pilot plant test; slight to moderate aeration; no agitation. Plus 22% water. Crevice attack (tendency to concentration-cell corrosion)	78	10-25 (50-77)	17 d	<0.0001 in./yr	89
Type 410 stainless steel	...	All	21 (70)	...	Poor	121
Type 410 stainless steel	...	...	Room	...	Attacked	121
Type 430 stainless steel	...	All	21 (70)	...	Poor	121
Titanium						
Titanium	...	30	80 (176)	...	0.02 (0.8)	90
Titanium	...	100	Boiling	...	0.013 (0.52)	90
Heat- and corrosion-resistant alloys						
Carpenter 20	Chemical processing; field or pilot plant test; no aeration; no agitation. Plus 22% water	78	50-60 (122-140)	17 d	0.0018 in./yr	89
Carpenter 20	Chemical processing; field or pilot plant test; slight to moderate aeration; no agitation. Plus 22% water	78	10-25 (50-77)	17 d	<0.0001 in./yr	89
Noble metals						
Silver	...	All	Boiling	...	<0.05 (<2)	4

Chloroform

Chloroform, CCl_3, also known as trichloromethane, formyl trichloride, and methenyl trichloride, is a colorless, nonflammable liquid with a boiling point of 61.2 °C (142 °F). Chloroform is used as a solvent, in medicine, and for organic synthesis.

Material Summaries

The following material summaries were compiled from a survey of the available literature. Inclusion of a material description under a given environment does not imply that it is the most appropriate material for corrosion service in that environment. Likewise, exclusion of a given material does not imply that it is not suitable for corrosion service applications in that environment.

Aluminum. Aluminum alloy 1100 was found to be resistant to chloroform with a trace of water. However, in the same test using temperatures up to the boiling point of 61 °C (142 °F), anhydrous chloroform was found to be corrosive to alloy 1100.

Corrosion Behavior of Various Metals and Alloys in Chloroform

Material	Condition, other factors, comments	Concen-tration, %	Temperature, °C (°F)	Duration	Corrosion rate, mm/yr (mils/yr) or other	Ref
Coppers						
70-30 cupronickel	Dry	...	...	...	Suitable	93
90-10 cupronickel	Dry	...	...	...	Suitable	93
Admiralty brass	Dry	...	...	...	Suitable	93
Aluminum bronze	Dry	...	...	...	Suitable	93
Ampco 8, aluminum bronze	Generally suitable. Conditions such as aeration or temperature could restrict use	...	...	...	<0.5 (<20)	96
Architectural bronze	Dry	...	...	...	Suitable	93
Brass	Dry	...	...	...	Suitable	93
Cartridge brass	Dry	...	...	...	Suitable	93
Commercial bronze	Dry	...	...	...	Suitable	93
Electrolytic copper	Dry	...	...	...	Suitable	93
Free-cutting brass	Dry	...	...	...	Suitable	93

(Continued)

Corrosion Behavior of Various Metals and Alloys in Chloroform (Continued)

Material	Condition, other factors, comments	Concentration, %	Temperature, °C (°F)	Duration	Corrosion rate, mm/yr (mils/yr) or other	Ref
Muntz metal	Dry	...	...	...	Suitable	93
Naval brass	Dry	...	...	...	Suitable	93
Nickel silver	Dry	18	...	...	Suitable	93
Phosphor bronze	5% Sn. Dry	...	...	...	Suitable	93
Phosphor bronze	8% Sn. Dry	...	...	...	Suitable	93
Phosphor copper	Dry	...	...	...	Suitable	93
Red brass	Dry	...	...	...	Suitable	93
Silicon bronze	Low. Dry	...	...	...	Suitable	93
Silicon bronze	High. Dry	...	...	...	Suitable	93
Titanium						
Titanium	...	100	Boiling	...	nil	20
Titanium	Plus water	50	Boiling	...	0.12 (4.7)	20
Titanium	...	Vapor & liquid	Boiling	...	0.000	90
Titanium	Plus 50% HNO3	50	95 (203)	...	0.000	90
Lead, tin, and zinc						
Lead	Practically resistant; Pb recommended for use	...	24-62 (75-143)	...	<500 μm/yr (<20)	95
Noble metals						
Silver	Dry or wet	...	Boiling	...	<0.05 (<2)	10
Others						
Magnesium	...	100	Room	...	Suitable	119

Chlorosulfonic Acid

Chlorosulfonic acid, ClSO3H, also known as chlorosulfuric acid and sulfuric chlorohydrin, is an oily liquid with a boiling point of 158 °C (316 °F). It is formed from sulfur trioxide and hydrogen chloride, but decomposes in water to form hydrochloric acid and sulfuric acid. It is a vigorous dehydrating agent and is used in manufacturing synthetic drugs, poison gas, and saccharin.

Material Summaries

The following material summaries were compiled from a survey of the available literature. Inclusion of a material description under a given environment does not imply that it is the most appropriate material for corrosion service in that environment. Likewise, exclusion of a given material does not imply that it is not suitable for corrosion service applications in that environment.

Aluminum (99.5%) is resistant to chlorosulfonic acid at room temperature up to 70 °C. It is used in reaction vessels, stirrers, and feed pipes for the sulphonation of aliphatic alcohols. Aluminum is resistant to chlorosulfonic acid at room temperature and is used in vessels and pipes for so-called fog-forming acid (mixture of chlorosulfonic acid with approximately 50% sulfur trioxide). Aluminum is unusable at room temperature in the presence of water.

Copper. Copper bronze (without zinc) is fairly resistant to chlorosulfonic acid at temperatures up to 150 °C, if water and air are excluded. It is used in boilers in the manufacture of toluenesulfonyl chloride from toluene and chlorosulfonic acid.

Irons and Steels. Iron (pure), cast iron, and steel are resistant to chlorosulfonic acid at room temperature and up to 130 °C, if water is excluded. It is used in vessels, barrels, pipes for transportation and shipping of chlorosulfonic acid and also in mixture with sulfur trioxide for mild steel. Irons are resistant to corrosion at 0 °C and are used for frederking vessels of cast iron for the manufacture of o-toluenesulfonyl chloride from toluene and chlorosulfonic acid. Irons are fairly resistant at 180 °C and are used in reaction vessels of mild steel for the manufacture of chlorosulfonic acid from contact gas (6 to 7% sulfur trioxide, balance mainly nitrogen) and hydrogen chloride. The condensers for the hot gaseous chlorosulfonic acid and absorbers (98% sulfuric acid) are also made of mild steel. Iron is unusable at room temperature, if water is present. It is not particularly resistant at 140 °C, but is used with mixtures of 98% chlorosulfonic acid, 1.5% sulfuric acid, and 0.5% hydrochloric acid. Cast silicon-irons (containing more than 14.5% silicon), such as Durichlor, are resistant to chlorosulfonic acid at room temperature.

Stainless Steels. Stainless steels containing approximately 17% chromium and those containing approximately 17% chromium with small additions of molybdenum behave like unalloyed steel. Chlorosulfonic acid is stored in carbon steel and stainless steel.

Austenitic Steels. Stabilized austenitic chromium-nickel steels containing 18 to 20% chromium and 8 to 11% nickel and those containing 16 to 18% chromium, 10 to 14% nickel, and 2.0 to 3.0% molybdenum behave like unalloyed steel in the presence of chlorosulfonic acid. The corrosion rate at room temperature is <0.1 mm/yr, but carries the risk of pitting in the presence of moisture.

Highly alloyed austenitic steels, such as Carpenter 20, are resistant to chlorosulfonic acid from room temperature to 50 °C, as well as to mixtures of 98% chlorosulfonic acid, 1.5% sulfuric acid, and 0.5% hydrochloric acid.

Lead. Lead is fairly resistant to corrosion by chlorosulfonic acid at room temperature. The maximum corrosion rate for lead is 0.8 mm/yr. It is also fairly resistant at 20 °C and is used in decomposition vessels for the elimination of the surplus of chlorosulfonic acid in sulphonation mixtures by adding water (hard lead).

Nickel. Nickel is fairly resistant to chlorosulfonic acid at room temperature, and has a corrosion rate of 0.05 to 0.50 mm/yr. Nickel-chromium alloys, such as Inconel, behave like nickel in the presence of chlorosulfonic acid. Monel alloys behave like nickel in the presence of chlorosulfonic acid.

Nickel-molybdenum alloys, such as Hastelloy B, Chlorimet 2, Bergit B, and Euzonit 70, are resistant to chlorosulfonic acid from room temperature up to 140 °C, whether or not moisture is present. They are resistant from room temperature to the boiling point and are used in sulphonation vessels of Hastelloy B for alkyl-aryl organics. These alloys are resistant at 40 °C and are used with mixtures of 45% chlorosulfonic acid, 50% sulfur trioxide, and 5% sulfuric acid in the manufacture of smoke screens, as well as for valves and pumps of Hastelloy B. Nickel-molybdenum alloys are resistant at 100 °C and are used with mixtures of 45% chlorosulfonic acid, 50% sulfur trioxide, 5% sulfuric acid. The corrosion rate for Hastelloy B is <0.05 mm/yr.

Platinum. Platinum, its alloys and less common metals, like gold, are resistant from room temperature up to the boiling point of chlorosulfonic acid. Platinum, gold, and tantalum are resistant up to 100 °C, with a corrosion rate of <0.05 mm/yr.

Tin. Chlorosulfonic acid reacts rapidly with tin.

Corrosion Behavior of Various Metals and Alloys in Chlorosulfonic Acid

Material	Condition, other factors, comments	Concentration, %	Temperature, °C (°F)	Duration	Corrosion rate, mm/yr (mils/yr) or other	Ref
Lead	During storage of chlorosulfonic acid + 50% SO₃	50	...	...	0.015 (0.6)	48
Tin	...					
Tin	...	...	20 (68)	...	Unsuitable	94
Tin	...	...	60 (140)	...	Unsuitable	94
Tin	...	...	100 (212)	...	Unsuitable	94
Titanium	...	100	Room	...	0.312 (12.48)	90

Chromic Acid

Chromic acid, H_2CrO_4, exists only in solution. The hydrate of chromium oxide, it is used in electroplating baths.

Material Summaries

The following material summaries were compiled from a survey of the available literature. Inclusion of a material description under a given environment does not imply that it is the most appropriate material for corrosion service in that environment. Likewise, exclusion of a given material does not imply that it is not suitable for corrosion service applications in that environment.

Aluminum. Aqueous solutions of chromic acid in concentrations up to $0.1N$ at ambient temperature had no effect on aluminum alloy 1100 in laboratory tests.

Copper. Aluminum bronzes should be avoided in the service of chromic acid.

Lead has high corrosion resistance to chromic acid and is widely used in its manufacture and handling. Lead performs well at acid concentrations up to 95% at ambient temperatures, up to 85% at 220 °C (428 °F), and up to 93% at 150 °C (302 °F). Below a concentration rate of 5%, the corrosion rate increases, but it is still relatively low. Lead exhibits the same excellent corrosion resistance to higher concentrations of chromic acid. In general, lead is also resistant to solutions containing salts of chromic acid.

Magnesium and its alloys are attacked very slowly by pure chromic acid. With the addition of the chloride ion in the chromic acid, the corrosion rate increases markedly. A boiling solution of 20% chromic acid is often used to cleanse corrosion products from magnesium alloys without endangering the base metal.

Titanium alloys generally are highly resistant to chromic acid over a wide range of temperatures and concentrations.

Corrosion Behavior of Various Metals and Alloys in Chromic Acid

Material	Condition, other factors, comments	Concentration, %	Temperature, °C (°F)	Duration	Corrosion rate, mm/yr (mils/yr) or other	Ref
Stainless steels						
12Cr stainless steel	...	1	100 (212)	2 d	0.01 (0.4)	87
12Cr stainless steel	...	15	100 (212)	2 d	0.860 (34)	87
18-8Mo stainless steel	...	1	100 (212)	2 d	0.008 (0.3)	87
18-8Mo stainless steel	...	15	100 (212)	2 d	2.57 (101)	87
18-8Ti stainless steel	...	1	100 (212)	2 d	0.013 (0.5)	87
18-8Ti stainless steel	...	15	100 (212)	2 d	5.84 (230)	87
27Cr stainless steel	...	1	100 (212)	2 d	0.01 (0.4)	87
27Cr stainless steel	...	15	100 (212)	2 d	0.97 (38)	87
Type 304 stainless steel	...	5	82 (180)	3 d	0.018 (0.7)	87
Type 304 stainless steel	...	10	82 (180)	3 d	0.15 (5.9)	87
Type 304 stainless steel	...	15	82 (180)	3 d	1.42 (56)	87
Type 304 stainless steel	...	15	100 (212)	2.5 d	2.49 (98)	87
Type 304 stainless steel	...	25	24 (75)	3 d	nil	87
Type 304 stainless steel	...	25	82 (180)	3 d	18.5 (730)	87
Type 304 stainless steel	(a)	10	21 (70)	...	Good	121
Type 304 stainless steel	(a)	50	21 (70)	...	Good	121
Type 316 stainless steel	...	5	82 (180)	3 d	0.074 (2.9)	87
Type 316 stainless steel	...	10	82 (180)	3 d	0.305 (12)	87
Type 316 stainless steel	...	15	82 (180)	3 d	0.460 (18)	87
Type 316 stainless steel	...	15	100 (212)	2.5 d	9.96 (392)	87
Type 316 stainless steel	...	25	24 (75)	3 d	0.018 (0.7)	87
Type 316 stainless steel	...	25	82 (180)	3 d	27.4 (1080)	87
Type 316 stainless steel	(a)	10	21 (70)	...	Good	121
Type 316 stainless steel	(a)	50	21 (70)	...	Good	121
Type 410 stainless steel	(a)	10	21 (70)	...	Fair	121
Type 410 stainless steel	(a)	50	21 (70)	...	Poor	121
Type 410 stainless steel	(a)	...	Room	...	Slightly attacked	121
Type 430 stainless steel	(a)	10	21 (70)	...	Good	121
Type 430 stainless steel	(a)	50	21 (70)	...	Poor	121
Aluminum						
Aluminum (99.0-99.5%)	Solution	...	20 (68)	...	Restricted applications	92
Aluminum alloys	Solution	...	20 (68)	...	Restricted applications	92
Coppers						
70-30 cupronickel	...	...	...	...	Not suitable	93
90-10 cupronickel	...	...	...	...	Not suitable	93
Admiralty brass	...	...	...	...	Not suitable	93
Aluminum bronze	...	...	...	...	Not suitable	93
Ampco 8, aluminum bronze	Generally not suitable	...	...	...	>0.5 (>20)	96
Architectural bronze	...	...	...	...	Not suitable	93
Brass	...	...	...	...	Not suitable	93
Cartridge brass	...	...	...	...	Not suitable	93
Commercial bronze	...	...	...	...	Not suitable	93
Electrolytic copper	...	...	...	...	Not suitable	93
Free-cutting brass	...	...	...	...	Not suitable	93
Muntz metal	...	...	...	...	Not suitable	93
Naval brass	...	...	...	...	Not suitable	93
Nickel silver	...	18	...	...	Not suitable	93
Phosphor bronze	5% Sn	...	...	...	Not suitable	93
Phosphor bronze	8% Sn	...	...	...	Not suitable	93
Phosphor copper	...	...	...	...	Not suitable	93
Red brass	...	...	...	...	Not suitable	93
Silicon bronze	Low	...	...	...	Not suitable	93
Silicon bronze	High	...	...	...	Not suitable	93

(Continued)

Corrosion Behavior of Various Metals and Alloys in Chromic Acid (Continued)

Material	Condition, other factors, comments	Concen-tration, %	Temperature, °C (°F)	Duration	Corrosion rate, mm/yr (mils/yr) or other	Ref
Titanium						
Ti-3Al-2.5V	ASTM Grade 9	10	Boiling	...	0.007 (0.3)	91
Ti-3Al-2.5V	ASTM Grade 9	30	Boiling	...	0.05 (2.1)	91
Ti-3Al-2.5V	ASTM Grade 9	50	Boiling	...	0.25 (10.1)	91
Titanium	Grade 7	10	Boiling	...	nil	33
Titanium	Grade 9	10	Boiling	...	0.008 (0.32)	33
Titanium	Grade 9	30	Boiling	...	0.053 (2.12)	33
Titanium	...	10	Boiling	...	0.003 (0.12)	90
Titanium	...	15	24 (75)	...	0.006 (0.24)	90
Titanium	...	15	82 (180)	...	0.015 (0.6)	90
Titanium	...	50	24 (75)	...	0.013 (0.52)	90
Titanium	...	50	82 (180)	...	0.028 (1.12)	90
Titanium	Plus 5% HNO_3	5	21 (70)	...	<0.003 (<0.12)	90
Titanium	Grade 9	50	Boiling	...	0.26 (10.4)	33
Titanium	...	10	Boiling	...	0.002 (0.1)	91
Titanium	...	30	Boiling	...	0.01 (0.4)	91
Titanium	...	50	Boiling	...	0.03 (1.4)	91
Titanium	Unalloyed	10	Boiling	...	0.003 (0.12)	86
Titanium	Unalloyed	15	24 (75)	...	0.005 (0.2)	86
Titanium	Unalloyed	15	82 (180)	...	0.015 (0.6)	86
Titanium	Unalloyed	36.5	90 (195)	...	0.046 (1.8)	86
Titanium	Unalloyed	50	24 (75)	...	0.013 (0.5)	86
Titanium	Unalloyed	50	82 (180)	...	0.025 (1.0)	86
Heat- and corrosion-resistant alloys						
44Co-31Cr-13W	(b)	2	65 (150)	...	nil	53
44Co-31Cr-13W	(b)	10	65 (150)	...	0.025 (1)	53
44Co-31Cr-13W	Heat treated 4 h at 899 °C (1650 °F) and furnace cooled. (b)	2	65 (150)	...	nil	53
44Co-31Cr-13W	Heat treated 4 h at 899 °C (1650 °F) and furnace cooled. (b)	10	65 (150)	...	0.625 (25)	53
44Co-31Cr-13W	(b)	2	65 (150)	...	nil	53
44Co-31Cr-13W	Heat treated 4 h at 899 °C (1650 °F), furnace cooled. (b)	2	65 (150)	...	nil	53
44Co-31Cr-13W	(b)	10	65 (150)	...	0.025 (1)	53
44Co-31Cr-13W	Heat treated 4 h at 899 °C (1650 °F), furnace cooled. (b)	10	65 (150)	...	0.625 (25)	53
50Co-20Cr-15W-10Ni	...	2	65 (150)	...	nil	53
50Co-20Cr-15W-10Ni	...	10	65 (150)	...	0.125 (5)	53
50Co-20Cr-15W-10Ni	(b)	2	65 (150)	...	nil	53
50Co-20Cr-15W-10Ni	(b)	10	65 (150)	...	0.125 (5)	53
53Co-30Cr-4.5W	(b)	2	65 (150)	...	nil	53
53Co-30Cr-4.5W	(b)	10	65 (150)	...	0.7 (28)	53
53Co-30Cr-4.5W	Heat treated 4 h at 899 °C (1650 °F). (b)	2	65 (150)	...	nil	53
53Co-30Cr-4.5W	Heat treated 4 h at 899 °C (1650 °F). (b)	10	65 (150)	...	0.575 (23)	53
53Co-30Cr-4.5W	(b)	2	65 (150)	...	nil	53
53Co-30Cr-4.5W	Heat treated 4 h at 899 °C (1650 °F), furnace cooled. (b)	2	65 (150)	...	nil	53
53Co-30Cr-4.5W	(b)	10	65 (150)	...	0.7 (28)	53
53Co-30Cr-4.5W	Heat treated 4 h at 899 °C (1650 °F), furnace cooled. (b)	10	65 (150)	...	0.57 (23)	53
Haynes alloy No. 25	(c)	2	Room	24 h	nil	68
Haynes alloy No. 25	(c)	2	66 (150)	24 h	nil	68
Haynes alloy No. 25	(c)	2	Boiling	24 h	0.08 (3.0)	68
Haynes alloy No. 25	(c)	10	Room	24 h	nil	68
Haynes alloy No. 25	...	10	Boiling	...	1.0 (40)	23
Haynes alloy No. 25	(c)	10	66 (150)	24 h	0.13 (5.0)	68
Haynes alloy No. 25	(c)	10	Boiling	24 h	1.04 (41)	68
Haynes alloy No. 25	(c)	20	Room	24 h	nil	68

(Continued)

Corrosion Behavior of Various Metals and Alloys in Chromic Acid (Continued)

Material	Condition, other factors, comments	Concentration, %	Temperature, °C (°F)	Duration	Corrosion rate, mm/yr (mils/yr) or other	Ref
Haynes alloy No. 25	(c)	20	66 (150)	24 h	0.53 (21)	68
Haynes alloy No. 25	(c)	20	Boiling	24 h	4.19 (165)	68
Haynes alloy No. 188	...	10	Boiling	...	1.37 (54)	23
Haynes alloy No. 556	...	10	Boiling	...	2.8 (110)	23
Incoloy 800	Solutions were prepared with reagent-grade chemicals. Test specimens were cold-rolled, annealed sheet, 2.84 mm (0.112 in.) thick. No pitting	5	80 (176)	7 d	0.041 (1.6)	44
Inconel 690	...	5	80 (176)	...	0.13 (5)	57
Inconel 601	Average of two tests	5	80 (176)	7 d	0.091 (3.6)	64
Multimet	(c)	2	66 (150)	24 h	nil	68
Multimet	(c)	10	66 (150)	24 h	0.2 (8.0)	68
Multimet	(c)	20	66 (150)	24 h	2.31 (91)	68
Multimet	(c)	2	Boiling	24 h	0.15 (6.0)	68
Multimet	Data were obtained using corrosion specimens prepared from 12-gage, solution heat-treated sheet. Rate is for the fifth 24-h test period, not steady-state rate	10	Boiling	24 h	9.09 (358)	68
Multimet	(c)	20	Boiling	24 h	>25.4 (>1000)	68
Zirconium						
Zr702	...	10-50	Boiling	...	<0.025 (<1)	15
Lead, tin, and zinc						
Lead	Practically resistant; Pb recommended for use	...	24 (75)	...	<0.5 (<20)	95
Tin	...	80	20 (68)	...	Resistant	94
Tin	...	80	60 (140)	...	Resistant	94
Tin	...	80	100 (212)	..	Resistant	94
Noble metals						
Silver	...	All	100 (212)	...	<0.05 (<2)	4
Silver	...	All	100 (212)	...	<0.05 (<2)	4
Others						
Magnesium	...	All	Room	...	Resistant	119

(a) Chemically pure. (b) As-cast specimens 38 mm x 25 mm x 6 mm (1.5 in. x 1 in. x 0.25 in.), 120-grit abrasive finish. Average of 24-h periods. (c) Data are steady-state as calculated from a minimum of five 24-h test periods. Data were obtained using corrosion specimens prepared from 12-gage solution heat-treated sheet.

Citric Acid

Citric acid, $(COOH)CH_2C(OH)(COOH)CH_2COOH$, also known as 2-hydroxy-1,2,3-propane tricarboxylic acid, is a colorless crystalline solid with a melting point of 153 °C (307 °F). Citric acid is soluble in water and alcohol. It is found in many plants, especially citrus fruits. The juice of unripe lemons is a commercial source of citric acid. The reaction of calcium citrate and dilute sulfuric acid yields citric acid and calcium sulfate, which may be separated by filteration. The food industry uses citric acid as a flavoring agent and as an antioxidant. Citric acid, formulated with propylene glycol and butylated hydroxy anisol, is used as a stabilizer for fats, greases, and tallow. Etching, textile dyeing, and printing operations use citric acid in various applications, and it is also used to adjust the pH in certain electroplating baths.

Material Summaries

The following material summaries were compiled from a survey of the available literature. Inclusion of a material description under a given environment does not imply that it is the most appropriate material for corrosion service in that environment. Likewise, exclusion of a given material does not imply that it is not suitable for corrosion service applications in that environment.

Aluminum. Aluminum alloy 1100 exhibits good resistance to citric acid at ambient temperature. In laboratory tests, higher concentrations of the citric acid solution had little effect on the corrosion rate, but an increase in temperature raised it substantially. The corrosion rate also increased in the presence of chlorides of heavy metals. Aluminum alloy 356.0 valves have been used to service citrus acid solutions. Fermenting vats, crystallizers, pipes, and other equipment made of aluminum have been used in manufacturing citric acid, because aluminum has no harmful effect on the organisms involved.

Stainless Steel. Type 316 stainless steel has been recommended for all concentrations of citric acid up to the boiling point, whereas type 304 has been used at moderate temperatures.

Zirconium. Zirconium resists corrosion in citric acid.

Additional Reading

J.M. Bastidas and J.D. Scantlebury, The Influence of Light on Corrosion Phenomena: The Behavior of Mild Steel in Citric Acid Solution, *Corros. Sci.*, 26(5), 341-347, 1986. MetAbs No. 86-352032. **Abstract:** Experiments using photopotential, galvanic current, ac impedance and harmonic analysis techniques were carried out to observe the effect of visible light on mild steel in a citric acid solution.

Y.M. Chen, T.J. O'Keefe, and W.J. James, Electrochemical Studies of Plasma-Formed Films of Tin, *Thin Solid Films, 129*(3-4), 205-215, 1985. MetAbs No. 87-350233. **Abstract:** The electrochemical behavior of plasma-formed Sn films on Al is compared with that of conventional beta-Sn.

M.Th. Makhlouf, A.A. Abdel-Hafez, and S.A. Ibrahim, Effect of Chelating 8-Hydroxyquinolin Derivatives on the Corrosion of Zinc in Polybasic Acids, *J. Electrochem. Soc. India, 35*(2), 89-92, 1986. MetAbs No. 87-350318. **Abstract:** The corrosion behavior of Zn in some polybasic acids covering a wide range of pH has been studied. The effect of 8-hydroxyquinoline and some of its derivatives on the corrosion of Zn in the presence of the polybasic acids (malonic and citric) as aggressive media has been investigated.

R.A. Speranzini, R.L. Tapping, and D.J. Disney, Corrosiveness of Decontamination Solutions to Sensitized AISI 304 Stainless Steel, *Corrosion, 43*(10), 632-641, 1987. MetAbs No. 88-350606. **Abstract:** An experimental study of the corrosiveness of citric acid, oxalic acid, and EDTA mixtures to sensitized AISI 304 stainless steel was conducted.

Corrosion Behavior of Various Metals and Alloys in Citric Acid

Material	Condition, other factors, comments	Concentration, %	Temperature, °C (°F)	Duration	Corrosion rate, mm/yr (mils/yr) or other	Ref
Stainless steels						
Type 304 stainless steel	...	20	Boiling	24 h	0.01 (0.4)	52
Type 304 stainless steel	...	10	21 (70)	...	Good	121
Type 304 stainless steel	...	10	Boiling	...	Good	121
Type 304 stainless steel	...	50	21 (70)	...	Good	121
Type 304 stainless steel	...	50	Boiling	...	Poor	121
Type 304 stainless steel	...	10	99-102 (210-215)	...	0.210 (8.3)	87
Type 316 stainless steel	...	20	Boiling	24 h	0.0125 (0.5)	52
Type 316 stainless steel	...	10	21 (70)	...	Good	121
Type 316 stainless steel	...	10	Boiling	...	Good	121
Type 316 stainless steel	...	50	21 (70)	...	Good	121
Type 316 stainless steel	...	50	Boiling	...	Good	121
Type 316 stainless steel	...	10	99-102 (210-215)	...	0.013 (0.5)	87
Type 409 stainless steel	...	6	Room	...	0.00	87
Type 409 stainless steel	...	10	Room	...	0.00	87
Type 409 stainless steel	...	6	Boiling	...	0.0025 (0.1)	87
Type 409 stainless steel	...	10	Boiling	...	0.0025 (0.1)	87
Type 410 stainless steel	...	10	21 (70)	...	Good	121
Type 410 stainless steel	...	10	Boiling	...	Poor	121
Type 410 stainless steel	...	50	21 (70)	...	Fair	121
Type 410 stainless steel	...	50	Boiling	...	Poor	121
Type 410 stainless steel	...	...	Room	...	Very slightly attacked	121
Type 410 stainless steel	...	10	99-102 (210-215)	...	0.260 (10.3)	87
Type 410 stainless steel	Plus 10% potassium ferricyanide	...	Room	...	Very slightly stained	121
Type 430 stainless steel	...	10	21 (70)	...	Good	121
Type 430 stainless steel	...	10	Boiling	...	Fair	121
Type 430 stainless steel	...	50	21 (70)	...	Good	121
Type 430 stainless steel	...	50	Boiling	...	Poor	121
Type 430 stainless steel	...	10	99-102 (210-215)	...	0.020 (0.8)	87
Type 444 stainless steel	...	20	Boiling	24 h	0.0075 (0.3)	52
Aluminum						
Aluminum-manganese alloys	Solution	...	20-100 (68-212)	...	Satisfactory	92
Coppers						
70-30 cupronickel	...	...	...	...	Suitable	93
90-10 cupronickel	...	...	...	...	Suitable	93
Admiralty brass	...	...	...	...	Suitable	93
Aluminum bronze	...	...	...	...	Suitable	93

(Continued)

Corrosion Behavior of Various Metals and Alloys in Citric Acid (Continued)

Material	Condition, other factors, comments	Concen-tration, %	Temperature, °C (°F)	Duration	Corrosion rate, mm/yr (mils/yr) or other	Ref
Ampco 8, aluminum bronze	Generally suitable	...	...	...	<0.05 (<2)	96
Architectural bronze	...	...	...	...	Fair	93
Brass	...	...	...	...	Suitable	93
Cartridge brass	...	...	...	...	Fair	93
Commercial bronze	...	...	...	...	Suitable	93
Electrolytic copper	...	...	...	...	Suitable	93
Free-cutting brass	...	...	...	...	Fair	93
Muntz metal	...	...	...	...	Fair	93
Naval brass	...	...	...	...	Fair	93
Nickel silver	...	18	...	...	Suitable	93
Phosphor bronze	5% Sn	...	...	...	Suitable	93
Phosphor bronze	8% Sn	...	...	...	Suitable	93
Phosphor copper	...	...	...	...	Suitable	93
Red brass	...	...	...	...	Suitable	93
Silicon bronze	Low	...	...	...	Suitable	93
Silicon bronze	High	...	...	...	Suitable	93
Titanium						
Titanium	Grade 12	50	Boiling	...	0.013 (0.52)	33
Titanium	...	10	100 (212)	...	0.009 (0.36)	90
Titanium	...	25	100 (212)	...	0.001 (0.04)	90
Titanium	...	50	60 (140)	...	0.000	90
Titanium	...	50	Boiling	...	0.127-1.27 (5.08-50.8)	90
Titanium	...	672	149 (301)	...	Corroded	90
Titanium	Aerated	50	100 (212)	...	<0.127 (<5.08)	90
Titanium	Grade 9	50	Boiling	...	0.38 (15.2)	33
Titanium	...	50	Boiling	...	0.35 (14)	91
Titanium	Grade 7	50	Boiling	...	0.025 (1)	33
Titanium-3Al-2.5V	ASTM Grade 9	50	Boiling	...	0.37 (15)	91
Heat- and corrosion-resistant alloys						
Ferralium 255	Plus 8% NaCl	5	141 (286)	...	<0.01 (0.1)	60
Incoloy 800	Solutions were prepared with reagent-grade chemicals. Test specimens were cold-rolled, annealed sheet, 2.84 mm (0.112 in.) thick. No pitting occurred	7	80 (176)	7 d	nil	44
Inconel 690	...	10	80 (176)	...	<0.03 (<1)	57
Inconel 601	...	10	80 (176)	7 d	<0.002 (<0.1)	64
Nickel 200	Laboratory immersion test	2	Room	...	0.02 (0.8)	44
Nickel 200	Laboratory immersion test	2	71 (160)	...	0.14 (5.5)	44
Nickel 200	Laboratory aerated test	2	82 (180)	...	0.85 (180)	44
Nickel 200	Laboratory immersion test	5	30 (86)	...	0.125 (5)	44
Nickel 200	Laboratory aerated test	5	30 (86)	...	0.375 (15)	44
Nickel 200	Laboratory immersion test	5	60 (140)	...	0.5 (20)	44
Nickel 200	Laboratory immersion test	58	Boiling	...	0.425 (17)	44
Zirconium						
Zr702	...	10-50	35-100 (95-212)	...	<0.025 (<1)	15
Zr702	...	10, 25, 50	100 (212)	...	<0.025 (<1)	15
Zr702	...	50	Boiling	...	<0.13 (<5)	15
Lead, tin, and zinc						
Lead	...	10	Boiling	...	0.025 (1.0)	2
Tin	Nonaerated solutions	...	20 (68)	...	Resistant	94
Tin	...	...	60 (140)	...	Unsuitable	94
Tin	...	...	100 (212)	...	Unsuitable	94
Tin	Nonaerated solutions	...	20 (68)	...	Resistant	94
Tin	...	...	60 (140)	...	Unsuitable	94
Tin	...	...	100 (212)	...	Unsuitable	94

(Continued)

Corrosion Behavior of Various Metals and Alloys in Citric Acid (Continued)

Material	Condition, other factors, comments	Concen-tration, %	Temperature, °C (°F)	Duration	Corrosion rate, mm/yr (mils/yr) or other	Ref
Noble metals						
Gold	...	20	Boiling	...	<0.05 (<2)	8
Gold	...	30	Boiling	...	<0.05 (<2)	8
Silver	...	0-30	Boiling	...	<0.05 (<2)	4
Silver	...	0-30	Boiling	...	<0.05 (<2)	4

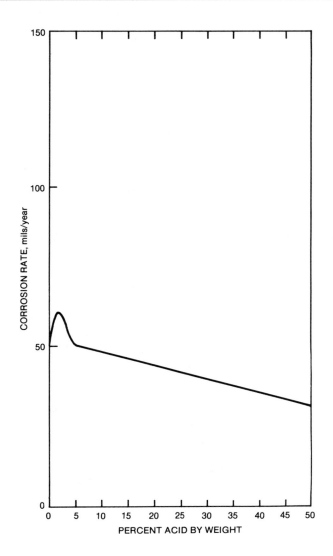

Aluminum. Effect of citric acid on alloy 1100 at 100 °C (212 °F). Source: *Guidelines for the Use of Aluminum with Food and Chemicals: Compatibility Data on Aluminum in the Food and Chemical Process Industries*, 5th ed., The Aluminum Association, Washington, DC, 1984, 25.

Copals

Copal is the general name for fossil and other hard resins found in almost all tropical countries. All are distinguished by their yellowish to yellowish-brown color and their solubility in chloral hydrate, alcohol, linseed oil, and turpentine. Their main use is in the manufacture of lacquers, varnishes, coatings, and adhesives.

Material Summaries

The following material summaries were compiled from a survey of the available literature. Inclusion of a material description under a given environment does not imply that it is the most appropriate material for corrosion service in that environment. Likewise, exclusion of a given material does not imply that it is not suitable for corrosion service applications in that environment.

Aluminum. Varnishes made from copal resins have been produced in aluminum alloy equipment.

Corrosion Behavior of Various Metals and Alloys in Copals

Material	Condition, other factors, comments	Concen- tration, %	Temperature, °C (°F)	Duration	Corrosion rate, mm/yr (mils/yr) or other	Ref
Silver	Pure and wet	...	400 (750)	...	<0.05 (<2)	10
Magnesium	...	100	Room	...	Suitable	119
Type 410 stainless steel	Varnish	...	Room	...	Unattacked	121

Cresol

Cresol, $CH_3C_6H_4OH$, also known as cresylic acid, methyl phenol, and tricresol, is a mixture of three isomers of cresol derived from coal tar and is used in making plastics, ore flotation, refining petroleum, and as a strong antiseptic. Orthocresol is a colorless solid with a melting point of 30 °C (86 °F) that is soluble in alcohol, but only slightly soluble in water. It is used in making disinfectants and as a plasticizer. Metacresol is a colorless liquid used in the manufacture of photographic developers, printing inks, and paint removers. It is also used as a leather preservative. The least soluble isomer, paracresol, is a colorless solid and is used in the production of dyes and pharmaceuticals.

Material Summaries

The following material summaries were compiled from a survey of the available literature. Inclusion of a material description under a given environment does not imply that it is the most appropriate material for corrosion service in that environment. Likewise, exclusion of a given material does not imply that it is not suitable for corrosion service applications in that environment.

Aluminum alloy 1100 had excellent resistance to 1, 3, and 100% solutions of cresol at ambient temperature. In other laboratory tests, cresol was very corrosive to aluminum alloy 1100 at the boiling point.

Corrosion Behavior of Various Metals and Alloys in Cresol

Material	Condition, other factors, comments	Concen- tration, %	Temperature, °C (°F)	Duration	Corrosion rate, mm/yr (mils/yr) or other	Ref
Stainless steels						
Type 304 stainless steel	Chemical processing; laboratory test; no aeration; no agitation. p- and m-cresol mixture, technical (alternately immersed)	...	Room	11 d	<0.0001 in./yr	89
Type 304 stainless steel	Chemical processing; laboratory test; no aeration; no agitation. p- and m-cresol mixture, technical (alternately immersed)	...	71 (160)	11 d	<0.0001 in./yr	89
Lead, tin, and zinc						
Tin	...	50	20 (68)	...	Resistant	94
Tin	...	50	60 (140)	...	Unsuitable	94
Tin	...	50	100 (212)	...	Unsuitable	94

(Continued)

Corrosion Behavior of Various Metals and Alloys in Cresol (Continued)

Material	Condition, other factors, comments	Concen-tration, %	Temperature, °C (°F)	Duration	Corrosion rate, mm/yr (mils/yr) or other	Ref
Noble metals						
Gold	...	Pure	Boiling	...	<0.05 (<2)	7
Platinum	...	Pure	Boiling	...	<0.05 (<2)	6
Silver	...	Pure	Boiling	...	<0.05 (<2)	10
Others						
Magnesium	...	100	Room	...	Suitable	119

Cupric Chloride

Cupric chloride, CuCl$_2$, also known as copper chloride, is a yellowish-brown solid that is soluble in water and alcohol. The dihydrate of cupric chloride, CuCl$_2 \cdot$H$_2$O, is a green crystalline solid that is soluble in water. Cupric chloride is used in the textile industry as a mordant in the dyeing and printing of fabrics. It is also used in refining gold, silver, and copper.

Material Summaries

The following material summaries were compiled from a survey of the available literature. Inclusion of a material description under a given environment does not imply that it is the most appropriate material for corrosion service in that environment. Likewise, exclusion of a given material does not imply that it is not suitable for corrosion service applications in that environment.

Titanium. Cupric chloride, a halide salt of an oxidizing cationic species, enhances the passivity of titanium alloys to the extent that corrosion rates are negligible.

Zirconium is highly resistant to corrosion by most saline solutions, but cupric chloride is an exception. Cupric chloride attacks zirconium and causes stress-corrosion cracking of zirconium alloys.

Additional Reading

Z. Szklarska-Smialowska, D. Grimes, and J. Park, The Kinetics of Pit Growth on Alloy 600 in Chloride Solutions at High Temperatures, *Corros. Sci.*, 27(8), 859-567, 1987. MetAbs No. 87-352919. **Abstract:** Alloy 600 tube specimens were subjected to corrosion in deaerated 0.1M NaCl solution at applied potentials more positive than the respective pit nucleation potentials, and in deaerated 200 ppm CuCl$_2$ solution at 150 and 280 °C under open circuit conditions.

Corrosion Behavior of Various Metals and Alloys in Cupric Chloride

Material	Condition, other factors, comments	Concen-tration, %	Temperature, °C (°F)	Duration	Corrosion rate, mm/yr (mils/yr) or other	Ref
Stainless steels						
Type 304 stainless steel	...	10	21 (70)	...	Poor	121
Type 304 stainless steel	Research (electrolysis); laboratory test. Severe pitting (maximum depth of pits over 0.010 in.)	10	...	1 d	0.174 in./yr	89
Type 304 stainless steel	Petroleum processing; field or pilot plant test; slight to moderate aeration. Plus cupric sulfate and sodium chloride. Severe pitting (maximum depth of pits over 0.010 in.). Crevice attack (tendency to concentration-cell corrosion)	...	16-27 (60-80)	233 d	<0.0001 in./yr	89
Type 316 stainless steel	Jewelry; laboratory test	10	102 (215)	2 d	2.1 in./yr	89
Type 316 stainless steel	Petroleum processing; field or pilot plant test; slight to moderate aeration. Plus cupric sulfate and sodium chloride. Moderate pitting (maximum depth of pits from 0.005 to 0.010 in.)	...	16-27 (60-80)	233 d	<0.0001 in./yr	89
Type 316 stainless steel	Automotive; laboratory test; no aeration; no agitation. Cuprous chloride, ammonia, magnesium oxide (carbon-monoxide absorption chamber). Severe pitting (maximum depth of pits over 0.010 in.)	...	Room	1 d	0.0565 in./yr	89
Type 316 stainless steel	...	10	21 (70)	...	Poor	121
Type 317 stainless steel	Chemical processing; laboratory test; no aeration; no agitation. Plus sodium chloride 226.7 g per 2345.9 ml, pressure 6 in. of mercury	7.66	26-27 (78-80)	7 d	0.0017 in./yr	89
Type 317 stainless steel	Chemical processing; laboratory test; strong aeration; no agitation. Plus sodium chloride 226.7 g per 2345.9 ml, pressure 6 in. of mercury	7.66	26-27 (78-80)	7 d	0.0002 in./yr	89

(Continued)

Corrosion Behavior of Various Metals and Alloys in Cupric Chloride (Continued)

Material	Condition, other factors, comments	Concen-tration, %	Temperature, °C (°F)	Duration	Corrosion rate, mm/yr (mils/yr) or other	Ref
Type 410 stainless steel	...	10	21 (70)	...	Poor	121
Type 410 stainless steel	...	...	Room	...	Attacked	121
Type 430 stainless steel	...	10	21 (70)	...	Poor	121
Coppers						
70-30 cupronickel	...	...	...	...	Fair	93
90-10 cupronickel	...	...	...	...	Fair	93
Admiralty brass	...	...	...	...	Fair	93
Aluminum bronze	...	...	...	...	Fair	93
Architectural bronze	...	...	...	...	Not suitable	93
Brass	...	...	...	...	Fair	93
Cartridge brass	...	...	...	...	Not suitable	93
Commercial bronze	...	...	...	...	Fair	93
Electrolytic copper	...	...	...	...	Fair	93
Free-cutting brass	...	...	...	...	Not suitable	93
Muntz metal	...	...	...	...	Not suitable	93
Naval brass	...	...	...	...	Not suitable	93
Nickel silver	...	18	...	...	Fair	93
Phosphor bronze	5% Sn	...	...	...	Fair	93
Phosphor bronze	8% Sn	...	...	...	Fair	93
Phosphor copper	...	...	...	...	Fair	93
Red brass	...	...	...	...	Fair	93
Silicon bronze	Low	...	...	...	Fair	93
Silicon bronze	High	...	...	...	Fair	93
Titanium						
Titanium	...	50	90 (194)	...	<0.003 (<0.12)	90
Titanium	...	20	Boiling	...	nil	90
Titanium	...	40	Boiling	...	0.005 (0.2)	90
Titanium	...	55	118 (244)	...	0.003 (0.12)	90
Heat- and corrosion-resistant alloys						
44Co-31Cr-13W	(a)	10	Room	...	0.013 (0.5)	53
44Co-31Cr-13W	Heat treated 4 h at 899 °C (1650 °F), furnace cooled. (a)	10	Room	...	0.05 (2)	53
44Co-31Cr-13W	(a)	10	Room	...	0.012 (0.5)	53
44Co-31Cr-13W	Heat treated 4 h at 899 °C (1650 °F), furnace cooled. (a)	10	Room	...	0.05 (2)	53
50Co-20Cr-15W-10Ni	...	10	Room	...	0.005 (0.2)	53
50Co-20Cr-15W-10Ni	(a)	10	Room	...	0.005 (0.2)	53
53Co-30Cr-4.5W	(a)	10	Room	...	0.012 (0.5)	53
53Co-30Cr-4.5W	Heat treated 4 h at 899 °C (1650 °F). (a)	10	Room	...	0.05 (2)	53
53Co-30Cr-4.5W	(a)	10	Room	...	0.012 (0.5)	53
53Co-30Cr-4.5W	Heat treated 4 h at 899 °C (1650 °F), furnace cooled. (a)	10	Room	...	0.05 (2)	53
Haynes alloy No. 25	...	2	Room	...	nil	124
Haynes alloy No. 25	Plus 5% NaCl	2	66 (150)	...	nil	124
Haynes alloy No. 25	Plus 5% NaCl	2	Boiling	...	<0.01 (0.1)	124
Haynes alloy No. 25	Plus 10% NaCl	5	66 (150)	...	nil	124
Haynes alloy No. 25	Plus 10% NaCl	5	Boiling	...	<0.02 (0.5)	124
Haynes alloy No. 25	...	10	Room	...	<0.01 (0.2)	124
Haynes alloy No. 25	Plus 10% NaCl	10	66 (150)	...	nil	124
Multimet	...	2	Room	...	nil	124
Multimet	Plus 5% NaCl	2	66 (150)	...	4.06 (160)	124
Multimet	Plus 5% NaCl	2	Boiling	...	23.3 (919)	124
Multimet	Plus 10% NaCl	5	66 (150)	...	nil	124
Multimet	Plus 10% NaCl	5	Boiling	...	>25.4 (>1000)	124
Multimet	...	10	Room	...	nil	124
Multimet	Plus 10% NaCl	10	66 (150)	...	nil	124

(Continued)

Corrosion Behavior of Various Metals and Alloys in Cupric Chloride (Continued)

Material	Condition, other factors, comments	Concentration, %	Temperature, °C (°F)	Duration	Corrosion rate, mm/yr (mils/yr) or other	Ref
Zirconium						
Zr702	...	5, 10, 20	35-100 (95-212)	...	>1.3 (>50)	15
Zr702	...	20, 40, 50	Boiling	...	>1.3 (>50)	15
Zr704	...	5, 10, 20	35-100 (95-212)	...	>1.3 (>50)	15
Zr704	...	20, 40, 50	Boiling	...	>1.3 (>50)	15
Zr705	...	5, 10, 20	35-100 (95-212)	...	>1.3 (>50)	15
Zr705	...	20, 40, 50	Boiling	...	>1.3 (>50)	15
Lead, tin, and zinc						
Lead	Corrosion rate too high to merit any consideration of Pb	10-40	24 (75)	...	>1270 μm/yr (>50)	95
Noble metals						
Palladium	...	100 g/L	Room	...	<0.25 (<10)	17
Platinum	...	100 g/L	Room	...	nil	5
Silver	...	All	100 (212)	...	Attacked	9

(a) As-cast specimens 38 mm x 25 mm x 6 mm (1.5 in. x 1 in. x 0.25 in.), 120-grit abrasive finish. Average of five 24-h periods.

Cupric Nitrate

Cupric nitrate, $Cu(NO_3)_2 \cdot 3H_2O$, also known as copper nitrate, is a blue, deliquescent, crystalline solid that is soluble in water. Cupric nitrate is used in electroplating copper on iron.

Material Summaries

The following material summaries were compiled from a survey of the available literature. Inclusion of a material description under a given environment does not imply that it is the most appropriate material for corrosion service in that environment. Likewise, exclusion of a given material does not imply that it is not suitable for corrosion service applications in that environment.

Copper. Wires of copper alloy Cu-23Zn-12Ni used in telephone equipment under the conditions of a 6-g load and a positive potential were observed to undergo stress-corrosion cracking within 2 years. Laboratory tests implied that nitrate salts were the cause. The same results were achieved in the laboratory using high humidity, a constant load of 386 MPa, and a potential applied so that the wires were anodic to the normal corrosion potential. Cracking was observed when the surface had a high nitrate concentration even without an applied potential. Wires made of Cu-20Ni resisted cracking under the same conditions.

Corrosion Behavior of Various Metals and Alloys in Cupric Nitrate

Material	Condition, other factors, comments	Concentration, %	Temperature, °C (°F)	Duration	Corrosion rate, mm/yr (mils/yr) or other	Ref
Stainless steels						
Type 304 stainless steel	...	10	21 (70)	...	Very good	121
Type 316 stainless steel	...	10	21 (70)	...	Very good	121
Type 410 stainless steel	...	10	21 (70)	...	Good	121
Type 410 stainless steel	...	...	Room	...	Unattacked	121
Type 430 stainless steel	...	10	21 (70)	...	Good	121
Coppers						
70-30 cupronickel	...	...	...	...	Fair	93
90-10 cupronickel	...	...	...	...	Fair	93
Admiralty brass	...	...	...	...	Fair	93
Aluminum bronze	...	...	...	...	Fair	93
Architectural bronze	...	...	...	...	Not suitable	93
Brass	...	...	...	...	Fair	93
Cartridge brass	...	...	...	...	Not suitable	93

(Continued)

Corrosion Behavior of Various Metals and Alloys in Cupric Nitrate (Continued)

Material	Condition, other factors, comments	Concentration, %	Temperature, °C (°F)	Duration	Corrosion rate, mm/yr (mils/yr) or other	Ref
Commercial bronze	...	...	...	...	Fair	93
Electrolytic copper	...	...	...	...	Fair	93
Free-cutting brass	...	...	...	...	Not suitable	93
Muntz metal	...	...	...	...	Not suitable	93
Naval brass	...	...	...	...	Not suitable	93
Nickel silver	...	18	...	...	Fair	93
Phosphor bronze	5% Sn	...	...	...	Fair	93
Phosphor bronze	8% Sn	...	...	...	Fair	93
Phosphor copper	...	...	...	...	Fair	93
Red brass	...	...	...	...	Fair	93
Silicon bronze	Low	...	...	...	Fair	93
Silicon bronze	High	...	...	...	Fair	93
Titanium						
Titanium	...	Saturated	Room	...	nil	90
Zirconium						
Zr702	...	40	Boiling	...	Weight gain	62
Zr702	BP 115 °C (239 °F)	40	Boiling	...	Weight gain	15
Zr705	...	40	Boiling	...	Weight gain	62
Zr705	BP 115 °C (239 °F)	40	Boiling	...	Weight gain	15
Tantalum and hafnium						
Hafnium	...	40	...	10 d	nil	11
Hafnium	...	40	...	10 d	nil	11
Noble metals						
Silver	...	All	Room	...	<0.05 (<2)	9
Others						
Niobium	...	40	Boiling	...	nil	2

Cupric Sulfate

Cupric sulfate, CuSO$_4$, also known as hydrocyanite and copper sulfate, is a greenish-white salt with a melting point of 200 °C (392 °F). It is soluble in water and used in copper-plating baths, dyestuffs, and germicides. Cupric sulfate (hydrated), CuSO$_4$·5H$_2$O, also known as blue vitriol, chalcanthite, and bluestone, is an azure blue material used in the leather industry. It is prepared by the reaction of sulfuric acid and copper. It is also obtained as a by-product from copper refineries.

Additional Reading

W.K. Blanchard, D.A. Koss, and L.A. Heldt, Slow Strain Rate Stress Corrosion Cracking Under Multiaxial Deformation Conditions: Technique and Application to Admiralty Brass, *Corrosion, 40*(3), 101-104, 1984. MetAbs No. 84-351478. **Abstract:** A set of straightforward experimental techniques is described for the examination of slow strain rate stress-corrosion cracking of sheet deforming under nearly all multiaxial deformation conditions which result in sheet thinning. Based on the local fracture strain as a failure criterion, the results contrast the stress-corrosion susceptibility in uniaxial tension with those in both plane strain and balanced biaxial tension.

Corrosion Behavior of Various Metals and Alloys in Cupric Sulfate

Material	Condition, other factors, comments	Concentration, %	Temperature, °C (°F)	Duration	Corrosion rate, mm/yr (mils/yr) or other	Ref
Stainless steels						
AM-363 stainless steel	...	...	Room	...	Unattacked	120
Type 304 stainless steel	Metal processing (plating); field or pilot plant test; strong aeration; rapid agitation. Plus 10% sulfuric acid, 9-10 g/L manganese dioxide	~5	70 (158)	63 d	<0.0001 in./yr	89

(Continued)

Corrosion Behavior of Various Metals and Alloys in Cupric Sulfate (Continued)

Material	Condition, other factors, comments	Concentration, %	Temperature, °C (°F)	Duration	Corrosion rate, mm/yr (mils/yr) or other	Ref
Type 304 stainless steel	...	10	21 (70)	...	Very good	121
Type 304 stainless steel	...	10	Boiling	...	Very good	121
Type 304 stainless steel	Metal processing; field or pilot plant test; no aeration; no agitation. Plus copper-refinery electrolyte, 200-235 g/L sulfuric acid, 20-22 g/L nickel ion as sulfate, pressure	~8-10	65 (150)	32.9 d	<0.0001 in./yr	89
Type 304 stainless steel	Metal processing; field or pilot plant test; no aeration; rapid agitation. Plus 0.4-0.8% sulfuric acid (evaporator). Saturated	~65	76-104 (170-220)	30 d	0.0002 in./yr	89
Type 316 stainless steel	Metal processing (plating); field or pilot plant test; strong aeration; rapid agitation. Plus 10% sulfuric acid, 9-10 g/L manganese dioxide	~5	70 (158)	63 d	<0.0001 in./yr	89
Type 316 stainless steel	...	10	21 (70)	...	Very good	121
Type 316 stainless steel	Metal processing; field or pilot plant test; no aeration; no agitation. Plus copper-refinery electrolyte, 200-235 g/L sulfuric acid, 20-22 g/L nickel ion as sulfate, pressure	~8-10	65 (150)	32.9 d	<0.0001 in./yr	89
Type 316 stainless steel	Metal processing; field or pilot plant test; no aeration; rapid agitation. Plus 0.4-0.8% sulfuric acid (evaporator). Saturated	~65	76-104 (170-220)	30 d	0.0002 in./yr	89
Type 316 stainless steel	...	10	Boiling	...	Very good	121
Type 317 stainless steel	Metal processing (plating); field or pilot plant test; strong aeration; rapid agitation. Plus 10% sulfuric acid, 9-10 g/L manganese dioxide	~5	70 (158)	63 d	<0.0001 in./yr	89
Type 317 stainless steel	Metal processing; field or pilot plant test; no aeration; rapid agitation. Plus 0.4-0.8% sulfuric acid (evaporator). Saturated	~65	76-104 (170-220)	30 d	0.0001 in./yr	89
Type 410 stainless steel	Plus 2% H_2SO_4	...	Room	...	Very slightly attacked	121
Type 410 stainless steel	...	10	21 (70)	...	Good	121
Type 410 stainless steel	...	10	Boiling	...	Fair	121
Type 430 stainless steel	Sensitized sample. Heat treated at 1093 °C (2000 °F) 1 h, air cooled. Intergranular corrosion rate. Plus Cu, 50% H_2SO_4	...	...	...	118.2 (4728)	41
Type 430 stainless steel	Nonsensitized sample. Heat treated at 760 °C (1400 °F) 1 h, water quenched. Intergranular corrosion rate. Plus Cu, 50% H_2SO_4	...	...	...	2.1 (84)	41
Type 430 stainless steel	...	10	21 (70)	...	Good	121
Type 430 stainless steel	...	10	Boiling	...	Good	121
Coppers						
70-30 cupronickel	(a)	...	...	...	Good	93
90-10 cupronickel	(a)	...	...	...	Good	93
Admiralty brass	(a)	...	...	...	Good	93
Aluminum bronze	(a)	...	...	...	Good	93
Ampco 8, aluminum bronze	Generally suitable. Conditions such as aeration or temperature could restrict use	...	...	...	<0.5 (<20)	96
Architectural bronze	...	...	...	...	Not suitable	93
Brass	(a)	...	...	...	Good	93
Cartridge brass	...	...	...	...	Not suitable	93
Commercial bronze	(a)	...	...	...	Good	93
Electrolytic copper	(a)	...	...	...	Good	93
Free-cutting brass	...	...	...	...	Not suitable	93
Muntz metal	...	...	...	...	Not suitable	93
Naval brass	...	...	...	...	Not suitable	93
Nickel silver	(a)	18	...	...	Good	93
Phosphor bronze	5% Sn. (a)	...	...	...	Good	93
Phosphor bronze	8% Sn. (a)	...	...	...	Good	93
Phosphor copper	(a)	...	...	...	Good	93
Red brass	(a)	...	...	...	Good	93
Silicon bronze	Low. (a)	...	...	...	Good	93
Silicon bronze	High. (a)	...	...	...	Good	93

(Continued)

Corrosion Behavior of Various Metals and Alloys in Cupric Sulfate (Continued)

Material	Condition, other factors, comments	Concentration, %	Temperature, °C (°F)	Duration	Corrosion rate, mm/yr (mils/yr) or other	Ref
Titanium						
Titanium	...	50	Boiling	...	nil	90
Titanium	Plus 2% H₂SO₄	Saturated	Room	...	0.018 (0.72)	90
Heat- and corrosion-resistant alloys						
Alloy 825	Metal processing (plating); field or pilot plant test; strong aeration; rapid agitation. Plus 10% sulfuric acid, 9-10 g/L manganese dioxide	~5	70 (158)	63 d	<0.0001 in./yr	89
Carpenter 20	Metal processing (plating); field or pilot plant test; strong aeration; rapid agitation. Plus 10% sulfuric acid, 9-10 g/L manganese dioxide	~5	70 (158)	63 d	<0.0001 in./yr	89
Carpenter 20	Metal processing; field or pilot plant test; no aeration; no agitation. Plus copper-refinery electrolyte, 200-235 g/L sulfuric acid, 20-22 g/L nickel ion as sulfate, pressure	~8-10	65 (150)	32.9 d	<0.0001 in./yr	89
Incoloy 800	Solutions were prepared with reagent-grade chemicals. Test specimens were cold-rolled, annealed sheet, 2.84 mm (0.112 in.) thick. No pitting	10	80 (176)	7 d	nil	44
Inconel 601	...	10	80 (176)	7 d	nil	64
Noble metals						
Iridium	...	100 g/L	100 (212)	...	nil	18
Palladium	...	100 g/L	100 (212)	...	nil	17
Platinum	...	100 g/L	100 (212)	...	nil	5
Rhodium	...	100 g/L	100 (212)	...	nil	29
Silver	...	All	Room-boiling	...	<0.05 (<2)	9
Silver	In NaCl	...	100 (212)	...	Attacked	9

(a) May be considered in place of a copper metal when some property, other than corrosion resistance, governs its use.

Susceptibility of Naval Brass to Stress-Corrosion Cracking in 0.1M Cupric Sulfate

Environment	Test potential (mV(SCE))	Strain ϵ_F to failure (%)	Reduction in area (%)	Strain ϵ_i at maximum load (%)	Ultimate tensile strength (MPa)
0.1 M CuSO₄	45 (corrosion potential)	14	12	13	330
0.1 M CuSO₄	300	11	9	11	320
0.1 M CuSO₄	540	9	9	8	299
0.1 M CuSO₄	−540	38	50	30	400
Air		38	53	30	403

Source: I.R. Kramer, B. Wu *et al.*, "Dislocation Distribution in Transgranular Stress Corrosion Cracking of Naval Brass," *Material Science and Engineering*, Vol 82, Sept 1986, 144.

Dichloroacetic Acid

Dichloroacetic acid, CHCl₂COOH, also known as dichloroethanoic acid, is a colorless, strong liquid acid with a boiling point of 194 °C (381 °F). It is soluble in water and alcohol. Dichloroacetic acid is prepared by the chlorination of acetic acid. It is used in organic synthesis.

Material Summaries

The following material summaries were compiled from a survey of the available literature. Inclusion of a material description under a given environment does not imply that it is the most appropriate material for corrosion service in that environment. Likewise, exclusion of a given material does not imply that it is not suitable for corrosion service applications in that environment.

Aluminum. Aluminum alloy 3003 in limited laboratory tests at 204 °C (400 °F) was attacked by dichloroacetic acid.

Additional Reading

H. Mansour, H.M. Moustafa, A. El-Wafa, and G.A. Noubi, Corrosion of Aluminium in Chloroacetic Acids, *Bull. Electrochem.*, 2(5), 449-451,

1986. MetAbs No. 87-350962. **Abstract:** The study is concerned with the corrosion of aluminum in mono-, di-, and trichloroacetic acids. The inhibitive effect of potassium thiocyanate, sodium azide, thiourea, thio- semicarbazide and alpha-amino acids (glycine, L-alanine, L-valine and L-leucine) on the corrosion of aluminum in trichloroacetic acid has been investigated. The effect of time and temperature has also been studied.

Corrosion Behavior of Various Metals and Alloys in Dichloroacetic Acid

Material	Condition, other factors, comments	Concentration, %	Temperature, °C (°F)	Duration	Corrosion rate, mm/yr (mils/yr) or other	Ref
Titanium	...	100	Boiling	...	0.007 (0.28)	90
Zr702	...	100	Boiling	...	<0.5 (<20)	15

Ether

Ether, $(C_2H_5)_2$, also known as ethyl ether, is a colorless liquid with a boiling point of 34.5 °C (93 °F). It is used as a solvent, a denaturant, and as an anesthetic in medicine. It is an organic compound in which two hydrocarbon radicals are joined by an atom of oxygen.

Material Summaries

The following material summaries were compiled from a survey of the available literature. Inclusion of a material description under a given environment does not imply that it is the most appropriate material for corrosion service in that environment. Likewise, exclusion of a given material does not imply that it is not suitable for corrosion service applications in that environment.

Aluminum. Aluminum alloy 3003 has excellent resistance to ether at ambient and elevated temperatures in laboratory tests. Ether has been processed, degreased, and handled in aluminum equipment. Valves of 356.0 aluminum alloy have been used successfully to service ether.

Corrosion Behavior of Various Metals and Alloys in Ether

Material	Condition, other factors, comments	Concentration, %	Temperature, °C (°F)	Duration	Corrosion rate, mm/yr (mils/yr) or other	Ref
Stainless steels						
Type 410 stainless steel	...	...	Room	...	Unattacked	121
Coppers						
70-30 cupronickel	...	...	...	...	Suitable	93
90-10 cupronickel	...	...	...	...	Suitable	93
Admiralty brass	...	...	...	...	Suitable	93
Aluminum bronze	...	...	...	...	Suitable	93
Ampco 8, aluminum bronze	Generally suitable	...	...	...	<0.05 (<2)	96
Architectural bronze	...	...	...	...	Suitable	93
Brass	...	...	...	...	Suitable	93
C11000	Methylbenzyl ether, N_2 atmosphere	...	...	2784 h	0.0025 max (0.1 max)	39
C11000	Methylbenzyl ether, air atmosphere	...	...	2784 h	0.0025 max (0.1 max)	39
C11000	Recovered butyl ether	...	...	288 h	nil	39
C11000	Dichloro ethyl ether residues	...	80 (175)	94 h	0.183-0.915 (7.2-36)	39
C11000	Crude dichloro ethyl ether	...	80 (175)	71 h	2.130-3.050 (84-120)	39
C11000	Dichloro ethyl ether	...	80 (175)	70 h	0.15 (6)	39
C11000	Dichloro ethyl ether	...	100 (212)	70 h	0.61 (24)	39
C11000	Dichloro ethyl ether	...	Boiling	70 h	0.183 (7.2)	39
C65500	Recovered butyl ether	...	...	288 h	0.0025 (0.1)	39
C65500	Dichloro ethyl ether residues	...	80 (175)	94 h	0.061-0.245 (2.4-9.6)	39
C65500	Crude dichloro ethyl ether	...	80 (175)	71 h	1.22-3.05 (48-120)	39
C65500	Dichloro ethyl ether	...	80 (175)	70 h	0.12 (4.8)	39

(Continued)

Corrosion Behavior of Various Metals and Alloys in Ether (Continued)

Material	Condition, other factors, comments	Concen-tration, %	Temperature, °C (°F)	Duration	Corrosion rate, mm/yr (mils/yr) or other	Ref
C65500	Dichloro ethyl ether	...	100 (212)	70 h	0.245 (9.6)	39
C65500	Dichloro ethyl ether	...	Boiling	70 h	0.213 (8.4)	39
Cartridge brass	...	...	...	...	Suitable	93
Commercial bronze	...	...	...	...	Suitable	93
Electrolytic copper	...	...	...	...	Suitable	93
Free-cutting brass	...	...	...	...	Suitable	93
Muntz metal	...	...	...	...	Suitable	93
Naval brass	...	...	...	...	Suitable	93
Nickel silver	...	18	...	...	Suitable	93
Phosphor bronze	5% Sn	...	...	...	Suitable	93
Phosphor bronze	8% Sn	...	...	...	Suitable	93
Phosphor copper	...	...	...	...	Suitable	93
Red brass	...	...	...	...	Suitable	93
Silicon bronze	Low	...	...	...	Suitable	93
Silicon bronze	High	...	...	...	Suitable	93
Noble metals						
Gold	...	Pure	Boiling	...	<0.05 (<2)	7
Platinum	...	Pure	Boiling	...	<0.05 (<2)	6
Silver	...	Pure	Boiling	...	<0.05 (<2)	10
Others						
Magnesium	...	100	Room	...	Suitable	119

Ethyl Alcohol

Ethyl alcohol, CH_3CH_2OH, also known as ethanol and grain alcohol, is a colorless, volatile liquid with a boiling point of 78.5 °C (172 °F) and a mild characteristic odor. It is soluble in water, chloroform, methyl alcohol, and ether. Ethyl alcohol is a very important commercial and industrial solvent and is used in the manufacture of many food extracts, pharmaceuticals, cleaning products, toiletries, antifreeze compounds, and fuels. Ethyl alcohol burns with a transparent blue flame, producing carbon dioxide and water. The vapor forms an explosive mixture with air and is used under compression as a fuel (gasohol) in some internal combustion engines. The alcoholic beverage industry bases a wide variety of products on the content of ethyl alcohol.

Material Summaries

The following material summaries were compiled from a survey of the available literature. Inclusion of a material description under a given environment does not imply that it is the most appropriate material for corrosion service in that environment. Likewise, exclusion of a given material does not imply that it is not suitable for corrosion service applications in that environment.

Aluminum. Laboratory tests have found that anhydrous ethyl alcohol corrodes aluminum alloys. However, in other laboratory tests, aluminum alloy 3003 resisted corrosion from aqueous solutions of ethyl alcohol up to 95% (commercial grade). Industry uses aluminum alloy equipment such as stills, heat exchangers, tanks, and piping for processing ethyl alcohol and products manufactured using ethyl alcohol.

Additional Reading

P.L. De Anna, The Effects of Water and Chloride Ions on the Electrochemical Behaviour of Iron and 304L Stainless Steel in Alcohols, *Corros. Sci.*, *25*(1), 43-53, 1985. MetAbs No. 85-350967. **Abstract:** The electrochemical behavior of pure iron and 304L stainless steel in protic organic media has been characterized by determination of current-potential potentiodynamic curves. The media studied were methyl, ethyl, isopropyl, n-butyl and 2-chloroethyl alcohols. The influence of water and chloride ion concentration on the cathodic and anodic electrochemical reactions has been investigated.

C. Monticelli, G. Brunoro, A. Frignani, and A. Marchi, Inhibitive Action of Some Schiff Bases and Amines Towards the Corrosion of Copper in an Aqueous Alcoholic Medium, *Surf. Coat. Technol.*, *27*(2), 175-186, 1986. MetAbs No. 86-351034. **Abstract:** Some Schiff bases and relative amines were tested as copper corrosion inhibitors in aqueous 25 vol.% ethanolic $0.1M$ NaCl solution at 30 °C. Polarization curves and weight loss measurements allowed the inhibitor efficiencies of the additives to be screened.

H. Jahnke and M. Schonborn, Electrochemical Corrosion Measurements in Motor Fuels Based on Methanol and Ethanol, *Werkst. Korros.*, *36*(12), 561-566, 1985. MetAbs No. 86-351152. **Abstract:** Possible alternative fuels such as ethanol and methanol can cause corrosion in mixture preparation systems, in contrast to the conventional petrol and diesel fuels. This phenomenon is due less to the pure alcohols than to the pollutants and additives. Electrochemical corrosion measurements were carried out on four selected steels, the influence of each constituent being investigated. The results of these measurements are given.

E.K. Oshe, V.P. Persiantseva, V.E. Zorina, and V.N. Alekseev, Passivation and Violation of Passivity of Aluminium in Water-Alcohol Media in the Presence of Surface Nonstoichiometric Oxide With and Without Inhibitors, 6th European Symposium on Corrosion Inhibitors, Ferrara, Italy, 16-20 Sept. 1985. MetAbs No. 86-351892. **Abstract:** Photoelectric polarization together with electron and Auger spectroscopies were used to study the passivity of Al in ethanol-water mixtures and the effects of inhibitors. Irrespective of the C_2H_5OH/H_2O ratio the surface oxide was an oxygen excess Al sesquioxide. Structure-sensitive properties of the oxide typical of a donor-acceptor bond mechanism of interaction were used to explain the effects of H_2O concentration on corrosion rates.

K. Otto, J.E. Anderson, L. Bartosiewicz, R.O. Carter, and C.A. Gierczak, Corrosion Produced by Burning Layers of Methanol and Ethanol, *Corros. Sci.*, 26(6), 455-466, 1986. MetAbs No. 86-352708. **Abstract:** Burning methanol and ethanol generate formic acid and acetic acid, respectively, as reaction products. These acids, concentrated in the liquid during fires, cause electrochemical corrosion and rust formation on metal substrates. In these experiments, small amounts of alcohol were burnt on 1020 steel coupons. Corrosion products were analyzed by FT-IR spectroscopy and by microscopy. Rates of rust formation were measured gravimetrically for various alcohol solutions, then compared with rates of deposit formation beneath fires of iso-octane.

U. Lechner-Knoblauch and E. Heitz, Corrosion of Zinc, Copper and Iron in Contaminated Non-Aqueous Alcohols, *Electrochim. Acta*, 32(6), 901-907, 1987. MetAbs No. 87-352342. **Abstract:** The corrosion of Zn, Fe and Cu in methanol and ethanol, both in the pure liquids and in alcohol solutions of HCOOH, CH_3COOH, HCOONa and CH_3COONa, was examined. The work was initiated to obtain deeper insight into the impact of such contaminants on corrosion in alcohols.

B. Elsener, S. Virtanen, and H. Boehni, Corrosion and Passivation of Amorphous and Crystalline Fe-Cr Alloys in Ethanol/Water/HCl Mixtures, *Electrochim. Acta*, 32(6), 927-934, 1987. MetAbs No. 87-352345. **Abstract:** The corrosion and passivation of Type 304 stainless steel and of amorphous alloys have been studied by polarization curves and impedance spectroscopy in deaerated ethanolic/0.5N HCl solutions with different water contents.

E. Cavalcanti, V.G. Wanderley, T.R. Miranda, and L. Uller, The Effect of Water, Sulphate and pH on the Corrosion Behaviour of Carbon Steel in Ethanolic Solutions, *Electrochim. Acta*, 32(6), 935-937, 1987. MetAbs No. 87-352346. **Abstract:** The corrosion behavior of 1010 carbon steel in ethanolic solutions containing different contents of water and sulfate has been investigated by corrosion immersion tests. The influence of pH has also been studied by adding different concentrations of sodium hydroxide to ethanolic solutions.

C.A. Farina and U. Grassini, Stress Corrosion Cracking in Non-Aqueous Media, *Electrochim. Acta*, 32(6), 977-980, 1987. MetAbs No. 87-352352. **Abstract:** Results concerning stress-corrosion cracking in nonaqueous solvents: methanol, ethanol, 2-propanol, dimethylformamide, acetonitrile and liquid ammonia are reported and discussed. The effectiveness of inhibition with controlled addition of water was verified in the case of methanol and liquid ammonia. Experimental data for 38NiCrMo4 and Fe52D steels give information on the role played by lithium perchlorate as supporting electrolyte.

V.K. Singh and V.B. Singh, Electrochemical Behavior of AISI 304 Stainless Steel: Corrosion, Passivity, and Pitting in Alcohols + H_2SO_4 Mixtures, *Corrosion*, 43(12), 756-762, 1987. MetAbs No. 88-350656. **Abstract:** The electrochemical behavior of austenitic AISI 304 stainless steel in alcoholic solutions (ethanol, isopropanol, and t-butanol) containing different concentrations of sulfuric acid (0.001-1.0M) has been investigated using potentiostatic and potentiodynamic techniques.

Corrosion Behavior of Various Metals and Alloys in Ethyl Alcohol

Material	Condition, other factors, comments	Concentration, %	Temperature, °C (°F)	Duration	Corrosion rate, mm/yr (mils/yr) or other	Ref
Stainless steels						
AM-363 stainless steel	...	...	Room	...	Unattacked	120
Type 304 stainless steel	...	...	21 (70)	...	Good	121
Type 304 stainless steel	Chemical processing; field or pilot plant test; no aeration; slight to moderate agitation. Plus 0.1% butyric acid, 0.5% sulfuric acid, 1% acetic acid, 5% ethyl acetate, 15% water	56	75 (167)	59 d	0.001 in./yr	89
Type 304 stainless steel	Plastic processing; field or pilot plant test; no aeration; slight to moderate agitation. Sensitized specimens. Plus 0.5% sulfuric acid, 1% butyraldehyde, 5% ethyl acetate, 15% water, 23% solids	56	75 (167)	132 d	0.02 in./yr	89
Type 304 stainless steel	Plastic processing; field or pilot plant test; no aeration; slight to moderate agitation. With carbon over the standard maximum. Plus 0.5% sulfuric acid, 1% butyraldehyde, 5% ethyl acetate, 15% water, 23% solids	56	75 (167)	132 d	0.0001 in./yr	89
Type 316 stainless steel	Chemical processing; field or pilot plant test; no aeration; slight to moderate agitation. Plus 0.1% butyric acid, 0.5% sulfuric acid, 1% acetic acid, 5% ethyl acetate, 15% water	56	75 (167)	59 d	0.0004 in./yr	89
Type 316 stainless steel	...	...	21 (70)	...	Very good	121
Type 316 stainless steel	Plastic processing; field or pilot plant test; no aeration; slight to moderate agitation. Plus 0.5% sulfuric acid, 1% butyraldehyde, 5% ethyl acetate, 15% water, 23% solids	56	75 (167)	132 d	<0.0001 in./yr	89

(Continued)

Corrosion Behavior of Various Metals and Alloys in Ethyl Alcohol (Continued)

Material	Condition, other factors, comments	Concentration, %	Temperature, °C (°F)	Duration	Corrosion rate, mm/yr (mils/yr) or other	Ref
Type 317 stainless steel	Plastic processing; field or pilot plant test; no aeration; slight to moderate agitation. Plus 0.5% sulfuric acid, 1% butyraldehyde, 5% ethyl acetate, 15% water, 23% solids	56	75 (167)	132 d	<0.0001 in./yr	89
Type 317 stainless steel	Plastic processing; field or pilot plant test; no aeration; slight to moderate agitation. Sensitized specimens. Plus 0.5% sulfuric acid, 1% butyraldehyde, 5% ethyl acetate, 15% water, 23% solids	56	75 (167)	132 d	<0.0001 in./yr	89
Type 410 stainless steel	...	...	21 (70)	...	Good	121
Type 410 stainless steel	...	...	Room	...	Unattacked	121
Type 430 stainless steel	...	...	21 (70)	...	Good	121
Coppers						
70-30 cupronickel	...	...	...	...	Suitable	93
90-10 cupronickel	...	...	...	...	Suitable	93
Admiralty brass	...	...	...	...	Suitable	93
Aluminum bronze	...	...	...	...	Suitable	93
Architectural bronze	...	...	...	...	Suitable	93
Brass	...	...	...	...	Suitable	93
Cartridge brass	...	...	...	...	Suitable	93
Commercial bronze	...	...	...	...	Suitable	93
Electrolytic copper	...	...	...	...	Suitable	93
Free-cutting brass	...	...	...	...	Suitable	93
Muntz metal	...	...	...	...	Suitable	93
Naval brass	...	...	...	...	Suitable	93
Nickel silver	...	18	...	...	Suitable	93
Phosphor bronze	5% Sn	...	...	...	Suitable	93
Phosphor bronze	8% Sn	...	...	...	Suitable	93
Phosphor copper	...	...	...	...	Suitable	93
Red brass	...	...	...	...	Suitable	93
Silicon bronze	Low	...	...	...	Suitable	93
Silicon bronze	High	...	...	...	Suitable	93
Titanium						
Titanium	...	95	Boiling	...	0.013 (0.5)	20
Heat- and corrosion-resistant alloys						
Alloy 825	Plastic processing; field or pilot plant test; no aeration; slight to moderate agitation. Plus 0.5% sulfuric acid, 1% butyraldehyde, 5% ethyl acetate, 15% water, 23% solids	56	75 (167)	132 d	0.0001 in./yr	89
Carpenter 20	Plastic processing; field or pilot plant test; no aeration; slight to moderate agitation. Plus 0.5% sulfuric acid, 1% butyraldehyde, 5% ethyl acetate, 15% water, 23% solids	56	75 (167)	132 d	<0.0001 in./yr	89
Noble metals						
Platinum	...	All	Boiling	...	<0.05 (<2)	6
Silver	...	All	Boiling	...	<0.05 (<2)	10
Others						
Magnesium	...	100	Room	...	Suitable	119

Ethyl Chloride

Ethyl chloride, CH_3CH_2Cl, also known as chloroethane, hydrochloric ether, and muriatic ether, is a colorless liquid or gas. It has a boiling point of 12.2 °C (54 °F), is soluble in alcohol and ether, and is slightly soluble in water. Ethyl chloride is used as a solvent for oils, resins, and waxes. It is used in medicine and as an intermediate in synthesis.

Corrosion Behavior of Various Metals and Alloys in Ethyl Chloride

Material	Condition, other factors, comments	Concen-tration, %	Temperature, °C (°F)	Duration	Corrosion rate, mm/yr (mils/yr) or other	Ref
Type 304 stainless steel	Chemical processing; laboratory test; no aeration. 1,2-dichloroethane	...	501-557 (935-1035)	1 d	0.03 in./yr	89
Titanium	...	100	Boiling	...	<0.13 (<5)	20
Gold	Wet and acid products	...	Boiling	...	<0.05 (<2)	7
Silver	Wet and acid products	...	Boiling	...	<0.05 (<2)	10
Platinum	Wet and acid products	...	Boiling	...	<0.05 (<2)	6
Zr702	...	100	Boiling	...	<0.13 (<5)	15

Ethylene Glycol

Ethylene glycol, CH_2OHCH_2OH, also known as glycol, ethylene alcohol, glycol alcohol, and dihydric alcohol, is a colorless liquid with a boiling point of 197.2 °C (385 °F). It is soluble in water and in alcohol. Ethylene glycol has a low freezing point, -25 °C (-13 °F), and is widely used as an antifreeze in automobiles and in hydraulic fluids. It is used as a solvent for nitrocellulose and in the manufacture of acrylonitrile, dynamites, and resins.

Material Summaries

The following material summaries were compiled from a survey of the available literature. Inclusion of a material description under a given environment does not imply that it is the most appropriate material for corrosion service in that environment. Likewise, exclusion of a given material does not imply that it is not suitable for corrosion service applications in that environment.

Aluminum. Aluminum alloy 3003 resists ethylene glycol under laboratory test conditions of both ambient temperature and refluxing, boiling, and condensing temperatures. Ethylene glycol has been processed and stored in aluminum alloy equipment. Automobile aluminum radiators and heat exchangers use inhibited ethylene glycol/water solutions for antifreeze protection. Violent reactions in aluminum alloys are possible if stagnant ethlylene glycol is present at 200 °C (392 °F) or above.

Additional Reading

F.M. Al-Kharafi, F.H. Al-Hajjar, and A. Katrib, 3-Phenyl-1,2,4-triazol-5-1 as a Corrosion Inhibitor for Copper, *Corros. Sci.*, 26(4), 257-264, 1986. MetAbs No. 86-352406. **Abstract:** The cathodic and anodic behavior of copper in 30% ethylene glycol solution containing 100 ppm SO_4^-, 100 ppm Cl^- and 100 ppm HCO_3^- has been studied in the presence of different concentrations of 3-phenyl-1,2,4-triazol-5-1.

C. Monticelli, G. Brunoro, G. Trabanelli, and A. Frignani, Corrosion in Solar Heating Systems. I. Copper Behavior in Water-Glycol Solutions, *Werkst. Korros.*, 37(9), 479-484, 1986. MetAbs No. 87-351792. **Abstract:** The corrosion behavior of metallic materials commonly used in solar heating systems is discussed. The results of an experimental study on Cu corrosion resistance in ethylene and propylene glycol/water solutions (1:1 by volume) constituting the most common bases of heat transfer fluids are given.

C. Monticelli, G. Brunoro, G. Trabanelli, and A. Frignani, Corrosion in Solar Heating Systems. II. Corrosion Behavior of AA 6351 in Water-/Glycol Solutions, *Werkst. Korros.*, 38(2), 83-88, 1987. MetAbs No. 87-351805. **Abstract:** Research was carried out to investigate the corrosion behavior of the metals most commonly used as construction materials for solar absorber plates. The corrosion resistance of the aluminum alloy AA 6351 toward common uninhibited heat transfer fluids, such as ethylene and propylene glycol/water mixtures, was tested.

S.E. Faidi, G. Jones, and J.D. Scantlebury, The Corrosion of Mild Steel in Ethylene Glycol Monoethyl Ether-Water Mixtures, *Electrochim. Acta*, 32(6), 947-953, 1987. MetAbs No. 87-352348. **Abstract:** The corrosion of mild steel in ethylene glycol monoethyl ether-water mixtures has been investigated. Viscosity, conductivity and dielectric measurements were carried out to investigate the physicochemical properties of the solutions and to relate these properties to the nature of the corrosion process.

Corrosion Behavior of Various Metals and Alloys in Ethylene Glycol

Material	Condition, other factors, comments	Concen-tration, %	Temperature, °C (°F)	Duration	Corrosion rate, mm/yr (mils/yr) or other	Ref
Stainless steels						
AM-363 stainless steel	...	...	Room	...	Unattacked	120
Type 304 stainless steel	Pharmaceutical processing; field or pilot plant test; no aeration; no agitation	...	-34 (-30)	112 d	0.0001 in./yr	89
Type 304 stainless steel	Pharmaceutical processing; field or pilot plant test; no aeration; no agitation	...	46 (115)	112 d	0.0001 in./yr	89
Type 304 stainless steel	...	All	21 (70)	...	Very good	121

(Continued)

Corrosion Behavior of Various Metals and Alloys in Ethylene Glycol (Continued)

Material	Condition, other factors, comments	Concentration, %	Temperature, °C (°F)	Duration	Corrosion rate, mm/yr (mils/yr) or other	Ref
Type 316 stainless steel	Pharmaceutical processing; field or pilot plant test; no aeration; no agitation	...	-34 (-30)	112 d	0.0001 in./yr	89
Type 316 stainless steel	Pharmaceutical processing; field or pilot plant test; no aeration; no agitation	...	46 (115)	112 d	0.0001 in./yr	89
Type 316 stainless steel	...	All	21 (70)	...	Very good	121
Type 410 stainless steel	...	All	21 (70)	...	Very good	121
Type 430 stainless steel	...	All	21 (70)	...	Very good	121
Coppers						
70-30 cupronickel	...	...	...	...	Suitable	93
90-10 cupronickel	...	...	...	...	Suitable	93
Admiralty brass	...	...	...	...	Suitable	93
Aluminum bronze	...	...	...	...	Suitable	93
Ampco 8, aluminum bronze	Generally suitable	...	...	...	<0.05 (<2)	96
Architectural bronze	(a)	...	...	...	Good	93
Brass	...	...	...	...	Suitable	93
C11000	Triethylene glycol solution, aerated	...	Room	1344 h	nil	122
C11000	(b)	...	175 (345)	2560 h	0.04 (1.6)	122
C11000	(b)	...	175 (345)	3320 h	0.01 (0.4)	122
C11000	(b)	...	175 (345)	8328 h	0.025 (1.0)	122
C11000	(b)	87-95	160 (320)	2880 h	0.0075 (0.3)	122
C11000	(b)	...	160 (320)	5760 h	0.0025 (0.1)	122
C11000	(c)	15	99 (210)	2400 h	0.58 (23)	122
C11000	Glycol maleate	...	79 (175)	305 h	0.02 (0.8)	122
C26000	(b)	...	175 (345)	2560 h	0.05 (2.0)	122
C26000	(b)	...	175 (345)	3320 h	0.015 (0.6)	122
C26000	(b)	...	175 (345)	8328 h	0.035 (1.4)	122
C26000	(b)	...	160 (320)	2880 h	0.0075 (0.3)	122
C26000	(b)	...	160 (320)	5760 h	0.0025 (0.1)	122
C51000	(d)	15	99 (210)	2880 h	0.0075-0.01 (0.3-0.4)	122
C60800	(d)	15	99 (210)	2880 h	0.0025-0.0075 (0.1-0.3)	122
C61800	(c)	15	99 (210)	2400 h	0.48 (19)	122
C63000	(d)	15	99 (210)	2880 h	0.0025-0.18 (0.1-0.7)	122
C65500	(d)	15	99 (210)	2880 h	0.02-0.025 (0.8-1.0)	122
C71500	(c)	15	99 (210)	2400 h	0.46 (18)	122
Cartridge brass	(a)	...	...	...	Good	93
Commercial bronze	...	...	...	...	Suitable	93
Electrolytic copper	...	...	...	...	Suitable	93
Free-cutting brass	(a)	...	...	...	Good	93
Muntz metal	(a)	...	...	...	Good	93
Naval brass	(a)	...	...	...	Good	93
Nickel silver	...	18	...	...	Suitable	93
Phosphor bronze	5% Sn	...	...	...	Suitable	93
Phosphor bronze	8% Sn	...	...	...	Suitable	93
Phosphor copper	...	...	...	...	Suitable	93
Red brass	...	...	...	...	Suitable	93
Silicon bronze	Low	...	...	...	Suitable	93
Silicon bronze	High	...	...	...	Suitable	93
Others						
Magnesium	May need inhibitors	...	Room	...	Suitable	119

(a) May be considered in place of a copper metal when some property, other than corrosion resistance, governs its use. (b) Triethylene glycol air conditioning system. (c) Ethylene glycol solution. Plus 0.03-0.05% H_2SO_4. Second run. (d) Ethylene glycol solution. Plus 0.03% H_2SO_4.

Fatty Acids

Fatty acids, $C_nH_{2n+1}COOH$, are organic acids of the aliphatic or open-chain structure. They are found in the form of glycerol esters in common animal fats and vegetable fatty oils, hence the name "fatty acids." They are very stable and only weakly acidic, their acidic qualities decreasing with increasing formula weight. The simplest member of the group is formic acid. Other examples are butyric acid, valeric acid, palmitic acid, stearic acid, and oleic acid. These acids react with alcohol to form esters and water. Fatty acids are used as lubricants in cosmetics and in soaps and detergents.

Material Summaries

The following material summaries were compiled from a survey of the available literature. Inclusion of a material description under a given environment does not imply that it is the most appropriate material for corrosion service in that environment. Likewise, exclusion of a given material does not imply that it is not suitable for corrosion service applications in that environment.

Cast Iron. Unalloyed cast iron can be used to handle concentrated fatty acids, but will be attacked by more dilute solutions. Austenitic nickel cast irons exhibit adequate resistance to stearic acid.

Aluminum. Aluminum alloy 1100 is mildly attacked by fatty acids at ambient temperature in laboratory tests. Anhydrous fatty acids at the boiling point were very corrosive to aluminum alloys in other tests. Fatty acids and their derivatives have been processed and handled in aluminum alloy storage tanks, settling and receiving tanks, separators, condensors, and vapor and steam trace lines.

Copper. Fatty acids attack copper and copper alloys in the presence of moisture and air. The rate of attack is also influenced by the temperature and presence of impurities. Copper alloys C11000, C26000, and C65500 had corrosion rates of 0.50 to 1.25 mm/yr (20 to 50 mils/yr) when tested at 25 to 100 °C (75 to 212 °F) in stearic acid. Under severe conditions, fatty acids attack copper alloys at a higher rate than other organic acids. Specimens of C71000 (copper nickel, 20%) and C71500 (copper nickel, 30%) had corrosion rates of 0.064 mm/yr (2.6 mils/yr) and 0.059 mm/yr (2.4 mils/yr), respectively, when submerged just below the liquid level in tests conducted for 400 h in a copper-lined wooden splitting tank containing a mixture of 60% fatty acids, 39% water, and 1.17% sulfuric acid heated to 100 °C (212 °F) and agitated violently with an open steam jet. Similar specimens of C71000 and C71500, when submerged to 150 mm (6 in.) from the tank bottom, had corrosion rates of 0.178 and 0.185 mm/yr (7.0 and 7.3 mils/yr), respectively.

Nickel. In general, fatty acids such as stearic and lauric acid are not very corrosive to nickel-base alloys. Inorganic impurities such as chlorides and oxidizing salts in the fatty acids determine the corrosion rate.

Corrosion Behavior of Various Metals and Alloys in Fatty Acids

Material	Condition, other factors, comments	Concentration, %	Temperature, °C (°F)	Duration	Corrosion rate, mm/yr (mils/yr) or other	Ref
Steel						
Steel	Butyric acid	...	Room	...	0.15 (6)	22
Stainless steels						
Type 304 stainless steel	Butyric acid	...	Room	...	<0.02 (<1)	22
Type 304 stainless steel	Butyric acid	...	115 (240)	...	0.08 (3)	22
Type 304 stainless steel	Butyric acid	...	Boiling 163 (325)	...	1.42 (56)	22
Type 304 stainless steel	Chemical (distillation) processing; field or pilot plant test; strong aeration; slight to moderate agitation. Crude fatty acids, mixed. Crevice attack (tendency to concentration-cell corrosion)	...	100 (212)	43 d	0.0213 in./yr	89
Type 304 stainless steel	Soap (distillation) processing; field or pilot plant test; no aeration; rapid aeration. Animal fatty acids, 60% free pitch (high-vacuum column)	40	226 (440)	163 d	<0.0001 in./yr	89
Type 304 stainless steel	Soap (distillation) processing; field or pilot plant test; no aeration; rapid agitation. Fatty acids vapor and liquid from animal foot, 20% stripping steam (high-vacuum column)	90	215 (420)	163 d	0.0005 in./yr	89
Type 304 stainless steel	Soap (distillation) processing; field or pilot plant test; no aeration; rapid agitation. Fatty acids vapor and liquid from animal foot, 20% stripping steam (high-vacuum column)	90	215 (420)	163 d	0.00022 in./yr	89
Type 304 stainless steel	...	100	21 (70)	...	Good	121
Type 316 stainless steel	Butyric acid	...	Room	...	<0.0254 (<1)	22
Type 316 stainless steel	Butyric acid	...	115 (240)	...	0.076 (3)	22
Type 316 stainless steel	Butyric acid	...	Boiling 163 (325)	...	0.127 (5)	22
Type 316 stainless steel	Chemical (distillation) processing; field or pilot plant test; strong aeration; slight to moderate agitation. Crude fatty acids, mixed. Crevice attack (tendency to concentration-cell corrosion)	...	100 (212)	43 d	0.0049 in./yr	89

(Continued)

Corrosion Behavior of Various Metals and Alloys in Fatty Acids (Continued)

Material	Condition, other factors, comments	Concen-tration, %	Temperature, °C (°F)	Duration	Corrosion rate, mm/yr (mils/yr) or other	Ref
Type 316 stainless steel	Soap (distillation) processing; field or pilot plant test; no aeration; rapid aeration. Animal fatty acids, 60% free pitch (high-vacuum column)	40	226 (440)	163 d	<0.0001 in./yr	89
Type 316 stainless steel	Soap (distillation) processing; field or pilot plant test; no aeration; rapid agitation. Fatty acids vapor and liquid from animal foot, 20% stripping steam (high-vacuum column)	90	215 (420)	163 d	<0.0001 in./yr	89
Type 316 stainless steel	...	100	21 (70)	...	Very good	121
Type 410 stainless steel	...	100	21 (70)	...	Good	121
Type 430 stainless steel	...	100	21 (70)	...	Good	121
Aluminum						
Aluminum (>99.5%)	Higher. Commercial	...	20-boiling point (68-boiling point)	..	Restricted applications	92
Aluminum-manganese alloys	Higher. Commercial	...	20-boiling point (68-boiling point)	...	Restricted applications	92
Coppers						
70-30 cupronickel	Palmitic acid. (a)	...	...	...	Good	93
90-10 cupronickel	Palmitic acid. (a)	...	...	...	Good	93
Admiralty brass	Palmitic acid. (a)	...	...	...	Good	93
Aluminum bronze	Palmitic acid. (a)	...	...	...	Good	93
Ampco 8, aluminum bronze	Generally suitable. Conditions such as aeration or temperature could restrict use	...	...	...	<0.508 (<20)	96
Architectural bronze	Palmitic acid	...	...	...	Fair	93
Brass	Palmitic acid. (a)	...	...	...	Good	93
Cartridge brass	Palmitic acid	...	...	...	Fair	93
Commercial bronze	Palmitic acid. (a)	...	...	...	Good	93
Copper	Butyric acid	...	Room	...	0.0508 (2)	22
Electrolytic copper	Palmitic acid. (a)	...	...	...	Good	93
Free-cutting brass	Palmitic acid	...	...	...	Fair	93
Muntz metal	Palmitic acid	...	...	...	Fair	93
Naval brass	Palmitic acid	...	...	...	Fair	93
Nickel silver	Palmitic acid. (a)	18	...	...	Good	93
Phosphor bronze	Palmitic acid. 5% Sn. (a)	...	...	...	Good	93
Phosphor bronze	Palmitic acid. 8% Sn. (a)	...	...	...	Good	93
Phosphor copper	Palmitic acid. (a)	...	...	...	Good	93
Red brass	Palmitic acid. (a)	...	...	...	Good	93
Silicon bronze	Palmitic acid. Low. (a)	...	...	...	Good	93
Silicon bronze	Palmitic acid. High. (a)	...	...	...	Good	93
Silicon bronze	Butyric acid	...	Room	...	0.0508 (2)	22
Titanium						
Titanium	Butyric acid. Normal. Undiluted	...	Room	...	nil	90
Lead, tin, and zinc						
Tin	>C_6	...	20 (68)	...	Resistant	94
Tin	>C_6	...	60 (140)	...	Resistant	94
Tin	>C_6	...	100 (212)	...	Unsuitable	94
Noble metals						
Gold	...	Pure	Boiling	...	<0.05 (<2)	8
Platinum	...	Pure	400 (750)	...	<0.05 (<2)	6
Silver	...	...	400 (750)	...	<0.05 (<2)	4
Silver	...	Pure	400 (750)	...	<0.05 (<2)	10
Silver	...	...	400 (750)	...	<0.05 (<2)	4
Silver	Butyric acid	...	Boiling	...	<0.05 (<2)	4
Silver	Butyric acid	...	Boiling	...	<0.05 (<2)	4
Others						
Magnesium	...	All	Room	...	Unsuitable	119

(a) May be considered in place of a copper metal when some property, other than corrosion resistance, governs its use.

Ferric Chloride

Ferric chloride, $FeCl_3$, is a brown crystalline solid that melts at 300 °C and is soluble in water, alcohol, and glycerol. It is also known as anhydrous ferric chloride, ferric trichloride, Flores martis, and iron chloride. Ferric chloride is used as a coagulant for sewage and industrial wastes, as an oxidizing and chlorinating agent, as a disinfectant, in copper etching, and as a mordant. In addition, this compound is employed in the ferric chloride test, which is used to assess the relative corrosion resistance of stainless and nickel-base alloys. The ferric chloride test has been shown to be an appropriate measure of the suitability of such alloys for service in paper mill bleach plants and seawater.

Material Summaries

The following material summaries were compiled from a survey of the available literature. Inclusion of a material description under a given environment does not imply that it is the most appropriate material for corrosion service in that environment. Likewise, exclusion of a given material does not imply that it is not suitable for corrosion service applications in that environment.

Copper. Aluminum bronzes should be avoided for service in ferric chloride.

Metallic Glasses. The tendency of glassy $Fe_{40}Ni_{40}P_{14}B_6$ to undergo stress-corrosion cracking and hydrogen embrittlement in acidic electrolytes was studied. Specimens immersed in aqueous ferric chloride solution at the free corrosion potential failed by stress-corrosion cracking.

The corrosion behavior of glassy alloys is strongly influenced by additions of metallic elements, especially those that form films on the alloy surface, that is, film former additions. The beneficial effect of chromium additions has been demonstrated for glassy iron-base, cobalt-base, and nickel-base alloys. In one study, it was shown that a chromium content of 7 at.% in a glassy $Ni-Cr-P_{15}B_5$ alloy resulted in an undetectably small corrosion rate in 10% ferric chloride.

Osmium is dissolved fairly rapidly in ferric chloride at 100 °C (212 °F).

Platinum. A 10% addition of rhodium to platinum reduces the corrosion rate in 100 g/L ferric chloride at 100 °C (212 °F) from 16.7 to 0.2 mm/yr (660 to 50 mils/yr). Alloys containing more than 60% Ag are rapidly attacked by ferric chloride.

Palladium is generally resistant to corrosion by most single acids, alkalis, and aqueous solutions of many common salts, but when air is present it is attacked by ferric chloride. In a 100 g/L solution of ferric chloride, a 10% addition of platinum decreased the room-temperature corrosion rate of palladium from 11.9 to 8.6 mm/yr (469 to 339 mils/yr). A 30% platinum addition further decreased the corrosion rate to 1.8 mm/yr (71 mils/yr).

Titanium. Halide salts of oxidizing cationic species enhance the passivity of titanium alloys such that negligible corrosion rates can be expected. Examples include ferric chloride, cupric chloride, and nickel chloride solutions and their bromide counterparts.

Zirconium is highly resistant to corrosion by most saline solutions, but ferric chloride is an exception. Ferric chloride attacks zirconium, causing stress-corrosion cracking.

Additional Reading

M.D. Archer and R.J. McKim, The Stress Corrosion Behavior of Glassy Fe-40Ni-20B Alloy in Aqueous Acidic Media, *Corrosion*, *39*(3), 91-98, 1983. MetAbs No. 83-351274. **Abstract:** The stress corrosion behavior of commercially available glassy Fe-40Ni-20B alloy was investigated. Constant strain testing was carried out in aqueous solutions of ferric chloride, polythionic acid and hydrochloric acid. Weight loss and selective dissolution experiments at the free corrosion potential and linear polarization studies were also performed.

M.A. Pao and E. Klar, Corrosion Phenomena in Regular and Tin-Modified P/M Stainless Steels, in *Progress in Powder Metallurgy 1983*, Vol 39, 431-443, Metal Powder Industries Federation, Princeton, 1984. MetAbs No. 84-540899. **Abstract:** The corrosion behavior of P/M parts is heavily dependent on processing. Corrosion data collected over the past few years for three different corrosive media are summarized.

A.I. Grekula, V.P. Kujanpaa, and L.P. Karjalainen, Effect of Solidification Mode and Impurities on Pitting Corrosion in AISI 316 GTA Welds, *Corrosion*, *40*(11), 569-572, 1984. MetAbs No. 85-350443. **Abstract:** Pitting resistance was evaluated in autogenous GTA welds of approximately 30 commercial and laboratory heats of AISI 316 steel sheet by the standard ferric chloride immersion test and the potentiodynamic anodic polarization test in acid chloride solution.

R.J. Brigham, The Initiation of Crevice Corrosion on Stainless Steels, *Mater. Perform.*, *24*(12), 44-48, 1985. MetAbs No. 86-350395. **Abstract:** The variability that characterizes crevice corrosion initiation in stainless steels has been investigated as a function of temperature, crevice-forming material, and crevice tightness in laboratory tests consisting of immersion of Avesta 254SMO and Monit in ferric chloride.

B.E. Wilde, The Influence of Silicon on the Pitting Corrosion Resistance of an 18Cr-8Ni Stainless Steel, *Corrosion*, *42*(3), 147-151, 1986. MetAbs No. 86-351025. **Abstract:** The effect of Si additions to an 18Cr-8Ni stainless steel on the resistance to pit initiation in halide media is described. Pitting corrosion tests were conducted in acidified 10% ferric chloride solution.

J.R. Cahoon, M.N. Bassim, and E.G. Oman, Acoustic Emission During Corrosion, *Can. Metall. Q.*, *25*(1), 73-77, 1986. MetAbs No. 86-352573. **Abstract:** The corrosion of commercially pure Cu, commercially pure Al and mild steel in 10% ferric chloride solution was studied with respect to corrosion rate and rate of acoustic emission. Corrosion rates were established by weight loss measurements and acoustic emission.

M. Renner, U. Heubner, M.B. Rockel, and E. Wallis, Temperature as a Pitting and Crevice Corrosion Criterion in the FeCl3 Test, *Werkst. Korros.*, *37*(4), 183-190, 1986. MetAbs No. 87-350183. **Abstract:** The FeCl3 test is applied to an increasing extent for examining the resistance to pitting and crevice corrosion. Two methods having proved their value are described. The chemical properties of the FeCl3 solution with regard to hydrolysis, pH and redox potential behavior at various test temperatures are described. Results for high-alloy stainless steels and Ni alloys are presented, as are results for artificial seawater.

N. Saito, P.C. Searson, and R.M. Latanision, The Corrosion Performance of Microcrystalline Titanium-Modified 316 Stainless Steel, *Corros. Sci.*, *26*(8), 629-645, 1986. MetAbs No. 87-350209. **Abstract:** The corrosion performance of rapidly solidified, consolidated rapidly solidified, and conventionally processed Ti-modified nuclear grade 316 stainless steel was studied.

E. Angelini and R. Zucchi, Corrosion Behavior of Various Duplex Stainless Steels in the Welded Condition, *Br. Corros. J.*, 21(4), 257-213, 1986. MetAbs No. 87-351176. **Abstract:** A number of duplex stainless steels, whose ferrite content ranged from 25 to 70%, were studied for evidence of corrosion in the aged and welded conditions. Microstructural reasons for differences in corrosion properties have been investigated, together with the influence of base alloy composition. The corrosion performance of duplex stainless steels was tested in highly aggressive media—sulfuric acid and ferric chloride solutions.

E.L. Hibner, Modification of Critical Crevice Temperature Test Procedures for Nickel Alloys in a Ferric Chloride Environment, *Mater. Perform.*, 26(3), 37-40, 1987. MetAbs No. 87-351346. **Abstract:** Techniques exist presently for ranking alloys for crevice corrosion resistance by determining their critical crevice temperature in 6 to 10% $FeCl_3$ environments. Laboratory studies were conducted on Ni alloys to evaluate the effect of $FeCl_3$ concentration and test procedure on critical crevice temperature results. A modified test procedure was developed that yields more reproducible results with less data scatter than existing techniques.

S.C. Srivastava and M.B. Ives, Dissolutions of Inclusions in Low-Alloy Steel Exposed to Chloride-Containing Environments, *Corrosion, 43*(11), 687-692, 1987. MetAbs No. 88-350475. **Abstract:** The role played by nonmetallic inclusions in the nucleation of pitting corrosion in low-alloy steels is determined by the detailed analysis of the inclusions in an AISI 1536 steel and their behavior on exposure to ferric chloride and sodium chloride solutions at various pH values.

Corrosion of Various Metals and Alloys in Ferric Chloride

Material	Condition, other factors, comments	Concentration, %	Temperature, °C (°F)	Duration	Corrosion rate, mm/yr (mils/yr) or other	Ref
Stainless steels						
ALFA-I and ALFA-II	Rubber band test measuring crevice corrosion. Plain specimen. Average weight loss	10	21.1 (70)	72 h	0.0336 g/cm^2	98
ALFA-I and ALFA-II	Rubber band test measuring crevice corrosion. Welded specimen. Average weight loss	10	21.1 (70)	72 h	0.0327 g/cm^2	98
Type 304 stainless steel	...	10	21 (70)	...	Poor	121
Type 304 stainless steel	Research; laboratory test	10	Room	1 d	0.145 in./yr	89
Type 316 stainless steel	Chemical processing; slight aeration; rapid agitation. Containing ammonia and fatty acids	...	102 (216)	106 d	<0.0001 in./yr	89
Type 316 stainless steel	...	10	Room	...	16 (640)	51
Type 316 stainless steel	...	10	21 (70)	...	Poor	121
Type 316 stainless steel	Field or pilot plant test; slight to moderate aeration; no agitation	~36	25 (77)	61 d	Corrosion	89
Type 410 stainless steel	...	10	21 (70)	...	Poor	121
Type 410 stainless steel	...	...	Room	...	Attacked	121
Type 430 stainless steel	...	10	21 (70)	...	Poor	121
Coppers						
70-30 cupronickel	...	...	...	...	Not suitable	93
90-10 cupronickel	...	...	...	...	Not suitable	93
Admiralty brass	...	...	...	...	Not suitable	93
Aluminum bronze	...	...	...	...	Not suitable	93
Ampco 8, aluminum bronze	Generally not suitable	...	...	...	>0.5 (>20)	96
Architectural bronze	...	...	...	...	Not suitable	93
Brass	...	...	...	...	Not suitable	93
Cartridge brass	...	...	...	...	Not suitable	93
Commercial bronze	...	...	...	...	Not suitable	93
Electrolytic copper	...	...	...	...	Not suitable	93
Free-cutting brass	...	...	...	...	Not suitable	93
Muntz metal	...	...	...	...	Not suitable	93
Naval brass	...	...	...	...	Not suitable	93
Nickel silver	...	18	...	...	Not suitable	93
Phosphor bronze	5% Sn	...	...	...	Not suitable	93
Phosphor bronze	8% Sn	...	...	...	Not suitable	93
Phosphor copper	...	...	...	...	Not suitable	93
Red brass	...	...	...	...	Not suitable	93
Silicon bronze	Low	...	...	...	Not suitable	93
Silicon bronze	High	...	...	...	Not suitable	93
Titanium						
Ti-3-8-6-4-4	...	10	Boiling	...	nil	33
Ti-550	...	10	Boiling	...	nil	33

(Continued)

Corrosion of Various Metals and Alloys in Ferric Chloride (Continued)

Material	Condition, other factors, comments	Concen-tration, %	Temperature, °C (°F)	Duration	Corrosion rate, mm/yr (mils/yr) or other	Ref
Ti-5Ta	...	10	Boiling	...	nil	33
Ti-6-2-1-.8	...	10	Boiling	...	nil	33
Ti-6-2-4-6	...	10	Boiling	...	0.06 (2.4)	33
Ti-6-4	...	10	Boiling	...	nil	33
Ti-10-2-3	...	10	Boiling	...	nil	33
Titanium	...	10	19-26 (65-80)	36 d	0.00076 (0.03)	74
Titanium	Grade 7	10	Boiling	...	nil	33
Titanium	Grade 12	10	Boiling	...	nil	33
Titanium	Grade 7	30	Boiling	...	nil	33
Titanium	Grade 9	10	Boiling	...	nil	33
Titanium	...	10-20	Room	...	nil	90
Titanium	...	1-30	100 (212)	...	0.004 (0.16)	90
Titanium	...	10-40	Boiling	...	nil	90
Titanium	...	1-30	Boiling	...	nil	90
Titanium	...	50	150 (302)	...	0.003 (0.12)	90
Titanium	...	10	Boiling	...	0.00	90
Transage 207	...	10	Boiling	...	0.19 (7.6)	33
Heat- and corrosion-resistant alloys						
18Cr-2Ni-12Mn	...	10 wt%	Room	...	<0.025 (<1)	47
44Co-31Cr-13W	As cast. (a)	2	Room	...	0.07 (3)	53
44Co-31Cr-13W	Heat treated 4 h at 899 °C (1650 °F) and furnace cooled. (a)	2	Room	...	0.25 (10)	53
44Co-31Cr-13W	Heat treated 4 h at 899 °C (1650 °F) and furnace cooled. (a)	89	65 (150)	...	nil	53
44Co-31Cr-13W	As cast. (a)	2	Room	...	0.07 (3)	53
44Co-31Cr-13W	Heat treated 4 h at 899 °C (1650 °F) and furnace cooled. (a)	2	Room	...	0.25 (10)	53
50Co-20Cr-15W-10Ni	...	2	Room	...	nil	53
50Co-20Cr-15W-10Ni	As cast. (a)	2	Room	...	nil	53
53Co-30Cr-4.5W	As cast. (a)	2	Room	...	0.005 (0.2)	53
53Co-30Cr-4.5W	Heat treated 4 h at 899 °C (1650 °F). (a)	2	Room	...	0.005 (0.2)	53
53Co-30Cr-4.5W	As cast. (a)	2	Room	...	0.005 (0.2)	53
53Co-30Cr-4.5W	Heat treated 4 h at 899 °C (1650 °F) and furnace cooled. (a)	2	Room	...	0.005 (0.2)	53
Alloy 825	Chemical processing; slight aeration; rapid agitation. Containing ammonia and fatty acids	...	102 (216)	106 d	<0.0001 in./yr	89
Alloy 825	Field or pilot plant test; slight to moderate aeration; no agitation	~36	25 (77)	61 d	Corrosion	89
Carpenter 20	Chemical processing; slight aeration; rapid agitation. Containing ammonia and fatty acids	...	102 (216)	106 d	<0.0001 in./yr	89
Carpenter 20	Field or pilot plant test; slight to moderate aeration; no agitation	~36	25 (77)	61 d	Corrosion	89
Ferralium	...	10	Room	...	0.625 (25)	51
Ferralium 255	GTAW, base metal thickness of 3.1 mm (0.125 in.). Critical pitting temperature	10	≤25 (77)	120 h	...	88
Ferralium 255	GTAW, base metal thickness of 12.7 mm (0.5 in.). Critical pitting temperature	10	≤25 (77)	120 h	...	88
Ferralium 255	Autogenous welding. GTAW, base metal thickness of 25.4 mm (1.0 in.). Critical pitting temperature	10	≤15 (58)	120 h	...	88
Ferralium 255	GMAW (short arc), base metal thickness of 3.1 mm (0.125 in.). Critical pitting temperature	10	30 (86)	120 h	...	88
Ferralium 255	GMAW (short arc), base metal thickness of 6 mm (0.25 in.). Critical pitting temperature	10	30 (86)	120 h	...	88
Ferralium 255	GMAW (short arc), base metal thickness of 12.7 mm (0.5 in.). Critical pitting temperature	10	≤25 (77)	120 h	...	88
Ferralium 255	GMAW (spray), base metal thickness of 9.5 mm (0.375 in.). Critical pitting temperature	10	≤25 (77)	120 h	...	88
Ferralium 255	GMAW (spray), base metal thickness of 12.7 mm (0.5 in.). Critical pitting temperature	10	≤25 (77)	120 h	...	88
Ferralium 255	SMAW, base metal thickness of 3.1 mm (0.125 in.). Critical pitting temperature	10	30-35 (86-94)	120 h	...	88

(Continued)

Corrosion of Various Metals and Alloys in Ferric Chloride (Continued)

Material	Condition, other factors, comments	Concen-tration, %	Temperature, °C (°F)	Duration	Corrosion rate, mm/yr (mils/yr) or other	Ref
Ferralium 255	SMAW, base metal thickness of 6.4 mm (0.25 in.). Critical pitting temperature	10	30 (86)	120 h	...	88
Ferralium 255	SMAW, base metal thickness of 12.7 mm (0.5 in.). Critical pitting temperature	10	30 (86)	120 h	...	88
Ferralium 255	Reannealed at 1038 °C (1900 °F), water quenched. Critical pitting temperature	10	40 (104)	120 h	...	88
Ferralium 255	Mill-annealed at 1038 °C (1900 °F). Annealing treatment: 482 °C (900 °F), 1 h, water quenched	10	Room	...	0.23 (9)	88
Ferralium 255	Mill-annealed at 1038 °C (1900 °F). Annealing treatment: 927 °C (1700 °F), 1 h, water quenched	10	Room	...	10 (400)	88
Ferralium 255	Mill-annealed at 1038 °C (1900 °F), water quenched	10	Room	...	11.3 (450)	88
Ferralium 255	Mill-annealed at 1038 °C (1900 °F). Annealing treatment 1260 °C (2300 °F), 30 min, water quenched	10	Room	...	11.3 (450)	88
Ferralium 255	Mill-annealed at 1038 °C (1900 °F). Annealing treatment 1260 °C (2300 °F), 30 min, water quenched plus 1038 °C (1900 °F), 20 min, water quenched	10	Room	...	0	88
Haynes No. 188	Mill annealed	3.8	Room	24 h	nil	99
Haynes No. 188	Mill annealed	3.8	70 (160)	24 h	nil	99
Haynes No. 188	Mill annealed	3.8	Boiling	24 h	nil	99
Haynes No. 25	Mill annealed	3.8	Room	24 h	0.013 (0.5)	99
Haynes No. 25	Mill annealed	3.8	70 (160)	24 h	nil	99
Haynes No. 25	Mill annealed	3.8	Boiling	24 h	nil	99
Haynes No. 25	(b)	2	Room	24 h	nil	68
Haynes No. 25	(b)	10	Room	24 h	nil	68
Haynes No. 25	Plus 5% NaCl. (b)	2	66 (150)	24 h	nil	68
Haynes No. 25	Plus 10% NaCl. (b)	5	66 (150)	24 h	nil	68
Haynes No. 25	Plus 5% NaCl. (b)	2	Boiling	24 h	nil	68
Haynes No. 556	Mill annealed	3.8	Room	24 h	0.033 (1.3)	99
Haynes No. 556	Mill annealed	3.8	70 (160)	24 h	14 (550)	99
Haynes No. 556	Mill annealed	3.8	Boiling	24 h	36 (1419)	99
Inco C-276	Crevice corrosion	10	50 (122)	100 h	0.005 (0.2)	40
Inco C-276	Crevice corrosion	10	75 (167)	100 h	0.036 (1.4)	40
Incoloy 800	Solutions were prepared with reagent-grade chemicals. Test specimens were cold-rolled, annealed sheet, 2.84 mm (0.112 in.) thick. Pitting occurred after 7 d	5	80 (176)	42 d	10.7 (420)	44
Inconel 601	Pitting attack. Average of two tests	5	80 (176)	7 d	8.99 (354)	64
Multimet	(b)	2	Room	24 h	nil	68
Multimet	(b)	10	Room	24 h	nil	68
Multimet	Plus 5% NaCl. (b)	2	66 (150)	24 h	4.90 (193)	68
Multimet	Plus 10% NaCl. (b)	5	66 (150)	24 h	>25.4 (>1000)	68
Multimet	Plus 5% NaCl. (b)	2	Boiling	24 h	>25.4 (>1000)	68
Zirconium						
Zirconium	Uneven corrosion	10	19-26 (65-80)	36 d	0.01 (0.42)	74
Zr702	...	0-50	Room to 100 (room to 212)	...	>1.3 (>50)	15
Zr702	...	0-50	Boiling	...	>1.3 (>50)	15
Zr704	...	0-50	Room to 100 (room to 212)	...	>1.3 (>50)	15
Zr704	...	0-50	Boiling	...	>1.3 (>50)	15
Zr705	...	0-50	Room to 100 (room to 212)	...	>1.3 (>50)	15
Zr705	...	0-50	Boiling	...	>1.3 (>50)	15
Lead, tin, and zinc						
Lead	Corrosion rate too high to merit any consideration of Pb	20-30	24 (75)	...	>1270 μm/yr (>50)	95
Lead	...	100 g/L	Room	...	11.9 (469)	17
Lead	...	100 g/L	100 (212)	...	Rapid dissolution	17

(Continued)

Corrosion of Various Metals and Alloys in Ferric Chloride (Continued)

Material	Condition, other factors, comments	Concentration, %	Temperature, °C (°F)	Duration	Corrosion rate, mm/yr (mils/yr) or other	Ref
Tin	...	...	20 (68)	...	Unsuitable	94
Tin	...	...	60 (140)	...	Unsuitable	94
Tin	...	...	100 (212)	...	Unsuitable	94
Tantalum						
Tantalum	...	10	19-26 (65-80)	36 d	nil	74
Tantalum	Commercial sheet. (c)	30	Boiling	48 h	<0.025 (<1)	38
Tantalum	High purity. (c)	30	Boiling	48 h	<0.025 (<1)	38
Noble metals						
Iridium	...	100 g/L	100 (212)	...	nil	18
Osmium	...	100 g/L	100 (212)	...	3.0 (120)	26
Platinum	...	100 g/L	100 (212)	...	16.7 (6.57)	5
Platinum	...	100 g/L	Room	...	<0.25 (<10)	5
Rhodium	...	100 g/L	100 (212)	...	nil	29
Ruthenium	...	100 g/L	100 (212)	...	nil	18
Silver	...	<5	Room	...	<0.05 (<2)	9
Others						
Columbium alloy	Wrought 100% Cb; laboratory button; annealed at 1175 °C (2140 °F) for 30 min. (c)	30	Boiling	48 h	<0.025 (<1)	38
Columbium alloy	Wrought 100% Cb; electron-beam melted; annealed at 1400 °C (2552 °F) for 1 h. (c)	30	Boiling	48 h	<0.025 (<1)	38
Columbium alloy	Wrought 0.75% Zr, bal Cb; arc melted; annealed at 1400 °C (2552 °F) for 1 h. (c)	30	Boiling	48 h	<0.025 (<1)	38
Columbium alloy	Wrought 6.9% Ti, 0.81% Zr, bal Cb; arc melted; annealed at 1400 °C (2552 °F) for 1 h. (c)	30	Boiling	48 h	<0.025 (<1)	38
Columbium alloy	Wrought 100% Cb; arc melted; annealed at 1400 °C (2552 °F) for 1 h. (c)	30	Boiling	48 h	<0.025 (<1)	38
Columbium alloy	Wrought 8% Ti, bal Cb; arc melted; annealed at 1400 °C (2552 °F) for 1 h. (c)	30	Boiling	48 h	<0.025 (<1)	38
Magnesium	...	All	Room	...	Unsuitable	119
Niobium	...	10	Room	...	nil	2
Niobium	...	10	Boiling	...	nil	2
Niobium	...	10	19-26 (65-80)	36 d	nil	74

(a) Based on five 24-h test periods with cast specimens 38 mm x 25 mm x 6 mm (1.5 in. x 1 in. x 0.25 in.), 120-grit abrasive finish. (b) All data are steady-state as calculated from a minimum of five 24-h test periods. All data were obtained using corrosion specimens prepared from 12-gage, solution heat-treated sheet. (c) Average of three 48-h periods.

Stainless Steels: Crevice Corrosion Data in 10% Ferric Chloride

Alloy	Temperature at onset of crevice corrosion
AL 2205	20 °C (68 °F)
AL 29-4C	52 °C (125 °F)
AL 6XN	45 °C (113 °F)
AL 904L	18 °C (65 °F)
Alloy 625	45 °C (113 °F)
Altemp 625	40-45 °C (104-113 °F)
E-Brite	24 °C (75 °F)
Type 316	-3 °C (27 °F)
Type 317	2 °C (35 °F)

Note: ASTM Procedure G-48 using a 10% ferric chloride solution.
Source: Ref 120

Nickel Alloys: Critical Pitting Temperature

Alloy	Critical pitting temperature, °C
825	0.0, 0.0
904L	2.5, 5.0
Type 317LM stainless steel	2.5, 2.5
G	23.0, 25.0
G-3	25.0, 25.0
C-4	37.5, 37.5
625	35.0, 40.0
ALLCORR	52.5, 52.5
C-276	60.0, 65.0
C-22	70.0, 70.0

Note: Alloys evaluated in 6% ferric chloride for 24-h periods
Source: Ref 123

Heat- and Corrosion-Resistant Alloys: Comparative Crevice Corrosion Data in 6% Ferric Chloride

Alloy	Temperature at onset of crevice corrosion
Cabot alloy No. 625	45 °C
Hastelloy alloy G	30 °C
Source: Ref 67	

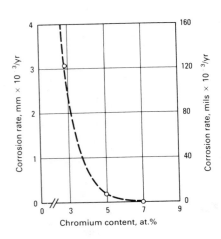

Metallic glass. Corrosion rates of metallic glasses of Ni-Cr-P$_{15}$B$_5$ in 10 wt% FeCl$_3$·6H$_2$O at 30 °C (85 °F) vs. chromium content. Source: *Metals Handbook*, 9th ed., Vol 13, Corrosion, ASM International, Metals Park, OH, 1987, 867.

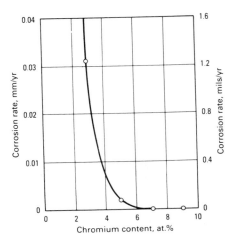

Amorphous nickel-chromium alloys. Effect of chromium content on the corrosion rates of amorphous Ni-Cr-P$_{15}$B$_5$ alloys in 10% FeCl$_3$·6H$_2$O at 30 ± 1 °C (85 ± 2 °F). The corrosion rate was estimated from weight loss during immersion for 168 h. Source: *Metals Handbook*, 9th ed., Vol 13, Corrosion, ASM International, Metals Park, OH, 1987, 866.

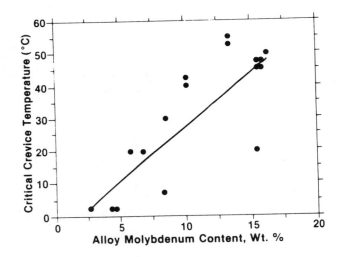

Nickel alloys. Critical crevice temperature for nickel alloys in 6% FeCl$_3$ determined by the modified MTI procedure. Source: E.L. Hibner, "Modification of Critical Crevice Temperature Test Procedures for Nickel-Alloys in a Ferritic Chloride Environment," *Materials Performance*, Vol 26, Mar 1987, 38.

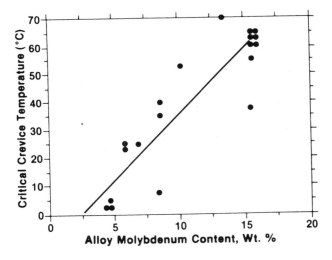

Nickel alloys. Critical crevice temperature for nickel alloys in 6% FeCl$_3$ determined by the MTI procedure. Source: E.L. Hibner, "Modification of Critical Crevice Temperature Test Procedures for Nickel-Alloys in a Ferritic Chloride Environment," *Materials Performance*, Vol 26, Mar 1987, 38.

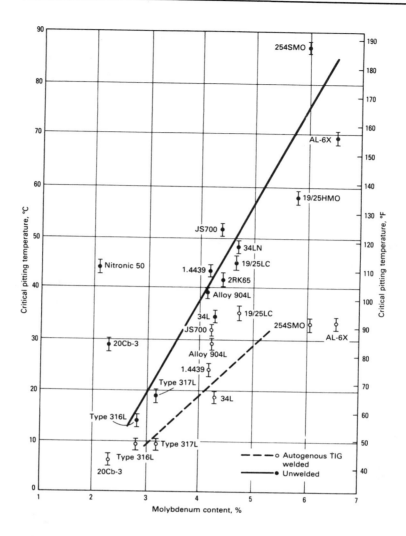

Austenitic stainless steels. Critical pitting temperature vs. molybdenum content of commercial austenitic steels after testing in 10% FeCl₃. Resistance to pitting corrosion, as measured by critical pitting temperature, increases with molybdenum content and decreases after autogenous gas tungsten arc welding. Source: A. Garner, "How Stainless Steel Welds Corrode," *Metal Progress*, Vol 27, Apr 1985, 32.

Ferric Sulfate

Ferric sulfate, $Fe_2(SO_4)_3 \cdot 9H_2O$, also known as iron sulfate, is a deliquescent solid composed of yellow rhombohedral crystals. It is soluble in water and decomposes when heated. Ferric sulfate is used as a disinfectant, a pigment, a soil conditioner, and as a chemical intermediate and analytical reagent.

Additional Reading

R. Bandy and D. Van Rooyen, Effect of Thermal Stabilization on the Low-Temperature Stress Corrosion Cracking of Inconel 600, *Corrosion*, 40(6), 281-284, 1984. MetAbs No. 84-352376. **Abstract:** The propensity of thermally stabilized Inconel 600 to undergo low-temperature stress-corrosion cracking in sulfur-bearing environments has been investigated with U-bends and slow strain rate testing. The results are compared with those of sensitized Inconel 600.

Corrosion Behavior of Various Metals and Alloys in Ferric Sulfate

Material	Condition, other factors, comments	Concen-tration, %	Temperature, °C (°F)	Duration	Corrosion rate, mm/yr (mils/yr) or other	Ref
Stainless steels						
Type 304 stainless steel	Chemical processing; field or pilot plant test; no aeration; rapid agitation. Containing ferric oxide slurry and water	5	18 (65)	32 d	<0.0001 in./yr	89
Type 304 stainless steel	...	10	21 (70)	...	Good	121
Type 304 stainless steel	Metal processing (pickling); field or pilot plant test; rapid agitation. Plus 0.5% citric acid; copper ions present. Crevice attack (tendency to concentration-cell corrosion)	10	77-99 (170-210)	38 d	0.0004 in./yr	89
Type 304 stainless steel	...	50	21 (70)	...	Good	121
Type 316 stainless steel	Chemical processing; field or pilot plant test; no aeration; rapid agitation. Containing ferric oxide slurry and water	5	18 (65)	32 d	<0.0001 in./yr	89
Type 316 stainless steel	Metal processing (pickling); field or pilot plant test; rapid agitation. Plus 0.5% citric acid; copper ions present. Crevice attack (tendency to concentration-cell corrosion)	10	77-99 (170-210)	38 d	0.0001 in./yr	89
Type 316 stainless steel	...	10	21 (70)	...	Good	121
Type 316 stainless steel	...	50	21 (70)	...	Good	121
Type 317 stainless steel	Chemical processing; field or pilot plant test; no aeration; rapid agitation. Containing ferric oxide slurry and water	5	18 (65)	32 d	<0.0001 in./yr	89
Type 410 stainless steel	...	10	21 (70)	...	Good	121
Type 410 stainless steel	...	50	21 (70)	...	Good	121
Type 430 stainless steel	Sensitized sample. Heat treated at 1093 °C (2000 °F) 1 h, air cool. Intergranular corrosion rate. Plus 50% H_2SO_4	...	...	...	109.1 (4364)	41
Type 430 stainless steel	Nonsensitized sample. Heat treated at 760 °C (1400 °F) 1 h, water quenched. Intergranular corrosion rate. Plus 50% H_2SO_4	...	...	...	3.7 (148)	41
Type 430 stainless steel	...	10	21 (70)	...	Good	121
Type 430 stainless steel	...	50	21 (70)	...	Good	121
Aluminum						
Aluminum (>99.5%)	Solution	...	20 (68)	...	Satisfactory	92
Aluminum-manganese alloys	Solution	...	20 (68)	...	Satisfactory	92
Coppers						
70-30 cupronickel	...	...	...	...	Not suitable	93
90-10 cupronickel	...	...	...	...	Not suitable	93
Admiralty brass	...	...	...	...	Not suitable	93
Aluminum bronze	...	...	...	...	Not suitable	93
Architectural bronze	...	...	...	...	Not suitable	93
Brass	...	...	...	...	Not suitable	93
Cartridge brass	...	...	...	...	Not suitable	93
Commercial bronze	...	...	...	...	Not suitable	93
Electrolytic copper	...	...	...	...	Not suitable	93
Free-cutting brass	...	...	...	...	Not suitable	93
Muntz metal	...	...	...	...	Not suitable	93
Naval brass	...	...	...	...	Not suitable	93
Nickel silver	...	18	...	...	Not suitable	93
Phosphor bronze	5% Sn	...	...	...	Not suitable	93
Phosphor bronze	8% Sn	...	...	...	Not suitable	93
Phosphor copper	...	...	...	...	Not suitable	93
Red brass	...	...	...	...	Not suitable	93
Silicon bronze	Low	...	...	...	Not suitable	93
Silicon bronze	High	...	...	...	Not suitable	93
Titanium						
Titanium	...	10	Room	...	nil	90

(Continued)

Corrosion Behavior of Various Metals and Alloys in Ferric Sulfate (Continued)

Material	Condition, other factors, comments	Concen-tration, %	Temperature, °C (°F)	Duration	Corrosion rate, mm/yr (mils/yr) or other	Ref
Heat- and corrosion-resistant alloys						
Carpenter 20	Chemical processing; field or pilot plant test; no aeration; rapid agitation; cast specimens. Containing ferric oxide slurry and water	5	18 (65)	32 d	<0.0001 in./yr	89
Carpenter 20	Metal processing (pickling); field or pilot plant test; rapid agitation; cast specimens. Plus 0.5% citric acid; copper ions present	10	77-99 (170-210)	38 d	nil	89
Inco C-276	Corrosion test ASTM G28. Unwelded, solution heat treated specimens	...	...	...	5.69 (224)	40
Inco C-276	Corrosion test ASTM G28. As-welded with the gas-tungsten-arc method	...	...	...	6.93 (273)	40
Zirconium						
Zr702	...	10	0-100 (32-212)	...	<0.05 (<2)	15
Lead, tin, and zinc						
Lead	Negligible corrosion; Pb recommended for use	10-20	24-79 (75-175)	...	<50 μm/yr (<2)	95
Others						
Magnesium alloy AZ61A	Specimen size, 75 x 25 x 1.5 mm (3 x 1 x 0.06 in.); surface preparation, HNO_3 pickling; volume of testing solution, 100 ml. Specimens were alternately immersed 30 s in solution and held 2 min in air	3	35 (95)	7 d	29.7 $g/m^2/d$ (19.2 $mg/in.^2/d$)	12

Ferrous Chloride

Ferrous chloride, $FeCl_2 \cdot 4H_2O$, also known as iron chloride and iron dichloride, is a green-blue deliquescent crystalline solid. It is soluble in water and alcohol and is used as a mordant in the dyeing of textiles. Ferrous chloride finds use in sewage treatment, in metallurgy, and in pharmaceutical preparations.

Corrosion Behavior of Various Metals and Alloys in Ferrous Chloride

Material	Condition, other factors, comments	Concen-tration, %	Temperature, °C (°F)	Duration	Corrosion rate, mm/yr (mils/yr) or other	Ref
Stainless steels						
Type 304 stainless steel	Chemical processing; field or pilot plant test; no aeration; rapid agitation. Saturated ferrous chloride water solution, plus 0.09% hydrochloric acid (evaporator)	...	135 (275)	1 d	0.0046 in./yr	89
Type 316 stainless steel	Chemical processing; field or pilot plant test; no aeration; rapid agitation. Saturated ferrous chloride water solution, plus 0.09% hydrochloric acid (evaporator)	...	135 (275)	1 d	0.0054 in./yr	89
Type 316 stainless steel	Chemical processing; field or pilot plant test; no aeration; rapid agitation. Plus 5% organic wastes, 3% resorcinol, 0.5% hydrochloric acid, abrasive iron residue, pH 1 (filter press). Severe pitting: maximum depth of pits over 0.010 in.; crevice attack (tendency to concentration-cell corrosion)	30	79 (175)	10 d	0.0017 in./yr	89
Type 316 stainless steel	Chemical processing; field or pilot plant test; no aeration; rapid agitation; sensitized specimens. Plus 5% organic wastes, 3% resorcinol, 0.5% hydrochloric acid, abrasive iron residue, pH 1 (filter press). Severe pitting: maximum depth of pits over 0.010 in.; crevice attack (tendency to concentration-cell corrosion)	30	79 (175)	10 d	0.0029 in./yr	89

(Continued)

Corrosion Behavior of Various Metals and Alloys in Ferrous Chloride (Continued)

Material	Condition, other factors, comments	Concentration, %	Temperature, °C (°F)	Duration	Corrosion rate, mm/yr (mils/yr) or other	Ref
Type 316 stainless steel	Chemical processing; field or pilot plant test; no aeration; rapid agitation; low-carbon grade (0.03% C max) specimens. Plus 5% organic wastes, 3% resorcinol, 0.5% hydrochloric acid, abrasive iron residue, pH 1 (filter press). Moderate pitting: maximum depth of pits from 0.005 to 0.010 in.; crevice attack (tendency to concentration-cell corrosion)	30	79 (175)	10 d	0.0017 in./yr	89
Type 316 stainless steel	Chemical processing (evaporation); laboratory test; no aeration; rapid agitation. Plus 0.07-2.5 g/L lead ion, 0.07 g/L tin ion as chlorides, pH 1.2	~16.5	66 (150)	1.75 d	0.006 in./yr	89
Type 316 stainless steel	Chemical processing (evaporation); laboratory test; no aeration; rapid agitation. Plus 0.07-2.5 g/L lead ion, 0.07 g/L tin ion as chlorides, pH 1.2. Slight pitting: maximum depth of pits from incipient to 0.005 in.	~16.5	66 (150)	1.75 d	0.08 in./yr	89
Type 317 stainless steel	Chemical processing; field or pilot plant test; no aeration; rapid agitation. Plus 5% organic wastes, 3% resorcinol, 0.5% hydrochloric acid, abrasive iron residue, pH 1 (filter press). Severe pitting: maximum depth of pits over 0.010 in.; crevice attack (tendency to concentration-cell corrosion)	30	79 (175)	10 d	0.0014 in./yr	89
Coppers					Good	93
70-30 cupronickel	(a)	...	...	...	Good	93
90-10 cupronickel	(a)	...	...	...	Good	93
Admiralty brass	(a)	...	...	...	Good	93
Aluminum bronze	(a)	...	...	...	Not suitable	93
Architectural bronze	...	...	...	...	Not suitable	93
Cartridge brass	...	...	...	...	Good	93
Commercial bronze	(a)	...	...	...	Good	93
Electrolytic copper	(a)	...	...	..	Not suitable	93
Free-cutting brass	...	...	...	...	Not suitable	93
Muntz metal	...	...	...	...	Not suitable	93
Naval brass	...	...	...	...	Good	93
Nickel silver	(a)	18	...	...	Good	93
Phosphor bronze	5% Sn. (a)	...	...	...	Good	93
Phosphor bronze	8% Sn. (a)	...	...	...	Good	93
Phosphor copper	(a)	...	...	...	Good	93
Red brass	(a)	...	...	...	Good	93
Silicon bronze	Low. (a)	...	...	...	Good	93
Silicon bronze	High. (a)	...	...	...		
Titanium						
Titanium	Plus 0.5% HCl	30	79 (175)	...	0.006 (0.24)	90
Titanium	Plus 0.5% HCl	30	79 (175)	...	0.006 (0.24)	90
Heat- and corrosion-resistant alloys						
Alloy 825	Chemical processing; field or pilot plant test; no aeration; rapid agitation. Plus 5% organic wastes, 3% resorcinol, 0.5% hydrochloric acid, abrasive iron residue, pH 1 (filter press). Severe pitting: maximum depth of pits over 0.010 in.; crevice attack (tendency to concentration-cell corrosion)	30	79 (175)	10 d	0.001 in./yr	89
Carpenter 20	Chemical processing; field or pilot plant test; no aeration; rapid agitation. Plus 5% organic wastes, 3% resorcinol, 0.5% hydrochloric acid, abrasive iron residue, pH 1 (filter press). Severe pitting: maximum depth of pits over 0.010 in.; crevice attack (tendency to concentration-cell corrosion)	30	79 (175)	10 d	0.0012 in./yr	89
Carpenter 20	Chemical processing (evaporation); laboratory test; no aeration; rapid agitation; cast specimens. Plus 0.07-2.5 g/L lead ion, 0.07 g/L tin ion as chlorides, pH 1.2	~16.5	66 (150)	1.75 d	0.004 in./yr	89
Carpenter 20	Chemical processing (evaporation); laboratory test; no aeration; rapid agitation; cast specimens. Plus 0.07-2.5 g/L lead ion, 0.07 g/L tin ion as chlorides, pH 1.2	~16.5	66 (150)	1.75 d	0.039 in./yr	89

(Continued)

Corrosion Behavior of Various Metals and Alloys in Ferrous Chloride (Continued)

Material	Condition, other factors, comments	Concen-tration, %	Temperature, °C (°F)	Duration	Corrosion rate, mm/yr (mils/yr) or other	Ref
Lead, tin, and zinc						
Lead	Pb may be used where this effect on service life can be tolerated	10-30	24 (75)	...	500-1270 μm/yr (20-50)	95
(a) May be considered in place of a copper metal when some property, other than corrosion resistance, governs its use.						

Ferrous Sulfate

Ferrous sulfate, $FeSO_4 \cdot 7H_2O$, also known as ferrisulpas, green copperas, green vitriol, iron sulfate, and melanterite, is composed of blue-green monoclinic crystals. It is soluble in water and is used as a mordant for dyeing wool in the textile industry. Ferrous sulfate is also used as a disinfectant and in the manufacture of ink.

Material Summaries

The following material summaries were compiled from a survey of the available literature. Inclusion of a material description under a given environment does not imply that it is the most appropriate material for corrosion service in that environment. Likewise, exclusion of a given material does not imply that it is not suitable for corrosion service applications in that environment.

Aluminum. Solid ferrous sulfate had no effect on aluminum alloy 3003, but mildly attacked (around 4 mils/yr) aluminum alloy 5154 in laboratory test conditions of ambient temperature and 100% relative humidity. Aqueous solutions of 0.001 to 10% ferrous sulfate mildly attacked (around 3 mils/yr) aluminum alloy 1100 in other tests at ambient temperature. Ferrous sulfate oxidizes at elevated temperatures to ferric sulfate, which is corrosive to aluminum alloys. Ferrous sulfate solutions have been handled in aluminum alloy A356.0 valves and aluminum spray tanks.

Corrosion Behavior of Various Metals and Alloys in Ferrous Sulfate

Material	Condition, other factors, comments	Concen-tration, %	Temperature, °C (°F)	Duration	Corrosion rate, mm/yr (mils/yr) or other	Ref
Stainless steels						
AM-363 stainless steel	...	...	Room	...	Attacked	120
Type 304 stainless steel	Metal processing; field or pilot plant test; no aeration; no agitation. With carbon over the standard maximum. Plus 19.5% sulfuric acid, 10% titanium dioxide as sulfate, 2-3% solids, 1.7 g/L titanium ion as sulfate, trace hydrogen sulfide (Dorr settling tank)	20	50-70 (122-158)	1 d	5.12 in./yr	89
Type 304 stainless steel	Chemical processing; field or pilot plant test; strong aeration; rapid agitation. Plus 16-18% ferric sulfate, 10% sodium chloride, 0.5-1% sodium hypochlorite, trace hydrochloric acid (cypress tank). Severe pitting: maximum depth of pits over 0.010 in.	20	95 (203)	1.8 d	0.19 in./yr	89
Type 304 stainless steel	Metal processing (pickling); field or pilot plant test; no aeration; rapid agitation. Plus some wetting agents, 2.5 pH (evaporator crystallizer). Severe pitting: maximum depth of pits over 0.010 in.; crevice attack (tendency to concentration-cell corrosion)	16	82-98 (180-210)	16 d	0.0006 in./yr	89
Type 304 stainless steel	Metal processing; field or pilot plant test; strong aeration; rapid agitation. Plus 5% sulfuric acid, 5% hydrofluoric acid	10	48 (120)	1.7 d	0.393 in./yr	89
Type 304 stainless steel	Metal processing (pickling); field or pilot plant test; no aeration; rapid agitation. Plus trace of wetting agents, 2.5 pH (evaporator crystallizer). Crevice attack (tendency to concentration-cell corrosion)	24	32-54 (90-130)	16 d	0.0001 in./yr	89
Type 316 stainless steel	Metal processing (pickling); field or pilot plant test; no aeration; rapid agitation. Plus trace of wetting agents, 2.5 pH (evaporator crystallizer). Crevice attack (tendency to concentration-cell corrosion)	24	32-54 (90-130)	16 d	0.0001 in./yr	89
(Continued)						

Corrosion Behavior of Various Metals and Alloys in Ferrous Sulfate (Continued)

Material	Condition, other factors, comments	Concentration, %	Temperature, °C (°F)	Duration	Corrosion rate, mm/yr (mils/yr) or other	Ref
Type 316 stainless steel	Metal processing; field or pilot plant test; strong aeration; rapid agitation. Plus 5% sulfuric acid, 5% hydrofluoric acid	10	48 (120)	1.7 d	0.191 in./yr	89
Type 316 stainless steel	Metal processing (pickling); field or pilot plant test; no aeration; rapid agitation. Plus some wetting agents, 2.5 pH (evaporator crystallizer). Crevice attack (tendency to concentration-cell corrosion)	16	82-98 (180-210)	16 d	0.0003 in./yr	89
Type 316 stainless steel	Chemical processing; field or pilot plant test; strong aeration; rapid agitation. Plus 16-18% ferric sulfate, 10% sodium chloride, 0.5-1% sodium hypochlorite, trace hydrochloric acid (cypress tank). Severe pitting: maximum depth of pits over 0.010 in.; crevice attack (tendency to concentration-cell corrosion)	20	95 (203)	1.8 d	0.07 in./yr	89
Type 316 stainless steel	Metal processing; field or pilot plant test; no aeration; no agitation. With carbon over the standard maximum. Plus 19.5% sulfuric acid, 10% titanium dioxide as sulfate, 2-3% solids, 1.7 g/L titanium ion as sulfate, trace hydrogen sulfide (Dorr settling tank). Slight pitting: maximum depth of pits from incipient to 0.005 in.; crevice attack (tendency to concentration-cell corrosion)	20	50-70 (122-158)	1 d	11.5 in./yr	89
Type 410 stainless steel	...	...	Room	...	Unattacked	121
Coppers						
70-30 cupronickel	(a)	...	...	...	Good	93
90-10 cupronickel	(a)	...	...	...	Good	93
Admiralty brass	(a)	...	...	...	Good	93
Aluminum bronze	(a)	...	...	...	Good	93
Ampco 8, aluminum bronze	Generally not suitable	...	...	...	>0.5 (>20)	96
Architectural bronze	...	...	...	...	Not suitable	93
Brass	(a)	...	...	...	Good	93
Cartridge brass	...	...	...	...	Not suitable	93
Commercial bronze	(a)	...	...	...	Good	93
Electrolytic copper	(a)	...	...	...	Good	93
Free-cutting brass	...	...	...	...	Not suitable	93
Muntz metal	...	...	...	...	Not suitable	93
Naval brass	...	...	...	...	Not suitable	93
Nickel silver	(a)	18	...	...	Good	93
Phosphor bronze	5% Sn. (a)	...	...	...	Good	93
Phosphor bronze	8% Sn. (a)	...	...	...	Good	93
Phosphor copper	(a)	...	...	...	Good	93
Red brass	(a)	...	...	...	Good	93
Silicon bronze	Low. (a)	...	...	...	Good	93
Silicon bronze	High. (a)	...	...	...	Good	93
Titanium						
Titanium	...	Saturated	Room	...	nil	90
Heat- and corrosion-resistant alloys						
Carpenter 20	Metal processing (pickling); field or pilot plant test; no aeration; rapid agitation. Plus trace of wetting agents, 2.5 pH (evaporator crystallizer)	24	32-54 (90-130)	16 d	0.0001 in./yr	89
Carpenter 20	Metal processing (pickling); field or pilot plant test; no aeration; rapid agitation. Plus some wetting agents, 2.5 pH (evaporator crystallizer)	16	82-98 (180-210)	16 d	0.0002 in./yr	89
Carpenter 20	Chemical processing; field or pilot plant test; strong aeration; rapid agitation; cast specimen. Plus 16-18% ferric sulfate, 10% sodium chloride, 0.5-1% sodium hypochlorite, trace hydrochloric acid (cypress tank). Severe pitting: maximum depth of pits over 0.010 in.; crevice attack (tendency to concentration-cell corrosion)	20	95 (203)	1.8 d	0.05 in./yr	89

(Continued)

Corrosion Behavior of Various Metals and Alloys in Ferrous Sulfate (Continued)

Material	Condition, other factors, comments	Concentration, %	Temperature, °C (°F)	Duration	Corrosion rate, mm/yr (mils/yr) or other	Ref
Lead, tin, and zinc						
Lead	Practically resistant; Pb recommended for use	10	24-100 (75-212)	...	<500 μm/yr (<20)	95
Tin	...	...	20 (68)	...	Unsuitable	94
Tin	...	...	60 (140)	...	Unsuitable	94
Tin	...	...	100 (212)	...	Unsuitable	94
Noble metals						
Platinum	...	All	Room	...	<0.05 (<2)	5
Silver	Attacked upon heating	All	Room	...	<0.05 (<2)	9

(a) May be considered in place of a copper metal when some property, other than corrosion resistance, governs its use.

Fluorine

Fluorine (F) is a chemical element (group VIIa, halogens) that melts at -219.62 °C and boils at -188.1 °C. It is a pale yellow, highly toxic, corrosive, flammable gas. It is the most electronegative of all elements and the most chemically energetic of all nonmetallic elements.

Fluorine is a high-tonnage chemical that is used in production of fluorides, in synthesis of fluorocarbons, and as an oxidizer for rocket fuels. Because of its severe oxidizing characteristics, special permits are required for shipping of fluorine, and all containers, piping, and processing equipment used for fluorine service must be passivated prior to use. Thereafter, they must be designated for exclusive fluorine service.

Material Summaries

The following material summaries were compiled from a survey of the available literature. Inclusion of a material description under a given environment does not imply that it is the most appropriate material for corrosion service in that environment. Likewise, exclusion of a given material does not imply that it is not suitable for corrosion service applications in that environment.

Aluminum. In laboratory tests, aluminum 1100 alloy was resistant to fluorine at temperatures up to 450 °C (842 °F). In the presence of moisture, hydrofluoric acid is formed, which corrodes aluminum alloys. Dry fluorine gas has been handled in aluminum alloy equipment. A durable protective coating is formed on the aluminum surfaces contacting the gas.

Stainless Steels. At lower temperatures, most austenitic stainless steels resist fluorine gas if the gas is completely dry. The presence of even small amounts of moisture results in accelerated attack, especially pitting and possibly stress-corrosion cracking.

Nickel Alloys. Although fluorine and chlorine are strong oxidizers that react with metal, Nickel 200 can be used successfully in such environments under certain conditions. At room temperature, Nickel 200 forms a protective fluoride film and is considered satisfactory for handling fluorine at low temperatures. At elevated temperatures, Nickel 201 is preferred.

Magnesium. Dry fluorine causes little or no corrosion of magnesium at room or slightly elevated temperatures. The presence of a small amount of water causes negligible attack by fluorine.

Niobium. Niobium is an important metal for chromium plating applications. It is particularly attractive when fluoride ions are also present. It has the highest resistance to attack by fluoride ions among reactive and refractory metals.

Gold. Dry fluorine can be handled by gold, within limitations.

Silver is not resistant to fluorine unless it is cathodically protected.

Tantalum. Fluorine attacks tantalum at room temperature.

Tin. Reactions of fluorine with tin become significant only at temperatures above 100 °C (212 °F).

Corrosion Behavior of Various Metals and Alloys in Fluorine

Material	Condition, other factors, comments	Concentration, %	Temperature, °C (°F)	Duration	Corrosion rate, mm/yr (mils/yr) or other	Ref
Stainless steels						
Type 304 stainless steel	Gas	100	...	...	Very good	121
Type 316 stainless steel	Gas	100	...	...	Very good	121
Type 410 stainless steel	Gas	100	...	...	Poor	121
Type 430 stainless steel	Gas	100	...	...	Very good	121

(Continued)

Corrosion Behavior of Various Metals and Alloys in Fluorine (Continued)

Material	Condition, other factors, comments	Concen-tration, %	Temperature, °C (°F)	Duration	Corrosion rate, mm/yr (mils/yr) or other	Ref
Titanium						
Titanium	...	5-20	Elevated	...	Rapid attack	90
Titanium	Commercial	Gas/liquid	Gas-109 (229)	...	0.864 (34.56)	90
Titanium	HF free	Liquid	Gas-196 (385)	...	0.011 (0.44)	90
Titanium	HF free	Gas	Gas-196 (385)	...	0.011 (0.44)	90
Heat- and corrosion-resistant alloys						
Nickel 201	Dry	...	400 (752)	...	0.213 (8.4)	44
Nickel 201	Dry	...	450 (842)	...	0.579 (22.8)	44
Nickel 201	Dry	...	500 (932)	...	1.554 (61.2)	44
Nickel 201	Dry	...	600 (1112)	...	8.839 (348)	44
Nickel 201	Dry	...	650 (1202)	...	4.877 (192)	44
Nickel 201	Dry	...	700 (1292)	...	10.363 (408)	44

Fluosilicic Acid

Fluosilicic acid, H_2SiF_6, also known as hydrofluorosilicic acid, is a colorless liquid that is soluble in water. It is highly corrosive and toxic, attacking glass and stoneware. Fluosilicic acid is used in water fluoridation, electroplating, and in manufacturing enamels and cement.

Material Summaries

The following material summaries were compiled from a survey of the available literature. Inclusion of a material description under a given environment does not imply that it is the most appropriate material for corrosion service in that environment. Likewise, exclusion of a given material does not imply that it is not suitable for corrosion service applications in that environment.

Lead. The corrosion rates of chemical lead and 6% antimonial lead in fluosilicic acid decrease with the addition of sulfuric acid.

Corrosion Behavior of Various Metals and Alloys in Fluosilicic Acid

Material	Condition, other factors, comments	Concen-tration, %	Temperature, °C (°F)	Duration	Corrosion rate, mm/yr (mils/yr) or other	Ref
Stainless steels						
Type 304 stainless steel	Chemical processing; field or pilot plant test; slight to moderate aeration; slight to moderate agitation. Severe pitting: maximum depth of pits over 0.010 in.	9.1-23.1	63 (145)	90 d	0.038 in./yr	89
Type 304 stainless steel	Chemical processing; field or pilot plant test; strong aeration; slight to moderate agitation. Plus some hydrofluoric and phosphoric acids	10	60 (140)	19 d	Corrosion	89
Type 316 stainless steel	Chemical processing; field or pilot plant test; slight to moderate aeration; slight to moderate agitation	9.1-23.1	63 (145)	90 d	0.005 in./yr	89
Type 316 stainless steel	Chemical processing; field or pilot plant test; no aeration; rapid agitation. Severe pitting: maximum depth of pits over 0.010 in.; crevice attack (tendency to concentration-cell corrosion)	22	63 (145)	94 d	0.002 in./yr	89
Type 316 stainless steel	Chemical processing; field or pilot plant test; strong aeration; rapid agitation; low-carbon grade (0.03% C max) specimens	20	57 (135)	38 d	0.005 in./yr	89
Type 316 stainless steel	Chemical processing; field or pilot plant test; strong aeration; slight to moderate agitation. Plus some hydrofluoric and phosphoric acids	10	60 (140)	19 d	0.024 in./yr	89
Type 317 stainless steel	Chemical processing; field or pilot plant test; strong aeration; rapid agitation	20	57 (135)	38 d	0.005 in./yr	89

(Continued)

Corrosion Behavior of Various Metals and Alloys in Fluosilicic Acid (Continued)

Material	Condition, other factors, comments	Concentration, %	Temperature, °C (°F)	Duration	Corrosion rate, mm/yr (mils/yr) or other	Ref
Type 317 stainless steel	Chemical processing; field or pilot plant test; strong aeration; slight to moderate agitation. Plus some hydrofluoric and phosphoric acids	10	60 (140)	19 d	0.13 in./yr	89
Titanium						
Titanium	...	10	Room	...	47.5 (1900)	90
Heat- and corrosion-resistant alloys						
Alloy 825	Chemical processing; field or pilot plant test; strong aeration; rapid agitation	20	57 (135)	38 d	0.005 in./yr	89
Alloy 825	Chemical processing; field or pilot plant test; strong aeration; slight to moderate agitation. Plus some hydrofluoric and phosphoric acids	10	60 (140)	19 d	0.116 in./yr	89
Carpenter 20	Chemical processing; field or pilot plant test; strong aeration; rapid agitation. Slight pitting: maximum depth of pits from incipient to 0.005 in.	20	57 (135)	38 d	0.003 in./yr	89
Carpenter 20	Chemical processing; field or pilot plant test; strong aeration; slight to moderate agitation. Plus some hydrofluoric and phosphoric acids	10	60 (140)	19 d	0.025 in./yr	89
Zirconium						
Zr702	...	10	Room	...	>1.3 (>50)	15
Lead, tin and zinc						
Lead	Corrosion rate too high to merit any consideration of Pb	10	45 (113)	...	>1270 μm/yr (>50)	95
Lead	Chemical	5	45 (113)	...	1.3 (53)	130
Lead	6% antimonial	5	45 (113)	...	1.956 (77)	130
Lead	Chemical. Plus 5% H_2SO_4	5	45 (113)	...	0.2286 (9)	130
Lead	6% antimonial. Plus 5% H_2SO_4	5	45 (113)	...	0.3556 (14)	130
Lead	Chemical	10	45 (113)	...	1.626 (64)	130
Lead	Chemical. Plus 1% H_2SO_4	10	45 (113)	...	2.235 (88)	130
Lead	6% antimonial	10	45 (113)	...	2.921 (115)	130
Lead	6% antimonial. Plus 1% H_2SO_4	10	45 (113)	...	1.93 (76)	130
Lead	Chemical	1	45 (113)	...	0.1016 (4)	130
Lead	6% antimonial. Plus 10% H_2SO_4	1	45 (113)	...	0.2286 (9)	130
Tin	...	...	20 (68)	...	Unsuitable	94
Tin	...	...	60 (140)	...	Unsuitable	94
Tin	...	...	100 (212)	...	Unsuitable	94
Noble metals						
Silver	...	...	65 (150)	...	<0.05 (<2)	4
Others						
Magnesium	...	All	Room	...	Unsuitable	119

Formaldehyde

Formaldehyde, HCHO, also known as methanal, formol, and methylene oxide, is a colorless gas at room temperature. In solution with water, it is a colorless poisonous liquid with a pungent odor. Formaldehyde is used in the manufacture of plastics and resins by reaction with phenols, urea, and melamine. It is used as a preservative, a disinfectant, and as a chemical intermediate.

Material Summaries

The following material summaries were compiled from a survey of the available literature. Inclusion of a material description under a given environment does not imply that it is the most appropriate material for corrosion service in that environment. Likewise, exclusion of a given material does not imply that it is not suitable for corrosion service applications in that environment.

Aluminum. Formaldehyde has been distilled, stored, and shipped in aluminum alloy equipment. Valves of aluminum alloy 356.0 are used to handle formaldehyde.

Corrosion Behavior of Various Metals and Alloys in Formaldehyde

Material	Condition, other factors, comments	Concen-tration, %	Temperature, °C (°F)	Duration	Corrosion rate, mm/yr (mils/yr) or other	Ref
Stainless steels						
AM-363 stainless steel	...	...	Room	...	Slightly attacked	120
Type 304 stainless steel	Rayon processing; no aeration; slight to moderate agitation	5	98 (210)	560 d	0.001 in./yr	89
Type 304 stainless steel	Chemical processing; field or pilot plant test; no aeration; rapid agitation. Fractionating tower	10	104 (220)	87 d	0.0004 in./yr	89
Type 304 stainless steel	Chemical processing; field or pilot plant test; slight to moderate aeration; rapid agitation	30-70	54-60 (130-140)	99 d	<0.0001 in./yr	89
Type 304 stainless steel	...	40	21 (70)	...	Very good	121
Type 304 stainless steel	Chemical processing; field or pilot plant test; no aeration; rapid agitation. Nozzle on side of Para-form evaporator	84	87-93 (190-200)	35 d	0.0001 in./yr	89
Type 316 stainless steel	Rayon processing; no aeration; slight to moderate agitation	5	98 (210)	560 d	0.0001 in./yr	89
Type 316 stainless steel	Chemical processing; field or pilot plant test; no aeration; rapid agitation. Fractionating tower	10	104 (220)	87 d	0.0006 in./yr	89
Type 316 stainless steel	Chemical processing; field or pilot plant test; no aeration; rapid agitation	20	135 (275)	71 d	0.0001 in./yr	89
Type 316 stainless steel	Chemical processing; field or pilot plant test; slight to moderate aeration; rapid agitation	30-70	54-60 (130-140)	99 d	nil	89
Type 316 stainless steel	...	40	21 (70)	...	Very good	121
Type 316 stainless steel	Chemical processing; field or pilot plant test; no aeration; rapid agitation. Nozzle on side of Para-form evaporator	84	87-93 (190-200)	35 d	0.0001 in./yr	89
Type 317 stainless steel	Rayon processing; no aeration; slight to moderate agitation	5	98 (210)	560 d	<0.0001 in./yr	89
Type 317 stainless steel	Chemical processing; field or pilot plant test; no aeration; rapid agitation. Fractionating tower	10	104 (220)	87 d	<0.0001 in./yr	89
Type 317 stainless steel	Chemical processing; field or pilot plant test; no aeration; rapid agitation	20	135 (275)	71 d	0.0001 in./yr	89
Type 410 stainless steel	...	40	21 (70)	...	Good	121
Type 410 stainless steel	...	...	Room	...	Unattacked	121
Type 430 stainless steel	...	40	21 (70)	...	Good	121
Aluminum						
Aluminum (>99.5%)	Solution	...	20-100 (68-212)	...	Satisfactory	92
Coppers						
70-30 cupronickel	...	...	...	...	Suitable	93
90-10 cupronickel	...	...	...	...	Suitable	93
Admiralty brass	...	...	...	...	Suitable	93
Aluminum bronze	...	...	...	...	Suitable	93
Ampco 8, aluminum bronze	Generally suitable	...	...	...	<0.05 (<2)	96
Architectural bronze	...	...	...	...	Fair	93
Brass	...	...	...	...	Suitable	93
Cartridge brass	...	...	...	...	Fair	93
Commercial bronze	...	...	...	...	Suitable	93
Electrolytic copper	...	...	...	...	Suitable	93
Free-cutting brass	...	...	...	...	Fair	93
Muntz metal	...	...	...	...	Fair	93
Naval brass	...	...	...	...	Fair	93
Nickel silver	...	18	...	...	Suitable	93
Phosphor bronze	5% Sn	...	...	...	Suitable	93
Phosphor bronze	8% Sn	...	...	...	Suitable	93
Phosphor copper	...	...	...	...	Suitable	93
Red brass	...	...	...	...	Suitable	93
Silicon bronze	Low	...	...	...	Suitable	93
Silicon bronze	High	...	...	...	Suitable	93
Titanium						
Titanium	...	37	Boiling	...	<0.13 (<5)	20
Titanium	...	37	Boiling	...	nil	90

(Continued)

Corrosion Behavior of Various Metals and Alloys in Formaldehyde (Continued)

Material	Condition, other factors, comments	Concentration, %	Temperature, °C (°F)	Duration	Corrosion rate, mm/yr (mils/yr) or other	Ref
Zirconium						
Zr702	...	6-37	Boiling	...	<0.025 (<1)	15
Zr702	...	0-70	Room to 100 (room to 212)	...	<0.05 (<2)	15
Zr705	...	6-37	Boiling	...	<0.025 (<1)	15
Lead, tin, and zinc						
Lead	Practically corrosion resistant; Pb recommended for use	20-100	24-52 (75-125)	...	<500 μm/yr (<20)	95
Tin	...	40	20 (68)	...	Resistant	94
Tin	...	40	60 (140)	...	Resistant	94
Tin	...	40	100 (212)	...	Unsuitable	94
Noble metals						
Platinum	...	All	500 (930)	...	<0.05 (<2)	6
Silver	...	All	Boiling	...	<0.05 (<2)	10
Others						
Magnesium	...	All	...	...	Suitable	119
Niobium	...	37	Boiling	...	0.0025 (0.1)	2

Formic Acid

Formic acid, HCOOH, also known as methanoic acid, is a colorless, pungent, toxic, corrosive liquid that melts at 8.4 °C (47 °F) and is soluble in water, ether, and alcohol. It is the most highly ionized of the common organic acids and therefore the most corrosive. It reacts readily with many oxidizing and reducing compounds and is somewhat unstable as the concentration approaches 100%, decomposing to carbon monoxide and water.

Formic acid is used as a chemical intermediate and solvent, in dyeing and electroplating processes, and in fumigants. In a reaction with glycerol at 220 °C (430 °F), it is a source of allyl alcohol. Formic acid has also been employed in brewing (to assist fermentation), as a food preservative, and in the preparation of metallic formates and esters.

Material Summaries

The following material summaries were compiled from a survey of the available literature. Inclusion of a material description under a given environment does not imply that it is the most appropriate material for corrosion service in that environment. Likewise, exclusion of a given material does not imply that it is not suitable for corrosion service applications in that environment.

Cast Irons. High-chromium cast irons, although they exhibit adequate resistance to acetic acid, are more severely corroded by formic acid. High-silicon cast irons exhibit excellent resistance to most organic acids, including formic, in all temperature and concentration ranges.

Alloy Steels. Although they can be used for ambient-temperature storage of some high molecular weight organic acids, alloy steels are attacked rapidly by formic acid.

Stainless Steels. The 400 series stainless steels are usually not resistant to formic acid, except for very dilute, cool solutions. They are seldom used in formic acid service. Type 304 stainless steel has excellent resistance to formic acid at all concentrations at ambient temperatures, and it is the preferred material of construction for storage of the acid. However, type 304 stainless steel is resistant to only 1 to 2% formic acid at the atmospheric boiling temperature, and corrosion tests are advisable whenever type 304 stainless steel is considered for handling formic acid at elevated temperatures.

Type 316 stainless steel shows excellent resistance to formic acid in all concentrations at ambient temperatures and is resistant to at least 5% formic acid at the atmospheric boiling temperature. However, type 316 stainless steel can be seriously attacked by intermediate strengths of formic acid at higher temperatures, and corrosion tests are advisable.

The 20-type alloys, such as 20Cb-3, are more resistant to formic acid than type 316 stainless steel, and their use should be considered in higher concentrations at higher temperatures. Other alloys with chromium and nickel contents higher than those of type 316 stainless steel also show superior resistance to mixtures of formic acid and CH_3COOH and would be expected to perform better in formic acid. Duplex alloys are also reported to be superior to type 316 stainless steel. Weld overlays of 20-type alloys have also been used to alleviate the crevice corrosion of type 316 stainless steel—for example, under gaskets.

A low-carbon niobium-bearing variant of type 446 stainless steel—alloy S44627—appears to have exceptional corrosion resistance to formic acid in preliminary laboratory studies and plant usage. This alloy should be considered for handling formic acid.

Aluminum shows fair resistance to formic acid at any concentration at ambient temperatures as long as there is no contamination of the acid. However, contamination with a wide variety of materials—for example, heavy metal salts—can cause severe corrosion of aluminum. Aluminum has been used to ship concentrated formic acid of about 95 to 99% concentration.

Copper. Copper and its alloys, except yellow brasses which dezincify, respond in approximately the same manner as aluminum to exposure to formic acid. Aluminum bronze is reported to be a superior copper alloy for handling formic acid. The resistance of copper and its alloys to formic acid depends on the presence or absence of oxygen or other oxidizing agents. If free air or other oxidants are present, high corrosion rates will be encountered; if the acid is free of air and other oxidants, copper will provide usable resistance to formic acid at all concentrations to the atmospheric boiling point and even at higher temperatures. Copper and its alloys are probably the most widely used materials for handling formic acid.

Lead. Formic acid in most concentrations corrodes lead at rates that are high enough to preclude the use of lead in these acids.

Nickel. Several of the high-nickel alloys, such as Hastelloy B, Hastelloy C-276, and Hastelloy C-4, have shown outstanding resistance to formic acid in process equipment and are reported to exhibit very good resistance even at temperatures above the atmospheric boiling point.

Niobium. Niobium is resistant to formic acid.

Silver. Silver is resistant to formic acid.

Tantalum. Tantalum is resistant to formic acid.

Titanium has shown outstanding resistance to formic acid in laboratory tests and in field usage. However, titanium can be attacked at truly catastrophic rates by anhydrous formic acid. Additional work is needed to determine the precise conditions under which titanium is attacked in formic acid, and until these parameters have been established, titanium should be tested very carefully before use in formic acid approaching 100% concentration at elevated temperatures.

Zirconium. Zirconium is resistant to formic acid.

Additional Reading

I. Sekine and A. Chinda, Comparison of the Corrosion Behavior of Pure Iron, Nickel, Chromium and Type 304 Stainless Steel in Formic Acid Solution, *Corrosion*, 40(3), 95-100, 1984. MetAbs No. 84-351477. **Abstract:** To investigate the chemical components which contribute to the corrosion resistance of 304 stainless steel in formic acid solution, the natural electrode potential variation with time and the anodic polarization curves were measured for pure Fe, Ni, Cr and 304 steel in various concentrations of formic acid solution.

I. Sekine, S. Hatakeyama, and Y. Nakazawa, Corrosion Behaviour of Type 430 Stainless Steel in Formic and Acetic Acids, *Corros. Sci.*, 27(3), 275-288, 1987. MetAbs No. 87-351485. **Abstract:** The corrosion behavior of Type 430 stainless steel in formic and acetic acid solutions was investigated by measuring the corrosion weight loss, the polarization curve, the corrosion potential variation with time and the impedance at the steel-solution interface.

I. Sekine, S. Hatakeyama, and Y. Nakazawa, Effect of Water Content on the Corrosion Behaviour of Type 430 Stainless Steel in Formic and Acetic Acids, *Electrochim. Acta*, 32(6), 915-920, 1987. MetAbs No. 87-352343. **Abstract:** Corrosion of Type 430 stainless steel was studied in the formic acid-water and in the acetic acid-water systems. Weight-loss measurements were made at ambient temperature and at the solution boiling points.

M.T. Makhlouf, A.A. Abdel-Hafez, and K.M. Hassan, Corrosion of Zinc in Formic Acid Containing Some Organic Additives, *Trans. SAEST*, 21(4), 245-250, 1986. MetAbs No. 87-352809. **Abstract:** The corrosion behavior of Zn in 0.5*M* formic acid solution, either alone or in presence each of four selected organic compounds (8-hydroxy quinoline or in its sulphonamide derivatives) characterized by chelation, was studied.

I. Sekine, A. Masuko, and K. Senoo, Corrosion Behavior of AISI 316 Stainless Steel in Formic and Acetic Acid Solutions, *Corrosion*, 43(9), 553-560, 1987. MetAbs No. 88-350052. **Abstract:** The corrosion behavior of AISI 316 stainless steel in formic and acetic acids was investigated by measuring the corrosion weight loss, the polarization curve, the impedance at the steel/solution interface, and the variation of natural electrode potential with time.

G.B. Elder, Materials of Construction for Organic Acids, *Process Industries Corrosion—The Theory and Practice*, 287-296, 1987. MetAbs No. 88-350337. **Abstract:** The organic acids constitute an important group of chemicals that are handled industrially in large volume. The corrosion characteristics and materials (Al 1100 and 5086) used to manufacture and store formic, acetic and propionic acid are presented in detail.

Corrosion Behavior of Various Metals and Alloys in Formic Acid

Material	Condition, other factors, comments	Concentration, %	Temperature, °C (°F)	Duration	Corrosion rate, mm/yr (mils/yr) or other	Ref
Stainless steels						
Type 304 stainless steel	Test conducted in three 48-h periods	10	Boiling	48 h	0.6 (24)	47
Type 304 stainless steel	...	45	Boiling	...	1220 μm/yr (48)	100
Type 304 stainless steel	No activation	30	Boiling	24 h	2.025 (81)	52
Type 304 stainless steel	No activation	45	Boiling	24 h	...	52
Type 304 stainless steel	...	10	21 (70)	...	Good	121
Type 304 stainless steel	...	50	21 (70)	...	Good	121
Type 316 stainless steel	...	20	Boiling	...	0.08 (3.1)	51
Type 316 stainless steel	...	45	Boiling	...	280 μm/yr (11)	100
Type 316 stainless steel	No activation	30	Boiling	24 h	0.725 (29)	52
Type 316 stainless steel	No activation	45	Boiling	24 h	...	52
Type 316 stainless steel	...	10	21 (70)	...	Very good	121
Type 316 stainless steel	...	50	21 (70)	...	Very good	121
Type 410 stainless steel	...	10	21 (70)	...	Good	121

(Continued)

Corrosion Behavior of Various Metals and Alloys in Formic Acid (Continued)

Material	Condition, other factors, comments	Concen-tration, %	Temperature, °C (°F)	Duration	Corrosion rate, mm/yr (mils/yr) or other	Ref
Type 410 stainless steel	...	50	21 (70)	...	Poor	121
Type 410 stainless steel	...	...	Room	...	Attacked	121
Type 430 stainless steel	...	10	21 (70)	...	Fair	121
Type 430 stainless steel	...	50	21 (70)	...	Poor	121
Type 444 stainless steel	No activation	30	Boiling	24 h	0.85 (34)	52
Type 444 stainless steel	No activation	45	Boiling	24 h	5.3 (212)	52
Aluminum						
Aluminum (99.5%)	Solution	...	...	...	Restricted applications	92
Aluminum-manganese alloys	Solution	...	...	...	Restricted applications	92
Coppers						
70-30 cupronickel	...	...	...	...	Suitable	93
90-10 cupronickel	...	...	...	...	Suitable	93
Admiralty brass	...	...	...	...	Suitable	93
Aluminum bronze	...	...	...	...	Suitable	93
Ampco 8, aluminum bronze	Generally suitable	...	...	...	<0.05 (<2)	96
Architectural bronze	...	...	...	...	Fair	93
Brass	...	...	...	...	Suitable	93
C10300	(a)	40.0	Boiling	96 h	0.14 (5.5)	102
C10300	(a)	1.0	Boiling	96 h	0.02 (0.8)	102
C10300	(a)	5.0	Boiling	96 h	0.02 (0.7)	102
C10300	(a)	10.0	Boiling	96 h	0.02 (0.6)	102
C10300	(a)	20.0	Boiling	96 h	0.20 (7.8)	102
C10300	(a)	50.0	Boiling	96 h	0.26 (10.2)	102
C10300	(a)	60.0	Boiling	96 h	0.05 (2.0)	102
C10300	(a)	70.0	Boiling	96 h	0.76 (30.0)	102
C10300	(a)	80.0	Boiling	96 h	0.20 (7.8)	102
C10300	(a)	90.0	Boiling	96 h	0.22 (8.7)	102
C70600	(a)	1.0	Boiling	96 h	0.02 (0.9)	102
C70600	(a)	5.0	Boiling	96 h	0.02 (0.9)	102
C70600	(a)	10.0	Boiling	96 h	0.02 (0.7)	102
C70600	(a)	20.0	Boiling	96 h	0.40 (15.7)	102
C70600	(a)	40.0	Boiling	96 h	0.34 (13.3)	102
C70600	(a)	50.0	Boiling	96 h	0.54 (21.1)	102
C70600	(a)	60.0	Boiling	96 h	0.03 (1.3)	102
C70600	(a)	70.0	Boiling	96 h	0.76 (30.0)	102
C70600	(a)	80.0	Boiling	96 h	0.13 (5.0)	102
C70600	(a)	90.0	Boiling	96 h	0.19 (7.6)	102
Cartridge brass	...	...	...	...	Fair	93
Commercial bronze	...	...	...	...	Suitable	93
Electrolytic copper	...	...	...	...	Suitable	93
Free-cutting brass	...	...	...	...	Fair	93
Muntz metal	...	...	...	...	Fair	93
Naval brass	...	...	...	...	Fair	93
Phosphor bronze	5% Sn	...	...	...	Suitable	93
Phosphor bronze	8% Sn	...	...	...	Suitable	93
Phosphor copper	...	...	...	...	Suitable	93
Red brass	...	...	...	...	Suitable	93
Silicon bronze	Low	...	...	...	Suitable	93
Silicon bronze	High	...	...	...	Suitable	93
Titanium						
Ti-3-8-6-4-4	...	50	Boiling	...	0.98 (39.2)	33
Ti-3Al-2.5V	ASTM Grade 9	50	Boiling	...	5.0 (200)	91
Ti-550	...	50	Boiling	...	0.02 (0.8)	33
Ti-5Ta	...	50	Boiling	...	3.16 (126.4)	33

(Continued)

Corrosion Behavior of Various Metals and Alloys in Formic Acid (Continued)

Material	Condition, other factors, comments	Concentration, %	Temperature, °C (°F)	Duration	Corrosion rate, mm/yr (mils/yr) or other	Ref
Ti-6-2-4-6	...	50	Boiling	...	0.62 (24.8)	33
Ti-6-4	...	50	Boiling	...	7.92 (288)	33
Titanium	Grade 9	25	88 (190)	...	<0.13 (<5.2)	33
Titanium	Grade 9. Nitrogen-sparged	25	35 (95)	...	<0.13 (<5.2)	33
Titanium	Grade 9	50	Boiling	...	5.08 (203)	33
Titanium	Grade 7	45	Boiling	...	nil	33
Titanium	Grade 12	45, 50	Boiling	...	nil	33
Titanium	Grade 7	50	Boiling	...	0.01 (0.4)	33
Titanium	Grade 12	90	Boiling	...	0.56 (22.4)	33
Titanium	Aerated	10	100 (212)	...	0.005 (0.2)	90
Titanium	Aerated	25	100 (212)	...	0.001 (0.04)	90
Titanium	Aerated	50	100 (212)	...	0.001 (0.04)	90
Titanium	Aerated	90	100 (212)	...	0.001 (0.04)	90
Titanium	Nonaerated	10	100 (212)	...	nil	90
Titanium	Nonaerated	25	100 (212)	...	2.44 (97.6)	90
Titanium	Nonaerated	50	Boiling	...	3.20 (128)	90
Titanium	Nonaerated	90	100 (212)	...	3.00 (120)	90
Titanium	...	9	50 (122)	...	<0.127 (<5.08)	90
Titanium	Grade 7	90	Boiling	...	0.056 (2.24)	33
Titanium	...	50	Boiling	...	10.82 (433)	91
Transage 207	...	50	Boiling	...	0.90 (36)	33

Heat- and corrosion-resistant alloys

Material	Condition, other factors, comments	Concentration, %	Temperature, °C (°F)	Duration	Corrosion rate, mm/yr (mils/yr) or other	Ref
18Cr-2Ni-12Mn	Test conducted in three 48-h periods	10	Boiling	48 h	2 (80)	47
26Cr-1Mo	...	45	Boiling	...	76 µm/yr (3)	100
29Cr-4Mo	...	45	Boiling	...	50 µm/yr (2)	100
44Co-31Cr-13W	(b)	89	65 (150)	...	0.002 (0.1)	53
44Co-31Cr-13W	Heat treated 4 h at 899 °C (1650 °F), furnace cooled. (b)	89	65 (150)	...	nil	53
50Co-20Cr-15W-10Ni	(b)	89	65 (150)	...	0.002 (0.1)	53
53Co-30Cr-4.5W	(b)	89	65 (150)	...	0.002 (0.1)	53
53Co-30Cr-4.5W	Heat treated 4 h at 899 °C (1650 °F), furnace cooled. (b)	89	65 (150)	...	nil	53
Alloy 200	(c)	88	Boiling	24 h	0.31-0.34 (12.2-13.2)	101
Alloy 200	(c)	40	...	24 h	0.26-0.27 (10.3-10.5)	101
Alloy 400	(c)	88	Boiling	24 h	0.024-0.028 (0.97-1.1)	101
Alloy 400	(c)	40	...	24 h	0.038-0.068 (1.5-2.7)	101
Alloy 600	(c)	40	...	24 h	0.25 (10.0)	101
Alloy 625	(c)	88	Boiling	24 h	0.236-0.238 (9.3-9.4)	101
Alloy 625	(c)	40	...	24 h	0.17-0.19 (6.8-7.8)	101
Alloy 825	(c)	88	Boiling	24 h	0.064-0.08 (2.5-3.1)	101
Alloy 825	(c)	40	...	24 h	0.2 (7.9)	101
Alloy B-2	(c)	88	Boiling	24 h	0.00025-0.001 (0.01-0.04)	101
Alloy B-2	(c)	40	...	24 h	0.008-0.01 (0.31-0.40)	101
Alloy C-22	(c)	88	Boiling	24 h	0.023 (0.9)	101
Alloy C-276	(c)	88	Boiling	24 h	0.043-0.048 (1.7-1.9)	101
Alloy C-276	(c)	40	...	24 h	0.07-0.074 (2.8-2.9)	101
Alloy C-4	(c)	88	Boiling	24 h	0.05-0.076 (2.0-3.0)	101

(Continued)

Corrosion Behavior of Various Metals and Alloys in Formic Acid (Continued)

Material	Condition, other factors, comments	Concen-tration, %	Temperature, °C (°F)	Duration	Corrosion rate, mm/yr (mils/yr) or other	Ref
Alloy C-4	(c)	40	...	24 h	0.07-0.076 (2.9-3.0)	101
Alloy G	(c)	88	Boiling	24 h	0.099-0.12 (3.9-4.6)	101
Alloy G	(c)	40	...	24 h	0.013-0.0132 (5.0-5.2)	101
Alloy G-2	(c)	88	Boiling	24 h	0.05-0.067 (2.0-2.6)	101
Alloy G-3	(c)	88	Boiling	24 h	0.14-0.15 (5.4-5.9)	101
Alloy G-3	(c)	40	...	24 h	0.046-0.05 (1.8-2.1)	101
Cabot No. 625	Average of four 24-h periods	40	Boiling	24 h	0.19 (7.3)	67
Cabot No. 625	Average of four 24-h periods	88	Boiling	24 h	0.24 (9.3)	67
Carpenter Pyromet Alloy 102	Annealed	5	...	48 h	0.076 (3.04)	30
Carpenter Pyromet Alloy 102	Stress relieved at 843 °C (1550 °F) for ½ h, furnace cooled	5	...	48 h	0.076 (3.04)	30
Ferralium	...	20	Boiling	...	0.2 (6.5)	51
Hastelloy B-2	(d)	10	Boiling	...	<0.01 (0.3)	63
Hastelloy B-2	(d)	20	Boiling	...	<0.02 (0.6)	63
Hastelloy B-2	(d)	30	Boiling	...	<0.02 (0.7)	63
Hastelloy B-2	(d)	40	Boiling	...	<0.02 (0.7)	63
Hastelloy B-2	(d)	60	Boiling	...	<0.02 (0.5)	63
Hastelloy B-2	(d)	89	Boiling	...	<0.02 (0.5)	63
Hastelloy C-4	Unwelded. (d)	20	Boiling	...	0.07 (2.9)	68
Hastelloy C-4	As-welded. Gas tungsten arc welded. Values determined in laboratory tests. It is recommended that samples be tested under actual plant conditions	20	Boiling	...	0.09 (3.5)	68
Hastelloy C-4	Aged at 899 °C (1650 °F)	20	Boiling	100 h	0.09 (3.5)	68
Haynes No. 25	(e)	10	Room	24 h	nil	68
Haynes No. 25	(e)	20	Room	24 h	<0.01 (0.1)	68
Haynes No. 25	(e)	30	Room	24 h	...	68
Haynes No. 25	(e)	40	Room	24 h	<0.01 (0.1)	68
Haynes No. 25	(e)	60	Room	24 h	<0.01 (0.1)	68
Haynes No. 25	(e)	89	Room	24 h	<0.01 (0.1)	68
Haynes No. 25	(e)	10	66 (150)	24 h	nil	68
Haynes No. 25	(e)	20	66 (150)	24 h	<0.01 (0.1)	68
Haynes No. 25	(e)	30	66 (150)	24 h	...	68
Haynes No. 25	(e)	40	66 (150)	24 h	nil	68
Haynes No. 25	(e)	60	66 (150)	24 h	nil	68
Haynes No. 25	(e)	89	66 (150)	24 h	<0.01 (0.1)	68
Haynes No. 25	(e)	10	Boiling	24 h	0.20 (8.0)	68
Haynes No. 25	(e)	20	Boiling	24 h	0.25 (10)	68
Haynes No. 25	(e)	30	Boiling	24 h	...	68
Haynes No. 25	(e)	40	Boiling	24 h	0.38 (15)	68
Haynes No. 25	(e)	60	Boiling	24 h	0.51 (20)	68
Haynes No. 25	(e)	89	Boiling	24 h	0.15 (6.0)	68
Haynes No. 25	...	60	Boiling	...	0.61 (24)	23
Haynes alloy 6B	...	60	Boiling	...	1.22 (48)	23
Multimet	(e)	10	Room	24 h	nil	68
Multimet	(e)	20	Room	24 h	<0.01 (0.1)	68
Multimet	(e)	30	Room	24 h	...	68
Multimet	(e)	40	Room	24 h	<0.01 (0.1)	68
Multimet	(e)	60	Room	24 h	<0.01 (0.1)	68
Multimet	(e)	89	Room	24 h	nil	68
Multimet	(e)	10	66 (150)	24 h	nil	68
Multimet	(e)	20	66 (150)	24 h	<0.01 (0.1)	68
Multimet	(e)	30	66 (150)	24 h	...	68

(Continued)

Corrosion Behavior of Various Metals and Alloys in Formic Acid (Continued)

Material	Condition, other factors, comments	Concentration, %	Temperature, °C (°F)	Duration	Corrosion rate, mm/yr (mils/yr) or other	Ref
Multimet	(e)	40	66 (150)	24 h	nil	68
Multimet	(e)	60	66 (150)	24 h	<0.01 (0.1)	68
Multimet	(e)	89	66 (150)	24 h	nil	68
Multimet	(e)	10	Boiling	24 h	0.10 (4.0)	68
Multimet	(e)	20	Boiling	24 h	0.15 (6.0)	68
Multimet	(e)	30	Boiling	24 h	...	68
Multimet	(e)	40	Boiling	24 h	0.20 (8.0)	68
Multimet	(e)	60	Boiling	24 h	0.15 (6.0)	68
Multimet	(e)	89	Boiling	24 h	0.08 (3.0)	68
Nickel 200	Liquid in storage tank	90	Room	...	0.1 (4)	44
Nickel 200	Vapor in storage tank	90	Room	...	0.175 (7)	44
Nickel 200	Liquid in a still	90	100 (212)	...	0.45 (18)	44
Nickel 200	Vapor in a still	90	100 (212)	...	0.175 (7)	44
Nickel silver	...	18	...	...	Suitable	93
Lead, tin, and zinc						
Lead	Corrosion rate too high to merit any consideration of Pb	10-100	24-100 (75-212)	...	>1270 μm/yr (>50)	95
Tin	...	...	20 (68)	...	Unsuitable	94
Tin	...	...	60 (140)	...	Unsuitable	94
Tin	...	...	100 (212)	...	Unsuitable	94

(a) Laboratory tests in deaerated acid. (b) Cast specimen 38 mm x 25 mm x 6 mm (1.5 in. x 1 in. x 0.25 in.), 120-grit abrasive finish. Average of five 24-h periods. (c) Mill-annealed. Results based on four 24-h test periods. (d) Heat treated at 1066 °C (1950 °F), water quenched. Values determined in laboratory tests. It is recommended that samples be tested under actual plant conditions. (e) Twelve-gage, solution heat treated sheet. Calculated from a minimum of five 24-h periods. Values determined in laboratory tests. It is recommended that samples be tested under actual plant conditions.

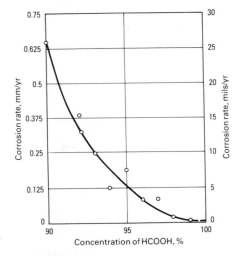

Aluminum alloy. Corrosion of aluminum alloy 5086 in formic acid at 45 °C (115 °F). Source: Chemical Processing Industry.

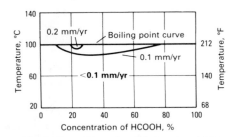

Nickel alloy. Corrosion of Hastelloy C in formic acid. Source: Haynes International.

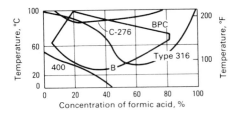

Nickel alloys. Isocorrosion curves (0.1 mm/yr, or 4 mils/yr) of various nickel-base alloys in formic acid. BPC, boiling point curve. Source: *Metals Handbook*, 9th ed., Vol 13, Corrosion, ASM International, Metals Park, OH, 1987, 649.

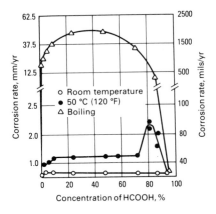

Aluminum alloy. Corrosion of aluminum alloy 1100-H14 in aqueous reagent grade formic acid solutions. Source: Chemical Processing Industry.

Gelatin

Gelatin, also known as glutin, is a protein found in many animal tissues including skin, cartilage, horn, and bone. Gelatin is used in leather dressings, in photography, in metallurgy, in the plastics industry, and in pharmaceuticals.

Material Summaries

The following material summaries were compiled from a survey of the available literature. Inclusion of a material description under a given environment does not imply that it is the most appropriate material for corrosion service in that environment. Likewise, exclusion of a given material does not imply that it is not suitable for corrosion service applications in that environment.

Aluminum. Aluminum alloys have excellent resistance to gelatin. In fact, aluminum is approved by the Pure Food and Drug Administration for use in the production of edible gelatin. Finished gelatin solutions are not handled in unprotected aluminum containers because of the corrosive presence of salt. Gelatin is obtained by the digestion of pork skins, calf skins, and animal bones in dilute solutions of phosphoric acid, hydrochloric acid, nitric acid, and sulfuric acid. The pH of the desired gelatin (pH ranges from 3 to 7) determines the concentration of the acid. The reaction occurs at 66 °C (150 °F) in aluminum vats. Aluminum alloy equipment has also been used in evaporators, piping, tubing, tanks, pumps, and conveyors.

Corrosion Behavior of Various Metals and Alloys in Gelatin

Material	Condition, other factors, comments	Concentration, %	Temperature, °C (°F)	Duration	Corrosion rate, mm/yr (mils/yr) or other	Ref
Stainless steels						
Type 304 stainless steel	Food processing; field or pilot plant test; no aeration; slight to moderate agitation. Plus <0.6% hydrochloric acid	...	13 (55)	11 d	0.0003 in./yr	89
Type 304 stainless steel	Food processing; field or pilot plant test; slight to moderate aeration; rapid agitation. Liquor, acidified with hydrochloric acid to pH 3.8-4.8	...	54-65 (130-150)	55 d	0.0001 in./yr	89
Type 304 stainless steel	Food processing; field or pilot plant test; slight to moderate aeration; rapid agitation. Evaporated. Plus 0.75% salts, acidified with hydrochloric acid to pH 3. Crevice attack (tendency to concentration-cell corrosion)	20-30	43 (110)	100 d	0.0004 in./yr	89
Type 316 stainless steel	Food processing; field or pilot plant test; no aeration; slight to moderate agitation. Plus <0.6% hydrochloric acid	...	13 (55)	11 d	0.0002 in./yr	89
Type 316 stainless steel	Food processing; field or pilot plant test; slight to moderate aeration; rapid agitation. Liquor, acidified with hydrochloric acid to pH 3.8-4.8	...	54-65 (130-150)	55 d	0.0001 in./yr	89
Type 316 stainless steel	Food processing; field or pilot plant test; slight to moderate aeration; rapid agitation. Evaporated. Plus 0.75% salts, acidified with hydrochloric acid to pH 3. Crevice attack (tendency to concentration-cell corrosion)	20-30	43 (110)	100 d	<0.0001 in./yr	89
Type 317 stainless steel	Food processing; field or pilot plant test; slight to moderate aeration; rapid agitation. Evaporated. Plus 0.75% salts, acidified with hydrochloric acid to pH 3. Crevice attack (tendency to concentration-cell corrosion)	20-30	43 (110)	100 d	<0.0001 in./yr	89
Coppers						
70-30 cupronickel	...	...	...	...	Suitable	93
90-10 cupronickel	...	...	...	...	Suitable	93
Admiralty brass	...	...	...	...	Suitable	93
Aluminum bronze	...	...	...	...	Suitable	93
Architectural bronze	...	...	...	...	Suitable	93
Brass	...	...	...	...	Suitable	93
Cartridge brass	...	...	...	...	Suitable	93
Commercial bronze	...	...	...	...	Suitable	93
Electrolytic copper	...	...	...	...	Suitable	93
Free-cutting brass	...	...	...	...	Suitable	93
Muntz metal	...	...	...	...	Suitable	93
Naval brass	...	...	...	...	Suitable	93
Nickel silver	...	18	...	...	Suitable	93
Phosphor bronze	5% Sn	...	...	...	Suitable	93
Phosphor bronze	8% Sn	...	...	...	Suitable	93

(Continued)

Corrosion Behavior of Various Metals and Alloys in Gelatin (Continued)

Material	Condition, other factors, comments	Concentration, %	Temperature, °C (°F)	Duration	Corrosion rate, mm/yr (mils/yr) or other	Ref
Phosphor copper	...	...	...	...	Suitable	93
Red brass	...	...	...	...	Suitable	93
Silicon bronze	Low	...	...	...	Suitable	93
Silicon bronze	High	...	...	...	Suitable	93
Lead, tin, and zinc						
Tin	...	...	20 (68)	...	Resistant	94
Tin	...	...	60 (140)	...	Resistant	94
Tin	...	...	100 (212)	...	Resistant	94
Noble metals						
Platinum	...	Pure	Boiling	...	<0.05 (<2)	6
Silver	...	Pure	Boiling	...	<0.05 (<2)	10
Others						
Magnesium	...	All	Room	...	Suitable	119

Gluconic Acid

Gluconic acid, $C_5H_6(OH)_5COOH$, also known as dextronic acid, is a white crystalline acid. It is obtained by the oxidation of glucose and is used in cleaning metals.

Corrosion Behavior of Various Metals and Alloys in Gluconic Acid

Material	Condition, other factors, comments	Concentration, %	Temperature, °C (°F)	Duration	Corrosion rate, mm/yr (mils/yr) or other	Ref
Stainless steels						
Type 304 stainless steel	Chemical processing; field or pilot plant test; no aeration; no agitation	50	43-66 (110-150)	99 d	<0.0001 in./yr	89
Type 304 stainless steel	Chemical processing; field or pilot plant test; pH 2 (evaporator, liquid level)	~50	60-66 (140-150)	99 d	<0.0001 in./yr	89
Type 316 stainless steel	Chemical processing; field or pilot plant test; pH 2 (evaporator, liquid level)	~50	60-66 (140-150)	99 d	<0.0001 in./yr	89
Type 316 stainless steel	Chemical processing; field or pilot plant test; no aeration; no agitation	50	43-66 (110-150)	99 d	<0.0001 in./yr	89
Others						
Silver	...	...	Boiling	...	<0.05 (<2)	4
Silver	...	All	Boiling	...	<0.05 (<2)	4
Titanium	...	50	Room	...	nil	90

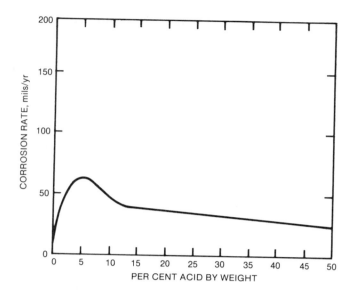

Aluminum. Effect of gluconic acid on alloy 1100 at 100 °C (212 °F). Source: *Guidelines for the Use of Aluminum with Food and Chemicals: Compatibility Data on Aluminum in the Food and Chemical Process Industries*, 5th ed., The Aluminum Association, Washington, DC, 1984, 33.

Glycerol

Glycerol, CH$_2$OHCHOHCH$_2$OH, also known as glycerin and glycyl alcohol, is a colorless nontoxic liquid with a sweet taste. It is the simplest trihydroxy alcohol and a valuable chemical intermediary. It is soluble in water and alcohol, but only partially soluble in ether and ethyl acetate. Glycerol is used in perfume and medicine, as an antifreeze, and in manufacturing soaps and explosives.

Material Summaries

The following material summaries were compiled from a survey of the available literature. Inclusion of a material description under a given environment does not imply that it is the most appropriate material for corrosion service in that environment. Likewise, exclusion of a given material does not imply that it is not suitable for corrosion service applications in that environment.

Cast Irons. Unalloyed cast irons can be used to handle glycerol, although slight discolorization of the glycerol may result. High-silicon cast irons also exhibit excellent resistance to glycerol.

Aluminum. Aluminum alloy 3003 is resistant to glycerol solutions at all temperatures in laboratory tests. Glycerol has been distilled, condensed, stored and shipped in aluminum alloy equipment. Aluminum alloy 356.0 valves have been used for handling glycerol.

Corrosion Behavior of Various Metals and Alloys in Glycerol

Material	Condition, other factors, comments	Concen-tration, %	Temperature, °C (°F)	Duration	Corrosion rate, mm/yr (mils/yr) or other	Ref
Stainless steels						
Type 304 stainless steel	Soap (distillation) processing; field or pilot plant test; slight to moderate aeration; rapid agitation. Concentrated glycerine saturated with salt, salt crystals. Slight pitting: maximum depth of pits from incipient to 0.005 in.; crevice attack (tendency to concentration-cell corrosion)	...	<160 (<320)	124 d	0.0079 in./yr	89
Type 304 stainless steel	Soap processing; field or pilot plant test; no aeration; no agitation. Glycerine saturated with salt (Wooster-Sanger evaporator). Severe pitting: maximum depth of pits over 0.010 in.; crevice attack (tendency to concentration-cell corrosion)	15-80	60-104 (140-220)	91 d	0.0003 in./yr	89

(Continued)

Corrosion Behavior of Various Metals and Alloys in Glycerol (Continued)

Material	Condition, other factors, comments	Concentration, %	Temperature, °C (°F)	Duration	Corrosion rate, mm/yr (mils/yr) or other	Ref
Type 316 stainless steel	Soap (distillation) processing; field or pilot plant test; slight to moderate aeration; rapid agitation. Concentrated glycerine saturated with salt, salt crystals. Moderate pitting: maximum depth of pits from 0.005 to 0.010 in.; crevice attack (tendency to concentration-cell corrosion)	...	<160 (<320)	124 d	0.0078 in./yr	89
Type 316 stainless steel	Soap processing; field or pilot plant test; no aeration; no agitation. Glycerine saturated with salt (Wooster-Sanger evaporator). Slight pitting: maximum depth of pits from incipient to 0.005 in.; crevice attack (tendency to concentration-cell corrosion)	15-80	60-104 (140-220)	91 d	0.0001 in./yr	89
Type 410 stainless steel	...	...	Room	...	Unattacked	121
Titanium						
Titanium	...	...	Room	...	nil	90
Heat- and corrosion-resistant alloys						
Alloy 825	Soap processing; field or pilot plant test; no aeration; no agitation. Glycerine saturated with salt (Wooster-Sanger evaporator). Crevice attack (tendency to concentration-cell corrosion)	15-80	60-104 (140-220)	91 d	<0.0001 in./yr	89
Carpenter 20	Soap processing; field or pilot plant test; no aeration; no agitation. Glycerine saturated with salt (Wooster-Sanger evaporator). Crevice attack (tendency to concentration-cell corrosion)	15-80	60-104 (140-220)	91 d	<0.0001 in./yr	89
Lead, tin, and zinc						
Lead	Practically resistant; Pb recommended for use	...	24 (75)	...	<500 μm/yr (<20)	95
Noble metals						
Gold	...	Pure	Boiling	...	<0.05 (<2)	7
Platinum	...	Pure	Boiling	...	<0.05 (<2)	6
Silver	...	Pure	Boiling	...	<0.05 (<2)	10
Others						
Magnesium	Chemically pure	100	Room	...	Suitable	119

Glycolic Acid

Glycolic acid, $CH_2OHCOOH$, also known as hydroxyacetic acid, is composed of colorless deliquescent leaflets that decompose at approximately 78 °C (172 °F). It is soluble in water, alcohol, and ether. Glycolic acid is used in dyeing, tanning, electropolishing, and in foodstuffs. It is produced by oxidizing glycol with dilute nitric acid.

Material Summaries

The following material summaries were compiled from a survey of the available literature. Inclusion of a material description under a given environment does not imply that it is the most appropriate material for corrosion service in that environment. Likewise, exclusion of a given material does not imply that it is not suitable for corrosion service applications in that environment.

Aluminum. Aluminum alloys 3003 and 5154 were reported to be attacked by glycolic acid at 100 °C (212 °F) in laboratory tests. Aluminum alloy containers have been used to ship and store glycolic acid solutions.

Corrosion Behavior of Various Metals and Alloys in Glycolic Acid

Material	Condition, other factors, comments	Concentration, %	Temperature, °C (°F)	Duration	Corrosion rate, mm/yr (mils/yr) or other	Ref
Zr702	...	...	40 (104)	...	<0.13 (<5)	15

Hydrobromic Acid

Hydrobromic acid, HBr, is a solution of hydrogen bromide in water, usually 40%. It is a strongly acidic liquid, which fumes when at a saturated concentration. Hydrobromic acid is used in medicine, analytical chemistry, and in the synthesis of alkyl and inorganic bromides. The bromides are usually soluble with the exception of the copper, gold, silver, mercury, lead, and thallium bromides and the heavy alkali ions with many bromo-complex anions.

Material Summaries

The following material summaries were compiled from a survey of the available literature. Inclusion of a material description under a given environment does not imply that it is the most appropriate material for corrosion service in that environment. Likewise, exclusion of a given material does not imply that it is not suitable for corrosion service applications in that environment.

Niobium. Niobium is resistant to hydrobromic acid at all concentrations and temperatures below 100 °C (212 °F).

Silver. The exposure of silver-lined reaction vessels to hydrobromic acid is limited to a concentration of 14% and room temperature.

Rhodium. In wrought or cast form, rhodium is attacked slowly at 100 °C (212 °F) by hydrobromic acid.

Tantalum. Tantalum is not attacked by hydrobromic acid or any of the bromides at ordinary temperatures.

Tin. Hot hydrobromic acid rapidly attacks tin.

Zirconium. Zirconium has good resistance against hydrobromic acid. Boiling hydrobromic acid in concentrations of 20, 45, and 48% registered corrosion rates of less than 0.13 mm/yr (5 mils/yr). Zirconium also exhibits a low pitting tendency in $1N$ hydrobromic acid.

Additional Reading

I. Uehara, T. Sakai, H. Ishikawa, E. Ishii, and M. Nakane, The Corrosion Behavior of Tantalum and Niobium in Hydrobromic Acid Solutions, *Corrosion, 42*(8), 492-499, 1986. MetAbs No. 86-352262. **Abstract:** The corrosion behavior of tantalum and niobium in hydrobromic acid solutions free from or containing bromine has been studied.

A. Frignani, G. Demertzis, and G. Trabanelli, Electrochemical Investigation of $Fe_{80}B_{20}$ Amorphous Alloy, *Mater. Chem. Phys., 16*(5-6), 569-574, 1987. MetAbs No. 87-352197. **Abstract:** The behavior of $Fe_{80}B_{20}$ amorphous alloy is compared to that of crystalline iron (Armco iron) in 0.1N HBr, HCl, $HClO_4$, and H_2SO_4.

Corrosion Behavior of Various Metals and Alloys in Hydrobromic Acid

Material	Condition, other factors, comments	Concentration, %	Temperature, °C (°F)	Duration	Corrosion rate, mm/yr (mils/yr) or other	Ref
Stainless steels						
Type 304 stainless steel	...	All	21 (70)	...	Poor	121
Type 304 stainless steel	Chemical processing (distillation); field or pilot plant test; no aeration; slight to moderate agitation. Various concentrations, decomposition products of ethylene dibromide. Severe pitting: maximum depth of pits over 0.010 in.; crevice attack (tendency to concentration-cell corrosion)	...	93-100 (200-212)	37 d	0.018 in./yr	89
Type 304 stainless steel	Chemical processing (distillation); field or pilot plant test; no aeration; no agitation. Plus hydrochloric acid, crude ethylene dibromide. Moderate pitting: maximum depth of pits from 0.005 to 0.010 in.; crevice attack (tendency to concentration-cell corrosion)	...	75 (168)	55 d	0.0274 in./yr	89
Type 316 stainless steel	Chemical processing (distillation); field or pilot plant test; no aeration; no agitation. Plus hydrochloric acid, crude ethylene dibromide. Moderate pitting: maximum depth of pits from 0.005 to 0.010 in.; crevice attack (tendency to concentration-cell corrosion)	...	75 (168)	55 d	0.0058 in./yr	89
Type 316 stainless steel	Chemical processing (distillation); field or pilot plant test; no aeration; slight to moderate agitation. Various concentrations, decomposition products of ethylene dibromide. Severe pitting: maximum depth of pits over 0.010 in.; crevice attack (tendency to concentration-cell corrosion)	...	93-100 (200-212)	37 d	0.018 in./yr	89
Type 316 stainless steel	...	All	21 (70)	...	Poor	121
Type 410 stainless steel	...	All	21 (70)	...	Poor	121
Type 430 stainless steel	...	All	21 (70)	...	Poor	121
Coppers						
70-30 cupronickel	...	...	...	...	Fair	93
90-10 cupronickel	...	...	...	...	Fair	93
Admiralty brass	...	...	...	...	Fair	93
		...	...	...	Fair	93

(Continued)

Corrosion Behavior of Various Metals and Alloys in Hydrobromic Acid (Continued)

Material	Condition, other factors, comments	Concen-tration, %	Temperature, °C (°F)	Duration	Corrosion rate, mm/yr (mils/yr) or other	Ref
	...	...	...	...	Fair	93
Aluminum bronze	...	...	...	...	Not suitable	93
Architectural bronze	...	...	...	...	Fair	93
Brass	...	...	...	...	Not suitable	93
Cartridge brass	...	...	...	...	Fair	93
Commercial bronze	...	...	...	...	Fair	93
Electrolytic copper	...	...	...	...	Not suitable	93
Free-cutting brass	...	...	...	...	Not suitable	93
Muntz metal	...	...	...	...	Not suitable	93
Naval brass	...	...	...	...	Fair	93
Nickel silver	...	18	...	...	Fair	93
Phosphor bronze	5% Sn	...	...	...	Fair	93
Phosphor bronze	8% Sn	...	...	...	Fair	93
Phosphor copper	...	...	...	...	Fair	93
Red brass	...	...	...	...	Fair	93
Silicon bronze	Low	...	...	...	Fair	93
Silicon bronze	High	...	...	...	Fair	93
Zirconium						
Zr702	BP 125 °C (257 °F); shallow pits	48	Boiling	...	<0.13 (<5)	15
Zr702	Plus 50% acetic acid (glacial)	24	Boiling	...	<0.025 (<1)	15
Zr705	BP 125 °C (257 °F); shallow pits	48	Boiling	...	<0.13 (<5)	15
Zr705	Plus 50% acetic acid (glacial)	24	Boiling	...	<0.025 (<1)	15
Lead, tin, and zinc						
Lead	Corrosion rate too high to merit any consideration of Pb	10-70	24 (75)	...	>1270 μm/yr (>50)	95
Tin	...	50	20 (68)	...	Unsuitable	94
Tin	...	50	60 (140)	...	Unsuitable	94
Tin	...	50	100 (212)	....	Unsuitable	94
Hafnium						
Hafnium	Pitting	40	...	10 d	0.025 (1.0)	11
Noble metals						
Gold	Specific gravity 1.7	...	Room	...	<0.05 (<2)	8
Iridium	Specific gravity 1.7	...	100 (212)	...	nil	29
Osmium	Specific gravity 1.7	...	100 (212)	...	1.8 (72)	17
Palladium	Fuming	...	Room	...	161.2 (6346)	17
Rhodium	Fuming	...	100 (212)	...	2.2 (87)	29
Ruthenium	...	62	100 (212)	...	nil	18
Silver	...	<14	Room	...	<0.05 (2)	4
Silver	...	<14	Room	...	<0.05 (<2)	4

Corrosion Rates of Tantalum and Niobium Exposed to Hydrogen-Bubbled 47 wt% Hydrobromic Acid Solutions

Temperature (C)	Test Period (Day)	Corrosion Rate			
		Tantalum		Niobium	
		(mdd)	(μm/y)	(mdd)	(μm/y)
50	8	ND[1]	ND	0.4 (ND)[2]	1.6 (ND)
50	14	ND	ND	0.3 (0.3)	1.2 (1.1)
75	8	ND	ND	2.9 (2.9)	12.2 (12.6)
100	8	1.0 (0.6)	2.2 (1.3)	18.3	77.7
100	14			14.4	61.2
124	8	1.6	3.5		
124	22	0.7	1.5		

(1) ND = not determined. (2) Values in parentheses represent the corrosion rates determined by analysis of the test solutions.
Source: I. Uehara, T. Sakai, *et al.,* The Corrosion Behavior of Tantalum and Niobium in Hydrobromic Acid Solutions, *Corrosion,* Vol 42, Aug 1986, 495.

Effects of Temperature and Bromine Concentrations on the Corrosion Rates of Tantalum and Niobium in 47 wt% Hydrobromic Acid Solutions

Temperature (C)	Test Period (Day)	Br_2 (mol/dm^3)	Corrosion Rate			
			Tantalum		Niobium	
			(mdd)	(μm/y)	(mdd)	(μm/y)
75	13	0.002	ND[1]		1.2 (1.2)[2]	4.9 (5.2)
75	13	0.021	ND		0.2 (0.5)	1.0 (2.0)
75	13	0.110	ND		0.2 (0.4)	0.6 (1.6)
100	8	0.002	0.3 (0.3)	0.5 (0.6)	2.6 (2.7)	11.2 (11.5)
100	8	0.008	ND		2.0 (2.0)	8.5 (8.4)
100	8	0.021	ND		1.9 (2.0)	8.0 (8.4)
100	9	> 0.5			1.0	4.3

(1) ND = not determined. (2) Values in parentheses represent the corrosion rates determined by analysis of the test solutions.
Source: I. Uehara, T. Sakai, *et al.,* The Corrosion Behavior of Tantalum and Niobium in Hydrobromic Acid Solutions, *Corrosion,* Vol 42, Aug 1986, 495.

Hydrochloric Acid

Hydrochloric acid, HCl, also known as muriatic acid, is a poisonous, corrosive, hazardous liquid that reacts with most metals to form explosive hydrogen gas and causes severe burns and irritation of eyes and mucous membranes. It is made by absorbing hydrogen chloride in water. Most acid is the by-product of chlorination. Pure acid is produced by burning chlorine and hydrogen. Hydrochloric acid is available in technical, recovered, food-processing, and reagent grades. Frequently, the commercial grades are slightly yellow as a result of impurities, notably dissolved iron. Reagent grade, which normally contains about 37.1% hydrochloric acid, is perfectly clear and colorless.

Hydrochloric acid is an important mineral acid with many uses, including acid pickling of steel, acid treatment of oil wells, chemical cleaning and processing, ore reduction, production of numerous chlorides, production of chlorine, and food processing.

Concentrated hydrochloric acid is transported and stored in rubber-lined tanks, although custom-fabricated polyester-reinforced thermoset plastic storage tanks have been used. Pipelines are usually plastic-lined steel. Processes involving aqueous acid are commonly carried out in glass-lined steel equipment. Nonmetallic materials are normally preferred because of the corrosive action of this strongest of acids on most metals.

Candidate metals and alloys for handling hydrochloric acid are judged to be those with corrosion rates under 0.5 mm/yr (20 mils/yr) when exposed to uncontaminated hydrochloric acid. In practice, contamination is not uncommon and can be catastrophic. Selection of a candidate metal should be based on extensive corrosion testing or, preferably, field experience, using the grade of acid that will be available.

Effect of Impurities. Hydrochloric acid recovered from the manufacture of fluorocarbons may contain trace amounts of hydrofluoric acid (HF). It has been reported that such acids may contain more than 0.5% HF. Commercial suppliers remove most of the fluoride from hydrochloric acid by selective absorption, and it is unlikely that a customer would receive acid containing as much as 0.5%, but glass-lined steel and the refractory metals, such as zirconium, niobium, tantalum, and titanium (but not molybdenum), have very low tolerance levels for fluorides. Zirconium is reported to tolerate less than 10 ppm. Tantalum may tolerate 10 ppm or more. The limits are undefined except for a few specific cases, and it is best to consider all of these metals and glass-lined steel to be essentially nonresistant to fluorides and to know the source and specification limits of the acid if these materials are used. Other species that can be oxidizing include palladium and cobalt.

The presence of ferric ions in hydrochloric acid has a profound effect on the corrosion of many metals and alloys otherwise resistant to hydrochloric acid. Nickel-base alloys, including Hastelloy B-2, the copper alloys, and unalloyed zirconium, are affected. Although the acid specification may be low in iron, acid can easily become contaminated during shipment and handling. The presence of nitric acid will result in high corrosion rates of low-chromium alloys such as Hastelloy C-276 and B-2.

Cupric ions have an accelerating effect on the corrosion of many metals that is similar to that of ferric ions. Like ferric ions, cupric ions can cause pitting and stress-corrosion cracking of zirconium. The presence of cupric ions can also lead to the autocatalytic acceleration of nickel-copper and copper-nickel alloys. It is unlikely that commercial acid would contain cupric salts. This is more of a problem of in-process contamination by exposure of copper-containing metals or introduction as an impurity in a chemical or raw material used in the process.

Aeration. Although less damaging than the presence of oxidizing metal salts, aeration accelerates the corrosion of many metals.

Chlorine. Contamination accelerates the corrosion of all metals except unalloyed tantalum and noble metals; however, unalloyed titanium can be protected by the presence of chlorine in dilute hydrochloric acid. Chlorine may be present in acid recovered from a chlorination process, but it would be removed before commercial sale.

Material Summaries

The following material summaries were compiled from a survey of the available literature. Inclusion of a material description under a given environment does not imply that it is the most appropriate material for corrosion service in that environment. Likewise, exclusion of a given material does not imply that it is not suitable for corrosion service applications in that environment.

Cast Irons. Use of cast irons is relatively limited in hydrochloric acid. Unalloyed cast iron is unsuitable for any hydrochloric acid service. Rapid corrosion occurs at a pH of 5 or lower, particularly if appreciable velocity is involved. Aeration or oxidizing conditions, such as the presence of metallic salts, result in rapid destructive attack of unalloyed cast irons even in very dilute hydrochloric acid solutions.

High-nickel austenitic cast irons offer some resistance to all hydrochloric acid concentrations at room temperature or below. High-chromium cast irons are not suitable for hydrochloric acid service.

High-silicon cast irons offer the best resistance to hydrochloric acid of any cast iron. When alloyed with 4 to 5% Cr, high-silicon cast iron is suitable for all concentrations of hydrochloric acid to 28 °C (80 °F). When high-silicon cast iron is alloyed with chromium, molybdenum, and higher silicon levels, the temperature for use can be increased. A high-silicon iron alloyed with small amounts of molybdenum, chromium, and copper has good resistance to all concentrations of hydrochloric acid up to temperatures as high as 95 °C (200 °F). It is one of the few metals commonly used for pumps and valves in handling commercial grades of acid. In concentrations up to 20%, ferric ions or other oxidizing agents inhibit corrosion attack on high-silicon iron alloyed with chromium. At over 20% acid concentration, oxidizers accelerate attack on the alloy. As in sulfuric acid, corrosion rates in high-silicon cast iron are initially high in the first 24 to 48 h of exposure then decrease to very low steady-state rates. Fluoride impurities are damaging.

Carbon and alloy steels are unsuitable for exposure to hydrochloric acid except during acid cleaning. Repeated acid cleaning of carbon steel is likely to result in significant pitting. Hardened alloy steels are subject to hydrogen embrittlement. This problem is aggravated by corrosion inhibitors, because they generally suppress the cathodic reaction, promoting atomic hydrogen absorption rather than molecular hydrogen evolution. Therefore, the jackets of glass-lined vessels should not be cleaned with hydrochloric (or sulfuric) acid to avoid hydrogen spalling.

Stainless Steels. The commonly used austenitic stainless steels, such as types 304 and 316, are not resistant to hydrochloric acid at any concentration and temperature. At ambient temperatures and above, corrosion rates are high. Nickel, molybdenum, and to a lesser extent copper impart some resistance to dilute acid, but pitting, local attack, and stress-corrosion cracking may result. Subambient temperatures will slow the corrosion rate, but will invite stress-corrosion cracking. Type 316 stainless steel has been known to crack in 5% hydrochloric acid at 0 °C (32 °F). At high corrosion rates (>0.25 mm/yr, or 10 mils/yr), stress-corrosion cracking is unlikely to occur. However, the corrosion products, particularly $FeCl_3$, will cause cracking. Chlorides can penetrate and destroy the passivity (oxide film) that is responsible for the corrosion resistance of stainless steels, and the corrosion engineer should resist every attempt to use stainless steels in environments containing chlorides.

The standard ferritic stainless steels, such as types 410 and 430, should not be considered, because their corrosion resistance to hydrochloric acid is lower than that of carbon steel. An exception is 29-4-2 stainless steel, which reportedly resists up to 1.5% hydrochloric acid to the boiling point and remains passive. However, it is not suitable at higher concentrations, and the alloy is susceptible to stress-corrosion cracking, although its resistance is reported to be high.

Some stainless steels—such as 20Cb-3, with its high nickel content (32 to 38%), 2 to 3% Mo, and 3 to 4% Cu—resist dilute hydrochloric acid at ambient temperatures. However, 20Cb-3 is susceptible to pitting and crevice attack in acid chlorides and should be used with caution.

Corrosion studies of sintered austenitic stainless steels have shown that the corrosion resistance improves significantly with increasing density in acidic environments such as dilute hydrochloric acid.

Aluminum is corroded by hydrochloric acid. The rate of attack increases with acid concentration and temperature. Metal purity plays a significant role in the degree of attack by hydrochloric acid. Increasing purity of the aluminum decreases the rate of attack by hydrochloric acid significantly. Inhibitors can be effective in reducing the corrosive effects of hydrochloric acid, particularly in dilute (<10%) solutions. Such inhibited acid has been used to clean aluminum equipment and containers.

Cemented Carbides. The corrosion rates of various cemented carbide compositions in warm (50 °C, or 120 °F) acids were investigated. From the rates observed for straight WC-Co compositions in hydrochloric acid, even though lower than the rates in H_2SO_4 and HNO_3, it was obvious that these compositions are not suitable for use in warm or hot hydrochloric acid solutions. The TiC-6.5Ni-5Mo composition exhibited moderately good resistance to hydrochloric acid, and several of the binderless compositions and a TaC-base cemented carbide exhibited very acceptable resistance.

Copper and copper alloys have limited utility in hydrochloric acid service (dilute concentrations only) because they are so sensitive to velocity, aeration, and oxidizing impurities. However, copper is one of the few common metals above hydrogen in the electromotive force (emf) series, and under reducing conditions, it can experience low corrosion rates. An example is the use of silicon bronze (CDA C65500) agitators and hardware in the manufacture of $ZnCl_2$ by dissolving zinc in hydrochloric acid, with the evolution of hydrogen.

Typical corrosion rates for silicon bronze in hydrochloric acid under nonaerated nonoxidizing conditions are 0.08 to 0.1 mm/yr (3 to 4 mils/yr) in up to 20% acid and 0.5 mm/yr (20 mils/yr) in concentrated acid at 25 °C (75 °F). At 70 °C (160 °F), rates are approximately 1 mm/yr (40 mils/yr) in up to 20% acid and over 6.4 mm/yr (250 mils/yr) in concentrated (35 to 37%) acid.

Aluminum bronzes are generally suitable for service in hydrochloric acid. Phosphor bronzes, although they are resistant to most nonoxidizing acids, are not suitable for hydrochloric acid service.

The corrosion rate of copper nickels in 2N hydrochloric acid at 25 °C (75 °F) may range from 2.3 to 7.6 mm/yr (90 to 300 mils/yr), depending on the degree of aeration and other factors. Specimens of C71000 (copper nickel, 20%) in stagnant 1% hydrochloric acid solutions at room temperature corrode at a rate of 305 μm/yr (12 mils/yr); in 10% hydrochloric acid, the rate is 790 μm/yr (31 mils/yr).

Lead has fair corrosion resistance to dilute hydrochloric acid (up to 15%) at 24 °C (75 °F); the corrosion rate increases at higher concentrations and at higher temperatures. The presence of 5% ferric chloride also accelerates corrosion. The corrosion rates of chemical lead and 6% antimonial lead in hydrochloric acid are retarded by the presence of H_2SO_4.

Metallic Glasses. The first published information on the corrosion behavior of metallic glasses, which appeared in 1974, concerned the Fe-Cr-P-C alloy system. A comparison was made of the corrosion rates of $Fe_{70}Cr_{10}P_{13}C_7$ and $Fe_{65}Cr_{10}Ni_5P_{13}C_7$ metallic glasses and a typical AISI type 304 stainless steel in hydrochloric acid of various concentrations at 30 °C (85 °F). The corrosion rates, calculated from gravimetric measurements, were relatively large for the stainless steel because of pitting attack, but the rates for the metallic glasses were so low that they could not be detected even after immersion for 168 h. This early work illuminates the distinct differences in corrosion behavior between crystalline stainless steel and iron-base metal-metalloid glasses.

A study was done comparing the corrosion rates of crystalline Fe-Cr alloys and amorphous Fe-Cr-P-C alloys in hydrochloric acid as a function of chromium concentration. At low chromium levels, the amorphous alloy corroded at a higher rate than the crystalline material. However, at slightly higher chromium levels (4 at.%), there was a significant decrease in the corrosion rate of the glassy alloy, but the crystalline material remained essentially unchanged. At an intermediate level of 8 at.% Cr, no corrosion of the glassy alloy was detected by weight loss experiments after immersion for 168 h. It was also found that the concentration of hydrochloric acid, which has a profound effect on corrosion behavior of crystalline alloys, had no effect on corrosion of the glassy Fe-Cr-P-C or Fe-Ni-Cr-P-C alloy systems, which exhibited no weight loss after exposure for 168 h.

The effect of chromium concentration on the corrosion behavior of amorphous iron-, nickel-, and cobalt-base alloys in 1N hydrochloric acid was investigated. In all cases, the corrosion rate decreased with increasing chromium concentration. In addition, the Fe-Cr-P-C alloy system, which exhibited the highest corrosion rate at low chromium contents, experienced no weight loss in immersion tests with a chromium concentration of as little as 8 at.%. Glassy $Fe_{73}Cr_7P_{15}B_5$ passivated spontaneously in 1N hydrochloric acid. Surface analysis by x-ray photoelectron spectroscopy showed that chromium and phosphorus were enriched and that nickel became depleted in the alloy substrate beneath the passive film.

The tendency of glassy $Fe_{40}Ni_{40}P_{14}B_6$ to undergo stress-corrosion cracking and hydrogen embrittlement in acidic electrolytes was studied. Elastically stressed specimens cathodically polarized in 1M hydrochloric acid failed by hydrogen embrittlement, whereas specimens anodically polarized in 1M hydrochloric acid failed by stress-corrosion cracking. These specimens were covered by an iron oxide film, and selective leaching (dealloying) of nickel from pits and cracks occurred.

Molybdenum increases the pitting resistance of glassy alloys and crystalline steels in hydrochloric acid. Addition of molybdenum to glassy $Fe-Mo-xP_{13}C_7$ alloys suppresses pitting and decreases the critical current density for passivation and the passive current density. As little as 4 at.% Mo prevents pitting in 1N hydrochloric acid, and small additions of molybdenum are more effective than chromium in decreasing corrosion rates.

Nickel. Commercially pure nickel (Nickel 200 and 201) and nickel-copper alloys (Monel 400) have room-temperature corrosion rates below 0.25 mm/yr (10 mils/yr) in air-free hydrochloric acid at concentrations up to 10%. In hydrochloric acid concentrations of less that 0.5%, these alloys have been used at temperatures up to about 200 °C (390 °F). Monel 400 has been used at concentrations below 20% at ambient temperatures under air-free conditions and under 10% concentration aerated, but penetration rates generally exceed 0.25 mm/yr (10 mils/yr) and may approach 1 mm/yr (40 mils/yr). Oxidizing agents, such as cupric and chromate ions, or aeration, increase the corrosion rate considerably. Under these conditions nickel-chromium-molybdenum alloys such as Inconel 625 or Hastelloy C-276 offer better corrosion resistance. They can be passivated by the presence of oxidizing agents.

Increasing the temperature affects the corrosion rate of Nickel 200 more than that of Monel 400 in 5% hydrochloric acid. When hydrochloric acid is formed by hydrolysis of chlorinated hydrocarbons, acid concentrations are often less than 0.5%. Under these conditions, Nickel 200 and Monel 400 have found application at temperatures below 200 °C (390 °F).

Inconel 600, although it has useful resistance to cold dilute hydrochloric acid, exhibits corrosion resistance that is inferior to that of Nickel 200 and Monel 400. However, this alloy is useful in handling wet halogenated solvents, because it has little, if any, catalytic effect on hydrolysis.

Inconel 825, Hastelloy G, and Inconel 625 contain appreciable amounts of chromium and increasing amounts of molybdenum, and they have useful resistance to all concentrations of hydrochloric acid below 40 °C

(100 °F). Inconel 625 has good resistance to concentrated reagent-grade acid at ambient temperatures.

These alloys have good resistance to dilute (<5%) acid at higher temperatures and are less affected by aeration than Nickel 200 and Monel 400. They are all very resistant to chloride stress-corrosion cracking. Resistance to pitting and crevice corrosion in acid chloride solutions improves with increasing chromium and molybdenum contents. Thus, Inconel 625 (22Cr-9Mo) is more resistant than Hastelloy G (22Cr-6.5Mo), which in turn is more resistant than Inconel 825 (21Cr-3Mo).

The most corrosion resistant of the nickel-base alloys to hydrochloric acid are Hastelloy B-2 (Ni-28Mo) and Hastelloy C-276 (Ni-16Cr-15.5Mo). Hastelloy B-2 is one of the few metals with a corrosion rate under 0.5 mm/yr (20 mils/yr) in all concentrations and at temperatures up to the atmospheric boiling point in nonaerated acid in the absence of oxidizing agents.

Accordingly, this alloy is used in a variety of processes involving hot hydrochloric acid or nonoxidizing chloride salts that are hydrolyzed to produce hydrochloric acid. Hastelloy B-2 experiences two isocorrosion curves—one at high temperatures near the boiling point and one at low temperature. This is due to variations in the oxygen content of the solutions. At the higher temperatures, the oxygen solubility is lower, and therefore, the corrosion rate is lower. The major weakness of the alloy is that its corrosion resistance decreases dramatically under oxidizing conditions. Chromium-containing alloys such as Hastelloy C-276 or Inconel 625 can be passivated when oxidizers are present and thus display much lower corrosion rates.

Hastelloy C-276 has excellent corrosion resistance (<0.13 mm/yr, or 5 mils/yr) in all concentrations of hydrochloric acid at room temperatures and good resistance (<0.5 mm/yr, or 20 mils/yr) to all concentrations up to 50 °C (120 °F). At concentrations under 10%, its resistance often exceeds that of Hastelloy B-2. Oxygen and strong oxidizing agents accelerate corrosion, although markedly less than for Hastelloy B-2.

Niobium is resistant to hydrochloric acid in all concentrations at temperatures below 100 °C (212 °F).

Gold. Refined gold is extremely resistant to all concentrations of hydrochloric acid at temperatures up to and above the atmospheric boiling point.

Iridium, although resistant to anodic corrosion in aqueous electrolytes, may be attacked in aqueous hydrochloric acid (and potassium cyanide) under the action of an alternating current.

Osmium is resistant to hydrochloric acid.

Palladium is readily corroded anodically in hydrochloric acid solutions. However, palladium alloys containing more than 20% gold are resistant to hydrochloric acid.

Platinum. Refined platinum is almost as resistant to hydrochloric acid as gold. It is slightly attacked by 36% acid at 100 °C (212 °F), the point at which gold shows no appreciable attack. A 10% addition of rhodium to platinum reduces the corrosion rate in 36% hydrochloric acid at 100 °C from 0.2 mm/yr (50 mils/yr) to zero. As an anode, platinum will resist attack in a wide variety of alkaline, neutral, and mildly acidic solutions, but is attacked by strong solutions.

Rhodium. In wrought or cast form, rhodium remains unattacked at 100 °C (212 °F) by concentrated hydrochloric acid.

Silver forms a protective chloride film in hydrochloric acid and thus is resistant to this acid as long as the film is not dissolved or disturbed. Results can be unsatisfactory under strongly aerating conditions when acid concentration and temperature are increased. At ambient temperatures, in the absence of oxidizing agents, silver resists hydrochloric acid in all concentrations, exhibiting a corrosion rate of less than 0.025 mm/yr (<1 mil/yr) at concentrations of 20% or lower. At the boiling point, corrosion rates vary from 0.025 mm/yr (1 mil/yr) at 5% to 0.5 mm/yr (20 mils/yr) at 20%. Increases in temperature, aeration, and velocity will increase corrosion rates.

Tantalum and its alloys are the most resistant to hydrochloric acid. Specific corrosion tests and many industrial applications show that tantalum is completely inert to hydrochloric acid in all concentrations under atmospheric pressure to at least 90 °C (195 °F). This has been demonstrated by long industrial experience. For example, bayonet heaters fabricated from tantalum with a wall thickness as thin as 0.33 mm (0.013 in.) have been in continuous industrial use in hydrochloric acid distilling units for over 20 years without being attacked.

Tantalum resists concentrations below 25% up to 190 °C (375 °F) and concentrations to 37% at temperatures to 150 °C (300 °F). It was found that tantalum is embrittled by concentrations of 25% or higher at 190 °C (375 °F). Corrosion rates at that temperature were less than 0.025 mm/yr (<1 mil/yr) at 25% concentration or less, 0.01 mm/yr (3.9 mils/yr) at 30%, and 0.29 mm/yr (11.6 mils/yr) at 37%. Embrittlement was most pronounced in 37% acid. It also was found that corrosion and embrittlement could be avoided by coupling tantalum with platinum. This discovery formed the basis for the later development of the titanium-palladium alloy. The possibility of hydrogen embrittlement should be considered whenever tantalum is used for handling concentrated solutions of hydrochloric acid above the boiling point of the acid. This tendency was not noted at or below the boiling point.

Additions of HNO_3 and ferric or cupric chlorides ($FeCl_3$ or $CuCl_2$) to hydrochloric acid tend to improve corrosion resistance of tantalum. Tantalum, like zirconium and titanium, is embrittled by the absorption of atomic hydrogen. This occurs if the metal is corroded in a nonoxidizing chemical or if it becomes the cathode of an electrolytic cell. For example, it is possible to embrittle tantalum plugs in a glass-lined vessel, if the vessel is equipped with an agitator of a metal lower in the emf series.

Researchers in other tests also found that tantalum and substitutional tantalum-base alloys became hydrogen embrittled in concentrated hydrochloric acid at 150 °C (300 °F). Corrosion rates of Ta-Nb alloys were conducted in hot and cold concentrated hydrochloric acid on alloys having various proportions of tantalum and niobium. The corrosion rate increased roughly in proportion to the niobium content of the alloy. Even though the 95Ta-5Nb alloy exhibited excellent resistance in all exposures, the attack was three times that obtained on pure tantalum.

The corrosion behavior of alloys in the Ti-Ta-Nb system in 5% hydrochloric acid at 100 °C (212 °F) was investigated. The corrosion rate dropped by a factor of 1.5 to 2 times less than that of titanium, with a total of 15 to 20% Nb or Ta in the alloy. At 20 to 30% additions of these elements, the corrosion rate dropped by a factor of 10 to 70 times less than that of titanium. Tantalum increased the corrosion resistance of the alloys more effectively than niobium.

The role of the structural factor in increasing the corrosion resistance of the titanium-tantalum-chromium and titanium-chromium alloys in a 5% hydrochloric acid solution at 100 °C (212 °F) was demonstrated. The corrosion rate of quenched alloys was 2 to 10 times or more lower than that of annealed alloys. As the tantalum content increases, the corrosion rate decreases for both quenched and annealed alloys. The ternary alloys with a tantalum to chromium ratio of 3:1 and binary titanium-tantalum alloys with 20% more tantalum were found to have good corrosion resistance.

Titanium. Although titanium has limited resistance to hydrochloric acid, it is, unlike other metals, passivated rather than corroded by the presence of dissolved oxygen, ferric and cupric ions, nitrates, chromates, chlorine, and other oxidizing impurities. In commercial applications involving hot dilute acid, enough impurities are often present to provide a high degree of protection. For example, the corrosion rate of unalloyed titanium in boiling 4% hydrochloric acid was lowered from 21.4 mm/yr (843 mils/yr) to 0.01 mm/yr (0.4 mils/yr) by the addition of 0.2% $FeCl_3$. No titanium alloy has resistance to concentrated grades of hydrochloric acid.

Zirconium. The resistance of zirconium to corrosion by hydrochloric acid exceeds that of most metals (exceptions are tantalum and such noble metals as gold and platinum). Corrosion rates are less that 0.13 mm/yr (5 mils/yr) at all concentrations up to the atmospheric boiling point and above, and aeration does not have an appreciable effect. Moreover, zirconium is not as susceptible to hydrogen embrittlement in hydrochloric acid as tantalum. In one study, tantalum lost 33% and 18% of its ductility after 1000 h in 11M hydrochloric acid and 11M hydrochloric acid + 7% gallium chloride ($GaCl_3$), respectively, at 70 °C (160 °F). Under the same testing conditions, zirconium remained unattacked and retained 100% of its ductility.

Although hydrochloric acid is highly reducing, the anodic polarization curves of zirconium still do not have the active region. This corrosion property explains the resistance of zirconium to crevice corrosion in chloride-containing environments. However, zirconium can suffer pitting and/or stress-corrosion cracking when it is anodically polarized to a potential at or exceeding the pitting potentials. The same types of corrosion problems can be developed in hydrochloric acid when strong oxidizing ions, such as ferric ions, are present. The presence of ferric ions polarizes the zirconium surface to a potential exceeding the pitting potential. Thus, local breakdown of the passive surface at preferred sites occurs, and a condition develops that favors pitting and/or cracking. Maintaining zirconium at a potential in its passive region (arbitrarily set at 50 to 100 mV below the corrosion potential) can counteract the detrimental effects resulting from the presence of ferric ions.

It is important to avoid galvanic effects when connecting zirconium to other metals immersed in an electrolyte, because zirconium, like all the reactive metals, is sensitive to hydrogen embrittlement when it is the cathode of an electrochemical cell.

Hafnium is resistant to dilute hydrochloric acid.

Additional Reading

W. Chu, Y. Wang, and C. Hsiao, Research of Hydrogen-Induced Cracking and Stress Corrosion Cracking in an Aluminum Alloy, *Corrosion*, 38(11), 561-570, 1982. MetAbs No. 83-350292. **Abstract:** For a high-strength Al alloy (7075, LC4), the dynamic processes of nucleation and propagation of hydrogen-induced delayed cracking of a charged and modified WOL specimen were followed metallographically.

I.J. Lefever and S.R. Saunders, Corrosion Behavior of Porous Sintered Metal Fibre Structures, *Bull. Cercle Etud. Metaux*, 14(19), 8-1 to 8-10, 1982. MetAbs No. 83-350508. **Abstract:** Synopsis of paper presented at the 21st Journees des Aciers Speciaux, St-Etienne, France, Apr. 1982. Porous sheets made from 12-22 μm diameter fibres of a stainless steel or some Ni-base alloys were exposed to combustion gases containing SO_2 and HCl.

M.D. Archer and R.J. McKim, The Stress Corrosion Behavior of Glassy Fe-40Ni-20B Alloy in Aqueous Acidic Media, *Corrosion*, 39(3), 91-98, 1983. MetAbs No. 83-351274. **Abstract:** The stress-corrosion behavior of commercially available glassy Fe-40 at.% Ni-20 at.% B alloy was investigated. Constant strain testing was carried out in aqueous solutions

of ferric chloride, polythionic acid and hydrochloric acid. Weight loss and selective dissolution experiments at the free corrosion potential and linear polarization studies were also performed.

N. Bui, A. Irhzo, R. Dabosi, and Y. Limouzin-Maire, On the Mechanism for Improved Passivation by Additions of Tungsten to Austenitic Stainless Steels, *Corrosion*, 39(12), 491-496, 1983. MetAbs No. 84-350836. **Abstract:** To elucidate the role of tungsten in improving the passivity of austenitic stainless steels, anodic polarization curves and X-ray photoelectron spectra have been obtained for pure W and W-containing steels passivated in 1N HCl, 0.1M NaCl and in Cl⁻ containing H_3PO_4.

J.P. Frayret, A. Caprani, H. Luc, and F. Priem, The Influence of Alloying Elements on the Electrochemical Behavior of Titanium: A Study of Two Commercial Alloys (TU$_2$, TA$_6$ V) in Hydrochloric Acid, *Corrosion*, 40(1), 14-21, 1984. MetAbs No. 84-351091. **Abstract:** Stationary behavior is investigated by plotting the stationary polarization curves (I, V) and by examination of the dissolution morphology with scanning microscopy.

J.D. Talati, G.A. Patel, and D.K. Gandhi, Maximum Utilization Current Density in Cathodic Protection. I. Aluminum in Acid Media, *Corrosion*, 40(2), 88-92, 1984. MetAbs No. 84-351165. **Abstract:** Cathodic protection of Al alloy AA 2017 (Al-4% Cu) in 2.5M HCl containing various dyes and of AA 2017 and AA 3003 (Al-1.3% Mn) in 2.0M trichloroacetic acid containing various amines as inhibitors has been studied.

J.P. Carter, B.S. Covino Jr., T.J. Driscoll, W. Riley, and M. Rosen, Gaseous Corrosion of Metals in a 60% H_2O, 40% HCl Environment, *Corrosion*, 40(5), 205-214, 1984. MetAbs No. 84-351925. **Abstract:** Laboratory tests were conducted on Co-base alloys for 15 days in a 60 vol.% H_2O, 40 vol.% HCl gaseous mixture. Two alloys were also exposed for a period of 66 days. Field tests were conducted in a rotary calciner and a fluidized bed decomposer using the more resistant alloys from the laboratory tests.

M.M. Hefny, A.G. Gad Allah, S.A. Salih, and M.S. El-Basiouny, Nature of the Corrosion Reaction at the Anodic Oxide Film on Titanium in HCl Solutions, *Corrosion*, 40(5), 245-249, 1984. MetAbs No. 84-351928. **Abstract:** The corrosion of the anodically formed oxide film on Ti has been studied in HCl solutions after the flow of the forming current ceases.

T.L. Yau and M. Maguire, Electrochemical Protection of Zirconium in Oxidizing Hydrochloric Acid Solutions, *Corrosion*, 40(6), 289-296, 1984. MetAbs No. 84-352377. **Abstract:** An electrochemical protection technique using cathodic polarization to maintain Zr below its critical repassivation potential was used to avoid pitting and stress corrosion cracking in hydrochloric acid containing ferric ions. Corrosion and pit penetration rates are reported for pickled, abraded and as-received surface conditions in 10, 20 and 37% HCl containing 50, 100 or 500 ppm Fe^{+3} at temperatures up to boiling.

W.M. Moore, C.T. Chen, and G.A. Shirn, A Voltammetric Investigation of A.C. Corrosion Phenomena at an Aluminum Electrode in Hydrochloric Acid, *Corrosion*, 40(12), 644-649, 1984. MetAbs No. 85-350469. **Abstract:** The electrochemical behavior of 99.999% pure Al in HCl has been studied by cyclic voltammetry, square-wave chronoamperometry and square-wave chronopotentiometry. High-speed cyclic voltammetry was studied thoroughly, and the effects of temperature, HCl concentration, potential sweep rate and cathodic potential limit were examined.

J.Y. Mui, Corrosion Mechanism of Metals and Alloys in the Silicon-Hydrogen-Chlorosilane System at 500 °C, *Corrosion*, 41(2), 63-69, 1985. MetAbs No. 85-350637. **Abstract:** To determine suitable materials of construction for a high-pressure fluidized-bed reactor and to develop a basic understanding of the corrosion mechanism of alloys and metals in a hydrochlorination reaction environment, selected materials were studied.

A. Handa, J. Kobayashi, and Y. Ujihira, Formation and Analysis of Corrosion Products Deposited on Steel Under HCl Atmosphere by Means of Conversion Electron Mossbauer Spectrometry at Room Temperature and 80K, *Appl. Surf. Sci.*, 20(4), 581-593, 1985. MetAbs No. 85-351755. **Abstract:** A conversion electron Mossbauer spectrometer, which allows measurement to be performed at low temperatures (80 K), was fabricated using a ceramic electron multiplier. It was used to discriminate the CEM spectrum of beta-FeOOH from gamma-FeOOH which were produced on steel (SM50 and SPCC-D) surfaces as corrosion products following exposure of steel in an air-HCl-H_2O atmosphere.

F. Zucchi and I.H. Omar, Plant Extracts as Corrosion Inhibitors of Mild Steel in HCl Solutions, *Surf. Technol.*, 24(4), 391-399, 1985. MetAbs No. 85-351811. **Abstract:** The effects of various plant extracts on the dissolution of mild steel in HCl solutions were studied. The additives investigated were Papaia, Poinciana pulcherrima, Cassia occidentalis and Datura stramonium seeds and Papaia, Calotropis procera B, Azydracta indica and Auforpio turkiale sap.

R.C. Newman, The Dissolution and Passivation Kinetics of Stainless Alloys Containing Molybdenum. I. Coulometric Studies of Fe-Cr and Fe-Cr-Mo Alloys, *Corros. Sci.*, 25(5), 331-339, 1985. MetAbs No. 85-351904. **Abstract:** The evolution of active current density with time has been measured on new surfaces of Fe-Cr and Fe-Cr-1.5 at.% Mo alloys. The solutions used were $1M$ and $4M$ HCl.

S.H. Sanad, H. Abbas, A.A. Ismail, and K.M. El-Sobki, Benzotriazole as a Corrosion Inhibitor for Brass, *Surf. Technol.*, 25(1), 39-48, 1985. MetAbs No. 85-352057. **Abstract:** The effect of benzotriazole on the corrosion of 67/33, 70/30, and 90/10 brasses in $0.1N$ HCl, $0.1N$ H_2SO_4 and $0.1N$ NH_4Cl was studied by means of immersion tests and galvanostatic measurements.

W.H. Smyrl, Digital Impedance for Faradaic Analysis. II. Electrodissolution of Copper in HCl, *J. Electrochem. Soc.*, 132(7), 1555-1562, 1985. MetAbs No. 85-352067. **Abstract:** The electrodissolution of Cu was studied experimentally by both steady-state and impedance (DIFA) techniques on a rotating disk.

W.H. Smyrl and L.L. Stephenson, Digital Impedance for Faradaic Analysis. III. Copper Corrosion in Oxygenated 0.1N HCl, *J. Electrochem. Soc.*, 132(7), 1563-1567, 1985. MetAbs No. 85-352068. **Abstract:** Impedance measurements have been made on Cu rotating disks corroding in oxygenated $0.1N$ HCl. A model is developed for the faradaic impedance of a corrosion couple consisting of an anodic dissolution reaction dominated by convective diffusion and a cathodic reaction under kinetic control.

Y.G. Kim, G.W. Yoon, and N.S. Stoloff, Effect of Boron on the Corrosion Behavior of Polycrystalline Ni_3Al, *Metall. Trans. A*, 16A(11), 2072-2073, 1985. MetAbs No. 85-352341. **Abstract:** The effects of boron additions on the corrosion behavior of Ni_3Al in HCl, H_2SO_4, NaCl and H_3PO_4 electrolytes were studied.

H.W. White, Study of Corrosion and Corrosion Inhibitor Species on Aluminum Surfaces, *Tunneling Spectroscopy—Capabilities, Applications and New Techniques*, Plenum Press, New York, 287-309, 1982. MetAbs No. 85-352371. **Abstract:** Applications of tunneling spectroscopy on the corrosion of Al and Al alloys in chlorinated solvents and acid media are reviewed, the mechanism of surface-reaction inhibition by chemical additives discussed, and the results related to the development of improved inhibitors and more resistant alloy

compositions. Media studied include CCl_4, trichloroethylene, and HCl, and the inhibitors were formamide, for the CCl_4, and acridine and thiourea for the HCl.

G. Schmitt and K. Bedbur, Investigations on Structural and Electronic Effects in Acid Inhibitors by AC Impedance, *Werkst. Korros.*, 36(6), 273-278, 1985. MetAbs No. 85-352443. **Abstract:** AC impedance investigations were performed on high-purity iron and mild steel in deaerated 10% hydrochloric acid under free corrosion at room temperature in the presence of quaternary ammonium compounds.

K.H. Adhe and P.R. Shibad, Adsorption of Acridine on Aluminium Base Alloys in Dilute Hydrochloric Acid Solution-Kinetic and Thermodynamic Parameters, *J. Electrochem. Soc. India*, 34(2), 138-142, 1985. MetAbs No. 86-350050. **Abstract:** The corrosion of Al-base alloys in $0.1N$ HCl and its inhibition using acridine were studied. The influence of temperature (28 to 70 °C) on corrosion of alloys Al 3S, Al-1Ni-0.5Fe and Al-0.1Zr was studied.

R.M. Oza, P.C. Vadher, A.B. Patel, and J.C. Vora, Mechanism of Corrosion Inhibition of Stainless Steel, *J. Electrochem. Soc. India*, 34(2), 143-146, 1985. MetAbs No. 86-350051. **Abstract:** The action of thiourea and its derivatives is studied for corrosion inhibition of AISI type 304 stainless steel in hydrochloric acid solutions. The mechanism of inhibition has been discussed.

J.P. Frayret, A. Caprani, T. Jaszay, and F. Priem, Influence of Aluminum and Vanadium on the Anodic Dissolution of Ti-Al and Ti-V Binary Alloys in Concentrated Hydrochloric Acid, *Corrosion*, 41(11), 656-664, 1985. MetAbs No. 86-350207. **Abstract:** To understand the combined roles of Al and vanadium in the dissolution-passivation mechanism of the ternary TA_6V alloy in hydrochloric acid, the roles of Al and V were investigated separately in Ti-Al and Ti-V binary alloys.

M.M. Nerodenko, L.M. Onoprienko, V.A. Gorban, and A.B. Goncharov, Corrosion Resistance of Welded Joints of Zirconium Alloy With 2.5% Niobium in Hydrochloric, Sulfuric and Phosphoric Acids, *Avtom. Svarka*, (8), 53-56, 1985. MetAbs No. 86-350415. **Abstract:** Corrosion resistance of TIG welded samples from Zr-Nb alloy (2.5% Nb, 0.056% oxygen, 0.0006% hydrogen and 0.0067% nitrogen) was determined by weight loss in boiling solutions of HCl, H_2SO_4 and H_3PO_4 and also in 20% solution of HCl with addition of 1 g/L $CuCl_2$. Potentiostat P-5827M was used for measuring electrochemical characteristics.

M. Magrini, P. Matteazzi, and A. Frignani, Structural Characterization and Electrochemical Behavior of Fe-Ni-Mo-B Amorphous Alloys, *Mater. Chem. Phys.*, 13(1), 71-83, 1985. MetAbs No. 86-350502. **Abstract:** Amorphous alloys obtained by the "melt-spinning" technique, with variable nickel and molybdenum contents, have been examined. Potentiodynamic anodic and cathodic polarization curves have been obtained for each of these amorphous alloys in various environments ($1N$ HCl, $1N$ H_2SO_4, 3% NaCl, $1N$ NaOH).

B.A. Abd-El-Nabey, M.M. Essa, and M.A. Shaban, 3-(Alditol-1-Yl)-1,2,4-Triazolo(3,4-a)Phthalazines as Inhibitors for the Acid Corrosion of Aluminium, *Surf. Technol.*, 26(2), 165-175, 1985. MetAbs No. 86-350542. **Abstract:** Corrosion inhibition by 3-(alditol-1-yl)-1,2,4-triazolo(3,4-a) phthalazine and some related compounds of commercial purity Al strip in hydrochloric acid was measured using chemical and electrochemical methods.

A.B. Rais, F. Dalard, and J.C. Sohm, Aluminum Pit Propagation in Acidic Media. I. Experimental Results, *Corros. Sci.*, 25(11), 1035-1046, 1985. MetAbs No. 86-350706. **Abstract:** Tunnel propagation has been studied in Al corroding in HCl + NaCl solutions (pH 1), at constant potential. An experimental method has been devised for preparing electrodes of very small active area (100 μm^2). The effects of potential, temperature, chloride concentration, pH and speed of rotation of the electrode have been studied.

M.N. Desai, C.B. Shah, and S.M. Desai, Alicyclic Compounds as Corrosion Inhibitors for Aluminium 57S in Hydrochloric Acid Solutions, *J. Electrochem. Soc. India, 34*(3), 173-176, 1985. MetAbs No. 86-350915. **Abstract:** Cyclohexanone, cyclohexanol, methylcyclohexanol and cyclohexylamine are investigated as inhibitors of corrosion of Al 57S in hydrochloric acid solutions.

M. Troquet and J. Pagetti, Cathodic Study of Zinc Behavior in a 1N HCl Medium by Means of Impedance Measurements: Influence of Phosphonium Salts Addition, *Mater. Chem. Phys., 14*(2), 193-198, 1986. MetAbs No. 86-350976. **Abstract:** Phenylbenzylphosphonium bromide has been shown to act basically as a cathodic inhibitor. Classical methods, such as weight loss, polarization resistance or corrosion intensity as a result of Tafel slope extrapolation, have been used.

W.A. Badawy, A.G. Gad-Allah, H.A. Abed El-Rahman, and M.M. Abouromia, Kinetics of the Passivation of Molybdenum in Acids and Alkali Solutions as Inferred From Impedance and Potential Measurements, *Surf. Coat. Technol., 27*(2), 187-196, 1986. MetAbs No. 86-351035. **Abstract:** The electrochemical behavior of mechanically polished Mo electrodes in different acid and alkali solutions was investigated using open-circuit potential and impedance measurements. The effect of the concentration of acid (HCl) and alkali (NaOH) on the electrochemical behavior of the Mo electrodes was also studied.

K. Choudhury, D. Das, C.K. Majumdar, K.R. Rao, and M. Adhikari, Mossbauer Studies of Corrosion and Inhibition, *Phys. Status Solidi (a), 91*(1), 29-35, 1985. MetAbs No. 86-351091. **Abstract:** The corrosion products of mild steel in an acid medium are identified by Mossbauer spectroscopy. The diffusion coefficient, which gives the rate of reaction, is measured to 0.14 x 10^{-12} cm^2/s. The retardation of corrosion by an inhibitor and a surfactant is also discussed.

A. Kawashima, K. Asami, and K. Hashimoto, An XPS Study of Passive Films on Nickel and Alloy 600 in Acids, *Corros. Sci., 25*(12), 1103-1114, 1985. MetAbs No. 86-351115. **Abstract:** Compositions of surface films formed on Ni and Alloy 600 in 1M HCl, 0.5M H$_2$SO$_4$ and 1/3M H$_3$PO$_4$ solutions were investigated as a function of polarization potential.

M. Studnicki, Syntheses of Derivatives of Alkylarylamines and Their Properties as Pickling Inhibitors of Carbon Steels and Stainless Steels, *Ind. Eng. Chem., Prod. Res. Dev., 25*(1), 96-102, 1986. MetAbs No. 86-351260. **Abstract:** Preparation and application of pickling inhibitors derivatives of alkylarylamines in hydrochloric acid and sulfuric acid are described.

W.R. Brakenbury and R. Grzeskowiak, An Ellipsometric Study of Mild Steel in Hydrochloric Acid Solutions, *Appl. Surf. Sci., 25*(3), 305-320, 1986. MetAbs No. 86-351483. **Abstract:** An ellipsometric study has been made on mild steel in hydrochloric acid solutions, in a situation where film growth is not expected. The results are considered to be due to roughening and have been interpreted in terms of a Fenstermaker-McCrackin type roughening model.

G.O. Davis, J. Kolts, and N. Sridhar, Polarization Effects in Galvanic Corrosion, *Corrosion, 42*(6), 329-336, 1986. MetAbs No. 86-351501. **Abstract:** Galvanic corrosion in couples of Hastelloy Alloys B-2 and G-3 was examined in boiling 10% sulfuric and ambient-temperature hydrochloric acids. The galvanic corrosion rates were determined by measurement of the galvanic current using (1) a zero resistance ammeter technique and (2) weight loss measurements.

J.D. Talati and D.K. Gandhi, Some Dyes Corrosion Inhibitors for Aluminium-Copper Alloy in Higher Concentrations of Hydrochloric Acid, *Indian J. Technol., 23*(6), 232-236, 1985. MetAbs No. 86-351588. **Abstract:** The inhibitive efficiency of some dyes for Al-4% Cu alloy (B26S) in 1.0 to 10.0M hydrochloric acid has been studied.

V.G. Gokhale, V.B. Mahale, and H.V. Sudhaker Nayak, 2-Sulfhydryl-Methylbenzimidazole as Inhibitor of Corrosion of Copper and Brass in 1N HCl, *Bull. Electrochem., 2*(3), 219-221, 1986. MetAbs No. 87-350177. **Abstract:** Inhibitive efficiency of 2-sulfhydryl-methylbenzimidazole (SMBZ) for Cu in 1N NaCl increased with inhibitor concentration and period of exposure.

K. Shimamura, A. Kawashima, K. Asami, and K. Hashimoto, Corrosion Behavior of Amorphous Nickel-Valve Metal Alloys in Boiling Concentrated Nitric and Hydrochloric Acids, *Sci. Rep. Res. Inst., Tohoku Univ. A, 33*(1), 196-210, 1986. MetAbs No. 87-350198. **Abstract:** The corrosion behavior of amorphous nickel-base alloys containing Ti, Zr, Nb, Ta and/or P in boiling 9N HNO$_3$ solutions with and without Cr^{6+} ion and in a boiling 6N HCl solution was investigated.

A.S. Fouda, M.N. Moussa, F.I. Taha, and A.I. Elneanaa, The Role of Some Thiosemicarbazide Derivatives in the Corrosion Inhibition of Aluminium in Hydrochloric Acid, *Corros. Sci., 26*(9), 719-726, 1986. MetAbs No. 87-350242. **Abstract:** The inhibitive action of some thiosemicarbazide derivatives toward the corrosion of Al in 2M HCl has been investigated by using thermometric, weight loss, and hydrogen evolution techniques.

I.H. Omar, F. Zucchi, and G. Trabanelli, Schiff Bases as Corrosion Inhibitors of Copper and Its Alloys in Acid Media, *Surf. Coat. Technol., 29*(2), 141-151, 1986. MetAbs No. 87-350278. **Abstract:** The inhibiting action of some Schiff bases on the corrosion of Cu and its alloys in hydrochloric and sulfuric acid solutions has been studied. The Schiff bases were synthesized by reacting salicyl aldehyde with aliphatic or aromatic amines. The behaviors of electrolytic Cu, Al brass and cupronickels (90Cu-10Ni and 70Cu-30Ni with 0.4 wt.% Fe) have been examined.

H. Bala and S. Szymura, Corrosion Behavior of the Ti$_{75}$Ni$_{20}$Si$_5$ (Ge$_5$) Metallic Glasses, *J. Mater. Sci. Lett., 5*(11), 1087-1088, 1986. MetAbs No. 87-350392. **Abstract:** The corrosion behavior of Ti$_{75}$Ni$_{20}$Si$_5$ and Ti$_{75}$Ni$_{20}$Ge$_5$ metallic glasses in Ar-saturated 5N HCl solution was investigated using a potentiokinetic polarization technique. The potentiokinetic polarization curves were determined for two different surface conditions, namely rinsed with acetone and alcohol, or etched in boiling concentrated HCl.

F.B. Glikina, N.L. Khar'kovskaya, N.A. Bychkova, and A.R. Kutikov, Protection of Boiler Steel Against Corrosion When Removing Dense Iron Oxide Deposits With Hydrochloric Acid, *Therm. Eng. (USSR), 32*(2), 106-108, 1985. MetAbs No. 87-350519. **Abstract:** An experimental investigation, using various reducing agents and inhibitors both separately and together in 4% hydrochloric acid at 60 °C for removal of deposits in boiler tubes, is reported. Paraformaldehyde, hydroxylamine sulfate, formaldehyde, formaldehyde sodium sulfoxylate, glyoxal and ethylene glycol and eight industrial inhibitors were investigated.

R.B. Diegle, C.R. Clayton, Y. Lu, and N.R. Sorensen, Evidence of Chemical Passivity in Amorphous Ni-20P Alloy, *J. Electrochem. Soc., 134*(1), 138-139, 1987. MetAbs No. 87-350834. **Abstract:** A study is discussed in which amorphous Ni-20P (at.%) exhibits chemical passivity in 0.2N HCl. No distinct mechanical barrier to diffusion, such as an oxide film, is present.

M.N. Desai, M.B. Desai, C.B. Shah, and S.M. Desai, Schiff Bases as Corrosion Inhibitors for Mild Steel in Hydrochloric Acid Solutions,

Corros. Sci., *26*(10), 827-837, 1986. MetAbs No. 87-351017. **Abstract:** Seven Schiff bases have been examined as corrosion inhibitors of mild steel in 1.0 to 6.0*N* solutions of HCl. Activation energies in the presence and absence of inhibitors have been evaluated.

A. Abras, A.A. Campos, A.V. de Carvalho, and L.O. Ladeira, Conversion Electron and X-Ray Mossbauer Studies of Boronized Low-Carbon Steel Under Corrosion and Oxidation Conditions, *Appl. Phys. A*, *A41*(3), 185-189, 1986. MetAbs No. 87-351404. **Abstract:** Iron-boride layers on low-carbon steel were produced by a thermomechanical diffusion process. The surface interaction products were identified by surface Mossbauer spectroscopy (CEMS and XMS).

da Costa, J.C. Rubim, and S.M. Agostinho, Spectroelectrochemical Study of the Corrosion of a Copper Electrode in Deaerated 1.0*M* HCl Solutions Containing Iron (III). Effect of the Corrosion Inhibitor Benzotriazole, *J. Electroanal. Chem. Interfacial Electrochem.*, *220*(2), 259-268, 1987. MetAbs No. 87-351563. **Abstract:** The corrosion rate of a Cu electrode in deaerated 1.0*M* HCl by Fe(III) ions, in the absence and presence of benzotriazole (BTAH), has been evaluated through weight-loss experiments using a rotating disk electrode.

Y. Roques, G. Mankowski, G. Chatainier, and F. Dabosi, Statistical Study of Pitting Corrosion of Zircaloy-4 in Aqueous and Methanolic Solutions of HCl, *Mater. Sci. Forum*, *8*, 105-111, 1986. MetAbs No. 87-352148. **Abstract:** Pitting corrosion of a Zr alloy was studied in chloride containing aqueous and methanolic solutions from a statistical point of view. The influence of various parameters such as prepolarization time, temperature, test potential and water content on pitting susceptibility was shown.

A. Frignani, G. Demertzis, and G. Trabanelli, Electrochemical Investigation of $Fe_{80}B_{20}$ Amorphous Alloy, *Mater. Chem. Phys.*, *16*(5-6), 569-574, 1987. MetAbs No. 87-352197. **Abstract:** The behavior of $Fe_{80}B_{20}$ amorphous alloy is compared to that of crystalline iron (Armco iron) in 0.1*N* HBr, HCl, $HClO_4$ and H_2SO_4.

H. Bala, The Acid Corrosion of Fe-P Alloys, *Werkst. Korros.*, *38*(1), 26-31, 1987. MetAbs No. 87-352230. **Abstract:** The effect of the P-content in iron (0.002 to 0.12% P) and the stirring rate on the corrosion rate of five Fe-P alloys in H_2SO_4 and HCl solutions (pH 0) has been investigated. A mechanism of the corrosion of Fe-P alloys, including the transfer of phosphine from the surface into the bulk of the solution by stirring, is discussed.

H. Bala and S. Szymura, Acid Corrosion Behavior of Amorphous and Crystalline $Ti_{75}_{20}Si_5$ Alloys, *Thin Solid Films*, *149*(2), 171-176, 1987. MetAbs No. 87-352233. **Abstract:** The corrosion resistance of amorphous and crystalline $Ti_{75}Ni_{20}Si_5$ alloy as well as that of pure crystalline titanium as a reference material were investigated in sulfuric and hydrochloric acids. Potentiokinetic polarization curves were obtained to determine their corrosion properties.

K. Ogino, A. Hida, S. Kishima, and S. Kumanomido, Susceptibility of Type 431 Stainless Steel to Erosion-Corrosion by Vibratory Cavitation in Corrosive Media, *Wear*, *116*(3), 299-307, 1987. MetAbs No. 87-352329. **Abstract:** Using the structural characteristics of type 431 stainless steel, which reveals a wide range of strength and corrosion resistance with tempering after quenching, its susceptibility to erosion-

corrosion was investigated as a function of tempering temperature. Tests were conducted under a vibratory cavitation condition of 6.5 kHz in cavitation media of 3% NaCl solution, 0.1*N* HCl and 0.1*N* H_2SO^4 at 22 °C.

N. Nigam and K. Srivastava, Role of Impurities on the Dissolution of Mild Steel in Acidic Media, *Anti-Corros. Methods Mater.*, *34*(5), 4-5, 1987. MetAbs No. 87-352383. **Abstract:** Sulfates, chlorides, nitrates and oxidizing agents were studied as impurities in sulfuric acid and hydrochloric acid in mild steel.

G. Rocchini, A Computerized Tool for Corrosion Rate Monitoring, *Corrosion*, *43*(6), 326-331, 1987. MetAbs No. 87-352495. **Abstract:** Two variations of the INTER1 program for determination of the corrosion rate of a metal are presented that are valid from a mathematical viewpoint only when the overall electrochemical reaction is controlled by the activation energy and contains two processes (one cathodic and the other anodic).

J.D. Talati and J.M. Daraji, Dyes as Corrosion Inhibitors for Aluminium Alloys in Acid Media. I. Triphenylmethane Dyes as Inhibitors for Aluminium-Magnesium Alloy in Hydrochloric Acid, *Trans. SAEST*, *21*(4), 233-243, 1986. MetAbs No. 87-352808. **Abstract:** The inhibitive efficiency of triphenylmethane dyes in HCl of various concentration up to 5*M* have been studied.

R.C. Newman and T. Shahrabi, The Effect of Alloyed Nitrogen or Dissolved Nitrate Ions on the Anodic Behavior of Austenitic Stainless Steel in Hydrochloric Acid, *Corros. Sci.*, *27*(8), 827-838, 1987. MetAbs No. 87-352917. **Abstract:** The anodic behavior of high-purity stainless steels, based on a 316L composition, has been studied at room temperature in HCl solutions from 1 to 6*M*.

B. Poulson, Localized Corrosion at Welds During Acid Cleaning, *Werkst. Korros.*, *38*(7), 359-367, 1987. MetAbs No. 87-352926. **Abstract:** An instance where a pre-commissioning hydrochloric acid clean caused localized corrosion of the heat-affected zones in a carbon steel containing 0.25/0.3% C (ASTM Grade 210C) is described. The factors influencing the occurrence of corrosion at welds during chemical cleaning have been examined.

T.P. Moffat, W.F. Flanagan, and B.D. Lichter, Effects of Alloy Chemistry on the Corrosion of FeNi Metal-Metalloid Metallic Glasses, *Corrosion*, *43*(10), 389-593, 1987. MetAbs No. 88-350600. **Abstract:** The polarization characteristics of $Fe_{40}Ni_{40}P_{14}B_6$ and $Fe_{40}Ni_{38}Mo_4B_{18}$ metallic glasses have been determined in 1*N* H_2SO_4 and 1*N* HCl. Results have been compared with those for metallic glasses of other compositions and with results for metalloid-free crystalline alloys.

S.C. Makwana, N.K. Patel, and J.C. Vora, Corrosion Inhibitors for the 3003 Al Alloy in Mixed Acid Solutions (HCl-H_3PO_4), *Trans. Soc. Adv. Electrochem. Sci. Technol.*, *12*(1), 15-19, 1977. MetAbs No. 77-351904.

E.L. Liening, Materials of Construction for Halogens, in *Process Industries Corrosion*, National Association of Corrosion Engineers, Houston, p 315.

J.P. Carter *et al.*, *Corrosion*, *40*(5), May 1984.

Corrosion Behavior of Various Metals and Alloys in Hydrochloric Acid

Material	Condition, other factors, comments	Concentration, %	Temperature, °C (°F)	Duration	Corrosion rate, mm/yr (mils/yr) or other	Ref
Irons and steels						
1020 steel	Laboratory test. Plus 60% water	40	500 (932)	15 d	2.1 (82.6)	182
1020 steel	Laboratory test. Plus 60% water	40	400 (752)	15 d	0.326 (12.8)	182
1020 steel	Laboratory test. Plus 60% water	40	300 (570)	15 d	0.700 (27.5)	182
1020 steel	Laboratory test. Plus 60% water	40	200 (392)	15 d	0.046 (1.8)	182
4130 steel	Laboratory test. Plus 60% water	40	500 (932)	15 d	1.70 (66.9)	182
4130 steel	Laboratory test. Plus 60% water	40	400 (752)	15 d	0.406 (15.9)	182
4130 steel	Laboratory test. Plus 60% water	40	300 (570)	15 d	0.87 (34.2)	182
4130 steel	Laboratory test. Plus 60% water	40	200 (392)	15 d	0.051 (2.0)	182
Armco iron	1.4N	...	45 (115)	3 h	13 (512)	31
ASTM 335	1.4N. Grade P22 (2Cr-1Mo)	...	45 (115)	3 h	10 (394)	31
ASTM 335	1.4N. Grade P5 (5Cr-0.5Mo)	...	45 (115)	3 h	3 (118)	31
ASTM 335	1.4N. Grade P9 (10Cr-1Mo)	...	45 (115)	3 h	6 (236)	31
ASTM A106 carbon steel	1.4N	...	45 (115)	3 h	23 (906)	31
ASTM A335	1.4N. Grade P11 (1.5Cr-0.25Mo)	...	45 (115)	3 h	4 (157)	31
Stainless steels						
AM-363 stainless steel	...	...	Room	...	Attacked	120
Carpenter Pyromet Alloy 102	Annealed	10	...	48 h	8.636 (345.4)	30
Carpenter Pyromet Alloy 102	Stress relieved at 843 °C (1550 °F) for ½ h, furnace cooled	10	...	48 h	9.144 (365.6)	30
Carpenter Pyromet Alloy 102	Annealed	Conc	...	48 h	11.43 (457.2)	30
Carpenter Pyromet Alloy 102	Stress relieved at 843 °C (1550 °F) for ½ h, furnace cooled	Conc	...	48 h	10.16 (406.4)	30
Jessop JS700	...	5	Boiling	48 h	37.87 (1.491 in./yr)	97
Jessop JS700	...	10	Room	48 h	0.457 (0.018 in./yr)	97
Jessop JS700	...	10	60 (140)	48 h	3.81 (0.150 in./yr)	97
Jessop JS700	...	10	Boiling	48 h	114.6 (4.51 in./yr)	97
Jessop JS700	1 volume concentrated HCl in 9 volumes ethylene diamine	10	Boiling	48 h	<0.025 (<0.001 in./yr)	97
Type 304 stainless steel	Annealed. All solutions from CP chemicals. Tests made in the laboratory	0.4	27 (80)	...	0.250 (10)	19
Type 304 stainless steel	...	All	21 (70)	...	Poor	121
Type 316 stainless steel	Annealed. All solutions from CP chemicals. Tests made in the laboratory	0.4	49 (120)	...	0.125 (5)	19
Type 316 stainless steel	...	All	21 (70)	...	Poor	121
Type 317L stainless steel	...	5	Boiling	48 h	42.95 (1.691 in./yr)	97
Type 317L Plus stainless steel	...	5	Boiling	48 h	36.93 (1.454 in./yr)	97
Type 410 stainless steel	...	All	21 (70)	...	Poor	121
Type 410 stainless steel	...	...	Room	...	Attacked	121
Type 430 stainless steel	...	All	21 (70)	...	Poor	121
Coppers						
70-30 cupronickel	...	...	...	...	Fair	93
90-10 cupronickel	...	...	...	...	Fair	93
Admiralty brass	...	...	...	...	Fair	93
Aluminum bronze	...	...	...	...	Fair	93
Ampco 8, aluminum bronze	Generally not suitable	>15	...	...	>0.5 (>20)	96
Ampco 8, aluminum bronze	Generally suitable. Conditions such as aeration or temperature could restrict use	To 15	...	...	<0.5 (<20)	96
Architectural bronze	...	...	...	...	Not suitable	93
Brass	...	...	...	...	Fair	93
Cartridge brass	...	...	...	...	Not suitable	93

(Continued)

Corrosion Behavior of Various Metals and Alloys in Hydrochloric Acid (Continued)

Material	Condition, other factors, comments	Concen-tration, %	Temperature, °C (°F)	Duration	Corrosion rate, mm/yr (mils/yr) or other	Ref
Commercial bronze	...	...	...	...	Fair	93
Copper	...	Conc	...	...	0.75 (30)	28
Electrolytic copper	...	...	...	...	Fair	93
Free-cutting brass	...	...	...	...	Not suitable	93
Muntz metal	...	...	...	...	Not suitable	93
Naval brass	...	...	...	...	Not suitable	93
Nickel silver	...	18	...	...	Fair	93
Phosphor bronze	5% Sn	...	...	...	Fair	93
Phosphor bronze	8% Sn	...	...	...	Fair	93
Phosphor copper	...	...	...	...	Fair	93
Red brass	...	...	...	...	Fair	93
Silicon bronze	Low	...	...	...	Fair	93
Silicon bronze	High	...	...	...	Fair	93
Titanium						
Ti-10-2-3	...	0.5	Boiling	...	1.10 (44)	33
Ti-10-2-3	Plus 0.1% $FeCl_3$	5	Boiling	...	0.008 (0.315)	33
Ti-3-8-6-4-4	...	0.5	Boiling	...	0.003 (0.12)	33
Ti-3-8-6-4-4	...	1.0	Boiling	...	0.058 (2.32)	33
Ti-3-8-6-4-4	...	1.5	Boiling	...	0.26 (10.4)	33
Ti-3-8-6-4-4	Aerated. pH 1	...	Boiling	...	nil	33
Ti-3-8-6-4-4	Plus 0.1% $FeCl_3$	5	Boiling	...	0.018 (0.70)	33
Ti-3Al-2.5V	ASTM Grade 9	1	Boiling	...	2.75 (110)	91
Ti-3Al-2.5V	ASTM Grade 9. Plus 0.2% $FeCl_3$	1	Boiling	...	0.005 (0.2)	91
Ti-3Al-2.5V	ASTM Grade 9	5	Boiling	...	26.3 (1055)	91
Ti-3Al-2.5V	ASTM Grade 9. Plus 0.2% $FeCl_3$	5	Boiling	...	0.03 (1.3)	91
Ti-3Al-2.5V	ASTM Grade 9	10	Boiling	...	>75 (>3000)	91
Ti-3Al-2.5V	ASTM Grade 9. Plus 0.2% $FeCl_3$	10	Boiling	...	0.3 (12)	91
Ti-550	...	0.5	Boiling	...	0.056 (2.24)	33
Ti-550	...	1.0	Boiling	...	0.64 (25.6)	33
Ti-550	Plus 0.1% $FeCl_3$	5	Boiling	...	0.393 (15.4)	33
Ti-5Ta	...	0.5	Boiling	...	0.013 (0.52)	33
Ti-5Ta	...	1.5	Boiling	...	2.10 (84)	33
Ti-5Ta	Plus 0.1% $FeCl_3$	5	Boiling	...	0.020 (0.78)	33
Ti-6-2-1-.8	...	0.5	Boiling	...	0.020 (0.8)	33
Ti-6-2-1-.8	...	1.0	Boiling	...	1.07 (42.8)	33
Ti-6-2-1-.8	Plus 0.1% $FeCl_3$	5	Boiling	...	0.051 (2.00)	33
Ti-6-2-4-6	...	0.5	Boiling	...	nil	33
Ti-6-2-4-6	...	1.0	Boiling	...	0.03 (1.2)	33
Ti-6-2-4-6	Aerated. pH 1	...	Boiling	...	0.01 (0.4)	33
Ti-6-2-4-6	Plus 0.1% $FeCl_3$	5	Boiling	...	0.068 (2.67)	33
Ti-6-4	...	1.0	Boiling	...	2.52 (100)	33
Ti-6-4	Aerated. pH 1	...	Boiling	...	0.60 (24)	33
Ti-6-4	Plus 0.1% $FeCl_3$	5	Boiling	...	0.015 (0.59)	33
Titanium	...	18	19-26 (65-80)	36 d	0.11 (4.5)	74
Titanium	...	37	19-26 (65-80)	36 d	17.7 (698)	74
Titanium	Grade 9	0.5	Boiling	...	1.08 (43.2)	33
Titanium	Grade 9	1	88 (190)	...	0.009 (0.36)	33
Titanium	Grade 9	3	88 (190)	...	3.10 (124)	33
Titanium	Grade 7. Deaerated	3	82 (1800	...	0.013 (0.52)	33
Titanium	Grade 7. Deaerated	5	82 (180)	...	0.051 (2.04)	33
Titanium	Grade 7. Deaerated	10	82 (180)	...	0.419 (16.7)	33
Titanium	Grade 9	1	Boiling	...	2.79 (111.6)	33
Titanium	Grade 9. Aerated	5	35 (95)	...	0.001 (0.04)	33
Titanium	Grade 9. Nitrogen saturated	5	35 (95)	...	0.185 (7.4)	33
Titanium	Grade 7	1.0	Boiling	...	0.008 (0.32)	33
Titanium	Grade 7	1.5	Boiling	...	0.03 (1.2)	33
Titanium	Grade 7	5.0	Boiling	...	0.23 (9.2)	33

(Continued)

Corrosion Behavior of Various Metals and Alloys in Hydrochloric Acid (Continued)

Material	Condition, other factors, comments	Concentration, %	Temperature, °C (°F)	Duration	Corrosion rate, mm/yr (mils/yr) or other	Ref
Titanium	Grade 12	0.5	Boiling	...	nil	33
Titanium	Grade 12	1.0	Boiling	...	0.04 (1.6)	33
Titanium	Grade 12	1.5	Boiling	...	0.25 (10)	33
Titanium	Grade 7. Hydrogen saturated	1-15	25 (75)	...	<0.025 (<1)	33
Titanium	Grade 7. Hydrogen saturated	20	25 (75)	...	0.102 (4.08)	33
Titanium	Grade 7. Hydrogen saturated	5	70 (158)	...	0.076 (3.04)	33
Titanium	Grade 7. Hydrogen saturated	10	70 (158)	...	0.178 (7.12)	33
Titanium	Grade 7. Hydrogen saturated	15	70 (158)	...	0.33 (13.2)	33
Titanium	Grade 7. Hydrogen saturated	3	190 (375)	...	0.025 (0.63)	33
Titanium	Grade 7. Hydrogen saturated	5	190 (375)	...	0.025 (1)	33
Titanium	Grade 7. Hydrogen saturated	10	190 (375)	...	8.9 (356)	33
Titanium	Grade 7. Oxygen saturated	3, 5	190 (375)	...	0.127 (5.0)	33
Titanium	Grade 7. Oxygen saturated	10	190 (375)	...	9.3 (366)	33
Titanium	Grade 7. Chlorine saturated	3, 5	190 (375)	...	<0.03 (<1.18)	33
Titanium	Grade 7. Chlorine saturated	10	190 (375)	...	29.0 (1141)	33
Titanium	Grade 7. Aerated	1, 5	70 (158)	...	<0.03 (<1.18)	33
Titanium	Grade 7. Aerated	10	70 (158)	...	0.05 (1.96)	33
Titanium	Grade 7. Aerated	15	70 (158)	...	0.15 (5.9)	33
Titanium	Grade 7. Plus 4% $FeCl_3$, 4% $MgCl_2$	19	82 (180)	...	0.49 (19.2)	33
Titanium	Grade 7. Plus 4% $FeCl_3$, 4% $MgCl_2$. Chlorine saturated	19	82 (180)	...	0.46 (18.1)	33
Titanium	Grade 7. Plus 5 g/L $FeCl_3$	10	Boiling	...	0.279 (10.9)	33
Titanium	Grade 7. Plus 16 g/L $FeCl_3$	10	Boiling	...	0.076 (2.99)	33
Titanium	Grade 7. Plus 16 g/L $CuCl_2$	10	Boiling	...	0.127 (5.0)	33
Titanium	Grade 12. Plus 2 g/L $FeCl_3$	4.2	91 (195)	...	0.058 (2.28)	33
Titanium	Grade 9. Plus 0.2% $FeCl_3$	1	Boiling	...	0.005 (0.19)	33
Titanium	Grade 9. Plus 0.2% $FeCl_3$	5	Boiling	...	0.033 (1.29)	33
Titanium	Grade 9. Plus 0.2% $FeCl_3$	10	Boiling	...	0.305 (12.0)	33
Titanium	Grade 9. Plus 0.1% $FeCl_3$	5	Boiling	...	0.008 (0.31)	33
Titanium	Grade 7. Plus 0.1% $FeCl_3$	5	Boiling	...	0.013 (0.51)	33
Titanium	Grade 12. Plus 0.1% $FeCl_3$	5	Boiling	...	0.020 (0.78)	33
Titanium	Grade 7. Plus 18% H_3PO_4, 5% HNO_3	18	77 (170)	...	nil	33
Titanium	Aerated	1	60 (140)	...	0.004 (0.16)	90
Titanium	Aerated	2	60 (140)	...	0.016 (0.64)	90
Titanium	Aerated	5	60 (140)	...	1.07 (42.8)	90
Titanium	Aerated	1	100 (212)	...	0.46 (18.4)	90
Titanium	Aerated	5	35 (95)	...	0.01 (0.4)	90
Titanium	Aerated	10	35 (95)	...	1.02 (40.8)	90
Titanium	Aerated	20	35 (95)	...	4.45 (178)	90
Titanium	...	0.1	Boiling	...	0.10 (4)	90
Titanium	...	1	Boiling	...	1.8 (72)	90
Titanium	Plus 4% $FeCl_3$ + 4% $MgCl_2$	19	82 (180)	...	0.51 (20.4)	90
Titanium	Plus 4% $FeCl_3$ + 4% $MgCl_2$ + Cl_2 saturated	19	82 (180)	...	0.46 (18.4)	90
Titanium	Chlorine saturated	5	190 (374)	...	<0.025 (<1)	90
Titanium	Chlorine saturated	10	190 (374)	...	28.5 (1140)	90
Titanium	Plus 200 ppm Cl_2	36	25 (77)	...	0.432 (17.28)	90
Titanium	Plus 1% HNO_3	5	40 (104)	...	nil	90
Titanium	Plus 1% HNO_3	5	95 (203)	...	0.091 (3.64)	90
Titanium	Plus 3% HNO_3	8.5	80 (176)	...	0.051 (2.04)	90
Titanium	Plus 5% HNO_3	1	Boiling	...	0.074 (2.96)	90
Titanium	Plus 5% HNO_3	5	40 (104)	...	0.025 (1)	90
Titanium	Plus 5% HNO_3	5	95 (203)	...	0.030 (1.2)	90
Titanium	Plus 10% HNO_3	5	40 (104)	...	nil	90
Titanium	Plus 10% HNO_3	5	95 (203)	...	0.183 (7.32)	90
Titanium	Plus 0.5% CrO_3	5	38 (100)	...	nil	90
Titanium	Plus 0.5% CrO_3	5	95 (203)	...	0.031 (1.24)	90
Titanium	Plus 1% CrO_3	5	38 (100)	...	0.018 (0.72)	90

(Continued)

Corrosion Behavior of Various Metals and Alloys in Hydrochloric Acid (Continued)

Material	Condition, other factors, comments	Concentration, %	Temperature, °C (°F)	Duration	Corrosion rate, mm/yr (mils/yr) or other	Ref
Titanium	Plus 1% CrO_3	5	95 (203)	...	0.031 (1.24)	90
Titanium	Plus 0.05% $CuSO_4$	5	38 (100)	...	0.040 (1.6)	90
Titanium	Plus 0.05% $CuSO_4$	5	93 (200)	...	0.091 (3.64)	90
Titanium	Plus 0.05% $CuSO_4$	5	38 (100)	...	0.091 (3.64)	90
Titanium	Plus 0.5% $CuSO_4$	5	93 (200)	...	0.061 (2.44)	90
Titanium	Plus 1% $CuSO_4$	5	38 (100)	...	0.031 (1.24)	90
Titanium	Plus 1% $CuSO_4$	5	93 (200)	...	0.091 (3.64)	90
Titanium	Plus 5% $CuSO_4$	5	38 (100)	...	0.020 (0.8)	90
Titanium	Plus 5% $CuSO_4$	5	93 (200)	...	0.061 (2.44)	90
Titanium	Plus 0.05% $CuSO_4$	5	Boiling	...	0.064 (2.56)	90
Titanium	Plus 0.5% $CuSO_4$	5	Boiling	...	0.084 (3.36)	90
Titanium	...	1	Boiling	...	2.12 (85)	91
Titanium	Plus 0.2% $FeCl_3$	1	Boiling	...	<0.125 (<5)	91
Titanium	...	5	Boiling	...	21 (840)	91
Titanium	Plus 0.2% $FeCl_3$	5	Boiling	...	<0.125 (<5)	91
Titanium	Plus 0.1% $FeCl_3$	5	Boiling	...	0.01 (0.4)	90
Titanium	...	10	Boiling	...	>50 (>2000)	91
Titanium	Plus 0.2% $FeCl_3$	10	Boiling	...	<0.125 (<5)	91
Titanium	Plus 1 g/L Ti^{4+}	10	Boiling	...	0.000	90
Titanium	Plus 5.0% $NaClO_3$	10.2	80 (176)	...	0.006 (0.24)	90
Titanium	Plus 2.5% $NaClO_3$	10.2	80 (176)	...	0.009 (0.36)	90
Titanium	Plus 18% H_3PO_4 + 5% HNO_3	18	77 (171)	...	0.000	90
Titanium	Plus 5.8 g/L Ti^{4+}	20	Boiling	...	0.000	90
Titanium	Grade 7	0.5	Boiling	...	nil	33
Transage 207	...	0.5	Boiling	...	0.005 (0.2)	33
Transage 207	...	1.0	Boiling	...	0.025 (1)	33
Transage 207	Plus 0.1% $FeCl_3$	5	Boiling	...	0.048 (1.88)	33
Heat- and corrosion-resistant alloys						
40Co-20Cr-15Ni-7Mo	...	Conc	110 (230)	50 h	47.5 (1900)	54
40Co-20Cr-15Ni-7Mo	...	50	110 (230)	50 h	55 (2200)	54
40Co-20Cr-15Ni-7Mo	...	10	102 (216)	50 h	71.75 (2870)	54
44Co-31Cr-13W	As cast. (a)	5	Room	...	0.7 (26)	53
44Co-31Cr-13W	Heat treated 4 h at 899 °C (1650 °F) and furnace cooled. (a)	5	Room	...	0.4 (16)	53
44Co-31Cr-13W	As cast. (a)	5	Room	...	0.65 (26)	53
44Co-31Cr-13W	Heat treated 4 h at 899 °C (1650 °F), furnace cooled. (a)	5	Room	...	0.4 (16)	53
50Co-20Cr-15W-10Ni	...	5	Room	...	0.6 (24)	53
50Co-20Cr-15W-10Ni	(a)	5	Room	...	0.6 (24)	53
53Co-30Cr-4.5W	As cast. (a)	5	Room	...	1.3 (52)	53
53Co-30Cr-4.5W	Heat treated 4 h at 899 °C (1650 °F). (a)	5	Room	...	0.225 (9)	53
53Co-30Cr-4.5W	As cast. (a)	5	Room	...	1.3 (52)	53
53Co-30Cr-4.5W	Heat treated 4 h at 899 °C (1650 °F), furnace cooled. (a)	5	Room	...	0.225 (9)	53
Cabot alloy No. 625	...	2.5	Room	100 h	nil	67
Cabot alloy No. 625	...	2.5	70 (158)	100 h	<0.02 (0.5)	67
Cabot alloy No. 625	...	2.5	Boiling	100 h	12 (472)	67
Cabot alloy No. 625	Average of four 24-h tests	5	70 (158)	...	0.86 (158)	67
Cast Illium G	...	5	21 (70)	...	≥0.10 (≥4)	126
Cast Illium G	...	7	21 (70)	...	0.10-0.37 (4-15)	126
Cast Illium G	...	7	50 (120)	...	>3.12 (>125)	126
Cast Illium G	...	10	21 (70)	...	≥0.10 (≥4)	126
Cast Illium G	...	16	50 (120)	...	>3.12 (>125)	126
Cast Illium G	...	22	21 (70)	...	1.25-3.12 (50-125)	126
Cast Illium G	...	22	50 (120)	...	>3.12 (>125)	126
Cast Illium G	...	32	41 (105)	...	>3.12 (>125)	126
Cast Illium G	...	Conc	21 (70)	...	>3.12 (>125)	126

(Continued)

Corrosion Behavior of Various Metals and Alloys in Hydrochloric Acid (Continued)

Material	Condition, other factors, comments	Concentration, %	Temperature, °C (°F)	Duration	Corrosion rate, mm/yr (mils/yr) or other	Ref
Co-20Cr	...	10	Boiling	...	250 (10,000)	35
Fe-47Cr (ferrite)	Reducing	10	Boiling	...	1461 g/dm²/d	58
Fe-47Cr (sigma)	Reducing	10	Boiling	...	7543 g/dm²/d	58
Hastelloy alloy G	Wrought	1	Room	...	0.003 (0.1)	126
Hastelloy alloy G	Wrought	1	65 (150)	...	0.003 (0.1)	126
Hastelloy alloy G	Wrought	2	Room	...	0.02 (0.8)	126
Hastelloy alloy G	Wrought	5	Room	...	0.09 (3.6)	126
Hastelloy alloy G	Wrought	5	65 (150)	...	2.32 (93)	126
Hastelloy alloy G	Wrought	10	Room	...	0.22 (8.9)	126
Hastelloy alloy G	Wrought	10	65 (150)	...	3.6 (144)	126
Hastelloy alloy G	Wrought	15	Room	...	0.25 (9.9)	126
Hastelloy alloy G	Wrought	15	65 (150)	...	4.8 (192)	126
Hastelloy alloy G	Wrought	37	65 (150)	...	7.67 (307)	126
Hastelloy alloy B-2	Sheet as solution heat-treated, 92 HRB	20	Boiling	...	0.36 (14)	63
Hastelloy alloy B-2	Sheet cold reduced 10%, 32 HRC	20	Boiling	...	0.36 (14)	63
Hastelloy alloy B-2	Sheet cold reduced 20%, 38 HRC	20	Boiling	...	0.36 (14)	63
Hastelloy alloy B-2	Sheet cold reduced 30%, 43 HRC	20	Boiling	...	0.33 (13)	63
Hastelloy alloy B-2	Sheet cold reduced 40%, 44 HRC	20	Boiling	...	0.36 (14)	63
Hastelloy alloy B-2	Sheet cold reduced 50%, 45 HRC	20	Boiling	...	0.36 (14)	63
Hastelloy alloy C-4	Heat-treated at 1066 °C (1950 °F), water quenched. (b)	10	75 (167)	...	0.91 (36)	16
Hastelloy alloy C-4	As gas tungsten arc welded. (b)	10	75 (167)	...	0.86 (34)	16
Hastelloy alloy C-4	Specimen aged 100 h at 899 °C (1650 °F). (b)	10	75 (167)	...	0.89 (35)	16
Hastelloy alloy B-2	All specimens were heat-treated at 1066 °C (1950 °F), water quenched. (b)	1	Boiling	...	0.02 (0.8)	63
Hastelloy alloy B-2	All specimens were heat-treated at 1066 °C (1950 °F), water quenched. (b)	2	Boiling	...	0.08 (3)	63
Hastelloy alloy B-2	All specimens were heat-treated at 1066 °C (1950 °F), water quenched. (b)	5	Boiling	...	0.13 (5)	63
Hastelloy alloy B-2	All specimens were heat-treated at 1066 °C (1950 °F), water quenched. (b)	10	Boiling	...	0.18 (7)	63
Hastelloy alloy B-2	All specimens were heat-treated at 1066 °C (1950 °F), water quenched. (b)	15	Boiling	...	0.28 (11)	63
Hastelloy alloy B-2	All specimens were heat-treated at 1066 °C (1950 °F), water quenched. (b)	20	Boiling	...	0.38 (15)	63
Hastelloy alloy B-2	As gas tungsten arc welded. (b)	20	Boiling	...	0.51 (20)	63
Haynes alloy No. 6B	Average of four 24-h test periods	2.5	Boiling	...	96.5 (3800)	23
Haynes alloy No. 6B	...	5	Boiling	24 h	>250 (10000)	23
Haynes alloy No. 25	Average of four 24-h test periods	1	Boiling	...	0.56 (22)	23
Haynes alloy No. 25	Average of four 24-h test periods	2.5	Boiling	...	57.4 (2260)	23
Haynes alloy No. 25	...	5	Boiling	24 h	188 (7400)	23
Haynes alloy No. 25	(c)	1	Room	24 h	<0.01 (0.1)	124
Haynes alloy No. 25	(c)	1	66 (150)	24 h	nil	124
Haynes alloy No. 25	(c)	1	Boiling	24 h	10.2 (400)	124
Haynes alloy No. 25	(c)	2	Room	24 h	<0.01 (0.1)	124
Haynes alloy No. 25	(c)	2	66 (150)	24 h	0.01 (0.1)	124
Haynes alloy No. 25	(c)	2	Boiling	24 h	>25.4 (>1000)	124
Haynes alloy No. 25	(c)	5	Room	24 h	0.61 (24)	124
Haynes alloy No. 25	(c)	5	66 (150)	24 h	12.0 (474)	124
Haynes alloy No. 25	(c)	5	Boiling	24 h	>25.4 (>1000)	124
Haynes alloy No. 25	(c)	10	Room	24 h	0.64 (25)	124
Haynes alloy No. 25	(c)	10	66 (150)	24 h	10.7 (420)	124
Haynes alloy No. 25	(c)	10	Boiling	24 h	>25.4 (>1000)	124
Haynes alloy No. 25	(c)	15	Room	24 h	0.74 (29)	124
Haynes alloy No. 25	(c)	15	66 (150)	24 h	14.0 (552)	124
Haynes alloy No. 25	(c)	15	Boiling	24 h	>25.4 (>1000)	124
Haynes alloy No. 25	(c)	20	Room	24 h	0.15 (6.0)	124
Haynes alloy No. 25	(c)	20	66 (150)	24 h	6.81 (268)	124
Haynes alloy No. 25	(c)	20	Boiling	24 h	>25.4 (>1000)	124

(Continued)

Corrosion Behavior of Various Metals and Alloys in Hydrochloric Acid (Continued)

Material	Condition, other factors, comments	Concentration, %	Temperature, °C (°F)	Duration	Corrosion rate, mm/yr (mils/yr) or other	Ref
Haynes alloy No. 25	(c)	25	Room	24 h	0.10 (4.0)	124
Haynes alloy No. 25	(c)	25	66 (150)	24 h	3.66 (144)	124
Haynes alloy No. 25	(c)	37	Room	24 h	0.05 (2.0)	124
Haynes alloy No. 25	(c)	37	66 (150)	24 h	1.73 (68)	124
Haynes alloy No. 25	Average of four 24-h test periods	10	Room	...	nil	23
Haynes alloy No. 188	Average of four 24-h test periods. Corrosion decreased from a high value	1	Boiling	...	nil	23
Haynes alloy No. 188	Average of four 24-h test periods	2.5	Boiling	...	61 (2400)	23
Haynes alloy No. 188	...	5	Boiling	24 h	140 (5500)	23
Haynes alloy No. 188	Average of four 24-h test periods. Corrosion rate oscillated during test period	10	Room	...	0.008-0.8 (0.3-31)	23
Haynes alloy No. 556	Average of four 24-h test periods. Corrosion rate decreased from a high value	1	Boiling	...	nil	23
Haynes alloy No. 556	Average of four 24-h test periods	2.5	Boiling	...	63.5 (2500)	23
Haynes alloy No. 556	...	5	Boiling	24 h	167.6 (6600)	23
Haynes alloy No. 556	Average of four 24-h test periods	10	Room	...	0.6 (23)	23
Inco alloy G-3	Duplicate specimens	10	66 (150)	1 week	87; 92 (2.2; 2.3)	40
Inco alloy C-276	Corrosion test ASTM G28. Unwelded, solution heat treated specimens. No grain separation on bending	...	...	...	5.72 (225)	40
Inco alloy C-276	Corrosion test ASTM G28. As-welded with the gas-tungsten-arc method. No grain separation on bending	...	...	...	5.94 (234)	40
Inco alloy G	...	10	66 (150)	...	144 (3.66)	40
Incoloy 825	...	5	Room	...	0.13 (5)	64
Incoloy 825	...	10	Room	...	0.18 (7)	64
Incoloy 825	...	15	Room	...	0.18 (7)	64
Incoloy 825	...	28	50 (120)	...	0.9 (36)	64
Incoloy 825	...	5	Room	...	0.124 (4.9)	43
Incoloy 825	...	5	40 (104)	...	0.452 (17.8)	43
Incoloy 825	...	5	66 (150)	...	2.007 (79.0)	43
Incoloy 825	...	10	Room	...	0.183 (7.2)	43
Incoloy 825	...	10	40 (104)	...	0.472 (18.6)	43
Incoloy 825	...	10	66 (150)	...	2.591 (102.0)	43
Incoloy 825	...	15	Room	...	0.185 (7.3)	43
Incoloy 825	...	20	40 (104)	...	0.437 (17.2)	43
Incoloy 825	...	20	66 (150)	...	1.524 (60.0)	43
Incoloy 825	...	Conc	40 (104)	...	12.2 (480)	43
Incoloy 825	...	Conc	66 (150)	...	28.7 (1130)	43
Inconel 600	H$_2$ saturated, velocity 16.5 ft/min	5	30 (86)	20 h	0.32 (13)	133
Inconel 600	Air saturated, velocity 16.5 ft/min	5	30 (86)	20 h	2.4 (97)	133
Inconel 600	H$_2$ saturated, 16.5 ft/min	5	85 (185)	20 h	39.7 (1590)	133
Inconel 600	Air saturated, 16.5 ft/min	5	85 (185)	20 h	48.7 (1950)	133
Inconel 600	Air saturated, no velocity	5.9	30 (86)	120 h	1.12 (45)	133
Inconel 600	Air saturated, no velocity	5.9	80 (176)	120 h	17.8 (710)	133
Inconel 625	...	25	66 (150)	...	0.92 (38)	64
Inconel 625	...	30	66 (150)	...	0.82 (34)	64
Inconel 625	...	5	66 (150)	...	1.8 (71)	64
Inconel 625	...	10	66 (150)	...	2.1 (81)	64
Inconel 625	...	15	66 (150)	...	1.7 (65)	64
Inconel 625	...	20	66 (150)	...	16.5 (650)	64
Inconel 625	...	25	66 (150)	...	0.96 (38)	64
Inconel 625	...	30	66 (150)	...	0.86 (34)	64
Inconel 625	...	37	66 (150)	...	0.38 (15)	64
Inconel 625	...	5	66 (150)	...	1.77 (71)	64
Inconel 625	...	10	66 (150)	...	2.02 (81)	64
Inconel 625	...	15	66 (150)	...	1.92 (65)	64
Inconel 625	...	20	66 (150)	...	1.25 (50)	64
Inconel 625	...	Conc	66 (150)	...	0.375 (15)	64

(Continued)

Corrosion Behavior of Various Metals and Alloys in Hydrochloric Acid (Continued)

Material	Condition, other factors, comments	Concen-tration, %	Temperature, °C (°F)	Duration	Corrosion rate, mm/yr (mils/yr) or other	Ref
Monel 400	No velocity, no aeration	0.5	Boiling	10 d	0.725 (29)	134
Monel 400	No velocity, no aeration	1	Boiling	10 d	1.05 (42)	134
Monel 400	No velocity, no aeration	5	Boiling	10 d	1.1 (44)	134
Multimet	(c)	1	Room	24 h	<0.01 (0.1)	124
Multimet	(c)	1	66 (150)	24 h	nil	124
Multimet	(c)	1	Boiling	24 h	9.40 (370)	124
Multimet	(c)	2	Room	24 h	<0.01 (0.1)	124
Multimet	(c)	2	66 (150)	24 h	nil	124
Multimet	(c)	2	Boiling	24 h	22.7 (934)	124
Multimet	(c)	5	Room	24 h	0.43 (17)	124
Multimet	(c)	5	66 (150)	24 h	8.71 (343)	124
Multimet	(c)	5	Boiling	24 h	>25.4 (>1000)	124
Multimet	(c)	10	Room	24 h	0.33 (13)	124
Multimet	(c)	10	66 (150)	24 h	14.5 (572)	124
Multimet	(c)	10	Boiling	24 h	>25.4 (>1000)	124
Multimet	(c)	15	Room	24 h	0.38 (15)	124
Multimet	(c)	15	66 (150)	24 h	10.9 (431)	124
Multimet	(c)	15	Boiling	24 h	>25.4 (>1000)	124
Multimet	(c)	20	Room	24 h	0.20 (8.0)	124
Multimet	(c)	20	66 (150)	24 h	10.8 (424)	124
Multimet	(c)	20	Boiling	24 h	>25.4 (>1000)	124
Multimet	(c)	25	Room	24 h	0.15 (6.0)	124
Multimet	(c)	25	66 (150)	24 h	17.4 (687)	124
Multimet	(c)	37	Room	24 h	0.28 (11)	124
Multimet	(c)	37	66 (150)	24 h	>25.4 (>1000)	124
Zirconium						
Zirconium	Became brittle	18	19-26 (65-80)	36 d	0.06 (0.09)	74
Zirconium	...	37	19-26 (65-80)	36 d	0.002 (0.08)	74
Zirconium	...	37	110 (230)	7 d	0.48 (18.75)	74
Zirconium	Plus 20% HNO_3	20	Room	...	Dissolved	36
Zirconium	Plus 10% HNO_3	10	Room	...	Dissolved	36
Zr702	...	2	225 (435)	...	<0.025 (<1)	15
Zr702	...	5	Room	...	<0.025 (<1)	15
Zr702	...	10	35 (95)	...	<0.025 (<1)	15
Zr702	...	20	35 (95)	...	<0.025 (<1)	15
Zr702	...	32	30 (85)	...	<0.025 (<1)	15
Zr702	...	32	82 (180)	...	<0.025 (<1)	15
Zr702	Plus Cl_2 gas. Pitting	20	58 (135)	...	0.13-0.25 (5-10)	15
Zr702	Plus Cl_2 gas	37	58 (135)	...	<0.13 (<5)	15
Zr702	Plus 100 ppm $FeCl_3$. Stress-corrosion cracking observed	10	30 (85)	...	<0.025 (<1)	15
Zr702	Plus 100 ppm $FeCl_3$. Pitting rate	10	105 (220)	...	<0.13 (<5)	15
Zr702	Plus 100 ppm $FeCl_3$	20	105 (220)	...	<0.13 (<5)	15
Zr702	Plus 100 ppm $FeCl_3$. Stress-corrosion cracking observed	37	53 (125)	...	0.13-0.25 (5-10)	15
Zr702	Plus 20% HNO_3	20	Room	...	Dissolved	15
Zr702	Plus 10% HNO_3	10	Room	...	Dissolved	15
Zr704	Plus 100 ppm $FeCl_3$. Stress-corrosion cracking observed	10	30 (85)	...	<0.05 (<2)	15
Zr705	...	2	225 (435)	...	<0.025 (<1)	15
Zr705	Plus 100 ppm $FeCl_3$. Stress-corrosion cracking observed	10	30 (85)	...	<0.025 (<1)	15
Lead, tin, and zinc						
Lead	Pb may be used where this effect on service life can be tolerated	0-10	24 (75)	...	500-1270 μm/yr (20-50)	95
Lead	...	36	Room	...	<0.25 (<10)	17
Lead	...	36	100 (212)	...	1.3 (51)	17

(Continued)

Corrosion Behavior of Various Metals and Alloys in Hydrochloric Acid (Continued)

Material	Condition, other factors, comments	Concen-tration, %	Temperature, °C (°F)	Duration	Corrosion rate, mm/yr (mils/yr) or other	Ref
Lead	Specific gravity 1.6	...	Room	...	nil	17
Lead	Specific gravity 1.6	...	100 (212)	...	2.5 (100)	17
Lead	Chemical	1	24 (75)	...	610 μm/yr (24)	131
Lead	6% Sb	1	24 (75)	...	840 μm/yr (33)	131
Lead	Chemical	5	24 (75)	...	410 μm/yr (16)	131
Lead	6% Sb	5	24 (75)	...	510 μm/yr (20)	131
Lead	Chemical	10	24 (75)	...	560 μm/yr (22)	135
Lead	6% Sb	10	24 (75)	...	1090 μm/yr (43)	131
Lead	Chemical	15	24 (75)	...	790 μm/yr (31)	135
Lead	6% Sb	15	24 (75)	...	3810 μm/yr (150)	135
Tin	Hydrogen	6	...	...	60 mg/dm^2/d	59
Tin	Oxygen	6	...	...	11,100 mg/dm^2/d	59
Tin	...	10	20 (68)	...	Unsuitable	94
Tin	...	10	60 (140)	...	Unsuitable	94
Tin	...	10	100 (212)	...	Unsuitable	94
Tin	...	Conc	20 (68)	...	Unsuitable	94
Tin	...	Conc	60 (140)	...	Unsuitable	94
Tin	...	Conc	100 (212)	...	Unsuitable	94
Tantalum and hafnium						
Hafnium	...	20	...	8 d	0.005 (0.2)	11
Hafnium	...	20	...	8 d	0.005 (0.2)	11
Tantalum	...	18	19-26 (65-80)	36 d	nil	74
Tantalum	...	37	19-26 (65-80)	36 d	nil	74
Tantalum	...	37	110 (230)	7 d	nil	74
Tantalum	...	1	Boiling	...	<0.02 (<1)	37
Tantalum	...	1	190 (375)	...	<0.02 (<1)	37
Tantalum	...	5	Boiling	...	<0.02 (<1)	37
Tantalum	...	5	190 (375)	...	<0.02 (<1)	37
Tantalum	...	10	Boiling	...	<0.02 (<1)	37
Tantalum	...	10	190 (375)	...	<0.02 (<1)	37
Tantalum	...	15	Boiling	...	<0.02 (<1)	37
Tantalum	...	15	190 (375)	...	<0.02 (<1)	37
Tantalum	...	20	Boiling	...	<0.02 (<1)	37
Tantalum	...	20	190 (375)	...	<0.02 (<1)	37
Tantalum	Susceptible to embrittlement	25	190 (375)	...	<0.05 (<2)	37
Tantalum	Susceptible to embrittlement	30	190 (375)	...	<0.15 (<6)	37
Tantalum	Average of 29 tests of 90-h duration on 8 lots of tantalum	Conc	190 (375)	...	<0.07 (<30)	37
Tantalum	...	20	21 (70)	...	nil	42
Tantalum	...	20	100 (70)	...	nil	42
Tantalum	...	Conc	21 (70)	...	nil	42
Tantalum	...	Conc	100 (212)	...	nil	42
Tantalum	Commercial sheet (d)	15	Boiling	48 h	<0.025 (<1)	33
Tantalum	Commercial sheet (d)	20	Boiling	48 h	<0.025 (<1)	33
Tantalum	High purity (d)	15	Boiling	48 h	<0.025 (<1)	33
Tantalum	High purity (d)	20	Boiling	48 h	<0.025 (<1)	33
Tantalum-molybdenum alloy	Contains 0% Ta. Solutions saturated with oxygen	Conc	55 (131)	...	1.8 mg/dm^2/d	56
Tantalum-molybdenum alloy	Contains 10.1% Ta. Solutions saturated with oxygen	Conc	55 (131)	...	1.7 mg/dm^2/d	56
Tantalum-molybdenum alloy	Contains 20.1% Ta. Solutions saturated with oxygen	Conc	55 (131)	...	1.8 mg/dm^2/d	56
Tantalum-molybdenum alloy	Contains 30.0% Ta. Solutions saturated with oxygen	Conc	55 (131)	...	0.9 mg/dm^2/d	56
Tantalum-molybdenum alloy	Contains 40.0% Ta. Solutions saturated with oxygen	Conc	55 (131)	...	1.0 mg/dm^2/d	56
Tantalum-molybdenum alloy	Contains 50.0% Ta. Solutions saturated with oxygen	Conc	55 (131)	...	1.0 mg/dm^2/d	56

(Continued)

Corrosion Behavior of Various Metals and Alloys in Hydrochloric Acid (Continued)

Material	Condition, other factors, comments	Concentration, %	Temperature, °C (°F)	Duration	Corrosion rate, mm/yr (mils/yr) or other	Ref
Tantalum-molybdenum alloy	Contains 61.2% Ta. Solutions saturated with oxygen	Conc	55 (131)	...	0.0 mg/dm^2/d	56
Tantalum-molybdenum alloy	Contains 82.8% Ta. Solutions saturated with oxygen	Conc	55 (131)	...	0.0 mg/dm^2/d	56
Tantalum-molybdenum alloy	Contains 91.4% Ta. Solutions saturated with oxygen	Conc	55 (131)	...	0.0 mg/dm^2/d	56
Tantalum-molybdenum alloy	Contains 100% Ta. Solutions saturated with oxygen	Conc	55 (131)	...	0.0 mg/dm^2/d	56
Noble metals						
Gold	...	36	Room-100 (212)	...	<0.05 (<2)	8
Iridium	...	36	100 (212)	...	nil	29
Osmium	...	36	Room	...	nil	17
Osmium	...	36	100 (212)	...	<0.25 (<10)	17
Rhodium	...	35	100 (212)	...	nil	29
Ruthenium	...	36	100 (212)	...	nil	18
Silver	Limited aeration	5	100 (212)	...	0.035 (1.4)	135
Silver	Strong aeration	5	20 (70)	...	0.04 (1.6)	135
Silver	Limited aeration	15	20 (70)	...	0.007 (0.28)	135
Silver	Strong aeration	15	20 (70)	...	0.085 (3.3)	135
Silver	Limited aeration	25	20 (70)	...	0.14 (5.5)	135
Silver	Strong aeration	25	20 (70)	...	0.36 (14.2)	135
Silver	Limited aeration	36	20 (70)	...	0.07 (2.8)	135
Silver	Strong aeration	36	100 (212)	...	2.5 (100)	135
Others						
85WC-15Co	...	10	22 (72)	48 h	0.14 g/m^2/h (0.09 mg/in.^{2}/h)	34
85WC-15Co	...	10	22 (72)	48 h	0.12 g/m^2/h (0.08 mg/in.^{2}/h)	34
94WC-6Co	...	10	22 (72)	48 h	0.09 g/m^2/h (0.06 mg/in.^{2}/h)	34
94WC-6Ni	...	10	22 (72)	48 h	0.03 g/m^2/h (0.02 mg/in.^{2}/h)	34
Cb alloy	Wrought 100% Cb; laboratory button; annealed at 1175 °C (2140 °F) for 30 min. Sample embrittled. (d)	15	Boiling	48 h	0.45 (18)	33
Cb alloy	Wrought 100% Cb; laboratory button; annealed at 1175 °C (2140 °F) for 30 min. Sample embrittled. (d)	20	Boiling	48 h	0.95 (38)	33
Cb alloy	Wrought 100% Cb; arc melted; annealed at 1400 °C (2552 °F) for 1 h. Sample embrittled. (d)	15	Boiling	48 h	0.22 (9)	33
Cb alloy	Wrought 100% Cb; arc melted; annealed at 1400 °C (2552 °F) for 1 h. Sample embrittled. (d)	20	Boiling	48 h	0.6 (24)	33
Cb alloy	Wrought 100% Cb; electron-beam melted; annealed at 1400 °C (2552 °F) for 1 h. Sample embrittled. (d)	15	Boiling	48 h	0.22 (9)	33
Cb alloy	Wrought 100% Cb; electron-beam melted; annealed at 1400 °C (2552 °F) for 1 h. Sample embrittled. (d)	20	Boiling	48 h	0.52 (21)	33
Cb alloy	Wrought 0.75% Zr, bal Cb; arc melted; annealed at 1400 °C (2552 °F) for 1 h. Sample embrittled. (d)	15	Boiling	48 h	0.25 (10)	33
Cb alloy	Wrought 0.75% Zr, bal Cb; arc melted; annealed at 1400 °C (2552 °F) for 1 h. Sample embrittled. (d)	20	Boiling	48 h	0.52 (21)	33
Cb alloy	Wrought 8% Ti, bal Cb; arc melted; annealed at 1400 °C (2552 °F) for 1 h. (d)	15	Boiling	48 h	0.32 (13)	33
Cb alloy	Wrought 8% Ti, bal Cb; arc melted; annealed at 1400 °C (2552 °F) for 1 h. (d)	20	Boiling	48 h	0.7 (28)	33
Cb alloy	Wrought 6.9% Ti, 0.81% Zr, bal Cb; arc melted; annealed at 1430 °C (2606 °F) for 1 h. (d)	15	Boiling	48 h	0.27 (11)	33
Cb alloy	Wrought 6.9% Ti, 0.81% Zr, bal Cb; arc melted; annealed at 1400 °C (2552 °F) for 1 h. Sample embrittled in stenciled area only. (d)	20	Boiling	48 h	0.775 (31)	33

(Continued)

Corrosion Behavior of Various Metals and Alloys in Hydrochloric Acid (Continued)

Material	Condition, other factors, comments	Concen-tration, %	Temperature, °C (°F)	Duration	Corrosion rate, mm/yr (mils/yr) or other	Ref
Cb alloy	Wrought 50% V, 50% Cb; arc melted. Not tested for embrittlement. (d)	15	Boiling	48 h	2.07 (83)	33
		All	Room	...	Unsuitable	119
Magnesium	...	1	Boiling	...	<0.02 (<1)	37
Niobium	...	1	190 (375)	...	<0.02 (<1)	37
Niobium	...	1	190 (375)	...	<0.05 (<2)	37
Niobium	Susceptible to embrittlement	5	Boiling	...	<0.02 (<1)	37
Niobium	Susceptible to embrittlement	5	190 (375)	...	<0.12 (<5)	37
Niobium	Susceptible to embrittlement	10	Boiling	...	<6.35 (<25)	37
Niobium	Susceptible to embrittlement	15	Boiling	...	>12 (>500)	37
Niobium	Susceptible to embrittlement	15	190 (375)	...	<1.2 (<50)	37
Niobium	Susceptible to embrittlement	20	Boiling	...	nil	2
Niobium	...	1	Boiling	...	0.025 (1.0)	2
Niobium	...	37	Room	...	0.25 (10)	2
Niobium	...	37	60 (140)	...	0.5 (20)	2
Niobium	Plus Cl₂	37	60 (140)	...	0.025 (1.0)	2
Niobium	Plus 0.1% FeCl₃	10	Boiling	...	0.125 (5.0)	2
Niobium	Plus 0.6% FeCl3	10	Boiling	...	0.05 (2.0)	2
Niobium	Plus 35% FeCl₂ and 2% FeCl₃	10	Boiling	...	nil	74
Niobium	...	18	19-26 (65-80)	36 d	0.05 (0.12)	74
Niobium	...	37	19-26 (65-80)	36 d	0.1 (4)	74
Niobium	Tarnished	37	110 (230)	7 d	nil	2
Niobium	Aerated	15	Room-60 (140)	...	0.025 (1.0)	2
Niobium	Aerated	15	100 (212)	...	0.025 (1.0)	2
Niobium	Aerated	30	35 (95)	...	0.05 (2.0)	2
Niobium	Aerated	30	60 (140)	...	0.125 (5.0)	2
Niobium	Aerated	30	100 (212)	...		2

(a) Based on five 24-h test periods with cast specimens 38 mm x 25 mm x 6 mm (1.5 in. x 1 in. x 0.25 in.), 120-grit abrasive finish. (b) Determined in laboratory tests. It is recommended that samples be tested under actual plant conditions. (c) All specimens prepared from 12-gage, solution heat-treated sheet. Calculated on a minimum of five 24-h test periods. (d) Average of three 48-h periods.

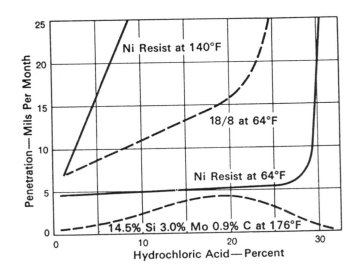

Cast irons. Corrosion rate of high-nickel and high-silicon molybdenum alloy irons compared to 18-8 stainless steel when exposed to hydrochloric acid at various concentrations. Source: "Physical and Corrosion Properties," in *Source Book on Ductile Iron*, A.H. Rauch, Ed., American Society for Metals, Metals Park, OH, 1977, 367.

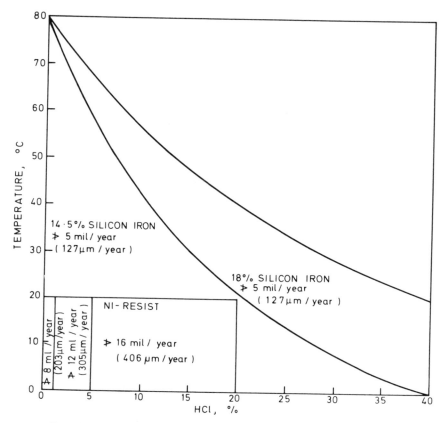

Cast irons. Corrosion rates of cast iron in hydrochloric acid. Source: H.T. Angus, *Cast Iron: Physical and Engineering Properties*, 2nd ed., Butterworths, London, 1976, 323.

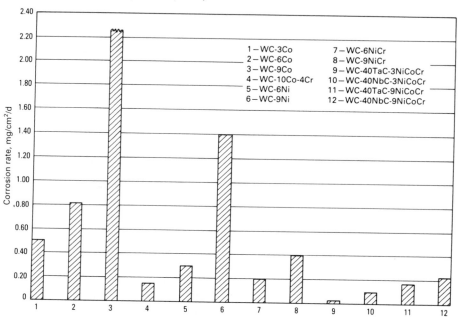

Cemented carbides. Corrosion resistance of cemented carbides in 22% hydrochloric acid at room temperature. Source: E. Kay, T. Bader, Ch. Hohenrainer, L. Schmid, and R. Glatzle, Korrosionsresistent hochverschlei festye Hartmetalle, *Werkst. Korros.,* May 1986, and E. Kay and L. Schmid, "New Hardmetal Alloys with Improved Erosion and Corrosion Resistance," as reported in *Metals Handbook*, 9th ed., Vol 13, Corrosion, ASM International, Metals Park, OH, 1987, 852.

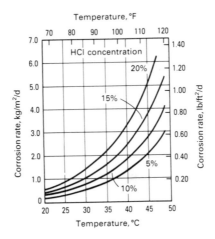

Low-carbon steel. Effect of temperature on corrosion of low-carbon steel in uninhibited hydrochloric acid. Source: Chemical Processing Industry.

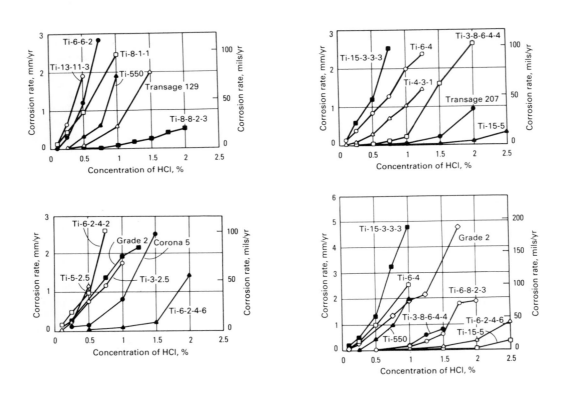

Titanium. General corrosion of annealed titanium alloys in naturally aerated hydrochloric acid solution. Source: *Metals Handbook*, 9th ed., Vol 13, Corrosion, ASM International, Metals Park, OH, 1987, 680.

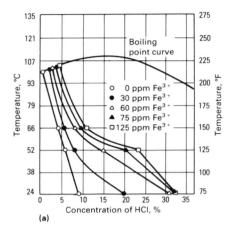 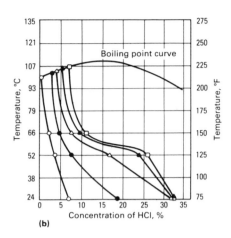 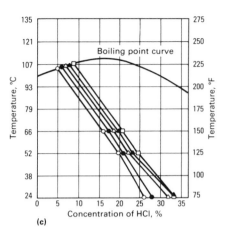

(a) **(b)** **(c)**

Titanium. Effect of minute ferric ion concentrations on the useful corrosion resistance of grade 2 titanium (a), grade 12 titanium (b), and grade 7 titanium (c) in naturally aerated hydrochloric acid solutions. 0.127-mm/yr (5-mils/yr) isocorrosion lines are shown. Source: *Metals Handbook*, 9th ed., Vol 13, Corrosion, ASM International, Metals Park, OH, 1987, 683.

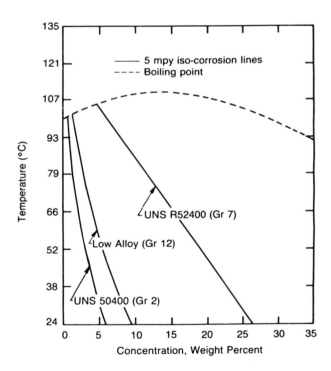

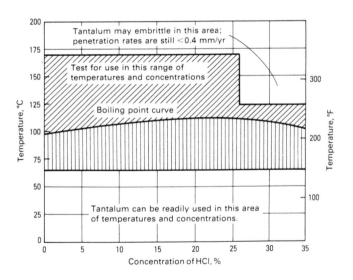

Titanium. Corrosion of titanium alloys in naturally aerated hydrochloric acid solutions. Source: T.F. Degnan, "Materials Construction for Hydrochloric Acid," in *Process Industries Corrosion*, B.J. Moniz and W.I. Pollock, Ed., National Association of Corrosion Engineers, Houston, 1986, 170.

Tantalum. Corrosion of tantalum in hydrochloric acid at various concentrations and temperatures. Source: M. Stern and C.R. Bishop, Corrosion and Electrochemical Behavior, in *Columbium and Tantalum*, F.T. Sisco and E. Epremian, Ed., John Wiley & Sons, New York, 1963, and "Tantalum, Corrosion Data, Comparative Charts and Coating Characteristics," General Technologies Corporation.

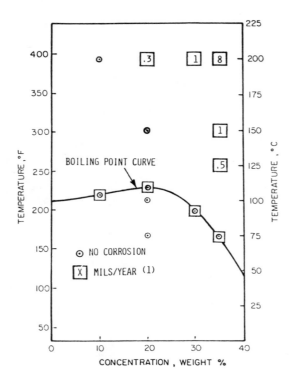

Tantalum. Corrosion resistance of tantalum in hydrochloric acid. Source: R.H. Burns, F.S. Shuker, Jr., *et al.*, "Industrial Applications of Corrosion-Resistant Tantalum, Niobium, and Their Alloys," in *Refractory Metals and Their Industrial Applications* (STP 849), R.E. Smallwood, Ed., ASTM, Philadelphia, 1984, 60.

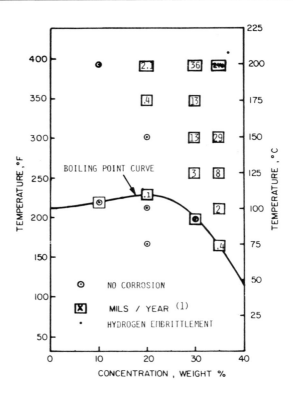

Tantalum. Corrosion resistance of KBI alloy 40 in hydrochloric acid (KBI Alloy 40 is a Ta-40Nb alloy). Source: R.H. Burns, F.S. Shuker, Jr., *et al.*, "Industrial Applications of Corrosion-Resistant Tantalum, Niobium, and Their Alloys," in *Refractory Metals and Their Industrial Applications* (STP 849), R.E. Smallwood, Ed., ASTM, Philadelphia, 1984, 59.

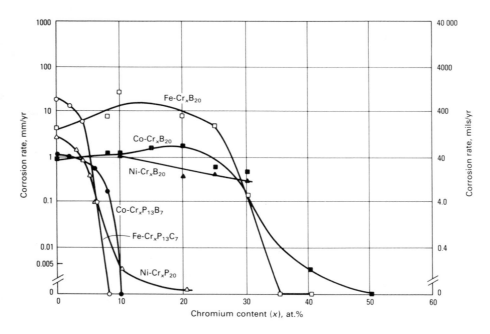

Various alloys. The influence of chromium content on the corrosion rates of iron-, cobalt-, and nickel-base amorphous alloys in $1N$ hydrochloric acid. Source: *Metals Handbook*, 9th ed., Vol 13, Corrosion, ASM International, Metals Park, OH, 1987, 867.

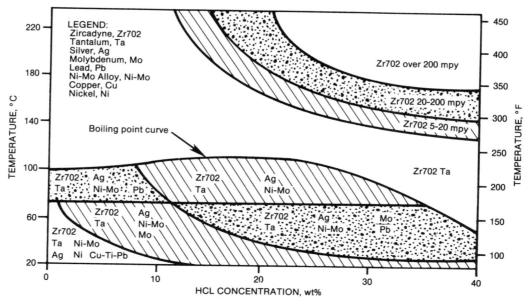

Corrosion resistance of materials to hydrochloric acid

Various alloys. Corrosion resistance of various materials to hydrochloric acid. These materials exhibit a corrosion rate of less than 20 mils/yr, except for zirconium and tantalum, which have corrosion rates of less than 5 mils/yr. Source: Teledyne Wah Chang Albany.

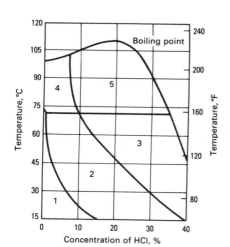

a)

Metals with reported corrosion rates of <0.5 mm/yr (<20 mils/yr) in HCl

Zone 1	Zone 2	All zones (including 5)
ACI CN-7M(a)(c)(f)	Silicon bronze(b)(f)	
Monel 400(b)(c)(f)	Silicon cast iron(c)(g)	Platinum
Copper(b)(c)(f)		Tantalum
Nickel 200(b)(c)(f)	**Zone 3**	Silver(c)(f)
Silicon bronze(b)(c)(f)		Zirconium(c)(f)
Silicon cast iron(c)(g)	Silicon cast iron(c)(g)	Hastelloy B-2(c)(f)
Tungsten		Molybdenum(c)(f)
Titanium, grade 7	**Zone 4**	
Titanium, grade 2(d)	Tungsten	
	Titanium, grade 7(e)	

(a) <2% HCl at 25 °C (75 °F). (b) No aeration. (c) No FeCl₃ or CuCl₂ contamination. (d) <10% HCl at 25 °C (75 °F). (e) <5% HCl at boiling temperature. (f) No free chlorine. (g) Contains chromium, molybdenum, and nickel

b)

Various alloys. Various alloys for hydrochloric acid service. Source: D.L. Gaver, Ed., *Corrosion Data Survey*, 6th ed., National Association of Corrosion Engineers, Houston, 1985, 180-181.

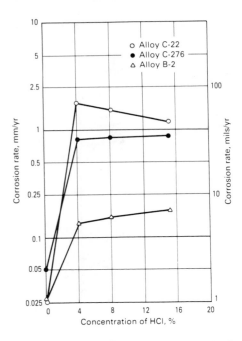

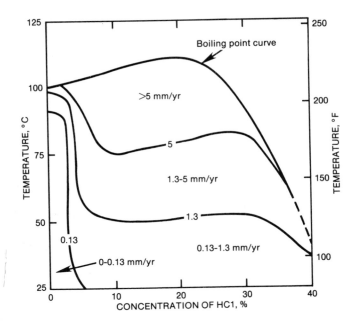

Various alloys. Effect of hydrochloric acid on the corrosion of various alloys in 15% hydrochloric acid at 80 °C. Source: N. Sridhar, Paper 182, presented at "Corrosion/86," National Association of Corrosion Engineers, Houston, 1986.

Hastelloy G. Isocorrosion diagram for Hastelloy G in hydrochloric acid. Source: *Metals Handbook*, 9th ed., Vol 13, Corrosion, ASM International, Metals Park, OH, 1987, 1163.

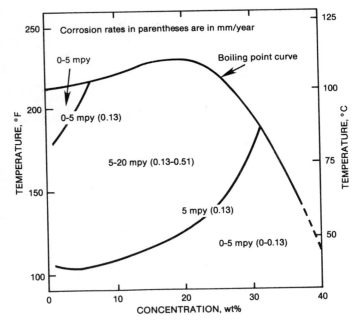

a)

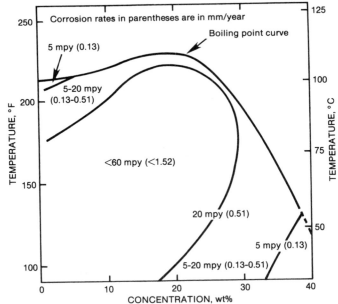

b)

(Continued)

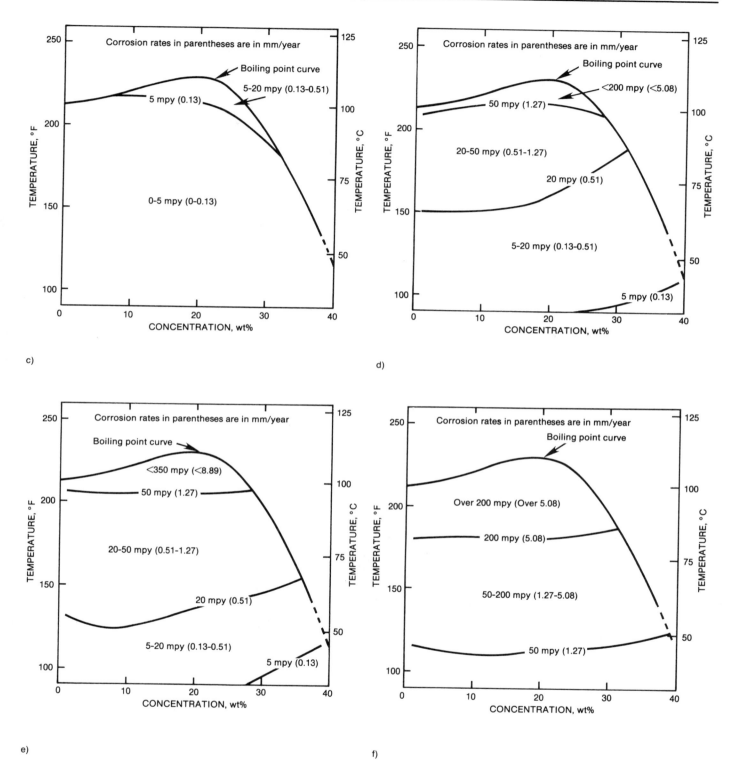

Hastelloy B-2. Resistance to (a) hydrochloric acid, (b) hydrochloric acid purged with oxygen, (c) hydrochloric acid purged with nitrogen, (d) hydrochloric acid with 50 ppm ferric ions, (e) hydrochloric acid with 100 ppm ferric ions, and (f) hydrochloric acid with 500 ppm ferric ions. All test specimens were solution heat-treated and in the unwelded condition. Source: Haynes International, 1984.

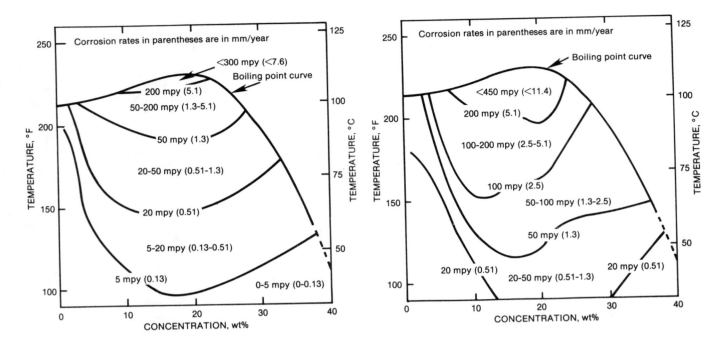

a)

b)

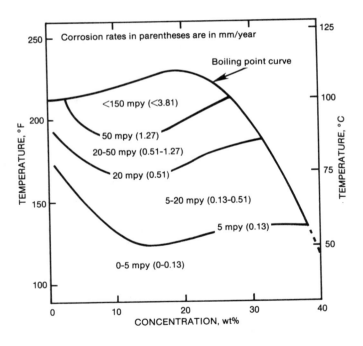

c)

Hastelloy C-276. Resistance to (a) hydrochloric acid, (b) hydrochloric acid purged with oxygen, and (c) hydrochloric acid purged with nitrogen. Test specimens for (a) and (b) were heat treated at 1121 °C (2050 °F), rapid quenched, and in the unwelded condition; for (c) test specimens were solution heat-treated and in the unwelded condition. Source: Haynes International, 1984.

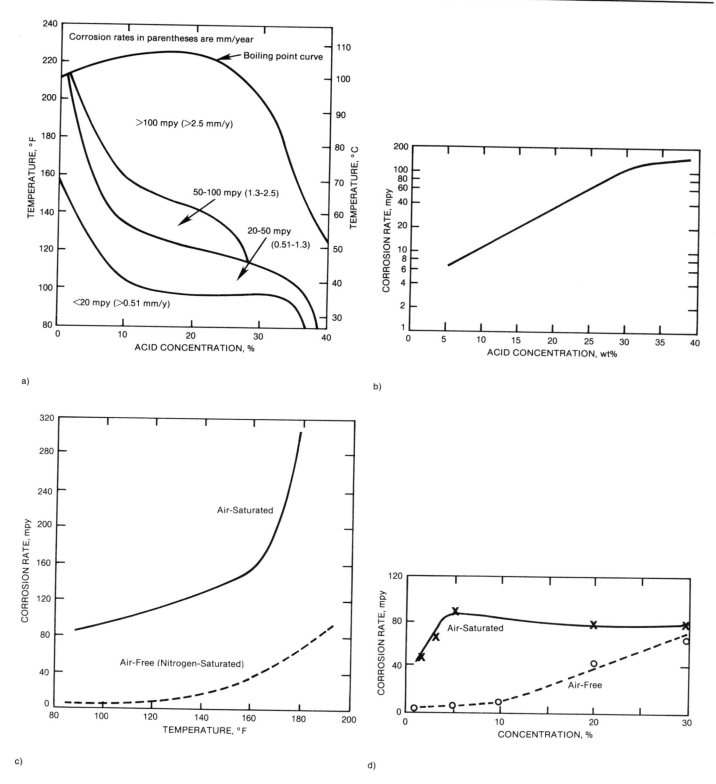

Nickel alloys. Corrosion rates in hydrochloric acid for (a) Incoloy alloy 825, based on laboratory tests in pure acid; (b) Inconel alloy 600, at room temperature; (c) Monel alloy 400 in 5% hydrochloric acid; and (d) Nickel 200 in hydrochloric acid at 86 °F (the air-free samples were nitrogen saturated). Source: Inco Alloys International.

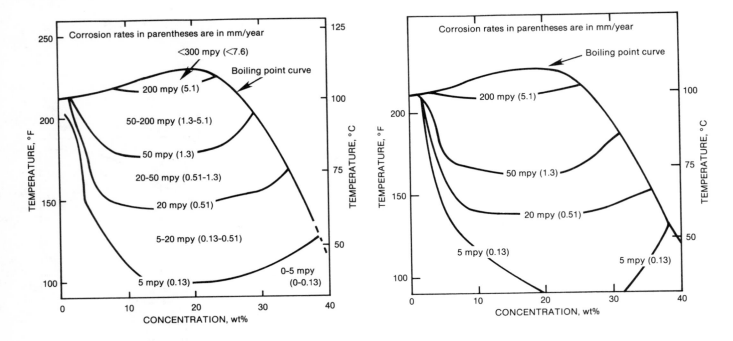

a)

b)

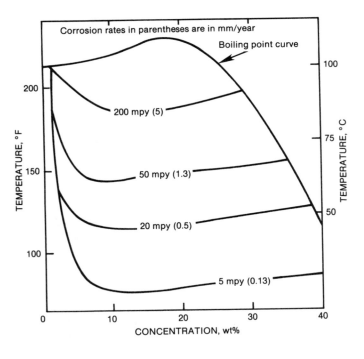

c)

Nickel alloys. Resistance to hydrochloric acid. (a) Hastelloy C-4, test specimens were solution heat-treated at 1066 °C (1950 °F), rapid quenched and in the unwelded condition. (b) Hastelloy C-22, test specimens were solution heat-treated and in the unwelded condition; and (c) Hastelloy G-30, test specimens were heat-treated at 1177 °C (2150 °F), rapid quenched and in the unwelded condition. Source: Haynes International.

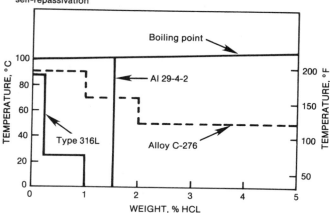

Regions outlined exhibit corrosion rates less than 25 mm/a(10 mpy) and self-repassivation

Nickel and nickel-base alloys. Comparison of corrosion resistance of AL 29-4-2, Nickel alloy C-276, and type 316L stainless steel in dilute hydrochloric acid. Source: Allegheny Ludlum Corporation, 1982.

Hydrofluoric Acid and Hydrogen Fluoride

Anhydrous hydrogen fluoride (AHF) and hydrofluoric acid (aqueous hydrogen fluoride) are of great industrial importance. Hydrofluoric acid (HF), a colorless, fuming, poisonous, highly corrosive, extremely reactive liquid, is used in large quantities for pickling of stainless steels and other metals, acid treating of wells, and etching of glass. Other uses include production of aluminum fluoride and synthetic cryolite for aluminum production; production of fluorinated organics such as aerosol propellants, special-purpose solvents, refrigerants, and plastics; formulation of atomic-energy feed materials; manufacture of elemental fluorine; preparation of fluorides and fluoborates; dissolving of ores; and cleaning of stone and brick.

Anhydrous hydrogen fluoride is the foundation of the multibillion dollar fluorocarbon industry, which encompasses essentially all refrigerants, fire-extinguishing agents, ultrasonic cleaning fluids, fluorocarbon plastics, and fluorocarbon elastomers. A popular process for alkylation of petroleum to enhance yields of gasoline depends on the use of anhydrous hydrogen fluoride.

Both aqueous hydrofluoric acid and anhydrous hydrogen fluoride are hazardous chemicals that are highly corrosive to skin, eyes, lungs, and mucous membranes. Fluoride salts, although added to potable waters to prevent tooth decay, are toxic in higher concentrations. Painful, persistent burns and often deep-seated ulcerations result from contact with aqueous hydrofluoric acid or anhydrous hydrogen fluoride, and inhalation of high concentrations of the vapors causes lung damage. The Occupational Safety and Health Administration has ruled that an employee's exposure to hydrofluoric acid vapor in any 8-h work shift of a 40-h work week shall not exceed a time-weighted average of 3 ppm hydrofluoric acid vapor by volume.

Anhydrous hydrogen fluoride is manufactured by the reaction of H_2SO_4 and calcium fluoride (CaF_2) in horizontal kiln-like reactors, usually constructed of steel with a high-nickel alloy liner at the feed and discharge ends. The popular Buch process premixes the CaF_2 and H_2SO_4 in a high-nickel alloy mixer that reduces corrosion of the steel reactor. The reaction is endothermic and therefore requires a source of heat.

Information on suitable materials of construction for handling hydrofluoric acid is presented in various sources. However, many factors that are not shown on charts can influence the performance of these materials, and adequate experience or testing under the proposed conditions is necessary to avoid serious corrosion problems. The duration of the test is important because most metals form protective films or scales that decrease initially high rates to the low rates found in commercial use. Therefore, the validity of short-term rates should be discounted unless the validity of the short-term test has been confirmed by longer tests.

Materials Commonly Used. Materials in common use in hydrofluoric acid service are listed in the Materials Selection for Hydrofluoric Acid Service table. This information, although not exhaustive, can be considered to be a valid guide for initial design and cost estimates of equipment to be used for handling most commercial hydrofluoric acids and is reliable for final material selection for service in acids known to be of normal commercial quality and to contain no impurities that might result in unusual corrosion. The information in this table assumes that the acid will be received and stored at ambient temperatures only. Where no temperature range is given, the data should be considered to be valid only for ambient-temperature service.

Unsuitable Materials. Metals considered unsuitable for hydrofluoric acid service can be divided into four groups: velocity-sensitive, hydrogen-sensitive, component-sensitive, and notch-sensitive.

Velocity-sensitive metals include copper, copper alloys other than copper nickels, and straight chromium stainless steels (such as type 410).

Hydrogen-sensitive metals are further divided into two subgroups— hydrogen embrittlement sensitive and hydrogen blistering sensitive. Metals sensitive to hydrogen embrittlement are steels and iron alloys, and welds and heat-affected zones with hardnesses of 22 HRC or higher. Fine-grain steels (without inclusion-shape control) are sensitive to hydrogen blistering.

Component-sensitive metals comprise high-zinc uninhibited brasses, and alloys of, or containing appreciable amounts of, silicon, tantalum, zirconium, titanium, and niobium. Notch-sensitive metals are free-machining steel, high-phosphorus steels, and cast irons.

High-Temperature Gas. A series of short-term corrosion tests conducted on the rate of attack of hot, gaseous anhydrous hydrogen fluoride on various metals showed that Nickel 200, Monel 400, and Inconel 600 all have useful resistance to gaseous anhydrous hydrogen fluoride at temperatures up to 600 °C (1110 °F) and that austenitic stainless steels are inferior to carbon steel in this regard. Although corrosion rates were exaggerated and distorted by the short 3- to 15-h test periods, other data confirm the general ranking of the materials. Although the tests were run for only 36 h, the results agree with experience.

Inconel 600 has been successfully used in the hydrofluorination of metal oxides at temperatures of 370 to 590 °C (700 to 1095 °F). Nickel 200 and the copper-nickel alloys are susceptible to intergranular embrittlement by sulfur compounds at temperatures above about 300 °C (570 °F). Trace amounts of these compounds are present in commercial anhydrous hydrogen fluoride. Inconel 600 resists embrittlement and has been successfully used at these temperatures in gaseous hydrofluoric acid environments. It should be noted that many nickel alloys, including Hastelloy C-276 and Inconel 625, undergo metallurgical changes, such as aging or long-range ordering at temperatures above 400 to 500 °C (750 to 930 °F). Hardness and susceptibility to hydrogen embrittlement also increase. Inconel 600 is relatively unaffected.

Material Summaries

The following material summaries were compiled from a survey of the available literature. Inclusion of a material description under a given environment does not imply that it is the most appropriate material for corrosion service in that environment. Likewise, exclusion of a given material does not imply that it is not suitable for corrosion service applications in that environment.

Carbon and Alloy Steels. Hardened carbon and alloy steels exhibit hydrogen embrittlement, and steel plate and pipelines suffer hydrogen blistering and stepwise cracking in the presence of either aqueous or anhydrous hydrofluoric acid. Corrosion of steel by nonoxidizing acids is accompanied by the formation of atomic hydrogen, which then either combines to form gaseous molecular hydrogen or is absorbed by the steel. Because of the small quantities of sulfides and arsenic that it contains, hydrofluoric acid inhibits the formation of molecular hydrogen and thus promotes absorption of atomic hydrogen into the steel. Once absorbed, the atomic hydrogen may migrate to dislocations in hardened steel and cause hydrogen embrittlement or may recombine at laminations or inclusions and produce blistering.

Carbon steels have useful corrosion resistance in the range of 64 to 100% hydrofluoric acid. Resistance to aqueous acid is limited to ambient temperatures. Liquid anhydrous hydrogen fluoride is commonly handled in carbon steel at temperatures up to 65 °C (150 °F). Gaseous anhydrous hydrogen fluoride is less corrosive and can be handled at temperatures up to 300 °C (570 °F).

Although Interstate Commerce Commission regulations permitted transportation of aqueous hydrofluoric acid of 60% or greater concentration in steel containers that were passivated with 58% acid, one study found that even passivated drums developed excessive hydrogen pressure from corrosion with 60% acid. The results of this testing indicate that the minimum concentration should be 64%. In practice, the closest commercial grade is 70% hydrofluoric acid, and the maximum recommended temperature for storage and handling is 30 °C (90 °F).

Alloy steels often have higher corrosion rates than carbon steels. In one case, a section of low-temperature pipe (ASTM A333, grade 9) containing nickel and copper was installed in a carbon steel piping system handling a mixture of organics and anhydrous hydrogen fluoride at a temperature above ambient. The section failed by uniform thinning, whereas the carbon steel fittings on either end were relatively unaffected.

It has been found that dilute acids (1.4 to 1.7N hydrofluoric, sulfuric, perchloric, and hydrochloric) used for chemical cleaning of heat exchangers corrode iron and carbon steel at about equivalent rates, but that hydrofluoric acid causes exceptionally high corrosion rates on steels containing 1.25 to 18% Cr (ASTM A335 grades and type 430 stainless steel).

Many failures of alloy steel fasteners in anhydrous hydrogen fluoride service have occurred, particularly with fasteners made of the Cr-Mo steel ASTM A193, grade B7. A better choice for high-strength fasteners is grade B7M, which is the same as grade B7, but tempered to a lower hardness (201 to 235 HB). However, bolts made of this material are subject to cracking under stresses beyond the yield point in hydrofluoric acid service. In addition, the above-mentioned range of hardness is difficult for manufacturers to meet while still fulfilling minimum tensile requirements.

Stainless Steels. The use of stainless steels in hydrofluoric acid service is generally rather limited. Austenitic stainless steels have good resistance to liquid anhydrous hydrogen fluoride at somewhat elevated temperatures. Unpublished data show corrosion rates of less than 0.13 mm/yr (<5 mils/yr) for type 304 stainless steel at 100 °C (210 °F), but high corrosion rates at 150 °C (300 °F). Type 304 stainless steel has good resistance to anhydrous hydrogen fluoride gas up to 200 °C (390 °F). Cast ACI CF-8M stainless steel is used for anhydrous hydrogen fluoride pumps. However, both type 304 stainless steel and carbon steel have been known to fail by direct impingement of anhydrous hydrogen fluoride streams.

Austenitic stainless steels have limited resistance to dilute hydrofluoric acid. Type 304 stainless steel has poor resistance to any significant concentration, but type 316 has useful resistance at ambient temperatures and concentrations below 10%.

Cold-worked type 303 stainless steel failed rapidly when used as a fastener material in a hydrofluoric acid plant. Cold-worked type 304 stainless steel fasteners (ASTM A193, grade B8, class 2) had few failures.

Annealed austenitic stainless steels are resistant but not immune to stress-corrosion cracking by hydrofluoric acid. In one study, types 304 and 316 both failed from transgranular cracking in impure 12% hydrofluoric acid at 70 °C (160 °F); type 304 failed in hot 40 to 50% hydrofluoric acid. However, these conditions are more severe than are reasonable for the use of stainless steels in hydrofluoric acid. This study also reported that cold-worked 18-8 stainless steel did not suffer stress-corrosion cracking in a 7-day test in anhydrous hydrogen fluoride at 70 °C (150 °F). Another study showed that the threshold Cl⁻ ion concentration necessary to cause intergranular stress-corrosion cracking of sensitized type 304 stainless steel was greatly reduced by the presence of fluorides.

Higher alloys such as 20Cb-3 stainless steel and Incoloy 825 have good resistance to all concentrations of hydrofluoric acid at ambient temperatures and to 0 to 10% concentrations at 70 °C (160 °F). The preferred material for pumps and valves for 70% hydrofluoric acid at ambient temperatures and for valve trim for anhydrous hydrogen fluoride is ACI CN-7M casting alloy.

Aluminum. Hydrofluoric acid is corrosive to aluminum alloys, and for most alloy compositions, its corrosive action is uniform and imparts a bright and silvery appearance to the metal. Hydrofluoric acid has been used as an etchant in the preparation of decorative patterns on aluminum.

Copper. In general, the use of copper in hydrofluoric acid service, regardless of hydrofluoric acid concentration, is limited by its susceptibility to aeration and velocity effects. The major exception is alloy C71500 (copper nickel, 30%), which has good resistance to both aqueous and anhydrous hydrofluoric acid. Unlike some other copper alloys, C71500 is not sensitive to velocity effects. Red brass (85% Cu minimum, remainder mostly zinc) has been used for pipes, fittings, and valves handling hydrofluoric acid, but only for acid concentrations of 1% or less. In this application, limited aeration had no significant adverse effect, but metal failure occurred at a site involving alternate wet and dry conditions.

Lead. The resistance of lead to corrosion by hydrofluoric acid is only fair. However, lead is used to handle hydrofluoric acid because it is the only low-priced metal that has adequate corrosion resistance. The corrosion rate in this acid (if it is free of air) is less than 510 μm/yr (20 mils/yr) for a wide range of temperatures and concentrations. Hydrofluoric acid rapidly attacks lead when dilute, but has little effect at strengths of 52 to 70%.

Magnesium is rapidly attacked by all mineral acids except hydrofluoric acid and chromic acid. Hydrofluoric acid does not attack magnesium to an appreciable extent, because it forms an insoluble, protective magnesium fluoride film on the magnesium; however, pitting develops at low acid concentrations. With increasing temperature, the rate of attack increases at the liquid line, but to a negligible extent elsewhere.

Molybdenum has good resistance to both aqueous and anhydrous hydrofluoric acid. The corrosion rates of molybdenum in 25 to 50% hydrofluoric acid at 100 °C (210 °F) are 0.4 to 0.5 mm/yr (16 to 20 mils/yr) in aerated acid. Rates in the absence of air are so small as to be negligible.

Nickel and Nickel Alloys

Nickel 200 is less resistant than Monel 400 to aqueous hydrofluoric acid. Also, oxygen has a greater accelerating effect on corrosion of Nickel 200. In aqueous hydrofluoric acid, use of Nickel 200 is limited to completely air-free systems below 80 °C (175 °F). Although there are reports of stress-corrosion cracking of Nickel 200 in aqueous hydrofluoric acid, they appear to be related to such impurities as cupric fluoride (CuF_2). Nickel 200 is one of the most resistant alloys to hot anhydrous hydrogen fluoride vapor, but it may be embrittled by sulfur compound impurities.

Monel 400 is used extensively in hydrofluoric acid alkylation units and in the manufacture and handling of hydrofluoric acid. It has excellent resistance to liquid hydrofluoric acid over the entire concentration range in the absence of oxygen to at least 150 °C (300 °F).

Monel 400 is subject to stress-corrosion cracking when exposed to wet vapors of hydrofluoric acid in the presence of oxygen. Cracking is intergranular. In one investigation, Monel 400 showed transgranular stress-corrosion cracking in the vapor phase of dilute hydrofluoric acid solutions (up to 0.5% hydrofluoric acid) at temperatures up to 95 °C (200 °F). The cracking susceptibility did not depend on the presence of oxygen, and no cracking was found in the liquid phase.

The mechanism of cracking was unknown until it was found that aqueous hydrofluoric acid solutions containing appreciable concentrations of cupric chloride ($CuCl_2$) would cause rapid cracking of stressed Monel 400. The least resistant nickel-copper composition corresponds to that of Monel 400 (33% Cu). Copper-nickel alloys with 30% or less nickel are resistant.

The reason that stress-corrosion cracking is usually limited to the vapor phase rather than liquid is the enrichment of a thin layer of aqueous hydrofluoric acid in the vapor with copper fluoride corrosion products. The presence of oxygen accelerates corrosion and forms CuF_2 from CuF. The much greater dilution of corrosion products prevents reaching a critical concentration of CuF_2 in the liquid phase.

Inconel 600 is resistant to dilute aqueous hydrofluoric acid at ambient temperatures and to anhydrous hydrogen fluoride. It has been used in valves and other equipment in place of Monel 400 to avoid possible stress-corrosion cracking. It is the most widely used alloy for hot hydrofluoric acid vapors, combining excellent chemical resistance and comparatively good metallurgical stability.

High-Performance Nickel Alloys. The Hastelloy alloys (C-276, B-2, G, and G-3) and Inconel 625 all have good-to-excellent resistance to aqueous and anhydrous hydrofluoric acid and to high-temperature hydrofluoric acid vapors. The presence of air or oxidizing agents can cause fairly high corrosion rates in hot aqueous acids.

Niobium, although resistant to most organic and mineral acids, is non-resistant to both aqueous and anhydrous hydrofluoric acid in even trace amounts. Metals and welding products that contain appreciable amounts of niobium will suffer accelerated corrosion by hydrofluoric acid under certain circumstances. The presence of several percent niobium in Monel 400 welds has been known to cause preferential weld attack.

Noble Metals. The noble metals, including gold, silver, and platinum, are all more or less unaffected by anhydrous hydrogen fluoride or by aqueous hydrofluoric acid of any concentration at ambient temperatures and, in most cases, to the boiling point or higher. Silver is widely used in stills, heating coils, and condensers for pure hydrofluoric acid. The resistance of silver to hydrofluoric acid can be affected by the presence of sulfides and oxygen. Silver is not passivated by hydrofluoric acid, as it is by the other halide acids. Platinum and gold are unaffected at high temperatures.

Tantalum. Although immune to attack by almost all acids, tantalum is nonresistant to both aqueous and anhydrous hydrofluoric acid, even in trace amounts. Under certain circumstances, hydrofluoric acid will cause accelerated corrosion of metals and welding products that contain appreciable amounts of tantalum.

In fact, hydrofluoric acid is the best solvent for tantalum. The rate of attack varies from slow for dilute acid to rapid for concentrated solutions. The rate of attack by hydrofluoric acid can be greatly accelerated by the addition of HNO_3 and other oxidizing agents, such as H_2O_2. Embrittlement of the metal due to the absorption of atomic (nascent) hydrogen can occur when the metal is attacked by hydrofluoric acid. However, when sufficient HNO_3 is present, hydrogen embrittlement does not occur, even after nearly all of the tantalum is dissolved—for example, by severe pickling. The rate of hydrogen absorption is greatly reduced in dilute hydrofluoric acid if the tantalum is made positive by impressing 2 to 10 V on the material in an electrolytic cell. Embrittlement by hydrogen does not occur when tantalum is made positive. In solution of hydrofluoric acid, which prevents the formation of the protective oxide film, tantalum is less noble than zinc, manganese, aluminum, and zirconium.

Attack on tantalum apparently does not occur in chromium plating baths containing F⁻. In one test, a corrosion rate of 0.0005 mm/yr (0.02 mil/yr) was observed on a sample placed in a chromium plating bath for 2½ months. The solution contained 40% chromium trioxide (CrO_3) and 0.5% F⁻ ion at a temperature of 55 to 60 °C (130 to 140 °F).

The corrosion resistance of tantalum-tungsten alloys was also studied in 50% KOH at 30 and 80 °C (85 and 175 °F), 20% hydrofluoric acid at 20 °C (70 °F), and KOH:$3K_3Fe(CN)_6$ mixture (concentration not given).

In the hydroxide solutions, a maximum corrosion rate was obtained at about 60 at.% tantalum. Although the alloy system reportedly represents a continuous series of solid solutions, a maximum electrical resistance also was found at the same composition. In 20% hydrofluoric acid solution, the tantalum-tungsten alloy system essentially exhibits the relatively low corrosion rates associated with tungsten, except when the tantalum concentration exceeds 80 at.%, at which concentration corrosion increases markedly. Alloys containing more than 18% tungsten show no corrosion in 20% hydrofluoric acid, thus offering an advantage over pure tantalum. Other tests have been conducted on tantalum and tantalum-tungsten alloys having tungsten contents ranging from 8.7 to 20.4% in 20% hydrofluoric acid. This work showed that tantalum and tantalum-tungsten alloys containing less than about 20% tungsten were more susceptible to attack by 20% hydrofluoric acid than was previously reported. Tantalum-tungsten alloys showed little improvement over tantalum when tested in the KOH:$3K_3Fe(CN)_6$ mixture.

Tin. Although the rate of attack is slow, tin reacts readily with hydrofluoric acid.

Titanium. Hydrofluoric acid solutions (as well as anhydrous hydrofluoric acid) can aggressively attack titanium and titanium alloys over the full range of concentrations and temperatures. Metals and welding products containing appreciable amounts of titanium will under certain circumstances suffer accelerated corrosion by hydrofluoric acid. Although the addition of oxidizing species, such as HNO_3, will tend to reduce corrosion

and retard hydrogen uptake in hydrofluoric acid solutions, significant rates of attack still prevail. Inhibition of corrosion can be achieved in very dilute acid fluoride solutions when an excess of complexing metal ions is present. In the absence of these complexing metal ions, solutions containing more than 20 ppm F⁻ may attack titanium when solution pH falls below 6 to 7.

Zirconium is attacked by aqueous and anhydrous hydrofluoric acid in even the lowest concentrations. Metals and welding products that contain appreciable amounts of zirconium will suffer accelerated corrosion by hydrofluoric acid under certain circumstances.

Additional Reading

P. Mayer, A.V. Manolescu, and E.M. Rasile, Corrosion of Medium-Carbon Steel in Aqueous Solutions Containing Fluoride Ions at 300 °C, *Corrosion 40*(4), 186-189, 1984. MetAbs No. 84-351895. **Abstract:** The accelerated internal corrosion in boiler evaporators results from an unfavorable coincidence of adverse thermohydraulic conditions, boiler water contamination and fabrication defects. Boiler tube material (medium-carbon steel, Type SA210) was exposed in static autoclaves to aqueous solutions of HF, FeF_3 and NiF_2 at 300 °C and the rates of attack and morphology of the resulting scales were established.

A. Frignani, C. Monticelli, G. Brunoro, M. Zucchini, and I.H. Omar, Inhibitors for Armco Iron and ASTM A106 Plain Steel in Hydrofluoric Acid. *Br. Corros. J.*, *22*(2), 103-107, 1987. MetAbs No. 87-352389. **Abstract:** Different classes of organic substance (acetylenic derivatives, nitrogen containing additives, and/or sulphur containing additives) were tested as inhibitors for corrosion of ASTM A106 plain steel and Armco iron in hot diluted hydrofluoric acid solutions.

G. Marsh and P. Elliott, Aspects of High Temperature Hydrofluorination of Cobalt, *High Temp. Technol.*, *3*(4), 215-218, 1985. MetAbs No. 87-352691. **Abstract:** Accelerated kinetics of cobalt oxidation associated with the presence of flowing anhydrous hydrogen fluoride and air at 650 °C are described.

Materials Selection for Hydrofluoric Acid Service

Material	Acid concentration, %	Applications	Comments
Steel (100% up to 66 °C, or (150 °F; 70% up to 32 °C, or 90 °F)	70-100(a)	All welded tanks 13-mm (½-in.) minimum wall. A thickness allowance of 6 mm (¼ in.) for acid in the 70 to 80% range is suggested. Pipe: extra heavy, seamless or welded. Fittings: extra heavy, forged, slag-free welds. Valves: forged steel, outside screw and yoke. Pressure gauges, pumps, centrifugal or positive displacement	Hydrogen embrittlement of hardened steels may be encountered in storage facilities or in subsequent process equipment. Alloy steel bolts (ASTM A-193 B7) have cracked. A few failures of "as-welded" mild steel are known in HF alkylation reactors. Steel with a hardness greater than 22 HRC and/or plastically strained are subject to hydrogen embrittlement failure. Vessels should be either stress relieved or hardness of welds and heat-affected zones should be controlled (NACE Recommended Practice RP-04-72) or both. Alloy steel bolts should also be hardness controlled (ASTM A-193 B7M) and should not be over tightened. Hydrogen blistering can occur, predominantly in fine-grain practice steels such as ASTM A-516. Inclusion shape-controlled plate steels should be used to minimize blistering. Alloy steel piping (A-333 Grade 9) corrodes more rapidly. Cast iron, ductile iron, or malleable iron fittings have been found to be unacceptable. Trim in valves and pumps should be of a resistant alloy: CN-7M, nickel-copper Alloy 400 (UNS N04400) or cobalt-base hard-facing alloy.(b) Steel parts in contact become cemented together by iron-fluoride corrosion products.(c) Bourdon tubes or diaphragms should be welded steel or a resistant alloy. Down to 60% strength, acid may be stored in mild steel if inhibited with at least 1.5% H_2SO_4
Stainless steel (ACI CF-8M)	80-100	Pumps	Reported to be better than cast steel. Limited to ambient temperature
Nickel-chromium-iron alloy 600 (UNS N06600)	80-100	Equipment	Used in place of nickel-copper Alloy 400 (UNS N04400) in AHF to avoid stress-corrosion cracking
Alloy 20 (d) (ACI CN-7M)	80-100	Pumps and valves	...

(Continued)

Materials Selection for Hydrofluoric Acid Service (Continued)

Material	Acid concentration, %	Applications	Comments
Copper in acid free of air and silicon dioxide	All	Tubes and gaskets	Reported to be highly velocity-sensitive and is useful only in low velocity and stagnant conditions. However, copper 90/10 copper-nickel (UNS C70600), and silicon bronze did not de-nickelify in hot dilute (1 to 5%) HF, while 70/30 copper-nickel (UNS C71500) and Alloy 400 (UNS N04400) did
Nickel-copper alloy 400 (UNS N04400)	All	Pipe, fittings, heat exchangers, vessels, and valves	This alloy of 66% nickel and 31.5% copper is widely used and can be used over the entire range of concentrations at temperatures up to the atmospheric boiling point if "air-free" conditions are maintained. Where air or oxygen cannot be excluded, corrosion rates, usually in the range of 0.07 to 0.4 mm/yr (3 to 15 mils/yr), occur at room temperature. At higher temperatures with air present, corrosion rates are usually in the range of 0.1 to 1.2 mm/yr (5 to 50 mils/yr). Severe liquid level attack can also occur in the presence of air. In addition to higher corrosion rates, this alloy is subject to stress-corrosion cracking in moist, aerated vapors of hydrogen fluoride and to a much lesser extent in aerated solutions of the acid. Dissolved copper accelerates attack. In practice, occurrence of stress-corrosion cracking may either be avoided by complete exclusion of oxygen or may be minimized by stress relieved welded or cold-formed parts at 535 °C (1000 °F) minimum followed by slow cooling. Niobium-free (d) welding products are preferred. Relatively free of velocity effects
Alloy B-2 (UNS N10665)	All	...	Adverse effects of dissolved oxygen similar to those of Alloy 400. This alloy type reported to be susceptible to intergranular corrosion if not solution annealed
70/30 copper-nickel (UNS C71500)	All	...	Similar to the nickel-copper alloy above in unaerated aqueous hydrofluoric acid, but possesses only limited resistance in aerated solutions. Resistant to stress cracking
Tetrafluoroethylene, fluoroethylene propylene, perfluoroalkane, and monochlorotrifluorethylene	A	Linings and gaskets	Subject to permeation. Rate depends upon thickness and temperature. Not normally a problem with thicker linings such as used in lined pipe
Fluoroelastomer	All	Gaskets	...

(a) Most HF is manufactured from sulfuric acid and fluorspar. Trace impurities in either reagent may find their way into the product acid. This may cause some unusual failures. (b) Alkylation plant pumps are carbon steel with nickel-copper Alloy 400 (UNS N04400) and cobalt alloy (AMS 5373B and AMS 5387) seal rings. (c) The adherent corrosion product film on carbon steel is protective and reduces corrosion rates under velocity conditions. (d) Niobium carbides and, to a lesser extent, titanium carbides are attacked by AHF. Welds in alloys that contain these elements have been known to be preferentially attacked.

Corrosion Behavior of Various Metals and Alloys in Hydrofluoric Acid

Material	Condition, other factors, comments	Concentration, %	Temperature, °C (°F)	Duration	Corrosion rate, mm/yr (mils/yr) or other	Ref
Irons and steels						
Armco iron	1.7N	...	45 (115)	3 h	14 (551)	31
ASTM A106 carbon steel	1.7N	...	45 (115)	3 h	26 (1.02 in./yr)	31
ASTM A335	1.7N. Grade P11 (1.5Cr-0.25Mo)	...	45 (115)	3 h	290 (11.4 in./yr)	31
ASTM A335	1.7N. Grade P22 (2Cr-1Mo)	...	45 (115)	3 h	640 (25.2 in./yr)	31
ASTM A335	1.7N. Grade P5 (5Cr-0.5Mo)	...	45 (115)	3 h	>290 (>11.4 in./yr)	31
ASTM A335	1.7N. Grade P9 (10Cr-1Mo)	...	45 (115)	3 h	330 (13 in./yr)	31
Stainless steels						
Type 304 stainless steel	Chemical processing; field or plant test; no aeration; rapid agitation. Plus 17 vol% water vapor, 10 vol% sulfuric acid, 1 vol% fluosilicic acid, vapors and condensate	72 vol%	176 (350)	14 d	Corrosion	89
Type 304 stainless steel	Chemical processing; field or plant test; no aeration; no agitation. Plus 1.5-2.5% hydrofluosilicic acid, 1.2% sulfuric acid, 0.01-0.03% iron ion	60-65	-1.1 to 26 (30-80)	28 d	Corrosion	89
Type 304 stainless steel	Chemical processing; field or plant test; strong aeration; rapid agitation. Plus 30% air, 12% water, 7% sulfuric acid, 1% silicon tetrafluoride vapors	50	176 (350)	7 d	0.133 in./yr	89

(Continued)

Corrosion Behavior of Various Metals and Alloys in Hydrofluoric Acid (Continued)

Material	Condition, other factors, comments	Concen-tration, %	Temperature, °C (°F)	Duration	Corrosion rate, mm/yr (mils/yr) or other	Ref
Type 304 stainless steel	Chemical processing; field or plant test; strong aeration; rapid agitation. Plus 30% air, 12% water, 7% sulfuric acid, 1% silicon tetrafluoride vapors	50	176 (350)	7 d	0.139 in./yr	89
Type 304 stainless steel	Petroleum processing; field or plant test; no aeration; no agitation. Plus isobutane, regeneration-tower top, vapors. Severe pitting: maximum depth of pits over 0.010 in.	~46.5	98-104 (210-220)	49 d	0.0634 in./yr	89
Type 304 stainless steel	Petroleum processing; field or plant test; no aeration; no agitation. Plus isobutane, regeneration-tower top, vapors. Severe pitting: maximum depth of pits over 0.010 in.	~46.5	98-104 (210-220)	49 d	Corrosion	89
Type 304 stainless steel	Glass processing; field or plant test; no aeration; slight to moderate agitation, with carbon over the standard maximum. Glass-etching solution, plus 9% ammonium bifluoride, water during 200 h and 49% hydrofluoric acid, 15% ammonium bifluoride, sulfuric acid, water during 24 h	37	75 (167)	9.3 d	Corrosion	89
Type 304 stainless steel	Glass processing; field or plant test; no aeration; slight to moderate agitation, with carbon over the standard maximum. Glass-etching solution, plus 14% ammonium bifluoride, water during 72 h, and 40% hydrofluoric, plus 15% ammonium bifluoride, 4% ammonium fluosilicate, water during 176 h	29	60 (140)	10.3 d	0.140 in./yr	89
Type 304 stainless steel	Chemical processing; field or plant test; no aeration; rapid agitation. Plus 0.2% hydrofluosilicic acid. Severe pitting: maximum depth of pits over 0.010 in.	12	83 (182)	7.2 d	0.160 in./yr	89
Type 304 stainless steel	Petroleum processing; field or plant test; no aeration, no agitation. Plus 71% organic fluorides, 19% benzene. Severe pitting: maximum depth of pits over 0.010 in.	6	135 (275)	226 d	0.012 in./yr	89
Type 316 stainless steel	Mining; field or plant test; no aeration; slight to moderate agitation. Commercial grade	70	21 (70)	42 d	0.49 in./yr	89
Type 316 stainless steel	Chemical processing; field or plant test; no aeration; no agitation. Plus 1.5-2.5% hydrofluosilicic acid, 1.2% sulfuric acid, 0.01-0.03% iron ion	60-65	-1.1 to 26 (30-80)	28 d	Corrosion	89
Type 316 stainless steel	Chemical processing; field or plant test; no aeration; rapid agitation. Plus 17 vol% water vapor, 10 vol% sulfuric acid, 1 vol% fluosilicic acid, vapors and condensate	72 vol%	176 (350)	14 d	0.24 in./yr	89
Type 316 stainless steel	Chemical processing; field or plant test; no aeration; rapid agitation. Plus 17 vol% water vapor, 10 vol% sulfuric acid, 1 vol% fluosilicic acid, vapors and condensate	72 vol%	176 (350)	14 d	>0.38 in./yr	89
Type 316 stainless steel	Glass processing; field or plant test. Plus 50% sulfuric acid. Severe pitting: maximum depth of pits over 0.010 in.	50	Room to 60 (room to 140)	4 d	0.99 in./yr	89
Type 316 stainless steel	Chemical processing; field or plant test; strong aeration; rapid agitation. Plus 30% air, 12% water, 7% sulfuric acid, 1% silicon tetrafluoride vapors	50	176 (350)	7 d	0.103 in./yr	89
Type 316 stainless steel	Chemical processing; field or plant test; strong aeration; rapid agitation. Plus 30% air, 12% water, 7% sulfuric acid, 1% silicon tetrafluoride vapors	50	176 (350)	7 d	0.113 in./yr	89
Type 316 stainless steel	Petroleum processing; field or plant test; no aeration; no agitation. Plus isobutane, regeneration-tower top, vapors. Severe pitting: maximum depth of pits over 0.010 in.	~46.5	98-104 (210-220)	49 d	0.001 in./yr	89
Type 316 stainless steel	Petroleum processing; field or plant test; no aeration; no agitation. Severe pitting: maximum depth of pits over 0.010 in.	38	110 (230)	2 d	2.0 in./yr	89
Type 316 stainless steel	Glass processing; field or plant test; no aeration; slight to moderate agitation. Glass-etching solution, plus 9% ammonium bifluoride, water during 200 h and 49% hydrofluoric acid, 15% ammonium bifluoride, sulfuric acid, water during 24 h	37	75 (167)	9.3 d	Corrosion	89

(Continued)

Corrosion Behavior of Various Metals and Alloys in Hydrofluoric Acid (Continued)

Material	Condition, other factors, comments	Concen-tration, %	Temperature, °C (°F)	Duration	Corrosion rate, mm/yr (mils/yr) or other	Ref
Type 316 stainless steel	Glass processing; field or plant test; no aeration; slight to moderate agitation. Glass-etching solution, plus 14% ammonium bifluoride, water during 72 h, and 40% hydrofluoric, plus 15% ammonium bifluoride, 4% ammonium fluosilicate, water during 176 h	29	60 (140)	10.3 d	0.1 in./yr	89
Type 316 stainless steel	Chemical processing; field or plant test; no aeration; rapid agitation. Plus 0.2% hydrofluosilicic acid. Severe pitting: maximum depth of pits over 0.010 in.	12	83 (182)	7.2 d	0.701 in./yr	89
Type 316 stainless steel	Petroleum processing; field or plant test; no aeration, no agitation. Plus 71% organic fluorides, 19% benzene. Moderate pitting: maximum depth of pits from 0.005 to 0.010 in.	6	135 (275)	226 d	0.012 in./yr	89
Type 410 stainless steel	...	...	Room	...	Attacked	121
Coppers						
70-30 cupronickel	May be considered in place of a copper metal when some property, other than corrosion resistance, governs its use	...	...	...	Good	93
90-10 cupronickel	...	...	...	...	Fair	93
Admiralty brass	...	...	...	...	Not suitable	93
Aluminum bronze	...	...	...	...	Fair	93
Ampco 8, aluminum bronze	Generally suitable. Conditions such as aeration or temperature could restrict use	...	...	...	<0.5 (<20)	96
Architectural bronze	...	...	...	...	Not suitable	93
Brass	...	...	...	...	Not suitable	93
Cartridge brass	...	...	...	...	Not suitable	93
Commercial bronze	...	...	...	...	Fair	93
Electrolytic copper	...	...	...	...	Fair	93
Free-cutting brass	...	...	...	...	Not suitable	93
Muntz metal	...	...	...	...	Not suitable	93
Naval brass	...	...	...	...	Not suitable	93
Nickel silver	...	18	...	...	Fair	93
Phosphor bronze	5% Sn	...	...	...	Fair	93
Phosphor bronze	8% Sn	...	...	...	Fair	93
Phosphor copper	...	...	...	...	Fair	93
Red brass	...	...	...	...	Fair	93
Silicon bronze	Low	...	...	...	Fair	93
Silicon bronze	High	...	...	...	Fair	93
Titanium						
Titanium	...	1	26 (79)	...	127 (5080)	90
Titanium	Anhydrous	100	Room	...	0.127-1.27 (5.08-50.8)	90
Heat- and corrosion-resistant alloys						
44Co-31Cr-13W	Heat treated 4 h at 899 °C (1650 °F) and furnace cooled. (a)	5	Room	...	1.37 (55)	53
44Co-31Cr-13W	(a)	5	Room	...	1.47 (59)	53
44Co-31Cr-13W	Heat treated 4 h at 899 °C (1650 °F), furnace cooled. (a)	5	Room	...	1.37 (55)	53
50C0-20Cr-15W-10Ni	(a)	5	Room	...	0.125 (5)	53
50Co-20Cr-15W-10Ni	...	5	Room	...	0.125 (0.5)	53
53Co-30Cr-4.5W	(a)	5	Room	...	1.3 (52)	53
53Co-30Cr-4.5W	Heat treated 4 h at 899 °C (1650 °F). (a)	5	Room	...	0.8 (32)	53
53Co-30Cr-4.5W	(a)	5	Room	...	1.3 (52)	53
53Co-30Cr-4.5W	Heat treated 4 h at 899 °C (1650 °F), furnace cooled. (a)	5	Room	...	0.8 (32)	53
Alloy 825	Mining; field or plant test; no aeration; slight to moderate agitation. Commercial grade	70	21 (70)	42 d	0.14 in./yr	89
Alloy 825	Glass processing; field or plant test. Plus 50% sulfuric acid	50	Room to 60 (room to 140)	4 d	0.026 in./yr	89

(Continued)

Corrosion Behavior of Various Metals and Alloys in Hydrofluoric Acid (Continued)

Material	Condition, other factors, comments	Concen-tration, %	Temperature, °C (°F)	Duration	Corrosion rate, mm/yr (mils/yr) or other	Ref
Alloy 825	Petroleum processing; field or plant test; no aeration; no agitation. Plus 71% organic fluorides, 19% benzene	6	135 (275)	226 d	0.0041 in./yr	89
Carpenter 20	Mining; field or plant test; no aeration; slight to moderate agitation. Commercial grade	70	21 (70)	42 d	0.15 in./yr	89
Carpenter 20	Chemical processing; field or plant test; no aeration; rapid agitation; cast. Plus 17 vol% water vapor, 10 vol% sulfuric acid, 1 vol% fluosilicic acid, vapors and condensate	72 vol%	176 (350)	14 d	0.43 in./yr	89
Carpenter 20	Chemical processing; field or plant test; strong aeration; rapid agitation; cast. Plus 30% air, 12% water, 7% sulfuric acid, 1% silicon tetrafluoride, vapors	50	176 (350)	7 d	0.081 in./yr	89
Haynes No. 25	(b)	5	Room	...	0.13 (5.0)	68
Haynes No. 25	(b)	25	Room	...	0.30 (12)	68
Haynes No. 25	(b)	45	Room	...	0.51 (20)	68
Inconel 617	Vapor. (c)	10	80 (175)	...	1.12 (44)	44
Inconel 617	Vapor. (c)	20	80 (175)	...	0.81 (32)	44
Inconel 617	Vapor. (c)	30	80 (175)	...	2.08 (82)	44
Inconel 617	Vapor. (c)	40	80 (175)	...	2.16 (85)	44
Inconel 617	Vapor. (c)	48	80 (175)	...	2.64 (104)	44
Inconel 617	Liquid. (c)	10	80 (175)	...	3.20 (126)	44
Inconel 617	Liquid. (c)	20	80 (175)	...	7.67 (302)	44
Inconel 617	Liquid. (c)	30	80 (175)	...	10.06 (396)	44
Inconel 617	Liquid. (c)	40	80 (175)	...	10.77 (424)	44
Inconel 617	Liquid. (c)	48	80 (175)	...	10.87 (428)	44
Multimet	(b)	5	Room	...	0.13 (5.0)	68
Multimet	(b)	25	Room	...	0.94 (37)	68
Multimet	(b)	45	Room	...	1.32 (52)	68
Zirconium						
Zr702	...	0-100	Room	...	>1.3 (>50)	15
Lead, tin, and zinc						
Tin	...	40	20 (68)	...	Unsuitable	94
Tin	...	40	60 (140)	...	Unsuitable	94
Tin	...	40	100 (212)	...	Unsuitable	94
Tin	...	75	20 (68)	...	Unsuitable	94
Tin	...	75	60 (140)	...	Unsuitable	94
Tin	...	75	100 (212)	...	Unsuitable	94
Tantalum						
Tantalum	...	40	25 (76)	3 h	Rapid	42
Noble metals						
Gold	...	40	Room	...	<0.05 (<2)	8
Iridium	...	40	Room	...	nil	29
Osmium	...	40	Room	...	nil	17
Rhodium	...	40	Room	...	nil	29
Ruthenium	...	49	Room	...	nil	18
Silver	...	<50	Boiling	...	<0.05 (<2)	4
Others						
Cobalt	Static	50	25 (77)	...	0.72 (29)	54
Cobalt	Static	Conc	25 (77)	...	0.4 (16)	54
Magnesium	...	5-60	Room	...	Suitable	119

(a) Cast specimen 38 mm x 25 mm x 6.4 mm (1.5 in. x 1 in. x 0.25 in.), 120-grit abrasive finish. Average of five 24-h periods. (b) Specimens prepared from 12-gage, solution heat-treated sheet. (c) Average of two tests.

Corrosion of Hastelloy Alloys in Aqueous Hydrofluoric Acid

Concentration HF, %	Temperature °C (°F)	Corrosion rate							
		Hastelloy B		Hastelloy C		Hastelloy D		Hastelloy F	
		mm/yr	mils/yr	mm/yr	mils/yr	mm/yr	mils/yr	mm/yr	mils/yr
5	Room	0.1	4	0.025	1	0.025	1	0.05	2
25	Room	0.13	5	0.13	5	0.15	6	0.3	12
40	Room	0.07	2.6	0.074	2.9	0.025	1	. . .	. . .
40	54 (130)	0.025	1	0.025	10	0.07	2.6	. . .	. . .
45	Room	0.076	3	0.15	6	0.1	4	0.38	15
50	Boiling (95 °C, or 205 °F)	. . .	. . .	4.6	180	. . .	. . .	. . .	. . .
60	Room	0.04	1.6	0.09	3.6	0.06	2.4	. . .	. . .
65	Boiling (70 °C, or 160 °F)	. . .	. . .	0.43	17	. . .	. . .	. . .	. . .
98	34–44 (95–110)	0.1	4	0.025	1	. . .	. . .	. . .	. . .

Source: T.F. Degnan, "Materials of Construction for Hydrofluoric Acid and Hydrogen Fluoride," in *Process Industries Corrosion*, B.J. Moniz and W.I. Pollock, Ed., National Association of Corrosion Engineers, Houston, 1986.

Corrosion of Various Nickel-Base Alloys in Hydrofluoric Acid

Alloy	Corrosion rate, mm/yr (mils/yr)			
	2% HF		5% HF	
	70 °C (160 °F)	Boiling	70 °C (160 °F)	Boiling
C-276	0.24 (9.5)	0.076 (3)	0.25 (10)	0.1 (4)
C-22	0.23 (9.4)	0.94 (37)	0.34 (13.5)	0.84 (33)
625	0.5 (20)	. . .	0.4 (16)	. . .
C-4	0.43 (17)	. . .	0.38 (15)	. . .
200	. . .	. . .	0.46 (18)	. . .
600	. . .	. . .	0.23 (9)	. . .
B-2	. . .	. . .	0.38 (15)	. . .
G-3	. . .	. . .	0.5 (20)	. . .
G-30	(10)	. . .	0.76 (30)	. . .

Source: T.F. Degnan, "Materials of Construction for Hydrofluoric Acid and Hydrogen Fluoride," in *Process Industries Corrosion*, B.J. Moniz and W.I. Pollock, Ed., National Association of Corrosion Engineers, Houston, 1986.

Effect of Aeration on Corrosion of Two Nickel-Base Alloys in 70% Hydrofluoric Acid

Alloy	Corrosion rate			
	Nitrogen blanket		Oxygen blanket	
	mm/yr	mils/yr	mm/yr	mils/yr
C-276	0.008	0.3	0.94	37
400	0.013	0.5	0.58	23

Source: T.F. Degnan, "Materials of Construction for Hydrofluoric Acid and Hydrogen Fluoride," in *Process Industries Corrosion*, B.J. Moniz and W.I. Pollock, Ed., National Association of Corrosion Engineers, Houston, 1986.

Corrosion of Metals and Alloys in Hydrofluoric Acid Gas

Alloy	Corrosion rate	
	mm/yr	mils/yr
Hastelloy C	0.008	0.3
Inconel 600	0.018	0.7
Hastelloy B	0.05	2
Nickel 200	0.23	9
Nickel 201	0.36	14
Monel 400	0.33	13
Monel K-500	0.4	16
70–30 copper-nickel	0.4	16

Source: T.F. Degnan, "Materials of Construction for Hydrofluoric Acid and Hydrogen Fluoride," in *Process Industries Corrosion*, B.J. Moniz and W.I. Pollock, Ed., National Association of Corrosion Engineers, Houston, 1986.

Effect of Oxygen on Corrosion of Alloy 400 in Hydrofluoric Acid Solutions

Concentration of oxygen in purge gas, ppm	Corrosion rate							
	Boiling (112 °C, or 234 °F) 38% HF				Boiling (108 °C, or 226 °F) 48% HF			
	Liquid phase		Vapor phase		Liquid phase		Vapor phase	
	mm/yr	mils/yr	mm/yr	mils/yr	mm/yr	mils/yr	mm/yr	mils/yr
<5	0.24	9.5	0.17	6.8	0.28	11	0.076	3
<500	0.43	17	0.3	12	0.56	22	0.1	4
1500	0.79	31	1.24	49	0.7	28	0.61	24
2500	0.74	29	0.46	18	0.69	27	0.23	9
3500	0.86	34	1.37	54	0.86	34	0.74	29
4700	1.3	53	2.7	107	1.1	43	2.1	83
10 000	1.2	46	0.64	25	1.2	48	1.9	75

Source: Inco Alloys International.

Corrosion of Metals and Alloys by Gaseous Anhydrous Hydrofluoric Acid at Elevated Temperatures

Metal	Corrosion rate at temperature, °C (°F)					
	500 (930)		550 (1020)		600 (1110)	
	mm/yr	mils/yr	mm/yr	mils/yr	mm/yr	mils/yr
Nickel 200	0.9	36	...	...	0.9	36
Monel 400	1.2	48	1.2	48	1.8	72
Copper	1.5	60	...	...	1.2	48
Inconel 600	1.5	60	...	...	1.5	60
Aluminum alloy 1100	4.9	192	...	...	14.6	576
Magnesium G	13.8	542	...	...	...	...
1020 steel	15.5	612	14.6	576	7.6	300
Type 430 stainless steel	1.5	60	9.1	360	11.6	456
Type 304 stainless steel	...	...	...	...	13.4	528
Type 347 stainless steel	183	7200	457	18 000	177	6960
Type 309Cb stainless steel	5.8	228	42.7	1680	168	6600
Type 310 stainless steel	12.2	480	100.6	3960	305	12 000

Source: T.F. Degnan, "Materials of Construction for Hydrofluoric Acid and Hydrogen Fluoride," in *Process Industries Corrosion*, B.J. Moniz and W.I. Pollock, Ed., National Association of Corrosion Engineers, Houston, 1986.

Corrosion of Nickel Stainless Steels and Chromium-Nickel-Molybdenum-Iron Alloys in Aqueous Hydrofluoric Acid

Concentration HF, %	Temperature °C	°F	Test duration, days	Corrosion rate									
				Type 304		Type 316		Type 309Cb		Alloy 20Cb-3		Incoloy 825	
				mm/yr	mils/yr	mm/yr	mils/yr	mm/yr	mils/yr	mm/yr	mils/yr	mm/yr	mils/yr
0.05	60	140	10	0.3	12	...	...	0.25	10	...	...	...	...
0.1	60	140	10	0.64	25	...	...	0.69	27	...	...	...	...
0.15	60	140	10	1.2	47	...	...	1.1	44	...	...	...	...
0.2	60	140	10	1.6	62	...	...	1.4	54	...	...	...	...
10	16	60	30	0.01	0.4	<0.002	<0.1	...	...	...	...	...	...
20	102	215	3	...	...	...	...	...	...	...	...	1.04	41
38	110	230	2	...	...	51	2000	...	...	...	...	...	...
38	Boiling		4	...	...	...	...	...	...	...	...	0.25	10
48	Boiling		4	...	...	...	...	...	...	...	...	0.23	9
50	60	140	35	...	...	...	...	...	...	...	...	0.05	2
65	60	140	35	...	...	...	...	...	...	...	...	0.13	5
70	60	140	35	...	...	...	...	...	...	...	...	0.13	5
70	21	70	42	...	...	1.24	49	...	...	0.38	15	0.35	14
90	4	40	0.2	0.9	35	...	...	...	...	...	...	...	...
90	21	70	1	0.76	30	...	...	...	...	...	...	...	...
90	21	70	1	0.28	11(a)	...	...	...	...	...	...	...	...
98	34–44	95–110	3.5	...	...	0.05	2	...	...	...	...	...	...

(a) Velocity: 0.14 to 0.43 m/s (0.4 to 1.4 ft/s)

Source: T.F. Degnan, "Materials of Construction for Hydrofluoric Acid and Hydrogen Fluoride," in *Process Industries Corrosion*, B.J. Moniz and W.I. Pollock, Ed., National Association of Corrosion Engineers, Houston, 1986.

Corrosion of Metals and Alloys in Anhydrous Hydrogen Fluoride

Metal	15–25 (60–80)		25–40 (80–100)		40–95 (100–200)		55 (130)		70 (160)		80–90 (180–190)	
	mm/yr	mils/yr	mm/yr	mils/yr	mm/yr	mils/yr	mm/yr	mils/yr	mm/yr	mils/yr	mm/yr	mils/yr
Carbon steel	0.07	2.8	0.16	6.2	...	...	0.35	14	...	...	2.3	89
Low-alloy steel	0.15	6	0.14	5.9	...	...	...	...	...	...	2	78
Austenitic stainless steel	0.16	6.2	0.12	4.8	...	...	...	...	...	...	0.06	2.4
Monel 400	0.08	3.2	0.02	0.9	0.12	4.7	...	...	...	...	...	...
Copper	0.33	12.9	...	...	...	...	...	...	...	...	...	...
Nickel 200	0.06	2.5	...	...	...	...	...	...	0.12	4.6	...	...
70–30 copper-nickel	...	...	0.05	2	...	...	0.008	0.3	...	...	0.25	10
80–20 copper-nickel	...	...	0.13	5.2	...	...	...	...	...	...	...	...
Red brass	0.76	30	0.4	16	...	...	...	...	...	...	1.3	50
Admiralty brass	0.25	10	0.33	12.8	...	...	0.01	0.4	...	...	0.5	20
Aluminum-bronze	0.37	14.4	...	...	...	...	...	...	...	...	...	...
Phosphorus-bronze	0.5	20	0.48	18.8	...	...	...	...	...	...	1.5	60
Inconel 600	...	...	0.067	2.6	...	...	...	...	...	...	...	...
Duriron	...	...	1.1	45	...	...	...	...	...	...	...	...
Aluminum	0.52	20.4	...	...	...	...	...	...	...	...	24.8	976
Magnesium	0.13	5.2	0.43	17.1	...	...	nil		...	...	nil	

Source: T.F. Degnan, "Materials of Construction for Hydrofluoric Acid and Hydrogen Fluoride," in *Process Industries Corrosion*, B.J. Moniz and W.I. Pollock, Ed., National Association of Corrosion Engineers, Houston, 1986.

Corrosion of Selected Metals and Alloys in Commercial Hydrofluoric Acid Solutions

Metal	50%				65%				70%			
	Liquid		Vapor		Liquid		Vapor		Liquid		Vapor	
	mm/yr	mils/yr	mm/yr	mils/yr	mm/yr	mils/yr	mm/yr	mils/yr	mm/yr	mils/yr	mm/yr	mils/yr
Platinum	nil		nil		nil		nil		...	...	...	...
Silver	0.009	0.36	nil		0.018	0.72	0.0005	0.02	0.018	0.72	0.00025	0.01
Monel 400	0.46	18.12	0.12	4.68	0.13	4.8	0.058	2.28	0.14	5.4	0.05	2.03
Magnesium	0.21	8.4	0.03	1.2	0.058	2.28	0.058	2.28	...	...	...	...
Hastelloy C	0.74	29.3	0.6	24	0.19	7.55	0.24	9.6	...	...	...	...
Illium R	0.22	8.65	0.08	3.23	0.2	8	0.02	0.84	...	...	...	...

Source: T.F. Degnan, "Materials of Construction for Hydrofluoric Acid and Hydrogen Fluoride," in *Process Industries Corrosion*, B.J. Moniz and W.I. Pollock, Ed., National Association of Corrosion Engineers, Houston, 1986.

Corrosion of Wrought Copper Alloys in Anhydrous Hydrofluoric Acid

Temperature		C51000		C44400		C71500	
°C	°F	µm/yr	mils/yr	µm/yr	mils/yr	µm/yr	mils/yr
16–27	60–80	510	20	255	10	180	7
27–38	80–100	480	18.8	480	18.8	...	...
82–88	180–190	1525	60	510	20	255	10

(a) These values are representative of results on copper alloys having high copper content, such as copper, aluminum bronze, silicon bronze, and inhibited admiralty metal. Corrosion rates for C23000 are between those for C44400 and C51000.

Source: T.F. Degnan, "Materials of Construction for Hydrofluoric Acid and Hydrogen Fluoride," in *Process Industries Corrosion*, B.J. Moniz and W.I. Pollock, Ed., National Association of Corrosion Engineers, Houston, 1986.

Corrosion of Steel in Hydrofluoric Acid at Ambient Temperature

Concentration of HF, %	Corrosion rate	
	mm/yr	mils/yr
58.	3	120
60.	2.53	99.6
61.	2.1	81.6
62.	1.5	58.8
63.	0.24	9.6
64.	0.05	2.0
65.	0.055	2.2
67.5.	0.048	1.9
69.9.	0.064	2.5

Source: T.F. Degnan, "Materials of Construction for Hydrofluoric Acid and Hydrogen Fluoride," in *Process Industries Corrosion*, B.J. Moniz and W.I. Pollock, Ed., National Association of Corrosion Engineers, Houston, 1986.

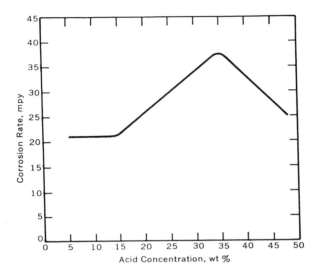

Inconel 600. Corrosion rates in hydrofluoric acid at 75 °C (167 °F). Source: Inco Alloys International, 1962.

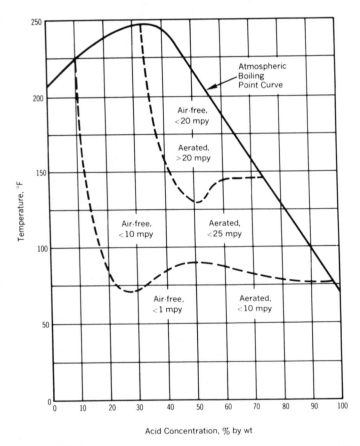

Monel 400. Isocorrosion charts of Monel 400 in hydrofluoric acid. Source: Inco Alloys International, 1984.

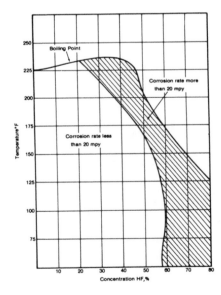

Lead. Corrosion resistance of lead to air-free hydrofluoric acid. Source: *Lead for Corrosion Resistant Applications: A Guide*, Lead Industries Association, Inc. New York.

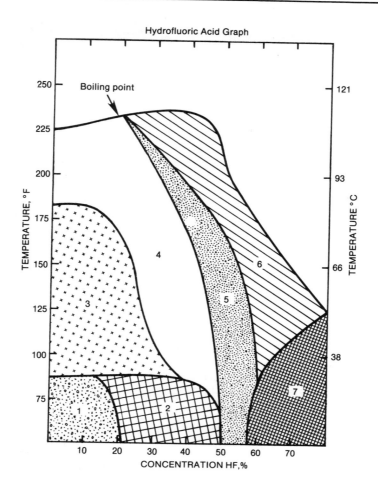

CODE FOR HYDROFLUORIC ACID GRAPH

Materials in shaded zone have reported corrosion rate of >20 mpy

ZONE 1
20Cr 30Ni
25Cr 20 Ni steel
70Cu 30Ni[1]
66Ni 32Cu[1]
54Ni 15Cr 16Mo
Copper[1]
Gold
Lead[1]
Nickel[1]
Nickel cast iron
Platinum Silver

ZONE 2
20Cr 30 Ni
70Cu 30 Ni1
54Ni 15Cr 16Mo
66Ni 32Cu[1]
Copper[1]
Gold
Lead[1]
Nickel[1]
Platinum
Silver

ZONE 3
20Cr 30Ni
70Cu 30Ni[1]
54Ni 15Cr 16Mo
66Ni 32Cu[1]
Copper[1]
Gold
Lead[1]
Platinum
Silver

ZONE 4
70Cu 30Ni[1]
66Ni 32Cu[1]
54Ni 15Cr 16Mo
Gold
Lead[1]
Platinum
Silver

ZONE 5
70Cu 30Ni[1]
6Ni 32Cu[1]
54Ni 15Cr 16Mo
Gold
Lead[1]
Platinum
Silver

ZONE 6
66Ni 32Cu[1]
54Ni 15Cr 16Mo
Gold
Platinum
Silver

ZONE 7
66Ni 32Cu[1]
54Ni 15Cr 16Mo
Gold
Platinum
Silver

[1]No air

Metals and alloys. Corrosion of selected metals and alloys in boiling 48% hydrofluoric acid. Source: T.F. Degnan, "Materials of Construction for Hydrofluoric Acid and Hydrogen Fluoride," in *Process Industries Corrosion*, B.J. Moniz and W.I. Pollock, Ed., National Association of Corrosion Engineers, Houston, 1986.

Hydrogen

Hydrogen, H_2, is a tasteless, colorless, odorless gas that may be liquified by cooling under pressure. Hydrogen is used in welding, in the production of ammonia, methanol, and other chemicals, for the hydrogenation of oil and coal, and for the reduction of metallic oxide ores. It is obtained by the dissociation of water and as a by-product in the electrolysis of brine solutions. Molecular hydrogen at ambient temperature is relatively innocuous to most metals. However, atomic hydrogen is detrimental to most metals.

Material Summaries

The following material summaries were compiled from a survey of the available literature. Inclusion of a material description under a given environment does not imply that it is the most appropriate material for corrosion service in that environment. Likewise, exclusion of a given material does not imply that it is not suitable for corrosion service applications in that environment.

Carbon steel. Dry hydrogen gas is often stored and handled successfully in carbon steel equipment at ambient temperature.

Alloy Steels. Alloy steels used in refining petroleum and processing hydrocarbons interact with hydrogen. Prolonged exposure, especially at elevated temperatures, results in loss of ductility and premature failure. Hydrogen attack, which is observed in actual service, is the chemical reaction of hydrogen at elevated temperatures with metal carbides to form methane. The inability of the methane to diffuse out of steel results in blistering and fissuring. The effect of decarburization combined with fissuring results in a loss of strength and ductility.

Aluminum. Hydrogen has been produced and stored in aluminum alloy equipment.

Copper. Copper and its alloys are not attacked by hydrogen unless they contain oxygen. Oxygen-bearing copper heated in hydrogen or hydrogen-bearing gases is invaded by the hydrogen, which reacts with the oxygen to form water. If the temperature is above 375 °C (705 °F), the water is converted to a high-pressure steam, which produces fissures and reduces the ductility of the metal. This condition is known as hydrogen embrittlement, which at any level, can cause catastrophic failure. This reaction is especially important when oxygen-containing copper is bright annealed in reducing atmospheres containing small amounts (1 to 5%) of hydrogen. Annealing of tough pitch coppers, for example C11000, which contains small amounts of copper oxide, in such reducing atmospheres at temperatures above 475 °C (900 °F) may lead to severe embrittlement, especially if annealing times are long. Therefore, tough pitch coppers, which may be welded or brazed, should not be exposed to hydrogen if they will later be used in service at temperatures above 370 °C (700 °F). When copper must be heated in a hydrogen environment, an oxygen-free or deoxidized copper with high residual deoxidizer content, where the oxygen is tied up in complex oxides that do not react appreciably with hydrogen, should be selected. No hydrogen embrittlement problems have been encountered with these materials. Deoxidized coppers with low residual deoxidizer contents, for example C12000, contain copper oxide in smaller amounts than the tough pitch coppers, but are still susceptible to hydrogen embrittlement.

Niobium. Niobium reacts with hydrogen gas above 250 °C (480 °F). At 100 °C (212 °F), niobium is inert in hydrogen.

Silver. Silver can be exposed to hydrogen up to 700 °C (1290 °F).

Tantalum. Tantalum dissolves hydrogen at comparatively low temperatures to a maximum solubility of 50 at.%. Although tantalum generally does not react with molecular hydrogen below 250 °C (480 °F), it can absorb 740 times its own weight at red heat. Tantalum containing more than 150 ppm of hydrogen loses it ductility. When undergoing deformation, tantalum can absorb molecular hydrogen at room temperature. Atomic hydrogen can be absorbed by tantalum even at room temperature. When this material is heated to about 800 °C (1470 °F), or even higher in a vacuum, it loses all its hydrogen. If the metal has not been permanently damaged, it may be restored to its original condition by annealing or degassing at 800 °C (1470 °F). The presence of hydrogen in tantalum increases its hardness and electrical resistivity, whereas it decreases ductility, strength, and density.

Tin. Below its melting point, tin does not react with hydrogen.

Zirconium. Zirconium, which has an oxide film, resists hydrogen absorption up to 760 °C (1400 °F). Zirconium will eventually suffer hydrogen embrittlement in an all-hydrogen environment, with hydrogen absorption beginning at 310 °C (590 °F). Hydrogen may be removed from zirconium by prolonged vacuum annealing at temperatures above 750 °C (1380 °F).

Additional Reading

E.N. Pugh and R.A. Yeske, Stress Corrosion Cracking of High-Strength Aluminum Alloys, 1980. MetAbs No. 81-351361. **Abstract:** A study was made of the mechanism of hydrogen embrittlement in Al-Zn-Mg alloys and of the role of hydrogen in the intergranular stress-corrosion cracking of these alloys. Up to 300 ppm (1 at.%) hydrogen was introduced into a high-purity Al-5.6Zn-2.6Mg alloy, either by room-temperature polishing with aqueous slurries or alumina particles or by exposure to water vapor-saturated air at 70 °C, and subsequent tensile tests (stress rate approximately 0.0001/s) in inert environments caused brittle intergranular fracture.

J.A. Wert, Observations on Hydrogen-Induced Delayed Plasticity and Cracking in 4340 Steel, *Corrosion*, *39*(2), 71-73, 1983. MetAbs No. 83-351058. **Abstract:** In an attempt to further understand crack tunneling behavior, a series of hydrogen-assisted cracking experiments was conducted with 4340 steel. Average crack advance rates were measured by potential drop methods coupled with SEM observations of the fractured sample.

A. Brown and C.L. Jones, Hydrogen-Induced Cracking in Pipeline Steels, *Corrosion*, *40*(7), 330-336, 1984. MetAbs No. 84-352600. **Abstract:** Work conducted at the British Gas Engineering Research Station using laboratory tests of the BP and NACE type to assess the hydrogen-induced cracking is described. Various grades of linepipe and fittings steels have been studied and the metallurgical parameters controlling hydrogen-induced cracking resistance have been established. In particular, the effects of nonmetallic inclusions, sulfur content, alloy segregation, and microstructure are described.

Z.J. Su, D. Stone, J. Wanagel, and C.Y. Li, The Effect of Cold Work on Hydrogen Attack in a 2.25 Cr-1Mo Steel, *Res. Mech.*, *13*(4), 243-250, 1985. MetAbs No. 85-351086. **Abstract:** Steel specimens, 2.25 Cr-1Mo (A387) both with and without cold work, are exposed to high-pressure hydrogen at 600 °C. A comparison of the cavity number density data suggest that prior cold work enhances hydrogen attack by accelerating the rates of methane bubble nucleation and growth in the 2.25Cr-1Mo steels.

T.A. Parthasarathy, H.F. Lopez, and P.G. Shewmon, Hydrogen Attack Kinetics of 2.25 Cr-1 Mo Steel Weld Metals, *Metall. Trans. A*, *16A*(6), 1143-1149, 1985. MetAbs No. 85-351390. **Abstract:** The kinetics of hydrogen attack of the base metals and the weld metals of two quenched and tempered 2.25Cr-1Mo steel weldments made by different techniques (SMAW and SAW) were studied at 460 to 590 °C and 10 to 23 MPa hydrogen.

Y.B. Wang, W.Y. Chu, and C.M. Hsiao, Hydrogen Induced Slow Crack Growth in Mild Steel and Pure Iron, *Corrosion*, *41*(7), 427-429, 1985. MetAbs No. 85-352105. **Abstract:** Hydrogen-induced slow crack growth occurs in 1020 steel, commercial purity iron, and high-purity iron in a constant load specimen, either dynamically charged or precharged. The threshold values of the hydrogen-induced delayed failure were approximately 0.5 and 0.45, respectively, for the 1020 steel and the high-purity iron.

M.F. Stevens and I.M. Bernstein, The Role of Aging Reactions in the Hydrogen Embrittlement Susceptibility of an HSLA Steel, *Metall. Trans. A*, *16A*(10), 1879-1886, 1985. MetAbs No. 85-352256. **Abstract:** Hydrogen embrittlement susceptibility, as measured from room temperature precharged tensile specimens, indicates that the type, extent, and morphology of carbide precipitation are all important in determining the degree and mode of degradation. At equivalent charging conditions, embrittlement is virtually eliminated by aging to produce fine scale clustering of Ti (carbon, nitrogen), even when concurrent with cementite precipitation.

G.L. Powell and W.G. Northcutt Jr., Internal Hydrogen Embrittlement of Uranium-5.7 Niobium Alloy, *J. Nucl. Mater.*, *132*(1), 47-51, 1985. MetAbs No. 86-350007. **Abstract:** Internal hydrogen embrittlement of U-5.7Nb alloy appears as an enhanced microvoid coalescence fracture mode and a loss in tensile ductility for hydrogen concentrations less than $23\,\mu g/g$ in specimens that were prepared using an 800 °C solution anneal and a very rapid water quench.

P.K. Datta, K.N. Strafford, and A.L. Dowson, Environment/Mechanical Interaction Processes and Hydrogen Embrittlement of Titanium, *Mech. Corros. Prop. A, Key Eng. Mater.*, *A8*, 203-216, 1985. MetAbs No. 86-350055. **Abstract:** Although extensive studies have been carried out to characterize the degradation behavior of Ti in complex H-O-S environments, little attention has been given to the contamination and embrittlement of the metal substrate. The degradation of Ti (IMI115, IMI130, IMI155) in hydrogen, oxygen and/or sulfur environments at 300 to 500 °C has been studied and has been shown to involve the simultaneous occurrence of oxidation, hydrogen absorption, and hydride precipitation reactions.

L.B. Traylor and C.E. Price, A Comparison of Hydrogen and Mercury Embrittlement in Monel at Room Temperature, *J. Eng. Mater. Technol. (Trans. ASME)*, *108*(1), 31-36, 1986. MetAbs No. 86-350626. **Abstract:** Slow strain rate tensile tests were performed on annealed and cold drawn Monel 400 and Monel R405 at room temperature in air, mercury, and electrolyte hydrogen. Hydrogen and mercury caused embrittlement, with the fractures having the same specific features.

C.E. Price and R.S. Fredell, A Comparative Study of the Embrittlement of Monel 400 at Room Temperature by Hydrogen and by Mercury, *Metall. Trans. A*, *17A*(5), 889-898, 1986. MetAbs No. 86-351113. **Abstract:** Slow strain rate tensile tests were performed at room temperature on Monel 400 specimens of grain sizes 35 to 500 μm in air, mercury, and electrolytically generated hydrogen. Specimens of grain size 250 μm were tested at a range of strain rates in the three environments.

Z.A. Foroulis, High Temperature Degradation of Structural Materials in Environments Encountered in the Petroleum and Petrochemical Industries: Some Mechanistic Observations, *Anti-Corros. Methods Mater.*, *32*(11), 4-9, 1985. MetAbs No. 86-351179. **Abstract:** This paper reviews some of the important processes underlying high-temperature degradation of structural materials used in the petroleum and petrochemical industries. Particular emphasis is placed on degradation processes involving the interaction of structural metals and alloys with environments containing sulfidizing, carburizing and halogenizing species.

T. Livne, X. Chen, and W.W. Gerberich, Temperature Effects on Hydrogen Assisted Crack Growth in Internally Charged AISI 4340 Steel, *Scr. Metall.*, *20*(5), 659-662, 1986. MetAbs No. 86-352077. **Abstract:** Stage II crack growth kinetics were studied as a function of test temperature for AISI 4340 steel internally charged with hydrogen. Standard compact tension specimens of 4340 were machined, fatigue pre-cracked, electrochemically charged for 24 h, and then cadmium-plated to prevent hydrogen effusion. Models of crack growth behavior are proposed to account for the significant differences observed in growth kinetics between externally and internally charged specimens.

W. David, K. Schleithoff, and F. Schmitz, Hydrogen-Induced Crack Formation in the Low-Alloy Steel 26NiCrMoV14 5 With a Yield Strength of Approximately 850 N/mm^2, *Z. Werkstofftech.*, *17*(6), 205-211, 1986. MetAbs No. 86-352444. **Abstract:** In recent years, intergranular stress-corrosion cracking has occurred worldwide in the shrink-fitted discs of low-pressure turbine rotors made of low-alloy steels. Both anodic stress-corrosion cracking and hydrogen-induced crack formation have been mentioned in the literature as possible failure mechanisms. Clarification of the role of hydrogen-induced cracking was sought by carrying out a variety of tests with low-alloy steel.

M. Takemoto, Effect of Loading Mode on the Hydrogen-Assisted Fracture of an Ultra High-Strength Steel, *Corrosion*, *42*(10), 585-592, 1986. MetAbs No. 87-350020. **Abstract:** An experimental study on the effects of loading mode and hydrogen charging sequence on the hydrogen-assisted cracking of quenched and tempered AISI 4135 steel were conducted to determine the mechanism of hydrogen embrittlement. The cracking susceptibility and fracture mode were greatly affected by the loading mode and hydrogen charging sequence.

Y. Kobayasha and Z. Szklarska-Smialowska, A Study of the Hydrogen-Induced Degradation of Two Steels Differing in Sulfur Content, *Metall. Trans. A*, *17A*(12), 2255-2263, 1986. MetAbs No. 87-350169. **Abstract:** Two steels with different sulfur contents, 0.003 and 0.024 wt.%, were cathodically charged under three different conditions and brought to fracture in tension immediately after charging or after aging at room temperature. All hydrogen-charged specimens showed embrittlement, with a little higher loss of ductility in the high S steel.

D. Warren, Hydrogen Effects on Steel, *Mater. Perform.*, *26*(1), 38-48, 1987. MetAbs No. 87-351322. **Abstract:** Hydrogen can be introduced into steel either by the steel-making or fabrication processes or from subsequent service conditions. Hydrogen can enter and leave steel without making its presence known, or it can cause insidious damage: blisters, embrittlement, or even attack on carbide phases.

M. Arpaia, P.G. Orsini, and P. Pernice, Hydrogen Embrittlement of High Strength Steel Wires Under Cathodic Polarization, *Mater. Chem. Phys.*, *16*(5-6), 501-509, 1987. MetAbs No. 87-352196. **Abstract:** The conditions leading to failure, under cathodic polarization, of high-strength wires used to prestress concrete tubes, have been studied. A mechanism of nucleation and growth of microcracks in areas charged with hydrogen has been evidenced.

J.F. Kiefner and R.J. Eiber, *Study Shows Shift in Line Pipe Service Problems, Oil Gas J.*, *85*(13), 98-100, 1987. MetAbs No. 87-352431. **Abstract:** An analysis of 60 gas pipeline failures experienced from 1979-1986 showed that causes of failure did not differ significantly from those experienced prior to 1979. Three new types of failure were identified—hydrogen-induced cracking of high-strength steels, a case of unusually long ductile fracture propagation in a 16-in. diameter line, and bacterial corrosion. Examples of hydrogen-induced stress cracking are presented.

L.J. Qiao, *Hydrogen-Induced Cracking and Stress Corrosion Cracking of Austenitic Stainless Steel Under Mode III Loading, Corrosion*, *43*(8), 479-483, 1987. MetAbs No. 87-352843. **Abstract:** Hydrogen-induced cracking of austenitic stainless steel under mode III loading can occur during dynamic charging of hydrogen. The torsional angle, i.e., the torsional plastic deformation, enlarged continuously during dynamic charging under a constant torque until the specimen was twisted to failure.

T. Iwadate, T. Nomura, and J. Watanabe, *Hydrogen Effect on Remaining Life of Hydroprocessing Reactors, Corrosion*, *44*(2), 103-112, 1988. MetAbs No. 88-351088. **Abstract:** Old vintage 2.25Cr-1Mo steels used for high-temperature/pressure hydroprocessing reactors have a high potential for temper embrittlement. The cracks caused by hydrogen embrittlement have been experienced in a stainless steel overlay and base metal of hydroprocessing reactors.

Corrosion Behavior of Various Metals and Alloys in Hydrogen

Material	Condition, other factors, comments	Concentration, %	Temperature, °C (°F)	Duration	Corrosion rate, mm/yr (mils/yr) or other	Ref
Stainless steels						
Type 304 stainless steel	Petroleum processing; field or pilot plant test; no aeration; rapid agitation. Approximately 20% hydrocarbons, 2-10 grains/100 ft^3 hydrogen sulfide during 1 week, then 2 grains/100 ft^3 average, trace hydrogen chloride	~80	510 (950)	250 d	<0.0001 in./yr	89
Coppers					Suitable	93
70-30 cupronickel	...	...	...	...	Suitable	93
90-10 cupronickel	...	...	...	...	Suitable	93
Admiralty brass	...	...	...	...	Suitable	93
Aluminum bronze	...	...	...	...	<0.05 (<2)	96
Ampco 8, aluminum bronze	Generally suitable	...	...	...		
Architectural bronze	...	...	...	...	Suitable	93
Brass	...	...	...	...	Suitable	93
Cartridge brass	...	...	...	...	Suitable	93
Commercial bronze	...	...	...	...	Suitable	93
Electrolytic copper	...	...	...	...	Suitable	93
Free-cutting brass	...	...	...	...	Suitable	93
Muntz metal	...	...	...	...	Suitable	93
Naval brass	...	...	...	...	Suitable	93
Nickel silver	...	18	...	...	Suitable	93
Phosphor bronze	5% Sn	...	...	...	Suitable	93
Phosphor bronze	8% Sn	...	...	...	Suitable	93
Phosphor copper	...	...	...	...	Suitable	93
Red brass	...	...	...	...	Suitable	93
Silicon bronze	Low	...	...	...	Suitable	93
Silicon bronze	High	...	...	...	Suitable	93
Heat- and corrosion-resistant alloys						
Alloy 814	Plus 2% methane. Undescaled. Metal loss is 13 μm. Maximum attack is 363 μm	...	1095 (2000)	100 h	0.82 mg/cm^2	132
Alloy 814	Plus 2% methane. Descaled. Metal loss is 13 μm. Maximum attack is 363 μm	...	1095 (2000)	100 h	-0.73 mg/cm^2	132
Incoloy 800	Plus 2% methane. Undescaled. Metal loss is 132 μm. Maximum attack is 7615 μm	...	1095 (2000)	100 h	33.74 mg/cm^2	132
Incoloy 800	Plus 2% methane. Descaled. Metal loss is 132 μm. Maximum attack is 7615 μm	...	1095 (2000)	100 h	29.89 mg/cm^2	132
MA 956	Plus 2% methane. Undescaled. Metal loss is 10 μm. Maximum attack is 10 μm	...	1095 (2000)	100 h	0.07 mg/cm^2	132
MA 956	Plus 2% methane. Descaled. Metal loss is 10 μm. Maximum attack is 10 μm	...	1095 (2000)	100 h	-0.42 mg/cm^2	132
Noble metals						
Platinum	...	Pure	1000 (1830)	...	<0.05 (<2)	6
Silver	...	Pure	700 (1290)	...	<0.05 (<2)	8

Relative Resistance to Hydrogen Embrittlement of Various Alloys in High-Pressure Hydrogen at Room Temperature

Alloy	Stress concentration factor, K_t	Pressure		Ratio H_2/He(a)
		MPa	ksi	
250 maraging steel	8	69	10	0.12
Type 410 stainless steel	8	69	10	0.22
1042 steel (quenched and tempered)	8	69	10	0.22
17-7PH (TH1050)	8	69	10	0.23
HP9-4-20 alloy steel	8	69	10	0.24
H-11 high-strength steel	8	69	10	0.25
Inconel alloy X-750	6.3	48	7	0.26
René 41	8	69	10	0.27
ED nickel	8	69	10	0.31
4140 steel	8	69	10	0.40
Inconel alloy 718	8	69	10	0.46
MP35N	6.3	69	10	0.50
Type 440C stainless steel	8	69	10	0.50
Ti-6Al-4V (solution treated and aged)	8	69	10	0.58
Monel alloy 400	6.3	48	7	0.65
D-979 stainless steel	6.3	48	7	0.69
Nickel 270	8	69	10	0.70
CG27 stainless steel	6.3	48	7	0.72
ASTM A515, grade 70	8	69	10	0.73
HY-100 steel	8	69	10	0.73
ASTM A372, type IV	8	69	10	0.74
1042 steel (normalized)	8	69	10	0.75
Inconel alloy 625	8	34	5	0.76
ASTM A517, grade F	8	69	10	0.77
ASTM A533, type B	8	69	10	0.78
Waspaloy	6.3	48	7	0.78
Ti-6Al-4V (annealed)	8	69	10	0.79
1020 steel	8	69	10	0.79
HY-80 steel	8	69	10	0.80
Inconel alloy 706	6.3	48	7	0.80
Ti-5Al-2.5Sn	8	69	10	0.81
ARMCO iron	8	69	10	0.86
P/M Inconel alloy 718	6.3	48	7	0.86
Type 304 stainless steel	8	69	10	0.87
Type 321 stainless steel	8	34	5	0.87
Hastelloy alloy X	8	34	5	0.87
Type 305 stainless steel	8	69	10	0.89
Astroloy	8	34	5	0.90
Type 347 stainless steel	8	34	5	0.91
Haynes alloy 188	6.3	48	7	0.92
Type 304N stainless steel	6.3	103	15	0.93
Type 310 stainless steel	8	69	10	0.93
Beryllium-copper	8	69	10	0.93
RA330	6.3	48	7	0.95
A-286	8	69	10	0.97
21-6-9 stainless steel	6.3	48	7	0.97
Aluminum alloy 7075-T73	8	69	10	0.98
Incoloy alloy 802	6.3	48	7	0.99
Aluminum alloy 6061-T6	8	69	10	1.00
Copper (C10100)	8	69	10	1.00
Type 316 stainless steel	8	69	10	1.00
Incoloy alloy 903	8	34	5	1.00

(a) Ratio of notched strength in hydrogen to notched strength in helium

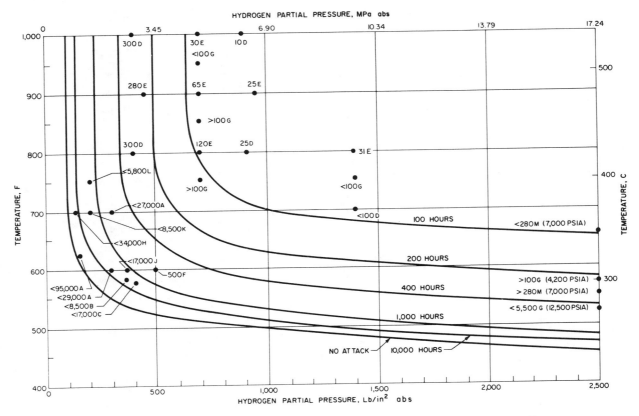

HYDROGEN PARTIAL PRESSURE, MPa abs

HYDROGEN PARTIAL PRESSURE, Lb/in² abs

Carbon steel. Time for incipient attack of carbon steel in hydrogen service. Source: *Corrosion Data Survey: Metals Section*, 6th ed., National Association of Corrosion Engineers, Houston, 1985, 174.

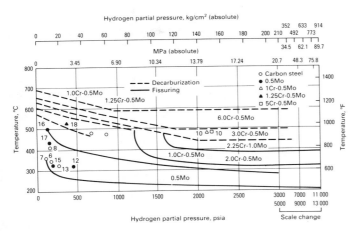

Hydrogen partial pressure, kg/cm² (absolute)

MPa (absolute)

Hydrogen partial pressure, psia

Steels. Nelson curve defining safe upper limits for steels in hydrogen service. Source: G.R. Prescott, "Materials Problems in the Hydrogen-Carbon Processing Industries," in *Alloys for the Eighties*, Climax Molybdenum Company, 303-315.

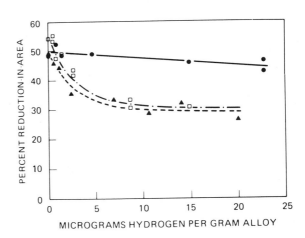

Uranium/niobium alloy. The effect of hydrogen content on the tensile reduction in area of alpha double prime-U-5.7Nb alloy. Closed triangle: 0.06 mm/s crosshead speed, 800 °C anneal. Open square: 0.06 mm/s crosshead speed, 850 °C anneal. Closed circle: 21 mm/s crosshead speed, 800 °C anneal. Source: G.L. Powell and W.G. Northcutt, Jr., "Internal Hydrogen Embrittlement of Uranium-5.7 Niobium Alloy," *Journal of Nuclear Materials*, Vol 132, May 1985, 49.

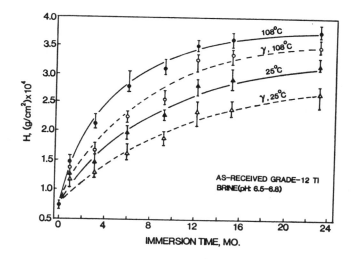

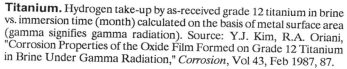

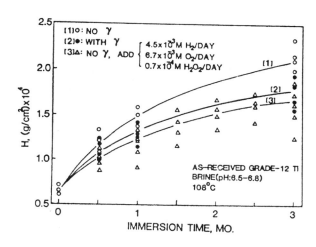

Titanium. Hydrogen take-up by as-received grade 12 titanium in brine vs. immersion time (month) calculated on the basis of metal surface area (gamma signifies gamma radiation). Source: Y.J. Kim, R.A. Oriani, "Corrosion Properties of the Oxide Film Formed on Grade 12 Titanium in Brine Under Gamma Radiation," *Corrosion*, Vol 43, Feb 1987, 87.

Titanium. Effect of additions of hydrogen, oxygen, and water together on the hydrogen take-up by as-received Grade 12 titanium in brine at 108 °C. Source: Y.J. Kim, R.A. Oriani, "Brine Radiolysis and Its Effects on the Corrosion of Grade 12 Titanium," *Corrosion*, Vol 43, Feb 1987, 92-97.

Hydrogen Chloride

Hydrogen chloride, HCl, is a fuming, highly toxic gas that is soluble in water, alcohol, and ether. It is used in polymerization, isomerization, and the synthesis of vinyl chloride and alkyl chloride.

Material Summaries

The following material summaries were compiled from a survey of the available literature. Inclusion of a material description under a given environment does not imply that it is the most appropriate material for corrosion service in that environment. Likewise, exclusion of a given material does not imply that it is not suitable for corrosion service applications in that environment.

Cast Irons. Hydrogen chloride and chlorine gas may be handled in cast iron. Unalloyed cast iron can be used in dry hydrogen chloride up to 205 °C (400 °F), but if moisture is present, unalloyed cast iron is unacceptable at any temperature.

Aluminum. Hydrogen chloride corrodes aluminum alloys at all temperatures, but the rate increases as the temperature increases. Dry hydrogen chloride has been handled in aluminum equipment.

Gold. Gold is resistant to hydrogen chloride up to 870 °C (1600 °F).

Platinum. Platinum is resistant to dry hydrogen chloride even at elevated temperatures.

Nickel. Dry hydrogen chloride is resisted by Nickel 200 at low temperatures. Nickel 201 and Inconel alloy 600 are the preferred alloys for use at elevated temperatures. For example, Nickel 201 had a corrosion rate in dry hydrogen chloride of about 0.075 mm/yr (3 mil/yr) in a 500-h laboratory test at 499 °C (930 °F). Inconel alloy 600 corrodes in wet hydrogen chloride, although the corrosion rates are the same as those for dry hydrogen chloride at temperatures above the dew point. The metal corrodes in hydrogen chloride to form a film of metal chloride. This film is protective at intermediate temperatures, but the film volatilizes at higher temperatures and the surface again corrodes to form another film.

Titanium. Titanium alloys have a protective oxide film that resists attack by dry hydrogen chloride at temperatures above 150 °C (300 °F).

Additional Reading

J.P. Carter *et al.*, *Corrosion*, 40(5), May 1984.

M.H. Brown *et al.*, *Ind. Eng. Chem.*, 39, 839, 1947.

Inco Corrosion Engineering Bulletin, CEB-3.

Corrosion Behavior of Various Metals and Alloys in Hydrogen Chloride

Material	Condition, other factors, comments	Concentration, %	Temperature, °C (°F)	Duration	Corrosion rate, mm/yr (mils/yr) or other	Ref
Stainless steels						
Type 304 stainless steel	Research; laboratory test; rapid agitation. Hydrogen chloride, dry	...	204 (400)	...	<0.005 in./yr	89
Type 304 stainless steel	Textile processing; field or pilot plant test; slight to moderate aeration; no agitation. Hydrogen chloride made by volatilizing 31.5% hydrochloric acid solution (shaft leading to wool-rag carbonizer). Slight pitting (maximum depth of pits from incipient to 0.005 in.). Crevice attack (tendency to concentration-cell corrosion)	...	104 (220)	37 d	0.0065 in./yr	89
Type 304 stainless steel	Metal (pickling); field or pilot plant test; strong aeration; slight to moderate agitation. Hydrogen chloride fumes from tank containing approximately 19% hydrochloric acid. Severe pitting (maximum depth of pits over 0.010 in.)	...	71-82 (160-180)	41 d	0.0086 in./yr	89
Type 304 stainless steel	Atomic energy; field or pilot plant test; low-carbon grade (0.03% C max). Hydrogen chloride, dry	...	499 (930)	21 d	0.011 in./yr	89
Type 304 stainless steel	Chemical processing; field or pilot plant test; no aeration; rapid agitation. Hydrogen chloride, dry, plus 2% acetic acid, 3% acetyl chloride	95	11 (52)	14 d	0.196 in./yr	89
Type 316 stainless steel	Petroleum processing; field or pilot plant test. Hydrogen chloride, dry, pressure	...	82 (180)	234 d	0.0075 in./yr	89
Type 316 stainless steel	Textile processing; field or pilot plant test; slight to moderate aeration; no agitation. Hydrogen chloride made by volatilizing 31.5% hydrochloric acid solution (shaft leading to wool-rag carbonizer). Slight pitting (maximum depth of pits from incipient to 0.005 in.). Crevice attack (tendency to concentration-cell corrosion)	...	104 (220)	37 d	0.0036 in./yr	89
Type 316 stainless steel	Metal (pickling); field or pilot plant test; strong aeration; slight to moderate agitation. Hydrogen chloride fumes from tank containing approximately 19% hydrochloric acid. Severe pitting (maximum depth of pits over 0.010 in.)	...	71-82 (160-180)	41 d	0.0071 in./yr	89
Type 316 stainless steel	Research; laboratory test; rapid agitation. Hydrogen chloride, dry	...	204 (400)	...	<0.005 in./yr	89
Type 316 stainless steel	Chemical processing; field or pilot plant test; no aeration; rapid agitation. Hydrogen chloride, dry, plus 2% acetic acid, 3% acetyl chloride	95	11 (52)	14 d	0.139 in./yr	89
Titanium						
Titanium	Gas. Air mixture	...	25-100 (77-212)	...	nil	90
Heat- and corrosion-resistant alloys						
Alloy 825	Metal (pickling); field or pilot plant test; strong aeration; slight to moderate agitation. Hydrogen chloride fumes from tank containing approximately 19% hydrochloric acid. Severe pitting (maximum depth of pits over 0.010 in.)	...	71-82 (160-180)	41 d	0.0059 in./yr	89
Carpenter 20	Metal (pickling); field or pilot plant test; strong aeration; slight to moderate agitation. Hydrogen chloride fumes from tank containing approximately 19% hydrochloric acid. Slight pitting (maximum depth of pits from incipient to 0.005 in.)	...	71-82 (160-180)	41 d	0.0086 in./yr	89
Carpenter 20	Chemical processing; field or pilot plant test; no aeration; rapid agitation. Hydrogen chloride, dry, plus 2% acetic acid, 3% acetyl chloride	95	11 (52)	14 d	0.042 in./yr	89
Nickel 201	Wet, moisture content about 0.25%	...	538 (1000)	4 h	3 (120)	44
Nickel 201	Wet, moisture content about 0.25%	...	538 (1000)	8 h	1.75 (70)	44
Nickel 201	Wet, moisture content about 0.25%	...	538 (1000)	20 h	0.7 (28)	44
Nickel 201	Dry	...	538 (1000)	20 h	0.925 (37)	44
Noble metals						
Gold	Dry	...	870 (1600)	...	<0.05 (<2)	8
Gold	Dry	...	870 (1600)	...	<0.05 (<2)	8
Platinum	Dry. Corrosion rate is increased by the presence of steam or oxidizing agents	...	1200 (2190)	...	<0.1 (<4)	6
Silver	Dry. Protected by a layer of silver chloride that forms rapidly on the surface	...	430 (805)	...	<0.05 (<2)	8

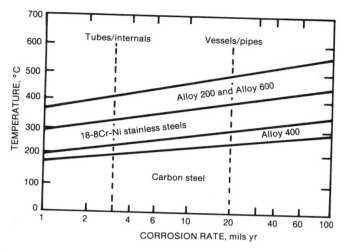

Various alloys. Upper temperature design limits for various alloys in hydrogen chloride. Source: T.F. Degnan, "Materials of Construction for Hydrochloric Acid and Hydrogen Chloride," in *Process Industries Corrosion*, B.J. Moniz and W.I. Pollock, Ed., National Association of Corrosion Engineers, Houston, 1986, 267.

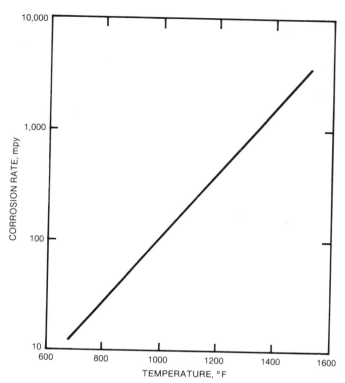

Inconel 600. Corrosion rates in dry hydrogen gas. Source: Inco Alloys International, 1962.

Hydrogen Cyanide

Hydrogen cyanide, HCN, also known as hydrocyanic acid, prussic acid, and formonitrile, is a very poisonous colorless gas with a characteristic fragrance of bitter almonds. Small amounts of hydrogen cyanide derivatives in combination with glucose and benzaldehyde are found in nature in apricot, peach, cherry, and plum pits. It liquifies at 26 °C (79 °F) and is soluble in water, alcohol, and ether. Hydrogen cyanide is usually sold commercially as an aqueous solution containing 2 to 10% hydrogen cyanide. The aqueous solutions of hydrogen cyanide decompose slowly to form ammonium formate. In some uses, it is preferable to generate hydrogen cyanide as needed, thus eliminating handling and storage problems. Hydrogen cyanide is used in manufacturing cyanide salts, acrylonitrile, and dyes. It is also used as a horticultural fumigant.

Material Summaries

The following material summaries were compiled from a survey of the available literature. Inclusion of a material description under a given environment does not imply that it is the most appropriate material for corrosion service in that environment. Likewise, exclusion of a given material does not imply that it is not suitable for corrosion service applications in that environment.

Aluminum. Hydrogen cyanide has been manufactured in aluminum alloy reactor towers, heat exchangers, tanks, and piping. Aluminum alloy 3003 resisted hydrogen cyanide at ambient temperature in laboratory tests.

Copper. Copper and copper alloys can be used to handle hydrogen cyanide.

Gold. Gold is rapidly attacked by hydrogen cyanide in the presence of oxygen.

Titanium. Titanium alloys have a protective oxide film that resists attack by hydrogen cyanide at temperatures above 150 °C (300 °F).

Corrosion Behavior of Various Metals and Alloys in Hydrogen Cyanide

Material	Condition, other factors, comments	Concentration, %	Temperature, °C (°F)	Duration	Corrosion rate, mm/yr (mils/yr) or other	Ref
Stainless steels						
Type 304 stainless steel	Chemical processing; field or pilot plant test; no aeration; no agitation. Liquid hydrocyanic acid	...	7 (45)	169 d	<0.0001 in./yr	89
Type 316 stainless steel	Chemical processing; field or pilot plant test; no aeration; no agitation. Liquid hydrocyanic acid	...	7 (45)	169 d	<0.0001 in./yr	89
Type 410 stainless steel	...	...	Room	...	Attacked	121
Coppers						
70-30 cupronickel	...	...	...	...	Not suitable	93
90-10 cupronickel	...	...	...	...	Not suitable	93
Admiralty brass	...	...	...	...	Not suitable	93
Aluminum bronze	...	...	...	...	Not suitable	93
Architectural bronze	...	...	...	...	Not suitable	93
Brass	...	...	...	...	Not suitable	93
C11000	Average penetration rate of stripping still 173-218 μm/yr (6.8-8.6 mils/yr); at top of HCN refining still 54-60 μm/yr (2.1-2.4 mils/yr); at base of stripping still 1033-1186 μm/yr (40.7-46.7 mils/yr); at base of partial condenser 1534-14170 μm/yr (60.4-558 mils/yr). (a)	...	...	573 h	...	138
C11000	Average penetration rate of stripping still 155-609 μm/yr (6.1-24.0 mils/yr); at top of HCN refining still 18-25 μm/yr (0.7-1.0 mils/yr); nil at base of stripping still; at base of partial condenser 478 μm/yr (18.8 mils/yr). (a)	...	...	671 h	...	138
C11000	Ethylene cyanohydrin residues. Average penetration rate 5-35 μm/yr (0.2-1.4 mils/yr)	...	70 (158)	3144 h	...	138
C11000	Ethylene cyanohydrin residues. Average penetration rate 13 μm/yr (0.5 mils/yr)	...	30-90 (86-194)	2232 h	...	138
C11000	Cyanohydrin stripping still products (kettle). Average penetration rate 690 μm/yr (27 mils/yr)	...	...	1621 h	...	138
C65500	Average penetration rate of stripping still 229-244 μm/yr (9.0-9.6 mils/yr); at top of HCN refining still 18-25 μm/yr (0.7-1.0 mils/yr); at base of stripping still 777-1145 μm/yr (30.6-45.1 mils/yr); at base of partial condenser 1138-5385 μm/yr (44.8-212 mils/yr). (a)	...	...	573 h	...	138
C65500	Average penetration rate of stripping still 137-503 μm/yr (5.4-19.8 mils/yr); at base of stripping still 275 μm/yr (10.8 mils/yr); at base of partial condenser 343 μm/yr (13.5 mils/yr). (a)	...	...	671 h	...	138
C65500	Ethylene cyanohydrin residues. Average penetration rate 40 μm/yr (1.6 mils/yr)	...	30-90 (86-194)	2232 h	...	138
C65500	Cyanohydrin stripping still products (kettle). Average penetration rate 35 μm/yr (1.4 mils/yr)	...	...	1621 h	...	138
Cartridge brass	...	...	...	...	Not suitable	93
Commercial bronze	...	...	...	...	Not suitable	93
Electrolytic copper	...	...	...	...	Not suitable	93
Free-cutting brass	...	...	...	...	Not suitable	93
Muntz metal	...	...	...	...	Not suitable	93
Naval brass	...	...	...	...	Not suitable	93
Nickel silver	...	18	...	...	Not suitable	93
Phosphor bronze	5% Sn	...	...	...	Not suitable	93
Phosphor bronze	8% Sn	...	...	...	Not suitable	93
Phosphor copper	...	...	...	...	Not suitable	93
Red brass	...	...	...	...	Not suitable	93
Silicon bronze	Low	...	...	...	Not suitable	93
Silicon bronze	High	...	...	...	Not suitable	93

(a) All data from separate specimens; differences at similar locations imply expected variability.

Hydrogen Peroxide

Hydrogen peroxide, H_2O_2, is a colorless, viscous, unstable liquid that has a boiling point of 158 °C (316 °F). It is soluble in water and in alcohol. The highly reactive hydrogen peroxide molecule is often used as an intermediate in chemical synthesis involving oxidation, epoxidation, and hydroxylation. Hydrogen peroxide has been used as an oxidizer in various fuel mixtures for rockets and torpedos. Hydrogen peroxide at low concentrations (around 3%) is used as an antiseptic in medicine and at higher concentrations as an antimicrobial agent to sterilize processing equipment and packaging materials for aseptic packaging. It is widely used as a bleaching agent for wool, cotton, groundwood pulp, and cosmetically in formulations for bleaching hair.

Material Summaries

The following material summaries were compiled from a survey of the available literature. Inclusion of a material description under a given environment does not imply that it is the most appropriate material for corrosion service in that environment. Likewise, exclusion of a given material does not imply that it is not suitable for corrosion service applications in that environment.

Aluminum. Aluminum alloy equipment has been used in distilling, shipping, and storing hydrogen peroxide. Aluminum alloy 1060 has been the choice for long-term storage, whereas the 5XXX series alloys have been selected for short-term storage. Piping of aluminum alloy 6063 has been used in the service of hydrogen peroxide. In laboratory conditions of ambient temperature and chloride-free hydrogen peroxide, aluminum alloys 1060, 5052, and 6063 were resistant to attack.

Nickel. Nickel alloy 600 resists alkaline solutions containing hydrogen peroxide.

Tantalum. Tantalum is not attacked by hydrogen peroxide at ordinary temperatures.

Titanium. The corrosion rate of titanium alloys depends on the concentration, temperature, and pH of the hydrogen peroxide solutions. Corrosion rates are low in dilute neutral solutions, but increase rapidly in alkaline solutions due to the formation of soluble titanium-peroxyl compounds. In concentrated (90%) hydrogen peroxide solutions, the corrosion rate is rapid.

Additional Reading

J.E.O. Mayne and J.A. Burkill, Role of Hydrogen Peroxide in Inhibition of Corrosion of Iron, *Br. Corros. J., 21*(4), 221-224, 1986. MetAbs No. 87-351171. **Abstract:** The reduction of oxygen at an Fe cathode has been examined previously using a polarographic method. The study showed that cathodically formed hydrogen peroxide plays an important part in the process of inhibition, probably via the formation of peroxyl compounds.

Corrosion Behavior of Various Metals and Alloys in Hydrogen Peroxide

Material	Condition, other factors, comments	Concentration, %	Temperature, °C (°F)	Duration	Corrosion rate, mm/yr (mils/yr) or other	Ref
Stainless steels						
Type 304 stainless steel	...	10	21 (70)	...	Very good	121
Type 304 stainless steel	Chemical processing; laboratory test; no aeration; rapid agitation. Stabilized with sulfuric acid	30	29 (85)	6 d	<0.0001 in./yr	89
Type 304 stainless steel	Cosmetic processing; laboratory test; no aeration; no agitation. Stabilized with acetanilide and phosphoric acid	6.1	Room	30 d	<0.0001 in./yr	89
Type 304 stainless steel	Cosmetic processing; laboratory test; no aeration; rapid agitation. Stabilized with acetanilide	3	Room	30 d	<0.0001 in./yr	89
Type 304 stainless steel	Chemical processing; field or pilot plant test; strong aeration; rapid agitation. Plus acetic acid, cationic resin, acetylated castor oil during 8 h; and alkaline wash, water wash, sodium sulfate during 6 h (epoxydation reactor). Crevice attack (tendency to concentration-cell corrosion)	50	100 (212)	1 d	0.027 in./yr	89
Type 316 stainless steel	Chemical processing; field or pilot plant test; strong aeration; rapid agitation. Plus acetic acid, cationic resin, acetylated castor oil during 8 h; and alkaline wash, water wash, sodium sulfate during 6 h (epoxydation reactor). Crevice attack (tendency to concentration-cell corrosion)	50	100 (212)	1 d	0.008 in./yr	89
Type 316 stainless steel	Chemical processing; field or pilot plant test; strong aeration; rapid agitation; sensitized specimens. Plus acetic acid, cationic resin, acetylated castor oil during 8 h; and alkaline wash, water wash, sodium sulfate during 6 h (epoxydation reactor). Crevice attack (tendency to concentration-cell corrosion)	50	100 (212)	1 d	0.059 in./yr	89
Type 316 stainless steel	...	10	21 (70)	...	Very good	121
Type 410 stainless steel	...	10	21 (70)	...	Good	121
Type 410 stainless steel	...	...	Room	...	Unattacked	121
Type 430 stainless steel	...	10	21 (70)	...	Good	121

(Continued)

Corrosion Behavior of Various Metals and Alloys in Hydrogen Peroxide (Continued)

Material	Condition, other factors, comments	Concen-tration, %	Temperature, °C (°F)	Duration	Corrosion rate, mm/yr (mils/yr) or other	Ref
Titanium						
Titanium	Grade 7. pH 1	5	23 (72)	...	0.062 (2.44)	33
Titanium	Grade 7. pH 4	5	23 (72)	...	0.010 (0.39)	33
Titanium	Grade 7. pH 1	5	66 (150)	...	0.127 (5.0)	33
Titanium	Grade 7. pH 4	5	66 (150)	...	0.046 (1.81)	33
Titanium	Grade 7. Plus 500 ppm Ca^{2+}, pH 1	5	66 (150)	...	nil	33
Titanium	Grade 7. Plus 500 ppm Ca^{2+}, pH 1	20	66 (150)	...	0.76 (29.9)	33
Titanium	Grade 7. Plus 5% NaCl, pH 1	20	66 (150)	...	0.008 (0.315)	33
Titanium	...	3	Room	...	<0.127 (<5.08)	90
Titanium	...	6	Room	...	<0.127 (<5.08)	90
Titanium	...	30	Room	...	<0.305 (<12.2)	90
Titanium	Plus 2% NaOH	1	60 (140)	...	55.9 (2236)	90
Titanium	pH 4	5	66 (151)	...	0.061 (2.44)	90
Titanium	pH 1	5	66 (151)	...	0.152 (6.08)	90
Titanium	pH 1	20	66 (151)	...	0.69 (27.6)	90
Titanium	Grade 2. pH 1. (a)	5	23 (73)	...	0.064 (2.5)	27
Titanium	Grade 2. pH 4.3. (a)	5	23 (73)	...	0.013 (0.5)	27
Titanium	Grade 2. pH 1. (a)	5	66 (150)	...	0.152 (6.0)	27
Titanium	Grade 2. pH 4.3. (a)	5	66 (150)	...	0.061 (2.4)	27
Titanium	Grade 2. pH 1. Plus 500 ppm Ca^{2+}. (a)	5	66 (150)	...	nil	27
Titanium	Grade 2. pH 1. (a)	20	66 (150)	...	0.686 (27.0)	27
Titanium	Grade 2. pH 1. Plus 500 ppm Ca^{2+}. (a)	20	66 (150)	...	nil	27
Titanium	Grade 2. Plus 20 g/L NaOH	10 g/L	60 (140)	...	55.9 (2200.0)	27
Titanium	Grade 2. pH 11. (a)	0.75 g/L	70 (160)	...	0.42 (16.5)	27
Titanium	Grade 2. Plus 10 g/L NaOH plus 10 g/L Na_2SiO_3 plus 0.5 g/L Na_3PO_4	3.5 g/L	60 (140)	...	nil	27
Titanium	pH 11	0.08	70 (158)	...	0.42 (16.8)	90
Zirconium						
Zr702	...	50	100 (212)	...	<0.05 (<2)	15
Noble metals						
Silver	...	All	Room	...	Peroxide decomposed	9
Others						
Magnesium	...	All	Room	...	Unsuitable	119
Niobium	...	30	Room	...	0.025 (1.0)	2
Niobium	...	30	Boiling	...	0.5 (20)	2

(a) Acid solutions were prepared with HCl additions.

Hydrogen Sulfide

Hydrogen sulfide, H_2S, also known as hydrogen disulfide, is a flammable, toxic, colorless, malodorous gas that is soluble in water and in alcohol. It boils at -60 °C (-76 °F). This gas requires careful handling because of its toxicity and explosiveness. It is especially dangerous from the standpoint of toxicity, because it can paralyze the olfactory nerves. Its explosiveness stems from a low ignition temperature (260 °C, or 500 °F) and a wide flammability range (from 4.3 to 44 vol% in air). Upon burning, hydrogen sulfide liberates a considerable amount of heat. It is produced by water hydrolysis of elements higher in the hydrogen scale and by acid hydrolysis of sulfides.

Hydrogen sulfide reacts with the elements fluorine, chlorine, bromine, and iodine to form the corresponding halogen acids. When hydrogen sulfide is introduced into solutions of heavy metals such as silver, lead, copper, and manganese, metal sulfides are formed. Such reactions form the basis for separation of these heavy metals in classical wet qualitative analytical methods and for tarnishing of silver. Hydrogen sulfide also reacts with a large number of organic compounds.

When dissolved in water, hydrogen sulfide is a weak acid and is therefore corrosive because it is a source of hydrogen ions. In the absence of buffering ions, water equilibrated with 1 atm of hydrogen sulfide has a pH of about 4. However, under high-pressure formation conditions, pH values as low as 3 have been calculated.

Hydrogen sulfide is used as an analytical reagent, as a source of sulfur, in the preparation of sulfides (sodium sulfide and sodium hydrosulfide) and sulfur-bearing organic compounds (mercaptans, thiophenes, and organic sulfides), for purification of hydrochloric and sulfuric acids, in the production of extreme pressure lubricants, in the formulation of rare-earth phosphors for use in color television tubes, and in removal of copper, cadmium, and titanium from spent catalysts.

Material Summaries

The following material summaries were compiled from a survey of the available literature. Inclusion of a material description under a given environment does not imply that it is the most appropriate material for corrosion service in that environment. Likewise, exclusion of a given material does not imply that it is not suitable for corrosion service applications in that environment.

Alloy steels used in oil and natural gas wells and pipelines are often subject to corrosion by hydrogen sulfide. For the casing of deep wells, high-strength alloy steels are usually required. Furthermore, very hostile environments are often encountered—in particular, high hydrogen sulfide levels. In deep gas wells, for example, formations have been encountered with hydrogen sulfide concentrations ranging from less than 1% to greater than 50%. In addition, temperatures up to 200 °C (390 °F) can be found, along with pressures to 140 MPa (20 ksi). Also, hydrogen sulfide is often found in combination with chloride-containing brines and carbon dioxide, which add to the harshness of the environment.

Chemical inhibition is frequently used in deep wells to control weight loss corrosion from hydrogen sulfide. However, hydrogen sulfide can also produce embrittlement of high-strength steels. This phenomena, known as sulfide stress cracking, depends on hydrogen sulfide concentration and temperature among other factors.

Linepipe steels can be susceptible to a specialized form of hydrogen damage when hydrogen sulfide is present in oil and gas. This type of embrittlement, known as hydrogen-induced cracking or stepwise cracking, results from the accumulation of hydrogen at internal surfaces within the steel such as interfaces at nonmetallic inclusions. Microcracks that form at these interfaces grow in a stepwise fashion toward the surface of the pipe, resulting in failure. Several failures due to hydrogen-induced cracking have been reported, and when they occur, they can be catastrophic.

Aluminum. In laboratory tests, aluminum alloys 1100 and 3003 have suffered mild attack (corrosion rates of about 0.05 mm/yr, or 2 mils/yr) by aqueous solutions of hydrogen sulfide and by hydrogen sulfide gas. Aluminum alloys have been used in refineries for handling hydrocarbon liquids and vapors containing hydrogen sulfide. These applications have included bubble caps, heat exchangers, and roofs on storage tanks for sour crude oils.

Copper. Moist hydrogen sulfide gas, as well as other sulfur compounds such as sodium sulfide and potassium sulfide, react with copper and copper-zinc alloys to form CuS. Reaction rates depend on alloy composition: alloys containing more than 20% Zn have considerably better resistance than lower zinc alloys or copper. Hot, wet hydrogen sulfide vapors corrode C26000, C28000, and C44300 at rates of only 50 to 75 μm/yr (2 to 3 mils/yr), but the rates for C11000 and C23000 under the same conditions are 1250 to 1625 μm/yr (50 to 65 mils/yr).

Nickel. Nickel alloy B-2 is susceptible to hydrogen embrittlement in hydrogen sulfide-containing environments even in the annealed condition.

Incoloy alloy 825 is used to resist the corrosive conditions in sour gas and oil wells. The environments include hydrogen sulfide and carbon dioxide in sour crude and gas at high temperatures and pressures. The NACE test was used to evaluate alloys for such service. The test consists of exposure of stressed, steel-coupled C-rings to a room-temperature solution of 5% sodium chloride with 0.5% acetic acid and saturated with hydrogen sulfide. The specimens of Incoloy alloy 825 were stressed at 100% of yield strength (0.2% offset). No failure occurred in the test period of 48 or 50 days.

Monel alloy K-500 has been found to be resistant to a sour gas environment. After 6 days of continuous immersion in saturated (3500 ppm) hydrogen sulfide solutions at acidic and basic pH (ranging from 1.0 to 11.0), U-bend specimens of age-hardened sheet showed no cracking. There was some tightly adherent black scale. Hardness of the specimens ranged from 28 to 40 HRC.

Alloy 800 has good resistance to hydrogen sulfide, a substance often encountered in petrochemical processing. Specimens of alloy 800 exposed to process gases containing hydrogen sulfide in various areas of a catalytic reformer exhibited corrosion rates of less than 0.03 mm/yr (1 mil/yr).

Palladium. Hydrogen sulfide at temperatures above 600 °C (1110 °F) attacks palladium and produces a low-melting phase. The standard electrode potential is approximately +0.83 V at 25 °C (75 °F).

Tantalum. Over the temperature range commonly used in solution processes, tantalum is inert to hydrogen sulfide.

Tin. From 25 to 100 °C (75 to 212 °F), hydrogen sulfide has little apparent effect on tin, but above 100 °C (212 °F), stannous sulfide (SnS) forms.

Titanium. The oxide film on titanium alloys provides an effective barrier to attack by hydrogen sulfide (as well as by most other gases). Corrosion rates are near zero over the full concentration range to temperatures well beyond boiling.

Tests in acidic NaCl brine environments containing hydrogen sulfide indicate that titanium alloys are immune to stress-corrosion cracking at stress levels up to their yield strengths. Elevated temperature tests in hydrogen sulfide brines indicate that Ti-3Al-8V-6Cr-4Mo-4Zr is susceptible to stress-corrosion cracking.

Zinc. Hydrogen sulfide is harmless to zinc because insoluble zinc sulfide (ZnS) is formed.

Zirconium. Zirconium is resistant to stress-corrosion cracking in hydrogen sulfide.

Additional Reading

P.B. Narayan, J.W. Anderegg, and O.N. Carlson, An ESCA Study of Sulfidation of Fe-25 Wt.-% Cr Alloy in H$_2$S at 50 to 400 °C, *Corrosion*, *39*(6), 236-241, 1983. MetAbs No. 83-352025. **Abstract:** The surface reaction of polycrystalline Fe-25 wt.% Cr alloy with H$_2$S was studied in situ with ESCA at 50 to 400 °C at pressures of 0.005 to 5 torr of H$_2$S, with and without pre-exposure to oxygen.

J.C. Turn Jr., B.E. Wilde, and C.A. Troianos, On the Sulfide Stress Cracking of Line Pipe Steels, *Corrosion*, *39*(9), 364-370, 1983. MetAbs No. 84-350036. **Abstract:** The mechanical properties of low-strength linepipe steel for energy-related industries may degrade by hydrogen-induced blister cracking and sulfide stress cracking if employed in sour service. Constant load tests in hydrogen sulfide saturated 5% sodium chloride plus 0.5% acetic acid solution have been conducted on linepipe steels (Grade X-42 to X-70).

Y. Yoshino, Metallurgical Influences on the Hydrogen Uptake by Steel in H$_2$S Environment, *Corrosion*, *39*(11), 435-444, 1983. MetAbs No.

84-350521. **Abstract:** This study details the hydrogen uptake by nine steels with varying Cr content (2Cr-Mo, 9Cr-Mo, 16Cr-Ni-Cu) naturally corroding in an acidic H2S.

S.W. Ciaraldi, Microstructural Observations on the Sulfide Stress Cracking of Low-Alloy Steel Tubulars, *Corrosion*, *40*(2), 77-81, 1984. MetAbs No. 84-351163. **Abstract:** Microstructural studies were performed on typical sour service steel specimens (4130 Gr C-75-2, 4130 Gr L-80, 4130 Gr 90SS and 4130 Gr 95SS) which had failed in laboratory sulfide stress cracking tests.

B.J. Berkowitz and F.H. Heubaum, The Role of Hydrogen in Sulfide Stress Cracking of Low-Alloy Steels, *Corrosion*, *40*(5), 240-244, 1984. MetAbs No. 84-351927. **Abstract:** It is generally accepted that sulfide stress cracking failures are the result of hydrogen embrittlement. However, the evidence heretofore has been mostly circumstantial. Experimental evidence is provided which establishes the causality of H and the contributory roles of H2S and anodic dissolution.

B.D. Craig, Effect of Copper on the Protectiveness of Iron Sulfide Films, *Corrosion*, *40*(9), 471-474, 1984. MetAbs No. 84-353067. **Abstract:** An explanation of the mechanisms behind the effects of Cu on the corrosion and hydrogen permeation rates of pipeline steels in H2S environments is offered. Over narrow pH ranges, Cu can either enhance or reduce the corrosion rate and likewise the H permeation rate.

T. Taira, Y. Kobayashi, K. Matsumoto, and K. Tsukada, Resistance of Line Pipe Steels to Wet Sour Gas, *Corrosion*, *40*(9), 478-486, 1984. MetAbs No. 84-353069. **Abstract:** Extensive analyses were conducted using three API 5LX steels (X70, X65, X52) to explore the effects of metallurgical factors on the resistance of linepipe steels to hydrogen-induced cracking and sulfide stress cracking.

T.E. Graedel, J.T. Plewes, J.P. Franey, G.W. Kammlott, and R.C. Stoffers, Sulfidation Under Atmospheric Conditions of Cu-Ni, Cu-Sn and Cu-Zn Binary and Cu-Ni-Sn and Cu-Ni-Zn Ternary Systems, *Metall. Trans. A*, *16A*(2), 275-284, 1985. MetAbs No. 85-350456. **Abstract:** The corrosion susceptibility of binary and ternary alloys can be assessed by controlled exposures to corrosive environments. To conduct such studies, 24 high-purity alloys from the Cu-Ni, Cu-Sn and Cu-Zn binary and Cu-Ni-Sn and Cu-Ni-Zn ternary systems were exposed to atmospherically realistic concentrations of hydrogen sulfide in humidified air. The resulting sulfurization of the samples is presented in a series of chromatic plots.

Y. Yoshino and A. Ikegaya, Pitting and Stress Cracking of 12Cr-Ni-Mo Martensitic Stainless Steels in Chloride and Sulfide Environments, *Corrosion*, *41*(2), 105-113, 1985. MetAbs No. 85-350645. **Abstract:** Laboratory melted 12Cr-Ni-Mo steels were tested in chloride/sulfide solutions at 60 °C and at room temperature to evaluate their resistance to pitting and stress cracking in connection with environmental and metallurgical factors.

R. Garber, T. Wad F.B. Fletcher, and T.B. Cox, Sulfide Stress Cracking Resistant Steels for Heavy Section Wellhead Components, *J. Mater. Energy Syst.*, *7*(2), 91-103, 1985. MetAbs No. 85-352278. **Abstract:** The development of low-alloy steels for heavy section wellhead equipment which will be subject to hydrogen sulfide stress-corrosion cracking is described. The continuous cooling transformation behavior of nine steels was evaluated by dilatometry.

M.D. Tumuluru, Sulfide Stress Corrosion Cracking of Quenched and Tempered AISI 4137-H Steel, *Mater. Perform.*, *24*(7), 38-43, 1985. MetAbs No. 85-352299. **Abstract:** The sulfide stress-corrosion cracking resistance of quenched and tempered AISI 4137-H steel was studied using the NACE test on smooth tensile specimens. The variables studied included the effects of temperature.

P.B. Narayan, A.J. Bevolo, C.W. Chen, and O.N. Carlson, An Auger and Depth Profiling Study of the Sulfidation of Iron and Fe-25Cr Alloy in H2S, *J. Vac. Sci. Technol. A*, *3*(5), 1992-1995, 1985. MetAbs No. 86-350042. **Abstract:** Polycrystalline Fe and an Fe-25Cr alloy were exposed from 200 to 300 °C in an H2S-Ar mixture at one atmosphere pressure. Depth profiling was conducted on the sulfidized specimen in an Auger spectrometer.

J.A. Larson, New Developments in High Alloy Cast Steels, *Steel Founders' Res. J.*, (10), 1-9, 1985. MetAbs No. 86-350219. **Abstract:** The commonly used austenitic stainless steels can be subjected to extremely high corrosion rates in applications such as secondary oil recovery, the use of deeper oil wells, geothermal streams for power generation, the proposed systems for coal conversion, and scrubber systems. The important types of corrosion and the effect of temperature, chloride level, pH and H2S content on the corrosion behavior of stainless steels are discussed. The most recent high alloy specifications and chemistry modifications are described.

B.L. Jones, Pipeline Steels for Sour-Gas Transport, *Steel India*, *8*(1), 1-15, 1985. MetAbs No. 86-350413. **Abstract:** Transport of sour gas through conventional HSLA (X65, X70, X52) pipelines can lead to failure from cracking through two mechanisms—hydrogen-induced cracking and sulfide stress-corrosion cracking. The details of these cracking mechanisms and the metallurgical means available to help combat them are discussed. A design philosophy for steels able to resist sour-gas environments is outlined.

R.D. Kane, Role of H2S in Behavior of Engineering Alloys, *Int. Met. Rev.*, *30*(6), 291-301, 1985. MetAbs No. 86-350732. **Abstract:** In this review, the behavior of low-alloy steels in H2S-containing environments is discussed. Emphasis is placed on the various types of corrosion and cracking that can occur, their origin and mechanisms, and methods of control.

C.J. Thomas, R.G. Edyvean, R. Brook, and W.G. Ferguson, Environmentally Assisted Crack Growth in a Martensitic Stainless Steel, *Mater. Sci. Eng.*, *78*(1), 55-63, 1986. MetAbs No. 86-351021. **Abstract:** The response of a martensitic stainless steel, En56C, to environmental stress cracking as a function of heat treatment has been examined. The as-quenched, 400, 550 and 650 °C temper conditions were studied. The threshold stress-intensity for stress-corrosion cracking was determined in dry H2S gas and the crack growth rate measured in distilled water and in acidified 3.5% NaCl solution at pH 3 (NACE solution).

A. Martinez and S. Toesca, Reactivity of Copper-Doped, Brass-Plated Steel Cords With Dry Hydrogen Sulfide, *Reactiv. Solids*, *1*(3), 263-273, 1986. MetAbs No. 86-351440. **Abstract:** The reactivity of Cu-doped, brass-plated steel cords has been investigated between 130 to 305 °C under a pressure of 60 mbar of hydrogen sulfide.

G.I. Ogundele and W.E. White, Some Observations on the Corrosion of Carbon Steel in Sour Gas Environments: Effects of H2S and H2S/CO2/CH4/C3H8 Mixtures, *Corrosion*, *42*(7), 398-408, 1986. MetAbs No. 86-351726. **Abstract:** Experimental results and analyses on the corrosion of carbon steel in simulated aqueous sour gas environments are reported. Tests were performed at temperatures and pressures up to 95 °C and 4.2 MPa (600 psig), respectively. Detailed thermodynamic and kinetic analyses of the experimental data were used to explain the observed corrosion behavior by partial reconstruction of the experimental polarization characteristics from theory.

J.P. Orchard and D.J. Young, Gas-Phase Composition Effects on the Iron Sulfide Scaling Reaction, *J. Electrochem. Soc.*, *133*(8), 1734-1741,

1986. MetAbs No. 86-352285. **Abstract:** Pure Fe has been sulfidized in $H_2S/H/N$ gas mixtures at temperatures in the range 793 to 1073 K. The gas mixtures corresponded to equilibrium sulfur partial pressures of 6.5 $\times 10^{-5}$ to 6.5×10^{-1} Pa and were diluted up to 60% with nitrogen.

F. Terasaki, H. Ohtani, A. Ikeda, and M. Nakanishi, Steel Plates for Pressure Vessels in Sour Environment Applications, *Proc. Inst. Mech. Eng. A, Power Process Eng.*, 200(A3), 141-158, 1986. MetAbs No. 86-352428. **Abstract:** It is well known that wet hydrogen sulfide can cause embrittlement of steels, hydrogen-induced cracking and sulfide stress-corrosion cracking. Several fractures of pipelines handling sour crude oil or gas has led to vigorous research on these problems. The paper considers the mechanism and factors involved in hydrogen-induced cracking.

W. Haumann and F.O. Koch, Effects of the Behavior of HFI Welded Pipes for Sour Service, *3R Int.*, 25(5), 261-266, 1986. MetAbs No. 87-350202. **Abstract:** This paper deals with metallurgical factors influencing the susceptibility to hydrogen-induced cracking as well as hydrogen sulfide stress-corrosion cracking and describes the development of pipeline steels and high frequency induction welded pipes for sour service.

K.K. Chawla, J.M. Rigsbee, and J.B. Woodhouse, Hydrogen-Induced Cracking in Two Linepipe Steels, *J. Mater. Sci.*, 21(11), 3777-3782, 1986. MetAbs No. 87-350292. **Abstract:** Linepipe steels are susceptible to hydrogen-induced cracking in wet, sour gas environments. Two commercially produced linepipe Mn steels were investigated with regard to hydrogen-induced cracking on cathodic charging.

G. Guntz, C. Jollain, B. Sala, B. Heritier, and B. Baroux, Influence of the Austenite-Ferrite Ratio on the Corrosion Resistance and Mechanical Properties, *Bull. Cercle Etud. Metaux*, 15(11), 14, 1986. MetAbs No. 87-350691. **Abstract:** The effects of alloying elements on the mechanical characteristics, phase balance and corrosion resistance of duplex stainless steels containing 22% Cr, 5% Ni and 3% Mo are described. The strength of the austenite and ferrite phases and hot workability were determined with variations in alloy composition. Corrosion studies concentrated on the effect of alloying elements and ferrite content on resistance to stress-corrosion cracking.

M.D. Tumuluru, Sulfide Stress Corrosion Cracking in Low-Alloy Steel Inertia Friction Welds, *Weld. J.*, 66(3), 61s-72s, 1987. MetAbs No. 87-351336. **Abstract:** Sulfide stress corrosion cracking behavior of quenched and tempered low-alloy steel inertia friction welds was studied using the NACE test on smooth tensile specimens. Inertia friction welds were made between AISI 4137-H steel and Grade E pipe. The welds (drill pipes) were quenched and tempered to 33 HRC.

A.K. Agrawal, W.N. Stiegelmeyer, and J.H. Payer, Corrosion and Cracking Behavior of a Martensitic 12Cr-3.5NiFe Alloy in Simulated Sour Gas Environments, *Mater. Perform.*, 26(3), 24-29, 1987. MetAbs No. 87-351344. **Abstract:** The superior corrosion resistance of 12% Cr martensitic stainless steels over that of low-alloy steels makes them of interest for gas and oil production applications. In this study, the corrosion and environmental cracking behaviors of a 12Cr-3.5Ni alloy have been evaluated in simulated down hole sour gas environments at 27, 82, and 149 °C.

A. Miyasaka, M. Iino, K. Nakajima, Corrosion Products Formed on Low-alloy Steel Surface Under High Pressure Sour Gas Environments, *Trans. Iron Steel Inst. Jpn.*, 25(10), B-277, 1985. MetAbs No. 87-352641. **Abstract:** The corrosion behavior of low-alloy steels for oil country tubular goods were reported under H_2S-CO_2 substitute ocean water environments.

R.A. King and R.G. Miller, Sulfide—The Unwelcome Part of the Sulphur Cycle, *Chem. Eng. (UK)*, (438), 38-39, 1987. MetAbs No. 87-352642. **Abstract:** Known reserves of oil are generally sour (i.e., H_2S-containing) following pressure-preservation injections of surface waters containing sulfate and bacteria capable of reducing it to give the H_2S. This can crack and corrode high-strength carbon steels used in the drilling rigs. Search for a solution thus turns towards chemistry, as instanced by continuous inhibition via a carrier fluid. Difficulties and disadvantages of this approach and the use of coatings are discussed.

A. Rauscher and Z. Lukacs, Effect of Hydrogen Sulfide on the Corrosion Behavior of Titanium, *Werkst. Korros.*, 38(6), 326-329, 1987. MetAbs No. 87-352649. **Abstract:** The effect of hydrogen sulfide on the electrochemical and corrosion behavior of VT1-0 commercial titanium has been studied in acidic solutions using polarization and analytical methods.

M. Barteri, F. Mancia, A. Tamba, and R. Bruno, Microstructural Study and Corrosion Performance of Duplex and Superaustenitic Steels in Sour Well Environment, *Corrosion*, 43(9), 518-525, 1987. MetAbs No. 88-350048. **Abstract:** A study has been made of mill-annealed and cold-worked duplex Dalmine D22 and D25 stainless steels (75 and 140 ksi) and of cold-worked superaustenitic Dalmine D28-32 steel (110 ksi). The materials have been tested under conditions typical of oil and natural gas wells operating in a severe environment. The effect of environment variables and cold-working on corrosion properties, particularly sulfide stress-corrosion cracking, has been investigated.

J.H. Payer, S.P. Pednekar, and W.K. Boyd, Sulfide Stress Cracking Susceptibility of Nickel Containing Steels, *Metall. Trans. A*, 17A(9), 601-1610, 1986. MetAbs No. 86-352241. **Abstract:** A systematic evaluation of the sulfide-stress cracking behavior of five steels with Ni contents ranging from 0-3% was conducted in an acidified chloride solution saturated with H_2S at room temperature (NACE solution). The relative cracking susceptibility of the steels was determined from threshold stresses in constant-load tension tests and threshold stress intensities shown by precracked double-cantilever-beam specimens.

E.W. Filler, Nickel-Beryllium Alloys Resistance to Sulfide Stress Cracking, *Corrosion*, 12, 89-101, 1984. MetAbs No. 85-350794. **Abstract:** Wrought (BERYLCO alloy 440) and cast (BERYLCO alloy 42C) Ni-Be alloys are suitable for use in environments containing hydrogen sulfide (sour gas). Testing was performed according to NACE Standard TM-01-77, covering ambient temperature testing of metals for resistance to cracking failure when subjected to tensile stresses in low pH aqueous environment containing hydrogen sulfide.

J.R. Scott, Aluminum Pipeline Gas History—An Update, *Mater. Perform.*, 24(2), 27-29, 1985. MetAbs No. 85-350804. **Abstract:** Information pertaining to Al pipelines, originally generated through a survey performed in 1963 and other histories, is updated. Case histories are presented for the following types of lines: natural gas, sour gas, peracetic acid and fuming nitric acid, and jet fuel.

Corrosion Behavior of Various Metals and Alloys in Hydrogen Sulfide

Material	Condition, other factors, comments	Concen-tration, %	Temperature, °C (°F)	Duration	Corrosion rate, mm/yr (mils/yr) or other	Ref
Stainless steels						
Type 304 stainless steel	Chemical processing; field or pilot plant test. Hydrogen sulfide (generator, vapors)	...	...	56 d	<0.0001 in./yr	89
Type 304 stainless steel	Chemical processing; field or pilot plant test; no aeration; no agitation. Hydrogen sulfide, water (extraction unit). Slight pitting: maximum depth of pits from incipient to 0.005 in.; crevice attack (tendency to concentration-cell corrosion)	...	80-150 (176-302)	160 d	<0.0001 in./yr	89
Type 304 stainless steel	Petroleum processing; field or pilot plant test; no aeration; rapid agitation. Plus 3-17 mol% ammonia, 7-12% carbon dioxide, small amounts of chlorides, cyanides and hydrocarbons (vapors)	85-65 mol%	127 (260)	288 d	<0.0001 in./yr	89
Type 304 stainless steel	Petroleum processing; field or pilot plant test; strong aeration; slight to moderate agitation. Plus air and nitrogen. Crevice attack (tendency to concentration-cell corrosion)	98	32 (90)	188 d	<0.0001	89
Type 316 stainless steel	Chemical processing; field or pilot plant test. Hydrogen sulfide (generator, vapors)	...	...	56 d	<0.0001 in./yr	89
Type 316 stainless steel	Chemical processing; field or pilot plant test; no aeration; no agitation. Hydrogen sulfide, water (extraction unit). Slight pitting: maximum depth of pits from incipient to 0.005 in.; crevice attack (tendency to concentration-cell corrosion)	...	80-150 (176-302)	160 d	<0.0001 in./yr	89
Type 316 stainless steel	Chemical processing; field or pilot plant test; no aeration. Hydrogen-sulfide gas saturated with water vapor	...	38-77 (100-170)	60 d	0.0001 in./yr	89
Type 316 stainless steel	Petroleum processing; field or pilot plant test; no aeration; rapid agitation. Plus 3-17 mol% ammonia, 7-12% carbon dioxide, small amounts of chlorides, cyanides and hydrocarbons (vapors)	85-65 mol%	127 (260)	288 d	<0.0001 in./yr	89
Type 316 stainless steel	Petroleum processing; field or pilot plant test; strong aeration; slight to moderate agitation. Plus air and nitrogen. Slight pitting: maximum depth of pits from incipient to 0.005 in.	98	32 (90)	188 d	<0.0001	89
Coppers						
70-30 cupronickel	Dry	...	...	...	Suitable	93
70-30 cupronickel	Moist	...	...	...	Fair	93
90-10 cupronickel	Dry	...	...	...	Suitable	93
90-10 cupronickel	Moist	...	...	...	Not suitable	93
Admiralty brass	Dry	...	...	...	Suitable	93
Admiralty brass	Moist	...	...	...	Fair	93
Aluminum bronze	Dry	...	...	...	Suitable	93
Aluminum bronze	Moist	...	...	...	Not suitable	93
Architectural bronze	Dry	...	...	...	Suitable	93
Architectural bronze	Moist	...	...	...	Fair	93
Brass	Dry	...	...	...	Suitable	93
Brass	Moist	...	...	...	Fair	93x
Cartridge brass	Dry	...	...	...	Suitable	93
Cartridge brass	Moist	...	...	...	Fair	93
Commercial bronze	Dry	...	...	...	Suitable	93
Commercial bronze	Moist	...	...	...	Not suitable	93
Electrolytic copper	Dry	...	...	...	Suitable	93
Electrolytic copper	Moist	...	...	...	Not suitable	93
Free-cutting brass	Dry	...	...	...	Suitable	93
Free-cutting brass	Moist	...	...	...	Fair	93
Muntz metal	Dry	...	...	...	Suitable	93
Muntz metal	Moist	...	...	...	Fair	93
Naval brass	Dry	...	...	...	Suitable	93
Naval brass	Moist	...	...	...	Fair	93
Nickel silver	Dry	18	...	...	Suitable	93
Nickel silver	Moist	18	...	...	Fair	93
Phosphor bronze	5% Sn. Dry	...	...	...	Suitable	93
Phosphor bronze	8% Sn. Dry	...	...	...	Suitable	93

(Continued)

Corrosion Behavior of Various Metals and Alloys in Hydrogen Sulfide (Continued)

Material	Condition, other factors, comments	Concen-tration, %	Temperature, °C (°F)	Duration	Corrosion rate, mm/yr (mils/yr) or other	Ref
Phosphor bronze	5% Sn. Moist	...	...	...	Not suitable	93
Phosphor bronze	8% Sn. Moist	...	...	...	Not suitable	93
Phosphor copper	Dry	...	...	...	Suitable	93
Phosphor copper	Moist	...	...	...	Not suitable	93
Red brass	Dry	...	...	...	Not suitable	93
Red brass	Moist	...	...	...	Suitable	93
Silicon bronze	Low. Dry	...	...	...	Not suitable	93
Silicon bronze	High. Dry	...	...	...	Suitable	93
Silicon bronze	Low. Moist	...	...	...	Suitable	93
Silicon bronze	High. Moist	...	...	...	Not suitable	93
Titanium					Not suitable	93
Titanium	Water saturated	...	21 (70)	...	<0.003 (<0.12)	90
Titanium	Steam and 0.077% mercaptans	7.65	93-110 (200-230)	...	nil	90
Heat- and corrosion-resistant alloys						
Carpenter 20	Chemical processing; field or pilot plant test; no aeration; no agitation. Hydrogen sulfide, water (extraction unit). Slight pitting: maximum depth of pits from incipient to 0.005 in.	...	80-150 (176-302)	160 d	<0.0001 in./yr	89
Carpenter 20	Chemical processing; field or pilot plant test; no aeration. Hydrogen-sulfide gas saturated with water vapor	...	38-77 (100-170)	60 d	<0.0001 in./yr	89
Alloy 825	Chemical processing; field or pilot plant test; no aeration; no agitation. Hydrogen sulfide, water (extraction unit). Slight pitting: maximum depth of pits from incipient to 0.005 in.; crevice attack (tendency to concentration-cell corrosion)	...	80-150 (176-302)	160 d	0.0002 in./yr	89
Noble metals						
Gold	Moist	...	Room	...	<0.05 (<2)	8
Iridium	Moist	...	Room	...	nil	18
Osmium	Moist	...	Room	...	<0.25 (<10)	26
Palladium	Moist	...	Room	...	nil	17
Platinum	Moist. Pt is blackened but unattacked in hydrogen sulfide to 1000 °C (1830 °F)	...	Room	...	Blackened	6
Rhodium	Moist	...	Room	...	nil	29
Rhodium	Moist at room temperature	...	100 (212)	...	nil	18
Rhodium	Moist	...	Room	...	nil	18
Silver	...	...	Room	...	Attacked	4
Silver	...	...	Room	...	Attacked	4
Silver	...	All	Room	...	Blackened	9
Others						
Magnesium	...	100	Room	...	Suitable	119

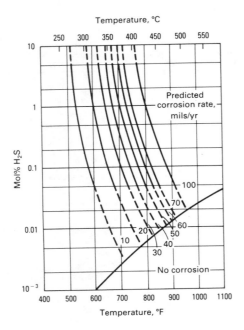

Carbon steel. Effect of temperature and hydrogen sulfide content on high-temperature H_2S/H_2 corrosion of carbon steel (gas oil desulfurizers). Source: J. Gutzeit, "High Temperature Sulfide Corrosion of Steels," *Process Industries Corrosion—The Theory and Practice*, National Association of Corrosion Engineers, Houston, 1986.

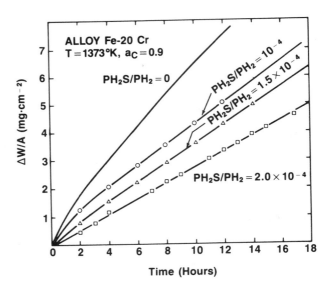

Fe-20Cr. Carburization kinetic data for Fe-20Cr alloy at 1373 K in the presence and absence of H_2S/H_2. Source: T.A. Ramanarayanan and D.J. Srolovitz, "Carburization Mechanisms of High Chromium Alloys," *Journal of the Electrochemical Society*, Vol 132, Sept 1875, 2272.

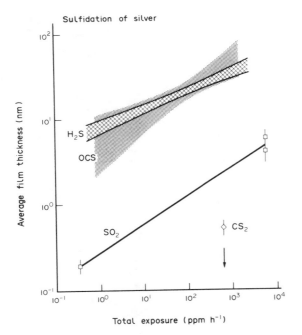

Silver. The thickness of the Ag_2S corrosion film as a function of total exposure to H_2S, OCS, SO_2 and CS_2. All exposures were made with RH $= 92 \pm 4\%$, $t = 21$ °C. Source: J.P. Franey, G.W. Kammlott, *et al.*, "The Corrosion of Silver by Atmospheric Sulfurous Gases," *Corrosion Science*, Vol 25, July 1985, 133.

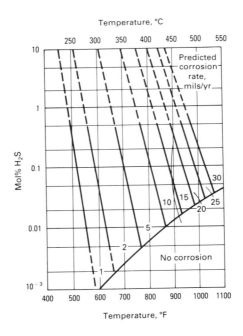

Stainless steel. Effect of temperature and hydrogen sulfide content on high-temperature H_2S/H_2 corrosion of 12% Cr stainless steel. Source: J. Gutzeit, "High Temperature Sulfide Corrosion of Steels," *Process Industries Corrosion—The Theory and Practice,* National Association of Corrosion Engineers, Houston, 1986.

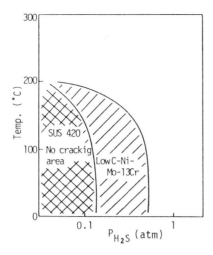

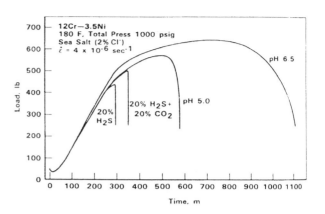

Stainless steel. No cracking area in H_2S environment. Source: T. Kurisu, M. Kimura, *et al.*, "Corrosion Resistance of Low C-Ni-13Cr Stainless Steels in CO_2/H_2O Environments," *Transactions of the Iron and Steel Institute of Japan*, Vol 25, April 1985, B-133.

Stainless steel. Load vs. time-to-failure in slow strain rate tests at 82 °C (180 °F) in sea salt brine in the presence and absence of active gases. Source: A.K. Agrawal and W.N. Stiegelmeyer, "Corrosion and Cracking Behavior of a Martensitic 12Cr-3.5Ni-Fe Alloy in Simulated Sour Gas Environments, *Materials Performance*, Vol 26, Mar 1987, 24-29.

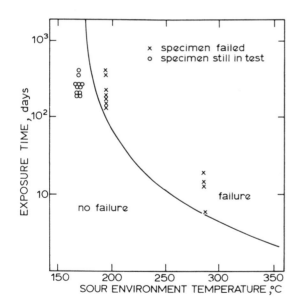

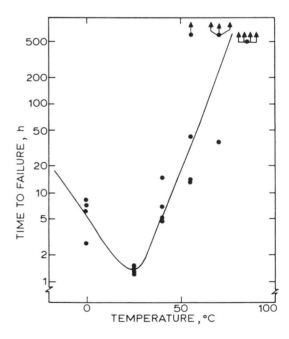

Hastelloy C-276. Stress-corrosion cracking behavior of Hastelloy C-276 versus testing temperature for specimens heat treated at 260 °C for 250 h. Environment: 25% sodium chloride, 0.5% acetic acid, and 1 g/L of sulfur and hydrogen sulfide. Source: R.D. Kane, Roles of H_2S in Behaviour of Engineering Alloys, The Institute of Metals and the American Society for Metals, 1985.

High-strength low-alloy steel. Time to failure for sulfide stress cracking versus temperature, showing minimum resistance at ~25 °C for a high-strength low-alloy steel (C-Mn composition). Source: R.D. Kane, Roles of H_2S in Behaviour of Engineering Alloys, The Institute of Metals and the American Society for Metals, 1985.

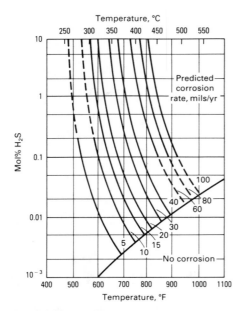

Low-alloy steel. Effect of temperature and hydrogen sulfide content on high-temperature H_2S/H_2 corrosion of 5Cr-0.5Mo steel (gas oil desulfurizers). Source: J. Gutzeit, "High Temperature Sulfide Corrosion of Steels," *Process Industries Corrosion—The Theory and Practice,* National Association of Corrosion Engineers, Houston, 1986.

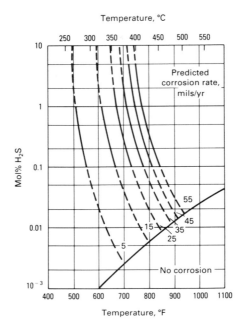

Alloy steel. Effect of temperature and hydrogen sulfide content on high-temperature H_2S/H_2 corrosion of 9Cr-1Mo steel (gas oil desulfurizers). Source: J. Gutzeit, "High Temperature Sulfide Corrosion of Steels," *Process Industries Corrosion—The Theory and Practice,* National Association of Corrosion Engineers, 1986.

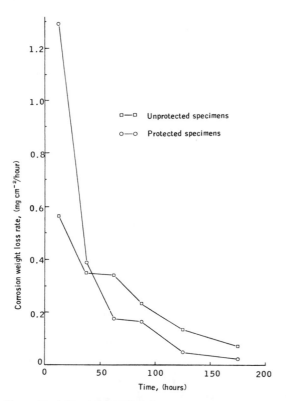

Low-alloy steel. The effect of FEP/MoS_2 coating on corrosion weight loss rate of EN 42 steel in NACE solution with H_2S bubbling continuously at 60 °C. Source: A.C.C. Tseung, T. Sriskandarajah, *et al.*, "A Method for the Inhibition of Sulphide Stress Corrosion Cracking in Steel. I. Electrochemical Aspects," *Corrosion Science*, Vol 25, June 1985, 390.

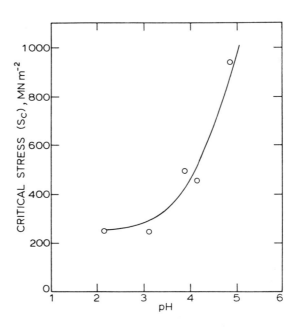

API casing steel. Effect of pH on sulfide stress cracking resistance of an API casing steel (C-Mn composition). Source: R.D. Kane, Roles of H_2S in Behaviour of Engineering Alloys, The Institute of Metals and the American Society for Metals, 1985.

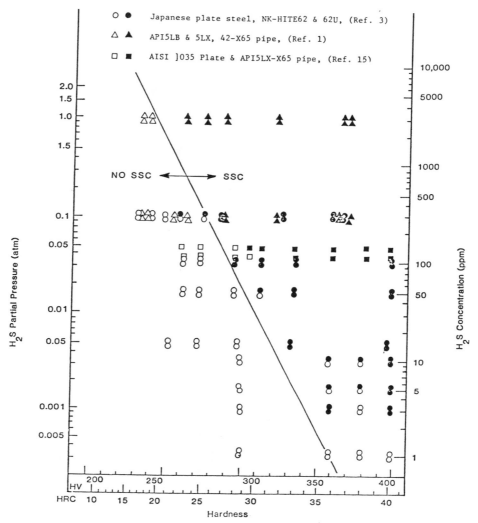

Steels. Relationship between hydrogen sulfide concentration, partial pressure, and hardness in the heat-affected zone. Source: A. Omar *et al.,* "Corrosion/81," Paper No. 237, National Association of Corrosion Engineers, Houston, 1981.

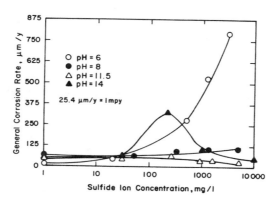

1040 steel. General corrosion rate versus sulfide ion concentration of 1040 steel in aqueous solutions of varying pH. Source: R.D. Kane, Roles of H₂S in Behaviour of Engineering Alloys, The Institute of Metals and the American Society for Metals, 1985.

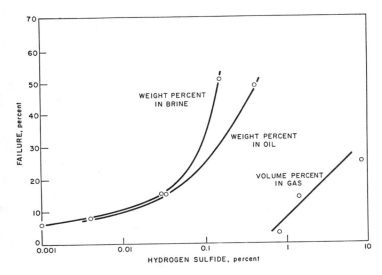

Steels. Effect of hydrogen sulfide concentration on frequency of cracking of 112 to 128 ksi yield strength steels in sour crude oils. Source: A. Omar *et al.,* "Corrosion/81," Paper No. 237, National Association of Corrosion Engineers, Houston, 1981.

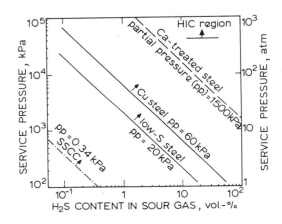

Steels. Critical hydrogen sulfide concentration for stepwise cracking for various linepipe steels. Source: R.D. Kane, Roles of H_2S in Behaviour of Engineering Alloys, The Institute of Metals and the American Society for Metals, 1985.

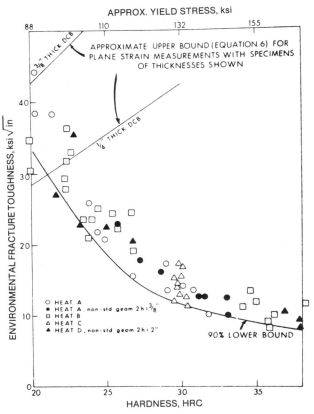

4130 steel. Sulfide corrosion cracking resistance of laboratory quenched and tempered AISI 4130 steel. Source: R.D. Kane, Roles of H_2S in Behaviour of Engineering Alloys, The Institute of Metals and the American Society for Metals, 1985.

Hydroiodic Acid

Hydroiodic acid, HI, is a colorless solution of dissolved hydrogen iodide gas in water (commercially at a strength of 10% hydrogen iodide). It is prepared by the reaction of iodine and hydrosulfuric acid or by the reaction of phosphorus plus iodine plus water followed by distillation. Concentrated hydroiodic acid reacts with the oxygen of the air to form free iodine, which gives a brownish color to the solution. It also gives an idea of the reducing nature of this acid. It is an important reagent in organic chemistry and is used commercially in the preparation of iodides.

Material Summaries

The following material summaries were compiled from a survey of the available literature. Inclusion of a material description under a given environment does not imply that it is the most appropriate material for corrosion service in that environment. Likewise, exclusion of a given

material does not imply that it is not suitable for corrosion service applications in that environment.

Niobium. Niobium is resistant to hydroiodic acid at all concentrations and at temperatures below 100 °C (212 °F).

Silver. Silver can only be exposed to dilute hydroiodic acid at room temperature.

Tin. Hot hydroiodic acid rapidly attacks tin.

Zirconium. Zirconium has a corrosion rate of less than 0.025 mm/yr (<1 mil/yr) in boiling 47% hydroiodic acid solutions. Results of pitting potential measurements indicate that zirconium has a lower pitting tendency in 1N hydroiodic acid than in 1N hydrochloric acid.

Corrosion Behavior of Various Metals and Alloys in Hydroiodic Acid

Material	Condition, other factors, comments	Concentration, %	Temperature, °C (°F)	Duration	Corrosion rate, mm/yr (mils/yr) or other	Ref
Titanium						
Titanium	Grade 2	10	Boiling	...	nil	32
Titanium	Grade 2	57	25 (75)	...	0.15 (6)	32
Lead, tin, and zinc						
Lead	Corrosion rate too high to merit any consideration of Pb	10-50	24 (75)	...	>1270 μm/yr (>50)	95
Noble metals						
Gold	Specific gravity 1.75	Dilute	Room	...	<0.05 (<2)	8
Iridium	Specific gravity 1.75	...	Room to 100 (212)	...	nil	29
Osmium	Specific gravity 1.75	...	100 (212)	...	3.7 (148)	17
Palladium	Specific gravity 1.75	...	Room	...	65.7 (2587)	17
Rhodium	Specific gravity 1.75	...	100 (212)	...	nil	29
Ruthenium	...	60	100 (212)	...	nil	18
Silver	...	Dilute	Room	...	<0.25 (<10)	4
Silver	...	Dilute	Room	...	<0.25 (<10)	4

Hypochlorites

Hypochlorites are compounds containing the ion ClO_3^- that are formed when chlorine reacts with an alkali. The ClO_3^- ion is an oxidizing agent, and these alkaline salts are among the most corrosive. Hypochlorite salts include those of sodium, calcium, lithium, strontium, and barium, although sodium hypochlorite enjoys the most applications. Sodium hypochlorite is sold in two strengths, the household bleach strength of 5.25% and the commercial bleach strength of 13%. "Liquid chlorine" refers to the 10% solution used in treating swimming pools. Hypochlorite solutions are used for bleaching pulp, odor control, waste treatment/disposal, and water purification. Hypochlorite solutions decompose to release chlorine. This decomposition rate depends on concentration, temperature, pH, ionic strength, light, and the presence of trace metal contaminants such as cobalt, nickel, and copper that act as catalysts.

Material Summaries

The following material summaries were compiled from a survey of the available literature. Inclusion of a material description under a given environment does not imply that it is the most appropriate material for corrosion service in that environment. Likewise, exclusion of a given material does not imply that it is not suitable for corrosion service applications in that environment.

Nickel. Alkaline solutions containing hydrogen peroxide do not affect Alloy 600.

Platinum. When air is present, hypochlorite solutions attack platinum.

Tantalum. Only strong alkaline hypochlorite solutions affect tantalum.

Titanium. Titanium has excellent resistance to ClO_3^- compounds.

Corrosion Behavior of Various Metals and Alloys in Hypochlorites

Material	Condition, other factors, comments	Concentration, %	Temperature, °C (°F)	Duration	Corrosion rate, mm/yr (mils/yr) or other	Ref
Tin	...	...	20 (68)	...	Unsuitable	94
Tin	...	...	60 (140)	...	Unsuitable	94
Tin	...	...	100 (212)	...	Unsuitable	94

Hypochlorous Acid

Hypochlorous acid, HOCl, is a weak, unstable acid existing only in solution. Hypochlorous acid decomposes upon standing. The rate of decomposition depends on the concentration, pH, exposure to light, and the presence of contaminants that act as catalysts, for example, cobaltous hydroxide. Hypochlorous acid is a powerful oxidizing agent and is used in bleaching operations. The compound may be prepared by the reaction of chlorine monoxide and water, sodium hypochlorite and an acid, or chlorine with an aqueous suspension of mercuric oxide.

Material Summaries

The following material summaries were compiled from a survey of the available literature. Inclusion of a material description under a given environment does not imply that it is the most appropriate material for corrosion service in that environment. Likewise, exclusion of a given material does not imply that it is not suitable for corrosion service applications in that environment.

Tantalum. Tantalum is not attacked by hypochloric acid at ordinary temperatures.

Titanium. Titanium alloys generally are highly resistant to attack over a wide range of concentrations and temperatures.

Corrosion Behavior of Various Metals and Alloys in Hypochlorous Acid

Material	Condition, other factors, comments	Concen-tration, %	Temperature, °C (°F)	Duration	Corrosion rate, mm/yr (mils/yr) or other	Ref
Silver	...	...	Room	...	Attacked	4
Silver	...	...	Room	...	Attacked	4
Titanium	Plus ClO and Cl_2 gases	17	38 (100)	...	0.000	90

Iodine

Iodine, I, is a nonmetallic element with an orthorhombic crystal structure, a violet to black color, and a melting point of 114 °C (237 °F). This poisonous element sublimes readily and is easily purified in this manner. It is insoluble in water, but is soluble in common solvents such as alcohol, ether, and carbon tetrachloride. Iodine is used as a germicide, an antiseptic, in dyes, tinctures, and pharmaceuticals. It is also used in the production of vanadium metal in the McKechnie-Seybolt process, which is the reduction of vanadium pentoxide in the presence of iodine. Iodine is used in a similar manner in the production of high-purity zirconium.

Material Summaries

The following material summaries were compiled from a survey of the available literature. Inclusion of a material description under a given environment does not imply that it is the most appropriate material for corrosion service in that environment. Likewise, exclusion of a given material does not imply that it is not suitable for corrosion service applications in that environment.

Aluminum. Alcohol solutions of iodine were found to be corrosive to aluminum alloys in laboratory tests.

Magnesium. Dry iodine causes little or no corrosion of magnesium at room or slightly elevated temperatures. The presence of a small amount of water causes some attack by iodine. Wet iodine below the dew point of any aqueous phase causes severe attack of magnesium.

Gold. Wet or dry iodine can be handled by gold within limitations.

Silver. Silver is not resistant to iodine, unless it is cathodically protected.

Palladium. Palladium is generally resistant to corrosion by most single acids, alkalis, and aqueous solutions of many common salts. When air is present, iodine attacks palladium to a negligible extent.

Ruthenium. Alcohol solutions of iodine attack ruthenium slowly.

Tantalum. Tantalum is totally inert to iodine up to 150 °C (300 °F), and if iodine is dissolved in solutions of salts or acids, it likewise has no effect. Iodine begins to attack tantalum at about 300 °C (570 °F).

Tin. Tin is readily attacked by iodine at room temperature.

Titanium. Titanium alloys exhibit outstanding resistance over the full range of concentrations and to relatively high temperatures in iodine-containing media. However, the susceptibility of titanium alloys to crevice corrosion should be considered when used with iodide solutions.

Zirconium. Zirconium is quite resistant to pitting corrosion in iodide solutions.

Additional Reading

T. Kubo, Y. Wakashima, H. Imahashi, and M. Nagai, Effects of Intermetallic Particles on the SCC Initiation of Zirconium Alloys, *J. Nucl. Mater.*, 132(2), 126-136, 1985. MetAbs No. 85-352038. **Abstract:** To investigate effects of intermetallic particles on stress-corrosion cracking of Zr alloys, tensile tests were conducted in an iodine atmosphere using Zr plate with different amounts of impurities and Zircaloy-2 plate.

B. Cox and R. Haddad, Methyl Iodide as a Promoter of the SCC of Zirconium Alloys in Iodine Vapor, *J. Nucl. Mater.*, 137(2), 115-123, 1986.

MetAbs No. 86-350894. **Abstract:** The effect of the presence of organic-iodine contaminants, or specifically methyl iodide, in an iodine environment during stress-corrosion tests on Zircaloy-2 was evaluated.

R. Haddad and B. Cox, On the Initiation of Cracks in Zircaloy Tubes by Iodine and Cs/Cd Vapors, *J. Nucl. Mater.*, *138*(1), 81-88, 1986. MetAbs No. 86-351422. **Abstract:** Single, short (5 s) compressive stress cycles on sealed fuel cladding tubes of low Ni Zircaloy-2 previously equilibrated with either iodine or Cs/Cd produced stress-corrosion cracks.

T. Kubo, T. Motomiya, and Y. Wakashima, Low-Cycle Corrosion Fatigue of Zircaloy-2 in Iodine Atmospheres, *J. Nucl. Mater.*, *140*(2),

185-196, 1986. MetAbs No. 87-350077. **Abstract:** Low-cycle fatigue tests have been performed on Zircaloy-2 by a reversed-bending method in inert and iodine atmospheres at 623 K.

K.-N. Choo, S.-I. Pyun, and J.-K. Choi, A Study on the Mechanism of Iodine-Induced Stress-Corrosion Cracking of Zircaloy-4, *J. Nucl. Mater.*, *149*(3), 289-295, 1987. MetAbs No. 87-352769. **Abstract:** The iodine-induced stress-corrosion cracking of Zircaloy-4 plate has been studied by the constant elongation rate test and U-bend test methods. To systematically evaluate the effects of stress states on the stress-corrosion cracking behavior, four kinds of specimens were prepared from as-annealed Zircaloy-4 plate.

Corrosion Behavior of Various Metals and Alloys in Iodine

Material	Condition, other factors, comments	Concen-tration, %	Temperature, °C (°F)	Duration	Corrosion rate, mm/yr (mils/yr) or other	Ref
Stainless steels						
Type 304 stainless steel	Research; laboratory test; no aeration; no agitation. Pressure 400 mm Hg	...	450 (842)	...	0.12 in./yr	89
Type 304 stainless steel	Soap processing; field or plant test; no aeration; no agitation. Plus 90% nonionic detergent, some hydrochloric acid	10	22 (72)	90 d	0.002 in./yr	89
Type 304 stainless steel	Soap processing; field or plant test; no aeration; rapid agitation. Plus 11% isopropyl alcohol, 2% hydrochloric acid, remainder nonionic detergent	9.3	22 (72)	90 d	0.0071 in./yr	89
Type 316 stainless steel	Research; laboratory test; no aeration; no agitation. Pressure 400 mm Hg	...	450 (842)	...	0.081 in./yr	89
Type 316 stainless steel	Soap processing; field or plant test; no aeration; no agitation. Plus 90% nonionic detergent, some hydrochloric acid	10	22 (72)	90 d	0.0003 in./yr	89
Type 316 stainless steel	Soap processing; field or plant test; no aeration; rapid agitation. Plus 11% isopropyl alcohol, 2% hydrochloric acid, remainder nonionic detergent	9.3	22 (72)	90 d	0.0023 in./yr	89
Type 410 stainless steel	...	...	Room	...	Attacked	121
Aluminum						
Aluminum (99.0-99.5%)	Dry solid	...	20 (68)	...	Excellent	92
Aluminum (99.0-99.5%)	Solution	...	20 (68)	...	Excellent	92
Titanium						
Titanium	Dry or moist gas	...	25 (77)	...	0.1 (4)	90
Titanium	In H2O + KI	...	Room	...	nil	90
Titanium	In alcohol	Saturated	Room	...	Pitted	90
Heat- and corrosion-resistant alloys						
Alloy 825	Soap processing; field or plant test; no aeration; no agitation. Plus 90% nonionic detergent, some hydrochloric acid	10	22 (72)	90 d	0.0001 in./yr	89
Alloy 825	Soap processing; field or plant test; no aeration; rapid agitation. Plus 11% isopropyl alcohol, 2% hydrochloric acid, remainder nonionic detergent	9.3	22 (72)	90 d	0.0039 in./yr	89
Carpenter 20	Soap processing; field or plant test; no aeration; no agitation. Plus 90% nonionic detergent, some hydrochloric acid	10	22 (72)	90 d	0.0002 in./yr	89
Carpenter 20	Soap processing; field or plant test; no aeration; rapid agitation. Plus 11% isopropyl alcohol, 2% hydrochloric acid, remainder nonionic detergent	9.3	22 (72)	90 d	0.0073 in./yr	89
Others						
Magnesium	Dry crystals	100	Room	...	Suitable	119

Lactic Acid

Lactic acid, CH3CHOHCOOH, also known as 2-hydroxypropanoic acid, is a hygroscopic liquid that exists in three isometric forms. *l*-lactic acid is found in blood and animal tissue as a product of glucose and glycogen metabolism. *d*-lactic acid is obtained by fermentation of sucrose (corn refining). The racemic mixture is present in foods prepared by bacterial fermentation or prepared synthetically. Lactic acid is soluble in water, alcohol, and ether. It is used as a solvent, in manufacturing confectionery, and in medicine.

Material Summaries

The following material summaries were compiled from a survey of the available literature. Inclusion of a material description under a given environment does not imply that it is the most appropriate material for corrosion service in that environment. Likewise, exclusion of a given material does not imply that it is not suitable for corrosion service applications in that environment.

Aluminum. Aluminum alloy 3003 suffered mild attack (0.075 mm/yr, or 3 mils/yr) in aqueous solutions of lactic acid (0.05 to 80%) during laboratory tests. When the temperature was raised to 100 °C (212 °F), lactic acid became very corrosive, with the greatest rate occurring at 5% concentration.

Copper. Aluminum bronzes generally are suitable for service in lactic acid.

Zirconium. Zirconium resists corrosion in lactic acid.

Corrosion Behavior of Various Metals and Alloys in Lactic Acid

Material	Condition, other factors, comments	Concentration, %	Temperature, °C (°F)	Duration	Corrosion rate, mm/yr (mils/yr) or other	Ref
Stainless steels						
AM-363 stainless steel	...	...	Room	...	Slightly attacked	120
Type 304 stainless steel	...	10	21 (70)	...	Good	121
Type 304 stainless steel	No activation	20	Boiling	24 h	1.825 (73)	52
Type 316 stainless steel	...	10	21 (70)	...	Good	121
Type 316 stainless steel	No activation	20	Boiling	24 h	0.0025 (0.1)	52
Type 410 stainless steel	...	10	21 (70)	...	Poor	121
Type 410 stainless steel	...	...	Room	...	Slightly attacked	121
Type 430 stainless steel	...	10	21 (70)	...	Poor	121
Type 444 stainless steel	No activation	20	Boiling	24 h	0.005 (0.2)	52
Aluminum						
Aluminum (>99.5%)	Solution	...	20 (68)	...	Satisfactory	92
Coppers						
70-30 cupronickel	...	...	...	...	Suitable	93
90-10 cupronickel	...	...	...	...	Suitable	93
Admiralty brass	...	...	...	...	Suitable	93
Aluminum bronze	...	...	...	...	Suitable	93
Ampco 8, aluminum bronze	Generally suitable	...	...	...	<0.05 (<2)	96
Architectural bronze	...	...	...	...	Fair	93
Brass	...	...	...	...	Suitable	93
Cartridge brass	...	...	...	...	Fair	93
Commercial bronze	...	...	...	...	Suitable	93
Electrolytic copper	...	...	...	...	Suitable	93
Free-cutting brass	...	...	...	...	Fair	93
Muntz metal	...	...	...	...	Fair	93
Naval brass	...	...	...	...	Fair	93
Nickel silver	...	18	...	...	Suitable	93
Phosphor bronze	5% Sn	...	...	...	Suitable	93
Phosphor bronze	8% Sn	...	...	...	Suitable	93
Phosphor copper	...	...	...	...	Suitable	93
Red brass	...	...	...	...	Suitable	93
Silicon bronze	Low	...	...	...	Suitable	93
Silicon bronze	High	...	...	...	Suitable	93
Titanium						
Titanium	...	10-85	100 (212)	...	<0.127 (<5.08)	90
Titanium	...	10	Boiling	...	<0.127 (<5.08)	90

(Continued)

Corrosion Behavior of Various Metals and Alloys in Lactic Acid (Continued)

Material	Condition, other factors, comments	Concen-tration, %	Temperature, °C (°F)	Duration	Corrosion rate, mm/yr (mils/yr) or other	Ref
Heat- and corrosion-resistant alloys						
40Co-20Cr-15Ni-7Mo	...	10	104 (219)	50 h	nil	54
Inconel 601	...	10	80 (176)	7 d	0.925 (36.4)	64
Inconel 690	...	10	80 (176)	...	<0.03 (<1)	57
Incoloy 800	No pitting. (a)	10	80 (176)	7 d	<0.003 (<0.1)	44
Nickel 200	Laboratory immersion test	2	Room	...	0.052 (2.1)	44
Nickel 200	In vacuum evaporator	10-22	54 (130)	...	1.275 (51)	44
Nickel 200	Laboratory immersion test	85	Room	...	0.067 (2.7)	44
Nickel 200	Liquid phase in vacuum evaporator	To 85	49-82 (120-180)	...	0.25 (10)	44
Nickel 200	Vapor phase in vacuum evaporator	To 85	49-82 (120-180)	...	0.27 (11)	44
Zirconium						
Zr702	...	10-100	148 (298)	...	<0.025 (<1)	15
Zr702	...	10-85	35 (95 to boiling)	...	<0.025 (<1)	15
Noble metals						
Gold	...	All	Boiling	...	<0.05 (<2)	8
Silver	...	...	Boiling	...	<0.05 (<2)	4
Silver	...	...	Boiling	...	<0.05 (<2)	4
Others						
Niobium	...	10-85	Boiling	...	0.025 (1.0)	2

(a) Solutions were prepared with reagent-grade chemicals. Test specimens were cold-rolled, annealed sheet, 2.84 mm (0.112 in.) thick.

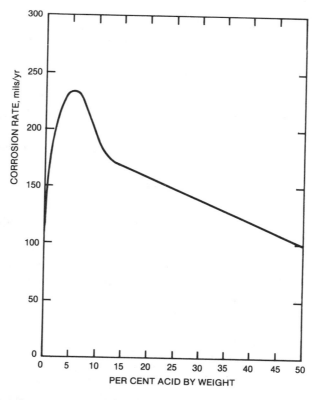

Aluminum. Effect of lactic acid on alloy 1100 at 100 °C (212 °F). Source: *Guidelines for the Use of Aluminum with Food and Chemicals: Compatibility Data on Aluminum in the Food and Chemical Process Industries*, 5th ed., The Aluminum Association, Washington, DC, 1984, 33.

Liquid Metals

The various types of corrosion reactions (direct dissolution, corrosion product formation, elemental transfer, alloying, compound reduction, and environmentally assisted cracking) must be considered in materials selection for liquid-metal containment. In many cases, particularly at low temperature or with less aggressive liquids, liquid-metal corrosion is not an important factor, and many materials, both metals and ceramics, would suffice. Under more severe conditions, however, an understanding of the various types of liquid-metal corrosion is necessary to select or develop a compatible containment material. For example, for applications in high-temperature molten lithium, most oxides would be unstable with respect to this liquid metal, low-chromium steels would decarburize, and alloys containing large amounts of nickel or manganese would suffer extensive preferential dissolution and irregular attack. Materials selection would then be limited to higher chromium ferritic/martensitic steels or high-purity refractory metals and alloys.

Because two or more concurrent corrosion reactions are possible, and because consideration of all of the applicable materials consequences may lead to opposite strategies, materials selection for liquid-metal environments can become quite complex and may require optimization of several factors rather than minimization of any particular one. In addition, an assessment of the suitability of a given material for liquid-metal service must be based on the knowledge of its total corrosion response.

Material Summaries

The following material summaries were compiled from a survey of the available literature. Inclusion of a material description under a given environment does not imply that it is the most appropriate material for corrosion service in that environment. Likewise, exclusion of a given material does not imply that it is not suitable for corrosion service applications in that environment.

Cast Irons

Unalloyed cast iron is used as a melting crucible for such low-melting metals as lead, zinc, cadmium, magnesium, and aluminum.

Carbon and Low-Alloy Steels

Plain carbon steels are not satisfactory for long-term containment of molten aluminum. Low-carbon steels have poor resistance to attack by liquid antimony. Low-alloy steels have good resistance to liquid bismuth at temperatures up to 700 °C (1290 °F). Bismuth alloys are more aggressive. Low-alloy steels exhibit good serviceability in liquid cadmium at temperatures up to 700 °C (1290 °F). One of the most aggressive of all liquid metals that cannot be contained by carbon or low-alloy steels at elevated temperatures is gallium. Carbon and low-alloy steels have poor resistance to molten indium. Low-alloy steels are resistant to molten lead at temperatures up to 600 °C (1110 °F), but are attacked more aggressively by lead-base alloys.

Although plain carbon steels are virtually unattacked by mercury under nonflowing or isothermal conditions, the presence of either a temperature gradient or liquid flow can lead to drastic attack. The corrosion mechanism appears to be one of dissolution, with the rate of attack increasing rapidly with temperatures above 500 °C (930 °F). Alloy additions of chromium, titanium, silicon, and molybdenum, alone or in combination, provide resistance to 600 °C (1110 °F). Where applicable, the attack of ferrous alloys by mercury can be reduced to negligible amounts by the addition of 10 ppm Ti to the mercury; this raises the useful limit of operating temperatures to 650 °C (1200 °F). Additions of metal with a higher affinity for oxygen than titanium, such as magnesium, may be required to prevent oxidation of the titanium and loss of the inhibitive action.

Plain carbon and low-alloy steels are generally suitable for long-term use in sodium and sodium-potassium alloys at temperatures to 450 °C (840 °F). Beyond these temperatures, stainless steels are required. Low-alloy steels are resistant to molten tin only at temperatures up to 150 °C (300 °F). Alloys of tin are more aggressive. Most engineering metals and alloys show poor resistance to molten zinc, and carbon steels are no exception.

Stainless Steels

The 18-8 stainless steels are highly resistant to liquid sodium or sodium-potassium alloys. Mass transfer is not expected up to 540 °C (1000 °F) and remains at moderately low levels up to 870 °C (1600 °F). Accelerated attack of stainless steels in liquid sodium occurs with oxygen contamination, with a noticeable effect occurring at about 0.02% oxygen by weight.

Exposure to molten lead under dynamic conditions often results in mass transfer in common stainless alloy systems. Particularly severe corrosion can occur in strongly oxidizing conditions.

Stainless steels are generally attacked by molten aluminum, zinc, antimony, bismuth, cadmium, and tin.

Niobium

Niobium resists attack in many liquid metals to relatively high temperatures. These include bismuth below 510 °C (950 °F), gallium below 400 °C (750 °F), lead below 850 °C (1560 °F), lithium below 1000 °C (1830 °F), mercury below 600 °C (1110 °F), sodium, potassium, and sodium-potassium alloys below 1000 °C (1830 °F), thorium-magnesium eutectic below 850 °C (1560 °F), uranium below 1400 °C (2550 °F), and zinc below 450 °C (840 °F). The presence of excessive amounts of nonmetallic impurities (for example, gases) may reduce the resistance of niobium to these liquid metals.

Because liquid metals are excellent heat transfer media, they can be used in very compact thermal systems, such as the fast breeder reactor, reactors for space vehicles, and fusion reactors. Niobium is a serious candidate as a material for high-efficiency reactors.

Niobium resists attack by sodium vapor at high temperatures and pressures. The Nb-1Zr alloy is used for the end caps in high-pressure sodium vapor lamps used for highway lighting.

Noble Metals

Gold is attacked by all low-melting alloys, including mercury, sodium, potassium, lead, tin, bismuth, and iridium.

Silver. All the low-melting molten metals attack silver, including mercury, sodium, potassium, lead, tin, bismuth, and indium.

Platinum. A number of low-melting metals, including lead, tin, antimony, zinc, and arsenic, will readily alloy with and attack platinum at their melting temperatures. Low-melting phases are formed with silicon, phosphorus, bismuth, and boron, and salts or compounds of these metals can be detrimental at high temperatures under reducing conditions.

Iridium shows excellent resistance to attack by a wide range of molten metals. Iridium is unattacked by gallium, lithium, potassium, sodium, indium, mercury, and bismuth at temperatures up to 200 °C (360 °F) above their respective melting points under an atmosphere of argon. It is only slowly attacked by molten lead, tellurium, cadmium, antimony, tin, calcium, silver, and gold. On the other hand, the metal is readily attacked by molten copper, aluminum, zinc, and magnesium.

Ruthenium exhibits good resistance to attack by molten lithium, sodium, potassium, copper, silver, and gold when it is heated in an atmosphere of argon. No solution attack by these metals occurs up to 100 °C (180 °F) above their melting points, although grain-boundary penetration is observed with sintered and unworked ruthenium. Ruthenium is also resistant to attack by molten lead, and at temperatures up to 700 °C (1290 °F), attack by liquid bismuth is extremely slight. The solubility of ruthenium in bismuth at this temperature is 0.029%. At 1200 °C (2190 °F), it is 0.016%.

Ruthenium is also unattacked by mercury at temperatures up to 550 °C (1020 °F). Ruthenium is apparently unattacked at lower temperatures by gallium, but there is some attack at temperatures 400 °C (720 °F) above the melting point of gallium. Similarly, bismuth dissolves ruthenium very slowly at 700 °C (1290 °F), with the dissolution occurring uniformly at the ruthenium surface.

Ruthenium is attacked by molten aluminum or zinc at all temperatures above their melting points. This attack appears to consist of uniform dissolution of the surface and does not result in the formation of intermetallic compounds or grain-boundary penetration. On the other hand, attack by magnesium and antimony occurs with the formation of an intermetallic compound at the interface, which appears to have some protective value.

Rhodium. At temperatures 200 °C (360 °F) above their melting points, gold, silver, mercury, cesium, potassium, sodium, and gallium have negligible corrosive action on rhodium, but unlike iridium and ruthenium, rhodium is rapidly dissolved by lead and bismuth.

Tantalum

Tantalum and some tantalum-base alloys exhibit good resistance to many liquid metals. Such tantalum materials exhibit remarkable resistance to several liquid metals even to high temperatures (900 to 1100 °C, or 1650 to 2010 °F) in the absence of oxygen or nitrogen. The severity of attack on tantalum by liquid metals may be markedly increased by increasing temperature. Because operating temperatures somewhat in excess of 700 °C (1290 °F) are desirable in many cases, refractory metals, including tantalum and niobium, seem to be particularly promising materials of construction for containing liquid metals.

Liquid aluminum reacts rapidly with tantalum to form the stable compound aluminum (Al_3Ta). Liquid bismuth has little action on tantalum at temperatures below 1000 °C (1830 °F) and exerts no detrimental effects on the stress-rupture properties of tantalum at 815 °C (1500 °F), but it causes some intergranular attack at 1000 °C (1830 °F). Tantalum is only slightly attacked by calcium at 1200 °C (2190 °F). A crucible with a wall thickness of 0.15 mm (5.8 mils) was reduced to 0.13 mm (5.3 mils) after 12 days of exposure to calcium at 1200 °C (2190 °F).

Similar lack of corrosion resistance to cesium was found for tantalum as reported for niobium. Refluxing capsule tests indicated surface dissolution and severe attack after 720 h at 980 and 1370 °C (1800 and 2500 °F). The resistance of tantalum to molten gallium is considered to be good at temperatures to 450 °C (840 °F), but poor at temperatures above 600 °C (1110 °F). Tantalum is highly resistant to liquid lead at temperatures to 1000 °C (1830 °F), with a rate of attack of less than 0.025 mm/yr (1 mil/yr).

It exhibits no detrimental effects when stress-rupture tests are conducted in molten lead at 815 °C (1500 °F).

Tantalum possesses good resistance to molten lithium at temperatures up to 1000 °C (1830 °F). Its service ability with lithium is similar to that of niobium in that corrosion resistance depends on oxygen concentration. Tantalum metal will exhibit good corrosion resistance to lithium as long as the oxygen concentration of the tantalum is maintained below 100 to 200 ppm.

Specimens of T-111 and T-222 (Ta-9.6W-2.4Hf-0.01C) alloys, oxygen contaminated to 500 ppm and welded in argon, were exposed to lithium at 750 and 1200 °C (1380 and 2190 °F) for 100 h. Evaluation indicated no attack in the weld areas; however, intergranular penetration was observed in the base metal of both alloys. Heat treatment at 1315 °C (2400 °F) eliminated the attack. In addition, a method of inhibiting the corrosion of tantalum by liquid lithium at temperatures above 1000 °C (1830 °F) by the addition of 0.15 to 1.5 at.% Si to the lithium has been discussed.

In one investigation, simulated nuclear-fuel element specimens, consisting of uranium mononitride (UN) fuel cylinders clad with tungsten-lined T-111 alloy, were exposed in a pumped lithium loop operated at 1040 °C (1905 °F) for up to 7500 h. The lithium flow velocity was 1.5 m/s (5 ft/s) in the specimen test section. A cladding crack was simulated in one specimen exposed for 50,000 h by an axial slot machined through both the cladding and the tungsten liner.

All of the fuel element specimens appeared to be in excellent condition after the tests. No evidence of any chemical compatibility problems between the specimens and the flowing lithium was found. Except for a slight reduction in the oxygen content of the T-111, very little change in chemistry was observed in the T-111 or the UN. No microstructural changes were observed in the UN, but bands of fine precipitates were seen in the T-111 after the lithium exposure. These precipitates were thought to be the result of thermal aging, not lithium exposure.

Direct exposure of the UN to the lithium through the simulated cladding crack resulted in some erosion of the UN and in some nitrogen contamination of the T-111 cladding in the area of the defect. The T-111 in the fuel element clad specimens was ductile after the long-term lithium exposure. Thermal aging at 1040 °C (1905 °F), however, resulted in the T-111 becoming sensitive to hydrogen embrittlement during post-test handling and testing.

Tantalum is unattacked by molten magnesium at 1150 °C (2100 °F). The limited amount of corrosion testing of refractory metals in mercury is summarized below. The results for tantalum are consistent with the solubility information. In static tests, tantalum exhibited good resistance to mercury at temperatures to 600 °C (1110 °F). Refluxing capsule tests showed no attack of tantalum up to 760 °C (1400 °F). The corrosion resistance of tantalum to mercury was further documented in a two-phase natural-circulation loop test that ran for 19,975 h with a boiling temperature of 650 °C (1200 °F) and superheat temperature of 705 °C (1300 °F).

Post-test evaluation of the loop revealed no corrosion. As a result of the inertness of tantalum to mercury attack demonstrated in this long-term experiment, tantalum was evaluated as a replacement material for Croloy 9M steel in a mercury boiler.

The compatibility of tantalum and potassium at 600, 800, and 1000 °C (1110, 1470, and 1830 °F) was studied in static capsule tests. As the oxygen concentration of potassium was increased, the amount of tantalum in the potassium was also found to increase. The results indicated the formation of an unidentified ternary oxide phase that is either nonadherent or dissolved when the potassium is dissolved for chemical analysis. When the tantalum specimens contained oxygen above a certain threshold concentration, potassium penetrated the tantalum, and intergranular, as well as transgranular, attack was observed. The threshold levels for intergranular attack at the test temperatures were found to be 500, 700, and 1000 ppm oxygen, respectively. The mechanism of attack was believed to be the formation of a ternary oxide phase.

Tantalum is only slightly attacked by silver at 1200 °C (2190 °F); a tantalum crucible tested in silver at this temperature for 35 days showed a loss in wall thickness of 0.02 mm (0.8 mil). Liquid sodium, potassium, or alloys of these elements have little effect on tantalum at temperatures up to 1000 °C (1830 °F), but oxygen contamination of sodium causes increases in corrosion. Sodium does not alloy with tantalum.

The presence of oxygen in liquid sodium leads to slight weight loss of tantalum in flowing systems. In addition, extensive intergranular and transgranular attack of tantalum by sodium was observed. This attack was attributed to the high (390 ppm) oxygen concentration of the tantalum before exposure to the sodium.

The compatibility of tantalum alloys T-111 and Ta-10W with static sodium was demonstrated in capsules tested at 1315 °C (2400 °F) for 6271 and 300 h, respectively. No corrosion was found in either alloy.

Corrosion of candidate construction materials for stills to extract radioactive polonium-210 from bismuth by distillation at temperatures of 450 to 950 °C (840 to 1740 °F) was investigated. Tellurium, which is chemically similar to polonium, was used as a nonradioactive substitute for polonium. Of the materials investigated, tantalum appeared to be the most satisfactory from the standpoint of fabricability and long-term corrosion resistance. Tantalum was corroded at rates up to 0.5 μm/h (0.02 mil/h) during the initial 100 to 200 h of exposure; the rate decreased to less than 0.05 μm/h (0.002 mil/h) after 400 h for concentrations of tellurium of less than 30% in bismuth.

In static tests, the thorium-magnesium eutectic had no appreciable effect on tantalum at 1000 °C (1830 °F). No measurable corrosion of tantalum by the thorium-magnesium eutectic was noted in dynamic tests for 28 days with a temperature range of 700 to 840 °C (1290 to 1545 °F). Extensive tests on components for molten-metal fuel reactors revealed that tantalum is a satisfactory material for several thousand hours of service in high-temperature circulating loops containing a molten magnesium-thorium alloy with a composition in the range of the magnesium-rich eutectic.

Short-term tests indicated that the practical upper limit for tantalum as a container material for uranium is about 1450 °C (2640 °F). However, attack below this temperature is also significant, because a tantalum crucible with a wall thickness of 1.5 mm (0.06 in.) was completely corroded within a test period of 50 h at 1275 °C (2325 °F). Other investigations showed that tantalum is not attacked by uranium-magnesium and plutonium-magnesium alloys at 1150 °C (2100 °F). Extensive tests on components for molten-metal fuel reactors revealed that tantalum is a satisfactory material for several thousand hours of service in several liquid-metal environments.

Tantalum is attacked by zinc, the surface of which is abraded in zinc at 440 °C (825 °F); also, molten zinc attacks tantalum at significant rates at temperatures above 450 °C (840 °F). Tantalum showed appreciable attack from molten zinc at 750 °C (1380 °F). However, one industrial zinc producer observed excellent corrosion resistance at 500 °C (930 °F). The maintenance of the oxide film on the tantalum may account for the latter result.

The intermetallic compounds YSb, ErSb, LaSb, and YBi have little effect on tantalum at 1800 to 2000 °C (3270 to 3630 °F), but antimony vapor

severely attacks tantalum at temperatures of 1000 °C (1830 °F) and higher.

Titanium

Several metals, both in liquid and solid form, have been found to induce cracking in contact with titanium alloys. The first reported incidence stemmed from a cracked compressor disk in contact with cadmium-plated steel bolts. Initial speculation hinted that the exposure temperature may have been above the melting point of cadmium, leading to liquid-metal embrittlement. However, later work found that cracking would occur well below the melting point of cadmium, such as at room temperature for Ti-6Al-4V.

Those metals known to cause cracking of titanium alloys include cadmium, mercury, zinc, and certain silver brazing alloys. The titanium alloys that are known to be susceptible to cracking in cadmium include commercially pure titanium (ASTM grade 3) with more than 0.2% oxygen, Ti-4Al-4Mn, Ti-8Mn, Ti-31V-11Cr-3Al, Ti-6Al-4V, and Ti-8Al-1Mo-1V. It is likely that most other titanium alloys are susceptible, but have not been tested.

Alloys tested and found to crack in mercury include commercially pure titanium (ASTM grade 4, ~0.3% oxygen), Ti-8Mn, Ti-31V-11Cr-3Al, Ti-6Al-4V, and Ti-8Al-1Mo-1V. As with cadmium, other alloys are probably susceptible, but have not been tested.

Zinc, in both solid and liquid form, has been reported to cause cracking of titanium alloys. However, there is conflicting evidence in the literature as to whether this is actually the case.

Silver and silver brazing alloys have been shown to cause cracking in titanium alloys that are particularly sensitive to stress-corrosion cracking. These alloys include Ti-8Al-1Mo-1V, Ti-5Al-2.5Sn, and Ti-7Al-4Mo. As with cadmium, both solid and liquid forms of silver may produce cracking. Susceptibility for Ti-6Al-4V is considered to be above 345 °C (650 °F).

Titanium exhibits good resistance to many liquid metals at moderately elevated temperatures, where corrosion rates increase with temperature and flow rate. These metals include molten aluminum, sodium, potassium, sodium-potassium mixtures, magnesium, tin, and lead. In contrast, useful performance of titanium in molten lithium, bismuth, zinc, gallium, cadmium, and mercury is limited to relatively low temperatures. Liquid mercury below 150 °C (300 °F) does not appear to affect titanium unless wetting of freshly exposed (mechanically damaged) surfaces occurs. Liquid cadmium, silver, and mercury may cause stress-corrosion cracking of titanium alloys.

Zirconium and Hafnium

Liquid cesium and liquid mercury cause stress-corrosion cracking of zirconium alloys. Hafnium is superior to zirconium and Zircaloy alloys in corrosion resistance in molten alkali metals.

Additional Reading

M.G. Adamson and E.A. Aitken, On the Caesium, Tellurium Fission Product-Induced Attack and Embrittlement of Stainless Steel Cladding in Oxide Fuel Pins, *J. Nucl. Mater.*, 132(2), 160-166, 1985. MetAbs No. 85-352039. **Abstract:** Attempts are made to rationalize the observed out-of-pile Cs-Te dependences of fission product-assisted inner surface attack and fission product-assisted liquid metal embrittlement in terms of Cs-Te thermochemistry and phase equilibria. The possibility of synergistic coupling between oxidative FCCI and FPLME in irradiated fuel pins is also examined.

S.P. Lynch, "Cleavage" of Aluminium Single Crystals in Liquid Metal Environments, *Mater. Sci. Eng.*, 72(2), L33-L37, 1985. MetAbs No.

85-352107. **Abstract:** Dislocation cell structures were observed by transmission electron microscopy of material beneath cleavage-like fracture surfaces of Al single crystals cracked in a liquid metal environment.

O.K. Chopra, D.L. Smith, P.F. Tortorelli, J.H. DeVan, and D.K. Sze, Liquid-Metal Corrosion, *Fusion Technol.*, *8*(2-I), 1956-1969, 1985. MetAbs No. 85-352282. **Abstract:** A review of corrosion and environmental effects on the mechanical properties of candidate structural alloys for use with liquid metals in fusion reactors is presented.

S.P. Lynch, Mechanisms of Stress-Corrosion Cracking and Liquid-Metal Embrittlement in Al-Zn-Mg Bicrystals, *J. Mater. Sci.*, *20*(9), 3329-3338, 1985. MetAbs No. 85-352287. **Abstract:** Metallographic and fractographic studies of intercrystalline fracture in high-purity Al-6Zn-3Mg bicrystals in inert, liquid metal, and water environments are described. The effects of variations in grain-boundary microstructure on fracture and the effects of cathodically charging specimens with hydrogen prior to testing in inert environments were also investigated.

O.K. Chopra and D.L. Smith, Corrosion of Ferrous Alloys in a Flowing Lithium Environment, *J. Nucl. Mater.*, 133-134, 861-866, 1985. MetAbs No. 85-352322. **Abstract:** Corrosion data on weight loss and internal penetration are presented for ferritic and austenitic stainless steels exposed for up to 6500 h at 700 and 755 K in a forced-circulation Li loop.

L.B. Traylor and C.E. Price, A Comparison of Hydrogen and Mercury Embrittlement in Monel at Room Temperature, *J. Eng. Mater. Technol. (Trans. ASME)*, *108*(1), 31-36, 1986. MetAbs No. 86-350626. **Abstract:** Slow strain rate tensile tests were performed on annealed and cold drawn Monel 400 and Monel R405 at room temperature in air, Hg, and electrolyte hydrogen.

J.A. Kapp, D. Duquette, and M.H. Kamdar, Crack Growth Behavior of Aluminum Alloys Tested in Liquid Mercury, *J. Eng. Mater. Technol. (Trans. ASME)*, *108*(1), 37-43, 1986. MetAbs No. 86-350627. **Abstract:** Crack growth rate measurements have been made in three Hg embrittled Al alloys each under three loading conditions. The alloys were 1100-0, 6061-T651, and 7075-T651. The loading conditions were fixed displacement static loading, fixed load static loading, and fatigue loading at two frequencies.

S.P. Lynch, A Fractographic Study of Hydrogen-Assisted Cracking and Liquid-Metal Embrittlement in Nickel, *J. Mater. Sci.*, *21*(2), 692-704, 1986. MetAbs No. 86-350869. **Abstract:** Metallographic and fractographic studies of crack growth in Ni polycrystals and single crystals in a number of environments are described.

P.C.S. Wu, Liquid-Metal Corrosion, in *Encyclopedia of Materials Science and Engineering*, Vol 4, Pergamon Press, Oxford, 2550-2551, 1986. MetAbs No. 86-352434. **Abstract:** Various mechanisms of liquid-metal corrosion are described.

W.A. Zdaniewski, Effect of Segregated Cr on Degradation of (Ti, Cr)B$_2$ Exposed to Liquid Aluminum, *J. Electrochem. Soc.*, *133*(9), 1777-1781, 1986. MetAbs No. 87-350010. **Abstract:** The effect of stress and microstructural variations on the structural integrity of polycrystalline (Ti, Cr)B$_2$ exposed to a liquid Al environment at 970 °C is discussed.

B.A. Wilkinson, D.A. Hammon, and G.R. Edwards, An Examination of Methods for Analysis of Liquid Metal Corrosion, *J. Mater. Energy Syst.*, *8*(3), 243-245, 1986. MetAbs No. 87-350787. **Abstract:** Methods of analyzing liquid metal penetration data are discussed and compared.

H.U. Borgstedt, G. Frees, and G. Drechsler, Corrosion of Stainless Steel in Flowing PbLi Eutectic, *J. Nucl. Mater.*, 141-143, 561-565, 1986. MetAbs No. 87-350868. **Abstract:** The corrosion of AISI 304 in a flowing Li-Pb environment is studied. Corrosion effects after an exposure of up to 5750 h are evaluated.

O.K. Chopra and D.L. Smith, Compatibility of Ferrous Alloys in a Forced Circulation Pb-17Li System, *J. Nucl. Mater.*, 141-143, 566-570, 1986. MetAbs No. 87-350869. **Abstract:** Corrosion data have been obtained on ferritic HT-9 and Fe-9Cr-1Mo steel and austenitic Type 316 stainless steel in a flowing Pb-17 at.% Li environment at 371 to 482 °C. The corrosion behavior is evaluated by measurement of weight loss as a function of time and temperature.

P.F. Tortorelli and J.H. DeVan, Corrosion of Fe-Cr-Mn Alloys in Thermally Convective Lithium, *J. Nucl. Mater.*, 141-143, 579-583, 1986. MetAbs No. 87-350871. **Abstract:** A series of austenitic Fe-Cr-Mn steels was exposed to circulating Li at temperatures up to 500 °C. Two groups of the alloys, which contained 12 to 30 wt% Mn and 2 to 20 wt% Cr, were sequentially exposed for periods greater than 3000 h in a type 316 stainless steel thermal convection loop.

O.K. Chopra and D.L. Smith, Influence of Temperature and Lithium Purity on Corrosion of Ferrous Alloys in a Flowing Lithium Environment, *J. Nucl. Mater.*, 141-143, 584-591, 1986. MetAbs No. 87-350872. **Abstract:** Corrosion data have been obtained on ferritic HT-9 and Fe-9Cr-1Mo steel and austenitic Type 316 stainless steel in a flowing Li environment at temperatures between 372 to 538 °C. The corrosion behavior is evaluated by measurements of weight loss as a function of time and temperature. A metallographic characterization of materials exposed to a flowing Li environment is presented.

P.F. Tortorelli and J.H. DeVan, Corrosion of Ferrous Alloys Exposed to Thermally Convective Pb-17 at.% Li, *J. Nucl. Mater.*, 141-143, 592-598, 1986. MetAbs No. 87-350873. **Abstract:** A type 316 stainless steel thermal convection loop with type 316 stainless steel coupons and a Fe-9Cr-1Mo steel loop containing Fe-12Cr-1MoVW steel specimens circulated molten Pb-17 at.% Li at a maximum temperature of 500 °C. Specimens were exposed for more than 6000 h. Mass loss and surface characterization data were compared for these two alloys.

M. Broc, P. Fauvet, T. Flament, and J. Sannier, Compatibility of 316L Stainless Steel With Liquid and Solid Tritium Breeding Materials, *J. Nucl. Mater.*, 141-143, 611-616, 1986. MetAbs No. 87-350877. **Abstract:** Corrosion of 316L stainless steel in flowing 17Li-83Pb has been investigated at 400 and 450 °C for up to 3000 h. The influence of temperature, time, microstructure of steel, alloy velocity and cold trap purification on corrosion rate is presented.

T. Suzuki and I. Mutoh, The Downstream Effect in the Corrosion of Metallic Materials in a Type 316 Stainless Steel Sodium Loop System, *J. Nucl. Mater.*, *140*(1), 56-62, 1986. MetAbs No. 87-351074. **Abstract:** Experimental results of the downstream effect in Na corrosion are presented for specimens of three kinds of Type 316 stainless steels, another austenitic steel and a Mo-coated austenitic steel in a Type 316 stainless steel sodium loop system at 700 and 600 °C.

S. Prakash, V.K. Tewari, and A. Gupta, Effect of Liquid Zinc on Armco Iron With Relevance to Pots Used in Galvanizing, *Steel Res.*, *58*(5), 220-225, 1987. MetAbs No. 87-352136. **Abstract:** This investigation deals with the comparative study of liquid zinc attack on Armco iron and Tisco A grade iron at 450 to 550 °C. The effect of variables, e.g., time of contact and temperature, on weight loss of iron for specimens of similar geometry has been studied.

S.P. Lynch and P. Trevena, Stress Corrosion Cracking and Liquid Metal Embrittlement in Pure Magnesium, *Corrosion*, *44*(2), 113-124, 1988. MetAbs No. 88-351089. **Abstract:** Metallographic and fractographic observations of crack growth in pure magnesium in dry air, aqueous, and liquid alkali metal environments are described.

C.E. Price and R.S. Fredell, A Comparative Study of the Embrittlement of Monel 400 at Room Temperature by Hydrogen and by Mercury, *Metall. Trans. A, 17A*(5), 889-898, 1986. MetAbs No. 86-351113.

Abstract: Slow strain rate tensile tests were performed at room temperature on Monel 400 specimens of grain sizes 35 to 500 μm in air, mercury, and electrolytically generated hydrogen. Specimens of grain size 250 μm were tested at a range of strain rates.

Corrosion Behavior of Various Metals and Alloys in Liquid Metals

Material	Condition, other factors, comments	Concentration, %	Temperature, °C (°F)	Duration	Corrosion rate, mm/yr (mils/yr) or other	Ref
Irons and steels						
Gray cast iron	In mercury, MP -38.8 °C	...	300 (570)	...	Unknown	104
Gray cast iron	In mercury, MP -38.8 °C	...	600 (1110)	...	Unknown	104
Gray cast iron	In sodium, potassium and mixtures, MP -12.3 to 97.9 °C. Short term use only	...	300 (570)	...	0.025-0.25 (1.0-10)	104
Gray cast iron	In sodium, potassium and mixtures, MP -12.3 to 97.9 °C. No structural possibilities	...	600 (1110)	...	>0.25 (>10)	104
Gray cast iron	In gallium, MP 29.8 °C	...	300 (570)	...	Unknown	104
Gray cast iron	In gallium, MP 29.8 °C	...	600 (1110)	...	Unknown	104
Gray cast iron	In bismuth-lead-tin, MP 97 °C. Considered for long-term use	...	300 (570)	...	<0.025 (<1.0)	104
Gray cast iron	In bismuth-lead-tin, MP 97 °C.	...	600 (1110)	...	Unknown	104
Gray cast iron	In bismuth-lead, MP 125 °C	...	300 (570)	...	Unknown	104
Gray cast iron	In bismuth-lead, MP 125 °C	...	600 (1110)	...	Unknown	104
Gray cast iron	In tin, MP 321.9 °C. Short-term use only	...	300 (570)	...	0.025-0.25 (1.0-10)	104
Gray cast iron	In tin, MP 321.9 °C. No structural possibilities	...	600 (1110)	...	>0.25 (>10)	104
Gray cast iron	In bismuth, MP 271.3 °C	...	300 (570)	...	Unknown	104
Gray cast iron	In bismuth, MP 271.3 °C	...	600 (1110)	...	Unknown	104
Gray cast iron	In lead, MP 327 °C. Considered for long-term use at 327 °C (621 °F)	...	300 (570)	...	<0.025 (<1.0)	104
Gray cast iron	In lead, MP 327 °C	...	600 (1110)	...	Unknown	104
Gray cast iron	In indium, MP 156.4 °C	...	300 (570)	...	Unknown	104
Gray cast iron	In indium, MP 156.4 °C	...	600 (1110)	...	Unknown	104
Gray cast iron	In lithium, MP 186 °C	...	300 (570)	...	Unknown	104
Gray cast iron	In lithium, MP 186 °C	...	600 (1110)	...	Unknown	104
Gray cast iron	In thallium, MP 303 °C	...	300 (570)	...	Unknown	104
Gray cast iron	In thallium, MP 303 °C	...	600 (1110)	...	Unknown	104
Gray cast iron	In cadmium, MP 321 °C. Considered for long-term use at 321 °C (610 °F)	...	300 (570)	...	<0.025 (<1.0)	104
Gray cast iron	In cadmium, MP 321 °C. Considered for long-term use	...	600 (1110)	...	<0.025 (<1.0)	104
Gray cast iron	In zinc, MP 419.5 °C. No structural possibilities	...	600 (1110)	...	>0.25 (>10)	104
Gray cast iron	In antimony, MP 630.5 °C. No structural possibilities at 630.5 °C (1167 °F)	...	600 (1110)	...	>0.25 (>10)	104
Gray cast iron	In magnesium, MP 651 °C. Considered for long-term use at 651 °C (1204 °F)	...	600 (1110)	...	<0.025 (<1.0)	104
Gray cast iron	In aluminum, MP 660 °C. No structural possibilities at 660 °C (1220 °F)	...	600 (1110)	...	>0.25 (>10)	104
Stainless steels						
Type 304 stainless steel	In zinc. No internal attack noted	...	454 (850)	50 h	0.35 (14.1)	63
Type 446 stainless steel	In zinc. No internal attack noted	...	454 (850)	50 h	0.23 (9.3)	63
Aluminum						
Aluminum (99.0-99.5%)	Molten bismuth	...	...	...	Excellent	92
Aluminum (99.0-99.5%)	Molten lead	...	...	...	Excellent	92
Coppers						
70-30 cupronickel	...	...	...	...	Not suitable	93
90-10 cupronickel	...	...	...	...	Not suitable	93
Admiralty brass	...	...	...	...	Not suitable	93
Aluminum bronze	...	...	...	...	Not suitable	93
Architectural bronze	...	...	...	...	Not suitable	93
Brass	...	...	...	...		

(Continued)

Corrosion Behavior of Various Metals and Alloys in Liquid Metals (Continued)

Material	Condition, other factors, comments	Concentration, %	Temperature, °C (°F)	Duration	Corrosion rate, mm/yr (mils/yr) or other	Ref
Cartridge brass	...	...	...	...	Not suitable	93
Commercial bronze	...	...	...	...	Not suitable	93
Electrolytic copper	...	...	...	...	Not suitable	93
Free-cutting brass	...	...	...	...	Not suitable	93
Muntz metal	...	...	...	...	Not suitable	93
Naval brass	...	...	...	...	Not suitable	93
Nickel silver	...	...	...	...	Not suitable	93
Phosphor bronze	...	18	...	...	Not suitable	93
Phosphor bronze	5% Sn	...	...	...	Not suitable	93
Phosphor copper	...	...	...	...	Not suitable	93
Red brass	...	...	...	...	Not suitable	93
Silicon bronze	Low	...	...	...	Not suitable	93
Silicon bronze	High	...	...	...	Not suitable	93
Titanium						
Titanium	Molten lead	...	816 (1503)	...	Attacked	90
Titanium	Molten lead	...	324-593 (615-1101)	...	Good	90
Titanium	Molten lithium	...	316-482 (601-900)	...	nil	90
Titanium	Molten magnesium	...	760 (1400)	...	Limited resistance	90
Titanium	In bismuth-lead	...	300 (570)	...	<0.1 (<4)	103
Titanium	In bismuth-lead	...	600 (1110)	...	0.13-1.3 (5-50)	103
Titanium	In gallium	...	400 (750)	...	0.1 (4)	103
Titanium	In gallium	...	450 (840)	...	>1.0 (>40)	103
Titanium	In lithium	...	850 (1560)	...	0.1-1.0 (4-40)	103
Titanium	In magnesium	...	750 (1380)	...	0.1 (4)	103
Titanium	In magnesium	...	850 (1560)	...	0.1-1.0 (4-40)	103
Titanium	In lead	...	400 (750)	...	<0.13 (<5)	103
Titanium	In lead	...	600-950 (1110-1740)	...	0.1-1.0 (4-40)	103
Titanium	In mercury	...	150 (300)	...	<0.1 (<4)	103
Titanium	In mercury	...	150-300 (300-570)	...	0.1-1.0 (4-40)	103
Titanium	In sodium, potassium	...	600 (1110)	...	<0.1 (<4)	103
Titanium	In sodium, potassium	...	800 (1470)	...	0.1-1.0 (4-40)	103
Titanium	In tin	...	350 (660)	...	<0.1 (<4)	103
Titanium	In tin	...	600 (1110)	...	0.1-1.0 (4-40)	103
Titanium	In aluminum	...	750 (1380)	...	<0.1 (<4)	103
Titanium	In aluminum	...	850 (1560)	...	>0.1 (>4)	103
Titanium	In cadmium	...	500 (930)	...	>1.0 (>40)	103
Titanium	In zinc	...	445 (830)	...	>1.0 (>40)	103
Titanium	...	100	Up to 38 (up to 100)	...	Satisfactory	90
Titanium	...	100	Room	...	nil	90
Titanium	...	...	371 (701)	...	3.03 (121)	90
Titanium	Plus iron	...	371 (701)	...	0.079 (3.16)	90
Titanium	Plus copper	...	371 (701)	...	0.063 (2.52)	90
Titanium	Plus zirconium	...	371 (701)	...	0.033 (1.32)	90
Titanium	Plus magnesium	...	371 (701)	...	0.083 (3.32)	90
Heat- and corrosion-resistant alloys						
Alloy 800H	In zinc. No internal attack noted	...	454 (850)	50 h	0.28 (11.0)	63
Hastelloy alloy X	In zinc. No internal attack noted. Dissolved	...	454 (850)	50 h	>0.6 (>24.0)	63
Haynes No. 25	In zinc. No internal attack noted	...	454 (850)	50 h	0.06 (2.3)	63
Haynes No. 188	In zinc. No internal attack noted	...	454 (850)	50 h	0.06 (2.5)	63
Haynes No. 556	In zinc. No internal attack noted	...	454 (850)	50 h	0.04 (1.6)	63
Haynes No. 625	In zinc. No internal attack noted. Dissolved	...	454 (850)	50 h	>0.6 (>24.0)	63
Lead, tin, and zinc						
Lead	Corrosion rate too high to merit any consideration of lead	100	24 (75)	...	>1270 μm/yr (>50)	95

(Continued)

Corrosion Behavior of Various Metals and Alloys in Liquid Metals (Continued)

Material	Condition, other factors, comments	Concentration, %	Temperature, °C (°F)	Duration	Corrosion rate, mm/yr (mils/yr) or other	Ref
Tantalum						
Tantalum	In aluminum as Al₃Ta	...	Molten	...	Not resistant	105
Tantalum	In antimony	...	To 1000 (1830)	...	Not resistant	105
Tantalum	In bismuth	...	To 900 (1650)	...	No attack	105
Tantalum	In cadmium	...	Molten	...	No attack	105
Tantalum	In gallium	...	To 450 (840)	...	No attack	105
Tantalum	In lead	...	To 1000 (1830)	...	No attack	105
Tantalum	In lithium	...	To 1000 (1830)	...	No attack	105
Tantalum	In magnesium	...	To 1150 (2100)	...	No attack	105
Tantalum	In mercury	...	To 600 (1110)	...	No attack	105
Tantalum	In potassium	...	To 900 (1650)	...	No attack	105
Tantalum	In sodium	...	To 900 (1650)	...	No attack	105
Tantalum	In sodium-potassium alloys	...	To 900 (1650)	...	No attack	105
Tantalum	In zinc	...	To 500 (930)	...	No attack/variable depending on temperature and concentration	105
Tantalum	In tin	...	...	...	Variable depending on temperature and concentration	105
Tantalum	In uranium	...	...	...	Variable depending on temperature and concentration	105
Tantalum	In Mg-37Th, in helium	...	To 800 (1470)	...	Satisfactory	105
Tantalum	In Bi-5 to 10U, in helium	...	To 1100 (2010)	...	Satisfactory	105
Tantalum	In Bi-5U-0.3Mn, in helium	...	To 1050 (1920)	...	Satisfactory	105
Tantalum	In Bi-10U-0.5Mn in helium	...	To 1160 (2120)	...	Satisfactory	105
Tantalum	In Al-18Th-6U. Failed	...	To 1000 (1830)	...	Not resistant	105
Tantalum	In U-10Fe. Failed	...	To 900 (1650)	...	Not resistant	105
Tantalum	In U-Cr (eutectic). Failed	...	To 900 (1650)	...	Not resistant	105
Tantalum	In YSb-intermetallic compound	...	To 1800-2000 (3270-3630)	...	Satisfactory	105
Tantalum	In YBi-intermetallic compound	...	To 1800-2000 (3270-3630)	...	Satisfactory	105
Tantalum	In ErSb-intermetallic compound	...	To 1800-2000 (3270-3630)	...	Satisfactory	105
Tantalum	In LaSb-intermetallic compound	...	To 1800-2000 (3270-3630)	...	Satisfactory	105
Tantalum	In plutonium-cobalt-cerium	...	To 650 (1200)	...	Variable depending on temperature and concentration	105
Others						
Magnesium	Salts	All	Room	...	Unsuitable	119

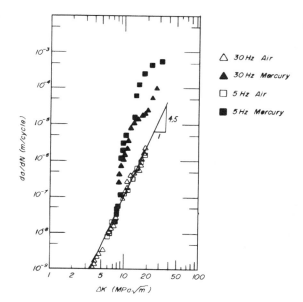

Aluminum. Fatigue loading results for 6061-T651 aluminum alloy exposed to mercury. Open triangle: 30 Hz, air. Closed triangle: 30 Hz, mercury. Open square: 5 Hz, air. Closed square: 5 Hz, mercury. Source: J.A. Kapp, D. Duquette, *et al.*, "Crack Growth Behavior of Aluminum Alloys Tested in Liquid Mercury," *Journal of Engineering Materials and Technology*, Vol 108, Jan 1986, 38.

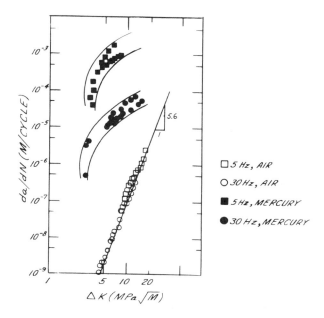

Aluminum. Fatigue loading results for 7075-T651 aluminum alloy exposed to mercury. Open square: 5 Hz, air. Open circle: 30 Hz, air. Closed square: 5 Hz, mercury. Closed circle: 30 Hz, mercury. Source: J.A. Kapp, D. Duquette, *et al.*, "Crack Growth Behavior of Aluminum Alloys Tested in Liquid Mercury," *Journal of Engineering Materials and Technology*, Vol 108, Jan 1986, 38.

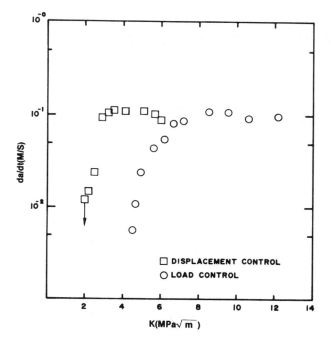

Aluminum. Static loading results for 7075-T651 aluminum alloy exposed to mercury. Source: J.A. Kapp, D. Duquette, *et al.*, "Crack Growth Behavior of Aluminum Alloys Tested in Liquid Mercury," *Journal of Engineering Materials and Technology*, Vol 108, Jan 1986, 40.

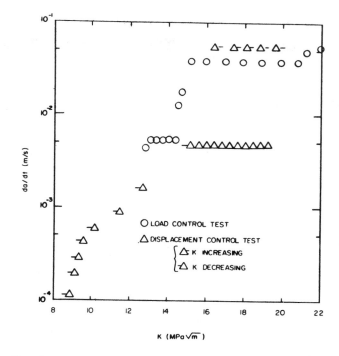

Aluminum. Static loading results for 6061-T651 aluminum alloy exposed to mercury. Source: J.A. Kapp, D. Duquette, *et al.*, "Crack Growth Behavior of Aluminum Alloys Tested in Liquid Mercury," *Journal of Engineering Materials and Technology*, Vol 108, Jan 1986, 39.

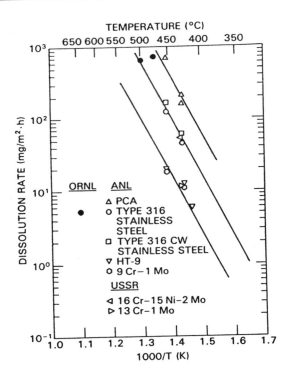

Stainless steel. Arrhenius plot of corrosion rate data for austenitic type 316 stainless steel and ferritic HT-9 alloy and Fe-9Cr-1Mo steel in flowing Pb-17Li. Data are normalized for $V = 1.5$ m/s. Source: O.K. Chopra, D.L. Smith, *et al.*, "Liquid-Metal Corrosion," *Fusion Technology*, Vol 8, Sept 1985, 1962.

Lithium Chloride

Lithium chloride, LiCl, is a white deliquescent solid with a melting point of 614 °C (1140 °F). It is soluble in water and alcohol and dehumidifies air for industrial drying and for air conditioning. Lithium chloride burns with a crimson flame and is used in pyrotechnics. It is also used as a pyrotechnic in welding and brazing fluxes.

Material Summaries

The following material summaries were compiled from a survey of the available literature. Inclusion of a material description under a given environment does not imply that it is the most appropriate material for corrosion service in that environment. Likewise, exclusion of a given material does not imply that it is not suitable for corrosion service applications in that environment.

Aluminum. Under laboratory conditions of 100% relative humidity and ambient temperature, aluminum alloys 3003, 5154, and 6061 were found to be resistant to solid lithium chloride. When the temperature was increased to 54 °C (130 °F), mild attack occurred. Tested in aqueous solutions of 1 to 40%, aluminum alloys 3003, 5052, and 6061 showed local pitting and mild attack (0.075 mm/yr, or 3 mils/yr) at both ambient temperature and 50 °C (122 °F).

Additional Reading

L. Brossard, Potentiodynamic Investigation of Copper in LiCl Solutions, *Corrosion, 40*(8), 420-425, 1984. MetAbs No. 84-352701. **Abstract:** The dissolution of copper has been investigated in an aqueous solution of pH 4 having up to 6M LiCl at temperatures from 22 to 64 °C.

S. Rambert and D. Landolt, Anodic Dissolution of Binary Single Phase Alloys. II. Behavior of CuPd, NiPd and AgAu in LiCl, *Electrochim. Acta, 31*(11), 1433-1441, 1986. MetAbs No. 87-350827. **Abstract:** The anodic dissolution behavior of the binary single-phase alloys CuPd, NiPd and AgAu in 12M LiCl is being investigated on a rotating disk electrode. Auger electron spectroscopy is employed to study the influence of applied charge on the surface composition of Cu20Pd and Ni20Pd and results are compared to previous data for AgPd alloys.

Corrosion Behavior of Various Metals and Alloys in Lithium Chloride

Material	Condition, other factors, comments	Concentration, %	Temperature, °C (°F)	Duration	Corrosion rate, mm/yr (mils/yr) or other	Ref
Lead	Corrosion rate too high to merit any consideration of Pb	...	24 (75)	...	>1270 μm/yr (>50)	95
Platinum	...	All	Boiling	...	<0.05 (<2)	5
Silver	...	All	Boiling	...	<0.05 (<2)	9
Titanium	...	50	149 (301)	...	nil	90
Type 304 stainless steel	Air conditioning (evaporator); field or pilot plant test; no aeration; rapid agitation. With carbon over the standard maximum. Stress-corrosion cracking	30	116 (240)	40 d	<0.0001 in./yr	89
Type 304 stainless steel	Chemical (dehydration) processing; field or pilot plant test; no aeration; slight to moderate agitation. With carbon over the standard maximum. Concentration: 30% during 26 days, 25% calcium chloride during 146 days, vacuum (bottom of column)	30	-7 to 20 (20-68)	172 d	<0.0001 in./yr	89
Type 304 stainless steel	Air conditioning (evaporator); field or pilot plant test; no aeration; slight to moderate agitation. Plus vapors from a boiling 30% lithium-chloride solution. Stress-corrosion cracking	...	116 (240)	40 d	Corrosion	89
Type 316 stainless steel	Air conditioning (evaporator); field or pilot plant test; no aeration; rapid agitation. Stress-corrosion cracking	30	116 (240)	40 d	<0.0001 in./yr	89
Type 316 stainless steel	Chemical (dehydration) processing; field or pilot plant test; no aeration; slight to moderate agitation. Concentration: 30% during 26 days, 25% calcium chloride during 146 days, vacuum (bottom of column)	30	-7 to 20 (20-68)	172 d	<0.0001 in./yr	89
Type 316 stainless steel	Air conditioning (evaporator); field or pilot plant test; no aeration; slight to moderate agitation. Plus vapors from a boiling 30% lithium-chloride solution. Severe pitting (maximum depth of pits over 0.010 in.). Stress-corrosion cracking	...	116 (240)	40 d	0.0069 in./yr	89

Magnesium Chloride

Magnesium chloride, $MgCl_2$, also known as chloromagnesite, is a colorless crystalline solid with a melting point of 712 °C (1312 °F). It is soluble in water and alcohol and is used in the ceramic and textile industries. Magnesium chloride is formed by heating hydrated magnesium chloride crystals in a current of dry hydrogen chloride or by heating magnesium ammonium chloride. Hydrated magnesium chloride, $MgCl_2 \cdot 6H_2O$, also known as bischophite, is a white deliquescent solid formed by the reaction of magnesium carbonate (or hydroxide, oxide or metal) and hydrogen chloride. It is used in disinfectants, fire extinguishers, and paper manufacture.

Material Summaries

The following material summaries were compiled from a survey of the available literature. Inclusion of a material description under a given environment does not imply that it is the most appropriate material for corrosion service in that environment. Likewise, exclusion of a given material does not imply that it is not suitable for corrosion service applications in that environment.

Aluminum. Tested under laboratory conditions of ambient temperature and 100% relative humidity, aluminum alloy 3003 resisted solid magnesium chloride. In other tests at ambient temperature, aqueous solutions of magnesium chloride with concentrations up to 10% produced localized pitting, but overall aluminum alloy 1001 showed good resistance.

Amorphous Metals. The stress-corrosion cracking behavior of a glassy $Fe_{32}Ni_{36}Cr_{14}P_{12}B_6$ alloy in boiling magnesium chloride (125 °C, or 255 °F) was studied by means of constant extension rate tensile tests and constant strain tests. Stress-corrosion cracking observed at the corrosion potential and anodic overpotentials could be prevented with a slight cathodic polarization. After studying the fracture surface, the conclusion was reached that the surface corrosion allowed hydrogen entry and therefore subsequent embrittlement.

Stainless Steels. The austenitic, ferritic and martensitic stainless steels display wide variability in their resistance to pitting and stress-corrosion cracking in magnesium chloride. A more detailed investigation should be performed if stainless steels are to be used in the presence of magnesium chloride, especially at elevated temperatures.

Zirconium. Zirconium resists stress-corrosion cracking in magnesium chloride.

Additional Reading

W.-Y. Chu, J. Yao, and C.-M. Hsiao, Stress Corrosion Cracking of Austenitic Stainless Steel Under Compressive Stress, *Corrosion*, 40(6), 302-306, 1984. MetAbs No. 84-352379. **Abstract:** Stress corrosion cracking of 304 and 321 austenitic stainless steel in boiling 42% $MgCl_2$ solution under compressive stress was investigated. Specimens with surface residual compressive stress, U-bend specimens, and notched compressive specimens of modified WOL type were used.

W.-Y. Chu, H.L. Wang, and C.-M. Hsiao, The Mechanism of Slow Crack Growth and Stress Corrosion Cracking in Austenitic Stainless Steel, *Corrosion, 40*(9), 487-492, 1984. MetAbs No. 84-353070. **Abstract:** The mechanisms of hydrogen-induced slow crack growth of 321 and 310 steels and stress-corrosion cracking of 321 steel in boiling $MgCl_2$ were investigated.

P. Muraleedharan, H.S. Khatak, J.B. Gnanamoorthy, and P. Rodriguez, Metallurgical Effect of Cold Work on Stress Corrosion Cracking Behavior of Types 304 and 316 Stainless Steels, *Metall. Trans. A, 16A*(2), 285-289, 1985. MetAbs No. 85-350457. **Abstract:** The influence of cold work (prestraining) in the range 2.3 to 56% on stress-corrosion cracking properties of 304 and 316 stainless steels in boiling $MgCl_2$ solution at 154° C was investigated using a constant load method.

J.-I. Sakai, M. Honda, K. Masamura, and I. Matsushima, Critical Contents of Nickel and Chromium Required for SCC Resistance of High Alloy Oil Country Tubular Goods, *Corrosion, 41*(2), 80-84, 1985. MetAbs No. 85-350640. **Abstract:** Stress-corrosion cracking test results of 10-37% Cr, 25-45% Ni, 3% Mo, balance Fe alloys are given.

R.F. Sandenbergh and R.M. Latanision, The Stress Corrosion Cracking of a Glassy $Fe_{32}Ni_{36}Cr_{14}P_{12}B_6$ Alloy, *Corrosion, 41*(7), 369-374, 1985. MetAbs No. 85-352101. **Abstract:** The stress-corrosion cracking of a glassy $Fe_{32}Ni_{36}Cr_{14}P_{12}B_6$ alloy in boiling $MgCl_2$ at 125 °C was studied by means of constant extension rate tensile and constant strain tests.

G. Herbsleb and W. Schwenk, The Influence of Dynamic Mechanical Parameters on Stress Corrosion Cracking of Steel–A Review, *Corrosion, 41*(8), 431-437, 1985. MetAbs No. 85-352330. **Abstract:** It has been demonstrated that with stress-corrosion cracking time-dependent parameters and critical stress levels are highly important.

T. Nakayama and M. Takano, Stress Corrosion Behavior of AISI 304 Stainless Steel in a Boiling 42% $MgCl_2$ Solution Under a Cyclic Slow Strain Rate Technique, *Corrosion, 41*(10), 592-597, 1985. MetAbs No. 86-350065. **Abstract:** Stress-corrosion cracking behavior of AISI 304 stainless steel rod and plate specimens in boiling 42% $MgCl_2$ was investigated. A thermal cyclic stress test was also conducted.

R. Oltra, J.C. Colson, and A. Desestret, The Electrochemical Effect of Chromium, Nickel, and Molybdenum Additions on the Stress Corrosion Cracking of Austenitic Stainless Steels in a Chloride Solution, *Corrosion, 42*(1), 44-50, 1986. MetAbs No. 86-350594. **Abstract:** A study has been made of the influence of Cr, Ni, and Mo additions on concurring mechanical and electrochemical processes, the balance of which determines the cracking susceptibility of austenitic stainless steel.

R.H. Jones and R. Wang, Stress Corrosion Cracking Behavior of an Amorphous FeCrNiW Alloy, *Corrosion, 42*(9), 504-513, 1986. MetAbs No. 86-352574. **Abstract:** Stress corrosion tests of an amorphous FeCrNiW alloy and wrought crystalline AISI 304 stainless steel alloys in boiling $MgCl_2$ were conducted. The time-to-failure was determined as a function of maximum tensile stress.

Y. Yoshino, Stress Corrosion Cracking of CrNi Martensitic Stainless Steel in Concentrated $MgCl_2$ Solutions, *Corrosion, 42*(10), 592-600, 1986. MetAbs No. 87-350021. **Abstract:** The stress-corrosion cracking of CrNi martensitic stainless steels was studied in 42% $MgCl_2$ solution, with a particular emphasis on intercritical heat treatment.

R.G. Melcher, C.E. Crowder, J.C. Tou, and D.I. Townsend, Oxygen Depletion in Corroded Steel Vessels, *Am. Ind. Hyg. Assoc. J., 48*(7), 608-612, 1987. MetAbs No. 87-352454. **Abstract:** Although steel treated with $MgCl_2$ has shown high corrosion rates when in a warm humid atmosphere, the rapid and extensive oxygen depletion observed in a $MgCl_2$ evaporator was much greater than expected. The reason for this unexpected oxygen depletion was investigated in the laboratory.

L.-J. Qiao, Hydrogen-Induced Cracking and Stress Corrosion Cracking of Austenitic Stainless Steel Under Mode III Loading, *Corrosion, 43*(8), 479-483, 1987. MetAbs No. 87-352843. **Abstract:** Hydrogen-induced cracking of austenitic stainless steel under mode III loading can occur during dynamic charging of hydrogen. Stress-corrosion cracking of austenitic stainless steel in a boiling $MgCl_2$ solution can also occur under mode III loading.

B.E. Wilde, The Influence of Silicon on the Stress Corrosion Cracking Resistance of 18Cr-8Ni-Base Stainless Steels, *Corrosion, 43*(10), 610-613, 1987. MetAbs No. 88-350602. **Abstract:** As part of a program to develop a stainless steel resistant to pitting, intergranular corrosion, and general corrosion while improving the stress-corrosion cracking resistance, the influence of Si additions to an 18Cr-8Ni stainless alloy was investigated.

L.-J. Qiao, W.-Y. Chu, C.-M. Hsiao, and J.-D. Lu, Stress Corrosion Cracking and Hydrogen-Induced Cracking in Austenitic Stainless Steel Under Mode II Loading, *Corrosion, 44*(1), 50-55, 1988. MetAbs No. 88-350929. **Abstract:** Stress-corrosion cracking and hydrogen-induced cracking of AISI 321 stainless steel under Mode II loading were investigated with notched specimens.

ASTM Standard G 35, ASTM, Philadelphia.

H. Chiang and M.A. Streicher, "Corrosion/85," 1895, p 353.

R.M. Labanision and R.W. Staehle, "Fundamental Aspects of Stress-Corrosion Cracking," Stress-Corrosion Cracking Conference, National Association of Corrosion Engineers, Houston, 1967, p 214.

Corrosion Behavior of Various Metals and Alloys in Magnesium Chloride

Material	Condition, other factors, comments	Concentration, %	Temperature, °C (°F)	Duration	Corrosion rate, mm/yr (mils/yr) or other	Ref
Stainless steels						
AM-363 stainless steel	...	...	Room	...	Attacked	120
Type 304 stainless steel	...	10	21 (70)	...	Fair	121

(Continued)

Corrosion Behavior of Various Metals and Alloys in Magnesium Chloride (Continued)

Material	Condition, other factors, comments	Concentration, %	Temperature, °C (°F)	Duration	Corrosion rate, mm/yr (mils/yr) or other	Ref
Type 304 stainless steel	Metal processing; field or pilot plant test; no aeration; slight to moderate agitation. Plus 0.8% sodium chloride, 0.4% calcium chloride, traces of iron, copper, nickel, manganese and sulfates, pH 5-6 (heating coil). Slight pitting: maximum depth of pits from incipient to 0.005 in.; crevice attack (tendency to concentration-cell corrosion)	36-35	71 (160)	31 d	0.0002 in./yr	89
Type 304 stainless steel	Chemical processing; laboratory test; strong aeration; no agitation. Evaporator. Severe pitting: maximum depth of pits over 0.010 in. Stress-corrosion cracking	42	156 (312)	35 d	0.0001 in./yr	89
Type 304 stainless steel	Chemical (evaporation) processing; field or pilot plant test; no aeration; rapid agitation. Boil-down kettle	48	166 (330)	55 d	0.0043 in./yr	89
Type 316 stainless steel	...	10	21 (70)	...	Good	121
Type 316 stainless steel	Metal processing; field or pilot plant test; no aeration; slight to moderate agitation. Plus 0.8% sodium chloride, 0.4% calcium chloride, traces of iron, copper, nickel, manganese and sulfates, pH 5-6 (heating coil). Slight pitting: maximum depth of pits from incipient to 0.005 in.; crevice attack (tendency to concentration-cell corrosion)	36-35	71 (160)	31 d	0.0002 in./yr	89
Type 316 stainless steel	Chemical (evaporation) processing; field or pilot plant test; no aeration; rapid agitation. Boil-down kettle. Stress-corrosion cracking	48	166 (330)	55 d	0.0032 in./yr	89
Type 410 stainless steel	...	10	21 (70)	...	Fair	121
Type 410 stainless steel	...	...	Room	...	Slightly attacked	121
Type 430 stainless steel	...	10	21 (70)	...	Good	121
Aluminum						
Aluminum (>99.5%)	Solution	...	20 (68)	...	Satisfactory	92
Coppers						
70-30 cupronickel	(a)	...	...	...	Good	93
90-10 cupronickel	(a)	...	...	...	Good	93
Admiralty brass	...	...	...	...	Fair	93
Aluminum bronze	(a)	...	...	...	Good	93
Ampco 8, aluminum bronze	Generally suitable	...	...	...	<0.05 (<2)	96
Architectural bronze	...	...	...	...	Not suitable	93
Brass	...	...	...	...	Fair	93
Cartridge brass	...	...	...	...	Not suitable	93
Commercial bronze	(a)	...	...	...	Good	93
Electrolytic copper	(a)	...	...	...	Good	93
Free-cutting brass	...	...	...	...	Not suitable	93
Muntz metal	...	...	...	...	Not suitable	93
Naval brass	...	...	...	...	Not suitable	93
Nickel silver	(a)	18	...	...	Good	93
Phosphor bronze	5% Sn. (a)	...	...	...	Good	93
Phosphor bronze	8% Sn. (a)	...	...	...	Good	93
Phosphor copper	(a)	...	...	...	Good	93
Red brass	(a)	...	...	...	Good	93
Silicon bronze	Low. (a)	...	...	...	Good	93
Silicon bronze	High. (a)	...	...	...	Good	93
Titanium						
Titanium	Grade 7	Saturated	Boiling	...	nil	33
Titanium	...	5-20	100 (212)	...	<0.010 (<0.4)	90
Titanium	...	5-40	Boiling	...	0.005 (0.2)	90
Heat- and corrosion-resistant alloys						
Nickel 200	Plant test in evaporator concentrating mixture plus $CaCl_2$ under vacuum	To 50	Boiling	...	0.075 (3)	44

(Continued)

Corrosion Behavior of Various Metals and Alloys in Magnesium Chloride (Continued)

Material	Condition, other factors, comments	Concentration, %	Temperature, °C (°F)	Duration	Corrosion rate, mm/yr (mils/yr) or other	Ref
Zirconium						
Zr702	...	5-40	Room to 100 (room to 212)	...	<0.05 (<2)	15
Zr702	...	47	Boiling	...	nil	15
Zr705	...	47	Boiling	...	nil	15
Lead, tin, and zinc						
Lead	Corrosion rate too high to merit any consideration of Pb	10-100	24 (75)	...	>1270 μm/yr (>50)	95
Noble metals						
Platinum	...	All	Boiling	...	<0.05 (<2)	5
Silver	...	All	120 (250)	...	<0.05 (<2)	9
Silver	Melt	...	710 (1310)	...	Attacked	9
Others						
Magnesium	...	All	Room	...	Unsuitable	119
Niobium	...	47	Boiling	...	0.025 (1.0)	2

(a) May be considered in place of a copper metal when some property, other than corrosion resistance, governs its use.

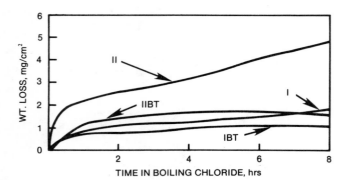

TiN and TiC coatings. Average cumulative weight loss of TiN and TiC coatings immersed in boiling magnesium chloride solution. I, TiN coatings; II, TiC coatings; BT, with bond coat and top sealant; no symbols, no bond coat, and no top sealant.

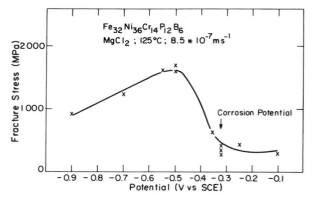

Metallic Glass. Tensile properties of a glassy $Fe_{32}Ni_{36}Cr_{14}P_{12}B_6$ alloy in constant extension rate tensile tests at a rate of 8.5×10^{-7} ms^{-1} in boiling magnesium chloride at 125 °C as a function of electrochemical potential. Source: R.F. Sandenbergh and R.M. Latanision, "The Stress Corrosion Cracking of a Glassy $Fe_{32}Ni_{36}Cr_{14}P_{12}B_6$ Alloy," *Corrosion*, Vol 41, July 1985, 371.

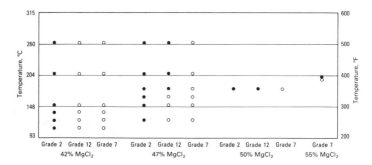

Titanium. Temperature guidelines for avoiding localized attack of grades 2, 7, and 12 titanium in concentrated magnesium chloride solutions in the absence of crevices. Closed circles denote susceptibility to attack. Source: R.W. Schutz and J.S. Grauman, "Selection of Titanium Alloys for Concentrated Seawater, NaCl and $MgCl_2$ Brines," in *Titanium 1986—Titanium Products and Applications*, proceedings of the Technical Program from the 1986 International Conference, San Francisco, Titanium Development Association, 1986.

Magnesium Hydroxide

Magnesium hydroxide, Mg(OH)$_2$, also known as magnesium hydrate and brucite, is a white powder that is very slightly soluble in water. It decomposes at 350 °C (662 °F). It is used in the extraction of magnesium metal and as a reagent in the sulfite wood pulp process. Magnesium hydroxide is formed by the reaction of sodium hydroxide and a soluble magnesium salt solution. Brucite, a mineral composed of magnesium hydroxide with occasional traces of iron and manganese, is a white to grayish translucent secondary mineral found with serpentine and metamorphic dolomites.

Material Summaries

The following material summaries were compiled from a survey of the available literature. Inclusion of a material description under a given environment does not imply that it is the most appropriate material for corrosion service in that environment. Likewise, exclusion of a given material does not imply that it is not suitable for corrosion service applications in that environment.

Aluminum. Aluminum alloys are generally considered poor choices for caustic service. In laboratory tests, the corrosion rate of aluminum alloy 1100 increased with the increasing pH of the magnesium hydroxide solution. In the construction industry, the contact of magnesium hydroxide-containing building materials with bare aluminum initially causes mild surface corrosion, which leaves a protective film that resists further attack.

Titanium. Titanium alloys generally resist all temperatures and concentrations of magnesium hydroxide. Hydrogen embrittlement may occur in alpha alloys when the temperature exceeds 80 °C (175 °F) and the pH is over 12. The addition of dissolved oxidizing species such as chlorate, hypochlorate, or nitrate compounds may extend resistance to higher temperatures.

Corrosion Behavior of Various Metals and Alloys in Magnesium Hydroxide

Material	Condition, other factors, comments	Concentration, %	Temperature, °C (°F)	Duration	Corrosion rate, mm/yr (mils/yr) or other	Ref
Coppers						
70-30 cupronickel	...	...	...	...	Suitable	93
90-10 cupronickel	...	...	...	...	Suitable	93
Admiralty brass	...	...	...	...	Suitable	93
Aluminum bronze	...	...	...	...	Suitable	93
Ampco 8, aluminum bronze	Generally suitable	...	...	...	<0.05 (<2)	96
Architectural bronze	...	...	...	...	Suitable	93
Brass	...	...	...	...	Suitable	93
Cartridge brass	...	...	...	...	Suitable	93
Commercial bronze	...	...	...	...	Suitable	93
Electrolytic copper	...	...	...	...	Suitable	93
Free-cutting brass	...	...	...	...	Suitable	93
Muntz metal	...	...	...	...	Suitable	93
Naval brass	...	...	...	...	Suitable	93
Nickel silver	...	18	...	...	Suitable	93
Phosphor bronze	5% Sn	...	...	...	Suitable	93
Phosphor bronze	8% Sn	...	...	...	Suitable	93
Phosphor copper	...	...	...	...	Suitable	93
Red brass	...	...	...	...	Suitable	93
Silicon bronze	Low	...	...	...	Suitable	93
Silicon bronze	High	...	...	...	Suitable	93

Maleic Acid

Maleic acid, HOOCCH:CHCOOH, also known as maleinic acid and toxilic acid, is a colorless crystalline dibasic acid with a melting point of 130 °C (266 °F). It is soluble in water and alcohol. Maleic acid is used in manufacturing synthetic resins, in textile processing, and in preserving oils and fats.

Material Summaries

The following material summaries were compiled from a survey of the available literature. Inclusion of a material description under a given environment does not imply that it is the most appropriate material for corrosion service in that environment. Likewise, exclusion of a given material does not imply that it is not suitable for corrosion service applications in that environment.

Aluminum. Under laboratory conditions of ambient temperature and 100% relative humidity, aluminum alloys 3003 and 5154 were resistant to solid maleic acid. In other laboratory tests, aluminum alloy 1100 endured mild attack (1.25 mm/yr, or 5 mils/yr) by 30% aqueous maleic acid solutions at 52 °C (126 °F) and corrosion at 100 °C (212 °F).

Corrosion Behavior of Various Metals and Alloys in Maleic Acid

Material	Condition, other factors, comments	Concentration, %	Temperature, °C (°F)	Duration	Corrosion rate, mm/yr (mils/yr) or other	Ref
Tin	Nonaerated solutions	...	20 (68)	...	Resistant	94
Tin	...	...	60 (140)	...	Unsuitable	94
Tin	...	...	100 (212)	...	Unsuitable	94
Tin	...	...	35 (95)	...	0.002 (0.08)	90
Titanium	...	18-20				

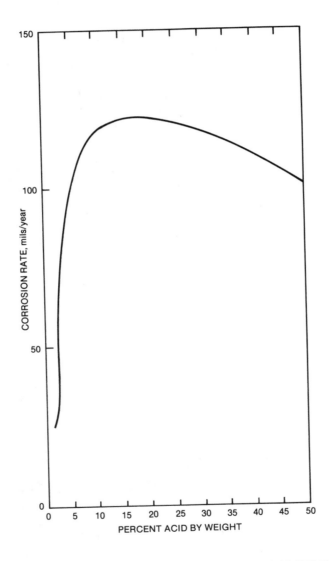

Aluminum. Effect of maleic acid on alloy 1100 at 100 °C (212 °F). Source: *Guidelines for the Use of Aluminum with Food and Chemicals: Compatibility Data on Aluminum in the Food and Chemical Process Industries*, 5th ed., The Aluminum Association, Washington, DC, 1984, 25.

Malic Acid

Malic acid, HOOCCH(OH)·CH2COOH, also known as hydroxysuccinic acid, is a colorless solid. It is soluble in water and alcohol. Malic acid exists in two optically active forms and a racemic mixture. It is used in medicine and found in apples and other fruits.

Material Summaries

The following material summaries were compiled from a survey of the available literature. Inclusion of a material description under a given environment does not imply that it is the most appropriate material for corrosion service in that environment. Likewise, exclusion of a given material does not imply that it is not suitable for corrosion service applications in that environment.

Aluminum. Laboratory tests have shown that aqueous solutions (up to 55%) of malic acid cause mild attack, 0.50 mm/yr (2 mils/yr), of aluminum alloy 1100 at ambient temperature, but cause corrosion at 100 °C (212 °F).

Corrosion Behavior of Various Metals and Alloys in Malic Acid

Material	Condition, other factors, comments	Concentration, %	Temperature, °C (°F)	Duration	Corrosion rate, mm/yr (mils/yr) or other	Ref
Stainless steels						
Type 304 stainless steel	Food processing; field or plant test; no aeration; rapid agitation. Concentrated apple juice, plus 72% soluble solids (mostly sugars), pH 3.3-3.45 (Majonnier vacuum pan)	2.1-2.7	57 (135)	42 d	<0.0001 in./yr	89
Type 304 stainless steel	Food processing; field or plant test; no aeration; no agitation. Apple sauce, plus 21% soluble solids (mostly sugars), trace sodium chloride, pH 3.4-3.7, temperature initially 102 °C (216 °F)	0.33-0.55	Room	57 d	<0.0001 in./yr	89
Type 304 stainless steel	Food processing; field or plant test; strong aeration; slight to moderate agitation. Fresh apple juice, plus 12-14% soluble solids (mostly sugars), pH 3.55-3.65 (tank bottom)	0.35-0.45	10-29 (50-85)	42 d	<0.0001 in./yr	89
Type 304 stainless steel	Food processing; field or plant test; strong aeration; slight to moderate agitation. Hard cider, plus 6.5-7.5% alcohol, 0.2-0.4% acetic acid, pH 3.55-3.65	0.35-0.45	18 (65)	88 d	<0.0001 in./yr	89
Type 316 stainless steel	Food processing; field or plant test; no aeration; rapid agitation. Concentrated apple juice, plus 72% soluble solids (mostly sugars), pH 3.3-3.45 (Majonnier vacuum pan)	2.1-2.7	57 (135)	42 d	<0.0001 in./yr	89
Type 316 stainless steel	Food processing; field or plant test; no aeration; no agitation. Apple sauce, plus 21% soluble solids (mostly sugars), trace sodium chloride, pH 3.4-3.7, temperature initially 102 °C (216 °F)	0.33-0.55	Room	57 d	<0.0001 in./yr	89
Type 316 stainless steel	Food processing; field or plant test; strong aeration; slight to moderate agitation. Fresh apple juice, plus 12-14% soluble solids (mostly sugars), pH 3.55-3.65 (tank bottom)	0.35-0.45	10-29 (50-85)	42 d	<0.0001 in./yr	89
Type 316 stainless steel	Food processing; field or plant test; strong aeration; slight to moderate agitation. Hard cider, plus 6.5-7.5% alcohol, 0.2-0.4% acetic acid, pH 3.55-3.65	0.35-0.45	18 (65)	88 d	<0.0001 in./yr	89
Type 410 stainless steel	...	...	Room	...	Unattacked	121
Aluminum						
Aluminum-manganese alloys	...	...	...	...	Satisfactory	92

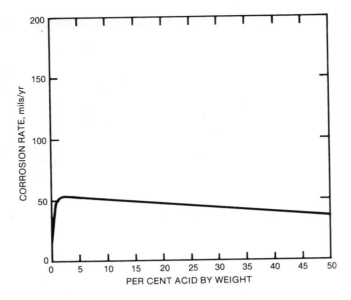

Aluminum. Effect of malic acid on alloy 1100 at 100 °C (212 °F). Source: *Guidelines for the Use of Aluminum with Food and Chemicals: Compatibility Data on Aluminum in the Food and Chemical Process Industries*, 5th ed., The Aluminum Association, Washington, DC, 1984, 33.

Methyl Alcohol

Methyl alcohol, CH_3OH, also known as methanol or wood alcohol, is a colorless, toxic, flammable liquid with a boiling point of 64.6 °C (147 °F). The principal toxic effect is on the nervous system, particularly the retinae. Methyl alcohol is miscible in all proportions with water, ethyl alcohol, and ether. It burns with a light blue flame producing water and carbon dioxide. This vapor forms an explosive mixture (6.0 to 36.5% by volume) with air. Methyl alcohol is an important inexpensive raw material that is synthetically produced for the organic chemical industry. Nearly half of the methyl alcohol manufactured is used in the production of formaldehyde. Other uses of methyl alcohol are as an antifreeze and fuel for automobiles and as an intermediate in the production of synthetic protein.

Material Summaries

The following material summaries were compiled from a survey of the available literature. Inclusion of a material description under a given environment does not imply that it is the most appropriate material for corrosion service in that environment. Likewise, exclusion of a given material does not imply that it is not suitable for corrosion service applications in that environment.

Aluminum. Aluminum alloy 1100 resists commercial methyl alcohol at all temperatures. In the same laboratory tests, the corrosion of aqueous solutions varied with their concentrations. Anhydrous methyl alcohol tested at the boiling point was corrosive. Aluminum alloy equipment has been used to process and handle methyl alcohol.

Titanium. Methyl alcohol causes stress-corrosion cracking in titanium and titanium alloys.

Zirconium. Mixtures of methyl alcohol and hydrochloric acid and mixtures of methyl alcohol and iodine cause stress-corrosion cracking of zirconium alloys.

Additional Reading

K. Otto, L. Bartosiewicz, and R.O. Carter, III, Steel Corrosion by Methanol Combustion Products, *Corros. Sci.*, 25(2), 117-131, 1985. MetAbs No. 85-351707. **Abstract:** Rust on 1020 steel, caused by methanol combustion products, was studied with a pulse flame combustor.

K. Ebtehaj, D. Hardie, and R.N. Parkins, The Stress Corrosion and Pre-Exposure Embrittlement of Titanium in Methanolic Solutions of Hydrochloric Acid, *Corros. Sci.*, 25(6), 415-429, 1985. MetAbs No. 85-352383. **Abstract:** When commercial purity titanium is strained in tension, either while immersed in a methanol-hydrochloric acid mixture or in air after prior exposure to the mixture, it suffers a loss in ductility that varies with strain rate.

J. Banas, K.-G. Schutze, and E. Heitz, Corrosion Studies on Zinc in a Methanol/Water/Lithium Chloride/Oxygen System, *J. Electrochem. Soc.*, 133(2), 253-259, 1986. MetAbs No. 86-350878. **Abstract:** The corrosion of Zn (99.999% pure) displays different effects in methanolic and aqueous chloride solutions. An evaluation of the polarization curves gives different kinetic parameters. The marked effect of chloride ions in methanol solutions is noticeable even in the ppm region.

D.D.N. Singh and M.K. Banerjee, Corrosion Behavior of Nickel in Methanol, *Corrosion, 42*(3), 156-161, 1986. MetAbs No. 86-351027. **Abstract:** Corrosion behavior of pure Ni in methanol containing different concentrations of water, chloride, and hydrogen ions has been studied using the potentiodynamic technique.

H. Jahnke and M. Schonborn, Electrochemical Corrosion Measurements in Motor Fuels Based on Methanol and Ethanol, *Werkst. Korros., 36*(12), 561-566, 1985. MetAbs No. 86-351152. **Abstract:** Electrochemical corrosion measurements were carried out on four steels, the influence of each constituent being investigated.

J.-P. Crousier, J. Crousier, M. Dubusc, and P.-L. Bonora, Behavior of Nickel in Methanol-Water Sulfuric Acid Solution, *Mater. Chem. Phys., 14*(6), 501-512, 1986. MetAbs No. 86-352420. **Abstract:** The electrochemical behavior of Ni in water-methanol-acid solutions has been investigated; the concentration of the three constituents of the solution has been varied extensively.

K. Otto, J.E. Anderson, L. Bartosiewicz, R.O. Carter, III, and C.A. Gierczak, Corrosion Produced by Burning Layers of Methanol and Ethanol, *Corros. Sci., 26*(6), 455-466, 1986. MetAbs No. 86-352708. **Abstract:** In these experiments, small amounts of alcohol were burnt on 1020 steel coupons. Corrosion products were analyzed by FT-IR spectroscopy and by microscopy. Rates of rust formation were measured gravimetrically for various alcohol solutions, then compared with rates of deposit formation beneath fires of iso-octane. In other experiments, acidity changes in liquid methanol and ethanol were measured as larger volumes of these fuels were burnt in beakers.

J. Banas, Passivity of Iron and Nickel in a CH_3OH-H_2O-H_2SO_4 System, *Electrochim. Acta, 32*(6), 871-875, 1987. MetAbs No. 87-352339. **Abstract:** The passivity of Fe and Ni has been investigated in methanolic solutions of sulfuric acid with various water contents.

U. Lechner-Knoblauch and E. Heitz, Corrosion of Zinc, Copper, and Iron in Contaminated Non-Aqueous Alcohols, *Electrochim. Acta, 32*(6), 901-907, 1987. MetAbs No. 87-352342. **Abstract:** The corrosion of Zn, Fe, and Cu in methanol and ethanol, both in the pure liquids and in alcohol solutions of HCOOH, CH_3COOH, HCOONa, and CH_3COONa, was examined.

F. Bellucci, P.-L. Bonora, G. Capobianco, J. Crousier, and J.-P. Crousier, A Contribution to the Study of the Electrochemical Behavior of Nickel in a Methanol-Water-Sulfuric Acid System, *Electrochim. Acta, 32*(6), 939-946, 1987. MetAbs No. 87-352347. **Abstract:** The influence of the experimental procedure and conditions on the electrochemical behavior of Ni was investigated. Experiments were performed on Ni sheet in $MeOH + 0.1N H_2SO_4$ with a water content of 1, 3 and 10%, respectively, as a function of metal purity grade, sample surface preparation, and fluid-dynamic conditions.

P.L. De Anna, The Effects of Water and Chloride Ions on the Electrochemical Behavior of Iron and 304L Stainless Steel in Alcohols, *Corros. Sci., 25*(1), 43-53, 1985. MetAbs No. 85-350967. **Abstract:** The electrochemical behavior of pure iron and 304L stainless steel in organic media has been characterized by determination of current-potential potentiodynamic curves. The media studied were methyl, ethyl, isopropyl, n-butyl, and 2-chloroethyl alcohols. The influence of water and chloride ion concentration on the cathodic and anodic electrochemical reactions has been investigated.

Corrosion Behavior of Various Metals and Alloys in Methyl Alcohol

Material	Condition, other factors, comments	Concentration, %	Temperature, °C (°F)	Duration	Corrosion rate, mm/yr (mils/yr) or other	Ref
Stainless steels						
AM-363 stainless steel	...	...	Room	...	Unattacked	120
Type 304 stainless steel	...	...	21 (70)	...	Good	121
Type 304 stainless steel	Rayon processing; field or pilot plant test; no aeration; rapid agitation. Plus 35% acetone, 8% 2,2-dimethoxy propane, 3% methyl acetate, 2% ethanol, 1% methylethyl ketone, 1% water	50	70 (158)	473 d	<0.0001 in./yr	89
Type 304 stainless steel	Rayon processing; field or pilot plant test; no aeration; rapid agitation. Plus 35% acetone, 8% 2,2-dimethoxy propane, 3% methyl acetate, 2% ethanol, 1% methylethyl ketone, 1% water	50	70 (158)	473 d	nil	89
Type 304 stainless steel	Paper (distillation) processing; field or pilot plant test; slight to moderate aeration; rapid agitation. Plus ammonia, hydrogen sulfide, 1-10 g/L various mercaptans, water and air (vapors). Crevice attack (tendency to concentration-cell corrosion)	15-95	82 (180)	762 d	<0.0001 in./yr	89
Type 304 stainless steel	Chemical processing. Plus 23% acetone, 15% methyl acetate, 2% water, 0.03% acetic acid, 16 psig pressure	60	74 (165)	355 d	<0.0001 in./yr	89
Type 316 stainless steel	...	...	21 (70)	...	Very good	121
Type 316 stainless steel	Paper (distillation) processing; field or pilot plant test; slight to moderate aeration; rapid agitation. Plus ammonia, hydrogen sulfide, 1-10 g/L various mercaptans, water and air (vapors)	15-95	82 (180)	762 d	<0.0001 in./yr	89
Type 316 stainless steel	Rayon processing; field or pilot plant test; no aeration; rapid agitation. Plus 35% acetone, 8% 2,2-dimethoxy propane, 3% methyl acetate, 2% ethanol, 1% methylethyl ketone, 1% water	50	70 (158)	473 d	<0.0001 in./yr	89

(Continued)

Corrosion Behavior of Various Metals and Alloys in Methyl Alcohol (Continued)

Material	Condition, other factors, comments	Concentration, %	Temperature, °C (°F)	Duration	Corrosion rate, mm/yr (mils/yr) or other	Ref
Type 316 stainless steel	Chemical processing. Plus 23% acetone, 15% methyl acetate, 2% water, 0.03% acetic acid, 16 psig pressure	60	74 (165)	355 d	nil	89
Type 317 stainless steel	Chemical processing. Plus 23% acetone, 15% methyl acetate, 2% water, 0.03% acetic acid, 16 psig pressure	60	74 (165)	355 d	nil	89
Type 410 stainless steel	...	...	21 (70)	...	Good	121
Type 410 stainless steel	...	...	Room	...	Unattacked	121
Type 430 stainless steel	...	...	21 (70)	...	Good	121
Aluminum						
Aluminum (>99.5%)	Solution	...	...	...	Satisfactory	92
Coppers						
70-30 cupronickel	...	...	...	...	Suitable	93
90-10 cupronickel	...	...	...	...	Suitable	93
Admiralty brass	...	...	...	...	Suitable	93
Aluminum bronze	...	...	...	...	Suitable	93
Architectural bronze	...	...	...	...	Suitable	93
Brass	...	...	...	...	Suitable	93
Cartridge brass	...	...	...	...	Suitable	93
Commercial bronze	...	...	...	...	Suitable	93
Electrolytic copper	...	...	...	...	Suitable	93
Free-cutting brass	...	...	...	...	Suitable	93
Muntz metal	...	...	...	...	Suitable	93
Naval brass	...	...	...	...	Suitable	93
Nickel silver	...	18	...	...	Suitable	93
Phosphor bronze	Low	...	...	...	Suitable	93
Phosphor bronze	High	...	...	...	Suitable	93
Phosphor copper	...	...	...	...	Suitable	93
Red brass	...	...	...	...	Suitable	93
Silicon bronze	Low	...	...	...	Suitable	93
Silicon bronze	High	...	...	...	Suitable	93
Titanium						
Ti-3Al-2.5V	ASTM Grade 9	100	Boiling	...	nil	91
Titanium	Grade 9	99	Boiling	...	nil	33
Titanium	...	100	Boiling	...	nil	91
Titanium	...	91	35 (95)	...	nil	90
Titanium	...	95	100 (212)	...	<0.01 (<0.4)	90
Heat- and corrosion-resistant alloys						
Inconel 601	...	...	80 (176)	7 d	nil	64
Incoloy 800	Solutions were prepared with reagent-grade chemicals. Test specimens were cold-rolled, annealed sheet, 2.84 mm (0.112 in.) thick. No pitting occurred	Absolute	80 (176)	7 d	nil	44
Noble metals						
Gold	...	Pure	Boiling	...	<0.05 (<2)	7
Platinum	...	Pure	Boiling	...	<0.05 (<2)	6
Silver	...	Pure	Boiling	...	<0.05 (<2)	10
Others						
Magnesium	...	100	Room	...	Unsuitable	119

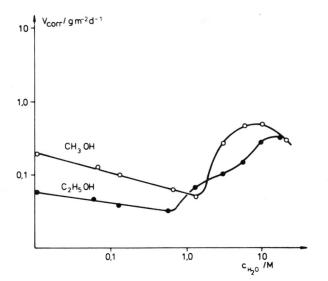

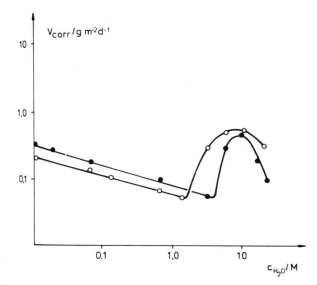

Zinc. Corrosion rates for zinc in CH_3OH/H_2O/50 ppm Cl^- and C_2H_5OH/H_2O/50 ppm Cl^-; duration of experiment 48 h, gassed with oxygen. Source: J. Banas, K.G. Schultze, *et al.*, "Corrosion Studies on Zinc in a Methanol/Water/Lithium Chloride/Oxygen System," *Journal of the Electrochemical Society*, Vol 133, Feb, 1986, 237.

Zinc. Corrosion rates for zinc in methyl alcohol solutions of differing water content, 50 ppm LiCl. Closed circle: gassed with nitrogen. Open circle: gassed with oxygen. Source: J. Banas, K.G. Schultze, *et al.*, "Corrosion Studies on Zinc in a Methanol/Water/Lithium Chloride/Oxygen System," *Journal of the Electrochemical Society*, Vol 133, Feb, 1986, 237.

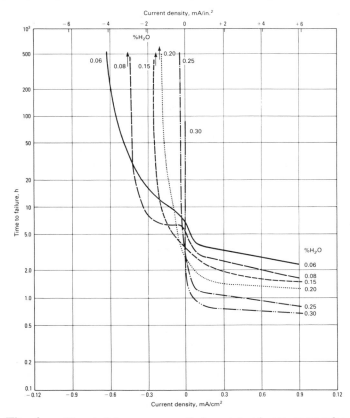

Titanium. Time to failure versus applied current and water content for cold-rolled and annealed Ti-6Al-4V stressed to 75% of yield strength in a methyl alcohol/water mixture. For 0.08, 0.15, and 0.20% water, there was no failure in time shown. Source: *Metals Handbook*, 9th ed., Vol 13, Corrosion, ASM International, Metals Park, OH, 1987, 691.

Nickel Chloride

Nickel chloride, $NiCl_2$, is a yellow deliquescent solid with a boiling point of 973 °C (1690 °F). Nickel chloride is soluble in water and alcohol. Nickel chloride (hydrated), $NiCl_2 \cdot 6H_2O$, is a gray deliquescent solid that is also soluble in water and alcohol. It is used in nickel plating.

Material Summaries

The following material summaries were compiled from a survey of the available literature. Inclusion of a material description under a given environment does not imply that it is the most appropriate material for corrosion service in that environment. Likewise, exclusion of a given material does not imply that it is not suitable for corrosion service applications in that environment.

Titanium. Halide salts of oxidizing cationic species enhance the passivity of titanium alloys such that negligible corrosion rates can be expected. Examples include nickel chloride and its bromide counterparts.

Aluminum. In laboratory tests conducted under conditions of 100% relative humidity at ambient and 54 °C (130 °F) temperatures, solid nickel chloride was very corrosive to alloys 3003, 5154, and 6061 at both temperatures.

Corrosion Behavior of Various Metals and Alloys in Nickel Chloride

Material	Condition, other factors, comments	Concentration, %	Temperature, °C (°F)	Duration	Corrosion rate, mm/yr (mils/yr) or other	Ref
Stainless steels						
Type 304 stainless steel	Metal plating; field or plant test; no aeration; no agitation; low-carbon grade (0.03% C max). Nickel chloride solution being evaporated. Slight pitting: maximum depth of pits from incipient to 0.005 in.	...	93 (200)	26 d	0.0015 in./yr	89
Type 316 stainless steel	Metal plating; field or plant test; no aeration; no agitation; low-carbon grade (0.03% C max). Nickel chloride solution being evaporated. Slight pitting: maximum depth of pits from incipient to 0.005 in.; crevice attack (tendency to concentration-cell corrosion)	...	93 (200)	26 d	0.0013 in./yr	89
Aluminum						
Ampco 8, aluminum bronze	Generally suitable. Conditions such as aeration or temperature could restrict use	...	...	...	<0.5 (<20)	96
Titanium						
Titanium	...	5	100 (212)	...	0.004 (0.16)	90
Titanium	...	20	100 (212)	...	0.003 (0.12)	90
Zirconium						
Zr702	...	5, 20	35-100 (95-212)	...	<0.025 (<1)	15
Zr702	...	5-20	100 (212)	...	<0.025 (<1)	15
Zr702	...	30	Boiling	...	nil	15
Zr705	...	30	Boiling	...	nil	15

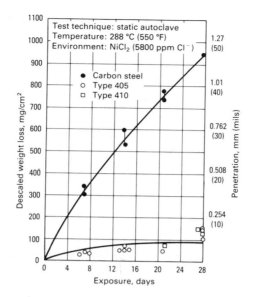

Steel. Corrosion of carbon steel and 12% Cr stainless steels in nickel chloride solutions. Source: *Metals Handbook*, 9th ed., Vol 13, Corrosion, ASM International, Metals Park, OH, 1987, 941.

Nitric Acid

Nitric acid, HNO_3, is a strong, fire-hazardous oxidant. It is a colorless or yellowish liquid that is miscible with water and boils at 86 °C (187 °F). Nitric acid, also known as *aqua fortis*, is used for chemical synthesis, explosives, and fertilizer manufacture, and in metallurgy, etching, engraving, and ore flotation.

Nitric acid is typically produced by the air oxidation of NH_3. This catalyzed reaction takes place at very high temperatures. The gaseous oxidation product is condensed to an aqueous liquid of about 65% concentration. During the high-temperature oxidation, corrosion of the plant materials is of secondary concern. The elevated operating temperatures dictate that the high-temperature properties of the materials are the primary design consideration. Corrosion considerations prevail during and after condensation and at lower temperatures.

The concentration of nitric acid up to 99% requires secondary processing to remove excess water. This involves mixing 65% nitric acid with another substance having a greater affinity for water (such as H_2SO_4), then separating the mixed acids by distillation and condensation processes.

Commercially produced nitric acid is available in concentrations from 52 to 99%. Nitric acid over 86% is described as fuming. Nitric acid up to 95% is stored and shipped in type 304 stainless steel. Concentrated acid above 95% is handled in Aluminum Association (AA) aluminum alloys 1100 or 3003, because although the corrosion rate of type 304 stainless steel increases rapidly above 95% concentration, that of aluminum 3003 remains essentially constant to 100%. A new stainless steel containing 4% Si—alloy A-610—exhibits excellent resistance to concentrated nitric acid; unfortunately, this advantage does not extend to lower concentrations.

Nitric acid is a strong oxidizing agent and attacks most metals, such as iron, by oxidizing the metal to the oxide. A secondary effect of oxidation is the generation of hydrogen at the metal/acid interface, which can cause hydrogen embrittlement of some materials, for example, high-strength steels. Metals and alloys that are able to form adherent oxide films, such as austenitic stainless steels and aluminum alloys, are protected by their oxide films from corrosion by nitric acid.

Material Summaries

The following material summaries were compiled from a survey of the available literature. Inclusion of a material description under a given environment does not imply that it is the most appropriate material for corrosion service in that environment. Likewise, exclusion of a given material does not imply that it is not suitable for corrosion service applications in that environment.

Aluminum. In laboratory tests, the action of nitric acid on aluminum alloys varies with concentration and with temperature and is increased by agitation or by the presence of nitrogen oxide. Aluminum shows an advantage over type 304 stainless steel at acid concentrations exceeding 95%; however, if acid concentration falls below 80%, or if the temperature rises above 40 °C (100 °F), much higher corrosion rates can be expected. The preferred aluminum alloys for nitric acid service are alloys 1100 and 3003. If higher strength is required, alloys 5052 or 5454 can be used. At room temperature, the rate at which nitric acid attacks alloy 1100 exhibits a maximum at an acid concentration of 20%. At concentrations exceeding 82%, the rate of attack is between 0 and 5 mils/yr.

Aluminum alloys are widely used in storage and shipping of fuming nitric acid. When inhibited with hydrofluoric acid, red fuming nitric acid is compatible with all aluminum alloys at temperatures up to at least 71 °C

(160 °F). Because solutions of the lower oxides of nitrogen, and the gases themselves, have only mild corrosive effects on aluminum alloys, these alloys have been used for catalytic oxidation of ammonia in production of nitric acid. The aluminum alloy equipment used in this process includes piping for supplying the ammonia and oxygen to the oxidizing reactor, refrigeration tanks for storage of raw materials, whirlwind gas mixers, autoclave parts, intermediate reservoirs, refining columns, heat exchangers for cooling of the acid prior to storage, and tanks and drums for storage and transportation of concentrated acid.

Cast Iron. All types of cast iron, except high-nickel austenitic iron, find some applications in nitric acid. The use of unalloyed cast iron in nitric acid is limited to low-temperature low-velocity concentrated acid service. Even in this service, caution must be exercised to avoid dilution of acid because the unalloyed and low-alloyed cast irons both corrode very rapidly in dilute or intermediate concentrations at any temperature. High-nickel austenitic cast irons exhibit essentially the same resistance as unalloyed cast iron to nitric acid and cannot be economically justified for this service.

High-chromium cast irons with chromium contents over 20% give excellent resistance to nitric acid, particularly in dilute concentrations. High-temperature boiling solutions attack these grades of cast iron. High-silicon cast irons also offer excellent resistance to nitric acid. Resistance is exhibited over essentially all concentration and temperature ranges with the exception of dilute, hot acids. High-silicon cast iron equipment has been used for many years in the manufacture and handling of nitric acid mixed with other chemicals, such as sulfuric acid, sulfates, and nitrates. Contamination of the nitric acid with HF, such as might be experienced in pickling solutions, may accelerate attack of the high-silicon iron to unacceptable levels.

Stainless steels have broad applicability in nitric acid service, primarily because of their chromium contents. Most AISI 300-series stainless steels exhibit good or excellent resistance in the annealed condition in concentrations from 0 to 65% up to the boiling point. More severe environments at elevated temperatures require alloys with higher chromium. In nitric acid cooler-condensers, such stainless alloys as 7-Mo PLUS (UNS S32950) and 2RE10 (UNS S31008), are candidates for service. Nitric acid is one of the few environments in which additions of molybdenum do not improve corrosion resistance. Thus, type 316L is inferior to type 304L in terms of resistance to nitric acid.

Corrosion of austenitic stainless steels by nitric acid is intensified by increases in temperature or acid concentration, or both. Nevertheless, there is a large useful range extending from 0 to 99% concentration and up to the boiling point below 50% concentration in which the predicted corrosion rate is less than 0.13 mm/yr (5 mils/yr).

Experience has shown that, although all austenitic stainless steels behave in this fashion, types 304 and 304L, when welded, are clearly superior to the others. Therefore, they are the most popular grades for nitric acid service.

The cast equivalents of wrought stainless steels are also generally resistant to nitric acid, but the normally higher carbon contents of cast alloys and the propensity of castings to have high-carbon surfaces often lead to selective intergranular corrosion in strong nitric acid.

Although austenitic stainless steels are commonly used in nitric acid, they are not without problems. One of the most prevalent is selective corrosion associated with chromium carbides precipitated around grain boundaries in the weld heat-affected zone (sensitization). Because few pieces of industrial equipment are made without welding, this is a serious shortcoming. The most popular method of avoiding this problem is to use stainless steels of low or extra-low carbon content when welding is planned.

Sensitization of stainless steel refers to the precipitation of chromium carbides and the resultant depletion of the matrix of chromium as a result of heating from 480 to 760 °C (900 to 1400 °F). The effect of such heating on corrosion rate in 65% nitric acid is detrimental in all cases. Sigma phase, which may also form during prolonged heating of austenitic stainless steels, is preferentially and rapidly attacked by 65% nitric acid. Solution heat treating the alloy will restore corrosion resistance.

The corrosion of austenitic stainless steels in nitric acid is accompanied by the formation of hexavalent chromium (Cr^{6+}), a complex chromium compound that increases the corrosivity of nitric acid solutions. The effect of Cr^{6+} buildup is clearly detrimental. In general, the presence of chlorides and fluorides in nitric acid solutions tends to increase the corrosion rate of stainless steels.

Selective corrosion along grain boundaries is common in austenitic stainless steels exposed to nitric acid, especially strong acid. There is some evidence to support the view that this cannot be entirely prevented; however, maintaining low carbon and avoiding sensitization will help.

For very concentrated acid (>95%), the addition of silicon to iron and to austenitic stainless steels is beneficial. Cast iron with 14% Si is very resistant to acid over 50% concentration. Recently, two new stainless alloys of 4 to 6% Si—alloys A-610 and A-611—have been produced. These new alloys have remarkable resistance to nitric acid to about 95%. At lower concentrations, they offer no advantage over type 304.

Corrosion studies of sintered austenitic stainless steels have shown that corrosion resistance improves significantly with increasing density in acidic environments such as dilute sulfuric, hydrochloric, and nitric acid.

Cemented Carbides. At 50 °C (120 °F), the straight WC-Co compositions undergo rapid attack in dilute nitric acid, but little attack in concentrated acid. Cemented TiC—especially the TiC-6.5Ni-5Mo composition—has poor resistance to nitric acid. Several of the binderless compositions and the TaC-base cemented carbide exhibit quite acceptable corrosion resistance in warm nitric acid.

Copper. Aluminum bronzes are not suitable for use in nitric acid.

Lead. Nitric, acetic, and formic acids in most concentrations corrode lead at rates high enough to preclude its use in these acids. However, although nitric acid rapidly attacks lead when dilute, it has little effect at strengths of 52 to 70%.

Molybdenum. Molybdenum is rapidly attacked by oxidizing agents such as nitric acid.

Nickel alloys are extensively used in the production of nitric acid. Alloy 617 is used for its high-temperature strength and corrosion resistance in the catalyst-support grids in high-pressure plants. In older plants, alloys 600 and 601 are used because of lower pressure. Alloy 800 is used in the heat-exchanger train. Where reboiling conditions exist, alloy 690 has given exceptional performance.

Chromium is an essential alloying element for corrosion resistance in nitric acid environments, because it readily forms a passive film in these environments. Thus, the higher chromium nickel alloys exhibit better resistance in nitric acid. In these types of environments, the highest chromium alloys, G-30 and 690, seem to exhibit the highest corrosion resistance. Molybdenum is generally detrimental to corrosion resistance in nitric acid. For example, alloy C-22 (with 13% Mo) is not as good as alloy G-3 (with 7% Mo). In pure nitric acid, stainless steels find the greatest application. In concentrated (98%) nitric acid, stainless steels containing both chromium and silicon are finding greater use. Because of the oxidizing nature of nitric acid, nitric acid streams are too severe for nickel-molybdenum alloys. The behavior of nickel-silicon alloys in nitric acid appears to depend on their microstructure and composition. Cast Hastelloy D, which consists of two phases (the nickel-silicon solid solution and the eutectic), does not show good resistance to any concentration of nitric acid. The Ni-9.5Si-2.5Cu-3Mo-2.75Ti cast alloy, which consists of a single phase, demonstrated high resistance to boiling concentrated nitric acid above 60% and to fuming (99%) nitric acid up to 80 °C (175 °F). However, the corrosion rates in more dilute acid were very high.

Niobium is completely resistant to nitric acid in all concentrations at temperatures below 100 °C (212 °F). Even in 70% nitric acid at 250 °C (480 °F), it has a corrosion rate of only 0.025 mm/yr (1 mil/yr). In chromium plating solutions, niobium exhibits only a slight weight change, and in the presence of small amounts of fluoride (F⁻) catalyst, its corrosion resistance exceeds that of tantalum.

In one study, niobium did not exhibit stress-corrosion cracking in 90% nitric acid at room temperature using the slow strain rate technique or in liquid bromine using the U-bend testing method. However, with particular types of surface contamination and preparation, niobium, like tantalum, was found to be sensitive to crevice corrosion at anodic potentials below those normally regarded as safe. Niobium is suited for handling hot, concentrated nitric acid. It can be considered for highly oxidizing solutions expected in chemical wastes, scrubber environments, and mining solutions.

Gold. Gold is resistant to nitric acid in concentrations up to 50% at the boiling point. It is attacked by concentrated nitric acid.

Palladium is generally resistant to corrosion by most single acids, but is attacked by nitric acid when air is present. Palladium alloys containing more than 20% Au are resistant to nitric acid. Addition of 2% Pt to palladium makes it resistant to the jewelers' nitric acid drop test used to determine equivalency with gold alloys, and addition of 10% Pt makes it completely resistant to nitric acid. Both iridium and rhodium are quite effective in improving the corrosion and tarnish resistance of palladium. Palladium alloys with 2% Ir or Rh are resistant to the nitric acid drop test.

Platinum. Up to 50% Cu can be added to platinum while still retaining its resistance to nitric acid.

Rhodium. In wrought or cast form, rhodium is unattacked at 100 °C (212 °F) by concentrated nitric acid.

Silver is attacked by nitric acid. Nitric acid that contains traces of nitrous acid attacks silver vigorously.

Tantalum is inert to nitric acid solutions in all concentrations and at all temperatures up to boiling. The presence of Cl⁻ in nitric acid does not reduce the corrosion resistance of the metal to this acid. The corrosion rate of tantalum to nitric acid at sub-boiling temperature is less than 0.4 μm/yr (0.015 mils/yr) for most concentrations and temperatures. In general, the use of tantalum at these temperatures would not be economical, considering the resistance offered by stainless steels. At temperatures near and above the normal boiling point of nitric acid, the superior resistance of tantalum becomes pronounced. Corrosion testing of tantalum for equipment to be used at these temperatures is recommended. Tantalum has been successfully used to handle fuming nitric acid at service conditions up to 5.5 MPa (800 psig) and 315 °C (600 °F) in chemical-processing equipment.

Considerable data have been accumulated on the corrosion resistance of tantalum-titanium alloys. Dilution of tantalum with titanium shows considerable promise for the possibility of providing a lower cost alloy with corrosion resistance almost comparable to that of tantalum in some select environments. In addition to dilution with a lower cost material, the resulting marked reduction in density is particularly advantageous, because corrosion applications generally require materials on a volume rather than a weight basis. Corrosion tests in 10 to 70% nitric acid at the boiling point and at 190 °C (375 °F) in sealed glass tubes were conducted on tantalum-titanium alloys ranging from pure tantalum to Ta-90Ti. All of these materials exhibited excellent behavior, with corrosion rates less than 0.025 mm/yr (1 mil/yr) and no indication of embrittlement.

Hydrogen embrittlement may occur when this alloy system is exposed to reducing corrosive conditions in tests conducted in sealed capsules. The tendency for hydrogen damage is markedly decreased as the tantalum concentration is increased.

Tin. Nitric acid reacts rapidly with tin over a wide range of concentrations, and the reaction is complex.

Titanium. Unalloyed titanium has been extensively used for handling and producing nitric acid in applications in which stainless steels have experienced significant uniform or intergranular attack. Titanium offers excellent resistance over the full concentration range at sub-boiling temperatures. As temperatures exceed 80 °C (175 °F), however, the corrosion resistance becomes highly dependent on nitric acid purity.

In hot, very pure solutions or vapor condensates of nitric acid, significant uniform corrosion rates may occur, particularly as temperatures increase. Mid-range nitric acid concentrations (20 to 70 wt%) are most aggressive when full inhibition to attack is not achieved in pure refreshed solutions. Under these conditions, semiprotective oxide surface films form that do not fully retard continued oxidation of the metal surface.

As the impurity levels increase in hot nitric acid solutions, the resistance of unalloyed titanium improves dramatically. In particular, relatively small amounts of certain dissolved metallic species, including Si^{4+}, Cr^{6+}, Fe^{3+}, Ti^{4+}, or various precious metal ions, can effectively inhibit the high-temperature corrosion of titanium in nitric acid. This inhibitive effect is very potent. Thus, titanium exhibits excellent resistance to recirculating nitric acid process streams, such as stripper reboiler loops in which steady-state levels of dissolved Ti^{4+} inhibitor are achieved. Hold tanks and stripper sumps are also good applications for similar reasons. Another good example of this inhibitive effect is the excellent performance of unalloyed titanium in evaporator reboilers and other components in the high-temperature metal-contaminated process streams used for U_3O_8 recovery.

The significant discrepancies and variations in titanium corrosion rates in hot nitric acid media reported by investigators over the years appear to be the result of these inhibitive metal ion effects. Because titanium corrosion is inhibited by its own corrosion product (Ti^{4+}), the titanium surface area to acid volume ratio, the test duration, and the rate of solution replenishment are critical to the rate obtained. The container material and acid purity (chemistry) will also be influential. Based on this information, it is clear that all design and operating factors must be taken into account when evaluating titanium for high-temperature concentrated nitric acid service.

Limited corrosion testing of alpha-beta and beta titanium alloys in boiling nitric acid indicates that increasing aluminum and beta alloying elements tend to decrease corrosion resistance. Alpha alloys are generally most resistant to hot nitric acid. Other studies have shown that high-purity (low iron, sulfur, and so on) unalloyed titanium does not experience the significant accelerated weldment attack in high-temperature nitric acid exhibited at times by the less pure unalloyed grades and the near-alpha alloys.

Titanium alloys exhibit good resistance to white fuming nitric acid. However, dangerous and violent pyrophoric reactions may occur with titanium alloys exposed to red fuming nitric acid or to nitrogen tetroxide. The critical variables are the nitrogen dioxide (NO_2) and water contents of the acid. Fuming nitric acid containing less than 1.4 to 2.0% water or more than 6% NO_2 may cause this rapid impact-sensitive reaction to occur. Both water and NO are effective inhibitors for this attack, but increasing oxygen and NO_2 are detrimental in this situation.

Zirconium. Zirconium is even more resistant to nitric acid than titanium. In 98% nitric acid at temperatures below the boiling point, and in 70% nitric acid at temperatures up to 250 °C (480 °F), the corrosion rate of zirconium is less than 0.13 mm/yr (<5 mils/yr). Recent autoclave tests showed that the corrosion rates of zirconium were less than 0.025 mm/yr (<1 mil/yr) in 80% nitric acid and 90% nitric acid at 120 to 150 °C (250 and 300 °F). Moreover, the corrosion rates were still under 0.025 mm/yr (<1 mil/yr) when zirconium was tested in boiling 30 to 70% nitric acid with up to 1% $FeCl_3$, 1% NaCl, 1% seawater, 1% Fe^{3+}, or 1.45% stainless steel at 205 °C (400 °F). These results indicated that the presence of heavy-metal ions and Cl^- in nitric acid has little effect on the corrosion resistance of zirconium.

Zirconium is normally susceptible to pitting in acidic oxidizing chloride solutions. However, NO_3^- ions effectively inhibit the pitting of zirconium. The minimum ratio of NO_3^- to Cl^- required to inhibit pitting of zirconium was determined to be 1 or 5. Nevertheless, the presence of appreciable amounts of HCl should be avoided, because zirconium is not resistant to aqua regia.

Polarization curves for zirconium in nitric acid show that a passive-to-active transition similar to that which occurs in H_2SO_4 takes place with increasing acid concentration. However, corrosion potentials are very noble because of the oxidizing nature of nitric acid. Common oxidizing agents, such as oxygen and Fe^{3+} ions, will not affect the corrosion resistance of zirconium. The polarization curves do suggest that, although corrosion rates are low, zirconium may be sensitive to stress in concentrated nitric acid. This is consistent with the observation of stress-corrosion cracking in U-bend specimens in more than 70% nitric acid. The slow strain rate technique can reveal cracking of zirconium in less than 70% nitric acid.

The primary concern in the use of zirconium for nitric acid service is cracking in concentrated nitric acid. Results of C-ring tests indicate that zirconium specimens will have a long life when they are stressed below the yield point.

Other concerns include the accumulation of chlorine gas in the vapor phase and the presence of noncomplexed F^- ions. Chlorine gas can be generated by the oxidation of chlorides by nitric acid. Areas that can trap chlorine gas should be avoided for zirconium equipment when Cl^- is present in nitric acid. Zirconium columns and reboilers are being used at one company to produce 67% nitric acid from 57% nitric acid. Previously, such materials as AISI type 304L stainless steel, titanium, and glass-lined steel were used. Titanium and type 304L stainless steel had relatively short service lives, whereas glass-lined steel presented maintenance problems.

A 27-ton zirconium heat exchanger is being used by one company to produce 65% nitric acid at 205 °C (400 °F). Before the use of zirconium, the company was faced with such problems as frequent replacement costs and downtime. In service since October 1984, the zirconium heat exchanger has already outperformed the stainless steel predecessor.

With proper design, zirconium can be used to handle a highly concentrated nitric acid. For example, an Israeli chemical plant uses zirconium tubes in a U-tube cooler that processes bleached nitric acid at concentrations between 98.5 and 99%. The unit cools the acid from 70 to 75 °C (160 to 170 °F) to 35 to 40 °C (95 to 100 °F). Previously, U-tube coolers were made from aluminum, which failed in 2 to 12 weeks. The zirconium has been in service for about 2 years, operating 24 h per day, 6 days a week.

Hafnium is unaffected by nitric acid in all concentrations. Hafnium alloys with 2.9, 17.3, 42.4, 59.5, and 81.4% Zr were evaluated for their corrosion resistance in various media. All of the alloys exhibited low corrosion rates (<0.0025 mm/yr, or 0.1 mil/yr) in the following boiling solutions: 30% nitric acid with or without 1% NaCl, 50% nitric acid with or without 1% NaCl, and 70% nitric acid with or without 1% NaCl. Transverse-cut U-bend specimens of these alloys were tested in 90% nitric acid at room temperature for 60 days. No cracking was observed.

Additional Reading

A. Zingales, G. Quartarone, and G. Moretti, Sigma Phase Intergranular Corrosion Effects in Austenitic Welds Containing Ferrite, *Corrosion 41*(3), 136-141, 1985. MetAbs No. 85-351100. **Abstract:** It has been suggested that the sigma phase and its preliminary phases are responsible for intergranular corrosion of Mo-containing austenitic stainless steels in such environments as 65 wt.% boiling nitric acid when the material is heat treated or when ferrite is introduced by welding. Data obtained for 316L steel joints welded by the TIG technique, annealed at 1100 °C and sensitized at 600-750 °C for different times, are discussed.

A.J. Sedriks, Corrosion of Nickel Alloys, in *Encyclopedia of Materials Science and Engineering*, Vol 2, Pergamon Press, Oxford, 1986. MetAbs No. 86-351945. **Abstract:** Nickel alloys are important corrosion-resistant materials in aggressive environments and are indicated to replace aluminium alloys and stainless steels as service temperature or environmental corrosivity increases. Ni-Cr alloys, particularly Inconel alloy 600, are studied.

A.M. El-Kot and A.A. Al-Suhybani, Organic and Inorganic Corrosion Inhibitors for Copper in nitric acid Studied by Two Methods, *Br. Corros. J.*, *22*(1), 29-31, 1987. MetAbs No. 87-351701. **Abstract:** The dissolution of copper in nitric acid solution has been studied by the thermometric technique. Free dissolution of copper in nitric acid is assumed to take place according to an autocatalytic mechanism involving the formation of HNO_2.

A.M. Shams El Din, F.M. Al-Kharafi, Z. Al-Fahd, and Y.A. El-Tantawy, Corrosion Behaviour of Nickel in Nitric Acid Solutions, *Corros. Prev. Control*, *32*(5), 92-98, 1985. MetAbs No. 86-351103. **Abstract:** The variation of the open-circuit potential of the Ni rod-type electrode in nitric acid solutions of increasing concentration is studied as a function of time.

A.S. Fouda, Influence of Some Thiophene Derivatives on the Corrosion of Iron in Nitric Acid Solution, *Monatsh. Chem.*, *117*(2), 159-165, 1986. MetAbs No. 86-351202. **Abstract:** Corrosion of Fe2M in nitric acid has been studied by electrochemical polarization and weight loss measurements. The effect of some thiophene derivatives has been investigated.

B.B. Vakil and B.N. Oza, Reaction Rate Studies for Corrosion of Brass in Nitric Acid in Presence of Colloidal Substances, *Trans. SAEST*, *21*(4), 251-254, 1986. MetAbs No. 87-352810. **Abstract:** The use of colloidal substances as corrosion inhibitors for 70/30 brass in nitric acid is investigated by thermometric and weight loss measurements.

B.S. Covino Jr, J.V. Scalera, T.J. Driscoll, and J.P. Carter, Dissolution Behavior of 304 Stainless Steel in HNO_3/HF Mixtures, *Metall. Trans. A*, *17A*(1), 137-149, 1986. MetAbs No. 86-350365. **Abstract:** The dissolution behavior of type 304 stainless steel was studied in typical pickling environments in an effort to reduce the unnecessary loss of Ni and Cr during the pickling process. Dissolution rates were determined for a 90-min exposure to HNO3/HF solutions ranging from 0.8 to 3.5M HNO3 and 0.5 to 2.6M HF at 30, 50, 70, and 90 °C and containing 0 to 0.21M dissolved Fe, Cr, or Ni.

C. Chakrabarty, M.M. Singh, and C.V. Agarwal, Inhibitive Action of Benzoic Acid and Its Derivatives on Dissolution of Aluminum Alloys in Nitric Acid, *Corrosion*, 39(12), 481-483, 1983. MetAbs No. 84-350834. **Abstract:** The inhibitive efficiency of benzoic acid and its hydroxy and nitro derivatives for 1060 and 3003 Al alloys in 20% nitric acid is assessed. Some insight into the possible mechanism of inhibition are provided. Weight loss and polarization experiments were carried out in air thermostat maintained at 35 °C.

C. Chakrabarty, M.M. Singh, and C.V. Agarwal, Preventing Corrosion of Aluminium in Nitric Acid by Tolyl Guanidine Derivatives, *Corros. Prev. Control*, 33(3), 72-76, 1986. MetAbs No. 86-352132. **Abstract:** The inhibitive effects of 1-p-tolylguanidine carbonate and some of its condensation products toward corrosion of Al (1060) alloy in 20% nitric acid at 35 and 45 °C are reported. Experiments were conducted with 50, 150, 250 and 500 ppm of the inhibitors.

C.C. Addison, N. Logan, and B. Mellor, Corrosion of Metals by Nitric Acid-Dinitrogen Tetroxide-Fluoride Mixtures: AISI 321 Stainless Steel, *Corrosion*, 44(1), 7-13, 1988. MetAbs No. 88-350924. **Abstract:** The inhibiting effect of fluoride on the corrosion of AISI 321 stainless steel by mixtures of 100% nitric acid and in nitrogen tetroxide, used as the oxidizer components of liquid rocket propellants, has been investigated, with particular regard to the influence of the N_2O_4 content of the mixture and the nature of the solid corrosion products formed.

C.L. Briant, C.S. O'Toole, and E.L. Hall, The Effect of Microstructure on the Corrosion and Stress Corrosion Cracking of Alloy 600 in Acidic and Neutral Environments, *Corrosion*, 42(1), 15-27, 1986. MetAbs No. 86-350593. **Abstract:** A study of corrosion and stress-corrosion cracking of Alloy 600 is presented. The primary purpose is to relate the corrosion susceptibility of the alloy after various heat treatments to the microstructure produced by these heat treatments. Corrosion susceptibility was evaluated with the 25% boiling nitric acid test. Stress corrosion susceptibility was determined by tests in 288 °C water containing either 0.2 or 8 ppm of oxygen.

C.L. Briant and E.L. Hall, Intergranular Corrosion of High Chromium Nickel-Base Alloys, *Corrosion*, 43(7), 437-440, 1987. MetAbs No. 87-352753. **Abstract:** The intergranular corrosion susceptibility of four high CrNi-base alloys is examined.

G. Lei, R.M. German, and H.S. Nayar, Corrosion Control in Sintered Austenitic Stainless Steels, *Progress in Powder Metallurgy 1983*, Vol 39, Metal Powder Industries Federation, Princeton, 1984, 391-410. MetAbs No. 84-540898. **Abstract:** Porous 316L stainless steel samples were made from water-atomized, prealloyed powder, pressed by cold isostatic pressing and sintered under a variety of conditions. The samples were examined for oxygen, carbon and nitrogen contents, density, crush strength and corrosion resistance in 10% nitric acid at 25 °C.

G. Lei, R.M. German, and H.S. Nayar, Influence of Sintering Variables on the Corrosion Resistance of 316L Stainless Steel, *Powder Metall. Int.*, 15(2), 70-76, 1983. MetAbs No. 86-351558. **Abstract:** Porous 316L stainless steel samples were made from water-atomized, prealloyed powder, pressed by cold isostatic pressing and sintered at 1350, 1250 and 1150 °C, at 90 and 45 min, under three different atmospheres (100% H_2, 75% H_2 and 25% H_2, balance N_2), with three different postsintering cooling rates. The samples were examined for oxygen, carbon and nitrogen contents, density, crush strength and corrosion resistance in 10% nitric acid at 25 °C.

G.A. Noubi, H. Mansour, and M.M. Kamal, Effect of Inorganic Salts on the Dissolution of Tin in Nitric Acid Solution, *J. Electrochem. Soc. India*. 34(1), 54-56, 1985. MetAbs No. 86-350472. **Abstract:** The dissolution of Sn in nitric acid solutions of varying concentrations has been studied by the thermometric method, and the dependence of the rise in temperature. The reaction number on solution concentration has been established. The effect of concentration of some inorganic additives KCl, KBr, KI, K_2SO_4, KNO_3, $K_2Cr_2O_7$ and Na_3PO_4 on the dissolution rate of Sn in 6.0N nitric acid has been examined.

H. Kajimura, H. Morikawa, and H. Nagano, Corrosion Resistance of Stainless Steels in Nitric Acid. II. Effect of Alloying Elements on the Corrosion Resistance of Stainless Steels in Nitric Acid, *Trans. Iron Steel Inst. Jpn.*, 25(4), B-131, 1985. MetAbs No. 86-350496. **Abstract:** The effect of alloying elements on the corrosion resistance of 25Cr-20Ni stainless steel in a boiling solution of nitric acid is reported.

H. Kajimura, K. Ogawa, H. Morikawa, M. Miura, and H. Nagano, Development of a Duplex Stainless Steel With High Corrosion Resistance to Nitric Acid. I. Corrosion Resistance of High Silicon Duplex Stainless Steels, *Trans. Iron Steel Inst. Jpn.*, 26(10), B.327, 1986. MetAbs No. 87-352439. **Abstract:** This paper reports the effect of alloying elements on the corrosion resistance of both base metal and weld metal in high Si stainless steel in nitric acid containing Cr^{6+} ions.

H. Mansour, M.H. Abu El-Wafa, and G.A. Noubi, Inhibition of Corrosion of Copper in Nitric Acid, *Bull. Electrochem.*, 2(2), 103-105, 1986. MetAbs No. 87-350401. **Abstract:** It is found that aniline, n-butylamine, sodium phosphate and sodium sulfate act as inhibitors on the corrosion of copper in 2N nitric acid. The effect of inhibitor concentration, time of immersion and temperature on the corrosion of Cu has been studied. Polarization measurements are carried out and the Tafel slopes are evaluated.

H. Tischner, B. Pieger, A. Kratzer, and E.M. Horn, A Cast Low Carbon Stainless Steel for Use in Nitric Acid at Higher Concentrations and Temperatures, *Werkst. Korros.*, 37(3), 119-129, 1986. MetAbs No. 86-351806. **Abstract:** This paper introduces three modifications of cast, low-carbon stainless steels with about 15 to 20% Cr, 13% Ni and 4.5 to 6.5% Si that can be used for pumps and valves in nitric acid plants. Mechanical and structural properties, castability, machinability and weldability are discussed.

H.S. Nayar, R.M. German, and W.R. Johnson, The Effect of Sintering on the Corrosion Resistance of 316L Stainless Steel, *Progress in Powder Metallurgy 1981*, Vol 37, Metal Powder Industries Federation, Princeton, 1982, 255-265. MetAbs No. 82-540727. **Abstract:** Porous 316L stainless steel specimens were fabricated from water-atomized, prealloyed powder by cold isostatic pressing and sintering. The sintered material was examined for corrosion resistance using a 24-h exposure to 10% nitric acid.

H.S. Nayar, R.M. German, W.R. Johnson, Effect of Sintering on the Corrosion Resistance of 316L Stainless Steel, *Ind. Heat.*, 48(12), 23-25, 1981. MetAbs No. 82-540678. **Abstract:** The corrosion resistance of P/M 316L stainless steel can be reduced when sintering is performed in nitrogen atmospheres. An experiment conducted to verify this observation and the effect of other sintering variables, such as dew point and cooling rate, on corrosion resistance, are reported.

I.C.G. Thanos, Investigation of Corrosion of a Rotating Iron Electrode in HNO3 by In Situ Raman Spectroscopy, *J. Electroanal. Chem. Interfacial Electrochem.*, 210(2), 259-264, 1986. MetAbs No. 87-350316.

Abstract: Iron products resulting during reduction/oxidation processes in 0.15M HNO$_3$ and 0.02M HNO$_3$ with and without excess of supporting electrolytes are detected by Raman spectroscopy.

I.V. Nel'zina, F.V. Zaplatina, and I.D. Radomysel'skii, Properties of P/M Kh25 Stainless Steel Produced by Hot Forging, *Sov. Powder Metall. Met. Ceram.*, 23(1), 34-37, 1984. MetAbs No. 86-540350. **Abstract:** This paper discusses how it is possible, using various sintering atmospheres (nitrogen, dissociated ammonia) and heat treatment conditions, to control the level of mechanical properties of hot-forged P/M Kh25 ferritic steel.

J.R. Scott, Aluminum Pipeline Gas History—An Update, *Mater. Perform.*, 24(2), 27-29 Feb. 1985. MetAbs No. 85-350804. **Abstract:** Information pertaining to Al pipelines, originally generated through a survey performed in 1963 and other histories, is updated. Case histories are presented for the following types of lines: natural gas, sour gas, peracetic acid and fuming nitric acid, and jet fuel.

K. Shimamura, A. Kawashima, K. Asami, and K. Hashimoto, Corrosion Behavior of Amorphous Nickel-Valve Metal Alloys in Boiling Concentrated Nitric and Hydrochloric Acids, *Sci. Rep. Res. Inst., Tohoku Univ. A*, 33(1), 196-210, 1986. MetAbs No. 87-350198. **Abstract:** The corrosion behavior of amorphous nickel-base alloys containing Ti, Zr, Cb, Ta and/or P in boiling 9N nitric acid solutions with and without Cr^{6+} ion and in a boiling 6N HCl solution was investigated.

K.P. Soni and I.M. Bhatt, Corrosion and Inhibition of Copper, Brass and Aluminium in Nitric Acid, Sulphuric Acid and Trichloroacetic Acid, *J. Electrochem. Soc. India*, 34(1), 76-77, 1985. MetAbs No. 86-350473. **Abstract:** A number of workers have studied corrosion of Al (1.0-1.5% Mn, 0.15% Cu, 0.75% Fe and 0.6% Si) in acid, alkali and neutral solutions; various organic and inorganic substances have also been investigated as inhibitors. Corrosion in acid media and inhibition by diphenyl thiourea and dithioglycolic acid are studied.

M.A. Pao and E. Klar, Corrosion Phenomena in Regular and Tin-Modified P/M Stainless Steels, *Progress in Powder Metallurgy 1983*, Vol 39, Metal Powder Industries Federation, Princeton, 1984, 431-443. MetAbs No. 84-540899. **Abstract:** The corrosion behavior of P/M parts is heavily dependent on processing. Corrosion data collected over the past few years for three different corrosive media are summarized.

M.A. Pao and E. Klar, On the Corrosion Resistance of P/M Austenitic Stainless Steels, "P/M-82 in Europe," International Powder Metallurgy Conference, Florence, Italy, 20-25 June 1982, Italiana di Metallurgia, Milan, Italy, 1982, 359-374. MetAbs No. 83-351047. **Abstract:** Effects of sintering temperature, atmosphere, dewpoint, cooling rate and part density upon nitrogen and oxygen content and corrosion resistance of regular and Sn- and Cu/Sn-modified P/M 304L and 316L austenitic Cr-Ni steels are described. Discussion of results takes into account the solubility of N in Cr-Ni steels in equilibrium with gaseous N and chromium nitride.

M.G.A. Khedr and B. Gaamaoune, Corrosion Behavior of Copper in Oxidizing and Non-Oxidizing Acid Mixtures, *Metaux-Corros.-Ind.*, 60(713), 1-8, 1985. MetAbs No. 85-352420. **Abstract:** The corrosion of Cu in the acid mixtures HNO$_3$-HCl, HNO$_3$-H$_3$PO$_4$, and H$_2$CrO$_4$-HCl has been studied by measurements of weight loss, potentiodynamic polarization and thermometric technique as a function of composition at a constant total concentration.

M.T. Makhlouf and Z.H. Khalil, Corrosion Behaviour of Copper Metal Treated With Hydroxystyryl Cyanine Dye, *J. Electrochem. Soc. India*, 35(4), 261-265, 1986. MetAbs No. 87-351507. **Abstract:** The effect of 2-(o-hydroxystyryl)pyridinium-1-methyl iodide cyanine dye on the corrosion behavior of Cu metal in nitric acid solution has been studied. Weight loss measurements, galvanostatic polarization curves, open-circuit potential variation of copper electrodes with time and the cathodic protective current values are given.

N.C. Subramanyam and S.M. Mayanna, Haloacetic Acids as Corrosion Inhibitors for Copper in Nitric Acid, *Indian J. Technol*, 24(1), 17-21, 1986. MetAbs No. 86-352167. **Abstract:** The corrosion behavior of copper in nitric acid containing chloro-, dichloro-, trichloro-, bromo- and iodoacetic acids has been studied using weight loss and polarization techniques.

P.H. Wilhelmsson, Special Stainless Steels for the Process Industry. II, *Stainless Steel Ind.*, 15(84), 7, 8, 9, 31, 1987. MetAbs No. 87-351783. **Abstract:** The resistance to attack in various acids of several duplex and highly alloyed stainless steels is discussed. Examples are given of their application in the process plant industry and the economic aspects of using these steels are considered.

P.K. Chauhan, K.B. Gaonkar, and H.S. Gadiyar, Ellipsometric-Electrochemical Study of the Passive Films Formed on Stainless Steels in 2N HNO$_3$, *J. Electrochem. Soc. India* 34(3), 164-168, 1985. MetAbs No. 86-350914. **Abstract:** Ellipsometric-electrochemical studies were carried out on the passive films formed on stainless steels 304, 304L and 316L in 2N nitric acid medium.

R.A. Arain and A.M. Shams el Din, A Thermometric Study of the Kinetics of Acid Dissolution of Four Copper Alloys Used in Desalination Plants, *Thermochim. Acta*, 89, 171-185, 1985. MetAbs No. 86-350273. **Abstract:** The dissolution of four copper alloys, commonly used in desalination plants, in nitric acid solutions of varying concentrations is studied by the thermometric technique.

R.J.L. Andon, R.C. Pemberton, and J.G.N. Thomas, Corrosion of Stainless Steels Under Heat Transfer Conditions in Nitric Acid, *Br. Corros. J.*, 21(2), 119-128, 1986. MetAbs No. 86-352160 **Abstract:** Novel test rigs are described for the study of the corrosion of metal specimens under controlled heat fluxes. Corrosion of stainless steels in nitric acid tests at various heat fluxes with steel surface temperature kept constant is discussed.

R.R. Kirchheiner, F. Hofmann, T. Hoffmann, and G. Rudolph, A Silicon-Alloyed Stainless Steel for Highly Oxidizing Conditions, *Mater. Perform.*, 26(1), 49-56, 1987. MetAbs No. 87-351323. **Abstract:** The austenitic CrNi steel VDM alloy 1815 LCSi based on 18Cr-15Ni with an addition of 4% Si exhibits an excellent corrosion resistance in highly oxidizing solutions. Ways of mastering this stainless steel from the fabrication and inspection of semifinished products up to appropriate welding are presented and discussed.

S. Gupta, M. Vajpeyi, B.J. Dhirendra, and G.N. Pandey, Determination of Corrosion of Stainless Steel (AISI 304) by Mixed Vapors of HCl and HNO$_3$, *Corros. Prev. Control*, 33(2), 47-50, 1986. MetAbs No. 86-351756. **Abstract:** The Mylius technique works well for many exothermic reactions in acid/metal systems in immersed conditions. The extent of corrosion of stainless steel exposed over mixed vapors of HCl and HNO$_3$ has been evaluated using the technique.

S.M. Sayed and H.A. El Shayeb, Study of the Dissolution of Lead in Nitric Acid by the Thermometric Technique, *Surf. Coat. Technol.*, 29(1), 51-58, 1986. MetAbs No. 86-352496. **Abstract:** The thermometric technique was used to study the dissolution of lead in nitric acid.

S.Z. Kostic, Effects of Cold Work and Galvanic Coupling on Corrosion of Chromium-Nickel Stainless Steels in Nitric Acid Solutions During Nitric Acid Production, *Br. Corros. J.*, 22(1), 53-55, 1987. MetAbs No. 87-351705. **Abstract:** Chromium-nickel stainless steels, otherwise chemically resistant, can suffer very high corrosion rates during nitric acid production using Pt-Rh catalyst. The corrosion of these steels is shown to be the result of the establishment of mixed electrode potentials between Cr-Ni steels and Pt-Rh deposits as well as of microgalvanic couples associated with the different potentials of strained and unstrained materials in nitric acid electrolyte.

T.P. Sastry and V.V. Rao, Anodic Protection of Mild Steel in Nitric Acid, *Corrosion*, 39(2), 55-60, 1983. MetAbs No. 83-351056. **Abstract:** The

applicability and efficiency of an anodic protection technique for controlling corrosion of mild steel in nitric acid of different concentrations at different temperatures are studied. Relevant polarization curves were obtained by potentiodynamic technique and the safe passive zone and the protection potentials to be applied were established by analyzing these curves.

Corrosion Behavior of Various Metals and Alloys in Nitric Acid

Material	Condition, other factors, comments	Concentration, %	Temperature, °C (°F)	Duration	Corrosion rate, mm/yr (mils/yr) or other	Ref
Stainless steels						
18Cr-2Ni-12Mn	Test conducted in three 48-h periods	20 wt%	93 (200)	48 h	0.375 (1.5)	47
7-Mo stainless steel	...	65	Boiling	...	0.18 (7.2)	136
AL 29-4C	...	10	149 (300)	...	0.0025 (0.1)	80
AL 29-4C	...	20	149 (300)	...	0.05 (2.2)	80
AL 29-4C	...	30	149 (300)	...	0.102 (4.1)	80
AM-363 stainless steel	...	...	Room	...	Slightly attacked	120
Carbon steel	...	25	Boiling	...	127 cm/month (50.0 in./month)	120
Carpenter Pyromet Alloy 102	Plus 3% HF. Annealed	15	...	48 h	4.318 (172.2)	30
Carpenter Pyromet Alloy 102	Plus 3% HF. Stress relieved at 843 °C (1550 °F) for ½ h, furnace cooled	15	...	48 h	4.318 (172.2)	30
Jessop JS700	Plus 3% HF	5	68 (155)	48 h	<0.051 (<0.002 in./yr)	97
Jessop JS700	...	25	Boiling	48 h	<0.051 (<0.002 in./yr)	97
Jessop JS700	Huey test	65	Boiling	48 h	<0.508 (<0.020 in./yr)	97
Type 304 stainless steel	...	10	21 (70)	...	Very good	121
Type 304 stainless steel	...	10	Boiling	...	Very good	121
Type 304 stainless steel	...	20	21 (70)	...	Very good	121
Type 304 stainless steel	Test conducted in three 48-h periods	20 wt%	93 (200)	48 h	0.027 (1.1)	47
Type 304 stainless steel	...	20	Boiling	...	Good	121
Type 304 stainless steel	...	25	Boiling	...	0.005 cm/month (0.0002 in./month)	120
Type 304 stainless steel	No activation	40	Boiling	24 h	0.06 (2.4)	52
Type 304 stainless steel	...	40	21 (70)	...	Very good	121
Type 304 stainless steel	...	40	Boiling	...	Good	121
Type 304 stainless steel	...	90	21 (70)	...	Very good	121
Type 304 stainless steel	...	100	21 (70)	...	Very good	121
Type 304 stainless steel	...	100	Boiling	...	Poor	121
Type 304L stainless steel	...	65	Boiling	...	0.24 (9.6)	136
Type 316 stainless steel	...	10	21 (70)	...	Very good	121
Type 316 stainless steel	...	10	Boiling	...	Very good	121
Type 316 stainless steel	...	20	21 (70)	...	Very good	121
Type 316 stainless steel	...	20	Boiling	...	Good	121
Type 316 stainless steel	No activation	40	Boiling	24 h	0.055 (2.2)	52
Type 316 stainless steel	...	40	21 (70)	...	Very good	121
Type 316 stainless steel	...	40	Boiling	...	Good	121
Type 316 stainless steel	...	90	21 (70)	...	Very good	121
Type 316 stainless steel	...	100	21 (70)	...	Very good	121
Type 316 stainless steel	...	100	Boiling	...	Poor	121
Type 317L stainless steel	...	25	Boiling	48 h	<0.051 (0.002 in./yr)	97
Type 347 stainless steel	...	65	Boiling	...	0.27 (10.8)	136
Type 347 stainless steel	Liquid	85.1	22 (77)	...	2.5 μm/yr (0.1)	137
Type 347 stainless steel	Vapor	85.1	22 (77)	...	2.5 μm/yr (0.1)	137
Type 347 stainless steel	Liquid	90.1	22 (77)	...	2.5 μm/yr (0.1)	137
Type 347 stainless steel	Vapor	90.1	22 (77)	...	2.5 μm/yr (0.1)	137
Type 347 stainless steel	Liquid	92.6	22 (77)	...	180 μm/yr (7.0)	137
Type 347 stainless steel	Vapor	92.6	22 (77)	...	2.5 μm/yr (0.1)	137
Type 347 stainless steel	Liquid	94.2	22 (77)	...	710 μm/yr (28.0)	137
Type 347 stainless steel	Vapor	94.2	22 (77)	...	58 μm/yr (2.3)	137
Type 347 stainless steel	Liquid	94.2	22 (77)	...	760 μm/yr (30.0)	137

(Continued)

Corrosion Behavior of Various Metals and Alloys in Nitric Acid (Continued)

Material	Condition, other factors, comments	Concentration, %	Temperature, °C (°F)	Duration	Corrosion rate, mm/yr (mils/yr) or other	Ref
Type 347 stainless steel	Vapor	96.3	22 (77)	...	970 μm/yr (38.0)	137
Type 347 stainless steel	Liquid	96.3	22 (77)	...	400 μm/yr (16.0)	137
Type 347 stainless steel	Liquid	98.5	22 (77)	...	1500 μm/yr (61.0)	137
Type 347 stainless steel	Vapor	98.5	22 (77)	...	1200 μm/yr (47.0)	137
Type 410 stainless steel	...	10	21 (70)	...	Good	121
Type 410 stainless steel	...	10	Boiling	...	Poor	121
Type 410 stainless steel	...	20	21 (70)	...	Good	121
Type 410 stainless steel	...	20	Boiling	...	Poor	121
Type 410 stainless steel	...	40	21 (70)	...	Good	121
Type 410 stainless steel	...	40	Boiling	...	Poor	121
Type 410 stainless steel	...	90	21 (70)	...	Poor	121
Type 410 stainless steel	...	100	21 (70)	...	Poor	121
Type 410 stainless steel	...	100	Boiling	...	Poor	121
Type 410 stainless steel	Plus 2% HCl	Conc	Room	...	Attacked	121
Type 430 stainless steel	...	10	21 (70)	...	Good	121
Type 430 stainless steel	...	10	Boiling	...	Good	121
Type 430 stainless steel	...	20	21 (70)	...	Good	121
Type 430 stainless steel	...	20	Boiling	...	Good	121
Type 430 stainless steel	...	40	21 (70)	...	Good	121
Type 430 stainless steel	...	40	Boiling	...	Good	121
Type 430 stainless steel	...	65	Boiling	...	0.91 (36.4)	136
Type 430 stainless steel	...	85.1	22 (77)	...	10 μm/yr (0.4)	137
Type 430 stainless steel	Liquid	85.1	22 (77)	...	2.5 μm/yr (0.1)	137
Type 430 stainless steel	Vapor	90	21 (70)	...	Good	121
Type 430 stainless steel	...	90.1	22 (77)	...	15 μm/yr (0.6)	137
Type 430 stainless steel	Liquid	90.1	22 (77)	...	690 μm/yr (27.0)	137
Type 430 stainless steel	Vapor	92.6	22 (77)	...	28 μm/yr (1.1)	137
Type 430 stainless steel	Liquid	92.6	22 (77)	...	690 μm/yr (27.0)	137
Type 430 stainless steel	Vapor	94.2	22 (77)	...	120 μm/yr (4.6)	137
Type 430 stainless steel	Liquid	94.2	22 (77)	...	740 μm/yr (29.0)	137
Type 430 stainless steel	Vapor	96.3	22 (77)	...	500 μm/yr (20.0)	137
Type 430 stainless steel	Liquid	96.3	22 (77)	...	1070 μm/yr (42.0)	137
Type 430 stainless steel	Vapor	98.5	22 (77)	...	1700 μm/yr (67.0)	137
Type 430 stainless steel	Liquid	98.5	22 (77)	...	1300 μm/yr (51.0)	137
Type 430 stainless steel	Vapor	100	21 (70)	...	Fair	121
Type 430 stainless steel	...	100	Boiling	...	Poor	121
Type 444 stainless steel	No activation	40	Boiling	24 h	0.0575 (2.3)	52
Aluminum						
Aluminum (99.0-99.5%)	Fuming	...	...	...	Satisfactory	92
Aluminum (>99.5%)	<80% solution	...	...	...	Satisfactory	92
Aluminum (>99.5%)	>80% solution	...	...	...	Satisfactory	92
Al-Mg₂Si alloys	Fuming	...	...	...	Satisfactory	92
Aluminum- manganese alloys	<80% solution	...	...	...	Satisfactory	92
Aluminum-manganese alloys	>80% solution	...	...	...	Satisfactory	92
Aluminum-silicon alloys	Fuming	...	...	...	Satisfactory	92
Coppers						
70-30 cupronickel	...	...	...	...	Not suitable	93
90-10 cupronickel	...	...	...	...	Not suitable	93
Admiralty brass	...	...	...	...	Not suitable	93
Aluminum bronze	...	...	...	...	Not suitable	93
Ampco 8, aluminum bronze	Generally not suitable	...	...	...	>0.5 (>20)	96
Architectural bronze	...	...	...	...	Not suitable	93

(Continued)

Corrosion Behavior of Various Metals and Alloys in Nitric Acid (Continued)

Material	Condition, other factors, comments	Concentration, %	Temperature, °C (°F)	Duration	Corrosion rate, mm/yr (mils/yr) or other	Ref
Brass	...	...	...	...	Not suitable	93
Cartridge brass	...	...	...	...	Not suitable	93
Commercial bronze	...	...	...	...	Not suitable	93
Copper	...	...	...	...	Not suitable	93
Electrolytic copper	...	32	...	...	240 (9450)	28
Free-cutting brass	...	...	...	...	Not suitable	93
Muntz metal	...	...	...	...	Not suitable	93
Naval brass	...	...	...	...	Not suitable	93
Nickel silver	...	18	...	...	Not suitable	93
Phosphor bronze	5% Sn	...	...	...	Not suitable	93
Phosphor bronze	8% Sn	...	...	...	Not suitable	93
Phosphor copper	...	...	...	...	Not suitable	93
Red brass	...	...	...	...	Not suitable	93
Silicon bronze	Low	...	...	...	Not suitable	93
Silicon bronze	High	...	...	...	Not suitable	93
Titanium						
Ti-10-2-3	...	25	Boiling	196 h	0.48 (18.9)	27
Ti-10-2-3	...	45	Boiling	196 h	1.2 (47.2)	27
Ti-10-2-3	...	70	Boiling	196 h	0.07 (2.8)	27
Ti-3-8-6-4-4	...	25	Boiling	196 h	1.13 (44.5)	27
Ti-3-8-6-4-4	...	45	Boiling	196 h	3.6 (141.7)	27
Ti-3-8-6-4-4	...	70	Boiling	196 h	1.46 (57.5)	27
Ti-3Al-2.5V	ASTM Grade 9	10	Boiling	...	0.08 (3.3)	91
Ti-3Al-2.5V	ASTM Grade 9	20	Boiling	...	0.26 (10.5)	91
Ti-3Al-2.5V	ASTM Grade 9	30	Boiling	...	0.49 (19.6)	91
Ti-3Al-2.5V	ASTM Grade 9	40	Boiling	...	0.69 (27.9)	91
Ti-3Al-2.5V	ASTM Grade 9	50	Boiling	...	0.45 (18.1)	91
Ti-3Al-2.5V	ASTM Grade 9	60	Boiling	...	0.35 (14.1)	91
Ti-3Al-2.5V	ASTM Grade 9	65	204 (399)	...	0.007 (0.3)	91
Ti-3Al-2.5V	ASTM Grade 9	70	Boiling	...	0.13 (5.4)	91
Ti-550	...	25	Boiling	196 h	0.83 (32.6)	27
Ti-550	...	45	Boiling	196 h	1.14 (44.9)	27
Ti-550	...	70	Boiling	196 h	0.30 (12)	27
Ti-5Ta	...	25	Boiling	196 h	0.04 (1.6)	27
Ti-5Ta	...	45	Boiling	196 h	0.08 (3.1)	27
Ti-5Ta	...	70	Boiling	196 h	0.03 (1.2)	27
Ti-6-2-1-0.8	...	25	Boiling	196 h	0.39 (15)	27
Ti-6-2-1-0.8	...	45	Boiling	196 h	0.73 (28.7)	27
Ti-6-2-1-0.8	...	70	Boiling	196 h	0.21 (8.3)	27
Ti-6-2-4-6	...	25	Boiling	196 h	4.3 (170)	27
Ti-6-2-4-6	...	45	Boiling	196 h	5.7 (224)	27
Ti-6-2-4-6	...	70	Boiling	196 h	0.78 (30.7)	27
Titanium	...	Conc	19-26 (65-80)	36 d	0.001 (0.05)	74
Titanium	Not refreshed	5-20	100 (212)	...	0.02 (0.8)	90
Titanium	Not refreshed	5-60	35 (95)	...	0.002-0.007 (0.08-0.28)	90
Titanium	Not refreshed	5-60	60 (140)	...	0.01-0.02 (0.4-0.8)	90
Titanium	...	10	Boiling	...	0.11 (4.4)	91
Titanium	Grade 9	10	Boiling	...	0.084 (3.30)	33
Titanium	Aerated	10	Room	...	0.005 (0.2)	90
Titanium	Aerated	10	40 (104)	...	0.003 (0.12)	90
Titanium	...	17	Boiling	...	0.076-0.102 (3.04-4.08)	90
Titanium	Aerated	20	40 (104)	...	0.005 (0.2)	90
Titanium	...	20	Boiling	...	0.2 (8.0)	91
Titanium	Not refreshed	20	290 (554)	...	0.4 (16)	90

(Continued)

Corrosion Behavior of Various Metals and Alloys in Nitric Acid (Continued)

Material	Condition, other factors, comments	Concentration, %	Temperature, °C (°F)	Duration	Corrosion rate, mm/yr (mils/yr) or other	Ref
		20	290 (554)	...	0.305 (12.2)	90
Titanium	Aerated	20.8	Boiling	...	0.127-0.295 (5.08-11.8)	90
Titanium	Plus 179 g/L NaNO₃ + 32 g/L NaCl					
Titanium	Grade 1	25	Boiling	196 h	0.15 (6)	27
Titanium	Grade 5	25	Boiling	196 h	0.67 (26.4)	27
Titanium	Grade 7	25	Boiling	196 h	0.17 (6.7)	27
Titanium	Grade 9	25	Boiling	196 h	0.18 (7)	27
Titanium	Grade 12	25	Boiling	196 h	0.18 (7)	27
Titanium	Plus 170 g/L NaNO₃ + 2.9 g/L NaCl	27.4	Boiling	...	0.483-2.92 (19.32-116.8)	90
Titanium	...	30	Boiling	...	0.5 (20.0)	91
Titanium	Grade 9	30	Boiling	...	0.497 (19.5)	33
Titanium	Aerated	30	Room	...	0.004 (0.16)	90
Titanium	Aerated	30	50 (122)	...	0.015 (0.6)	90
Titanium	Not refreshed	30-50	100 (212)	...	0.10-0.18 (4-7.2)	90
Titanium	Not refreshed	30-60	190 (374)	...	1.5-2.8 (60-112)	90
Titanium	Saturated with zirconyl nitrate	33-45	118 (244)	...	nil	90
Titanium	Plus 5% HF	35	25 (77)	...	452 (18,080)	90
Titanium	Plus 5% HF	35	35 (95)	...	571 (22,840)	90
Titanium	...	35	Boiling	...	0.127-0.508 (5.08-20.32)	90
Titanium	...	35	80 (176)	...	0.051-0.102 (2.04-4.08)	90
Titanium	...	40	Boiling	...	0.61 (24.4)	91
Titanium	...	40	Boiling	...	0.63 (25.2)	90
Titanium	Plus 0.01% K₂Cr₂O₇	40	Boiling	...	0.01 (0.4)	90
Titanium	Plus 0.01% CrO₃	40	Boiling	...	0.01 (0.4)	90
Titanium	Plus 0.01% FeCl₃	40	Boiling	...	0.68 (27.2)	90
Titanium	Plus 1% FeCl₃	40	Boiling	...	0.14 (5.6)	90
Titanium	Plus 1% NaClO₃	40	Boiling	...	0.31 (12.4)	90
Titanium	Plus 1% NaClO₃	40	Boiling	...	0.02 (0.8)	90
Titanium	Plus 1% Ce(SO₄)₂	40	Boiling	...	0.10 (4)	90
Titanium	Plus 0.1% K₂Cr₂O₇	40	Boiling	...	0.016 (0.64)	90
Titanium	Aerated	40	200 (392)	...	0.610 (24.4)	90
Titanium	Aerated	40	Room	...	0.002 (0.08)	90
Titanium	Aerated	40	50 (122)	...	0.016 (0.64)	90
Titanium	Grade 1	45	Boiling	196 h	0.39 (15)	27
Titanium	Grade 5	45	Boiling	196 h	0.86 (33.8)	27
Titanium	Grade 7	45	Boiling	196 h	0.38 (14.9)	27
Titanium	Grade 9	45	Boiling	196 h	0.54 (21.3)	27
Titanium	Grade 12	45	Boiling	196 h	0.27 (10.6)	27
Titanium	...	50	Boiling	...	0.61 (24.6)	91
Titanium	Aerated	50	Room	...	0.002 (0.08)	90
Titanium	Aerated	50	60 (140)	...	0.037 (1.48)	90
Titanium	...	60	Boiling	...	0.39 (15.9)	91
Titanium	Aerated	60	Room	...	0.001 (0.04)	90
Titanium	Aerated	60	60 (140)	...	0.040 (1.6)	90
Titanium	Plus 15% zirconyl nitrate	65	127 (261)	...	nil	90
Titanium	...	65	204 (399)	...	0.005 (0.2)	91
Titanium	...	70	Boiling	...	0.13 (5.2)	91
Titanium	Aerated	70	Room	...	0.005 (0.2)	90
Titanium	Aerated	70	70 (158)	...	0.040 (1.6)	90
Titanium	Aerated	70	270 (518)	...	1.22 (48.8)	90
Titanium	...	70	80 (176)	...	0.025-0.076 (1-3.04)	90
Titanium	...	70	Boiling	...	0.064-0.900 (2.56-36)	90

(Continued)

Corrosion Behavior of Various Metals and Alloys in Nitric Acid (Continued)

Material	Condition, other factors, comments	Concentration, %	Temperature, °C (°F)	Duration	Corrosion rate, mm/yr (mils/yr) or other	Ref
Titanium	Not refreshed	70	270 (518)	...	1.2 (48)	90
Titanium	Not refreshed	70	290 (554)	...	1.1 (44)	90
Titanium	Grade 1	70	Boiling	196 h	0.08 (3.1)	27
Titanium	Grade 5	70	Boiling	196 h	0.02 (0.8)	27
Titanium	Grade 7	70	Boiling	196 h	0.07 (2.8)	27
Titanium	Grade 9	70	Boiling	196 h	0.10 (4)	27
Titanium	Grade 12	70	Boiling	196 h	0.06 (2.4)	27
Titanium	White fuming	Liquid or vapor	Room	...	nil	90
Titanium	White fuming	...	82 (180)	...	0.152 (6.08)	90
Titanium	White fuming	...	122 (252)	...	<0.127 (<5.08)	90
Titanium	White fuming	...	160 (320)	...	<0.127 (<5.08)	90
Titanium	Red fuming with less than ~2% H_2O	...	Room	...	Ignition sensitive	90
Titanium	Red fuming with more than ~2% H_2O	...	Room	...	Not ignition sensitive	90
Transage 207	...	25	Boiling	196 h	8.0 (315)	27
Transage 207	...	45	Boiling	196 h	15.6 (614)	27
Transage 207	...	70	Boiling	196 h	0.95 (37.4)	27
Heat- and corrosion-resistant alloys						
44Co-31Cr-13W	As cast. (a)	10	Boiling	...	0.15 (6)	53
44Co-31Cr-13W	Heat treated 4 h at 899 °C (1650 °F) and furnace cooled. (a)	10	Boiling	...	0.15 (6)	53
44Co-31Cr-13W	Heat treated 4 h at 899 °C (1650 °F) and furnace cooled. (a)	40	65 (150)	...	0.05 (2)	53
44Co-31Cr-13W	As cast. (a)	40	65 (150)	...	0.8 (32)	53
50Co-20Cr-15W-10Ni	...	10	Boiling	...	0.012 (0.5)	53
50Co-20Cr-15W-10Ni	(a)	10	Boiling	...	0.012 (0.5)	53
50Co-20Cr-15W-10Ni	...	40	65 (150)	...	0.012 (0.5)	53
50Co-20Cr-15W-10Ni	As cast. (a)	40	65 (150)	...	0.012 (0.5)	53
53Co-30Cr-4.5W	As cast. (a)	10	Boiling	...	0.02 (0.8)	53
53Co-30Cr-4.5W	Heat treated 4 h at 899 °C (1650 °F). (a)	10	Boiling	...	0.025 (1)	53
53Co-30Cr-4.5W	Heat treated 4 h at 899 °C (1650 °F) and furnace cooled. (a)	10	Boiling	...	0.025 (1)	53
53Co-30Cr-4.5W	Heat treated 4 h at 899 °C (1650 °F). (a)	40	65 (150)	...	0.007 (0.3)	53
53Co-30Cr-4.5W	As cast. (a)	40	65 (150)	...	0.005 (0.2)	53
53Co-30Cr-4.5W	Heat treated 4 h at 899 °C (1650 °F) and furnace cooled. (a)	40	65 (150)	...	0.007 (0.3)	53
85WC-15Co	Tungsten carbide surface layer spalled	10	22 (72)	48 h	18.85 g/m²/h (12.16 mg/in.²/h)	34
85WC-15Co	Tungsten carbide surface layer spalled	10	22 (72)	48 h	19.82 g/m²/h (12.79 mg/in.²/h)	34
94WC-6Co	...	10	22 (72)	48 h	2.45 g/m²/h (1.58 mg/in.²/h)	34
94WC-6Ni	...	10	22 (72)	48 h	0.88 g/m²/h (0.57 mg/in.²/h)	34
Co-20Cr	...	11	Boiling	...	nil	35
Fe-47Cr (ferrite)	Oxidizing	65	Boiling	...	0.0205 g/dm²/d	58
Fe-47Cr (sigma)	Oxidizing	65	Boiling	...	0.861 g/dm²/d	58
Havar	...	10	Boiling	24 h	0.066 (2.6)	23
Haynes No. 6B	...	10	Boiling	24 h	0.023 (0.9)	23
Haynes No. 6B	...	70	Boiling	24 h	96.5 (3800)	23
Haynes No. 21	...	10	Boiling	24 h	0.025 (1.0)	23
Haynes No. 25	(b)	10	Room	24 h	nil	68
Haynes No. 25	(b)	10	66 (150)	24 h	nil	68
Haynes No. 25	(b)	10	Boiling	24 h	<0.02 (0.5)	68
Haynes No. 25	(b)	20	Room	24 h	nil	68
Haynes No. 25	(b)	20	66 (150)	24 h	nil	68
Haynes No. 25	(b)	20	Boiling	24 h	0.05 (2.0)	68
Haynes No. 25	(b)	30	Room	24 h	nil	68
Haynes No. 25	(b)	30	66 (150)	24 h	<0.01 (0.3)	68

(Continued)

Corrosion Behavior of Various Metals and Alloys in Nitric Acid (Continued)

Material	Condition, other factors, comments	Concen-tration, %	Temperature, °C (°F)	Duration	Corrosion rate, mm/yr (mils/yr) or other	Ref
Haynes No. 25	(b)	30	Boiling	24 h	0.10 (4.0)	68
Haynes No. 25	(b)	40	Room	24 h	nil	68
Haynes No. 25	(b)	40	66 (150)	24 h	<0.02 (0.5)	68
Haynes No. 25	(b)	40	Boiling	24 h	0.23 (9.0)	68
Haynes No. 25	(b)	50	Room	24 h	nil	68
Haynes No. 25	(b)	50	66 (150)	24 h	0.02 (0.8)	68
Haynes No. 25	(b)	50	Boiling	24 h	0.46 (18)	68
Haynes No. 25	(b)	60	Room	24 h	nil	68
Haynes No. 25	(b)	60	66 (150)	24 h	0.05 (2.0)	68
Haynes No. 25	(b)	60	Boiling	24 h	0.86 (34)	68
Haynes No. 25	(b)	65	Boiling	24 h	1.04 (41)	68
Haynes No. 25	(b)	70	Room	24 h	nil	68
Haynes No. 25	(b)	70	66 (150)	24 h	0.05 (2.0)	68
Haynes No. 25	(b)	70	Boiling	24 h	1.17 (46)	68
Haynes No. 188	...	10	Boiling	24 h	0.02 (0.8)	23
Haynes No. 188	(c)	65	Boiling	24 h	0.56 (22)	23
Haynes No. 556	(c)	65	Boiling	24 h	0.28 (11)	23
Inco alloy G-3	Huey test (ASTM Practice A-262-C) results	65	Boiling	...	14; 16 (0.36; 0.41)	40
Inco alloy G	...	65	Boiling	...	22 (0.56)	40
Inconel 601	...	5	Boiling	72 h	0.002 (0.1)	64
Inconel 601	...	10	Boiling	72 h	0.005 (0.2)	64
Inconel 601	...	20	Boiling	72 h	0.018 (0.7)	64
Inconel 601	...	30	Boiling	72 h	0.030 (1.2)	64
Inconel 601	...	40	Boiling	72 h	0.046 (1.8)	64
Inconel 601	...	50	Boiling	72 h	0.061 (2.4)	64
Inconel 601	...	60	Boiling	72 h	0.130 (5.1)	64
Inconel 601	...	70	Boiling	72 h	0.193 (7.6)	64
Inconel 617	Plus 3% HF	10	60 (140)	...	0.15 (6)	57
Inconel 617	Plus 3% HF	15	60 (140)	...	0.25 (10)	57
Inconel 617	Plus 2% HF	20	60 (140)	...	0.15 (6)	57
MP35N	...	10	Boiling	24 h	0.056 (2.2)	23
Multimet	(b)	10	Room	24 h	nil	68
Multimet	(b)	10	66 (150)	24 h	nil	68
Multimet	(b)	10	Boiling	24 h	<0.01 (0.3)	68
Multimet	(b)	20	Room	24 h	nil	68
Multimet	(b)	20	66 (150)	24 h	nil	68
Multimet	(b)	20	Boiling	24 h	0.02 (0.8)	68
Multimet	(b)	30	Room	24 h	nil	68
Multimet	(b)	30	66 (150)	24 h	nil	68
Multimet	(b)	30	Boiling	24 h	0.05 (2.0)	68
Multimet	(b)	40	Room	24 h	nil	68
Multimet	(b)	40	66 (150)	24 h	<0.01 (0.1)	68
Multimet	(b)	40	Boiling	24 h	0.10 (4.0)	68
Multimet	(b)	50	Room	24 h	nil	68
Multimet	(b)	50	66 (150)	24 h	<0.01 (0.3)	68
Multimet	(b)	50	Boiling	24 h	0.15 (6.0)	68
Multimet	(b)	60	Room	24 h	nil	68
Multimet	(b)	60	66 (150)	24 h	0.01 (0.4)	68
Multimet	(b)	60	Boiling	24 h	0.25 (10)	68
Multimet	(b)	65	Boiling	24 h	0.30 (12)	68
Multimet	(b)	70	Room	24 h	nil	68
Multimet	(b)	70	66 (150)	24 h	0.02 (0.8)	68
Multimet	(b)	70	Boiling	24 h	0.36 (14)	68
Nickel	...	1N	25 (75)	...	19 (770)	35
Nickel-20Cr	...	11	Hot	...	nil	35
Zirconium						
Zirconium	...	Conc	19-26 (65-80)	36 d	nil	74

(Continued)

Corrosion Behavior of Various Metals and Alloys in Nitric Acid (Continued)

Material	Condition, other factors, comments	Concentration, %	Temperature, °C (°F)	Duration	Corrosion rate, mm/yr (mils/yr) or other	Ref
Zr702	...	10-70	Room to 260 (room to 500)	...	<0.025 (<1)	15
Zr702	...	20	103 (215)	...	<0.025 (<1)	15
Zr702	Plus 1% Fe	65	120 (248)	...	<0.025 (<1)	15
Zr702	Plus 1% Fe	65	204 (400)	...	<0.025 (<1)	15
Zr702	Plus 1.45% 304 stainless steel	65	204 (400)	...	nil	15
Zr702	Plus 1% Cl⁻	70	120 (248)	...	nil	15
Zr702	Plus 1% seawater	70	120 (248)	...	nil	15
Zr702	Plus 1% FeCl₃	70	120 (248)	...	nil	15
Zr702	...	70	121 (250)	...	<0.025 (<1)	15
Zr702	Stress-corrosion cracking observed	70-98	Room to boiling	...	<0.025 (<1)	15
Zr704	...	20	103 (215)	...	<0.025 (<1)	15
Zr704	...	70	121 (250)	...	<0.025 (<1)	15
Zr705	...	20	103 (215)	...	<0.025 (<1)	15
Zr705	...	70	121 (250)	...	<0.025 (<1)	15
Lead, tin, and zinc						
Lead	...	1	24 (75)	...	3.5 (140)	130
Lead	...	1	50 (122)	...	15 (600)	130
Lead	...	5	24 (75)	...	41.25 (1650)	130
Lead	...	5	50 (122)	...	46.25 (1850)	130
Lead	...	10	24 (122)	...	85 (3400)	130
Lead	...	10	50 (122)	...	87.25 (3490)	130
Tin	Hydrogen	3	...	...	630 mg/dm²/d	59
Tin	Oxygen	3	...	...	640 mg/dm²/d	59
Tin	...	<25	20 (68)	...	Unsuitable	94
Tin	...	<25	60 (140)	...	Unsuitable	94
Tin	...	<25	100 (212)	...	Unsuitable	94
Tin	...	50	20 (68)	...	Unsuitable	94
Tin	...	50	60 (140)	...	Unsuitable	94
Tin	...	50	100 (212)	...	Unsuitable	94
Tin	...	95	20 (68)	...	Unsuitable	94
Tin	...	95	60 (140)	...	Unsuitable	94
Tin	...	95	100 (212)	...	Unsuitable	94
Tin	Fuming	...	20 (68)	...	Resistant	94
Tin	Fuming	...	60 (140)	...	Resistant	94
Tin	Fuming	...	100 (212)	...	Resistant	94
Tantalum and hafnium						
Hafnium	...	30	...	8 d	nil	11
Hafnium	Plus 1% NaCl	30	...	8 d	nil	11
Hafnium	...	50	...	8 d	nil	11
Hafnium	Plus 1% NaCl	50	...	8 d	nil	11
Hafnium	...	70	...	8 d	nil	11
Hafnium	Plus 1% NaCl	70	...	8 d	nil	11
Hafnium	...	70	...	8 d	nil	11
Tantalum	...	Conc	19-26 (65-80)	36 d	nil	74
Tantalum	...	1	Boiling	...	<0.02 (<1)	37
Tantalum	...	1	190 (375)	...	<0.02 (<1)	37
Tantalum	...	10	Boiling	...	<0.02 (<1)	37
Tantalum	...	10	190 (375)	...	<0.02 (<1)	37
Tantalum	...	20	100 (212)	...	nil	42
Tantalum	...	20	Boiling	...	<0.02 (<1)	37
Tantalum	...	20	190 (375)	...	<0.02 (<1)	37
Tantalum	...	30	Boiling	...	<0.02 (<1)	37
Tantalum	...	30	190 (375)	...	<0.02 (<1)	37
Tantalum	...	40	Boiling	...	<0.02 (<1)	37
Tantalum	...	40	190 (375)	...	<0.02 (<1)	37

(Continued)

Corrosion Behavior of Various Metals and Alloys in Nitric Acid (Continued)

Material	Condition, other factors, comments	Concentration, %	Temperature, °C (°F)	Duration	Corrosion rate, mm/yr (mils/yr) or other	Ref
Tantalum	...	50	Boiling	...	<0.02 (<1)	37
Tantalum	...	50	190 (375)	...	<0.02 (<1)	37
Tantalum	...	60	Boiling	...	<0.02 (<1)	37
Tantalum	...	60	190 (375)	...	<0.02 (<1)	37
Tantalum	...	65	Boiling	...	<0.02 (<1)	37
Tantalum	...	65	170 (338)	...	<0.0254 (<1)	42
Tantalum	...	65	190 (375)	...	<0.02 (<1)	37
Tantalum	Commercial sheet. (d)	65	Boiling	48 h	<0.025 (<1)	38
Tantalum	High purity. (d)	65	Boiling	48 h	<0.025 (<1)	38
Tantalum	...	70	Boiling	...	<0.02 (<1)	37
Tantalum	...	70	190 (375)	...	<0.02 (<1)	37
Tantalum	...	70	100 (212)	...	nil	42
Noble metals						
Gold	...	1-50	Boiling	...	<0.05 (<2)	8
Gold	...	70	Room	...	>0.05 (>2)	8
Gold	...	70	Boiling	...	0.15 (6)	8
Gold	...	95	100 (212)	...	nil	29
Iridium	...	95	100 (212)	...	Rapid dissolution	17
Osmium	...	70	Room	...	61.3 (2413)	17
Palladium	...	95	100 (212)	...	Rapid dissolution	17
Palladium	...	95	100 (212)	...	nil	29
Rhodium	...	95	100 (212)	...	nil	18
Ruthenium	...	...	Room	...	Rapid dissolution	4
Silver	...	...	Room	...	Rapid dissolution	4
Silver	...					
Others						
Cb alloy	Wrought 100% Cb; laboratory button; annealed at 1175 °C (2140 °F) for 30 min. (d)	65	Boiling	48 h	<0.025 (<1)	38
Cb alloy	Wrought 100% Cb; arc melted; annealed at 1400 °C (2552 °F) for 1 h. (d)	65	Boiling	48 h	<0.025 (<1)	38
Cb alloy	Wrought 100% Cb; electron-beam melted; annealed at 1400 °C (2552 °F) for 1 h. (d)	65	Boiling	48 h	<0.025 (<1)	38
Cb alloy	Wrought 0.75% Zr, bal Cb; arc melted; annealed at 1400 °C (2552 °F) for 1 h. (d)	65	Boiling	48 h	<0.025 (<1)	38
Cb alloy	Wrought 8% Ti, bal Cb; arc melted; annealed at 1400 °C (2552 °F) for 1 h. (d)	65	Boiling	48 h	<0.025 (<1)	38
Cb alloy	Wrought 6.9% Ti, 0.81% Zr, bal Cb; arc melted; annealed at 1430 °C (2606 °F) for 1 h. (d)	65	Boiling	48 h	<0.025 (<1)	38
Cb alloy	Wrought 50% V, 50% Cb; arc melted. (d)	65	Boiling	48 h	0.43 (17)	38
Cobalt	...	1N	25 (75)	...	223 (8900)	35
Magnesium	...	All	Room	...	Unsuitable	119
Niobium	...	1	Boiling	...	<0.07 (<3)	37
Niobium	...	1	190 (375)	...	<0.07 (<3)	37
Niobium	...	10	Boiling	...	<0.07 (<3)	37
Niobium	...	10	190 (375)	...	<0.07 (<3)	37
Niobium	...	20	190 (375)	...	<0.07 (<3)	37
Niobium	...	30	Boiling	...	<0.07 (<3)	37
Niobium	...	30	190 (375)	...	<0.07 (<3)	37
Niobium	...	40	Boiling	...	<0.07 (<3)	37
Niobium	...	40	190 (375)	...	<0.07 (<3)	37
Niobium	...	50	Boiling	...	<0.07 (<3)	37
Niobium	...	50	190 (375)	...	<0.07 (<3)	37
Niobium	...	60	Boiling	...	<0.07 (<3)	37
Niobium	...	60	190 (375)	...	<0.07 (<3)	37
Niobium	...	65	Room	...	nil	2
Niobium	...	65	Boiling	...	<0.07 (<3)	37
Niobium	...	65	190 (375)	...	<0.07 (<3)	37
Niobium	...	70	Boiling	...	<0.07 (<3)	37

(Continued)

Corrosion Behavior of Various Metals and Alloys in Nitric Acid (Continued)

Material	Condition, other factors, comments	Concentration, %	Temperature, °C (°F)	Duration	Corrosion rate, mm/yr (mils/yr) or other	Ref
Niobium	...	70	190 (375)	...	<0.07 (<3)	37
Niobium	...	70	250 (480)	...	0.025 (1.0)	2
Niobium	...	Conc	19-26 (65-80)	36 d	nil	74

(a) Based on five 24-h test periods with cast specimens 38 mm x 25 mm x 6 mm (1.5 in. x 1 in. x 0.25 in.), 120-grit abrasive finish. (b) All specimens prepared from 12-gage, solution heat-treated sheet. Calculated on a minimum of five 24-h test periods. (c) Based on an average of five 24-h test periods. (d) Average of three 48-h periods.

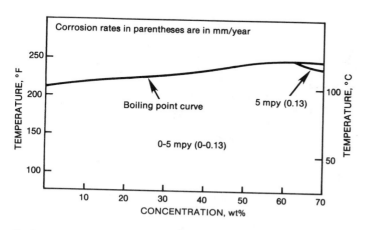

Stainless steel. Resistance to nitric acid of Ferralium Alloy 255. All test specimens were solution heat-treated and in the unwelded condition. Source: Haynes International, 1986.

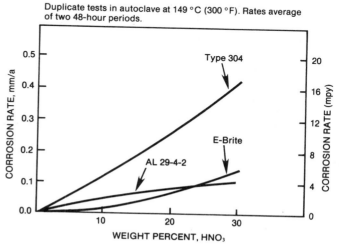

Stainless steel. Corrosion of AL 29-4-2 and other alloys in nitric acid at 149 °C (300 °F). Source: Allegheny Ludlum Corporation, 1982.

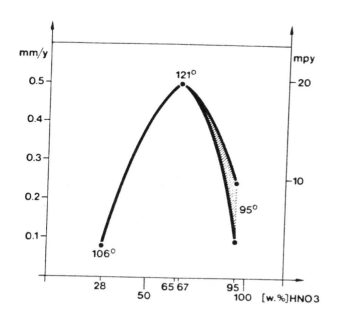

Stainless steel. Resistance of alloy 1815 (18Cr-15Ni-4Si) LCSi in nitric acid. Temperature in degrees Celsius. Source: R.R. Kirchheiner, F. Hofmann, *et al.*, "A Silicon-Alloyed Stainless Steel for Highly Oxidizing Conditions," *Materials Performance*, Vol 26, Jan 1987, 55.

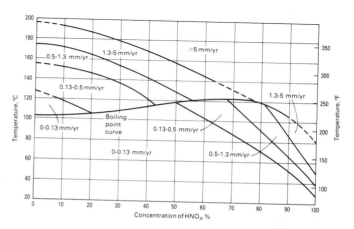

Stainless steel. Isocorrosion diagram for annealed type 304 stainless steel in nitric acid. Source: Chemical Processing Industry.

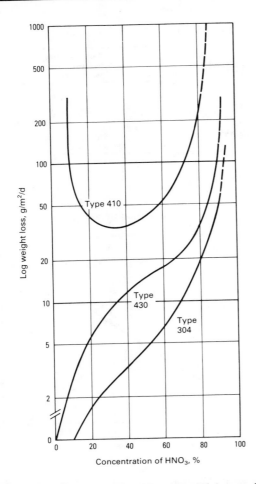

Stainless steel. Corrosion rates of various stainless steels in boiling nitric acid. Source: J.E. Tromen, in *Corrosion: Metal/Environment Reactions*, Vol 1, L.C. Shreir, Ed., Newness-Butterworths, 1976, 352.

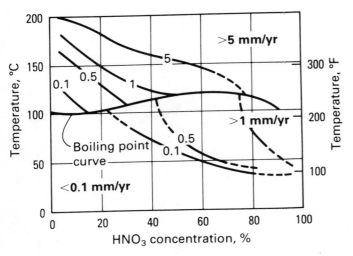

Stainless steel castings. Isocorrosion diagram for ACI CB-30 in nitric acid. Castings were annealed at 790 °C (1450 °F), furnace cooled to 540 °C (1000 °F), and then air cooled to room temperature. Source: *Metals Handbook*, 9th ed., Vol 13, Corrosion, ASM International, Metals Park, OH, 1987, 578.

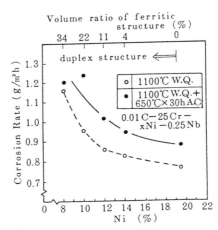

Stainless steel. Effect of nickel concentration on the corrosion of 25Cr steel in the boiling solution of $8N$ HNO_3 + 0.2 g/L Cr^{6+} ions. Source: H. Kajimura, H. Morikawa, *et al.*, Effect of Alloying Elements on the Corrosion Resistance of Stainless Steels in Nitric Acid, *Corrosion Resistance of Stainless Steels in Nitric Acid — Transactions of the Iron and Steel Institute of Japan*, 25, B-131, 1985.

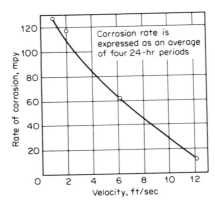

Stainless steel. Erosion corrosion of type 347 stainless steel by white fuming nitric acid at 108 °F. Source: M.G. Fontana, N.D. Green, *Corrosion Engineering*, McGraw-Hill, New York, 1967, 78.

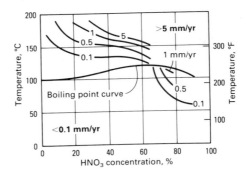

Stainless steel castings. Isocorrosion diagram for ACI CD-4MCu in nitric acid. The material was solution treated at 1120 °C (2050 °F) and water quenched. Source: *Metals Handbook*, 9th ed., Vol 13, Corrosion, ASM International, Metals Park, OH, 1987, 579.

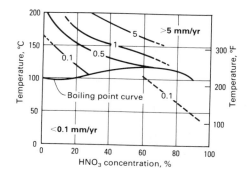

Stainless steel castings. Isocorrosion diagram for solution-treated quenched and sensitized ACI CF-3 in nitric acid. Source: *Metals Handbook*, 9th ed., Vol 13, Corrosion, ASM International, Metals Park, OH, 1987, 579.

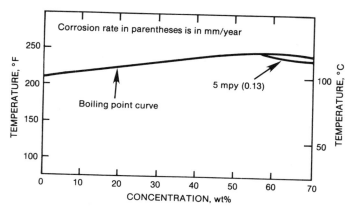

Hastelloy G-30. Resistance to nitric acid. All test specimens were heat treated at 1177 °C (2150 °F), rapid quenched, and in the unwelded condition. Source: Haynes International, 1987.

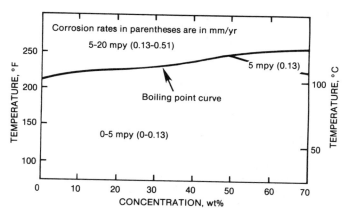

Hastelloy G-3. Resistance to nitric acid. All test specimens were solution heat-treated and in the unwelded condition. Source: Haynes International, 1984.

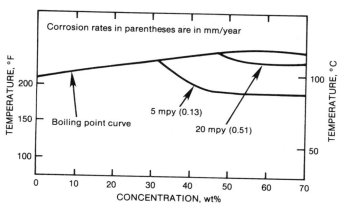

Hastelloy C-22. Resistance to nitric acid. All test specimens were solution heat-treated and in the unwelded condition. Source: Haynes International, 1984.

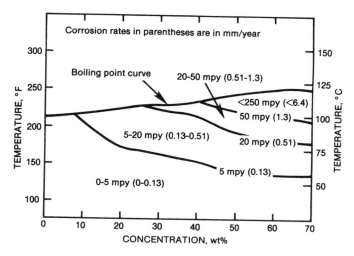

Hastelloy C-4. Resistance to nitric acid of Hastelloy C-4. All test specimens were solution heat-treated at 1066 °C (1950 °F), rapid quenched, and in the unwelded condition. Source: Haynes International, 1983.

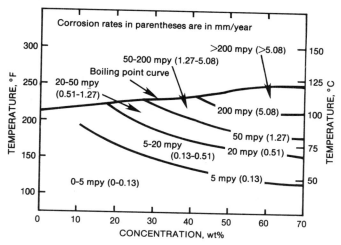

Hastelloy C-276. Resistance to nitric acid. All test specimens were heat-treated at 1121 °C (2050 °F), rapid quenched, and in the unwelded condition. Source: Haynes International, 1987.

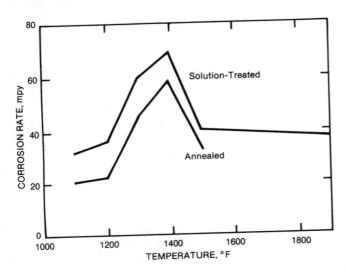

Inconel 625. Effect of sensitizing heat treatment (1 h at temperature) on corrosion of Inconel 625 in boiling 65% nitric acid (Huey test, average of five periods). Source: Inco Alloys International, 1985.

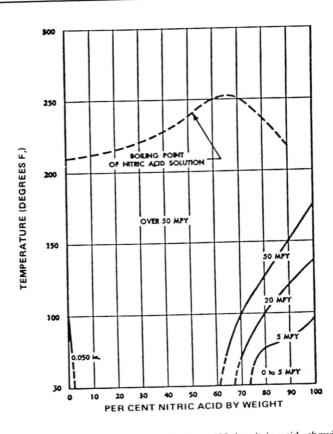

Aluminum. Corrosion rates of alloy 1100 in nitric acid, showing influence of concentration and temperature. Source: *Guidelines for the Use of Aluminum with Food and Chemicals: Compatibility Data on Aluminum in the Food and Chemical Process Industries*, 5th ed., The Aluminum Association, Washington, DC, 1984.

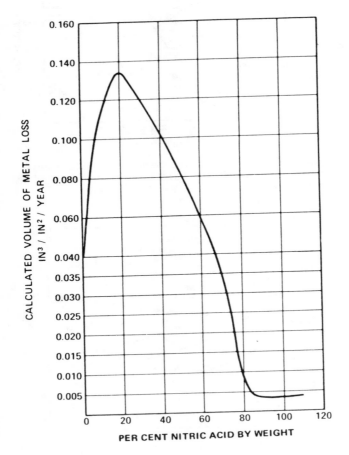

Aluminum. The resistance of alloy 1100 in nitric acid; results of 90-day tests at room temperature. Source: *Guidelines for the Use of Aluminum with Food and Chemicals: Compatibility Data on Aluminum in the Food and Chemical Process Industries*, 5th ed., The Aluminum Association, Washington, DC, 1984.

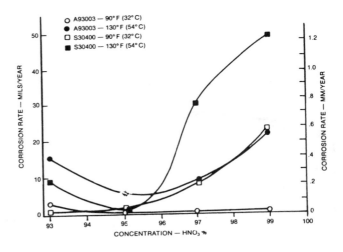

Aluminum. Corrosion rates of aluminum A93003 and stainless steel S30400 in concentrated nitric acid. Source: R.D. Crooks, "Materials of Construction for Nitric Acid," in *Process Industries Corrosion*, B.J. Moniz and W.I. Pollock, Ed., National Association of Corrosion Engineers, Houston, 1986, 259.

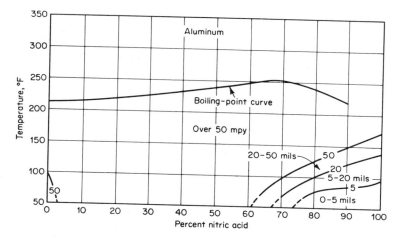

Aluminum. Corrosion of aluminum by nitric acid as a function of concentration and temperature. Source: *Guidelines for the Use of Aluminum with Food and Chemicals: Compatibility Data on Aluminum in the Food and Chemical Process Industries*, 5th ed., The Aluminum Association, Washington, DC, 1984.

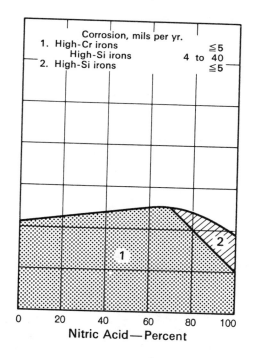

Cast iron. Useful life of plain and high-alloy iron castings in nitric acid. Source: "Physical and Corrosion Properties," in *Source Book on Ductile Iron*, A.H. Rauch, Ed., American Society for Metals, Metals Park, OH, 1977, 368.

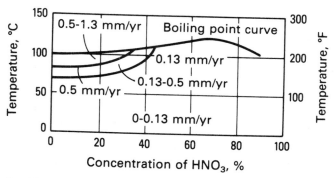

Cast iron. Corrosion of high-silicon cast iron in nitric acid as a function of concentration and temperature. Source: *Metals Handbook*, 9th ed., Vol 13, Corrosion, ASM International, Metals Park, OH, 1987, 569.

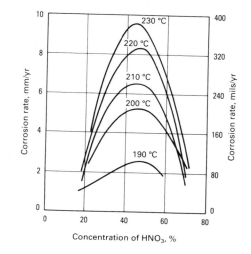

Titanium. Corrosion of unalloyed titanium in high-temperature nitric acid solutions. Source: *Metals Handbook*, Vol 13, Corrosion, ASM International, Metals Park, OH 1987, 678.

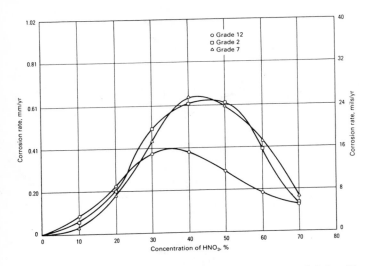

Titanium. Corrosion of titanium alloys in boiling, uninhibited nitric acid solutions. Acid solutions were refreshed every 24 h. Source: *Metals Handbook*, 9th ed., Vol 13, Corrosion, ASM International, Metals Park, OH, 1987, 678.

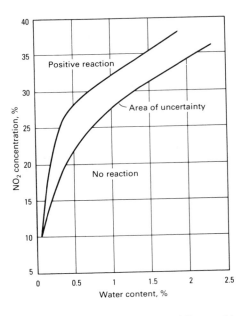

Titanium. Acid composition limits for avoiding rapid, pyrophoric reactions of titanium with red fuming nitric acid. Source: L.C. Gilbert and C.W. Fink, "Explosions of Titanium and Fuming Nitric Acid Mixtures," *Metal Progress*, Nov 1956, 93-96.

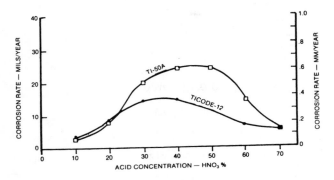

Titanium. Corrosion rate of titanium alloys in boiling nitric acid. Both titanium and titanium-palladium alloys are resistant to concentrated nitric acid from 65 to 90% and to dilute acid of less than 10%. At concentrations above 90%, however, titanium is subject to stress-corrosion cracking in nitric acid. Titanium is never used in red fuming nitric acid because a pyrophoric reaction can occur if water content is less than 1.34% and nitrous oxide exceeds 6%. Source: R.D. Crooks, "Materials of Construction for Nitric Acid," in *Process Industries Corrosion*, B.J. Moniz and W.I. Pollock, Ed., National Association of Corrosion Engineers, Houston, 1986, 261-262.

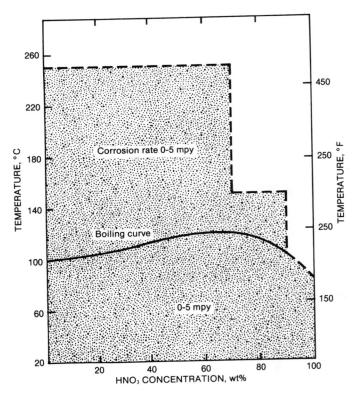

Zirconium. Corrosion of zirconium in nitric acid solutions. Source: "Zircadyne Corrosion Properties," Teledyne Wah Chang Albany, 1986.

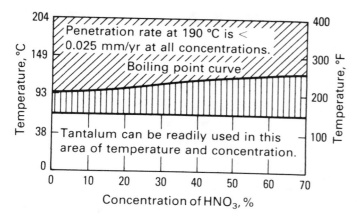

Tantalum. Corrosion resistance of tantalum in nitric acid of various concentrations and temperatures. Source: *Metals Handbook*, 9th ed., Vol 13, Corrosion, ASM International, Metals Park, OH, 1987, 731.

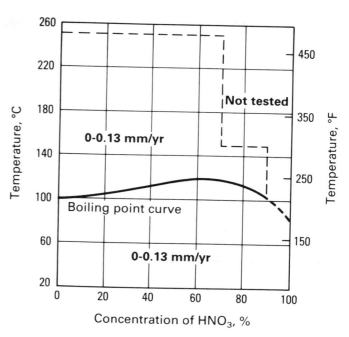

Zirconium. Isocorrosion diagram for zirconium in nitric acid. Source: "Zircadyne Corrosion Properties," Teledyne Wah Chang Albany, 1986.

Nitric Oxide

Nitric oxide, NO, also known as nitrogen oxide and nitrogen monoxide, is a colorless gas that will react with oxygen at room temperature to form nitrogen dioxide, N_2O_2, a reddish-brown gas. It is soluble in water and alcohol and is used primarily to form other compounds.

Material Summaries

The following material summaries were compiled from a survey of the available literature. Inclusion of a material description under a given environment does not imply that it is the most appropriate material for corrosion service in that environment. Likewise, exclusion of a given material does not imply that it is not suitable for corrosion service applications in that environment.

Copper. Instrument tubing at a new facility, a combination of copper (C12200) tubing and yellow brass (C27000) fittings, failed by stress-corrosion cracking after a few weeks. The new building was located near and downwind of another facility that occasionally vented small amounts of nitric oxide. Tests showed that brass samples would fail by stress-corrosion cracking if exposed to nitric oxide emissions.

Tantalum. Tantalum resists nitric oxide (as a 5% mixture in argon) at temperatures below 1125 °C (2050 °F). However, as the temperature is increased from 1195 to 1457 °C (2180 to 2670 °F), the reaction rate increased from 0.0065 to 0.076% area loss per second.

Corrosion Behavior of Various Metals and Alloys in Nitric Oxide

Material	Condition, other factors, comments	Concentration, %	Temperature, °C (°F)	Duration	Corrosion rate, mm/yr (mils/yr) or other	Ref
Silver	...	Pure	Room	...	Attacked	8

Nitric Tetroxide

Nitric tetroxide, N_2O_4, is also known as nitrogen peroxide and nitrogen dioxide, NO_2. It exists as a colorless solid, a yellow liquid, or a reddish-brown gas. It is soluble in water. Nitric tetroxide is used in the preparation of nitric acid and as an oxidizer with hydrazine rocket fuels.

Material Summaries

The following material summaries were compiled from a survey of the available literature. Inclusion of a material description under a given environment does not imply that it is the most appropriate material for corrosion service in that environment. Likewise, exclusion of a given material does not imply that it is not suitable for corrosion service applications in that environment.

Aluminum. Aluminum alloy missile fuel tanks handle nitric tetroxide under stringent moisture control.

Titanium. Titanium alloys are highly resistant to corrosion attack in nitric tetroxide. Titanium alloys will crack in nitric tetroxide containing excess dissolved oxygen (red nitric tetroxide), but will not crack in nitric tetroxide containing nitric oxide (oxygen-free or green nitric tetroxide). Rapid, pyrophoric reactions in titanium alloys are also possible in anhydrous nitric tetroxide gas atmospheres. The addition of small amounts of water or the presence of 0.6 to 1.0 wt% nitric acid inhibits metal attack.

Corrosion Behavior of Various Metals and Alloys in Nitric Tetroxide

Material	Condition, other factors, comments	Concentration, %	Temperature, °C (°F)	Duration	Corrosion rate, mm/yr (mils/yr) or other	Ref
Silver	...	Pure	Room	...	<0.05 (<2)	8

Nitrogen

Nitrogen, N_2, is a colorless, odorless, inert gas that comprises 80% of the earth's atmosphere. It serves as a diluent and controls natural burning and respiration rates, which would be much faster in higher concentrations of oxygen. Nitrogen is soluble in water and alcohol, but is essentially insoluble in most other liquids. It is essential to practically all forms of life and its compounds serve as foods or fertilizers. Nitrogen is used in the manufacture of ammonia and nitric acid. Nitrogen is essentially an inert gas at ambient and moderate temperatures. Therefore, it is easily handled by most metals. At elevated temperatures, nitrogen can be aggressive to metals and alloys.

Material Summaries

The following material summaries were compiled from a survey of the available literature. Inclusion of a material description under a given environment does not imply that it is the most appropriate material for corrosion service in that environment. Likewise, exclusion of a given material does not imply that it is not suitable for corrosion service applications in that environment.

Aluminum. Aluminum alloy equipment has been used to process and handle liquid nitrogen.

Niobium. At 100 °C (212 °F), niobium is inert in nitrogen. Niobium does react with nitrogen at temperatures above 350 °C (660 °F).

Silver. Silver can be exposed to nitrogen up to 500 °C (930 °F).

Tantalum. Tantalum experiences an increase in hardness, tensile strength, and electrical resistivity and a decrease in elongation and density with the presence of nitrogen in only a few atomic percent concentration (one atomic percent nitrogen in tantalum equals 780 ppm nitrogen).

Tin. Below its melting point of 232 °C (450 °F), tin does not react with nitrogen.

Titanium. Titanium alloys show low reaction rates in pure nitrogen atmospheres below 650 °C (1200 °F) due to the formation of a protective nitride surface film.

Zirconium. Zirconium is stable in nitrogen at temperatures up to 300 to 400 °C (570 to 750 °F).

Additional Reading

A. Levy and Y.-F. Man, The Effect of Temperature on the Erosion-Corrosion of 9Cr-1Mo Steel, *Wear, 111*(2), 161-172, 1986. MetAbs No. 86-352461. **Abstract:** The effect of test temperature on the nature of the scale formation and the substrate metal thickness loss by combined erosion-corrosion was determined for 9Cr-1Mo steel up to 900 °C in air and in undried nitrogen gas streams containing 130-μm Al_2O_3 particles.

Corrosion Behavior of Various Metals and Alloys in Nitrogen

Material	Condition, other factors, comments	Concentration, %	Temperature, °C (°F)	Duration	Corrosion rate, mm/yr (mils/yr) or other	Ref
Stainless steels						
Type 304 stainless steel	Rayon processing; field or pilot plant test; no aeration; rapid agitation. Plus 6% carbon dioxide, 1% carbon monoxide, traces of butanes, pentanes, water and aldehydes	90	30-55 (86-131)	1178 d	<0.0001 in./yr	89
Type 316 stainless steel	Rayon processing; field or pilot plant test; no aeration; rapid agitation. Plus 6% carbon dioxide, 1% carbon monoxide, traces of butanes, pentanes, water and aldehydes	90	30-55 (86-131)	1178 d	0.0001 in./yr	89
Aluminum						
Aluminum (99.0-99.5%)	...	...	High	...	Excellent	92
Coppers						
70-30 cupronickel	...	...	...	...	Suitable	93
90-10 cupronickel	...	...	...	...	Suitable	93
Admiralty brass	...	...	...	...	Suitable	93
Aluminum bronze	...	...	...	...	Suitable	93
Ampco 8, aluminum bronze	Dry. Generally suitable	...	...	...	<0.05 (<2)	96
Architectural bronze	...	...	...	...	Suitable	93
Brass	...	...	...	...	Suitable	93
Cartridge brass	...	...	...	...	Suitable	93
Commercial bronze	...	...	...	...	Suitable	93
Electrolytic copper	...	...	...	...	Suitable	93
Free-cutting brass	...	...	...	...	Suitable	93
Muntz metal	...	...	...	...	Suitable	93
Naval brass	...	...	...	...	Suitable	93
Nickel silver	...	18	...	...	Suitable	93
Phosphor bronze	5% Sn	...	...	...	Suitable	93
Phosphor bronze	8% Sn	...	...	...	Suitable	93
Phosphor copper	...	...	...	...	Suitable	93
Red brass	...	...	...	...	Suitable	93
Silicon bronze	Low	...	...	...	Suitable	93
Silicon bronze	High	...	...	...	Suitable	93
Noble metals						
Silver	...	Pure	500 (930)	...	<0.05 (<2)	8

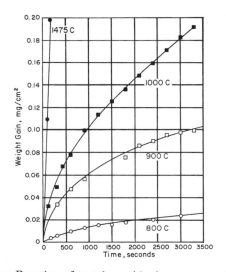

Tantalum. Reaction of tantalum with nitrogen at various temperatures. Source: C.A. Hampel, "Tantalum," in *Rare Metals Handbook*, 2nd ed., C.A. Hampel, Ed., Reinhold Publishing, New York, 1961, 505.

Nitrous Acid

Nitrous acid, HNO_2, is the aqueous solution of nitrogen trioxide. It is a moderately strong and rapid oxidizing agent used for diazotization.

Material Summaries

The following material summaries were compiled from a survey of the available literature. Inclusion of a material description under a given environment does not imply that it is the most appropriate material for corrosion service in that environment. Likewise, exclusion of a given material does not imply that it is not suitable for corrosion service applications in that environment.

Nickel. Alloy 600 resists corrosion from nitrous acid solutions in diazotizing baths used in the application of developed color dyes. Monel alloy 400 is severely attacked by nitrous acid in solutions over 0.5% at room temperature. Chromium-containing Incoloy alloys 800 and 825 are recommended for use with nitrous acid, because the metal forms a protective passive oxide film.

Corrosion Behavior of Various Metals and Alloys in Nitrous Acid

Material	Condition, other factors, comments	Concentration, %	Temperature, °C (°F)	Duration	Corrosion rate, mm/yr (mils/yr) or other	Ref
Aluminum (>99.5%)	Solution	...	...	...	Satisfactory	92
Aluminum-manganese alloys	Solution	...	...	...	Satisfactory	92
Silver	...	...	Room	...	Dissolution	4
Silver	...	...	Room	...	Dissolution	4
Type 410 stainless steel	...	...	Room	...	Slightly stained	121

Oleic Acid

Oleic acid, $C_{17}H_{33}COOH$, also known as red oil, elaine oil, and octadecenoic acid, is a yellowish unsaturated fatty acid with an aroma similar to lard. It is insoluble in water, but soluble in most organic solvents. Oleic acid is the main component in cooking and olive oils. It is used for making aluminum oleate, which thickens lubricating oil, and in the preparation of soaps and cosmetics.

Material Summaries

The following material summaries were compiled from a survey of the available literature. Inclusion of a material description under a given environment does not imply that it is the most appropriate material for corrosion service in that environment. Likewise, exclusion of a given material does not imply that it is not suitable for corrosion service applications in that environment.

Aluminum. Aluminum alloys 1100, 3003, and 6061 resisted oleic acid during laboratory tests at ambient temperature. Aluminum alloy tank cars have been used to ship oleic acid.

Cast Irons. Austenitic nickel cast irons exhibit adequate resistance to oleic acid.

Copper. Copper and copper-zinc alloys resist attack by pure oleic acid. The presence of air and water promotes the corrosion of these alloys, and temperature affects the rate of attack. Tested under conditions of 25 °C (75 °F), C51000 and C61300 had corrosion rates of less than 0.050 mm/yr (2 mils/yr) in oleic acid, whereas C26000 and C65500 had corrosion rates of 0.50 mm/yr (20 mils/yr).

Corrosion Behavior of Various Metals and Alloys in Oleic Acid

Material	Condition, other factors, comments	Concentration, %	Temperature, °C (°F)	Duration	Corrosion rate, mm/yr (mils/yr) or other	Ref
Stainless steels						
Type 410 stainless steel	...	...	Room	...	Unattacked	121
Coppers						
70-30 cupronickel	...	...	...	...	Suitable	93
90-10 cupronickel	...	...	...	...	Suitable	93

(Continued)

Corrosion Behavior of Various Metals and Alloys in Oleic Acid (Continued)

Material	Condition, other factors, comments	Concentration, %	Temperature, °C (°F)	Duration	Corrosion rate, mm/yr (mils/yr) or other	Ref
Admiralty brass	...	...	...	...	Suitable	93
Aluminum bronze	...	...	...	...	Suitable	93
Ampco 8, aluminum bronze	Generally suitable	...	...	...	<0.05 (<2)	96
Architectural bronze	...	...	...	...	Fair	93
Brass	...	...	...	...	Suitable	93
Cartridge brass	...	...	...	...	Fair	93
Commercial bronze	...	...	...	...	Suitable	93
Electrolytic copper	...	...	...	...	Suitable	93
Free-cutting brass	...	...	...	...	Fair	93
Muntz metal	...	...	...	...	Fair	93
Naval brass	...	...	...	...	Fair	93
Nickel silver	...	18	...	...	Suitable	93
Phosphor bronze	5% Sn	...	...	...	Suitable	93
Phosphor bronze	8% Sn	...	...	...	Suitable	93
Phosphor copper	...	...	...	...	Suitable	93
Red brass	...	...	...	...	Suitable	93
Silicon bronze	Low	...	...	...	Suitable	93
Silicon bronze	High	...	...	...	Suitable	93
Others						
Magnesium	...	100	Room	...	Suitable	119

Oxalic Acid

Oxalic acid, $HOOCCOOH \cdot 2H_2O$, also known as ethane dioic acid, is a poisonous, colorless crystalline solid that has a melting point of 189 °C (372 °F). It is soluble in water, alcohol, and ether. Oxalic acid is used in dyeing, bleaching, ink and rust removers, metal polishes, and as a chemical intermediate in the production of oxalates and purification of glycerols.

Material Summaries

The following material summaries were compiled from a survey of the available literature. Inclusion of a material description under a given environment does not imply that it is the most appropriate material for corrosion service in that environment. Likewise, exclusion of a given material does not imply that it is not suitable for corrosion service applications in that environment.

Aluminum. Under laboratory conditions of ambient temperature and 100% relative humidity, aluminum alloy 3003 had a corrosion rate of 0.50 mm/yr (20 mils/yr) in solid oxalic acid. Alloy 1100 suffered corrosion of 0.375 mm/yr (15 mils/yr) in aqueous solutions (0.1 to 12% oxalic acid) during tests run at ambient temperature. These solutions were also corrosive to alloy 1100 at 50 °C (122 °F) and at boiling temperatures. Aluminum alloy filters and crystallizers have been used with oxalic acid, because the aluminum salts do not discolor the product.

Cast Irons. High-silicon cast irons exhibit excellent resistance to oxalic acid at all temperatures and concentrations.

Copper. Aluminum bronzes are generally suitable for service in oxalic acid.

Zirconium. Zirconium resists corrosion in oxalic acid.

Additional Reading

M.A. Elmorsi, E.M. Mabrouk, R.M. Issa, and M.M. Ghoneim, Electrochemical Studies of the Corrosion of Some Cu-Zn Alloys in Organic Acids, *Surf. Coat. Technol.*, 30(3), 277-287, 1987. MetAbs No. 87-351667. **Abstract:** The electrochemical corrosion parameters, e.g., corrosion current density, corrosion rate and polarization resistance, of 63Cu-37Zn, 70Cu-30Zn and 58.81Cu-39.53Zn-1.66Pb alloys were measured in aqueous solutions of weak organic acids (oxalic, tartaric and succinic acid). Three techniques were used for these measurements, namely potentiodynamic, Tafel plot and polarization resistance using the model 350A-PARC corrosion measurement system. The effect of acid concentration and temperature on the corrosion parameters of such alloys is discussed.

R.A. Speranzini, R.L. Tapping, and D.J. Disney, Corrosiveness of Decontamination Solutions to Sensitized AISI 304 Stainless Steel, *Corrosion*, 43(10), 632-641, 1987. MetAbs No. 88-350606. **Abstract:** An experimental study of the corrosiveness of citric acid, oxalic acid, and EDTA mixtures to sensitized AISI 304 stainless steel was conducted. In initial tests, the corrosivity of various solutions at 125 °C was assessed by measuring anodic polarization curves and estimating corrosion current densities.

Corrosion Behavior of Various Metals and Alloys in Oxalic Acid

Material	Condition, other factors, comments	Concen-tration, %	Temperature, °C (°F)	Duration	Corrosion rate, mm/yr (mils/yr) or other	Ref
Stainless steels						
AL 2205		10	Boiling	...	0.13 (5.1)	120
AL 2205	Welded sample	10	Boiling	...	0.20 (7.8)	120
AL 29-4-2	Base metal	10	Boiling	...	0.02 (0.7)	81
AL 6XN	(a)	10	Boiling	...	0.274 (10.80)	120
AL 6XN	Welded sample	10	Boiling	...	0.277 (10.92)	120
AL 904L	Base metal	10	Boiling	...	0.69 (27.1)	120
ALFA-II	...	10	Boiling	...	122 (0.39924 in./month)	98
Alloy 625	(b)	10	Boiling	...	0.2 (6)	81
Altemp A-286	(a)	10	Boiling	...	0.37 (14.4)	98
E-Brite	...	10	Boiling	...	0.076 (3)	81
Type 304 stainless steel	(a)	10	21 (70)	...	Good	121
Type 304 stainless steel	...	10	Boiling	...	1.23 (48.5)	98
Type 304 stainless steel	...	10	Boiling	...	1.22 (0.004 in./month)	98
Type 304 stainless steel	...	10	Boiling	...	1.219 (48)	81
Type 316 stainless steel	(a)	10	21 (70)	...	Good	121
Type 316 stainless steel	...	10	Boiling	...	1.02 (40.08)	120
Type 316 stainless steel	Base metal	10	Boiling	...	0.991 (39.0)	120
Type 316L stainless steel	Welded sample	10	Boiling	...	1.02 (40.1)	120
Type 316L stainless steel	Base metal	10	Boiling	...	0.99 (39.0)	120
Type 409 stainless steel	Welded sample	10	Boiling	...	46 (0.1510 in./month)	98
Type 410 stainless steel	(b)	10	21 (70)	...	Poor	121
Type 410 stainless steel	...	...	Room	...	Slightly attacked	121
Type 430 stainless steel	...	10	21 (70)	...	Good	121
Type 430 stainless steel	...	10	Boiling	...	109 (0.35768 in./month)	98
Type 439 stainless steel	(b)	10	Boiling	...	55 (0.18 in./month)	98
Heat- and corrosion-resistant alloys	...					
Inconel 690	...	5	80 (176)	...	<0.03 (<1)	57
Inconel 690	...	10	80 (176)	...	<0.03 (<1)	57
Zirconium						
Zr702	...	0-100	100 (212)	...	<0.025 (<1)	15
Noble metals						
Gold	...	All	Boiling	...	<0.05 (<2)	8
Silver	...	...	Boiling	...	<0.05 (<2)	4
Silver	...	...	Boiling	...	<0.05 (<2)	4
Others						
Niobium	...	10	Boiling	...	1.25 (50)	2

(a) Average of five 48-h periods. (b) Average corrosion rates.

Oxygen

Oxygen, O_2, is a colorless, tasteless, gaseous element essential to almost all forms of life. It promotes respiration and combustion. Oxygen comprises 20% of the earth's atmosphere and is the most abundant element in seawater and in the earth's crust. It is slightly soluble in water and alcohol, but combines readily with most other elements to form oxides. The electrolysis of water produces both oxygen and hydrogen. Direct uses of oxygen are in welding, in metal-cutting, and in medicine. A purity of 99.5% oxygen is required for oxyacetylene torches, and a reduction of 0.5% decreases the welding efficiency by over 10%. Oxyhydrogen torches provide lower temperatures that are useful for welding light-gage aluminum and magnesium alloys and for underwater cutting.

Oxygen is very reactive with organic compounds like oil and grease. Therefore, equipment used to handle oxygen should be cleaned with great care.

Metal corrosion is influenced by the presence of oxidizing agents. On the positive side, oxidizing agents promote the formation of a protective oxide film on the surface of some metals such as aluminum, which prevents further corrosion. However, in some situations, oxidizing agents promote cathodic reactions that increase the corrosion rates. A dramatic example is the corrosion of Monel, which resisted attack by oxygen-free 5% sulfuric acid at room temperature, but with the addition of oxygen corroded at a rate in almost a direct proportion to the oxygen content. The oxygen need not be present in the entire acid, but only at the interface of metal, acid, and surrounding atmosphere.

Feedwater with dissolved oxygen will pit the internal surfaces of boiler, steel drum, economizer, and supply tubes. This corrosion in either the operating boiler or improperly stored idle boiler will reduce the reliability and the service life of the equipment.

Material Summaries

The following material summaries were compiled from a survey of the available literature. Inclusion of a material description under a given environment does not imply that it is the most appropriate material for corrosion service in that environment. Likewise, exclusion of a given material does not imply that it is not suitable for corrosion service applications in that environment.

Aluminum. Aluminum alloys retain mechanical properties at low temperatures and are therefore used in the manufacture, handling, and shipping of liquid oxygen. Valves of alloy A356.0 have been employed in the service of liquid oxygen. Aluminum has the lowest resistance to ignition in oxygen service of common metals.

Copper. Hospital oxygen systems use copper and copper alloy tubing to handle oxygen at room temperature. A copper oxide film forms when copper is heated in air or oxygen. At temperatures below 100 °C (212 °F), the film thickness increases logarithmically with time. An increase in temperature allows the scaling rate to increase irregularly, but the addition of pressure up to 1.6 kPa (12 torr) allows the rate to rise rapidly. The scaling rate increase is steady above 20 kPa (150 torr). The oxidation rate of copper is not affected by the presence of low concentrations of lead, oxygen, zinc, nickel, and phosphorus. However, the presence of silicon, magnesium, beryllium, and aluminum retard oxidation by forming a protective oxide film on the surface of copper.

Gold. Gold is resistant to oxygen to its melting point of 1063 °C (1945 °F).

Titanium. Titanium is not considered a suitable material for pure oxygen service.

Zirconium. Zirconium reacts with oxygen at temperatures above 540 °C (1000 °F) to form a white porous film of zirconium dioxide that is brittle. Prolonged exposure at temperatures above 700 °C (1290 °F) allows zirconium to absorb oxygen and become embrittled. Zirconium is not considered a suitable material for pure oxygen service.

Additional Reading

A. McMinn, F.F. Lyle Jr., and G.R. Leverant, Stress Corrosion Crack Growth in NiCrMoV Turbine Disc Steels, *Corrosion*, 41(9), 493-503, 1985. MetAbs No. 85-352342. **Abstract:** A study was made of the effects of metallurgical and environment variables on stress-corrosion cracking propagation rates in NiCrMoV turbine disc steels. Constant displacement tests, using wedge-opening-load specimens, were performed on steels with yield strengths in the range of 627 to 1124 MPa. One steel was temper-embrittled to study the effect of phosphorus segregation on stress-corrosion cracking growth rates. All tests were made at 157 °C in either pure water environments, or environments containing common ionic turbine contaminants (NaCl and NaOH), and gaseous turbine contaminants (air, oxygen, and carbon dioxide).

P.K. Datta, K.N. Strafford, and A.L. Dowson, Environment/Mechanical Interaction Processes and Hydrogen Embrittlement of Titanium, *Mech. Corros. Prop. A, Key Eng. Mater.*, A8, 203-216, 1985. MetAbs No. 86-350055. **Abstract:** The degradation of titanium (IMI115, IMI130, IMI155) in hydrogen, oxygen and/or sulfur containing environments at temperatures between 300 to 500 °C has been studied. The effect on mechanical integrity of substrate contamination, both by hydride precipitation and by interstitial oxygen and hydrogen, has been characterized in terms of the resistance to fatigue crack growth and fracture toughness.

W.M.M. Huijbregts, Oxygen and Corrosion Potential Effects on Chloride Stress Corrosion Cracking, *Corrosion*, 42(8), 456-462, 1986. MetAbs No. 86-352257. **Abstract:** Constant extension rate test experiments have been performed on AISI 304 at 200 °C in a 0.001M NaCl solution. During straining, the specimens were kept at constant potentials in the range of -400 to +425 normal hydrogen electrode.

Corrosion Behavior of Various Metals and Alloys in Oxygen

Material	Condition, other factors, comments	Concentration, %	Temperature, °C (°F)	Duration	Corrosion rate, mm/yr (mils/yr) or other	Ref
Aluminum						
Aluminum (99.0-99.5%)	...	...	<250 (<482)	...	Satisfactory	92
Aluminum (99.0-99.5%)	...	...	250-500 (482-932)	...	Restricted applications	92
Coppers						
70-30 cupronickel	...					
90-10 cupronickel	...	...	...	...	Suitable	93
Admiralty brass	...	...	...	...	Suitable	93
Aluminum bronze	...	...	...	...	Suitable	93
Ampco 8, aluminum bronze	Generally suitable. Conditions such as aeration or temperature could restrict use	...	...	...	Suitable	93
Architectural bronze	...	...	...	...	<0.5 (<20)	96
		...	...	...	Suitable	93

(Continued)

Corrosion Behavior of Various Metals and Alloys in Oxygen (Continued)

Material	Condition, other factors, comments	Concentration, %	Temperature, °C (°F)	Duration	Corrosion rate, mm/yr (mils/yr) or other	Ref
Brass	...	...	...	...	Suitable	93
Cartridge brass	...	...	...	...	Suitable	93
Commercial bronze	...	...	...	...	Suitable	93
Electrolytic copper	...	...	...	...	Suitable	93
Free-cutting brass	...	...	...	...	Suitable	93
Muntz metal	...	...	...	...	Suitable	93
Naval brass	...	...	...	...	Suitable	93
Nickel silver	...	18	...	...	Suitable	93
Phosphor bronze	5% Sn	...	...	...	Suitable	93
Phosphor bronze	8% Sn	...	...	...	Suitable	93
Phosphor copper	...	...	...	...	Suitable	93
Red brass	...	...	...	...	Suitable	93
Silicon bronze	Low	...	...	...	Suitable	93
Silicon bronze	High	...	...	...	Suitable	93
Lead, tin, and zinc						
Zinc	Boiled distilled water, specimens immersed in sealed flasks. (a)	...	Room	...	5.0 mg/dm^2/day (1.0)	140
Zinc	Boiled distilled water, specimens immersed in sealed flasks. (a)	...	40 (104)	...	9.4 mg/dm^2/day (1.9)	140
Zinc	Boiled distilled water, specimens immersed in sealed flasks. (a)	...	65 (149)	...	16.5 mg/dm^2/day (3.3)	140
Zinc	Oxygen bubbled slowly through the water. (a)	...	Room	...	43.0 mg/dm^2/day (8.6)	140
Zinc	Oxygen bubbled slowly through the water. (a)	...	40 (104)	...	68.6 mg/dm^2/day (13.7)	140
Zinc	Oxygen bubbled slowly through the water. (a)	...	65 (149)	...	62.0 mg/dm^2/day (12.4)	140
Noble metals						
Silver	Attack becomes appreciable at 200 °C (390 °F)	Pure	100 (212)	...	<0.05 (<2)	8
Others						
Magnesium	...	100	Room	...	Suitable	119

(a) High-grade zinc specimens, in duplicate, immersed for 7 days. Corrosion rate calculated after removal of corrosion products.

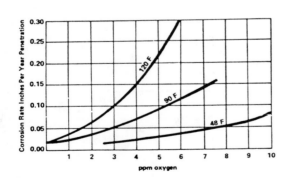

Low-carbon steel. Effect of oxygen concentration on the corrosion of low-carbon steel in tap water at different temperatures. Source: Betz Laboratories, Inc., Advertisement, *Materials Protection, 4*(10), 1965, 21.

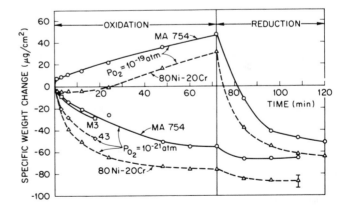

Alloy MA 754. Results of the kinetics experiments at $P_{O2} = 10^{-19}$ and 10^{-21} atm. Note that after 72 min, the specimens were subjected to reducing conditions in pure H_2. Alloy MA 754 contains 0.6% Y_2O_3; alloy 80Ni-20Cr contains no Y_2O_3. Source: D.N. Braski, P.D. Goodell, *et. al.,* "Effect of Y_2O_3 Dispersoids in 80Ni-20Cr Alloy on the Early Stages of Oxidation at Low-Oxygen Potential," *Oxidation of Metals,* Vol 25, Feb 1986, 34.

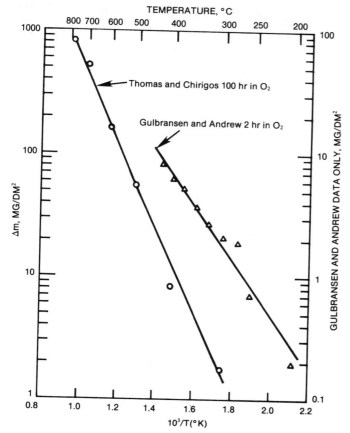

Zirconium. Effect of temperature on the corrosion of zirconium in oxygen. Source: B. Lustman, "Corrosion of Zirconium and Its Alloys," in *Metallurgy of Zirconium*, B. Lustman and F. Kerze, Ed., McGraw-Hill, New York, 1955, 614.

Iron. Effect of oxygen concentration on sodium polyphosphate as a corrosion inhibitor of iron showing beneficial effect of dissolved O_2 and Ca^{2+} during a 48-h test at 25 °C. Source: H.H. Uhlig and R.W. Revie, *Corrosion and Corrosion Engineering: An Introduction to Corrosion Science and Engineering*, 3rd ed., John Wiley & Sons, New York, 1985, 267.

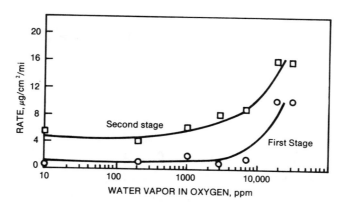

Uranium. Effect of water vapor on reaction of uranium (1-cm cubes) in oxygen at 200 °C. Source: J.H. Gittus, *Uranium*, Butterworths, Washington, DC, 1963, 396.

Ozone

Ozone, O_3, also known as activated oxygen, is an allotropic form of oxygen formed in nature by lightning in air and during the evaporation of water particularly by spray in the sea. It is an unstable blue gas with a distinctive odor. Ozone absorbs ultraviolet rays and acts as a natural blanket that protects the earth from harmful short-wave radiation from the sun. Ozone is a powerful oxidizer. It is used as an oxidant in the rubber industry, as a bleaching agent, as a water purifier, and to treat industrial wastes.

Material Summaries

The following material summaries were compiled from a survey of the available literature. Inclusion of a material description under a given environment does not imply that it is the most appropriate material for corrosion service in that environment. Likewise, exclusion of a given material does not imply that it is not suitable for corrosion service applications in that environment.

Aluminum. Ozonizers have been constructed of aluminum alloys.

Gold. Gold is resistant to ozone up to 100 °C (212 °F).

Silver. Ozone reacts with silver to form silver peroxide at 220 to 250 °C (430 to 480 °F). This black tarnish disappears above about 455 °C (850 °F).

Corrosion Behavior of Various Metals and Alloys in Ozone

Material	Condition, other factors, comments	Concentration, %	Temperature, °C (°F)	Duration	Corrosion rate, mm/yr (mils/yr) or other	Ref
Aluminum (>99.5%)	Dry	...	20 (68)	...	Excellent	92
Gold	With 98% oxygen	...	100 (212)	...	<0.05 (<2)	8
Gold	With 98% oxygen	...	100 (212)	...	<0.05 (<2)	8
Gold	With 98% oxygen	...	100 (212)	...	<0.05 (<2)	6
Platinum	With 98% oxygen	...	Room	...	<0.05 (<2)	8
Silver	With 98% oxygen	...	2-21 (35-70)	105 d	<0.0001 in./yr	89
Type 304 stainless steel	Water treatment; strong aeration; rapid agitation. Ozonated tap water	...	Room	60 d	0.0001 in./yr	89
Type 304 stainless steel	Chemical processing; field or pilot plant test; strong aeration; slight to moderate agitation. Ozone in air plus approximately 0.1 mg/L nitrogen pentoxide	0.23	2-21 (35-70)	105 d	<0.0001 in./yr	89
Type 316 stainless steel	Water treatment; strong aeration; rapid agitation. Ozonated tap water	...	Room	60 d	0.0004 in./yr	89
Type 316 stainless steel	Chemical processing; field or pilot plant test; strong aeration; slight to moderate agitation. Ozone in air plus approximately 0.1 mg/L nitrogen pentoxide	0.23				

Perchloric Acid

Perchloric acid, $HClO_4$, also known as Fraude's reagent, is a colorless, fuming, hygroscopic liquid that boils at 16 °C (61 °F). It is a strong oxidizer and is soluble in water. Cold dilute perchloric acid reacts with metals such as zinc and iron to yield hydrogen gas and the metallic perchlorate. Perchloric acid is used in electrolytic baths, electropolishing, explosives, analytical chemistry, and medicine.

Material Summaries

The following material summaries were compiled from a survey of the available literature. Inclusion of a material description under a given environment does not imply that it is the most appropriate material for corrosion service in that environment. Likewise, exclusion of a given material does not imply that it is not suitable for corrosion service applications in that environment.

Aluminum. Perchloric acid is very corrosive to aluminum alloys.

Tantalum. Tantalum is not attacked by perchloric acid at ordinary temperatures.

Titanium. Titanium alloys are generally highly resistant to perchloric acid over a wide range of concentrations and temperatures.

Additional Reading

B. Yan, G.C. Farrington, and C. Laird, Fatigue Life Behavior of Monocrystalline Copper in 0.1M Perchloric Acid, *Fatigue Fract. Eng. Mater. Struct.,* 8(3), 259-276, 1985. MetAbs No. 86-350182. **Abstract:** The fatigue lives of single crystals of copper have been studied in 0.1M $HClO_4$ under different polarization potentials. Perchloric acid was chosen for the aqueous environment because it allows one to control the corrosion reactions rigorously. Persistent slip band behavior and crack nucleation were studied during life, and fracture surfaces after failure.

H. Mansour, G.A. Noubi, and M.H. Abu-Elwafa, Inhibitive Effect of Pyridine Derivatives on the Corrosion of Zinc in Perchloric Acid, *J. Electrochem. Soc. India, 34*(4), 237-239, 1985. MetAbs No. 86-350903. **Abstract:** The study of the effect of pyridine, pyridine-3-aldehyde, pyridine-4-aldehyde and 4-amino pyridine on the corrosion of zinc in $0.5M$ perchloric acid is discussed.

B. Yan, E. Youngs, G.C. Farrington, and C. Laird, Pitting Morphology in Single Crystals of Copper During and After Cyclic Deformation in $0.1M$ Perchloric Acid, *Corros. Sci., 26*(2), 121-131, 1986. MetAbs No. 86-351191. **Abstract:** The morphologies of corrosion pits produced during cyclic deformation have been studied in copper single crystals exposed to corrosion, and by exposing previously cycled specimens to the same corrosive environment ($0.1M$ $HClO_4$) but without cycling.

K. Aramaki, M. Hagiwara, and H. Nishihara, The Synergistic Effect of Anions and the Ammonium Cation on the Inhibition of Iron Corrosion in Acid Solution, *Corros. Sci., 27*(5), 487-497, 1987. MetAbs No. 87-352134. **Abstract:** The synergistic effect of various anions and the tetra-n-butylammonium cation on the inhibition of iron corrosion in $1M$ $HClO_4$ and their joint adsorption on iron were studied by using an impedance and a polarization technique.

Corrosion Behavior of Various Metals and Alloys in Perchloric Acid

Material	Condition, other factors, comments	Concentration, %	Temperature, °C (°F)	Duration	Corrosion rate, mm/yr (mils/yr) or other	Ref
Tin	...	...	20 (68)	...	Unsuitable	94
Tin	...	...	60 (140)	...	Unsuitable	94
Tin	...	...	100 (212)	...	Unsuitable	94
Zr702	...	70	100 (212)	...	<0.05 (<2)	15

Petroleum Oils

Petroleum oils comprise a mixture of hydrocarbons including the liquid paraffin series, C_5H_{12} to $C_{16}H_{34}$, the cycloparaffin or naphthene series, $C_{17}H_{36}$ to $C_{27}H_{56}$, and the gases, CH_4 to C_4H_{10}. Petroleum is a heavy, flammable oil that is formed by the decomposition of animal and plant remains by fermentation or bacterial action in a low-temperature, high-pressure reaction. Crude oil may be designated as "sour" if it contains sulfur compounds. Petroleum is used mainly in the production of fuels and lubricants, but also provides raw materials for a wide range of chemicals called petrochemicals.

The corrosivity of petroleum oils during refining is related to original constituents such as hydrogen sulfide, carbon dioxide, and other sulfur-bearing chlorides, and heavy metals and products formed during refining. The reader is encouraged to pursue the corrosivity of each of these individual compounds rather than expect the data herein to be sufficient.

Material Summaries

The following material summaries were compiled from a survey of the available literature. Inclusion of a material description under a given environment does not imply that it is the most appropriate material for corrosion service in that environment. Likewise, exclusion of a given material does not imply that it is not suitable for corrosion service applications in that environment.

Carbon steel. The majority of petroleum oils are handled successfully with carbon steel equipment. Corrosion of steel in petroleum oils is almost always the result of associated sulfur compounds, carbon dioxide gas, or salts in the oil.

Aluminum. Aluminum alloy equipment has been used for pipelines, distillation columns, heat exchangers, storage tanks, piping, and valves handling petroleum oils because of its superior corrosion resistance compared to that of steel. However, due to the corrosive nature of some of the brines found in oil wells, it is necessary to test the brine of a specific oil field before use in aluminum alloy equipment. Sour crude (crude that contains sulfur compounds) that has previously been in contact with steel equipment may contain iron sulfide scale, which if deposited on the aluminum alloy equipment poses a corrosion hazard.

Additional Reading

M. El-Arabi and A. Mazur, Flow-Line Failure Resulting From Erosion-Corrosion in a High Production Oil Well, *Mater. Perform., 24*(9), 19-22, 1985. MetAbs No. 86-350018. **Abstract:** Severe erosion-corrosion has been experienced in the flow-line, downstream of the choke valve (of carbon steel) on a high-production oil well. A program of mitigation is discussed to remedy the problem.

R.S. Tresder, Corrosion in the Petroleum Industry, in *Encyclopedia of Materials Science and Engineering*, Vol 2, Pergamon Press, Oxford, 881-882, 1986. MetAbs No. 86-351934. **Abstract:** The major corrosion problems encountered in the production, transportation and refining of crude oil and natural gas are discussed and typical methods of corrosion control are described.

G. Guntz, C. Jollain, B. Sala, B. Heritier, and B. Baroux, Duplex Stainless Steel Tubings for Sour Gas and Oil Environment. Influence of the Austenite-Ferrite Ratio on the Corrosion Resistance and Mechanical Properties, *Bull. Cercle Etud. Metaux, 15*(11), 14, 1986. MetAbs No. 87-350691. **Abstract:** The effects of alloying elements on the mechanical characteristics, phase balance and corrosion resistance of duplex stainless steels containing 22% Cr, 5% Ni and 3% Mo are described. Corrosion studies concentrated on the effect of alloying elements and ferrite content on resistance to stress-corrosion cracking. Results on the influence of nitrogen, chromium, nickel, copper and tungsten on the various properties are summarized.

P. Kirkov, The Influence of Drag Reducers and Inhibitors on the Rate and Mechanism of Corrosion in Petroleum White Products in the Presence of Moisture, *Electrochim. Acta, 32*(6), 921-926, 1987. MetAbs No. 87-352344. **Abstract:** The correlation between concentration of moisture in petroleum white products and corrosion rate in an atmosphere of air, oxygen, nitrogen and hydrogen with and without the presence of inhibitors and drag reducers has been investigated by internal pit propagation in a closed pipeline system and metal cylinders. The carbon and chromium nickel steels used for construction of pipelines and storage vessels have been investigated.

I. von Hagen, R.K. Popperling, H. Schlerkmann, and U. Zeislmair, Answers to the Requirements on OCTG in Corrosive Wells, *3R Int., 25*(10), 538-544, 1986. MetAbs No. 87-352433. **Abstract:** Results of extensive research work toward the development of corrosion-resistant alloys for OCTG are presented. The mechanical strength of the materials at room temperature and at service temperatures up to 350 °C, as well as the long-term behavior of the mechanical strength at service temperatures, are of significance.

R.J. Jasinski and K.D. Efird, Electrochemical Corrosion Measurements in Crude Oil, *Corrosion, 43*(8), 476-478, 1987. MetAbs No. 87-352842. **Abstract:** An electrode assembly (probe) has been developed that allows the use of linear polarization methods to study corrosion in high-solution resistance environments, with no additional equipment or electrical shielding required, except those commonly used for low-solution resistance environments.

M. Fichera, R. Leonardi, and C.A. Farina, Fuel Ash Corrosion and Its Prevention With MgO Addition, *Electrochim. Acta, 32*(6), 955-960, 1987. MetAbs No. 87-352349. **Abstract:** Corrosion of 310 and 321 stainless steels in oil-fired boilers due to the presence of vanadium, Na and sulfur in low-grade fuels was investigated. By adding magnesium oxide in fuel oil the melting point of deposits taken from superheater tubes experience a considerable increase.

Corrosion Behavior of Various Metals and Alloys in Petroleum Oils (Refined, Sour)

Material	Condition, other factors, comments	Concentration, %	Temperature, °C (°F)	Duration	Corrosion rate, mm/yr (mils/yr) or other	Ref
Steels						
API N80	Crude oil, 0.8 MPa CO_2. Mixture conditioned with steel before test. Corrosion rate determined by coupon weight loss in hydrocarbon/water mixture	90	70 (158)	24 h	0.30	181
API N80	Crude oil, 0.8 MPa CO_2. Mixture conditioned with steel before test. Corrosion rate determined by electrochemical probe linear polarization in hydrocarbon/water mixture	90	70 (158)	24 h	0.28	181
API N80	Crude oil, 5.2 MPa CO_2. Mixture conditioned with steel before test. Corrosion rate determined by coupon weight loss in hydrocarbon/water mixture	90	85 (186)	24 h	0.01	181
API N80	Crude oil, 5.2 MPa CO_2. Mixture conditioned with steel before test. Corrosion rate determined by electrochemical probe linear polarization in hydrocarbon/water mixture	90	85 (186)	24 h	0.008	181
API N80	Crude oil, 0.8 MPa Ar. Mixture conditioned with steel before test. Corrosion rate determined by coupon weight loss in hydrocarbon/water mixture	90	70 (158)	24 h	0.41	181
API N80	Crude oil, 0.8 MPa Ar. Mixture conditioned with steel before test. Corrosion rate determined by electrochemical probe linear polarization in hydrocarbon/water mixture	90	70 (158)	24 h	0.36	181
API N80	Crude oil, 0.8 MPa CO_2 + 20 ppm H_2S. Mixture conditioned with steel before test. Corrosion rate determined by coupon weight loss in hydrocarbon/water mixture	90	70 (158)	24 h	0.24	181
API N80	Crude oil, 0.8 MPa CO_2 + 20 ppm H_2S. Mixture conditioned with steel before test. Corrosion rate determined by coupon weight loss in hydrocarbon/water mixture	90	70 (158)	24 h	0.30	181
API N80	Crude oil, 0.8 MPa CO_2 + 20 ppm H_2S. Mixture conditioned with steel before test. Corrosion rate determined by electrochemical probe linear polarization in hydrocarbon/water mixture	90	70 (158)	24 h	0.48	181
API N80	Crude oil, 0.8 MPa CO_2 + 20 ppm H_2S. Mixture conditioned with steel before test. Corrosion rate determined by electrochemical probe linear polarization in hydrocarbon/water mixture	90	70 (158)	24 h	0.13	181
API N80	Crude oil, 0.8 MPa CO_2 + 20 ppm H_2S. Mixture conditioned with steel before test. Corrosion rate determined by coupon weight loss in hydrocarbon/water mixture	95	70 (158)	24 h	0.04	181
API N80	Crude oil, 5.2 MPa CO_2. Mixture conditioned with steel before test. Corrosion rate determined by coupon weight loss in hydrocarbon/water mixture	95	85 (186)	24 h	0.08	181

(Continued)

Corrosion Behavior of Various Metals and Alloys in Petroleum Oils (Refined, Sour) (Continued)

Material	Condition, other factors, comments	Concentration, %	Temperature, °C (°F)	Duration	Corrosion rate, mm/yr (mils/yr) or other	Ref
API N80	Crude oil, 5.2 MPa CO_2. Mixture conditioned with steel before test. Corrosion rate determined by electrochemical probe linear polarization in hydrocarbon/water mixture	95	85 (186)	24 h	0.11	181
API N80	Crude oil, 0.8 MPa CO_2 + 20 ppm H_2S. Mixture conditioned with steel before test. Corrosion rate determined by electrochemical probe linear polarization in hydrocarbon/water mixture	95	70 (158)	24 h	0.03	181
API N80	Crude oil, 0.8 MPa CO_2 + 20 ppm H_2S. Mixture conditioned with steel before test. Corrosion rate determined by coupon weight loss in hydrocarbon/water mixture	95	70 (158)	24 h	0.13	181
API N80	Crude oil, 0.8 MPa CO_2 + 20 ppm H_2S. Mixture conditioned with steel before test. Corrosion rate determined by electrochemical probe linear polarization in hydrocarbon/water mixture	95	70 (158)	24 h	0.10	181
API N80	Crude oil, 0.8 MPa CO_2 + 20 ppm H_2S. Mixture conditioned with steel before test. Corrosion rate determined by electrochemical probe linear polarization in hydrocarbon/water mixture	98	70 (158)	24 h	0.02	181
API N80	Crude oil, 0.8 MPa CO_2 + 20 ppm H_2S. Mixture conditioned with steel before test. Corrosion rate determined by coupon weight loss in hydrocarbon/water mixture	98	70 (158)	24 h	0.04	181
Carbon steel	Cast. (a)	...	345 (650)	1000 h	3040 mg/cm^2 (196 mg/in.^{2})	107
Cast steel, seamless tubing	5% Cr. (a)	...	345 (650)	1000 h	1540 mg/cm^2 (99.2 mg/in.^{2})	107
Stainless steel, 18Cr-8Ni	(a)	...	345 (650)	1000 h	2.1 mg/cm^2 (30 mg/in.^{2})	107
Steel	Cast. 12% Cr. (a)	...	345 (650)	1000 h	6.4 mg/cm^2 (100 mg/in.^{2})	107
Steel, 2Ni-0.75 Cr	Cast. (a)	...	345 (650)	1000 h	2370 mg/cm^2 (153 mg/in.^{2})	107
Steel, 5Cr-0.5Mo	Cast. (a)	...	345 (650)	1000 h	730 mg/cm^2 (47 mg/in.^{2})	107
Steel, 5Cr-1W	Cast. (a)	...	345 (650)	1000 h	950 mg/cm^2 (61.5 mg/in.^{2})	107
Type 410 stainless steel	Petrol	...	Room	...	Unattacked	121
Aluminum						
Aluminum-manganese	Crude oil	...	250-500 (482-932)	...	Satisfactory	92
Aluminum-manganese alloys	...	...	...	...	Satisfactory	92
Aluminum (99.0-99.5%)	...	...	...	...	Satisfactory	92
Aluminum (99.0-99.5%)	Oils	...	<250 (<482)	...	Satisfactory	92
Aluminum (99.0-99.5%)	Crude oil	...	250-500 (482-932)	...	Satisfactory	92
Coppers						
Ampco 8, aluminum bronze	Sour. Generally suitable. Conditions such as aeration or temperature could restrict use	...	...	...	<0.5 (<20)	96
Ampco 8, aluminum bronze	Refined. Generally suitable	...	...	...	<0.05 (<2)	96

(a) Test in petroleum vapor under 780 N (175 lb) of pressure.

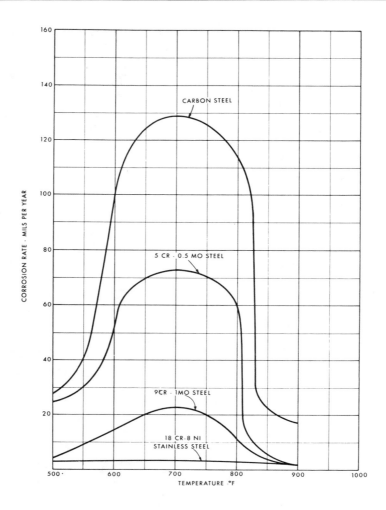

Steel. Corrosion of steels in crude oil containing 1.5% sulfur. Source: J.F. Bosich, *Corrosion Prevention for Practicing Engineers*, Barnes & Noble, New York, 1970, 214.

Phenol

Phenol, C_6H_5OH, also known as carbolic acid and phenylic acid, is a white poisonous crystalline solid that melts at 43 °C (110 °F) and boils at 182 °C (360 °F). Phenol has a sharp burning taste, a distinctive odor, and it irritates tissue. It is toxic not only by ingestion or inhalation, but also by skin absorption. Phenol is soluble in water, alcohol, and ether. It is used in the production of resins, germicides, weed killers, pharmaceuticals, and as a solvent in the refining of lubricating oils.

Material Summaries

The following material summaries were compiled from a survey of the available literature. Inclusion of a material description under a given environment does not imply that it is the most appropriate material for corrosion service in that environment. Likewise, exclusion of a given material does not imply that it is not suitable for corrosion service applications in that environment.

Aluminum. Aluminum alloy 3003 resisted attack by anhydrous phenol up to 50 °C (122 °F), but was mildly affected, 0.125 mm/yr (5 mils/yr), by aqueous solutions. Anhydrous phenol proved very corrosive at higher temperatures. Aluminum alloy drums, tubes, and A356.0 valves have been used to handle phenol.

Nickel. Nickel 200 protects phenol from contamination and discoloration and is therefore used to line steel storage tanks and tank cars.

Corrosion Behavior of Various Metals and Alloys in Phenol

Material	Condition, other factors, comments	Concentration, %	Temperature, °C (°F)	Duration	Corrosion rate, mm/yr (mils/yr) or other	Ref
Stainless steels						
AM-363 stainless steel	...	...	Room	...	Slightly attacked	120
Type 302 stainless steel	...	88	53 (125)	...	5 μm/yr (0.2)	139
Type 302 stainless steel	...	88	185 (365)	...	5 μm/yr (0.2)	139
Type 304 stainless steel	Chemically pure	...	21 (70)	...	Good	121
Type 304 stainless steel	...	100	315 (600)	...	25 μm/yr (1)	139
Type 310 stainless steel	...	100	315 (600)	...	25 μm/yr (1)	139
Type 316 stainless steel	Chemically pure	...	21 (70)	...	Good	121
Type 316 stainless steel	...	10	105 (220)	...	nil	139
Type 316 stainless steel	...	88	53 (125)	...	5 μm/yr (0.2)	139
Type 316 stainless steel	...	88	185 (365)	...	5 μm/yr (0.2)	139
Type 316 stainless steel	...	100	315 (600)	...	25 μm/yr (1)	139
Type 410 stainless steel	Chemically pure	...	21 (70)	...	Good	121
Type 410 stainless steel	...	...	Room	...	Attacked	121
Type 430 stainless steel	Chemically pure	...	21 (70)	...	Good	121
Type 430 stainless steel	...	10	105 (220)	...	nil	139
Aluminum						
Aluminum-manganese alloys	...	...	...	...	Restricted applications	92
Aluminum (99.0-99.5%)	...	...	...	...	Restricted applications	92
Coppers						
Ampco 8, aluminum bronze	Generally suitable. Conditions such as aeration or temperature could restrict use	...	...	...	<0.5 (<20)	96
Titanium						
Titanium	...	Saturated	25 (77)	...	0.102 (4.08)	90
Zirconium						
Zr702	...	Saturated	Room	...	<0.13 (<5)	15
Lead, tin, and zinc						
Lead	During sulfonation with 93% H_2SO_4 (66° Be)	...	120 (248)	...	0.075 (3)	48
Lead	Practically resistant; Pb recommended for use	90	24 (75)	...	<500 μm/yr (<20)	95
Tin	...	...	20 (68)	...	Resistant	94
Tin	...	...	60 (140)	...	Resistant	94
Tin	...	...	100 (212)	...	Unsuitable	94
Noble metals						
Gold	...	All	Boiling	...	<0.05 (<2)	7
Platinum	...	All	Boiling	...	<0.05 (<2)	6
Silver	...	All	Boiling	...	<0.05 (<2)	10
Others						
Magnesium	...	100	Room	...	Suitable	119

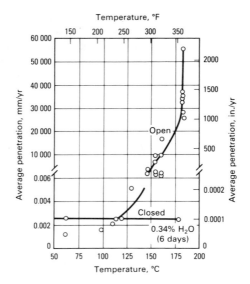

Aluminum. Effect of temperature of phenol. Rapid reaction above 120 °C (250 °F) can be stopped by small additions of steam or water. Source: *Metals Handbook*, 9th ed., Vol 13, Corrosion, ASM International, Metals Park, OH, 1987, 608.

Phosgene

Phosgene, $COCl_2$, also known as carbonyl chloride and chloroformyl chloride, is a colorless, poisonous gas produced by the action of chlorine and carbon monoxide. It condenses at 0 °C (32 °F) to a fuming liquid. Phosgene was used as a war gas, but is now used in the production of metal chlorides, pharmaceuticals, isocyanate resins, and perfumes.

Material Summaries

The following material summaries were compiled from a survey of the available literature. Inclusion of a material description under a given environment does not imply that it is the most appropriate material for corrosion service in that environment. Likewise, exclusion of a given material does not imply that it is not suitable for corrosion service applications in that environment.

Gold. Gold is resistant to phosgene at room temperature.

Corrosion Behavior of Various Metals and Alloys in Phosgene

Material	Condition, other factors, comments	Concentration, %	Temperature, °C (°F)	Duration	Corrosion rate, mm/yr (mils/yr) or other	Ref
Aluminum (>99.5%)	...	...	...	...	Satisfactory	92
Gold	...	...	Room	...	<0.05 (<2)	8
Gold	...	...	Room	...	<0.05 (<2)	8

Phosphoric Acid

The term "phosphoric acid" is normally used in reference to orthophosphoric acid (H_3PO_4). In anhydrous form, orthophosphoric acid is a white, crystalline solid that melts at 42.35 °C and forms a hemihydrate ($2H_3PO_4 \cdot H_2O$) that melts at 29.32 °C. This acid can be produced in virtually any desired concentration, but usually it is supplied as a solution containing from 75 to 85% phosphoric acid and melting at temperatures from 17.5 to 21.1 °C.

Phosphoric acid is obtained by two different means. The wet-process acid is obtained by reacting phosphate rock with concentrated sulfuric acid and concentrating the resulting dilute acid by evaporation. The furnace acid is obtained by calcining the phosphate rock to produce elemental phosphorus, which is then oxidized and reacted with water to produce phosphoric acid. This latter acid is very pure and is used as reagent grade.

The wet-process acid is used to make phosphatic fertilizers and usually contains a number of impurities, such as HF, sulfuric acid, and SiO_2. The percentage of these impurities depends on the source of the rock, the process of reaction with sulfuric acid, and the state of concentration of the phosphoric acid.

Particularly sensitive to the impurities in wet-process acid are the stainless steels, which are widely employed in phosphoric acid service.

In addition, a given alloy can corrode at different rates in wet-process acids from different manufacturers. Because of these differences, it is imperative that any comparison between alloys in this type of acid be made from tests conducted in the same batch of acid from the same source. It can also be seen that the wet-process acid can be considerably more corrosive than the reagent grade acid.

When heated to temperatures above 200 °C (390 °F), phosphoric acid loses its water of constitution, and salts of the resulting dehydrated acids are used in preparing some liquid fertilizers and some detergents. Use of these salts in detergents, however, has been severely restricted in an attempt to reduce pollution by phosphates. Phosphoric acid is also used in soft drinks and flavored syrups, in pharmaceuticals, in water treatment, in animal feeds, and for pickling of rustproof metals.

Material Summaries

The following material summaries were compiled from a survey of the available literature. Inclusion of a material description under a given environment does not imply that it is the most appropriate material for corrosion service in that environment. Likewise, exclusion of a given material does not imply that it is not suitable for corrosion service applications in that environment.

Cast Irons. All cast irons find some application in phosphoric acid, but the presence of contaminants must be carefully evaluated before selecting a material for this service. Unalloyed cast iron finds little use in phosphoric acid, with the exception of concentrated acids. Even in concentrated acids, use may be severely limited by the presence of fluorides, chlorides, or sulfuric acid.

High-nickel cast irons find some application in phosphoric acid at and slightly above room temperature. These cast irons can be used over the entire phosphoric acid concentration range. Impurities in the acid may greatly restrict the applicability of this grade of cast iron.

High-chromium cast irons exhibit generally low rates of attack in phosphoric acid up to 60% concentration. High-silicon cast irons show good-to-excellent resistance at all concentrations and temperatures of pure acid. The presence of fluoride ions (F^-) in phosphoric acid makes the high-silicon irons unacceptable for use.

Stainless Steels. Conventional straight-chromium stainless steels have very limited general corrosion resistance in phosphoric acid and exhibit lower rates only in very dilute or more highly concentrated solutions. Conventional austenitic stainless steels provide useful general corrosion resistance over the full range of concentrations up to about 65 °C (150 °F); use at temperatures up to the boiling point is possible for acid concentrations up to about 40%.

In commercial applications, however, wet-process phosphoric acid environments include impurities derived from the phosphate rock, such as chlorides, fluorides, and sulfuric acid. These three impurities accelerate corrosion, particularly pitting or crevice corrosion in the presence of the halogens. Higher alloyed materials than the conventional austenitic stainless steels are required to resist wet-process phosphoric acid. Candidate materials include alloy 904L, alloy 28, 20Cb-3, 20Mo-4, and 20Mo-6 stainless steels.

Cemented Carbides. The only cemented carbides that are subject to relatively rapid attack by phosphoric acid are the WC-Co compositions. The resistance of cemented TiC to corrosion by phosphoric acid is excellent, being somewhat better than that of cemented WC in hydrochloric and sulfuric acids.

Aluminum. In laboratory tests, aqueous solutions of phosphoric acid (5 to 85%) were corrosive to alloy 1100 and the corrosion rate increased with concentration at ambient temperature. The rate of attack was ~100 mils/yr at 5% and ~1200 mils/yr at 85% concentration. The action of phosphoric acid can be reduced by the addition of inhibitors. Aqueous solutions containing phosphoric acid and chromium trioxide have been used as cleaning solutions and as surface preparation for painting of aluminum alloys.

Copper. In general, copper and copper alloys provide satisfactory service in handling pure phosphoric acid solutions in various concentrations. The acid concentration seems to have less effect on the corrosion rate than the amount of impurities. The impure phosphoric acid produced by the sulfuric acid process may contain a markedly higher concentration of various ions than acid produced by the electric furnace process. These ions increase the corrosion rate up to 150 times, which limits the service lives of copper alloys.

Pure phosphoric acid produced by the electric furnace process contains only small quantities of impurities and is therefore only slightly corrosive to copper and its alloys. Inhibited admiralty metals C44300, C44400, and C44500 are suggested for solutions of pure phosphoric acid.

Accumulation of corrosion products on metal surfaces may also increase both the rate of corrosion and the possibility of pitting. Low-copper alloys, such as C46400 (naval brass), appear to form thin, adherent films of corrosion products. Copper, copper-silicon alloys, and other high-copper alloys form more voluminous, porous films or scales beneath which roughened or pitted surfaces are likely to be found.

The phosphoric acid vapors that condense in electrostatic precipitators at about 120 °C (250 °F) are noticeably more corrosive than solutions of pure phosphoric acid at the same or lower temperatures. The corrosion rates encountered in precipitators are so high that copper alloy wires will not give satisfactory service as electrodes. The high rate of corrosion is probably caused by an abundant supply of oxygen.

Although the corrosion rates of copper cooling tubes in phosphoric acid condensation chambers are high (about 10 mm/yr, or 400 mils/yr), the rates are lower than those of some other materials. Therefore, the use of copper tubes is feasible for this application.

Copper and copper alloys are used in heat-exchanger tubes, pipes, and fittings for handling phosphoric acid, although the corrosion rates of some of these alloys may be comparatively high. Laboratory tests were performed on groups of copper alloys in aerated and unaerated acid, with specimens at the water line, in quiet immersion, and totally submerged. Acid concentrations ranged from 5 to 90%, and temperatures ranged from 20 to 85 °C (70 to 185 °F) except for the copper-aluminum-silicon alloy, which was tested only in 6.5% phosphoric acid at 20 °C (70 °F) with specimens at the water line and in quiet immersion. Corrosion rates for alloy groups were as follows:

* Copper: 22 to 148 mils/yr

* Copper-zinc (70% Cu min): 5 to 280 mils/yr

* Copper-tin: 1 to 52 mils/yr

* Copper-nickel: 1 to 25 mils/yr

* Copper-silicon: 5 to 37 mils/yr

* Copper-aluminum-iron: 5 to 10 mils/yr

* Copper-aluminum-silicon: 11 to 97 mils/yr

Aluminum bronzes are generally suitable for service in phosphoric acid.

Lead has high corrosion resistance to phosphoric acid, as well as to chromic, sulfuric, and sulfurous acids, and is widely used in their manufacture and handling. It exhibits excellent corrosion resistance to higher concentrations of these acids at elevated temperatures.

Lead finds especially wide application in the manufacture of phosphoric acid from phosphate rock when sulfuric acid is used in the process. Corrosion rates are low for all acid concentrations up to 85%. The corrosion rate of 6% antimonial lead has been reported to be lower than that of chemical lead in a plant test using a solution containing 32% phosphoric acid, 0.4% sulfuric acid, and 1% chlorides at 88 °C (190 °F). In pure acid manufactured from elemental phosphor, lead corrodes at a higher rate because of the absence of sulfates.

Nickel alloys that are suitable for handling various concentrations of phosphoric acid include 20Cb-3 and alloys 825, C, G-3, G-30, and 625. Plant test results have shown that 20Cb-3 and alloys 825 and C have the highest corrosion resistance in dilute phosphoric acid process solutions. In very high-concentration phosphoric acid at high temperatures, alloy B-2 exhibits the highest resistance. The corrosion resistance in these acids seems to depend on molybdenum content.

It has been shown that in wet-process phosphoric acid, as opposed to furnace (reagent grade) acid, a high chromium content, such as in alloy G-30, improves corrosion resistance. In addition, Cl⁻ is inevitably present in these acids, and therefore, molybdenum and tungsten additions are beneficial.

Niobium is resistant to phosphoric acid at all concentrations and at temperatures below 100 °C (212 °F). In boiling 40 and 50% phosphoric acid with small amounts of F⁻ impurity (5 ppm), niobium has a corrosion rate of 0.25 mm/yr (10 mils/yr).

Silver can be used for handling phosphoric acid in all concentrations at temperatures from 160 to 200 °C (320 to 390 °F).

Tantalum exhibits superior resistance to boiling phosphoric acid at all concentrations. At a temperature in excess of boiling, the superiority of tantalum is evident. However, if the phosphoric acid contains more than a few parts per million of F⁻ ion, as is frequently the case with commercial acid, corrosive attack may occur.

In one study, the corrosion resistance of commercially pure tantalum to a mixture of phosphoric acid, potassium chloride, and water initially containing 60 to 260 ppm F⁻ was evaluated at 120 °C (250 °F) and at atmospheric pressure. Corrosion rates calculated from the test data were on the order of 0.0005 to 0.15 mm/yr (0.02 to 6 mils/yr), indicating good corrosion resistance.

Zirconium resists attack in phosphoric acid at concentrations up to 55% and at temperatures exceeding the boiling point. Above 55% phosphoric acid, the corrosion rate could increase greatly with temperature. The most interesting area of application of zirconium to phosphoric acid service is in dilute phosphoric acid at elevated temperatures. Tests have shown that zirconium outperforms some stainless alloys in 20% phosphoric acid at 150 °C (300 °F).

Anodic polarization curves for zirconium in phosphoric acid at near-boiling temperatures show that as concentration increases, the passive range diminishes gradually, and the passive current increases progressively. It appears that zirconium passivates more slowly in phosphoric acid than in other mineral acids.

If phosphoric acid contains more than a trace of F⁻ ion, attack on zirconium may occur. Because fluoride compounds are usually present in phosphoric acid, the use of zirconium has always been questioned. However, because P_2O_5 is an effective fluoride inhibitor for zirconium and a large amount of P_2O_5 is often present in phosphoric acid processes, tests should be performed to determine the suitability of zirconium in the actual phosphoric acid medium.

Additional Reading

N. Bui, A. Irhzo, R. Dabosi, and Y. Limouzin-Maire, On the Mechanism for Improved Passivation by Additions of Tungsten to Austenitic Stainless Steels, *Corrosion*, 39(12), 491-496, 1983. MetAbs No. 84-350836. **Abstract:** To elucidate the role of tungsten in improving the passivity of austenitic stainless steels, anodic polarization curves and X-ray photoelectron spectra have been obtained for pure W and W-containing steels passivated in 1N HCl, 0.1M NaCl and in Cl⁻ containing H_3PO_4.

Y.G. Kim, G.W. Yoon, and N.S. Stoloff, Effect of Boron on the Corrosion Behavior of Polycrystalline Ni₃Al, *Metall. Trans. A*, 16A(11), 2072-2073, 1985. MetAbs No. 85-352341. **Abstract:** The effects of boron additions on the corrosion behavior of Ni₃Al in HCl, H_2SO_4, NaCl and H_3PO_4 electrolytes were studied.

M.M. Nerodenko, L.M. Onoprienko, V.A. Gorban, and A.B. Goncharov, Corrosion Resistance of Welded Joints of Zirconium Alloy With 2.5% Niobium in Hydrochloric, Sulfuric and Phosphoric Acids, *Avtom. Svarka*, (8), 53-56, 1985. MetAbs No. 86-350415. **Abstract:** Corrosion resistance of TIG welded samples from Zr-Nb alloy (2.5% Nb, 0.056% oxygen, 0.0006% hydrogen, and 0.0067% nitrogen) was determined by weight loss in boiling solutions of HCl, H_2SO_4, and H_3PO_4 and also in 20% solution of HCl with addition of 1 g/L $CuCl_2$. Potentiostat P-5827M was used for measuring electrochemical characteristics.

S.H. Glarum and J.H. Marshall, The Anodic Dissolution of Copper Into Phosphoric Acid. I. Voltammetric and Oscillatory Behavior, *J. Electrochem. Soc.*, 132(12), 2872-2878, 1985. MetAbs No. 86-350437. **Abstract:** Anodic electrochemical dissolution of metals is often used in commercial electropolishing, and the copper/phosphoric acid system is a classic example. Surface films are believed essential for polishing, but their composition and role remain elusive. Current oscillations, which may by excited, have been attributed to film formation and breakdown. The information obtained from voltammetric measurements using rotating disk electrodes is examined.

S.H. Glarum and J.H. Marshall, The Anodic Dissolution of Copper Into Phosphoric Acid. II. Impedance Behavior, *J. Electrochem. Soc.*, 132(12), 2878-2885, 1985. MetAbs No. 86-350438. **Abstract:** Impedance measurements have been used to study the electrochemical dissolution of Cu rotating disk electrodes in phosphoric acid as a function of potential and current density.

N. Nassif, Influence of Impurities in Phosphoric Acid on the Corrosion Resistance of Some Commercially Produced Alloys, *Surf. Technol.*,

26(3), 189-198, 1985. MetAbs No. 86-350562. **Abstract:** The influence of Cl⁻, F⁻, S²⁻, SO₄²⁻, SiO₃²⁻, Fe³⁺, Al³⁺, Ca²⁺, and Mg²⁺ ions on the corrosion behavior of stainless steels 304 and 316, Incoloy 825, Inconel 625, Corronel 230, and Hastelloys C and G was investigated. The alloys were tested in 75% H_3PO_4 in the absence and presence of various concentrations of each of the impurities at 85 °C under reflux and stirring conditions.

A. Kawashima, K. Asami, and K. Hashimoto, An XPS Study of Passive Films on Nickel and Alloy 600 in Acids, *Corros. Sci.*, 25(12), 1103-1114, 1985. MetAbs No. 86-351115. **Abstract:** Compositions of surface films formed on Ni and Alloy 600 in $1M$ HCl, $0.5M$ H_2SO_4 and $0.33M$ H_3PO_4 solutions were investigated as a function of polarization potential.

J.D. Talati and J.M. Daraji, Dyes as Corrosion Inhibitors. II. Triphenyl Methane Dyes as Inhibitors for Aluminium—Copper Alloy in Phosphoric Acid, *J. Electrochem. Soc. India*, 35(3), 175-181, 1986. MetAbs No. 87-351501. **Abstract:** The inhibitive efficiency of triphenyl methane dyes for B26S Al in phosphoric acid increases with inhibitor concentration, but decreases with acid concentration.

P.H. Wilhelmsson, Special Stainless Steels for the Process Industry. II, *Stainless Steel Ind.*, 15(84), 7, 8, 9, 31, 1987. MetAbs No. 87-351783. **Abstract:** The resistance to attack in various acids of several duplex and highly alloyed stainless steels is discussed. Examples are given of their application in the process plant industry and the economic aspects of using these steels are considered.

F. El-Taib Heakal, A.S. Mogoda, A.A. Mazhar, and M.S. El-Basiouny, Kinetic Studies on the Dissolution of the Anodic Oxide Film on Titanium in Phosphoric Acid Solutions, *Corros. Sci.*, 27(5), 453-462, 1987. MetAbs No. 87-352133. **Abstract:** Capacitance and potential measurements versus time show a two-stage dissolution process in H_3PO_4 for the anodic oxide films formed galvanostatically on Ti.

B. Linder, Anodic Protection of Stainless Steel in Phosphoric Acid Containing Halide Ions, *Ind. Corros.*, 5(3), 12-17, 1987. MetAbs No. 87-352373. **Abstract:** Stainless steel is used to a large extent for storage, handling, and transportation of phosphoric acid without any special measures being taken from a corrosion point of view.

A.A. Mazhar, F. El-Taib Heakal, and A.S. Mogoda, Discussion on the Behavior of a Porous Anodic Film on Aluminum in H_3PO_4 Studied by Electrochemical Techniques, *Corrosion*, 44(6), 354-359, 1988. MetAbs No. 88-351718. **Abstract:** The dissolution behavior of anodic oxide films formed on Al (99.99%) in phosphoric acid solutions has been studied by impedance and potential measurements.

Corrosion Behavior of Various Metals and Alloys in Phosphoric Acid

Material	Condition, other factors, comments	Concentration, %	Temperature, °C (°F)	Duration	Corrosion rate, mm/yr (mils/yr) or other	Ref
Irons and steels						
Austenitic cast iron	Type 1. Aerated. (a)	5	30 (86)	1 d	2.8, 3.1 (112, 124)	156
Austenitic cast iron	Type 1. Aerated. (a)	5	87 (190)	0.88 d	9.2 (365)	156
Austenitic cast iron	Type 1. Not aerated. (a)	5	30 (86)	1 d	1.67, 2.2 (66, 90)	156
Austenitic cast iron	Type 1. Not aerated. (a)	5	87 (190)	0.88 d	6.9 (275)	156
Austenitic cast iron	Type 2. Not aerated. (a)	5	50 (122)	6 d	24.28 (956)	156
Austenitic cast iron	Type 2. Aerated. (a)	5	50 (122)	6 d	45.97 (1810)	156
Austenitic cast iron	Type D2. Not aerated. (a)	5	50 (122)	6 d	3.9 (154)	156
Austenitic cast iron	Type D2. Aerated. (a)	5	50 (122)	6 d	32 (1260)	156
Austenitic cast iron	Type 1. Not aerated. (a)	15	30 (86)	0.83 d	1.3 (52)	156
Austenitic cast iron	Type 1. Aerated. (a)	15	30 (86)	0.83 d	2.1 (84)	156
Austenitic cast iron	Type 1. Not aerated. (a)	15	87 (190)	0.83 d	8.1 (319)	156
Austenitic cast iron	Type 1. Aerated. (a)	15	87 (190)	0.83 d	12.5 (493)	156
Austenitic cast iron	Type 1. Not aerated. (a)	25	30 (86)	1 d	1.09 (43)	156
Austenitic cast iron	Type 1. Aerated. (a)	25	30 (86)	1 d	1.8 (72)	156
Austenitic cast iron	Type 1. Not aerated. (a)	25	87 (190)	0.83 d	12.9, 19.2 (510, 757)	156
Austenitic cast iron	Type 1. Aerated. (a)	25	87 (190)	0.83 d	13, 25.9 (512, 1023)	156
Austenitic cast iron	Type 2. Not aerated. (a)	85	30 (86)	1 d	5 (199)	156
Austenitic cast iron	Type 2. Aerated. (a)	85	30 (86)	1 d	5.1 (204)	156
Austenitic cast iron	Type 2. Aerated. (a)	85	50 (122)	1 d	21.9 (863)	156
Austenitic cast iron	Type 2. Aerated.	85	80 (176)	0.25 d	67.5 (2660)	156
Austenitic cast iron	Type 2. Aerated. (a)	85	30 (86)	12 d	2.2 (87)	156
Austenitic cast iron	Type D2. Aerated. (a)	85	30 (86)	12 d	6 (240)	156
Stainless steels						
AM-363 stainless steel	...	...	Room	...	Attacked	120
Carpenter 20Mo-6	Laboratory tests. Reagent grade concentrated	85	Boiling	144 h	0.660 (26)	145
Carpenter 20Mo-6	Laboratory tests. Wet process acid (68.9% phosphoric acid, 4.15% sulfuric acid, 1.85% iron, 5400 ppm fluorides, 2000 ppm chlorides). Samples activated immediately prior to test	68.9	100 (212)	144 h	0.076 (3)	145

(Continued)

Corrosion Behavior of Various Metals and Alloys in Phosphoric Acid (Continued)

Material	Condition, other factors, comments	Concentration, %	Temperature, °C (°F)	Duration	Corrosion rate, mm/yr (mils/yr) or other	Ref
Carpenter stainless steel No. 20Cb	...	10	101 (214)	96 h	<0.025 (<1)	156
Carpenter stainless steel No. 20Cb	...	50	110 (230)	96 h	0.431 (17)	156
Carpenter stainless steel No. 20Cb	...	60	Boiling	20 h	0.228 (9)	156
Carpenter stainless steel No. 20Cb	...	70	Boiling	20 h	0.279 (11)	156
Carpenter stainless steel No. 20Cb	CP grade. Three 24-h periods	85	160 (320)	24 h	1.37 (54)	156, 164
Carpenter stainless steel No. 20Cb	...	85	Boiling	20 h	0.965 (38)	156
Carpenter stainless steel No. 20Cb	...	86	97 (208)	96 h	0.05 (2)	156
Jessop JS700	...	20	Boiling	48 h	<0.051 (<0.002 in./yr)	97
Jessop JS700	...	54	121 (250)	48 h	0.061 (0.0024 in./yr)	97
Jessop JS700	...	60	Boiling	48 h	1.499 (0.059 in./yr)	97
Jessop JS700	...	85	Boiling	48 h	3.099 (0.122 in./yr)	97
Jessop JS700	Plus 2% HF	25	75 (167)	48 h	0.203 (0.008 in./yr)	97
Type 304 stainless steel	(b)	10	93 (200)	≥16 d	...	156, 157
Type 304 stainless steel	BP 101 °C (214 °F). Specimens activated before exposure. (b)	10	Boiling	0.08 d	nil	156, 158
Type 304 stainless steel	(b)	10	101 (214)	2 + 2 d	<0.025 (<1)	156, 159
Type 304 stainless steel	(b)	25	Boiling	5 d	0.025 (1)	156, 160
Type 304 stainless steel	BP 102 °C (216 °F). (b)	50	110 (230)	2 + 2 d	0.203 (8)	156, 159
Type 304 stainless steel	(b)	60	Boiling	0.83 d	...	156, 161
Type 304 stainless steel	BP 116 °C (240 °F). (b)	70	Boiling	0.83 d	...	156, 161
Type 304 stainless steel	BP 126 °C (259 °F). (b)	76	85 (185)	16 d	...	156, 162
Type 304 stainless steel	(b)	76	100 (212)	16 d	...	156, 162
Type 304 stainless steel	(b)	76	115 (239)	16 d	...	156, 162
Type 304 stainless steel	(b)	78-85	Room	≥16 d	<0.0025 (<0.1)	156, 157
Type 304 stainless steel	(b)	75-85	104 (220)	≥16 d	5.842 (230)	156, 157
Type 304 stainless steel	(b)	75-85	116 (240)	≥16 d	...	156, 161
Type 304 stainless steel	BP 146 °C (294 °F). (b)	80	Boiling	0.83 d	...	156, 162
Type 304 stainless steel	(b)	85	85 (185)	16 d	...	156, 162
Type 304 stainless steel	(b)	85	100 (212)	16 d	...	156, 162
Type 304 stainless steel	(b)	85	115 (239)	16 d	...	156, 162
Type 304 stainless steel	(b)	86	98 (208)	2 + 2 d	>25.4 (>1000)	156, 159
Type 304 stainless steel	No activation	50	Boiling	24 h	19.625 (785)	52
Type 304 stainless steel	(c)	10	21 (70)	...	Good	121
Type 304 stainless steel	Air free	10	21 (70)	...	Good	121
Type 304 stainless steel	Specimens activated before exposure. (b)	10	101 (214)	0.08 d	nil	156, 158
Type 304 stainless steel	(b)	10	101 (214)	2 + 2 d	<0.025 (<1)	156, 159
Type 304 stainless steel	(b)	50	110 (230)	2 + 2 d	0.203 (8)	156, 159
Type 304 stainless steel	(b)	78-85	Room	≥16 d	<0.002 (<0.1)	156, 157
Type 304 stainless steel	(b)	78-85	104 (220)	≥16 d	5.84 (230)	156, 157
Type 304 stainless steel	(b)	86	98 (208)	2 + 2 d	>25.4 (>1000)	156, 159
Type 304 stainless steel	(b)	25	102 (216)	5 d	0.025 (1)	156, 160
Type 316 stainless steel	(c)	10	21 (70)	...	Very good	121
Type 316 stainless steel	Air free	10	21 (70)	...	Good	121
Type 316 stainless steel	(b)	10	93 (200)	≥16 d	0.0025 (0.1)	156, 157
Type 316 stainless steel	BP 101 °C (214° F). Specimens activated before exposure. (b)	10	Boiling	0.08 d	...	156, 158
Type 316 stainless steel	(b)	10	93 (200)	≥16 d	0.005 (0.2)	156, 157
Type 316 stainless steel	(b)	10	93 (200)	≥16 d	0.002 (0.1)	156, 157
Type 316 stainless steel	(c)	10	93 (200)	≥16 d	0.005 (0.2)	156, 157
Type 316 stainless steel	...	10	101 (214)	96 h	<0.025 (<1)	156
Type 316 stainless steel	(b)	10	101 (214)	2 + 2 d	<0.025 (<1)	156, 159
Type 316 stainless steel	(b)	10	101 (214)	2 + 2 d	...	156, 159

(Continued)

Corrosion Behavior of Various Metals and Alloys in Phosphoric Acid (Continued)

Material	Condition, other factors, comments	Concen-tration, %	Temperature, °C (°F)	Duration	Corrosion rate, mm/yr (mils/yr) or other	Ref
Type 316 stainless steel	(b)					
Type 316 stainless steel	...	10	101 (214)	2 + 2 d	<0.025 (<1)	156, 159
Type 316 stainless steel	BP 102 °C (216 °F). (b)	20	Boiling	...	0.18 (7.2)	155
Type 316 stainless steel	(b)	25	Boiling	5 d	...	156, 160
Type 316 stainless steel	(b)	50	110 (230)	2 + 2 d	0.152 (6)	156, 159
Type 316 stainless steel	...	50	110 (230)	2 + 2 d	...	156, 159
Type 316 stainless steel	No activation	50	110 (230)	96 h	0.152 (6)	156
Type 316 stainless steel	...	50	Boiling	24 h	0.1875 (7.5)	52
Type 316 stainless steel	(b)	54	Boiling	...	0.55 (21.6)	155
Type 316 stainless steel	BP 116 °C (240 °F). (b)	60	115 (240)	0.83 d	2.7 (107)	156, 161
Type 316 stainless steel	BP 116 °C (240 °F). (b)	60	Boiling	0.83 d	2.718 (107)	156, 161
Type 316 stainless steel	...	60	Boiling	0.83 d	...	156, 161
Type 316 stainless steel	BP 126 °C (259 °F). (b)	60	Boiling	...	0.55 (21.6)	155
Type 316 stainless steel	BP 126 °C (259 °F). (b)	70	Boiling	0.83 d	5.385 (212)	156, 161
Type 316 stainless steel	(b)	70	Boiling	0.83 d	...	156, 161
Type 316 stainless steel	(b)	70	126 (259)	0.83 d	5.38 (212)	156, 161
Type 316 stainless steel	(b)	75-85	Room	≥16 d	<0.0025 (<0.1)	156, 157
Type 316 stainless steel	(b)	75-85	Room	≥16 d	...	156, 157
Type 316 stainless steel	...	75-85	104 (220)	≥16 d	0.127 (5)	156, 157
Type 316 stainless steel	(b)	75-85	104 (220)	...	0.127 (5)	156
Type 316 stainless steel	(b)	75-85	104 (220)	≥16 d	...	156, 157
Type 316 stainless steel	(b)	75-85	116 (240)	≥16 d	0.2337 (9.2)	156, 157
Type 316 stainless steel	(b)	76	85 (185)	16 d	0.0013 (0.05)	156, 162
Type 316 stainless steel	(b)	76	85 (185)	16 d	0.001 (0.05)	156, 162
Type 316 stainless steel	(b)	76	85 (185)	16 d	0.00	156, 162
Type 316 stainless steel	(b)	76	100 (212)	16 d	0.0356 (1.4)	156, 162
Type 316 stainless steel	(b)	76	100 (212)	16 d	0.0112 (0.44)	156, 162
Type 316 stainless steel	(c)	76	85 (185)	16 d	0.035 (1.4)	156, 162
Type 316 stainless steel	(c)	76	100 (212)	16 d	nil	156, 162
Type 316 stainless steel	(c)	76	115 (239)	16 d	0.011 (0.44)	156, 162
Type 316 stainless steel	(b)	76	115 (239)	16 d	0.018 (0.71)	156, 162
Type 316 stainless steel	(b)	76	115 (239)	16 d	0.17 (6.7)	156, 162
Type 316 stainless steel	(b)	76	115 (239)	16 d	0.0180 (0.71)	156, 162
Type 316 stainless steel	(b)	76	115 (239)	16 d	0.1702 (6.7)	156, 162
Type 316 stainless steel	(b)	78-85	Room	≥16 d	0.002 (0.1)	156, 157
Type 316 stainless steel	(c)	78-85	104 (220)	≥16 d	0.127 (5)	156, 157
Type 316 stainless steel	(b)	78-85	115 (239)	≥16 d	0.233 (9.2)	156, 157
Type 316 stainless steel	BP 146 °C (294 °F). (b)	80	145 (294)	0.83	20.142 (793)	156, 161
Type 316 stainless steel	BP 146 °C (294 °F). (b)	80	Boiling	0.83 d	...	156, 161
Type 316 stainless steel	(b)	80	Boiling	0.83 d	20.142 (793)	156, 161
Type 316 stainless steel	(b)	85	85 (185)	16 d	0.0035 (0.14)	156, 162
Type 316 stainless steel	(b)	85	85 (185)	16 d	0.003 (0.14)	156, 162
Type 316 stainless steel	(b)	85	85 (185)	16 d	0.0043 (0.17)	156, 162
Type 316 stainless steel	(b)	85	100 (212)	16 d	0.03 (1.19)	156, 162
Type 316 stainless steel	(b)	85	100 (212)	16 d	0.0302 (1.19)	156, 162
Type 316 stainless steel	(c)	85	100 (212)	16 d	0.0096 (0.38)	156, 162
Type 316 stainless steel	(c)	85	85 (185)	16 d	0.004 (0.17)	156, 162
Type 316 stainless steel	(b)	85	100 (212)	16 d	0.009 (0.38)	156, 162
Type 316 stainless steel	(b)	85	115 (239)	16 d	0.144 (5.7)	156, 162
Type 316 stainless steel	Plus 0.32% Cu. CP grade. Three 24-h periods	85	115 (239)	16 d	0.0170 (0.67)	156, 162
Type 316 stainless steel	(b)	85	160 (320)	24 h	11.3 (445)	156, 164
Type 316 stainless steel	Plus 0.04% Cu. CP grade. Three 24-h periods	85	115 (239)	16 d	0.1338 (5.7)	156, 162
Type 316 stainless steel	(b)	85	160 (320)	24 h	42.16 (1660)	156, 164
Type 316 stainless steel	...	86	97 (208)	2 + 2 d	0.406 (16)	156, 159
Type 316 stainless steel	(b)	86	97 (208)	96 h	0.406 (16)	156
Type 316 stainless steel	(b)	86	98 (208)	2 + 2 d	...	156, 159
Type 316 stainless steel	P₂O₅ equivalent 75-77%	86	98 (208)	2 + 2 d	0.406 (16)	156, 159
Type 316 stainless steel		104-106	104 (220)	...	0.012 (0.5)	156

(Continued)

Corrosion Behavior of Various Metals and Alloys in Phosphoric Acid (Continued)

Material	Condition, other factors, comments	Concentration, %	Temperature, °C (°F)	Duration	Corrosion rate, mm/yr (mils/yr) or other	Ref
Type 316L stainless steel	...	60	Boiling	20 h	2.717 (107)	156
Type 316L stainless steel	...	70	Boiling	20 h	5.384 (212)	156
Type 316L stainless steel	...	85	Boiling	20 h	20.14 (793)	156
Type 317L stainless steel	...	20	Boiling	48 h	<0.051 (<0.002 in./yr)	97
Type 317L stainless steel	...	85	Boiling	48 h	4.98 (0.196 in./yr)	97
Type 317L Plus stainless steel	...	85	Boiling	48 h	7.47 (0.294 in./yr)	97
Type 410 stainless steel	(c)	10	21 (70)	...	Good	121
Type 410 stainless steel	Air free	10	21 (70)	...	Poor	121
Type 410 stainless steel	...	10	Room	...	Slightly attacked	121
Type 430 stainless steel	Air free	10	21 (70)	...	Poor	121
Type 430 stainless steel	(c)	10	21 (70)	...	Good	121
Type 444 stainless steel	No activation	50	Boiling	24 h	0.11 (4.4)	52
Uddeholm alloy 904L	Laboratory tests. Reagent grade concentrated	85	Boiling	144 h	Not tested	145
Uddeholm alloy 904L	Laboratory tests. Wet process acid (68.9% phosphoric acid, 4.15% sulfuric acid, 1.85% iron, 5400 ppm fluorides, 2000 ppm chlorides). Samples activated immediately prior to test	68.9	100 (212)	144 h	0.178 (7)	145
Uddeholm 904L	(h)	70	160 (320)	87 d	55 mg/cm^2	145
Uddeholm 904L	(k)	70	188 (370)	87 d	158 mg/cm^2	145
Coppers						
70-30 cupronickel	84% P_2O_5. (b) (d)	116	60 (140)	...	0.0025 (0.1)	156
70-30 cupronickel	84% P_2O_5. (c) (d)	116	60 (140)	...	0.025 (1.0)	156
70-30 cupronickel	84% P_2O_5. (b) (d)	116	120 (248)	...	0.0508 (2.0)	156
70-30 cupronickel	84% P_2O_5. (c) (d)	116	120 (248)	...	0.2896 (11.4)	156
70-30 cupronickel	84% P_2O_5. (b) (d)	116	180 (356)	...	0.6655 (26.2)	156
70-30 cupronickel	84% P_2O_5. (c) (d)	116	180 (356)	...	2.0193 (79.5)	156
70-30 cupronickel	(e)	...	...	...	Good	93
90-10 cupronickel	(e)	...	...	...	Good	93
Admiralty brass	...	...	...	...	Fair	93
Aluminum bronze	(e)	...	...	...	Good	93
Ampco 8, aluminum bronze	Generally suitable. Conditions such as aeration or temperature could restrict use	...	...	...	<0.5 (<20)	96
	...	...	...	...	Not suitable	93
Architectural bronze	...	...	...	...	Fair	93
Brass	...	...	...	...	Not suitable	93
Cartridge brass	...	...	...	...	Good	93
Commercial bronze	(e)	...	...	...		
Copper	Totally submerged. (f)	5-90	20-85 (70-185)	...	0.55-3.7 (22-148)	153
Copper-aluminum-iron	Totally submerged. (f)	5-90	20-85 (70-185)	...	0.13-0.25 (5-10)	153
Copper-aluminum-silicon	(f)	6.5	20 (70)	...	0.28-2.4 (11-97)	153
Copper-nickel	Totally submerged. (f)	5-90	20-85 (70-185)	...	0.025-0.63 (1-25)	153
Copper-silicon	Totally submerged. (f)	5-90	20-85 (70-185)	...	0.13-0.93 (5-37)	153
Copper-tin	Totally submerged. (f)	5-90	20-85 (70-185)	...	0.025-1.30 (1-52)	153
Copper-zinc	(70% Cu minimum). Totally submerged. (f)	5-90	20-85 (70-185)	...	0.13-7.0 (5-280)	153
Electrolytic copper	(e)	...	...	...	Good	93
Free-cutting brass	...	...	...	...	Not suitable	93
Muntz metal	...	...	...	...	Not suitable	93
Naval brass	...	...	...	...	Not suitable	93
Nickel silver	(e)	18	...	...	Good	93
Phosphor bronze	5% Sn. (e)	...	...	...	Good	93
Phosphor bronze	8% Sn. (e)	...	...	...	Good	93
Phosphor copper	(f)	...	...	...	Good	93
Red brass	(e)	...	...	...	Good	93

(Continued)

Corrosion Behavior of Various Metals and Alloys in Phosphoric Acid (Continued)

Material	Condition, other factors, comments	Concen-tration, %	Temperature, °C (°F)	Duration	Corrosion rate, mm/yr (mils/yr) or other	Ref
Silicon bronze	Low. (e)	...	...	...	Good	93
Silicon bronze	High. (e)	...	...	...	Good	93
Titanium						
Titanium	...	85	19-26 (65-80)	36 d	0.17 (6.75)	74
Titanium	(g)	25	25 (75)	...	0.019 (0.74)	33
Titanium	(g)	30	25 (75)	...	0.056 (2.20)	33
Titanium	(g)	45	25 (75)	...	0.157 (6.18)	33
Titanium	(g)	8	52 (125)	...	0.02 (0.78)	33
Titanium	(g)	13	52 (125)	...	0.066 (2.59)	33
Titanium	(g)	15	52 (125)	...	0.52 (20.4)	33
Titanium	(g)	5	66 (150)	...	0.038 (1.49)	33
Titanium	(g)	7	66 (150)	...	0.15 (5.90)	33
Titanium	(g)	0.5	Boiling	...	0.071 (2.79)	33
Titanium	(g)	1.0	Boiling	...	0.14 (5.51)	33
Titanium	(h)	40	25 (75)	...	0.008 (0.31)	33
Titanium	(h)	60	25 (75)	...	0.07 (2.75)	33
Titanium	(h)	15	52 (125)	...	0.036 (1.41)	33
Titanium	(h)	23	52 (125)	...	0.15 (5.91)	33
Titanium	(h)	8	66 (150)	...	0.076 (2.99)	33
Titanium	(h)	15	66 (150)	...	0.104 (4.09)	33
Titanium	(h)	0.5	Boiling	...	0.050 (1.96)	33
Titanium	(h)	1.0	Boiling	...	0.107 (4.21)	33
Titanium	(h)	5.0	Boiling	...	0.228 (8.97)	33
Titanium	...	10-30	Room	...	0.020-0.051 (0.8-2.04)	90
Titanium	...	30-80	Room	...	0.051-0.762 (2.04-30.48)	90
Titanium	...	5.0	66 (151)	...	0.005 (0.2)	90
Titanium	...	6.0	66 (151)	...	0.117 (4.68)	90
Titanium	...	0.5	Boiling	...	0.094 (3.76)	90
Titanium	...	1.0	Boiling	...	0.266 (10.64)	90
Titanium	...	12	25 (77)	...	0.005 (0.2)	90
Titanium	...	20	25 (77)	...	0.076 (3.04)	90
Titanium	...	50	25 (77)	...	0.19 (7.6)	90
Titanium	...	9	52 (126)	...	0.03 (1.2)	90
Titanium	...	10	52 (126)	...	0.38 (15.2)	90
Titanium	...	5	Boiling	...	3.5 (140)	90
Titanium	...	10	80 (176)	...	1.83 (73.2)	90
Titanium	Plus 3% HNO_3	81	88 (190)	...	0.381 (15.24)	90
Heat- and corrosion-resistant alloys						
29Cr-4Mo	...	20	Boiling	...	nil	155
29Cr-4Mo	...	54	Boiling	...	0.03 (1.2)	155
29Cr-4Mo	...	60	Boiling	...	0.12 (4.8)	155
29Cr-4Mo-2Ni	...	20	Boiling	...	nil	155
29Cr-4Mo-2Ni	...	54	Boiling	...	0.03 (1.2)	155
29Cr-4Mo-2Ni	...	6	Boiling	...	0.12 (4.8)	155
40Co-20Cr-15Ni-7Mo	...	10	107 (225)	50 h	nil	54
44Co-31Cr-13W	(j)	50	Boiling	...	1.72 (68)	53
44Co-31Cr-13W	(j)	85	65 (150)	...	nil	53
44Co-31Cr-13W	Heat treated 4 h at 899 °C (1650 °F) and furnace cooled. (j)	50	Boiling	...	0.55 (22)	53
44Co-31Cr-13W	Heat treated 4 h at 899 °C (1650 °F) and furnace cooled. (j)	85	65 (150)	...	0.015 (0.6)	53
44Co-31Cr-13W	(j)	50	Boiling	...	1.7 (68)	53
44Co-31Cr-13W	Heat treated 4 h at 899 °C (1650 °F) and furnace cooled. (j)	50	Boiling	...	0.55 (22)	53
44Co-31Cr-13W	(j)	85	65 (150)	...	nil	53

(Continued)

Corrosion Behavior of Various Metals and Alloys in Phosphoric Acid (Continued)

Material	Condition, other factors, comments	Concentration, %	Temperature, °C (°F)	Duration	Corrosion rate, mm/yr (mils/yr) or other	Ref
44Co-31Cr-13W	Heat treated 4 h at 899 °C (1650 °F) and furnace cooled. (j)	85	65 (150)	...	0.015 (0.6)	53
50Co-20Cr-15W-10Ni	...	50	Boiling	...	0.1 (4)	53
50Co-20Cr-15W-10Ni	...	85	65 (150)	...	0.002 (0.1)	53
50Co-20Cr-15W-10Ni	(j)	50	Boiling	...	0.1 (4)	53
50Co-20Cr-15W-10Ni	(j)	85	65 (150)	...	0.002 (0.1)	53
53Co-30Cr-4.5W	Heat treated 4 h at 899 °C (1650 °F). (j)	85	65 (150)	...	nil	53
53Co-30Cr-4.5W	(j)	50	Boiling	...	0.3 (12)	53
53Co-30Cr-4.5W	Heat treated 4 h at 899 °C (1650 °F) and furnace cooled. (j)	50	Boiling	...	0.625 (25)	53
53Co-30Cr-4.5W	(j)	85	65 (150)	...	nil	53
53Co-30Cr-4.5W	Heat treated 4 h at 899 °C (1650 °F) and furnace cooled. (j)	85	65 (150)	...	nil	53
53Co-30Cr-4.5W	(j)	50	Boiling	...	0.3 (12)	53
53Co-30Cr-4.5W	(j)	85	65 (150)	...	nil	53
53Co-30Cr-4.5W	Heat treated 4 h at 899 °C (1650 °F). (j)	50	Boiling	...	0.625 (25)	53
Cabot alloy No. 625	Average of four 24-h periods	55	Boiling	24 h	0.16 (6.3)	67
Cabot alloy No. 625	...	70	116 (240)	96 h	0.30 (12)	67
Cabot alloy No. 625	...	70	149 (300)	96	0.28 (11)	67
Cabot alloy No. 625	Average of four 24-h periods	85	Boiling	24 h	1.7 (67)	67
Carpenter Pyromet Alloy 102	Plus 2% HF. Annealed	25	...	48 h	0.102 (4.08)	30
Carpenter Pyromet Alloy 102	Plus 2% HF. Stress relieved at 843 °C (1550 °F) for ½ h, furnace cooled	25	...	48 h	0.102 (4.08)	30
Carpenter 20Mo-6	(k)	70	160 (320)	87 d	34 mg/cm^2	145
Carpenter 20Mo-6	(m)	70	188 (370)	87 d	100 mg/cm^2	145
Durimet 20	...	78-85	115 (240)	...	0.233 (9.2)	156
Durimet 20	P_2O_5 equivalent 75-77%	104-106	104 (220)	...	0.002 (0.1)	156
Hastelloy B	(n)	10	Room	...	0.007 (0.3)	156
Hastelloy B	(n)	30	Room	...	0.007 (0.3)	156
Hastelloy B	(n)	50	Room	...	0.002 (0.1)	156
Hastelloy B	(n)	85	Room	...	nil	156
Hastelloy B	(n)	10	65 (150)	...	0.05 (2)	156
Hastelloy B	(n)	30	65 (150)	...	0.02 (0.8)	156
Hastelloy B	(n)	50	65 (150)	...	0.007 (0.3)	156
Hastelloy B	(n)	85	65 (150)	...	0.01 (0.4)	156
Hastelloy B	(n)	10	Boiling	...	0.025 (1)	156
Hastelloy B	(n)	30	Boiling	...	0.076 (3)	156
Hastelloy B	(n)	50	Boiling	...	0.076 (3)	156
Hastelloy B	(n)	85	Boiling	...	0.71 (28)	156
Hastelloy B-2	Chemically pure. Heat treated at 1066 °C (1950 °F), water quenched. (p)	10	Boiling	...	0.05 (2)	63
Hastelloy B-2	Chemically pure. Heat treated at 1066 °C (1950 °F), water quenched. (p)	30	Boiling	...	0.08 (3)	63
Hastelloy B-2	Chemically pure. Heat treated at 1066 °C (1950 °F), water quenched. (p)	50	Boiling	...	0.15 (6)	63
Hastelloy B-2	Chemically pure. Heat treated at 1066 °C (1950 °F), water quenched. (p)	85	Boiling	...	0.63 (25)	63
Hastelloy C	(q)	10	Room	...	0.002 (0.1)	156
Hastelloy C	(q)	30	Room	...	0.002 (0.1)	156
Hastelloy C	(q)	50	Room	...	0.002 (0.1)	156
Hastelloy C	(q)	85	Room	...	nil	156
Hastelloy C	(q)	10	65 (150)	...	0.005 (0.2)	156
Hastelloy C	(q)	30	65 (150)	...	0.002 (0.1)	156
Hastelloy C	(q)	50	65 (150)	...	0.007 (0.3)	156
Hastelloy C	(q)	85	65 (150)	...	0.007 (0.3)	156
Hastelloy C	(q)	10	Boiling	...	0.015 (0.6)	156
Hastelloy C	(q)	30	Boiling	...	0.101 (4)	156
Hastelloy C	(q)	50	Boiling	...	0.101 (4)	156
Hastelloy C	(q)	85	Boiling	...	1.14 (45)	156

(Continued)

Corrosion Behavior of Various Metals and Alloys in Phosphoric Acid (Continued)

Material	Condition, other factors, comments	Concentration, %	Temperature, °C (°F)	Duration	Corrosion rate, mm/yr (mils/yr) or other	Ref
Hastelloy C-4	Unwelded; Heat treated at 1066 °C (1950 °F), water quenched. (p)	85	Boiling	...	1.5 (61)	16
Hastelloy C-4	Determined in laboratory tests. As-welded; gas tungsten arc welded. (p)	85	Boiling	...	1.3 (52)	16
Hastelloy C-4	Determined in laboratory tests. Aged 100 h at 899 °C (1650 °F). (p)	85	Boiling	...	2.2 (85)	16
Hastelloy F	...	60	Boiling	20 h	2.46 (97)	156
Hastelloy F	...	70	Boiling	20 h	1.85 (73)	156
Hastelloy F	...	85	Boiling	20 h	30.48 (1200)	156
Hastelloy F	CP grade. Three 24-h periods	85	160 (320)	24 h	7.289 (287)	156, 164
Hastelloy G	Laboratory tests. Reagent grade concentrated	85	Boiling	144 h	0.660 (26)	145
Hastelloy G	(k)	70	160 (320)	87 d	35 mg/cm^2	145
Hastelloy G	(m)	70	188 (370)	87 d	83 mg/cm^2	145
Hastelloy G	...	30	102 (215)	...	0.101 (4)	156, 165
Hastelloy G	...	85	157 (316)	...	0.508 (20)	156, 165
Hastelloy G	Laboratory tests. Wet process acid (68.9% phosphoric acid, 4.15% sulfuric acid, 1.85% iron, 5400 ppm fluorides, 2000 ppm chlorides). Samples activated immediately prior to test	68.9	100 (212)	144 h	0.076 (3)	145
Haynes alloy No. 6B	...	85	Boiling	...	15.5 (610)	23
Haynes alloy No. 21	...	85	Boiling	...	17.3 (680)	23
Haynes alloy No. 25	(r)	10	Room	24 h	nil	68
Haynes alloy No. 25	(r)	30	Room	24 h	nil	68
Haynes alloy No. 25	(r)	50	Room	24 h	nil	68
Haynes alloy No. 25	(r)	85	Room	24 h	nil	68
Haynes alloy No. 25	(r)	10	66 (150)	24 h	<0.01 (0.1)	68
Haynes alloy No. 25	(r)	30	66 (150)	24 h	nil	68
Haynes alloy No. 25	(r)	85	Boiling	24 h	14.3 (562)	68
Haynes alloy No. 25	(r)	50	66 (150)	24 h	<0.01 (0.1)	68
Haynes alloy No. 25	(r)	85	66 (150)	24 h	<0.01 (0.1)	68
Haynes alloy No. 25	(r)	10	Boiling	24 h	<0.01 (0.2)	68
Haynes alloy No. 25	(r)	30	Boiling	24 h	0.05 (2.0)	68
Haynes alloy No. 25	(r)	50	Boiling	24 h	0.10 (4.0)	68
Haynes alloy No. 188	...	85	Boiling	...	13.5 (530)	23
Haynes alloy No. 556	...	85	Boiling	...	0.84 (33)	23
Haynes alloy No. 625	...	85	Boiling	...	19.2 (754)	23
Illium 98	Plus 2.9% H$_2$SO$_4$, traces of H$_2$SiF$_6$, Al and Fe phosphates. In strong filtrate seal tank	36	43 (110)	90 d	0.01 (0.4)	152
Illium 98	Plus 2.9% H$_2$SO$_4$. Some HF. Suspended CaSO$_4$. Reactor outlet just ahead of filter feed box. Agitation	36	77-84 (170-183)	90 d	0.038 (1.5)	152
Illium 98	Plus 2.9% H$_2$SO$_4$, traces of HF, H$_2$SiF$_6$, iron phosphate. Evaporator seal tank	52	40-50 (104-122)	61 d	0.015 (0.6)	152
Illium 98	Plus HF, H$_2$SiF$_6$, CaSO$_4$. In evaporator discharge of pump before heat	55	80-85 (175-185)	42 d	0.02 (0.8)	152
Illium 98	Plus 3-4% H$_2$SO$_4$, 3-4% CaSO$_4$, trace H$_2$SiF$_6$. In sump of evaporator seal tank	69	...	81 d	0.022 (0.9)	152
Illium 98	Plus small amounts of H$_2$SO$_4$ and H$_2$SiF$_6$. In slurry in reactor. Agitation at 110 ft/min	69	100 (212)	10 d	0.35 (14)	152
Illium 98	Spray. Plus H$_2$SiF$_6$, SiF$_4$, HF, phosphate rock, CaSO$_4$. Attached to top of baffle in reactor. Considerable agitation	69	65-85 (149-185)	10 d	0.38 (15)	152
Illium G	Plus 2.9% H$_2$SO$_4$, traces of H$_2$SiF$_6$, Al and Fe phosphates. In strong filtrate seal tank	36	43 (110)	90 d	0.066 (2.6)	152
Illium G	Plus 2.9% H$_2$SO$_4$. Some HF. Suspended CaSO$_4$. Reactor outlet just ahead of filter feed box. Agitation	36	77-84 (170-183)	90 d	0.10 (4)	152
Illium G	Plus 2.9% H$_2$SO$_4$, traces of HF, H$_2$SiF$_6$, iron phosphate. Evaporator seal tank	52	40-50 (104-122)	61 d	0.035 (1.4)	152
Illium G	Plus HF, H$_2$SiF$_6$, CaSO$_4$. In evaporator discharge of pump before heat	55	80-85 (175-185)	42 d	0.22 (8.7)	152
Illium G	Filtered. Small concentration of H$_2$SO$_4$ and H$_2$SiF$_6$. In filtrate seal tank	61	80 (176)	10 d	0.152 (6)	152

(Continued)

Corrosion Behavior of Various Metals and Alloys in Phosphoric Acid (Continued)

Material	Condition, other factors, comments	Concentration, %	Temperature, °C (°F)	Duration	Corrosion rate, mm/yr (mils/yr) or other	Ref
Illium G	Plus 3-4% H_2SO_4, 3-4% $CaSO_4$, trace H_2SiF_6. In sump of evaporator seal tank	69	...	81 d	0.035 (1.4)	152
Illium G	Plus small amounts of H_2SO_4 and H_2SiF_6. In slurry in reactor. Agitation at 110 ft/min	69	100 (212)	10 d	1.83 (72)	152
Illium G	Spray. Plus H_2SiF_6, SiF_4, HF, phosphate rock, $CaSO_4$. Attached to top of baffle in reactor. Considerable agitation	69	655-85 (149-185)	10 d	0.53 (21)	152
Inco alloy G	...	30	Boiling	...	0.10 (4)	40
Inco alloy G	...	85	Boiling	...	0.51 (20)	40
Inco alloy G-3	Duplicate specimens	30	Boiling	1 week	0.08 (3)	40
Inco alloy G-3	Duplicate specimens	85	Boiling	1 week	0.41, 0.43 (16, 17)	40
Incoloy 825	Recycle liquor from evaporator fume scrubber. Plus 20% H_2SiF_6, 1% H_2SO_4	15	75-85 (165-185)	16 d	0.025 (1)	151
Incoloy 825	Plus 20% HF in tank	20	21-30 (70-85)	13 d	0.035 (1.4)	151
Incoloy 825	Plus 2% H_2SO_4, 1% HF, 40% H_2O, $CaSO_4$. Slurry in digestor tank	20	80-93 (170-200)	117 d	0.017 (0.7)	151
Incoloy 825	Slurry, 27% P_2O_5, in acid transfer tank. Velocity 3 ft/s	37	65-88 (150-190)	46 d	0.017 (0.7)	151
Incoloy 825	Slurry plus 1.6% H_2SO_4, 1.5% H_2SiF_6, 0.12% HF, $CaSO_4$. In filter tank	31.4	46-60 (115-140)	8.3 d	<0.002 (<0.1)	151
Incoloy 825	Thickener in evaporated acid plus 1.7% HF, 2% H_2SO_4, 2% $CaSO_4$	54	52-65 (125-150)	51 d	0.012 (0.5)	151
Incoloy 825	Evaporator heated with hot gases plus 1-2% H_2SO_4, 1.5% HF, Na_2SiF_6	53	120 (250)	42 d	0.152 (6)	151
Incoloy 825	In wet separator on top of concentrating drum in vapors. Crude, plus HF	To 50-55	107-150 (255-300)	21 d	0.78 (31)	151
Incoloy 825	Defluorinator plus 1% H_2SO_4, HF. Violent agitation	75-80	120-157 (250-315)	8 d	3.04 (120)	151
Incoloy 825	(m)	70	188 (370)	87 d	141 mg/cm^2	145
Incoloy 825	(k)	70	160 (320)	87 d	55 mg/cm^2	145
Incoloy 825	...	60	Boiling	20 h	0.203 (8)	156
Incoloy 825	...	70	Boiling	20 h	0.177 (7)	156
Incoloy 825	...	85	Boiling	20 h	1.29 (51)	156
Incoloy 825	Pitted	78-85	104 (220)	...	0.254 (10)	156
Incoloy 825	P_2O_5 equivalent 75-77%	104-106	104 (220)	...	0.027 (1.1)	156
Inconel 600	(r)	10	101 (214)	2 + 2 d	<0.025 (<1.0)	156, 159
Inconel 600	(r)	50	110 (230)	2 + 2 d	4.470 (176)	156, 159
Inconel 600	(r)	86	98 (208)	2 + 2 d	1.168 (46)	156, 159
Inconel 600	Average. (r)	75	50 (122)	60 d	0.1499 (5.9)	156, 161
Inconel 600	In tank. Solution circulated. (r)	75	70 (158)	39 d	0.686 (27)	156, 161
Inconel 600	BP 160 °C (320 °F). (r)	85	Boiling	1 d	270.84 (14600)	156, 164
Inconel 600	Solution aerated. Composition similar to Inconel alloy 610 casting. (r)	75	75 (167)	2 d	1.321 (52)	156, 161
Inconel 617	(s)	10	80 (175)	...	0.005 (0.2)	44
Inconel 617	Plus 1% HF. (s)	10	80 (175)	...	0.023 (0.9)	44
Inconel 617	(s)	10	Boiling	...	0.003 (0.1)	44
Inconel 617	(s)	20	80 (175)	...	0.005 (0.2)	44
Inconel 617	Plus 1% HF. (s)	20	80 (175)	...	0.05 (2)	44
Inconel 617	(s)	20	Boiling	...	0.010 (0.4)	44
Inconel 617	Plus 1% HF. (s)	30	80 (175)	...	0.03 (1)	44
Inconel 617	(s)	30	80 (175)	...	0.010 (0.4)	44
Inconel 617	(s)	30	Boiling	...	0.013 (0.5)	44
Inconel 617	(s)	40	80 (175)	...	0.010 (0.4)	44
Inconel 617	Plus 1% HF. (s)	40	80 (175)	...	0.15 (6)	44
Inconel 617	(s)	40	Boiling	...	0.13 (5)	44
Inconel 617	(s)	50	80 (175)	...	0.018 (0.7)	44
Inconel 617	Plus 1% HF. (s)	50	80 (175)	...	0.20 (8)	44
Inconel 617	(s)	50	Boiling	...	0.79 (31)	44
Inconel 617	(s)	60	80 (175)	...	0.010 (0.4)	44

(Continued)

Corrosion Behavior of Various Metals and Alloys in Phosphoric Acid (Continued)

Material	Condition, other factors, comments	Concen-tration, %	Temperature, °C (°F)	Duration	Corrosion rate, mm/yr (mils/yr) or other	Ref
Inconel 617	Plus 1% HF. (s)	60	80 (175)	...	0.15 (6)	44
Inconel 617	(s)	60	Boiling	...	1.27 (50)	44
Inconel 617	(s)	70	80 (175)	...	0.010 (0.4)	44
Inconel 617	Plus 1% HF. (s)	70	80 (175)	...	0.015 (0.6)	44
Inconel 617	(s)	70	Boiling	...	0.97 (38)	44
Inconel 617	(s)	85	80 (175)	...	0.015 (0.6)	44
Inconel 617	Plus 1% HF. (s)	85	80 (175)	...	0.010 (0.4)	44
Inconel 617	(s)	85	Boiling	...	0.66 (26)	44
Monel 400	...	3.2	25 (77)	49 d	0.041 (1.6)	156, 161
Monel 400	...	3.2	100 (212)	0.17 d	0.1245 (4.9)	156, 161
Monel 400	...	10	101 (214)	2 + 2 d	0.254 (10)	156, 159
Monel 400	...	40	27 (80)	5 d	0.025 (1.0)	156, 161
Monel 400	...	50	110 (230)	2 + 2 d	0.1016 (4.0)	156, 159
Monel 400	Estimated	78-85	25 (77)	...	0.0025 (0.1)	156
Monel 400	...	78-85	49 (120)	...	0.025 (1.0)	156
Monel 400	...	78-85	104 (220)	...	0.226 (8.9)	156
Monel 400	...	90	98 (208)	2 + 2 d	0.025 (1.0)	156, 159
Monel 400	(b)	85	124 (255)	≥6d	0.254 (10)	156, 157
Monel 400	(c)	85	124 (255)	...	11.176 (440)	156, 157
Monel 400	...	85	160 (320)	1	114.935 (4525)	156, 163
Monel 400	(c)	117	60 (140)	≥6 d	<0.254 (<10)	156, 157
Monel 400	(b)	117	180 (356)	≥6 d	0.0838 (3.3)	156, 157
Monel 400	...	117	249-254 (480-490)	...	Excessive	156, 157
MP35N	...	85	Boiling	...	12.7 (500)	23
Multimet	(q)	10	Room	24 h	nil	68
Multimet	(q)	10	66 (150)	24 h	nil	68
Multimet	(q)	10	Boiling	24 h	<0.01 (0.1)	68
Multimet	(q)	30	Room	24 h	nil	68
Multimet	(q)	30	66 (150)	24 h	<0.01 (0.1)	68
Multimet	(q)	30	Boiling	24 h	<0.01 (0.3)	68
Multimet	(q)	50	Room	24 h	nil	68
Multimet	(q)	50	66 (150)	24 h	<0.01 (0.1)	68
Multimet	(q)	50	Boiling	24 h	0.08 (3.0)	68
Multimet	(q)	85	Room	24 h	nil	68
Multimet	(q)	85	66 (150)	24 h	<0.003 (0.1)	68
Multimet	(q)	85	Boiling	24 h	7.70 (303)	68
Nickel 200	Plant test in mixture of HCl and cresylic acid with phosphorus oxychloride. Test spool at liquid line	...	82 (180)	...	0.425 (17)	44
Nickel 200	(d)	40	27 (80)	5 d	0.025 (1.0)	156, 161
Nickel 200	Estimated. (d)	78-85	25 (77)	...	0.0076 (0.3)	156
Nickel 200	(d)	78-85	49 (120)	...	0.1067 (4.2)	156
Nickel 200	84% P_2O_5. Not aerated. (d)	116	60 (140)	...	0.330 (13)	156
Nickel 200	84% P_2O_5. Not aerated. (d)	116	120 (248)	...	58.52 (48)	156
Nickel 200	84% P_2O_5. Not aerated. (d)	116	180 (356)	...	...	156
Nickel 200	(d)	117	9-254 (48-490)	...	Excessive	156, 157
Worthite	CP grade. Three 24-h periods	85	160 (320)	24 h	3.27 (129)	156, 164
Zirconium						
Zirconium	Tarnished	85	19-26 (65-80)	36 d	0.0005 (0.02)	74
Zirconium	Plus 0.5% HNO_3	88	Room	...	nil	36
Zirconium	Plus 5% HNO_3	88	Room	...	Weight gain	36
Zr702	...	5-30	Room	...	<0.13 (<5)	15
Zr702	...	5-35	60 (140)	...	<0.13 (<5)	15
Zr702	...	5-50	100 (212)	...	<0.13 (<5)	15
Zr702	...	35-50	Room	...	<0.13 (<5)	15
Zr702	...	45	Boiling	...	<0.13 (<5)	15

(Continued)

Corrosion Behavior of Various Metals and Alloys in Phosphoric Acid (Continued)

Material	Condition, other factors, comments	Concentration, %	Temperature, °C (°F)	Duration	Corrosion rate, mm/yr (mils/yr) or other	Ref
Zr702	BP 108 °C (226 °F)	50	Boiling	...	<0.13 (<5)	15
Zr702	...	65	100 (212)	...	0.13-0.25 (5-10)	15
Zr702	BP 123-126 °C (253-259 °F)	70	Boiling	...	>1.3 (>50)	15
Zr702	...	85	38 (100)	...	0.13-0.5 (5-20)	15
Zr702	...	85	80 (175)	...	0.5-1.3 (20-50)	15
Zr702	BP 156 °C (313 °F)	85	Boiling	...	>1.3 (>50)	15
Zr702	Plus 0.5% HNO_3	88	Room	...	nil	15
Zr702	Plus 5% HNO_3	88	Room	...	Weight gain	15
Zr702	Plus 4% HNO_3	85	89 (190)	...	>1.3 (>50)	15
Zr704	BP 108 °C (226 °F)	50	Boiling	...	0.13-0.25 (5-10)	15
Zr705	BP 108 °C (226 °F)	50	Boiling	...	0.25-0.38 (10-15)	15
Zr705	...	65	100 (212)	...	<0.5 (<20)	15
Zr705	BP 123-126 °C (253-259 °F)	70	Boiling	...	>1.3 (>50)	15
Zr705	...	85	80 (175)	...	0.5-1.3 (20-50)	15
Zr705	BP 156 °C (313 °F)	85	Boiling	...	>1.3 (>50)	15
Zr705	Plus 4% HNO_3	85	89 (190)	...	>1.3 (>50)	15
Lead, tin, and zinc						
Lead	Practically resistant; Pb recommended for use	...	24-93 (75-200)	...	<500 μm/yr (<20)	95
Lead	...	20	21 (70)	...	0.086 (3.4)	154
Lead	...	30	21 (70)	...	0.124 (4.9)	154
Lead	...	40	21 (70)	...	0.144 (5.7)	154
Lead	...	50	21 (70)	...	0.162 (6.4)	154
Lead	...	85	21 (70)	...	0.04 (1.6)	154
Lead	Pure grade	80	21 (70)	...	0.325 (12.8)	154
Tin	...	25	20 (68)	...	Unsuitable	94
Tin	...	25	60 (140)	...	Unsuitable	94
Tin	...	25	100 (212)	...	Unsuitable	94
Tin	...	50	20 (68)	...	Unsuitable	94
Tin	...	50	60 (140)	...	Unsuitable	94
Tin	...	50	100 (212)	...	Unsuitable	94
Tin	...	95	20 (68)	...	Unsuitable	94
Tin	...	95	60 (140)	...	Unsuitable	94
Tin	...	95	100 (212)	...	Unsuitable	94
Tantalum and hafnium						
Hafnium	...	60	...	8 d	0.22 (8.5)	11
Hafnium	...	60	...	8 d	0.22 (8.5)	11
Tantalum	...	85	19-26 (65-80)	36 d	nil	74
Tantalum	...	85	25 (76)	...	nil	42
Tantalum	...	85	100 (212)	...	nil	42
Noble metals						
Iridium	...	...	100 (212)	...	nil	29
Osmium	...	Conc	100 (212)	...	nil	17
Palladium	...	100 g/L	100 (212)	...	<0.25 (<10)	17
Rhodium	...	100 g/L	100 (212)	...	nil	29
Silver	...	5	102 (215)	...	0.003 (0.12)	4
Silver	...	45	60 (14)	...	nil	4
Silver	...	45	110 (230)	...	0.007 (0.28)	4
Silver	...	67	60 (140)	...	0.004 (0.16)	4
Silver	...	67	125 (255)	...	0.02 (0.8)	4
Silver	...	85	60 (140)	...	0.002 (0.08)	4
Silver	...	85	140 (285)	...	0.048 (1.9)	4
Silver	...	85	160 (320)	...	0.306 (12)	4
Silver	...	5	102 (215)	...	0.003 (0.12)	4
Silver	...	45	60 (140)	...	nil	4
Silver	...	45	110 (230)	...	0.007 (0.28)	4

(Continued)

Corrosion Behavior of Various Metals and Alloys in Phosphoric Acid (Continued)

Material	Condition, other factors, comments	Concen-tration, %	Temperature, °C (°F)	Duration	Corrosion rate, mm/yr (mils/yr) or other	Ref
Silver	...	67	60 (140)	...	0.004 (0.16)	4
Silver	...	67	125 (255)	...	0.02 (0.8)	4
Silver	...	85	60 (140)	...	0.002 (0.08)	4
Silver	...	85	140 (285)	...	0.048 (1.9)	4
Silver	...	85	160 (320)	...	0.306 (12)	4
Others						
Cobalt	Static	50	25 (77)	...	0.27 (11)	54
Cobalt	Static	Conc	25 (77)	...	0.025 (1)	54
Havar	...	85	Boiling	...	>100 (>4000)	23
Magnesium	...	All	Room	...	Unsuitable	119
Niobium	...	60	Boiling	...	0.5 (20)	2
Niobium	...	85	Room	...	0.0025 (0.1)	2
Niobium	...	85	88 (190)	...	0.05 (2.0)	2
Niobium	...	85	100 (212)	...	0.125 (5.0)	2
Niobium	...	85	Boiling	...	3.75 (150)	2
Niobium	Plus 4% HNO3	85	88 (190)	...	0.025 (1.0)	2
Niobium	Plus 5 ppm F-	40-50	Boiling	...	0.25 (10)	2
Niobium	...	85	19-26 (65-80)	36 d	0.0005 (0.02)	74

(a) Ni-Resist series have found limited application in H3PO4 solutions. (b) Not aerated. (c) Aerated. (d) Laboratory tests. 84% P2O5. Very little application has been made of the high-copper low-nickel alloys in H3PO4 exposure. (e) May be considered in place of a copper metal when some property, other than corrosion resistance, governs its use. (f) Tests in aerated and unaerated H3PO4. Specimens at water line, in quiet immersion. (g) Grade 12. Naturally aerated. (h) Grade 7. Naturally aerated. (j) As cast, based on five 24-h test periods with cast specimens 38 mm x 25 mm x 6 mm (1.5 in. x 1 in. x 0.25 in.), 120-grit abrasive finish. (k) Wet process superphosphoric acid evaporator. (j) Wet process superphosphoric acid evaporator. Plus 3% sulfates, 6000 ppm fluorides. First stage. (m) Wet process superphosphoric acid evaporator. Plus 3% sulfates, 6000 ppm fluorides. Second stage. Residue formed on surface during exposure. The residue contained 81,000 ppm chlorides, 1500 ppm fluorides. (n) Steady-state data calculated from a minimum of five 24-h test periods. The most resistant of all the nickel-containing alloys in hot concentrated pure H3PO4. (p) Determined in laboratory tests. It is recommended that samples be tested under actual plant conditions. (q) Steady-state data calculated from a minimum of five 24-h test periods. (r) Specimens prepared from 12-gage, solution heat treated sheet. Determined in laboratory tests. Five 24-h test periods. (s) Pure. Laboratory. These materials are not normally used in H3PO4 solutions, because other alloys are more resistant. (t) Average of two tests.

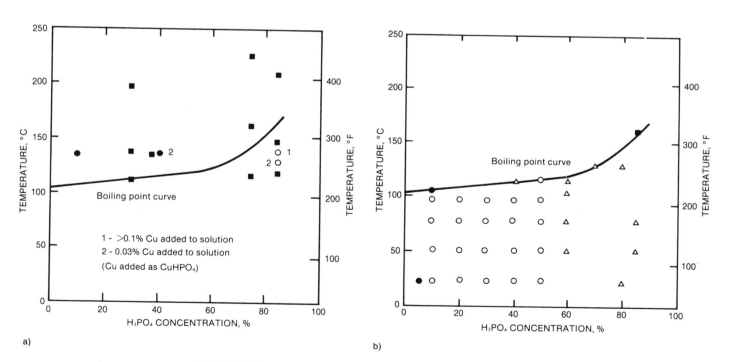

ACI CF-8. Isocorrosion diagrams for ACI CF-8 in phosphoric acid. (a) Test performed in a closed container at equilibrium pressure. (b) Tested at atmospheric pressure. Source: *Metals Handbook*, 9th ed., Vol 13, Corrosion, ASM International, Metals Park, OH, 1987, 579.

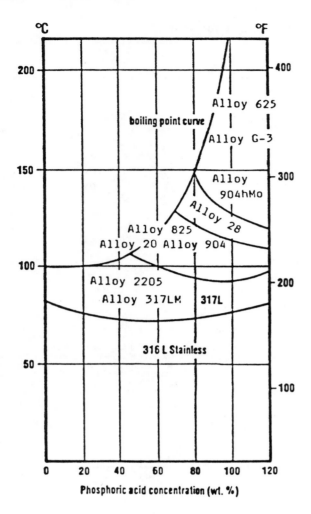

Various alloys. Areas of applicability for various alloys in phosphoric acid. Source: C.M. Schillmoller, "Corrosion in Phosphoric Acid Plants," in *Process Industries Corrosion*, B.J. Moniz and W.I. Pollock, Ed., National Association of Corrosion Engineers, Houston, 1986, 165.

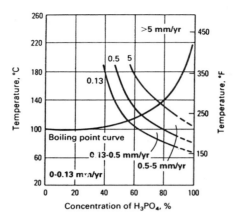

Zirconium. Isocorrosion diagram for zirconium in phosphoric acid. Source: "Zircadyne Corrosion Properties," Teledyne Wah Chang Albany, 1986.

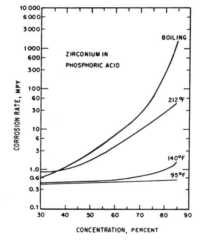

Zirconium. Corrosion rate of zirconium in phosphoric acid. Source: *ASTM Manual on Zirconium and Hafnium* (STP 639), J.H. Schemel, Ed., ASTM, Philadelphia, 1977, 37.

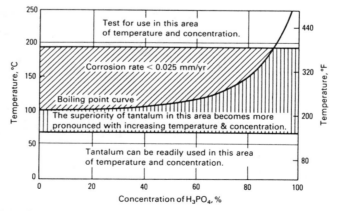

Tantalum. Corrosion resistance of tantalum in phosphoric acid of various concentrations and temperatures. Source: M. Stern and C.R. Bishop, Corrosion and Electrochemical Behavior, in *Columbium and Tantalum*, F.T. Sisco and E. Epremian, Ed., John Wiley & Sons, New York, 1963.

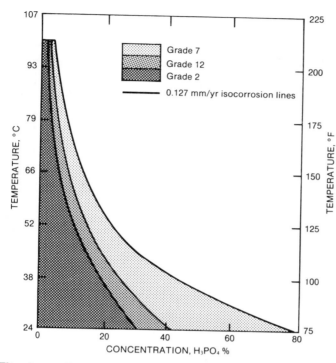

Titanium alloys. Isocorrosion diagram for titanium alloys in pure, naturally aerated phosphoric acid solutions. The 0.127-mm/yr (5-mils/yr) isocorrosion lines are indicated. Source: *Metals Handbook*, 9th ed., Vol 13, Corrosion, ASM International, Metals Park, OH 1987, 680.

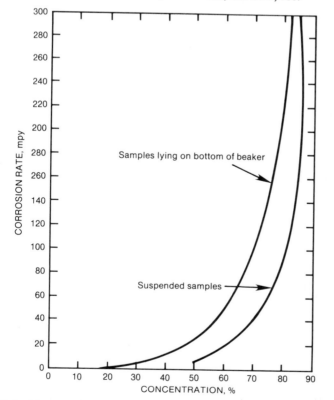

Nickel-base alloy. Corrosion of Inconel 625 in boiling phosphoric acid solutions. Source: Inco Alloys International, 1985.

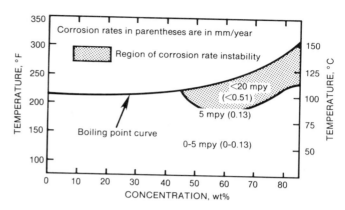

Nickel-base alloy. Resistance of Hastelloy B-2 to phosphoric acid. All test specimens were solution heat treated at 1066 °C (1950 °F), rapid quenched, and in the unwelded condition. Source: Haynes International, 1987.

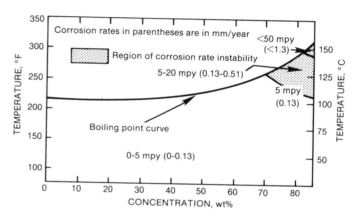

Nickel-base alloy. Resistance of Hastelloy C-4 to phosphoric acid. All test specimens were solution heat treated at 1066 °C (1950 °F), rapid quenched, and in the unwelded condition. Source: Haynes International, 1983.

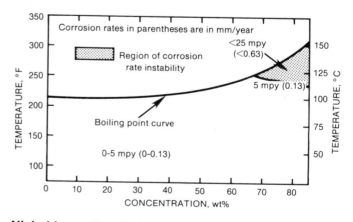

Nickel-base alloy. Resistance of Hastelloy C-276 to phosphoric acid. All test specimens were heat treated at 1121 °C (2050 °F), rapid quenched, and in the unwelded condition. Source: Haynes International, 1987.

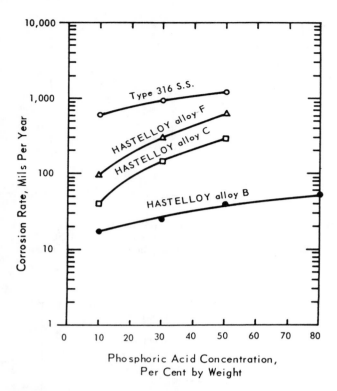

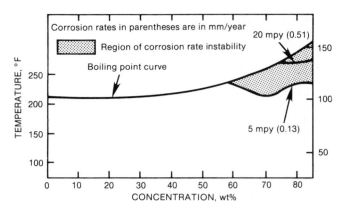

Nickel-base alloy. Resistance of Hastelloy G-30 to phosphoric acid. All test specimens were heat treated at 1177 °C (2150 °F), rapid quenched, and in the unwelded condition. Source: Haynes International, 1987.

Nickel-base alloys. Corrosion tests on nickel-base alloys and type 316 stainless steel in phosphoric acid at 190 °C (374 °F). Curves are included not only for Hastelloy B, but for Hastelloy C and F and type 316 stainless steel. Shown are the corrosion rates in pure phosphoric acid solutions at 190 °C (374 °F) for one 65-h period using sealed tubes above the boiling point. Source: "Corrosion Resistance of Nickel-Containing Alloys in Phosphoric Acid," The International Nickel Company, 1976.

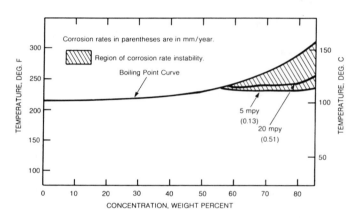

Nickel-base alloys. Corrosion resistance of Hastelloy C-22 to phosphoric acid. All test specimens were solution heat treated and in the unwelded condition. Source: Haynes International, 1984.

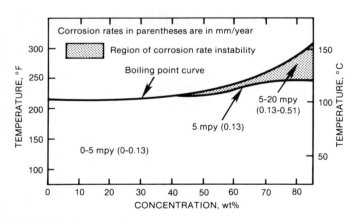

Nickel-base alloy. Resistance of Hastelloy G-3 to phosphoric acid. All test specimens were solution heat treated and in the unwelded condition. Source: Haynes International, 1987.

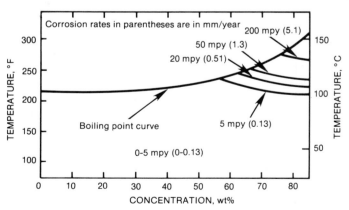

Duplex stainless steel. Resistance of Ferralium 255 to phosphoric acid. All test specimens were solution heat treated and in the unwelded condition.

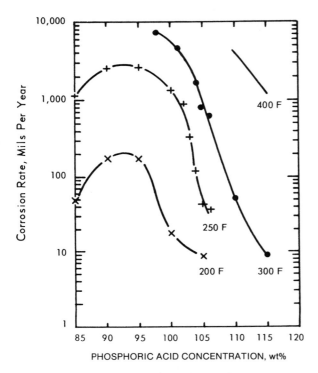

Stainless steel. Corrosion of type 317 stainless steel in phosphoric acid. Source: "Corrosion Resistance of Nickel-Containing Alloys in Phosphoric Acid," The International Nickel Company, 1976.

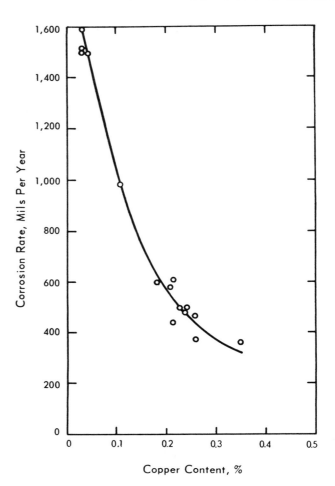

Stainless steel. Effect of copper content in type 316L stainless steel on resistance to corrosion in boiling 85% phosphoric acid. Source: "Corrosion Resistance of Nickel-Containing Alloys in Phosphoric Acid," The International Nickel Company, 1976.

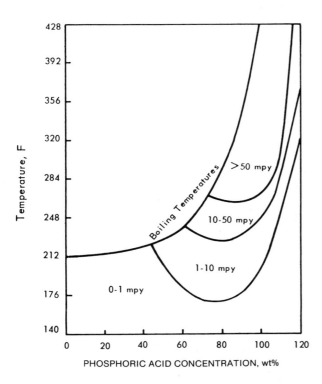

Stainless steel. Isocorrosion chart for type 316 stainless steel in furnace-grade phosphoric acid under mildly agitated conditions. Source: "Corrosion Resistance of Nickel-Containing Alloys in Phosphoric Acid," The International Nickel Company, 1976.

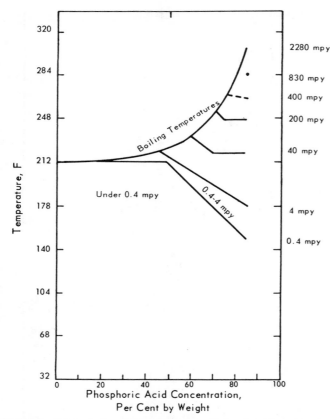

Stainless steel. Corrosion of wrought 18-9 stainless steel in phosphoric acid. Source: "Corrosion Resistance of Nickel-Containing Alloys in Phosphoric Acid," The International Nickel Company, 1976.

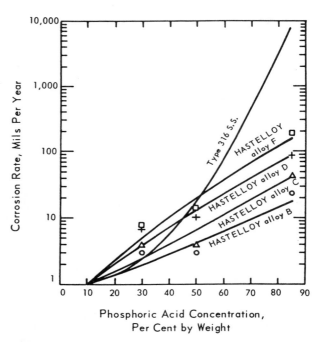

Stainless steel. Corrosion tests on nickel-base alloys and type 316 stainless steel in boiling phosphoric acid. Curves are included not only for Hastelloy B, but for Hastelloy C, D and F, and type 316 stainless steel. Shown are the corrosion rates in pure phosphoric acid solutions at the boiling point for three 48-h periods (five 24-h periods for Hastelloy D). Source: "Corrosion Resistance of Nickel-Containing Alloys in Phosphoric Acid," The International Nickel Company, 1976.

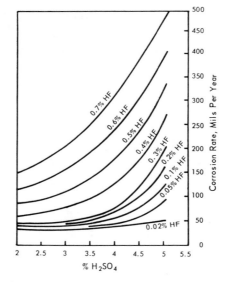

Stainless steel. Corrosion rate of type 316 stainless steel in 35% phosphoric acid at 88 °C (190 °F). Further evidence is found in a series of pilot plant tests in hot phosphoric acid containing hydrofluosilic acid and controlled contents of hydrofluoric and sulfuric acids, simulating wet-process acid. These three additions increase the corrosivity of the hot solution. Source: "Corrosion Resistance of Nickel-Containing Alloys in Phosphoric Acid," The International Nickel Company, 1976.

Phosphorus

Phosphorus, P, occurs in three distinct allotropes. The white phosphorus is a yellowish-white solid that is very poisonous, phosphorescent in the dark, and self-ignites in air. It has a melting point of 44 °C (111 °F) and is insoluble in water and alcohol. White phosphorus is used in manufacturing smoke screens, rat poisons, and matches. Red phosphorus is insoluble in all solvents, sublimes at 416 °C (780 °F), and is nonpoisonous. The black allotrope has lustrous crystals and is insoluble in most solvents. Phosphorus is essential to plant and animal nutrition, but does not occur naturally in the elemental form because of its reactivity. Most phosphorus ores are converted into phosphoric acid.

Material Summaries

The following material summaries were compiled from a survey of the available literature. Inclusion of a material description under a given environment does not imply that it is the most appropriate material for corrosion service in that environment. Likewise, exclusion of a given material does not imply that it is not suitable for corrosion service applications in that environment.

Aluminum. Aluminum alloy 1100 has shown to be resistant to solid and liquid white phosphorus during limited tests at ambient temperature. Molten phosphorus has been serviced by water-cooled aluminum alloy pans.

Osmium. Osmium burns in the vapor of phosphorus.

Tantalum. Tantalum filings heated in phosphorus vapor at 750 to 950 °C (1380 to 1740 °F) form tantalum phosphides.

Corrosion Behavior of Various Metals and Alloys in Phosphorus

Material	Condition, other factors, comments	Concentration, %	Temperature, °C (°F)	Duration	Corrosion rate, mm/yr (mils/yr) or other	Ref
Stainless steels						
Type 304 stainless steel	(a)	...	800 (1475)	30 d	380 μm (15.0)	63
Type 304 stainless steel	Research; laboratory test; no aeration; no agitation. With carbon over the standard maximum	...	65-70 (149-158)	...	0.0001 in./yr	89
Type 304 stainless steel	Chemical processing; field or pilot plant test; slight to moderate aeration; no agitation	...	60 (140)	185 d	<0.0001 in./yr	89
Type 304 stainless steel	Chemical (distillation) processing; field or pilot plant test; slight to moderate aeration; rapid agitation. Plus water, hydrogen, phosphine, hydrocarbon, traces of carbon dioxide and carbon monoxide, pH 3-6 (vapors, liquid)	...	80 (176)	112 d	0.0031 in./yr	89
Type 316 stainless steel	Chemical (distillation) processing; field or pilot plant test; slight to moderate aeration; rapid agitation. Plus water, hydrogen, phosphine, hydrocarbon, traces of carbon dioxide and carbon monoxide, pH 3-6 (vapors, liquid)	...	80 (176)	112 d	0.0029 in./yr	89
Type 316 stainless steel	Chemical processing; field or pilot plant test; slight to moderate aeration; no agitation	...	60 (140)	185 d	<0.0001 in./yr	89
Type 316 stainless steel	Research; laboratory test; no aeration; no agitation.	...	65-70 (149-158)	...	0.0001 in./yr	89
Type 317 stainless steel	Chemical (distillation) processing; field or pilot plant test; slight to moderate aeration; rapid agitation. Plus water, hydrogen, phosphine, hydrocarbon, traces of carbon dioxide and carbon monoxide, pH 3-6 (vapors, liquid)	...	80 (176)	112 d	0.0025 in./yr	89
Aluminum						
Aluminum (>99.5%)	...	...	...	...	Restricted applications	92
Heat- and corrosion-resistant alloys						
Alloy 800H	(a)	...	800 (1475)	30 d	280 μm (11.0)	63
Alloy 826	Chemical (distillation) processing; field or pilot plant test; slight to moderate aeration; rapid agitation. Plus water, hydrogen, phosphine, hydrocarbon, traces of carbon dioxide and carbon monoxide, pH 3-6 (vapors, liquid)	...	80 (176)	112 d	0.0024 in./yr	89
Carpenter 20	Chemical (distillation) processing; field or pilot plant test; slight to moderate aeration; rapid agitation; cast specimens. Plus water, hydrogen, phosphine, hydrocarbon, traces of carbon dioxide and carbon monoxide, pH 3-6 (vapors, liquid)	...	80 (176)	112 d	0.0028 in./yr	89
Hastelloy alloy S	(a)	...	800 (1475)	30 d	230 μm (9.0)	63

(Continued)

Corrosion Behavior of Various Metals and Alloys in Phosphorus (Continued)

Material	Condition, other factors, comments	Concen- tration, %	Temperature, °C (°F)	Duration	Corrosion rate, mm/yr (mils/yr) or other	Ref
Hastelloy alloy X	(a)	...	800 (1475)	30 d	75 μm (3.0)	63
Haynes alloy No. 188	(a)	...	800 (1475)	30 d	230 μm (9.0)	63
Haynes alloy No. 214	(a)	...	800 (1475)	30 d	205 μm (8.0)	63
Haynes alloy No. 556	(a)	...	800 (1475)	30 d	150 μm (6.0)	63

(a) Based on field tests in the combustion chamber of a fluid bed dryer used to dry sodium tripolyphosphate compounds.

Potassium Bromide

Potassium bromide, KBr, is a white crystalline hygroscopic solid that has a melting point of 730 °C (1346 °F). It has a bitter taste and is soluble in water. Potassium bromide is used in manufacturing photographic paper, soaps, and in medicine.

Material Summaries

The following material summaries were compiled from a survey of the available literature. Inclusion of a material description under a given environment does not imply that it is the most appropriate material for corrosion service in that environment. Likewise, exclusion of a given material does not imply that it is not suitable for corrosion service applications in that environment.

Aluminum. Potassium bromide solutions reacted with aluminum alloys during tests at ambient temperature.

Corrosion Behavior of Various Metals and Alloys in Potassium Bromide

Material	Condition, other factors, comments	Concen- tration, %	Temperature, °C (°F)	Duration	Corrosion rate, mm/yr (mils/yr) or other	Ref
Stainless steels						
Type 304 stainless steel	Chemical processing; field or pilot plant test; slight to moderate aeration; rapid agitation. Plus 25% potassium bromate, 1.5% potassium hydroxide, bromine, trace iron. Moderate pitting: maximum depth of pits from 0.005 to 0.010 in.	75	18 (65)	3.4 d	0.0078 in./yr	89
Type 304 stainless steel	Chemical processing; field or pilot plant test; slight to moderate aeration; slight to moderate agitation. Plus dissolved ammonia, pH 8-9.5 (filter)	Saturated	85 (185)	20 d	<0.0001 in./yr	89
Type 316 stainless steel	Chemical processing; field or pilot plant test; slight to moderate aeration; rapid agitation. Plus 25% potassium bromate, 1.5% potassium hydroxide, bromine, trace iron. Slight pitting: maximum depth of pits from incipient to 0.005 in.	75	18 (65)	3.4 d	0.0057 in./yr	89
Type 316 stainless steel	Chemical processing; field or pilot plant test; slight to moderate aeration; slight to moderate agitation. Plus dissolved ammonia, pH 8-9.5 (filter)	Saturated	85 (185)	20 d	<0.0001 in./yr	89
Type 410 stainless steel	...	...	Room	...	Slightly attacked	121
Aluminum						
Aluminum (>99.5%)	Solution	...	...	...	Satisfactory	92
Heat- and corrosion-resistant alloys						
Alloy 825	Chemical processing; field or pilot plant test; slight to moderate aeration; slight to moderate agitation. Plus dissolved ammonia, pH 8-9.5 (filter)	Saturated	85 (185)	20 d	<0.0001 in./yr	89
Carpenter 20	Chemical processing; field or pilot plant test; slight to moderate aeration; slight to moderate agitation. Plus dissolved ammonia, pH 8-9.5 (filter)	Saturated	85 (185)	20 d	<0.0001 in./yr	89
Titanium						
Titanium	...	Saturated	Room	...	nil	90

(Continued)

Corrosion Behavior of Various Metals and Alloys in Potassium Bromide (Continued)

Material	Condition, other factors, comments	Concen-tration, %	Temperature, °C (°F)	Duration	Corrosion rate, mm/yr (mils/yr) or other	Ref
Noble metals						
Platinum	...	All	Boiling	...	<0.05 (<2)	5
Platinum	Melt	...	760 (1400)	...	<0.05 (<2)	5
Silver	...	All	200-400 (390-750)	...	<0.05 (<2)	9

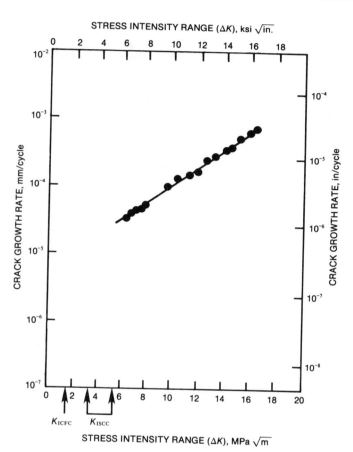

STRESS INTENSITY RANGE (ΔK), ksi $\sqrt{\text{in.}}$

CRACK GROWTH RATE, mm/cycle

CRACK GROWTH RATE, in/cycle

K_{ICFC} K_{ISCC}

STRESS INTENSITY RANGE (ΔK), MPa $\sqrt{\text{m}}$

Aluminum. Corrosion fatigue behavior of aluminum alloy 7079-T651 plate (S-L orientation). Temperature: 23 °C (73 °F); frequency: 4 cycle/s; stress ratio: $R = 0$. Source: M.O. Speidel, M.J. Blackburn, T.R. Beck, and J.Q. Feeney, "Corrosion Fatigue and Stress Corrosion Crack Growth in High Strength Aluminum Alloys, Magnesium Alloys and Titanium Alloys Exposed to Aqueous Solutions," in *Corrosion Fatigue: Chemistry, Mechanics and Microstructure*, O. Devereux, A.J. McEvily, and R.W. Staehle, Ed., National Association of Corrosion Engineers, Houston, 1973, 324-345.

Potassium Chloride

Potassium chloride, KCl, also known as potassium muriate and sylvite, is a colorless crystalline solid with a salty taste that melts at 776 °C (1420 °F). It is soluble in water, but insoluble in alcohol. Potassium chloride is used in fertilizers, pharmaceuticals, photography, and as a salt substitute.

Material Summaries

The following material summaries were compiled from a survey of the available literature. Inclusion of a material description under a given environment does not imply that it is the most appropriate material for corrosion service in that environment. Likewise, exclusion of a given material does not imply that it is not suitable for corrosion service applications in that environment.

Aluminum. Tested under laboratory conditions of ambient temperature and 100% relative humidity, aluminum alloys 3003 and 5154 resisted solid potassium chloride. Aluminum alloy hopper cars have been used to ship granular potassium chloride.

Copper. Aluminum bronzes are generally suitable for servicing potassium chloride.

Additional Reading

R.C. Newman, The Dissolution and Passivation Kinetics of Stainless Alloys Containing Molybdenum. II.—Dissolution Kinetics in Artificial Pits, *Corros. Sci.,* 25(5), 341-350, 1985. MetAbs No. 85-351905. **Abstract:** Artificial pit electrodes of Fe-Cr-Ni and Fe-Cr-Ni-Mo alloys have been polarized in a neutral 1M KCl solutions at 22 °C. The active dissolution kinetics in the nearly saturated pit environments has been determined.

J.-S. Chen, A. Bronson, and D.R. Knittel, Pitting Corrosion on Zirconium in KCl and KCl-H_2SO_4 Solutions, *Corrosion,* 41(8), 438-445, 1985. MetAbs No. 85-352331. **Abstract:** Electrochemical investigations of commercially pure Zr and Zr-2.5Nb immersed in KCl and KCl-H_2SO_4 solutions were performed.

I.A. Ammar, S. Darwish, M.W. Khalil, and A. Galal, Investigation of the Passivity of Tin in Neutral Media by Cyclic Galvanostatic Polarization, *Z. Werkstofftech.,* 16(12), 413-421, 1985. MetAbs No. 86-351232. **Abstract:** To understand the passivity of Sn in neutral mediums, two types of measurements have been performed in aerated unstirred KCl and Na_2SO_4 solutions (0.1, 0.5, 1.0 and 2.0M) and in phosphate buffer (pH 6.6 to 6.7). Open-circuit measurements and cyclic galvanostatic polarization measurements were taken.

A.A. Bahgat, E.E. Shaisha, N.A. Eissa, and M.S. Kany, Analysis of the Corrosion Products of an $Fe_{81}B_{13.5}Si_{3.5}C_2$ Amorphous Alloy, *Mater. Sci. Eng.,* 79(1), 43-46, 1986. MetAbs No. 86-351362. **Abstract:** The corrosion tendency and the products of the amorphous alloy $Fe_{81}B_{13.5}Si_{3.5}C_2$ in KCl solution were analyzed using the mass loss, X-ray diffraction, and Mossbauer effect techniques.

E.I. Sokolova, S.N. Raicheva, and M.R. Goulamali, Effect of Functional Groups in the Inhibitor on Its Protective Action, *C.R. Acad. Bulg. Sci.,* 39(4), 55-58, 1986. MetAbs No. 86-352499. **Abstract:** Gravimetric and galvanometric methods were used to study the effects of selected inhibitors on the corrosion of low-carbon steel in 0.5M Na_2SO_4 solution and of Cu in 0.1N KCl.

Corrosion Behavior of Various Metals and Alloys in Potassium Chloride

Material	Condition, other factors, comments	Concen-tration, %	Temperature, °C (°F)	Duration	Corrosion rate, mm/yr (mils/yr) or other	Ref
Stainless steels						
AM-363 stainless steel	...	...	Room	...	Attacked	120
Type 304 stainless steel	...	10	21 (70)	...	Good	121
Type 304 stainless steel	Chemical processing; field or pilot plant test; strong aeration; rapid agitation. Plus 13.95% potassium ion, 13.49% chloride ion, 0.59% sodium ion, 0.5% sulfate ion, 0.29% ferric oxide, 0.07% calcium ion, trace copper powder, 210 ppm amine acetate. Crevice attack (tendency to concentration-cell corrosion)	~25	50 (122)	29 d	0.0003 in./yr	89
Type 304 stainless steel	Chemical processing; field or pilot plant test; slight to moderate aeration; rapid agitation. Trace copper. Moderate pitting: maximum depth of pits from 0.005 to 0.010 in.	25	21 (70)	64 d	0.0002 in./yr	89
Type 304 stainless steel	Chemical processing; field or pilot plant test; slight to moderate aeration; slight to moderate agitation. Saturated solution, 2-7 g/L potassium hydroxide, 2-3 g/L potassium sulfate, 1 g/L potassium carbonate, 3.5 ppm calcium, specific gravity 1.18, pH 13.5. Slight pitting: maximum depth of pits from incipient to 0.005 in. Crevice attack (tendency to concentration-cell corrosion)	28	65 (150)	215 d	<0.0001 in./yr	89
Type 304 stainless steel	Chemical processing; field or pilot plant test; slight to moderate aeration; slight to moderate agitation. Plus 0.5% sodium sulfate, 0.05% sodium chloride, lead, copper, trace starch, pH 9-10 (Dorr clariflocculator, overflow weir). Severe pitting: maximum depth of pits over 0.010 in.	31.5	82 (180)	65 d	0.0002 in./yr	89

(Continued)

Corrosion Behavior of Various Metals and Alloys in Potassium Chloride (Continued)

Material	Condition, other factors, comments	Concentration, %	Temperature, °C (°F)	Duration	Corrosion rate, mm/yr (mils/yr) or other	Ref
Type 316 stainless steel	...	10	21 (70)	...	Very good	121
Type 316 stainless steel	Chemical processing; field or pilot plant test; strong aeration; rapid agitation. Plus 13.95% potassium ion, 13.49% chloride ion, 0.59% sodium ion, 0.5% sulfate ion, 0.29% ferric oxide, 0.07% calcium ion, trace copper powder, 210 ppm amine acetate. Crevice attack (tendency to concentration-cell corrosion)	~25	50 (122)	29 d	<0.0001 in./yr	89
Type 316 stainless steel	Chemical processing; field or pilot plant test; slight to moderate aeration; rapid agitation. Trace copper	25	21 (70)	64 d	<0.0001 in./yr	89
Type 316 stainless steel	Chemical processing; field or pilot plant test; slight to moderate aeration; slight to moderate agitation. Saturated solution, 2-7 g/L potassium hydroxide, 2-3 g/L potassium sulfate, 1 g/L potassium carbonate, 3.5 ppm calcium, specific gravity 1.18, pH 13.5. Slight pitting: maximum depth of pits from incipient to 0.005 in.	28	65 (150)	215 d	<0.0001 in./yr	89
Type 316 stainless steel	Chemical processing; field or pilot plant test; slight to moderate aeration; slight to moderate agitation. Plus 0.5% sodium sulfate, 0.05% sodium chloride, lead, copper, trace starch, pH 9-10 (Dorr clariflocculator, overflow weir)	31.5	82 (180)	65 d	0.0002 in./yr	89
Type 410 stainless steel	...	10	21 (70)	...	Good	121
Type 410 stainless steel	...	...	Room	...	Slightly attacked	121
Type 430 stainless steel	...	10	21 (70)	...	Good	121
Coppers						
70-30 cupronickel	...	...	...	...	Suitable	93
90-10 cupronickel	...	...	...	...	Suitable	93
Admiralty brass	(a)	...	...	...	Good	93
Aluminum bronze	(a)	...	...	...	Good	93
Ampco 8, aluminum bronze	Generally suitable	...	...	...	<0.05 (<2)	96
Architectural bronze	...	...	...	...	Not suitable	93
Brass	(a)	...	...	...	Good	93
Cartridge brass	...	...	...	...	Not suitable	93
Commercial bronze	(a)	...	...	...	Good	93
Electrolytic copper	(a)	...	...	...	Good	93
Free-cutting brass	...	...	...	...	Not suitable	93
Muntz metal	...	...	...	...	Not suitable	93
Naval brass	...	...	...	...	Fair	93
Nickel silver	...	18	...	...	Suitable	93
Phosphor bronze	5% Sn. (a)	...	...	...	Good	93
Phosphor bronze	8% Sn	...	...	...	Suitable	93
Phosphor copper	(a)	...	...	...	Good	93
Red brass	(a)	...	...	...	Good	93
Silicon bronze	Low. (a)	...	...	...	Good	93
Silicon bronze	High. (a)	...	...	...	Good	93
Titanium						
Titanium	...	Saturated	Room	...	nil	90
Titanium	...	Saturated	60 (140)	...	nil	90
Heat- and corrosion-resistant alloys						
Carpenter 20	Chemical processing; field or pilot plant test; slight to moderate aeration; slight to moderate agitation; cast specimens. Saturated solution, 2-7 g/L potassium hydroxide, 2-3 g/L potassium sulfate, 1 g/L potassium carbonate, 3.5 ppm calcium, specific gravity 1.18, pH 13.5	28	65 (150)	215 d	<0.0001 in./yr	89
Zirconium						
Zr702	...	Saturated	60 (140)	...	<0.025 (<1)	15
Zr702	...	Saturated	Room	...	<0.025 (<1)	15

(Continued)

Corrosion Behavior of Various Metals and Alloys in Potassium Chloride (Continued)

Material	Condition, other factors, comments	Concentration, %	Temperature, °C (°F)	Duration	Corrosion rate, mm/yr (mils/yr) or other	Ref
Lead, tin, and zinc						
Lead	Practically resistant; Pb recommended for use	0.25-8.0	8 (47)	...	<500 μm/yr (<20)	95
Tin	Pitting possible in stagnant solutions	...	20 (68)	...	Resistant	94
Tin	...	...	60 (140)	...	Unsuitable	94
Tin	...	...	100 (212)	...	Unsuitable	94

(a) May be considered in place of a copper metal when some property, other than corrosion resistance, governs its use.

Potassium Fluoride

Potassium fluoride, KF, is a colorless, deliquescent crystalline solid that has a melting point of 846 °C (1550 °F). Potassium fluoride has a salty taste and is poisonous. It is soluble in water, but insoluble in alcohol. Potassium fluoride is used in etching glass, preservatives, and insecticides.

Material Summaries

The following material summaries were compiled from a survey of the available literature. Inclusion of a material description under a given environment does not imply that it is the most appropriate material for corrosion service in that environment. Likewise, exclusion of a given material does not imply that it is not suitable for corrosion service applications in that environment.

Zirconium. Zirconium has good resistance to potassium fluoride at low temperatures, but resistance drops rapidly as the temperature is increased.

Additional Reading

W.A. Badawy, M.M. Ibrahim, M.M. Abou-Romia, and M.S. El-Basiouny, Kinetic Studies on the Dissolution Behavior of Anodic Oxide Films on Aluminum in KF Solutions, *Corrosion*, *42*(6), 324-328, 1986. MetAbs No. 86-351500. **Abstract:** A study was made to account for the dissolution of naturally developed and anodically formed oxide films on aluminum in KF solutions. The behavior of these oxide films was investigated by impedance and potential measurements.

Corrosion Behavior of Various Metals and Alloys in Potassium Fluoride

Material	Condition, other factors, comments	Concentration, %	Temperature, °C (°F)	Duration	Corrosion rate, mm/yr (mils/yr) or other	Ref
Magnesium	...	All	Room	...	Suitable	119
Zr702	pH 8.9	20	28 (82)	...	nil	15
Zr702	pH 8.9	20	90 (185)	...	>1.3 (>50)	15
Zr702	...	0.3	Boiling	...	<0.025 (<1)	15

Potassium Hydroxide

Potassium hydroxide, KOH, also known as caustic potash, lye, and potassium hydrate, is a white deliquescent crystalline solid that has a melting point of 360 °C (680 °F). It is soluble in water and alcohol. Potassium hydroxide is used as a mordant, mercerizing agent, in medicine, and in manufacturing soap and matches. It is a powerful cleansing bath for scouring metals and when used in steel-quenching baths gives a higher quenching rate than water alone without attacking the steel as a salt solution would. Potassium hydroxide is slightly more aggressive in the corrosion of metals and nonmetals than sodium hydroxide, but this may be due to its higher boiling point and likelihood of higher temperature exposure. Nickel alloys have been reported to be less sensitive to stress cracking in potassium hydroxide than in sodium hydroxide.

Material Summaries

The following material summaries were compiled from a survey of the available literature. Inclusion of a material description under a given environment does not imply that it is the most appropriate material for corrosion service in that environment. Likewise, exclusion of a given material does not imply that it is not suitable for corrosion service applications in that environment.

Aluminum. Potassium hydroxide is very corrosive to all aluminum alloys.

Copper. Aluminum bronzes are generally suitable for service in potassium hydroxide.

Nickel. Nickel 200 and 201 are used in the production of all concentrations and temperatures (including the molten stage) of potassium hydroxide. At temperatures exceeding 315 °C (600 °F), the lower carbon nickel 201 is used to avoid graphite precipitation. In situations where the dilute potassium hydroxide is evaporated to 50% concentration and contaminants such as chlorates and chlorides may be present, nickel 200 is extensively used. These contaminants can increase corrosion rates especially under velocity conditions. The resistance to corrosion and stress-corrosion cracking of nickel alloys increases with increasing nickel content, and alloys 400, 600, and C-276 may be used in situations requiring higher strength and resistance to other corrosive agents. However, these alloys can be attacked at higher temperatures and concentrations of potassium hydroxide.

Niobium. Niobium is embrittled at low concentrations (5%) of potassium hydroxide above room temperature.

Silver. Silver is not attacked at temperatures slightly below 500 °C (930 °F) by potassium hydroxide.

Iridium. Iridium is slightly attacked by potassium hydroxide.

Osmium. Osmium is attacked by potassium hydroxide.

Tantalum. Although tantalum is not dissolved by potassium hydroxide, the metal is destroyed by the continuous formation of surface scale layers. The rate of scale formation increases with concentration and temperature. Tantalum anode baskets have been successfully used in silver cyanide barrel platers, although the alkaline solutions contain potassium hydroxide. The positive voltage of the cell itself protected the tantalum anode basket from surface scale formation. Tantalum-tungsten alloys showed little improvement over tantalum when tested in a potassium hydroxide/potassium ferrocyanide mixture.

Titanium. Titanium alloys have low corrosion rates in potassium hydroxide solutions at sub-boiling temperatures. However, the corrosion rate increases significantly with higher temperatures and concentrations. Titanium alloys can experience hydrogen buildup and eventual embrittlement in potassium hydroxide solutions when temperatures exceed 80 °C (175 °F) and the pH is 12 or more. The addition of dissolved oxidizing compounds such as chlorates or hypochlorites to hot caustic solutions can extend the hydrogen resistance of titanium to somewhat higher temperatures.

Zirconium. Zirconium is fairly resistant to potassium hydroxide.

Additional Reading

K.B. Sarangapani, V. Balaramachandran, V. Kapali, S.V. Iyer, and M.G. Potdar, Aluminium as the Anode in Primary Alkaline Batteries, *Surf. Technol.*, *26*(1), 67-76, 1985. MetAbs No. 86-350406. **Abstract:** Self-corrosion and the anodic behavior of commercially pure Al (Al-2S) have been studied in potassium hydroxide solutions.

Corrosion Behavior of Various Metals and Alloys in Potassium Hydroxide

Material	Condition, other factors, comments	Concentration, %	Temperature, °C (°F)	Duration	Corrosion rate, mm/yr (mils/yr) or other	Ref
Stainless and carbon steels						
Low-carbon steel	Plus 13% KCl. Slight attack under spacer	13	30 (85)	207 d	0.013 (0.5)	111
Low-carbon steel	...	50	25 (80)	207 d	0.0013 (0.05)	111
Type 304 stainless steel	Petroleum processing; field or pilot plant test; slight to moderate aeration; rapid agitation. Plus 28% alkyl phenolate, 19% potassium isobutyrate, 0.8% sulfide, 0.4% mercaptans (bottom of "solutizer" regenerator tower). Slight pitting: maximum depth of pits from incipient to 0.005 in. Crevice attack (tendency to concentration-cell corrosion)	11.2	182-193 (360-380)	276 d	0.0023 in./yr	89
Type 304 stainless steel	Petroleum processing; field or pilot plant test; slight to moderate aeration; rapid agitation. With carbon over the standard maximum. Plus 28% alkyl phenolate, 19% potassium isobutyrate, 0.8% sulfide, 0.4% mercaptans (bottom of "solutizer" regenerator tower). Slight pitting: maximum depth of pits from incipient to 0.005 in. Crevice attack (tendency to concentration-cell corrosion)	11.2	182-193 (360-380)	276 d	0.0024 in./yr	89
Type 304 stainless steel	Chemical processing; field or pilot plant test; slight to moderate aeration; rapid agitation. With carbon over the standard maximum. Plus isopropanol solution of hexachlorocyclopentadiene. Slight pitting: maximum depth of pits from incipient to 0.005 in.	20	80 (176)	146 d	0.0002 in./yr	89
Type 304 stainless steel	Chemical processing; field or pilot plant test; slight to moderate aeration; slight to moderate agitation. Plus isopropanol solution of hexachlorocyclopentadiene	20	80 (176)	90 d	0.0001 in./yr	89

(Continued)

Corrosion Behavior of Various Metals and Alloys in Potassium Hydroxide (Continued)

Material	Condition, other factors, comments	Concentration, %	Temperature, °C (°F)	Duration	Corrosion rate, mm/yr (mils/yr) or other	Ref
Type 304 stainless steel	Chemical processing; field or pilot plant test; slight to moderate aeration; no agitation. With carbon over the standard maximum. Plus isopropanol solution of hexachloropentadiene (vapors). Slight pitting: maximum depth of pits from incipient to 0.005 in.	20	94 (202)	18 d	0.0004 in./yr	89
Type 304 stainless steel	Chemical processing; field or pilot plant test; slight to moderate aeration; rapid agitation. With carbon over the standard maximum. Plus isopropanol solution of hexachloropentadiene. Slight pitting: maximum depth of pits from incipient to 0.005 in.	20	94 (202)	19 d	0.0009 in./yr	89
Type 304 stainless steel	Petroleum processing; field or pilot plant test; no aeration; rapid agitation. Plus 37.8% potassium isobutyrate, 5.5% potassium sulfide, 2.1% potassium carbonate, 1.9% potassium mercaptides (reboiler)	25.2	139-142 (282-290)	140 d	Corrosion	89
Type 304 stainless steel	Petroleum processing; field or pilot plant test; no aeration; rapid agitation; With carbon over the standard maximum. Plus 37.8% potassium isobutyrate, 5.5% potassium sulfide, 2.1% potassium carbonate, 1.9% potassium mercaptides (reboiler)	25.2	139-142 (282-290)	140 d	Corrosion	89
Type 304 stainless steel	Chemical processing; field or pilot plant test; no aeration; rapid agitation. Plus 21.6% sodium hydroxide, approximately 3% ammonium hydroxide (evaporator)	32.4	120 (248)	60 d	0.0228 in./yr	89
Type 304 stainless steel	Chemical processing; field or pilot plant test; no aeration; rapid agitation. Plus 21.6% sodium hydroxide, approximately 3% ammonium hydroxide (evaporator)	32.4	120 (248)	60 d	0.0222 in./yr	89
Type 304 stainless steel	Chemical processing; field or pilot plant test; rapid agitation	~50	Boiling	3 d	0.13 in./yr	89
Type 304 stainless steel	Chemical processing; field or pilot plant test; no aeration; no agitation. Plus 50% sodium hydroxide	50	<93 (<200)	30 d	<0.0001 in./yr	89
Type 304 stainless steel	Chemical processing; field or pilot plant test; no agitation	~80	Boiling	4 d	0.1 in./yr	89
Type 304 stainless steel	Chemical processing; field or pilot plant test; rapid agitation	92-90	380 (716)	4 d	0.35 in./yr	89
Type 316 stainless steel	Petroleum processing; field or pilot plant test; slight to moderate aeration; rapid agitation. Plus 28% alkyl phenolate, 19% potassium isobutyrate, 0.8% sulfide, 0.4% mercaptans (bottom of "solutizer" regenerator tower). Slight pitting: maximum depth of pits from incipient to 0.005 in. Crevice attack (tendency to concentration-cell corrosion)	11.2	182-193 (360-380)	276 d	0.0041 in./yr	89
Type 316 stainless steel	Chemical processing; field or pilot plant test; slight to moderate aeration; rapid agitation. Plus isopropanol solution of hexachlorocyclopentadiene	20	80 (176)	146 d	0.0002 in./yr	89
Type 316 stainless steel	Chemical processing; field or pilot plant test; slight to moderate aeration; slight to moderate agitation. Plus isopropanol solution of hexachlorocyclopentadiene	20	80 (176)	90 d	0.0001 in./yr	89
Type 316 stainless steel	Chemical processing; field or pilot plant test; slight to moderate aeration; no agitation. Plus isopropanol solution of hexachloropentadiene (vapors). Slight pitting: maximum depth of pits from incipient to 0.005 in.	20	94 (202)	18 d	0.0003 in./yr	89
Type 315 stainless steel	Chemical processing; field or pilot plant test; slight to moderate aeration; rapid agitation. Plus isopropanol solution of hexachloropentadiene. Slight pitting: maximum depth of pits from incipient to 0.005 in.	20	94 (202)	19 d	0.0007 in./yr	89
Type 316 stainless steel	Chemical processing; field or pilot plant test; no aeration; rapid agitation. Plus 21.6% sodium hydroxide, approximately 3% ammonium hydroxide (evaporator)	32.4	120 (248)	60 d	0.0295 in./yr	89

(Continued)

Corrosion Behavior of Various Metals and Alloys in Potassium Hydroxide (Continued)

Material	Condition, other factors, comments	Concentration, %	Temperature, °C (°F)	Duration	Corrosion rate, mm/yr (mils/yr) or other	Ref
Type 316 stainless steel	Chemical processing; field or pilot plant test; no aeration; rapid agitation. Plus 21.6% sodium hydroxide, approximately 3% ammonium hydroxide (evaporator)	32.4	120 (248)	60 d	0.0292 in./yr	89
Type 316 stainless steel	Chemical processing; field or pilot plant test; rapid agitation	~50	Boiling	3 d	0.12 in./yr	89
Type 316 stainless steel	Chemical processing; field or pilot plant test; no aeration; no agitation. Plus 50% sodium hydroxide	50	<93 (<200)	30 d	<0.0001 in./yr	89
Type 316 stainless steel	Chemical processing; field or pilot plant test; no agitation	~80	Boiling	4 d	0.008 in./yr	89
Type 316 stainless steel	Chemical processing; field or pilot plant test; rapid agitation	92-90	380 (716)	4 d	0.25 in./yr	89
Coppers						
70-30 cupronickel	...	...	...	...	Suitable	93
90-10 cupronickel	...	...	...	...	Suitable	93
Admiralty brass	(a)	...	...	...	Good	93
Aluminum bronze	(a)	...	...	...	Good	93
Ampco 8, aluminum bronze	Generally suitable	...	...	...	<0.05 (<2)	96
Architectural bronze	...	...	...	...	Fair	93
Brass	(a)	...	...	...	Good	93
Cartridge brass	...	...	...	...	Fair	93
Commercial bronze	(a)	...	...	...	Good	93
Electrolytic copper	(a)	...	...	...	Good	93
Free-cutting brass	...	...	...	...	Fair	93
Muntz metal	...	...	...	...	Fair	93
Naval brass	...	...	...	...	Fair	93
Nickel silver	...	18	...	...	Suitable	93
Phosphor bronze	5% Sn. (a)	...	...	...	Good	93
Phosphor bronze	8% Sn. (a)	...	...	...	Good	93
Phosphor copper	(a)	...	...	...	Good	93
Red brass	(a)	...	...	...	Good	93
Silicon bronze	Low. (a)	...	...	...	Good	93
Silicon bronze	High. (a)	...	...	...	Good	93
Heat- and corrosion-resistant alloys						
Carpenter 20	Chemical processing; field or pilot plant test; rapid agitation	~50	Boiling	3 d	0.15 in./yr	89
Carpenter 20	Chemical processing; field or pilot plant test; no agitation	~80	Boiling	4 d	0.02 in./yr	89
Carpenter 20	Chemical processing; field or pilot plant test; rapid agitation; cast specimens	92-98	380 (716)	4 d	0.092 in./yr	89
Inconel	Plus 13% KCl	13	30 (85)	207 d	nil	111
Inconel	...	50	25 (80)	207 d	nil	111
Monel	Plus 13% KCl	13	30 (85)	207 d	nil	111
Monel	...	50	25 (80)	207 d	0.00005 (0.002)	111
Nickel	Plus 13% KCl	13	30 (85)	207 d	nil	111
Nickel	...	50	25 (80)	207 d	0.00008 (0.003)	111
Nickel 200	Saturated with KCl, 0.05% potassium chlorate. Liquid	30	Boiling	...	5.08 μm/yr (0.2)	44
Nickel 200	Saturated with KCl, 0.05% potassium chlorate. Vapor	30	Boiling	...	2.54 μm/yr (0.1)	44
Nickel 200	Saturated with KCl, 0.078% potassium chlorate. Liquid	47	Boiling	...	2.54 μm/yr (0.1)	44
Nickel 200	Saturated with KCl, 0.078% potassium chlorate. Vapor	47	Boiling	...	7.62 μm/yr (0.3)	44
Nickel 200	Velocity 21.6 ft/min	50	149 (300)	...	Gain	44
Nickel 200	Velocity 348 ft/min	50	149 (300)	...	Gain	44
Nickel 200	Velocity 21.6 ft/min	70	149 (300)	...	10.16 μm/yr (0.4)	44
Nickel 200	Velocity 348 ft/min	70	149 (300)	...	40.64 μm/yr (1.6)	44

(Continued)

Corrosion Behavior of Various Metals and Alloys in Potassium Hydroxide (Continued)

Material	Condition, other factors, comments	Concentration, %	Temperature, °C (°F)	Duration	Corrosion rate, mm/yr (mils/yr) or other	Ref
Titanium						
Titanium	...	10	Boiling	...	0.13 (5)	1
Titanium	...	10	Boiling	...	<0.127 (<5.08)	90
Titanium	Plus 13% KCl	13	29 (85)	...	nil	90
Titanium	Plus 13% KCl	13	29 (85)	207 d	0.023 (0.9)	111
Titanium	...	25	Boiling	...	0.3 (12)	1
Titanium	...	25	Boiling	...	0.305 (12.2)	90
Titanium	...	50	24 (75)	...	0.010 (0.4)	1
Titanium	...	50	27 (80)	207 d	0.01 (0.4)	111
Titanium	...	50	29 (85)	...	0.010 (0.4)	90
Titanium	Grade 9	50	150 (302)	...	9.21 (362)	33
Titanium	...	50	150 (302)	...	2.7 (108)	91
Titanium	...	50	Boiling	...	2.7 (106)	1
Titanium	...	50	Boiling	...	2.74 (109.6)	90
Titanium	Anhydrous	50	241-377 (467-712)	...	1.02-1.52 (40.8-60.8)	90
Ti-3Al-2.5V	ASTM Grade 9	50	150 (302)	...	9.07 (363)	91
Zirconium						
Zirconium	Plus 13% KCl	13	30 (85)	207 d	0.005 (0.2)	111
Zirconium	...	50	27 (80)	207 d	0.0015 (0.06)	111
Zirconium	...	50	27 (80)	...	<0.025 (<1)	15
Zr702	...	10	Boiling	...	<0.025 (<1)	15
Zr702	...	13	29 (85)	...	<0.025 (<1)	15
Zr702	Plus 13% KCl	25	Boiling	...	<0.025 (<1)	15
Zr702	...	50	Boiling	...	<0.13 (<5)	15
Zr702	...	50	241-377 (465-710)	...	>1.3 (>50)	15
Zr702	To anhydrous					
Lead, tin, and zinc						
Lead	Practically resistant; Pb recommended for use	0-50	24-60 (75-140)	...	<500 μm/yr (<20)	95
Tin	...	...	20 (68)	...	Unsuitable	94
Tin	...	...	60 (140)	...	Unsuitable	94
Tin	...	...	100 (212)	...	Unsuitable	94
Hafnium						
Hafnium	...	50	...	2 d	0.013 (0.5)	11
Noble metals						
Platinum	...	All	300 (570)	...	<0.05 (<2)	5
Platinum	Melt. Pt is attacked if strong oxidizers are present	...	300 (570)	...	<0.05 (<2)	5
Silver	Air must be excluded	All	300 (570)	...	<0.05 (<2)	9
Silver	Melt. Air must be excluded	...	350 (680)	...	<0.05 (<2)	9
Others						
Magnesium	...	All	Room	...	Suitable	119
Niobium	...	5-40	Room	...	Embrittlement	2
Niobium	...	1-5	98 (208)	...	Embrittlement	2

(a) May be considered in place of a copper metal when some property, other than corrosion resistance, governs its use.

Corrosion of Metals and Alloys in Potassium Hydroxide Solutions

Material	Corrosion rate			
	13% KOH(a)		50% KOH(b)	
	mm/yr	mils/yr	mm/yr	mils/yr
Titanium.............	0.023	0.9	0.01	0.4
Zirconium	0.005	0.2	0.0015	0.06
Nickel...............		nil	0.00008	0.003
Monel...............		nil	0.00005	0.002
Inconel..............		nil		nil
Low-carbon steel......	0.013	0.5(c)	0.0013	0.05

(a) 207-day test at 30 °C (85 °F); 13% KCl added to solution. (b) 207-day test at 25 °C (80 °F). (c) Slight attack under spacer. Source: Ref 62

Source: *Metals Handbook,* 9th ed., Vol 13, Corrosion, ASM International, Metals Park, OH, 1987, 1178.

Potassium Iodide

Potassium iodide, KI, is a white crystalline solid that melts at 686 °C (1260 °F). It is soluble in water and alcohol. Potassium iodide is used in analytical chemistry and photography. In medicine, potassium iodide is used to regulate the thyroid gland.

Material Summaries

The following material summaries were compiled from a survey of the available literature. Inclusion of a material description under a given environment does not imply that it is the most appropriate material for corrosion service in that environment. Likewise, exclusion of a given material does not imply that it is not suitable for corrosion service applications in that environment.

Aluminum. Limited testing of potassium iodide solutions at ambient temperature indicates a corrosion reaction with aluminum alloys comparable to that of sodium chloride.

Corrosion Behavior of Various Metals and Alloys in Potassium Iodide

Material	Condition, other factors, comments	Concentration, %	Temperature, °C (°F)	Duration	Corrosion rate, mm/yr (mils/yr) or other	Ref
Aluminum (>99.5%)	Solution	...	...	...	Satisfactory	92
AM-363 stainless steel	...	...	Room	...	Slightly attacked	120
Type 410 stainless steel	Plus 0.1% sodium carbonate, evaporated to dryness	Saturated	Room	...	Slightly attacked	121
Zr702	...	0-70	Room to 100 (room to 212)	...	<0.05 (<2)	15

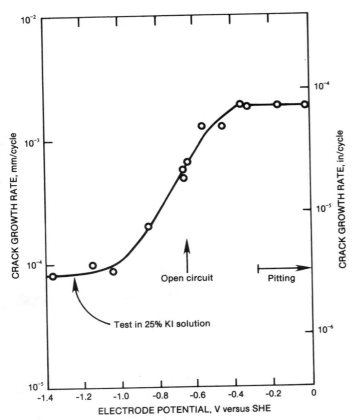

Aluminum. Corrosion fatigue behavior of aluminum alloy 7079-T651 plate (S-L orientation) in 25% potassium iodide solution. Temperature: 23 °C (73 °F); frequency: 4 cycles/s; stress ratio: $R = 0$. Source: M.O. Speidel, M.J. Blackburn, T.R. Beck, and J.A. Feeney, "Corrosion Fatigue and Stress Corrosion Crack Growth in High Strength Aluminum Alloys, Magnesium Alloys and Titanium Alloys Exposed to Aqueous Solutions," in *Corrosion Fatigue: Chemistry, Mechanics and Microstructure*, O. Devereux, A.J. McEvily, and R.W. Staehle, Ed., National Association of Corrosion Engineers, Houston, 1973, 324-345.

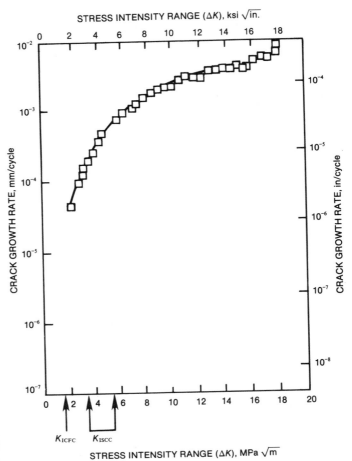

Aluminum. Corrosion fatigue behavior of aluminum alloy 7079-T651 plate (S-L orientation) in 25% potassium iodide solution. Temperature: 23 °C (73 °F); frequency: 4 cycles/s; stress ratio: $R = 0$. Source: M.O. Speidel, M.J. Blackburn, T.R. Beck, and J.A. Feeney, "Corrosion Fatigue and Stress Corrosion Crack Growth in High Strength Aluminum Alloys, Magnesium Alloys and Titanium Alloys Exposed to Aqueous Solutions," in *Corrosion Fatigue: Chemistry, Mechanics and Microstructure*, O. Devereux, A.J. McEvily, and R.W. Staehle, Ed., National Association of Corrosion Engineers, Houston, 1973, 324-345.

Potassium Sulfate

Potassium sulfate, K_2SO_4, also known as salt of Lemery and arcanite, is a colorless crystalline solid that melts at 1072 °C (1960 °F). It is soluble in water, but insoluble in alcohol. Potassium sulfate is used in manufacturing glass, aluminum, fertilizers, and in medicine.

Material Summaries

The following material summaries were compiled from a survey of the available literature. Inclusion of a material description under a given environment does not imply that it is the most appropriate material for corrosion service in that environment. Likewise, exclusion of a given material does not imply that it is not suitable for corrosion service applications in that environment.

Aluminum. During testing at ambient temperature and 100% relative humidity, aluminum alloys 3003 and 5154 resisted attack by solid potassium sulfate. When the temperature was increased to 54 °C (130 °F), these alloys endured mild attack (0.075 mm/yr, or 3 mils/yr).

Additional Reading

S.S. Abd El Rehim, A.C. Corrosion of Delta-52 Steel in K_2SO_4 Solutions, *Surf. Technol.*, 25(3), 223-228, 1985. MetAbs No. 86-350176. **Abstract:** The effect of a sinusoidal alternating current on the corrosion of Delta-52 (0.34% carbon) steel in K_2SO_4 solutions was investigated. A potentiodynamic anodic potential scan of the steel electrode was performed under the influence of superimposed alternating current.

Y.M. Chen, T.J. O'Keefe, and W.J. James, Electrochemical Studies of Plasma-Formed Films of Tin, *Thin Solid Films, 129*(3-4), 205-215, 1985. MetAbs No. 87-350233. **Abstract:** The electrochemical behavior of plasma-formed tin films on aluminum is compared with that of conventional beta-tin. Rest potential measurements in K_2SO_4 solutions (pH 3.4 to 5.9), auger analyses, and atomic absorption analyses were performed.

P.K. Chauhan, A. Sharma, and H.S. Gadiyar, Inhibition of the Corrosion of Mild Steel by Carbonyl Compounds in Potassium Sulfate Medium, *J. Electrochem. Soc. India, 35*(4), 251-256, 1986. MetAbs No. 87-351505. **Abstract:** Inhibition of the corrosion of mild steel in neutral potassium sulfate medium was investigated using several aldehydes and ketones. Detailed mechanisms regarding the structure of inhibitors and their performance have been considered.

Corrosion Behavior of Various Metals and Alloys in Potassium Sulfate

Material	Condition, other factors, comments	Concentration, %	Temperature, °C (°F)	Duration	Corrosion rate, mm/yr (mils/yr) or other	Ref
Stainless steels						
AM-363 stainless steel	...	...	Room	...	Unattacked	120
Type 410 stainless steel	...	...	Room	...	Unattacked	121
Aluminum						
Aluminum (99.0-99.5%)	Solution	...	20 (68)	...	Satisfactory	92
Aluminum-manganese alloys	Solution	...	20 (68)	...	Satisfactory	92
Coppers						
70-30 cupronickel	...	...	...	...	Suitable	93
90-10 cupronickel	...	...	...	...	Suitable	93
Admiralty brass	...	...	...	...	Suitable	93
Aluminum bronze	...	...	...	...	Suitable	93
Ampco 8, aluminum bronze	Generally suitable	...	...	...	<0.05 (<2)	96
Architectural bronze	(a)	...	...	...	Good	93
Brass	...	...	...	...	Suitable	93
Cartridge brass	(a)	...	...	...	Good	93
Commercial bronze	...	...	...	...	Suitable	93
Electrolytic copper	...	...	...	...	Suitable	93
Free-cutting brass	(a)	...	...	...	Good	93
Muntz metal	(a)	...	...	...	Good	93
Naval brass	(a)	...	...	...	Good	93
Nickel silver	...	18	...	...	Suitable	93
Phosphor bronze	5% Sn	...	...	...	Suitable	93
Phosphor bronze	8% Sn	...	...	...	Suitable	93
Phosphor copper	...	...	...	...	Suitable	93
Red brass	...	...	...	...	Suitable	93
Silicon bronze	Low	...	...	...	Suitable	93
Silicon bronze	High	...	...	...	Suitable	93
Titanium						
Titanium	...	10	Room	...	nil	90
Lead, tin, and zinc						
Tin	...	...	20 (68)	...	Resistant	94
Tin	...	...	60 (140)	...	Unsuitable	94
Tin	...	...	100 (212)	...	Unsuitable	94
Noble metals						
Platinum	...	All	Boiling	...	<0.05 (<2)	5
Platinum	Melt. Provided reducing agents are not present	...	Melting point	...	<0.05 (<2)	5
Silver	...	All	Boiling	...	<0.05 (<2)	9

(a) May be considered in place of a copper metal when some property, other than corrosion resistance, governs its use.

Potassium Thiocyanate

Potassium thiocyanate, KSCN, also known as potassium sulfocyanate and potassium rhodanide, is a colorless deliquescent crystalline solid that melts at 173 °C (343 °F) and decomposes at 500 °C (932 °F). Soluble in water and alcohol, it has no odor and a saline taste. Potassium thiocyanate is used in printing and dyeing textiles, freezing mixtures, manufacturing chemicals, photography and medicine.

Material Summaries

The following material summaries were compiled from a survey of the available literature. Inclusion of a material description under a given environment does not imply that it is the most appropriate material for corrosion service in that environment. Likewise, exclusion of a given material does not imply that it is not suitable for corrosion service applications in that environment.

Aluminum. Laboratory testing under conditions of 100% relative humidity and ambient temperature showed aluminum alloy 3003 to be resistant to solid potassium thiocyanate and aqueous solutions (including saturated) of potassium thiocyanate.

Additional Reading

M.G. Figueroa, R.C. Salvarezza and A.J. Arvia, Electrochemical Behavior of Copper in Potassium Thiocyanate. I. Dissolution, Passivation and Pitting Processes, *Electrochim. Acta, 31*(6), 671-680, 1986. MetAbs No. 86-352055. **Abstract:** The electrochemical behavior of copper in borate buffers containing KSCN was studied by potentiostatic and potentiodynamic techniques complemented with scanning electron microscopy and EDAX.

Corrosion Behavior of Various Metals and Alloys in Potassium Thiocyanate

Material	Condition, other factors, comments	Concentration, %	Temperature, °C (°F)	Duration	Corrosion rate, mm/yr (mils/yr) or other	Ref
Aluminum (99.0-99.5%)	Solution	...	20-100 (68-212)	...	Excellent	92
Aluminum-manganese alloys	Solution	...	20-100 (68-212)	...	Excellent	92

Propionic Acid

Propionic acid, CH_3CH_2COOH, also known as propanoic acid and methylacetic acid, is a clear, colorless liquid that boils at 140 °C (284 °F). It has a pungent odor and is soluble in water and alcohol. Propionic acid is used in nickel electroplating solutions, perfumes, artificial flavors, pharmaceuticals, and manufacturing propionates.

Material Summaries

The following material summaries were compiled from a survey of the available literature. Inclusion of a material description under a given environment does not imply that it is the most appropriate material for corrosion service in that environment. Likewise, exclusion of a given material does not imply that it is not suitable for corrosion service applications in that environment.

Alloy Steels. Alloy steel is attacked rapidly by propionic acid.

Stainless Steels. Type 304 stainless steel resists attack by propionic acid at room temperature and by its aqueous solutions with concentrations that are less than 50% at the boiling point. At the boiling temperature with concentrations ranging between 80 to 100%, type 304 stainless steel exhibits borderline passivity to propionic acid, and its use should be avoided. Type 316 stainless steel is recommended for use with hot concentrated solutions of propionic acid. Corrosion tests in the exact environment should be run to determine if intergranular attack is a problem before the use of a low-carbon grade (type 316L). Impurities strongly affect the corrosion rate.

Aluminum. Aluminum alloy 1100 resisted attack by aqueous solutions of propionic acid (0.5 to 100%) in tests at ambient temperature. However, propionic acid solutions became corrosive at higher temperatures and anhydrous propionic acid was very corrosive. Aluminum alloy tanks and drums have been used to ship, store, and handle propionic acid.

Copper. Copper has acceptable rates of corrosion in all concentrations of propionic acid in the absence of air.

Nickel. Incoloy alloy 800 has good resistance to propionic acid and is suitable for service, except in the most severe corrosive conditions.

Additional Reading

G.B. Elder, Materials of Construction for Organic Acids, *Process Industries Corrosion—The Theory and Practice*, National Association of Corrosion Engineers, Houston, 1986, 287-296. MetAbs No. 88-350337. **Abstract:** The corrosion characteristics and materials (Al 1100 and 5086, Cu-Ni, steel and Ti) used to manufacture and store propionic acid are presented in detail.

Corrosion Behavior of Various Metals and Alloys in Propionic Acid

Material	Condition, other factors, comments	Concentration, %	Temperature, °C (°F)	Duration	Corrosion rate, mm/yr (mils/yr) or other	Ref
Stainless steels						
Type 304 stainless steel	Chemical processing; field or pilot plant test; no aeration; rapid agitation. Plus 45% butyric acid, 5% heavy esters during 155 d, 96% acetic acid, 2% nonvolatiles, 1% propionic acid, 1% water during 38 d	50	121 (251)	193 d	0.002 in./yr	89
Type 304 stainless steel	Chemical processing; no aeration; rapid agitation. Plus 10-12% butyric acid, 4-7% acetic acid, remainder unknown. Severe pitting: maximum depth of pits over 0.010 in.	60-65	155 (311)	466 d	0.027 in./yr	89
Type 304 stainless steel	Chemical processing; field or pilot plant test; no aeration; slight to moderate agitation. Plus 16.5% glycol esters, 12% butyric acid, 1.5% acetic acid	70	156 (314)	566 d	0.017 in./yr	89
Type 304 stainless steel	Chemical processing; field or pilot plant test; slight to moderate aeration; slight to moderate agitation. Plus 12% butyric acid, 5% sulfuric acid	83	138 (280)	10 d	0.045 in./yr	89
Type 304 stainless steel	Chemical processing; field or pilot plant test; no aeration; slight to moderate agitation. Plus 5% sulfuric acid, 0.5% butyric acid, 0.5% decomposition products	94	150 (302)	12 d	0.0007 in./yr	89
Type 304 stainless steel	Chemical processing; field or pilot plant test; slight to moderate aeration; slight to moderate agitation. Plus 1% sulfuric acid	99	138 (280)	10 d	0.02 in./yr	89
Type 304 stainless steels	Rayon processing; field or pilot plant test; no aeration; rapid agitation	100	145 (293)	200 d	0.038 in./yr	89
Type 316 stainless steel	Chemical processing; field or pilot plant test; no aeration; rapid agitation. Plus 45% butyric acid, 5% heavy esters during 155 d, 96% acetic acid, 2% nonvolatiles, 1% propionic acid, 1% water during 38 d	50	121 (251)	193 d	0.0007 in./yr	89
Type 316 stainless steel	Chemical processing; no aeration; rapid agitation. Plus 10-12% butyric acid, 4-7% acetic acid, remainder unknown. Moderate pitting: maximum depth of pits from 0.005 to 0.010 in.	60-65	155 (311)	466 d	0.0061 in./yr	89
Type 316 stainless steel	Chemical processing; field or pilot plant test; no aeration; slight to moderate agitation. Plus 16.5% glycol esters, 12% butyric acid, 1.5% acetic acid. Slight pitting: maximum depth of pits from incipient to 0.005 in.	70	156 (314)	566 d	0.0046 in./yr	89
Type 316 stainless steel	Chemical processing; field or pilot plant test; slight to moderate aeration; slight to moderate agitation. Plus 12% butyric acid, 5% sulfuric acid	83	138 (280)	10 d	0.003 in./yr	89
Type 316 stainless steel	Chemical processing; field or pilot plant test; no aeration; slight to moderate agitation. Plus 5% sulfuric acid, 0.5% butyric acid, 0.5% decomposition products	94	150 (302)	12 d	0.00027 in./yr	89
Type 316 stainless steel	Chemical processing; field or pilot plant test; slight to moderate aeration; slight to moderate agitation. Plus 1% sulfuric acid	99	138 (280)	10 d	0.0043 in./yr	89
Type 316 stainless steels	Rayon processing; field or pilot plant test; no aeration; rapid agitation	100	145 (293)	200 d	0.012 in./yr	89
Type 317 stainless steel	Chemical processing; field or pilot plant test; no aeration; rapid agitation. Plus 45% butyric acid, 5% heavy esters during 155 d, 96% acetic acid, 2% nonvolatiles, 1% propionic acid, 1% water during 38 d	50	121 (251)	193 d	0.0004 in./yr	89
Type 317 stainless steel	Chemical processing; no aeration; rapid agitation. Plus 10-12% butyric acid, 4-7% acetic acid, remainder unknown	60-655	155 (311)	466 d	0.0039 in./yr	89
Type 317 stainless steel	Chemical processing; field or pilot plant test; no aeration; slight to moderate agitation. Plus 16.5% glycol esters, 12% butyric acid, 1.5% acetic acid	70	156 (314)	566 d	0.003 in./yr	89
Type 317 stainless steel	Chemical processing; field or pilot plant test; slight to moderate aeration; slight to moderate agitation. Plus 12% butyric acid, 5% sulfuric acid	83	138 (280)	10 d	0.0035 in./yr	89
Type 317 stainless steel	Chemical processing; field or pilot plant test; no aeration; slight to moderate agitation. Plus 5% sulfuric acid, 0.5% butyric acid, 0.5% decomposition products	94	150 (302)	12 d	0.00019 in./yr	89

(Continued)

Corrosion Behavior of Various Metals and Alloys in Propionic Acid (Continued)

Material	Condition, other factors, comments	Concentration, %	Temperature, °C (°F)	Duration	Corrosion rate, mm/yr (mils/yr) or other	Ref
Type 317 stainless steel	Chemical processing; field or pilot plant test; slight to moderate aeration; slight to moderate agitation. Plus 1% sulfuric acid	99	138 (280)	10 d	0.005 in./yr	89
Titanium						
Titanium	...	Vapor	190 (374)	...	Rapid attack	90
Heat- and corrosion-resistant alloys						
Nickel alloy 400	(a)	50	50 (120)	...	0.28 (11.0)	101
Nickel alloy 400	(a)	50	75 (165)	...	0.13 (5.0)	101
Nickel alloy 400	(a)	50	Boiling	...	0.076 (3.0)	101
Nickel alloy 400	(a)	80	50 (120)	...	0.4 (16.0)	101
Nickel alloy 400	(a)	80	75 (165)	...	0.15 (6.0)	101
Nickel alloy 400	(a)	80	Boiling	...	0.25 (10.0)	101
Nickel alloy 400	(a)	99	50 (120)	...	0.48 (19.0)	101
Nickel alloy 400	(a)	99	75 (165)	...	1.19 (47.0)	101
Nickel alloy 400	(a)	99	Boiling	...	0.53 (21.0)	101
Nickel alloy B	(a)	50	50 (120)	...	0.38 (15.0)	101
Nickel alloy B	(a)	50	75 (165)	...	0.1 (4.0)	101
Nickel alloy B	(a)	50	Boiling	...	0.05 (2.0)	101
Nickel alloy B	(a)	80	50 (120)	...	0.61 (24.0)	101
Nickel alloy B	(a)	80	75 (165)	...	0.3 (12.0)	101
Nickel alloy B	(a)	80	Boiling	...	0.13 (5.0)	101
Nickel alloy B	(a)	99	50 (120)	...	0.15 (6.0)	101
Nickel alloy B	(a)	99	75 (165)	...	0.64 (25.0)	101
Nickel alloy B	(a)	99	Boiling	...	0.28 (11.0)	101
Nickel alloy C	(a)	50	50 (120)	...	nil	101
Nickel alloy C	(a)	50	75 (165)	...	nil	101
Nickel alloy C	(a)	50	Boiling	...	0.025 (1.0)	101
Nickel alloy C	(a)	80	50 (120)	...	nil	101
Nickel alloy C	(a)	80	75 (165)	...	nil	101
Nickel alloy C	(a)	80	Boiling	...	0.025 (1.0)	101
Nickel alloy C	(a)	99	50 (120)	...	nil	101
Nickel alloy C	(a)	99	75 (165)	...	nil	101
Nickel alloy C	(a)	99	Boiling	...	0.025 (1.0)	101
Noble metals						
Gold	...	All	Boiling	...	<0.05 (<2)	8
Silver	...		Boiling	...	<0.05 (<2)	4
Silver	...		Boiling	...	<0.05 (<2)	4

(a) No attempt was made to control aeration.

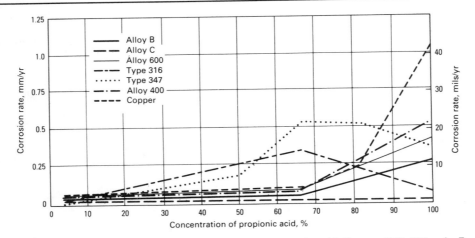

Various alloys. Corrosion of various alloys in boiling propionic acid. Source: G.B. Elder, in *Process Industries Corrosion*, National Association of Corrosion Engineers, Houston, 1975, 247.

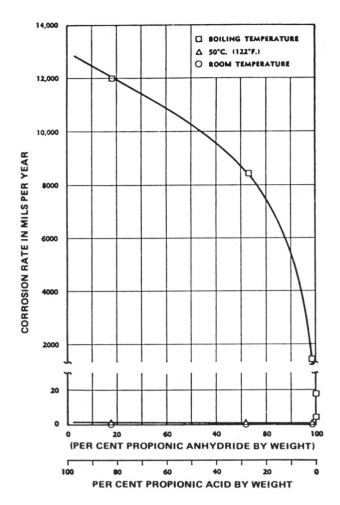

Aluminum. Effect of concentration and temperature on the resistance of alloy 1100 in propionic acid/propionic anhydride solutions. Source: *Guidelines for the Use of Aluminum with Food and Chemicals: Compatibility Data on Aluminum in the Food and Chemical Process Industries*, 5th ed., The Aluminum Association, Washington, DC, 1984, 50.

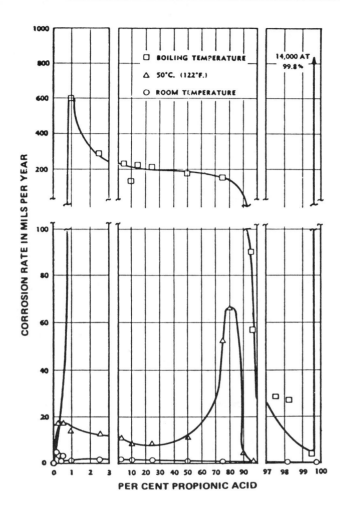

Aluminum. Effect of concentration and temperature on the resistance of alloy 1100 in propionic acid. Source: *Guidelines for the Use of Aluminum with Food and Chemicals: Compatibility Data on Aluminum in the Food and Chemical Process Industries*, 5th ed., The Aluminum Association, Washington, DC, 1984, 50.

Pyridine

Pyridine, C_5H_5N, is a yellowish, flammable, poisonous organic solvent with a very distinctive and penetrating odor. Pyridine is soluble in water, alcohol, benzene, and ether. It has a boiling point of 116 °C (240 °F). Pyridine is used in paints, medicine, and textile dyeing.

Material Summaries

The following material summaries were compiled from a survey of the available literature. Inclusion of a material description under a given environment does not imply that it is the most appropriate material for corrosion service in that environment. Likewise, exclusion of a given material does not imply that it is not suitable for corrosion service applications in that environment.

Aluminum. In laboratory tests at ambient temperature, aluminum alloys 1100 and 3003 resisted pyridine. Aluminum alloy 3003 experienced mild attack (0.075 mm/yr, or 5 mils/yr) in aqueous solutions of pyridine with concentrations of 1 and 5%. Aluminum alloy condensers and dephlegmators have serviced pyridine.

Additional Reading

K. Ramakrishnaiah and K. Subramanyam, Effect of Pyridine Compounds on the Corrosion of Aluminium, *J. Electrochem. Soc. India, 18*(1), 21-27, 1969. MetAbs No. 69-351236.

Corrosion Behavior of Various Metals and Alloys in Pyridine

Material	Condition, other factors, comments	Concentration, %	Temperature, °C (°F)	Duration	Corrosion rate, mm/yr (mils/yr) or other	Ref
Gold	...	All	Boiling	...	<0.05 (2)	7
Gold	...	All	Boiling	...	<0.05 (2)	8
Magnesium	Acid free	100	Room	...	Suitable	119
Platinum	...	All	Boiling	...	<0.05 (2)	6

Seawater

Seawater is a biologically active medium that contains a large number of microscopic and macroscopic organisms. Many of these organisms are commonly observed in association with solid surfaces in seawater, where they form biofouling films. Immersion of any solid surface in seawater initiates a continuous and dynamic process, beginning with adsorption of nonliving, dissolved organic material and continuing through the formation of bacterial and algal slime films and the settlement and growth of various macroscopic plants and animals. This process, by which the surfaces of all structural materials immersed in seawater become colonized, adds to the variability of the ocean environment in which corrosion occurs.

Bacterial Films. The process of colonization begins immediately upon immersion with the adsorption of a nonliving organic conditioning film. This conditioning film is nearly complete within the first 2 h of immersion, at which time the initial colonizing bacteria begin to attach in substantial numbers. The bacterial slime film develops over a period of 24 to 48 h in most natural seawaters, although further changes in the film can often be observed over more than a 2-week period.

The bacterial film changes the chemistry at the metal/liquid interface in various ways. As the biofilm grows, the bacteria in the film produce a number of organic by-products, including organic acids, hydrogen sulfide, and protein-rich polymeric materials commonly known as slime. The first effect of the composite film of bacteria and slime is to create a diffusion barrier between the liquid/metal interface and the bulk seawater. The barrier itself is over 90% water, so it does not in fact isolate the interface—instead it supports strong concentration gradients for various chemical species. As such, the water chemistry at the interface may be different from that in the bulk water, although the two are closely coupled through diffusive processes.

Oxygen and hydrogen, the two chemical species often implicated in corrosion, are also important in the metabolism of bacteria. A given bacterial slime film can be either a source or a sink for either oxygen or hydrogen. Moreover, these films are rarely continuous. Usually, they provide only spotty coverage of the metal surface. Thus, they are capable of inducing oxygen or other chemical concentration cells. Bacterial action on decaying matter in the slime film can also result in the production of ammonia and sulfides. Ammonia causes stress-corrosion cracking of copper alloys, and sulfides have been implicated in accelerated localized and/or uniform corrosion of copper alloys and steels.

Under anaerobic conditions, such as those found in marshy coastal areas, in which all the dissolved oxygen in the mud is used in the decay of organic matter, the corrosion rate of steel is expected to be very low. Under these conditions, however, the sulfate-reducing bacteria *desulfovibrio* use the hydrogen produced at the metal surface in reducing sulfates from the decaying material to sulfides, including hydrogen sulfide. The sulfides combine with iron from the steel to produce iron sulfide film, which is itself corrosive. The bacteria thus transform a benign environment into an aggressive one in which steel corrodes quite rapidly.

Even under open ocean conditions at air saturation, the presence of a bacterial slime film can result in anaerobic conditions at the metal surface. Oxygen-utilizing bacteria in the initial film may eventually increase sufficiently in number so that they use all of the oxygen diffusing through the film before it can reach the metal surface. This creates an anaerobic layer right next to the metal surface and provides a place where the sulfate-reducing organisms can flourish. The biofilm is able to change the chemistry of the electrolyte substantially at the water/metal interface. Thus, the corrosion rate may depend as much on the electrolyte as it does on the ambient bulk seawater chemistry.

Macrofouling Films. Within the first 2 to 3 days following immersion, the solid surface, already having acquired both conditioning and bacterial films, begins to be colonized by the macrofouling organisms. A heavy encrustation of these organisms can have detrimental effects on marine structures. In terms of corrosion, the effects of the macrofouling layer are similar to the microfouling mechanism. If the macrofoulers form a continuous layer, they decrease the availability of dissolved oxygen at the liquid/metal interface and can reduce the rate of corrosion. If the layer is discontinuous, they may induce oxygen or chemical concentration cells, thus leading to various types of localized corrosion.

Seawater Chemistry. Oceans cover over 70% of the earth's surface, with an average depth of about 2 miles. The average salt content of the sea is 3.5%, with the composition comprised of the following percentages: 77.76% $NaCl$, 10.88% $MgCl_2$, 4.74% $MgSO_4$, 3.60% $CaSO_4$, 2.46% K_2SO_4, 0.22% $MgBr_2$, and 0.34% $CaCO_3$. In addition, seawater contains measurable quantities of iodine, fluorine, arsenic, gold, silver, rubidium, copper, barium, phosphorus, manganese, lithium, lead, iron, strontium, and zinc. Ammonia is also present, with free oxygen, nitrogen, and other gases. In some seawater compositions, hydrogen sulfide is also present. Mineral and organic materials are also carried in suspension by the seawater, particularly near the mouths of rivers (Ref 1).

Material Summaries

The following material summaries were compiled from a survey of the available literature. Inclusion of a material description under a given environment does not imply that it is the most appropriate material for corrosion service in that environment. Likewise, exclusion of a given

material does not imply that it is not suitable for corrosion service applications in that environment.

Aluminum. Service experience with 1xxx, 3xxx, 5xxx, and 6xxx wrought aluminum alloys in marine applications, including structures, pipeline, boats, and ships, demonstrates their good resistance and long life under conditions of partial, intermittent, or total immersion. Casting alloys of the 356.0 and 514.0 types also show high resistance to seawater corrosion, and these alloys are used widely for fittings, housings, and other marine parts.

Among the wrought alloys, those of the 5xxx series are the most resistant and the most widely used because of their favorable strength and good weldability. Alloys of the 3xxx series are also highly resistant and are suitable where their strength range is adequate. With the 3xxx and 5xxx series alloys, thinning by uniform corrosion is negligible, and the rate of corrosion based on weight loss does not exceed about 5 μm/yr (0.2 mil/yr), which is generally less than 5% of the rate for unprotected low-carbon steel in seawater. Corrosion is mainly of the pitting or crevice type, characterized by deceleration of penetration with time from rates of 3 to 6 μm/yr (0.1 to 0.2 mil/yr) in the first year to average rates over a 10-year period of 0.8 to 1.5 μm/yr (0.03 to 0.06 mil/yr).

The aluminum-magnesium-silicon alloys are somewhat less resistant; although no general thinning occurs, weight loss may be two to three times that for 5xxx alloys. The more severe corrosion is reflected in larger and more numerous pits. Alloys of the 2xxx and 7xxx series, which contain copper, are considerably less resistant to seawater than 3xxx, 5xxx, and 6xxx alloys and are generally not used unprotected.

In a 10-year test of tidal and full-immersion exposure of seven 5xxx alloys and super-purity aluminum 1199, it was found that full immersion generally resulted in more extensive corrosion than tidal exposure, although the reverse relationship has also been observed. Tensile strength losses were 5% or less, and yield strength losses were less than 5% in the panels that were completely immersed. Losses were generally lower in those exposed to tidal immersion.

In a study of the corrosion resistance of aluminum alloy plate, with and without riveted or welded joints, in flowing seawater, all assemblies and panels underwent only moderate pitting and retained most of their original strength.

The corrosion behavior of aluminum alloys in deep seawater, as indicated from tests at a depth of 1.6 km (1 mile), is generally the same as at the surface, except that the rate of pit penetration may be higher and the effect of crevices somewhat greater. The corrosivity of unpolluted, full-strength seawater depends on several factors—dissolved oxygen content, pH, temperature, velocity of the water flow, and the presence or absence of heavy-metal ions, particularly copper. The corrosion rate tends to be increased by decreasing temperature, pH, and flow velocity and by increasing dissolved oxygen. The higher corrosion rate in deep water is not caused by low dissolved oxygen, but is caused by the combination of low pH and low temperature.

Surface water conditions at various tropical locations are benign to aluminum alloys because of their high temperature, high pH, and high oxygen concentrations and the virtual absence of heavy-metal contamination. A variety of aluminum alloys in the form of heat exchanger tubing have been tested for up to 3 years in surface water off Keahole Point, Hawaii, with no significant pitting or crevice corrosion.

Experience with seawater desalination units has demonstrated the high degree of resistance of aluminum alloys to deaerated seawater at temperatures up to 120 °C (250 °F). For example, a 11,355-L/day (3000-gal/day) multiflash aluminum unit at the Office of Saline Water Materials Test Center at Freeport, Texas, operated at 99% efficiency and with minimal corrosion for more than 3 years under process conditions selected to match those of a commercial installation. Such experience has shown, however, that galvanic attack of aluminum alloys in contact with dissimilar metals is more severe at elevated temperatures than at room temperature.

Cast Irons. Seawater presents some special problems for cast irons. Gray iron may experience graphitic corrosion in calm seawater. It will also be galvanically active in contact with most stainless steels, copper-nickel alloys, titanium, and Hastelloy C. Because these materials are frequently used in seawater structures, this potential for galvanic corrosion must be considered. In calm seawater, the corrosion resistance of cast iron is not greatly affected by the presence of crevices. However, intermittent exposure to seawater is very corrosive to unalloyed cast irons.

Use of high-alloy cast irons in water is relatively limited. High-nickel austenitic cast irons are used to increase the resistance of cast iron components to pitting in calm seawater. High-silicon cast iron is used to produce anodes for the cathodic protection systems used in seawater and brackish water.

Carbon Steels. Corrosion of steel in seawater is a function of water salinity, temperature, oxygen content, velocity, resistivity, and chemistry. The fatigue life of steel exposed to seawater is shorter than that of steel exposed to air because of corrosion fatigue. Steel immersed in seawater does not exhibit an endurance limit. Because there is no endurance limit, unprotected steel exposed to seawater is susceptible to fatigue failure even at low stress levels after long-term cyclic service. The corrosion fatigue effects are eliminated by the application of cathodic protection.

The corrosion of steels in aerated seawater is about the same overall as in aerated freshwater, but this is somewhat misleading because the improved electrical conductivity of seawater can lead to increased pitting. Furthermore, because of the improved conductance, the concentration cells can operate over long distances, and this leads to a more nonuniform attack than in freshwater. It is also well documented that alternate cycling of immersion and exposure to air produces more pitting attack than continuous immersion.

A study was done in England on the effects of various alloying additions and exposure conditions on the corrosion behavior of steel bars exposed to seawater for a period of 15 years. Although this study showed a beneficial effect of both copper and nickel additions, other studies reported no significant benefit. Interestingly, the corrosion rates of specimens completely immersed in seawater do not appear to depend on the geographical location of the test site; therefore, by inference, the mean temperature does not appear to play an important role.

This constancy of the corrosion rate in seawater has been attributed to the more rapid fouling of the exposed steel by marine organisms, such as barnacles and algae, in warmer seas. It is further speculated that this fouling offsets the increases expected from the temperature rise. For example, it has been demonstrated that, under laboratory conditions of rapidly flowing seawater where fouling is suppressed, a rise of 18 °C (32 °F) will approximately double the attack rate. In actual marine exposures, periods of rapid flow from tidal motion may not be effective, because the slack periods at reversal may allow marine organisms to attach themselves to the metal surface. If these organisms can survive the subsequent high flow, then a growth on the exposed surface can develop. This effectively reduces the velocity of seawater at the metal/water interface so that bulk flow rates are no longer rate determining.

Stainless Steels. For service in seawater, stainless steels must be chosen to resist chloride pitting. The amount of chloride that can be tolerated is expected to be higher with higher pH and cleaner stainless steel surfaces, that is, the absence of deposits. For example, type 304 stainless steel may resist pitting in chloride levels of 1000 ppm or higher in the absence of fouling, crevices, or stagnant conditions. The presence of one or more of these conditions can allow chlorides to concentrate at the metal surface and initiate pits. Several high-performance stainless steels have been used to resist chloride pitting in brackish water or seawater. High-performance austenitic grades have been useful in feedwater heaters, although duplex stainless steels may also be considered because of their high strength. Ferritic stainless steels have proved to be economically competitive in exchangers and condensers. High-performance austenitic and ferritic grades have been satisfactory for seawater-cooled units. These grades include MONIT, Al-29-4C, Usinor 290 Mo, Sea-Cure, AL-6X, AL-6XN, and 254SMO stainless steels.

Stainless steels are more likely to be attacked in low-velocity seawater or at crevices resulting from equipment design or attachment of barnacles. Type 304 and 316 stainless steels suffer deep pitting if the seawater flow rate decreases below about 1.5 m/s (5 ft/s) because of the crevices produced by fouling organisms. However, in one study, type 316 stainless steel provided satisfactory service as tubing in the heat recovery section of a desalination test plant with relatively high flow rates. Type 304 and 316 are frequently used for seawater heat exchange tubing when the flow rate is kept above about 10 ft/s.

The choice of stainless steel for seawater service can depend on whether stagnant conditions can be minimized or eliminated. For example, boat shafting of 17Cr-4Ni stainless steel has been used for trawlers where stagnant exposure and the associated pitting would not be expected to be a problem. When seagoing vessels are expected to be idle for extended periods, more resistant boat shaft materials, such as 22Cr-13Ni-5Mn stainless steel, are considered. Boat shafts with intermediate corrosion resistance are provided by 18Cr-2Ni-12Mn and high-nitrogen type 304 (type 304HN) stainless steel.

The possibility of galvanic corrosion must be considered if stainless steel is to be used in contact with other metals in seawater. Preferably, only those materials that exhibit closely related electrode potentials should be coupled to avoid attack of the less noble material. Galvanic differences have been used to advantage in the cathodic protection of stainless steel in seawater. Crevice corrosion and pitting of austenitic type 302 and 316 stainless steels have been prevented by cathodic protection, but type 410 and 430 stainless steels develop hydrogen blisters at current densities below those required for complete protection. Other factors that should be noted when applying stainless steels in seawater include the effects of high velocity, aeration, and temperature. Stainless steels generally show excellent resistance to high velocities, impingement attack, and cavitation in seawater. Also, stainless steels provide optimum service in aerated seawater because a lack of aeration at a specific site often leads to crevice attack. Very little oxygen is required to maintain the passive film on a clean stainless surface. Increasing the temperature from ambient to about 50 °C (120 °F) often reduces attack of stainless steels, possibly because of differences in the amount of dissolved oxygen, changes in the surface film, or changes in the resistance of the exposed sample area. Further temperature increases can result in increased corrosion, such as stress-corrosion cracking.

Cemented Carbides. A study was performed on the crevice corrosion resistance of cemented carbides in seawater with specimens of type 316 stainless steel, Teflon, and silicon carbide adjacent to the cemented carbide specimens. Of the five compositions tested, only the WC-6Co specimens showed any significant attack after 1 year. The attack was moderate and progressed the least against the silicon carbide and the most against the stainless steel.

Copper. An important use of copper alloys is in handling seawater in ships and tidewater power stations. Copper itself, although fairly useful, is usually less resistant to general corrosion than C44300 to C44500, C61300, C68700, C70600, or C71500. The superior performance of these alloys results from the combination of insolubility in seawater, erosion resistance, and biofouling resistance. Aluminum and phosphor bronzes are generally suitable for service in seawater. The corrosion rates of copper and its alloys in relatively quiescent seawater are typically less than 50 μm/yr (2 mils/yr).

In the laboratory and in actual service conditions, copper-nickel alloys C70600, C71500, C72200, and C71640 exhibit excellent corrosion resistance in seawater. Average corrosion rates for both C70600 and C71500 have been shown to range from 2 to 12 μm/yr (0.08 to 0.5 mil/yr), and long-term evaluations have revealed corrosion rates below 2.5 μm/yr (0.1 mil/yr) for both alloys after 14 years of exposure to quiescent and low-velocity seawater. Sixteen-year tests confirmed this same low corrosion rate.

Pitting Resistance. Alloys C70600 and C71500 both display excellent resistance to pitting in seawater. The average depth of the 20 deepest pits in C71500 observed at the end of a 16-year test was less than 127 μm (5 mils). Chromium-modified copper-nickel alloys, developed for resistance to high-velocity seawater, were evaluated in both low- and high-velocity conditions. The quiescent and low-velocity performances of C72200, C70600, and C71500 were compared; results showed uniform corrosion (5 to 25 μm/yr, or 0.2 to 1 mil/yr) on all three alloys. The chromium-containing alloys, however, were slightly more susceptible to localized attack in quiet seawater. Another study reported that the pitting behavior of C72200 is influenced by the presence of iron and chromium in or out of solid solution. The fraction of iron plus chromium in solution in C72200 must be kept higher than 0.7 to avoid pitting corrosion.

Velocity Effects. Recent work has demonstrated that, although the presence of 0.01 mg/L sulfide in aerated seawater can accelerate corrosion of copper-nickel alloys, the influence of seawater velocity is more significant. The corrosion resistance of copper alloys in flowing seawater depends on the growth and maintenance of a protective film of corrosion product layers. These alloys typically exhibit velocity-dependent corrosion rates. The more adherent and protective the film on a particular alloy, the higher its breakaway velocity and the greater its resistance to impingement attack or erosion-corrosion.

Some of the earliest work on copper-nickel alloys demonstrated the beneficial effects of iron additions on seawater impingement resistance. The effects of manganese level in association with iron in copper-nickel alloys have also been investigated. Additions of 2% iron and 2% manganese to a 70Cu-30Ni alloy (C71640) have been shown to be relatively beneficial, which indicates that alloys C71640 and C72200 are markedly more resistant than C70600 at velocities up to 9 m/s (30 ft/s). The chromium-modified copper-nickel alloys also provide increased resistance to impingement attack compared to copper-nickel-iron alloys. In jet impingement tests on several copper-base alloys at impingement velocities as high as 10 m/s (33 ft/s), no measurable impingement attack was observed on alloys C72200 and C71900 at 4.6 m/s (15 ft/s).

The behaviors of several copper-nickel alloys, including C71640 and C72200, have been characterized under conditions simulating partial blockage of a condenser tube. In the 1-year natural seawater tests, enhanced erosion-corrosion resistance was observed for the C71640 and C72200 alloys as compared to C70600 and C71500. Some localized pitting and/or crevice corrosion associated with the nonmetallic blockage device was noted for C71640 and C72200, with no such attack occurring for the C70600 and C71500 alloys. Superior performance of the modified copper-nickel alloys C72200 and C71640 was also observed under severely erosive conditions in seawater containing entrained sand.

Galvanic Effects. In general, the copper-base alloys are galvanically compatible with one another in seawater. The copper-nickel alloys are slightly cathodic (noble) to the nickel-free copper-base alloys, but the small differences in corrosion potential generally do not lead to serious galvanic effects unless unusually adverse anodic/cathodic area ratios are involved.

Studies have demonstrated the increased attack of less noble carbon steel coupled to copper-nickel alloys, the increased attack on the copper-nickel alloys when coupled to more noble titanium, and the general compatibility of copper-nickel alloys with aluminum bronze. Coupling copper-nickel alloys to less noble materials affords protection to the copper-nickel that effectively reduces its corrosion rate, thus inhibiting the natural fouling resistance of the alloy.

In short-term galvanic couple tests between alloy C70600 and several cast copper-base and ferrous alloys, the corrosion rate of cast 70Cu-30Ni was unaffected by coupling with an equal area of C70600, but some increased corrosion of other cast copper-base alloys was noted. Corrosion rates of cast stainless steels were reduced, with a resultant increase in the corrosion of C70600. Gray iron displayed the largest galvanic effect, whereas the corrosion rates of Ni-Resist cast irons nominally doubled. Although some caution should be exercised in using absolute values from any short-term tests, the relative degree of acceleration of corrosion from galvanic coupling was shown to be unaffected by extending some tests with Ni-Resist/C70600 couples to 1 year.

Effect of Oxygen, Depth, and Temperature. The corrosion of copper and copper-base alloys in clean seawater is cathodically controlled by oxygen reduction, with H^+ reduction being thermodynamically unfavorable. Dissolved oxygen retards corrosion by the promotion of a protective film on the copper alloy surface, but increases the rate of corrosion by depolarizing cathodic sites and oxidizing Cu^+ ions to more aggressive Cu^{2+} ions. Other factors, such as velocity, temperature, salinity, and ocean depth, affect the dissolved oxygen content of seawater, thus influencing the corrosion rate. In general, oxygen concentration decreases with increasing salinity, temperature, and depth. These factors can vary with depth in a complex manner and also may vary from location to location in the oceans of the world.

Although cathodic control by oxygen reduction suggests a strong dependence of corrosion rate on dissolved oxygen concentration, the growth of a protective oxide film on copper-nickel alloys minimizes the influence within the normally observed range of oxygen content found in seawater. Deep ocean testing indicated that the corrosion rates of copper and copper-nickel alloys do not change significantly for dissolved oxygen contents between 1 and 6 ml/L of seawater and consequently were not significantly affected by variations in depth of exposure.

Short-term laboratory tests indicated only a small increase in corrosion rate with increasing temperature up to 30 °C (85 °F). Long-term corrosion rate data from tests conducted at a coastal site near Panama agree very well with long-term data for exposures in Wrightsville Beach, North Carolina, where the seasonal temperature variation is 5 to 30 °C (40 to 85 °F). Final steady-state corrosion rates at both locations for C71500 ranged from 1 to 3 μm/yr (0.04 to 0.12 mils/yr).

Studies performed at higher temperatures relative to those in desalination plant environments show considerable disagreement in results. From 60 to 107 °C (140 to 225 °F), temperature may increase, decrease, or have no significant effect on the corrosion rates of copper-nickel alloys. Lower corrosion rates for C70600 over an intermediate temperature range were reported in seawater corrosion tests between 32 and 107 °C (90 and 225 °F) with controlled seawater chemistry; bicarbonate alkalinity, dissolved oxygen, and pH were noted as critical factors controlling corrosion. Other studies confirmed lower average corrosion rates at 40 °C (105 °F) than at lower temperatures. The variation in results reported in the literature can perhaps be explained by variations in seawater chemistry between test sites and/or control of operating conditions in desalination plants.

Effect of Chlorine. Coastal power plants that use seawater as a coolant have long used chlorine to control fouling and slime formation. The effect of chlorination, both continuous and intermittent, on the corrosion of copper-nickel alloys was studied. Continuous chlorine additions increased the corrosion rate of C70600 by a factor of two. Intermittent chlorination at a higher level controlled fouling, yet had no apparent effect on corrosion rates. A net reduction was noted in the corrosion rate of C71500 with continuous and most intermittent chlorine additions.

Seawater impingement tests were conducted on C70600, C71500, and C71640 with continuous additions of chlorine (and iron). Additions of 0.5 to 4.0 mg/L of chlorine caused increased susceptibility to impingement attack on C70600 at a velocity of 9 m/s (30 ft/s). Addition of chlorine up to 4.0 mg/L had little effect on the impingement resistance of C71500.

Polluted Cooling Waters. Polluted cooling waters, particularly in coastal harbors and estuaries, reportedly cause numerous premature failures of power station and shipboard condensers using copper-base alloys, including the copper nickels. During the early 1950s, polluted waters were identified as the most important contributing factor in the failure of condenser tubes.

The attack of copper-containing materials by polluted seawater has been addressed in numerous test programs. The primary causes of accelerated attack of copper-base alloys in polluted seawater are (1) the action of sulfate-reducing bacteria, under anaerobic conditions (for example, in bottom muds or sediments), on the natural sulfates present in seawater and (2) the putrefaction of organic sulfur compounds from decaying plant and animal matter within seawater systems during periods of extended shutdown. Partial putrefaction of organic sulfur compounds may also result in the formation of organic sulfides, such as cystine or glutathione, which can cause pitting of copper alloys in seawater.

A significant amount of work has recently been done on the behavior of copper alloys in sulfide-contaminated seawaters. Sulfides are added to the seawater by either bubbling hydrogen sulfide gas through the solution or by adding a sodium sulfide solution. In general, sulfide concentrations of the order of 1 ppm are sufficient to cause accelerated attack. For rapid corrosion to occur, the copper alloy must be exposed to a solution that contains oxygen as well as sulfide or must be alternately exposed to sulfide-bearing deaerated solutions, followed by exposure to sulfide-free aerated solutions. Alloy C70600 has been found to be susceptible to sulfide-induced attack in aerated seawater containing sulfide concentrations as low as 0.01 mg/L.

Lead. The corrosion of lead in seawater is relatively slight and may be retarded by incrustations of lead salts. A study has shown that at the same tropical location (Panama Canal Zone) the corrosion rate of lead in seawater is about four times the rate in fresh water.

Nickel. Nickel 200 and alloy 400 and nickel-base alloys containing chromium and iron are very resistant to flowing seawater, but in stagnant or very low velocity seawater, pitting or crevice corrosion can occur, especially under fouling organisms or other deposits. In moderate- and high-velocity seawater or brackish water, alloy 400 is frequently used for pump and valve trim and transfer piping. It has excellent resistance to cavitation erosion and exhibits corrosion rates less than 0.025 mm/year (1 mil/yr). Alloy 400 sheathing also provides economical seawater splash zone protection to steel offshore oil and gas platforms, pilings, and other structures. Although pitting can occur in alloy 400 under stagnant conditions, such pitting tends to slow down after fairly rapid initial attack and rarely exceeds 1.3 mm (50 mils) in depth. Age-hardened alloy K-500, with corrosion resistance similar to that of alloy 400, is frequently used for high-strength fasteners and pump and propeller shafting in freshwater and seawater applications.

Other nickel-base alloys containing chromium and molybdenum offer increased resistance to localized corrosion in stagnant seawater. In hot seawater applications, such as heat exchangers, highly alloyed materials such as alloys 625 or C-276 may be required. In addition, alloys 625, 400, and K-500 are frequently specified for Naval wetted components in contact with seawater. Specific high tensile strength requirements are met with alloy 718.

Niobium. Niobium is resistant to attack in seawater.

Palladium. As an electrode for cathodic protection use in seawater, palladium corrodes at a rate of 8.6 g/A · yr at a current density of 540 A/m^2 (50 A/ft^2). The current efficiency is 0.05%. In binary palladium-platinum alloys, the corrosion rate in this application becomes equal to that of platinum if the palladium content is less than 20%.

Tantalum is not attacked by seawater, either cold or hot.

Tin. In some instances of marine use, the formation of a hard, crusty oxidation product has been observed on tin-rich bearings. When free access of salt water to a bearing is possible, the cathodic relationship of the babbitt alloys to steel renders them unsuitable, and bearing alloys such as Zn-70Sn-1.5Cu are preferred.

In seawater or uninhibited brines, the high conductivity and predominance of chloride makes galvanic action at a soldered joint more likely to continue destructively, and soldered joints in copper, nickel, and their alloys may need protection by coatings. Although tin or tin-coated metals can be used in contact with aluminum alloys even in salt water, the soldering process introduces sufficient aluminum to the solder to render it susceptible to intergranular corrosion. If tin-zinc solders are used, the zinc can prevent serious embrittling action, although some corrosion will still occur under moist conditions.

Titanium. Because of the hard, tenacious titanium dioxide surface film that forms on titanium in normal passive environments, both unalloyed titanium and titanium alloys can withstand flowing seawater at velocities as high as 30 m/s (100 ft/s) with insignificant metal loss. In fact, high-speed water wheel tests in seawater indicate erosion rates for grade 5 titanium of approximately 0.013 mm/yr (5 mils/yr) at 46 m/s (150 ft/s). Jet impingement tests also involving seawater velocities of 46 m/s (150 ft/s) reveal rates of 0.03 to 0.06 mm/yr (1.2 to 24 mils/yr) for commercially pure titanium, with values of approximately 0.03 mm/yr (1.2 mils/yr) for welded and unwelded grade 5 titanium samples. Extremely low erosion rates are also reported for grade 2 titanium at various seawater locations.

Studies involving sand and emery particle-laden seawater indicate satisfactory erosion-corrosion resistance to flow rates of approximately 6 m/s (20 ft/s). The immunity of titanium to erosion-corrosion in silt-laden seawater flowing at approximately 2 m/s (6.5 ft/s) has been demonstrated in more than 20 years of outstanding service in seawater for the chemical, oil refining, desalination, and power industries. As a result of its immunity to ambient seawater corrosion, titanium is considered to be the technically correct material for many critical marine applications, including many naval and offshore components. Exposure of titanium to marine atmospheres, splash or tide zone, and soils also does not cause corrosion.

In near-neutral electrolytes such as seawater, active metals such as zinc, magnesium, and aluminum can lead to hydrogen uptake and eventual embrittlement when coupled to titanium above 80 °C (175 °F).

Titanium alloys exhibit negligible corrosion rates in seawater up to temperatures as high as 260 °C (500 °F), and extremely low corrosion rates of both unalloyed titanium and Ti-6Al-4V after up to 3 years of exposure in ambient seawater have been recorded. Pitting and crevice corrosion are totally absent in ambient seawater, even if marine deposits form and biofouling occurs. Titanium tubing exposed for 16 years to polluted and sulfide-containing seawater shows no evidence of corrosion. Similar reports of nil corrosion rates in ambient seawater have been reported for unalloyed titanium and titanium alloys such as Ti-5Al-2Sn, Ti-13V-11Cr-3Al, Ti-6Al-2Nb-1Ta-0.8Mo, and titanium-palladium.

The outstanding resistance of titanium alloys to cavitation damage has also been documented, and it has been confirmed that the harder, higher strength titanium alloys are more resistant to cavitation.

Zinc. The corrosion behavior of zinc in seawater is determined by the amounts of dissolved salts, principally chlorides and sulfates, in the water. The high chloride content of seawater would normally tend to increase corrosion, but the presence of magnesium and calcium ions inhibits the attack. The effect of time of exposure on the corrosion rate in natural waters indicates that the corrosion rate in seawater initially exceeds that in freshwater, but after about 2 years of exposure, the rate in seawater decreases so that it is approximately the same as that in fresh water.

The frequency with which seaside piers and ship hulls require repainting testifies to the corrosivity of seawater and the importance of taking adequate protective measures. The salts present in the North Sea amount to about 3.5% of the total, mainly sodium chloride with smaller amounts of magnesium and calcium salts. This produces a solution with a pH of about 8.

The corrosion resistance of zinc compares very favorably with that of other coating materials when totally immersed in seawater, possibly because of the slightly inhibitive action of the magnesium salts present. In tests, aluminum-, cadmium-, lead-, tin-, and zinc-coated specimens were immersed for 2 years. All except the zinc-coated specimens failed in this time. The zinc-coated specimens were then transferred to another test site and immersed for another 4 years. At the end of this time—a total of 6 years—the 915-g/m^2 (3-oz/ft^2) coatings were just ceasing to give complete protection to the basis steel. Therefore, it was concluded that the consumption of zinc is approximately 150 g/m^2 (0.5 oz/ft^2) of steel surface protected per year.

In most cases, zinc coatings would not be used alone when applied to steel immersed in seawater, but would form the first layer of a more elaborate protective system. Conditions within a few hundred yards of the surf line on beaches are intermediate between total immersion in seawater and normal exposure to a marine atmosphere. Such conditions have been studied in a series of tests carried out at Lighthouse Beach in Nigeria. At the high-water mark, about 45 m (50 yd) from the surf line on the tropical beach, conditions were extremely severe, and iron and zinc both corroded more rapidly than if they had actually been immersed in the sea.

Upon moving inland, however, it was found that both the salt content of the atmosphere and the rates of corrosion of iron and zinc fell off very rapidly. The values obtained only 1 km from the sea were similar to those obtained at inland sites.

Zirconium has excellent corrosion resistance to seawater, brackish water, and polluted water. Specimens with or without crevice attachment of Zr702 were placed in the Pacific Ocean at Newport, Oregon, for up to

129 days. All welded and nonwelded specimens exhibited negligible corrosion rates. Marine biofouling was observed; however, no corrosion was found beneath the marine organisms or within the crevices. Laboratory tests were preformed on Zr702 and Zr704 in boiling seawater for 275 days and in 200 °C (390 °F) seawater for 29 days. Both alloys were resistant to general, pitting, and crevice corrosion.

Tests of U-bend specimens with or without steel coupling of Zr702, nickel-containing Zr704, and nickel-free Zr704 were conducted in boiling seawater for 365 days. No cracking was observed during the testing period. Overstressing of the tested U-bend specimens indicated that all specimens were still ductile, except for the welded nickel-containing Zr704 with steel coupling. Steel-coupled nickel-containing Zr704 showed much higher hydrogen and oxygen absorption and formed hydrides, particularly in the weld heat-affected zone. Chemical analyses and metallographic examinations on other U-bends did not show evidence of hydride formation.

Reference

1   G.S. Brady and H.R. Clauser, Ed., *Materials Handbook*, 11th ed., McGraw-Hill, New York, 1977.

Additional Reading

A. Paola, F. DiQuarto, and C. Sunseri, A Photoelectrochemical Characterization of Passive Films on Stainless Steels, *Corros. Sci.*, 26(11), 935-948, 1986. MetAbs No. 87-350973. **Abstract:** Passive films on stainless steels for seawater service have been studied by means of photocurrent measurements. Four experimental ELI ferritic stainless steels (types 25Cr-4Ni-4Mo) and a commercial superaustenitic stainless steel (type 20Cr-18Ni-6Mo-N) have been investigated. Differences in the photoelectrochemical behavior have been attributed to the different nature of the passive films grown on ferritic or superaustenitic stainless steels. An interpretation is provided to explain the complex dependence of the photocurrent transients on the applied potential.

A.M. Beccaraia and G. Poggi, The Effect of Hydrostatic Pressure on the Corrosion Behavior of Aluminum and Nickel in Sea Water, *Corros. Prev. Control*, 34(2), 51-57, 1987. MetAbs No. 87-352490. **Abstract:** The corrosion resistance of Al in seawater was investigated as a function of hydrostatic pressure. Flat specimens were immersed in seawater in pressure vessels pressurized by a hydropneumatic pump. Measurements of the passive film breakdown potential and the protection against pitting potential were made over a range of hydrostatic pressure from 1 to 300 atm.

A.M. Beccaria and G. Poggi, Analysis of Admiralty Brass Corrosion Products in Sea Water and Brackish Water, *Analyst*, 111(8), 959-963, 1986. MetAbs No. 87-350506. **Abstract:** A method was developed for the separation and analysis of corrosion products formed on admiralty brass surfaces immersed in seawater at 40 °C and pH 8.2. This method is based on the selective dissolution of various oxidation compounds with suitable solvents (i.e., those which dissolve the metal matrix to only a negligible extent).

A.M. Beccaria and G. Poggi, Influence of Hydrostatic Pressure on Pitting of Aluminium in Sea Water, *Br. Corros. J.*, 20(4), 183-186, 1985. MetAbs No. 86-350681. **Abstract:** The effect of hydrostatic pressure on the corrosion of aluminium in seawater of pH 8.2 containing 7 ppm dissolved oxygen has been investigated at 20 °C.

A.T. Kuhn and J. Wellwood, Aqueous and Atmospheric Corrosion of Cobalt-Nickel Alloys, *Br. Corros. J.*, 21(4), 228-234, 1986. MetAbs No. 87-351173. **Abstract:** The corrosion of cobalt-nickel alloys at ambient temperatures is reviewed. In the aqueous phase, data for the anodic and

cathodic half-cell reactions are reported, as also for free corrosion. The literature (mainly patent) relating to corrosion inhibitors for atmospheric use is reviewed.

B.B. Moreton, Copper Alloys in Marine Environments Today and Tomorrow, *Corros. Prev. Control*, 33(1), 17-20, 1986. MetAbs No. 86-351363. **Abstract:** The excellent corrosion resistance and biofouling resistance of Cu-Ni alloys 70/30 and 90/10 have led to their extensive use in a number of areas. Offshore structures have demonstrated savings by using Cu-Ni sheathing on jacket structures. A test program to study sheathing protection on pilings at the Laque Center for Corrosion Technology is described. Other uses described are water intakes and screens for coastal power stations where they eliminate fouling problems and need for chlorination.

B.B. Moreton, Copper Alloys in Marine Environments Today and Tomorrow. I, *Corr. Prev. Control*, 32(6), 122-126, 1985. MetAbs No. 86-351057. **Abstract:** Copper alloys have varying degrees of corrosion resistance in seawater and varying degrees of resistance to marine fouling. Aluminum bronze and Cu-Ni alloys are the two most important Cu alloy groups for marine applications. The high strength Cu-Ni casting alloys developed by the Royal Navy (UK) for valve and pump bodies and the high-strength Cu-Ni-Sn spinodal alloys developed by Bell Labs for submarine cable repeater housings are relative newcomers.

C. Duran, E. Treiss, and G. Herbsleb, The Resistance of High Frequency Inductive Welded Pipe to Grooving Corrosion in Salt Water, *Mater. Perform.*, 25(9), 41-48, 1986. MetAbs No. 86-352527. **Abstract:** When exposed to neutral, salt-containing waters, electric resistance welded pipe in low-alloy steels with increased sulfur contents may suffer preferential corrosion attack in the weld area. This phenomenon, known as grooving corrosion, is discussed. The susceptibility to grooving corrosion is determined and quantitatively described by means of an accelerated potentiostatic exposure test.

C. Manfredi, S. Simison, and S.R. de Sanchez, Selection of Copper Base Alloys for Use in Polluted Seawater, *Corrosion*, 43(8), 458-464, 1987. MetAbs No. 87-352839. **Abstract:** The corrosion performance of different Cu alloys in polluted seawater has been studied. Investigations were conducted to determine the effect of sulfide on the materials covered with a natural protective film or treated with ferrous sulfate. These studies were done on cathodic (oxygen reduction) and anodic (metal cation dissolution) processes.

C. Matz, Stability of Adhesive Joints in High-Strength Aluminium Alloys to Aging and Chemical Attack, *Aluminium English*, 61(2), E118-E121, 1985. MetAbs No. 85-351003. **Abstract:** The determination of resistance to chemical attack relates mainly to the effect of water, corrosive aqueous solutions, fuels and hydraulic liquids on the strength of the adhesive bond. A comprehensive specification for use in aircraft production is developed, with which the stability of adhesive joints to aging and chemical attack can be accurately assessed with the aid of 25 different tests.

C. Vargel, Aluminium and the Sea, *Mater. Tech. (Paris)*, 74(5-6), 233-245, 1986. MetAbs No. 87-350195. **Abstract:** Use of the 5000 and 6000 series Al alloys in sea environments is discussed. Advanced means for exploiting deep offshore oil fields and for improving knowledge of underwater geology has resulted in several deep underwater survey vessels being built using aluminium alloys.

C.F. Britton, Internal Corrosion Monitoring of Subsea Pipelines, *Pipes Pipelines Int.*, 31(6), 12-18, 1986. MetAbs No. 87-350722. **Abstract:** Corrosion monitoring of pipelines is becoming an increasingly important aspect of operations, and more especially for the offshore systems, some of which have been in operation for up to 20 years in the North Sea. This paper describes the various systems available and details some of the requirements of the inspection authorities.

C.V. Roscoe, The Development of a New Duplex Stainless Steel, *Stainless Steel Ind.*, *13*(72), 12, 1985. MetAbs No. 85-351278. **Abstract:** Zeron 25 (25Cr-6Ni-2Mo), a ferritic-austenitic duplex stainless steel, has been successfully used in seawater applications. More recently, increasingly harsh environments have led to the development of a super-duplex type of stainless steel, Zeron 100, which gives much superior localized corrosion resistance to that displayed by traditional duplex and super-austenitic grades and shows marked improvements in mechanical properties.

Copper Alloys for a Marine Environment, *Met. Bull. Mon.*, (174), 75, 1985. MetAbs No. 85-351922. **Abstract:** Consumption of Cu alloys in the marine industry is about 100,000 tonnes/year, mainly in ships, propellers and condenser tubes. Major applications have also opened up in the offshore oil and gas industries and in desalination plants. Aluminum bronze and copper-nickel represent the two most important copper alloy groups in the marine sector, and their salient characteristics are outlined.

D.E. Dobb, J.P. Storvick, and G.K. Pagenkopf, Pretreatment Procedures for Corrosion Studies of Cupro-Nickel Alloys in Sea Water, *Corros. Sci.*, *26*(7), 525-536, 1986. MetAbs No. 87-350536. **Abstract:** The effects of surface roughness, degreasing, acid pickling, annealing and sample storage of 70/30 and 90/10 Cu-Ni alloys (CDA 715 and CDA 706, respectively) prior to seawater exposure were studied. The short-term (<1 day) corrosion behavior of each alloy was monitored by scanning Auger emission spectroscopy to determine which pretreatment parameters had the most influence.

D.E. Nivens, P.D. Nichols, J.M. Henson, G.G. Geesey, and D.C. White, Reversible Acceleration of the Corrosion of AISI 304 Stainless Steel Exposed to Seawater Induced by Growth and Secretions of the Marine Bacterium Vibrio Natriegens, *Corrosion*, *42*(4), 204-210, 1986. MetAbs No. 86-351329. **Abstract:** Growth of the nonsulfate-reducing marine bacterium *Vibrio natriegens* increased the corrosion current density of AISI 304 stainless steel coupons when grown in a marine medium.

D.F. Hasson, C. Zanis, L. Aprigliano, and C. Fraser, Corrosion and Corrosion-Fatigue Behavior of IN625 Weld Surfaced 3.25 Nickel Steel, *J. Mater. Energy Syst.*, *7*(3), 256-264, 1985. MetAbs No. 86-350481. **Abstract:** The corrosion and corrosion-fatigue behaviors of Inconel 625 weld metal surfaced onto 3.25% Ni steel using the gas metal arc welding-pulsed arc process are presented. General, crevice, and bent-beam stress-corrosion studies were performed. Completely reversed bending corrosion-fatigue and corrosion fatigue crack growth behaviors were also evaluated.

D.J. Tighe-Ford, J.N. McGrath, and L. Hodgkiss, Design Improvements for a Ship's Impressed-Current Cathodic Protection System Using Dimension and Conductivity Scaling (DACS), *Corros. Prev. Control*, *32*(5), 89-91, 1985. MetAbs No. 86-351101. **Abstract:** A cathodic protection system commonly used on ships consists of two anodes driven from one power supply controlled by a reference electrode amid ships. DACS uses a model ship, diluted seawater (to 1/60 the conductivity of seawater), and also a water flow of 1 m/s to represent a ship underway.

D.M. Aylor and P.J. Moran, Pitting Corrosion Behavior of 6061 Aluminum Alloy Foils in Sea Water, *J. Electrochem. Soc.*, *133*(5), 949-951, 1986. MetAbs No. 86-352066. **Abstract:** The corrosion of 6061 Al foil specimens and 6061 Al plate were compared. It was found that the metallurgical processes used in foil-making create smaller grains and electronegativity that aid in corrosion resistance.

D.M. Aylor and P.J. Moran, The Influence of Incubation Time on the Passive Film Breakdown of Aluminum Alloys in Sea Water, *J. Electrochem. Soc.*, *133*(5), 868-872, 1986. MetAbs No. 86-352062. **Abstract:** Potential-controlled electrochemical methods were used to characterize the pitting behavior of 6061 alloy Al in synthetic ocean water. Nonreproducible breakdown potentials and reproducible repassivation potentials were determined from cyclic anodic polarization. Reproducible breakdown and repassivation potentials were found from the quasi-stationary anodic polarization method.

E. Jones, Copper-Nickel Piping Systems for Offshore Seawater Platforms, *J. Met.*, *37*(3), 67-69, 1985. MetAbs No. 85-351335. **Abstract:** The two most common maintenance problems experienced by the offshore industry are corrosion and biofouling. These problems are most troublesome when steel piping is used for seawater distribution systems. A solution to these costly maintenance problems is use of an alternative piping material, 90/10 Cu-Ni (Alloy C70600), which is not only resistant to corrosion and marine growth, but is cost-effective over the life of the platform.

E.B. Shone and G.C. Grim, Experience With Seawater-Cooled Heat Transfer Equipment, *Mar. Eng. Rev.*, 20-23, 1986. MetAbs No. 86-351396. **Abstract:** The experience over 25 years with seawater systems in the Shell fleets is reviewed, with particular respect to materials selection. The limitations of materials currently used and the possibilities of using alternative high-performance materials in the future are discussed.

F. Blekkenhorst, G.M. Ferrari, C.J. Van Der Wekken, and F.P. Ijsseling, Development of High Strength Low Alloy Steels for Marine Applications. I. Results of Long Term Exposure Tests on Commercially Available and Experimental Applications, *Br. Corros. J.*, *21*(3), 163-176, 1986. MetAbs No. 87-350407. **Abstract:** High-strength low-alloy steels, both commercially available and experimentally prepared, were immersed at 45 and 90 m depths in the North Sea for periods ranging from 1.6 to 7.2 years. General corrosion, pitting corrosion and crevice corrosion behavior were evaluated after immersion.

F. Mazza, S. Torchio, and L. Ciaghi, Some Aspects of the Corrosion Behavior of Some Extra Low Interstitial Superferritic Stainless Steels in Chloride Environments Under Galvanic Coupling, *Corrosion*, *43*(5), 276-280, 1987. MetAbs No. 87-351915. **Abstract:** The effect of the galvanic coupling of some experimental extra low interstitial superferritic stainless steels with some less noble metallic materials was evaluated in synthetic seawater under constant strain rate conditions.

G. Bombara, M. Cavallini, and S. Maisano, Chemo-Mechanical Reliability of Metallic Materials in Deep Ocean Environments. II, *Anti-Corros. Methods Mater.*, *33*(3), 4-7, 1986. MetAbs No. 87-350505. **Abstract:** The mechanism of hydrogen embrittlement causing delayed brittle failure under stress in steels immersed in seawater is discussed.

G. Haynes and R. Baboian, Electrochemical Observations as Related to Marine Atmospheric Corrosion of Chrome-Flashed Stainless Steels, *J. Electrochem. Soc.*, *132*(12), 2967-2969, 1985. MetAbs No. 86-350441. **Abstract:** Chrome-flashed 301 stainless steel and chrome-flashed 434 stainless steel undergo localized corrosion when constantly immersed in chloride-containing environments for extended periods of time. Chrome flashing, however, provides improved resistance to localized corrosion for both alloys in marine atmospheric (and automotive) environments where intermittent wetting occurs. Cyclic potentiodynamic polarization data and the mixed potential theory can be used to determine the mechanisms of corrosion and explain this behavior.

G.P. Sheldon, N.W. Polan, H. Jain, T.M. Ahn, and P. Soo, Stress Corrosion of ASTM Grade-2 and Grade-12 Titanium in Simulated Rock Salt

Brines at 83 °C, *Corrosion, 41*(7), 375-380, 1985. MetAbs No. 85-352102. **Abstract:** Slow strain rate tensile tests were conducted on Grade 2 and Grade 12 titanium in simulated rock salt brines at approximately 83 °C. Optical and scanning electron microscopy results are discussed to elucidate the fracture mechanism.

G.P. Sheldon and N.W. Polan, Field Testing of Power Utility Condenser Tube Alloys, *J. Mater. Energy Syst., 6*(4), 313-319, 1985. MetAbs No. 85-351443. **Abstract:** The performances of various copper alloys (C71500, C70600, C19400, and C443) after four years exposure in condenser stream-side and cooling water environments of three operating power utility plants are described.

G.W. Lorimer, F. Hasan, J. Iqbal, and N. Ridley, Observation of Microstructure and Corrosion Behavior of Some Aluminium Bronzes, *Br. Corros. J., 21*(4), 244-248, 1986. MetAbs No. 87-351175. **Abstract:** The short-term corrosion behavior of four as-cast commercial aluminium bronzes has been examined by immersing the materials in artificial seawater for various lengths of time.

H. Meissner, Sea-Water—In Situ Experiments Using Aluminium Materials in the Arabian Gulf, *Aluminium, 61*(2), 91-93, 1985. MetAbs No. 85-351002. **Abstract:** As part of a cooperation between various research bodies and the Saudi-Arabian "University of Petroleum and Minerals" in Dharan, a seawater testing facility was available for a period of 4.5 years so that the corrosion behavior of aluminium in this hot climatic zone could be investigated.

H.P. Dhar, Corrosion Behavior of 70Cu-30Ni Alloy in $0.5M$ NaCl and in Synthetic Seawater, *Corrosion, 41*(4), 193-196, 1985. MetAbs No. 85-351434. **Abstract:** Electrochemical corrosion rates of 70Cu-30Ni alloy have been measured in oxygenated $0.5M$ NaCl and in synthetic seawater by the Tafel extrapolation procedure using a rotating disk electrode system.

H.P. Dhar, Corrosion of Cu and Cu-Ni Alloys in $0.5M$ NaCl and in Synthetic Seawater, *Corrosion, 41*(6), 317-323, 1985. MetAbs No. 85-351730. **Abstract:** Electrochemical corrosion rates of Cu and Cu-Ni alloys have been measured in oxygenated $0.5M$ NaCl and in synthetic seawater using the Tafel extrapolation procedure. In addition, Cu corrosion has been measured with the linear polarization procedure.

H.P. Goddard, Corrosion of Aluminium Alloys, in *Encyclopedia of Materials Science and Engineering*, Vol 2, Pergamon Press, Oxford, 1986. MetAbs No. 86-351940. **Abstract:** The corrosion resistance of commercial aluminum (approximately 99.6% Al) in seawater is studied.

H.P. Hack and J.R. Scully, Galvanic Corrosion Prediction Using Long- and Short-Term Polarization Curves, *Corrosion, 42*(2), 79-90, 1986. MetAbs No. 86-350811. **Abstract:** Long-term potentiostatic polarization curves of up to 120 days duration were developed for the following materials in seawater: 90-30 copper-nickel (C70600), Monel 400 (N04400), Inconel 625 (N06625), Navy M-bronze (C92200), Ni-Al bronze (C95800), HY-80 steel, Ti 50 (R50400), 70-30 copper-nickel (C71500) and anode grade Zn (MIL-STD 18001). In addition, short-term potentiodynamic polarization curves were developed at four scan rates and two pre-exposure levels for all materials.

H.S. Campbell, The Corrosion Factor in Marine Environments, *Met. Mater., 1*(8), 479-483, 1985. MetAbs No. 85-352451. **Abstract:** The various types of corrosion that occur in the four related marine environments identified by the author are reviewed, and the suitability of common corrosion-resistant materials for each situation is discussed. Also included are sections on combined corrosion and mechanical effects and on certain aspects of cathodic protection.

I. Ogilvie, Copper Alloys in Marine Environments, *Corros. Coatings S. Afr., 13*(1), 2, 1986. MetAbs No. 86-351923. **Abstract:** The aluminium bronzes and cupronickels are increasingly being used for their superior performance in seawater. The stable adherent oxide film of the former gives excellent erosion/corrosion protection, but, unlike copper nickel of not less than 70% Cu, indifferent biofouling resistance. Various applications of 70/30 copper nickel and 90/10 copper nickel in seawater are described. Since 1960, the increasing pollution of coastal waters has adversely affected the life of admiralty and Al brasses.

J. Larsen-Basse, Performance of OTEC Heat Exchanger Materials in Tropical Seawaters, *J. Met., 37*(3), 24-27, 1985. MetAbs No. 85-351332. **Abstract:** The corrosion of several Al alloys in flowing Hawaiian surface seawater and water from 600 m depth for exposure periods up to three years has been studied. The alloys tested in cold water were Alclad (7072/3003 and 3004 and bare 3004 and 5052).

J. Larsen-Basse and K.-F. Lam, Corrosion Tests in Hawaiian Geothermal Fluids, in *International Congress on Metallic Corrosion*, Vol 3, National Research Council of Canada, Ottawa, 641-648, 1984. MetAbs No. 84-352953. **Abstract:** Exposure tests were conducted in Hawaiian binary geothermal brine on a variety of weld materials, including 316L stainless, Al7075, A366 carbon steel and Hastelloy C-276.

J. Prybylowski and R. Ballinger, Influence of Microstructure on the Environmentally Assisted Cracking of Inconel 718, *Corrosion, 43*(2), 111-117, 1987. MetAbs No. 87-351305. **Abstract:** The effect of grain boundary precipitation on the environmental behavior of Inconel 718 was determined. The performance of conventionally heat treated material was compared with that of direct-aged material. Straining electrode tests with cathodic polarization at room temperature and fatigue tests in aqueous environments ranging from 30 to 288 °C were performed.

J. Sefaja and J. Malina, Electrochemical Aspects of Steel Corrosion in Sea Water, *Surf. Technol., 26*(4), 369-380, 1985. MetAbs No. 86-350579. **Abstract:** Electrochemical determinations of the corrosion parameters of construction steel DIN St 12 and an experimental alloy (2.8 wt.% Cr) were made in synthetic seawater under defined hydrodynamic conditions. The direct method of measuring polarization resistance and voltametric and comparative analytical methods were used.

J.F. Conde, G.C. Booth, and A.F. Taylor, Protection Against Hot Corrosion in Marine Gas Turbines, *Mater. Sci. Technol., 2*(3), 314-317, 1986. MetAbs No. 86-351607. **Abstract:** Under certain conditions, the high-temperature components of gas turbines used for the propulsive machinery and auxiliaries in ships may be subjected to hot corrosion resulting from sea salt contamination and ingestion of sulfur from the fuel (normally diesel or gas oil with a S content of about 1.0 wt.%). Carbon formed by incomplete combustion or pyrolysis of fuel, particularly under fuel-rich conditions in high-energy density combustion systems, may exacerbate corrosion by chemical effects or physical erosion.

J.F. Rau, T.W. Michie, and S.N. Smith, Cathodic Protection of a Guyed Tower in 1000 Feet of Water, *Mater. Perform., 25*(3), 50-56, 1986. MetAbs No. 86-351088. **Abstract:** The Lena guyed tower and its 20 associated guylines were installed in 1000 ft of water in 1983 in Mississippi Canyon Block 280 in the Gulf of Mexico. The design, installation, post-construction inspection, and routine monitoring of the 2.4 million pounds of anodes (Al-Hg or Al-In alloys) that provide underwater protection for the tower and guylines are reviewed.

J.G. Davis, Cast-On Zinc Anodes, *Pipeline Gas J., 214*(2), 14-16, 1987. MetAbs No. 87-351311. **Abstract:** A new process has been developed that allows Zn anodes to be directly cast onto the surface of steel pipelines.

This process has been used to provide corrosion protection for steel pipelines in marine environments.

J.M. Boulet, J.C. Bavay, and P. Bourgain, Superferritic Stainless Steel 290Mo: A High Performance Alloy for Seawater Applications, *Bull. Cercle Etud. Metaux*, 15(11), 12, 1986. MetAbs No. 87-350693. **Abstract:** Stainless steel with 29% Cr-4% Mo and stabilized with titanium is a superferritic alloy which has been specially developed for use in chloride environments, particularly for the multi-tubular condensers of power stations located by the sea or an estuary. The high performance of 290Mo stainless steel is analyzed on the basis of electrochemical pitting corrosion tests in chloride solutions carried out on laboratory superferritic stainless steels containing various combinations of alloying elements Cr, Mo, Ni, Ti or Nb.

J.P. Frick, L.R. Scharfstein, T.M. Parrill, and G. Haaland, Corrosion of 90-10 Cupronickel Alloys in Seawater Systems, *J. Met.*, 37(3), 28-30, 1985. MetAbs No. 85-351333. **Abstract:** The presence of a detrimental Fe-based grain boundary phase that develops during extended time at sensitizing temperature in heat exchanger tubes is documented.

J.P. Randin, Corrosion Resistance of Nickel in Artificial Sweat and Synthetic Seawater, *Werkst. Korros.*, 38(5), 233-236, 1987. MetAbs No. 87-352614. **Abstract:** The corrosion resistance of Nickel 200 has been determined in artificial sweats (perspiration) and in synthetic seawater by several electrochemical methods.

J.R. Pickens, J.R. Gordon, and J.A.S. Green, The Effect of Loading Mode on the Stress Corrosion Cracking of Aluminum Alloy 5083, *Metall. Trans A*, 14A(5), 925-930, 1983. MetAbs No. 83-351381. **Abstract:** The role of hydrogen embrittlement in the stress-corrosion cracking of Al-Mg alloys was investigated using commercial Al-4.4 wt.% Mg alloy, 5083. The susceptibility of this alloy in a saline environment was evaluated in Mode I (tension) and Mode III (torsion), using precracked fracture toughness specimens.

K. Nisancioglu, O. Lunder, and H. Holtan, Improving the Corrosion Resistance of Aluminum Alloys by Cathodic Polarization in Aqueous Media. *Corrosion*, 41(5), 247-257, 1985. MetAbs No. 85-351572. **Abstract:** An efficient method of improving the corrosion resistance of aluminum alloys appears to be cathodic polarization within a certain potential range in unbuffered salt solutions of neutral pH. An appreciable improvement of the corrosion resistance of alloys in the 1000, 3000, and 6000 series is discussed.

K. Rohrig, High-Alloy Cast Stainless Steels With Improved Seawater Resistance, *Stainless Steel Ind.*, 13(74), 8-11, 1985. MetAbs No. 85-352453. **Abstract:** From the outset, the development of cast stainless steels has run parallel to that of the corresponding wrought materials. However, the special requirements of the foundry industry with regard to casting and weldability, particularly in thick sections, has necessitated some slight modifications in the composition. This paper discusses the casting versions of the high alloy austenitic stainless steels and the duplex stainless steels which are being used increasingly in wrought form for seawater service especially in offshore installations.

K.A. Lucas and M.J. Robinson, The Influence of Lattice Hydrogen Content on the Hydrogen-Assisted Cracking of High Strength Steel, *Corros. Sci.*, 26(9), 705-717, 1986. MetAbs No. 87-350241. **Abstract:** The susceptibility of BS4360 grade 50D carbon-manganese steel to hydrogen-assisted cracking was measured in a range of aqueous environments including artificial seawater at applied cathodic potentials. The diffusible lattice H content of the steel was determined electrochemically and related to the threshold stress intensity to cause cracking.

K.D. Efird, Failure of Monel Ni-Cu-Al Alloy K-500 Bolts in Seawater, *Mater. Perform.*, 24(4), 37-40, 1985. MetAbs No. 85-351329. **Abstract:** Monel Ni-Cu-Al Alloy K-500 bolts failed by cracking after short periods of service as subsea riser clamp bolts on Occidental Petroleum Caledonia, Ltd.'s Piper Alpha platform in the UK North Sea.

K.E. Perumal, Solution of Severe Corrosion Problems in Chemical Process Industries With Special Stainless Steels, *Tool Alloy Steels*, 20(2), 53-61, 1986. MetAbs No. 86-352151. **Abstract:** In the application of stainless steels for process equipment in chemical industries the common stainless steels like types 304, 316 and 321, including the low-carbon varieties, have some inherent limitations. These are their poor resistance to general corrosion in reducing and less oxidizing acids and their susceptibility to pitting and stress-corrosion cracking in sulfide- and chloride-containing solutions. The economical solution to these problems is to upgrade the stainless steel with respect to its corrosion resistance by changing the alloy chemistry: increasing the Ni and Mo contents and adding elements like Cu. Four such grades are UNS N08904, UNS N08028, UNS S31254, and UNS S31803. Situations where the above upgraded steels find applications and promise as materials of construction in chemical process industries are described. Four major applications are described — organic reactions involving sulfuric acid as catalyst, drying of polymer products, seawater or chloride-containing waters, and pulp bleaching plants.

K.R. Trethewey and I. Pinwill, The Dezincification of Free-Machining Brasses in Sea Water, *Surf. Coat. Technol.*, 30(3), 289-307, 1987. MetAbs No. 87-351668. **Abstract:** New effects are reported in the microstructures of dezincified free-machining brasses and interpreted as variations in porosity within the attacked material. Kinetic studies show that a parabolic-type rate law is followed.

L. Admiraal, F.P. Ijsseling, B.H. Kolster, and J. Van Der Veer, Influence of Temperature on Corrosion Product Film Formation on CuNi10Fe in the Low Temperature Range. II. Studies on Corrosion Product Film Formation and Properties in Relation to Microstructure and Iron Content, *Br. Corros. J.*, 21(1), 33-43, 1986. MetAbs No. 86-351185. **Abstract:** Earlier experiments have shown seawater temperature to exercise a strong influence on the corrosion behavior of CuNi10Fe alloys. Investigations attempting to correlate the corrosion product layer properties, and hence the corrosion rate, with microstructural effects are described. Alloy Fe content and heat treatment were varied, exposure being carried out at 20 and 40 °C under conditions promoting uniform attack.

M. Eashwar, S. Iyer, and U. Venkatakrishna, Microfouling on Cathodically Protected Mild Steel in Sea Water, *Bull. Electrochem.*, 2(4), 341-343, 1986. MetAbs No. 87-350956. **Abstract:** The influence of cathodic protection on the rate of microfouling on mild steel was investigated in natural seawater. Cathodic protection was applied at current densities of 0.12 and 0.22 mA/cm^2 using sacrificial zinc anodes.

M. Eashwar, V. Ananth, S. Palaraj, and G. Subramanian, Biofouling Studies Relating to Cathodic Protection of Some Metals in Seawater, *Bull. Electrochem.*, 1(1), 19-21, 1985. MetAbs No. 86-350962. **Abstract:** Biofouling studies relating to cathodic protection of mild steel, stainless steel and brass in seawater have been conducted in the shallow waters of Mandapam coast, India, to understand the role of biological factors operating. Subjects of the investigations were the response to cathodic protection of marine fouling, the occurrence and the growth rate of calcareous deposits.

M. Miyasaka and N. Ogure, Stress Corrosion Cracking of Austenitic Cast Irons in Seawater and Brine, and Its Prevention, *Corrosion*, 43(10), 582-588, 1987. MetAbs No. 88-350599. **Abstract:** Stress-corrosion cracking behavior of austenitic cast irons, ASTM A436 Type 2 and A439

Type D2, in NaCl solutions was studied. Initially, constant tensile load tests were conducted for the stress-corrosion cracking experiment using smooth round-bar specimens to examine influences of applied stress, alloying elements, temperature, NaCl concentration, dissolved oxygen concentration, and potential on stress-corrosion cracking behavior. Protection methods against stress-corrosion cracking are discussed based on the test results.

M.A. Pao and E. Klar, "On the Corrosion Resistance of P/M Austenitic Stainless Steels," Association Italiana di Metallurgia, Milan, 359-374, 1982. MetAbs No. 83-351047. **Abstract:** Effects of sintering temperature, atmosphere, dewpoint, cooling rate and part density upon nitrogen and oxygen content and corrosion resistance of regular and Sn- and Cu/Sn-modified P/M 304L and 316L austenitic Cr-Ni steels are described. Discussion of results takes into account the solubility of nickel in Cr-Ni steels in equilibrium with gaseous nickel and chromium nitride.

M.D. Carpenter, R. Francis, L.M. Philips, and J.W. Oldfield, Electrochemical Tests to Assess Resistance to Crevice Corrosion in Sea Water of Some Duplex Stainless Steels, *Br. Corros. J.*, *21*(1), 45-48, 1986. MetAbs No. 86-351186. **Abstract:** An electrochemical test was used to evaluate the resistance to crevice corrosion in seawater of some commercial stainless steels. The results for established alloys correlate well with known service performance, and give confidence in the use of the technique to predict the behavior of newer materials.

M.N. Fokin and V.A. Kotenev, Ellipsometric Investigation of Adsorption of Sodium Oleate From Aqueous Solution on Smooth Aluminum, *Prot. Met. (USSR) (Translation)*, *21*(6), 740-744, 1985. MetAbs No. 86-352476.

M.R. Watts, Duplex Stainless Steels for Oil Field Recovery, *Chart. Mech. Eng.*, *34*(6), 32-34, 1987. MetAbs No. 87-352419. **Abstract:** Given the location of most oil fields, it is normal for the injection water to be a mixture of brackish aquifer water, seawater, or the produced water which came to the surface with the oil. This article describes how the corrosion problems were overcome by using special duplex stainless steels.

N. Mukhopadhyay and S. Baskaran, Characterization of Corrosion Products on Cupronickel 70:30 Alloy in Sulfide-Polluted Seawater, *Corrosion*, *42*(2), 113-117, 1986. MetAbs No. 86-350814. **Abstract:** The intermittent occurrence of dissolved sulfide in seawater up to a level of 100 ppb was observed when seawater was flowing in an experimental setup through Cu alloy tubes at 0.16 m/s for varying time periods from 1 to 12 months.

N. Totsuka, E. Lunarska, G. Cragnolino, and Z. Szklarska-Smialowska, Effect of Hydrogen on the Intergranular Stress Corrosion Cracking of Alloy 600 in High Temperature Aqueous Environments, *Corrosion*, *43*(8), 505-514, 1987. MetAbs No. 87-352847. **Abstract:** Slow strain rate tests on differently shaped tensile specimens machined from two heats of Alloy 600 tubing were conducted at 350 °C in deaerated aqueous solutions containing small amounts of lithium hydroxide and boric acid at different partial pressures of hydrogen, using a recirculating autoclave system. In addition, split half tube specimens cut from the same two heats of Alloy 600 were subjected to reverse U-bend testing in pure water and steam at 363 and 400 °C, respectively, using two static autoclaves.

N. Totsuka and Z. Szklarska-Smialowska, Activation Energy for IGSCC of Alloy 600 in an Aqueous Solution Containing Dissolved Hydrogen at 300 to 350 °C, *Scr. Metall.*, *21*(1), 45-47, 1987. MetAbs No. 87-350917. **Abstract:** A modified slow strain rate test has been used to determine the activation energy for intergranular stress-corrosion cracking of alloy 600 in a slightly alkaline water solution containing dissolved hydrogen at 310 to 350 °C.

O.E. Abdel-Salam and G.M. Abo-Elenien, Passivation of Mechanically Polished, Chemically Etched and Anodized Zirconium in Various Aqueous Solutions: Open-Circuit Potential Measurements, *Mater. Sci. Forum*, *8*, 605-611, 1986. MetAbs No. 87-352193. **Abstract:** The reactivity and corrosion rate of zirconium in aqueous solutions is tested by the measurement of open-circuit potentials of mechanically polished, chemically etched and anodized Zr in acidic, neutral and alkaline solutions. The variation of the potential with time, pH in different solutions, and with successive injection of oxygen and nitrogen provides an appropriate index of the extent of the surface reactivity.

P. Lovland, Use of Advanced Steel and Alloy Mounts in Seawater, Process Systems, *Anti-Corros. Methods Mater.*, *34*(1), 8-9, 1987. MetAbs No. 87-351425. **Abstract:** Materials used in seawater and process systems of offshore production platforms should not require to be replaced nor be too expensive, but should be manufactured easily and to a high quality. Most relevant are cupronickel 90-10 UNS C70600 and high-alloyed stainless steels, e.g., those containing 6% Mo.

P.D. Goodman, Effect of Chlorination on Materials for Sea Water Cooling Systems: A Review of Chemical Reactions, *Br. Corros. J.*, *22*(1), 56-62, 1987. MetAbs No. 87-351706. **Abstract:** The electrode and the chemical reactions likely to occur on electrochlorination of seawater are reviewed. The levels of Cl required to control fouling and the effects of pressure are also discussed. The reactions of chlorine with both common pollutants and chemical additions present in seawater are reviewed, as are the effects of chlorinated seawater on the corrosion of Cu and ferrous alloys.

P.J. Tate, Failure Analysis—Three Cases of Corrosion Involving Stainless Steels in Chloride Environments, *Prakt. Metallogr.*, *24*(1), 38-42, 1987. MetAbs No. 87-351493. **Abstract:** Three case histories of failures are provided demonstrating improper choice of stainless steel types for the service environment. The cases are: countersunk stainless steel (316) screw on coastal vessel, trim tab to hydraulic ram pivot pin on seagoing vessel, and damaged handrail system in a bathing pool.

P.K. Chauhan and H.S. Gadiyar, An XPS Study of the Corrosion of Cu-10 Ni Alloy Polluted Sea-Water: The Effect of $FeSO_4$ Addition, *Corros. Sci.*, *25*(1), 55-68, 1985. MetAbs No. 85-350968. **Abstract:** The corrosion behavior and the composition of surface films formed on Cu-10Ni alloy in unpolluted and polluted seawater have been investigated by XPS.

P.R. Shibad and K.N. Adhe, Effect of Addition Agents on the Corrosion Behavior of Copper Base Alloys in Salt Waters, *Trans. Indian Inst. Met.*, *38*(1), 17-22, 1985. MetAbs No. 85-352350. **Abstract:** Corrosion studies on Al brass, admiralty brass, Sn bronze and Cu-Ni alloys in 3% NaCl solution and synthetic seawater have been carried out with and without the addition of inhibitors such as $FeSO_4$ (1 and 5 ppm), Na_2CrO_4 (5 ppm) + NaH_2PO_4 (1:9), Na_2MoO_4 (20 ppm) and addition of NH_4OH (10 ppm) as pollutant. Electrochemical measurements such as potential-time and potential-current have been carried out.

R. Francis, Effect of Pollutants on Corrosion of Copper Alloys in Sea Water. I. Ammonia and Chlorine, *Br. Corros. J.*, *20*(4), 167-174, 1985. MetAbs No. 86-350679. **Abstract:** The results of seawater corrosion tests on five Cu alloy heat exchanger materials are presented. The tests were undertaken to determine whether ammonia, commonly present as a pollutant in seawater, would adversely affect their corrosion behavior.

R. Francis, Effect of Pollutants on Corrosion of Copper Alloys in Sea Water. II. Sulfide and Chlorine, *Br. Corros. J.*, *20*(4), 175-182, 1985. MetAbs No. 86-350680. **Abstract:** Seawater corrosion tests of five Cu alloy heat exchanger materials were undertaken to examine the effects of sulfide, commonly present as a pollutant in seawater, on their corrosion behavior, particularly in the presence of chlorine.

R. Francis, The Effects of Chlorine on the Properties of Films on Copper Alloys in Sea Water, *Corros. Sci.*, 26(3), 205-212, 1986. MetAbs No. 86-351581. **Abstract:** The films formed on aluminium brass and 90/10 copper-nickel in seawater dosed with chlorine have been studied.

R. Johnsen and E. Bardal, Cathodic Properties of Different Stainless Steels in Natural Seawater, *Corrosion*, 41(5), 296-302, 1985. MetAbs No. 85-351571. **Abstract:** The cathodic properties of a number of stainless steels, which were exposed to natural seawater flowing at 0 to 2.5 m/s and polarized to potentials from -300 to 950 mV SCE, have been studied.

R. Murakami and W.G. Ferguson, The Effects of Cathodic Potential and Calcareous Deposits on Corrosion Fatigue Crack Growth Rate in Seawater for Two Offshore Structural Steels, *Fatigue Fract. Eng. Mater. Struct.*, 9(6), 477-488, 1986. MetAbs No. 87-351659. **Abstract:** The effects of cathodic protection potential, corrosion products and stress ratio on corrosion fatigue crack growth rate have been studied on offshore structural steels. These materials were cathodically polarized in seawater and 3% sodium chloride solution at three potentials.

R.C. Salvarezza, M.F.L. de Mele, H.H. Videla, and F.R. Goni, Electrochemical Behavior of Aluminum in Human Plasma, *J. Biomed. Mater. Res.*, 19(9), 1073-1084, 1985. MetAbs No. 86-350183. **Abstract:** The electrochemical behavior of 99.99 Al% in isotonic saline solutions is studied using potentiostatic and potentiodynamic polarization techniques complemented with scanning electron microscopy and dispersive X-ray analysis.

R.J. Gray, J.C. Griess, R.S. Crouse, and J.H. DeVan, Examination of Aluminum Tubing Pitted in Stagnant Water (Retroactive Coverage), in *Microstructural Science*, Vol 6, Elsevier North-Holland, New York, 261-278, 1978. MetAbs No. 82-350801. **Abstract:** A demonstration is being conducted to determine the feasibility of an annual cycle energy system as an energy balance system for heating and cooling a house. A part of the initial demonstration involved the testing of ½ in. diameter series 1100 Al alloy, finned tubing as the basic thermal transfer via a 15% methanol brine solution. This examination includes optical and scanning electron microscopy displays of the holes and energy dispersive X-ray analyses of the products contiguous to the holes.

R.L. Tapping, Surface Studies of Austenitic Alloys Subjected to Crevice Corrosion in Sea Water, *Corros. Sci.*, 25(6), 363-376, 1985. MetAbs No. 85-352379. **Abstract:** Scanning Auger microscopy has been used to characterize the surface films formed on several austenitic Fe-Ni-Cr alloys subjected to crevice corrosion in seawater. Comparisons were made between corroded and noncorroded areas in an attempt to relate alloy and oxide compositional differences to corrosion susceptibility.

R.P. Frankenthal and P.C. Milner, Hydrogen Evolution Kinetics on a High-Carbon Steel and on Tin in Seawater, *Corrosion*, 42(1), 51-53, 1986. MetAbs No. 86-350595. **Abstract:** The rate of corrosion of steels in seawater may be controlled by the rate of the cathodic reaction. In the absence of dissolved oxygen, hydrogen evolution is the most probable cathodic reaction. Although there have been studies of the hydrogen evolution reaction on Fe in well-defined, simple solutions, no such studies exist for commercial steels in seawater. One means of protecting steel against corrosion is to coat it with a metal that has a higher overpotential, such as Sn.

R.P. Singh, O.P. Modi, M.N. Mungole, and K.P. Singh, Corrosion of 2.25Cr-1Mo Ferritic Steel in Sulfuric Acid and Sea Water, *Br. Corros. J.*, 20(1), 28-31, 1985. MetAbs No. 85-351883. **Abstract:** The corrosion behavior of 2.25Cr-1Mo ferritic steel in different concentrations

(0.05-5N) of sulfuric acid and in seawater has been studied by potentiodynamic polarization measurements at scan rates of 45 mV/min. The experiments were performed on steels in two different conditions, cold worked and annealed at 850 °C for 2 h in vacuum (0.1 Pa), and the effect of microstructure was also analyzed.

S. Elbeik, A.C. Tseung, and A.L. Mackay, The Formation of Calcareous Deposits During the Corrosion of Mild Steel in Sea Water, *Corros. Sci.*, 26(9), 669-680, 1986. MetAbs No. 87-350239. **Abstract:** The formation of calcareous deposits at the sea/air interface on corroding mild steel has been investigated using a scanning electron microscope, and by EDAX and X-ray distribution mapping. The mechanism for the formation of these calcareous deposits is discussed and the identification of cathodic and anodic sites on the steel surface is presented.

S. Maxwell, Effect of Cathodic Protection on the Activity of Microbial Biofilms, *Mater. Perform.*, 25(11), 53-56, 1986. MetAbs No. 87-350345. **Abstract:** The study was performed to determine the effect of a -950 mV cathodic potential on the activity of the biofilm formed, and the production of sulfide within that biofilm. 50D mild steel (BS 4360 Grade 5D) corrosion coupons, both unprotected and protected with a sacrificial anode, were exposed in the estuarine waters of Aberdeen Harbor. The activities of the bacterial biofilms were determined using radiorespirometric methods.

S. Maxwell and W.A. Hamilton, Effect of Cathodic Protection on the Activity of Microbial Biofilms, *Ind. Corros.*, 5(2), 14-17, 1987. MetAbs No. 87-352128. **Abstract:** Impressed current or sacrificial anode systems are used to protect the subsea structures of offshore platforms and rigs. The steel is considered protected when a potential of -850 mV (Cu:CuSO₄) is achieved. In many cases, the potential is further reduced to -950 mV to protect the steel from corrosion caused by the activity of sulfate-reducing bacteria. Some operators have questioned therefore presence of sulfide-containing deposits under marine macrofouling, indicating that sulfate-reducing bacteria are active, on structures protected to -950 mV. The decreased potential, however, is not applied to prevent the activity of sulfate-reducing bacteria, but is based on a theoretical level which will allow passivity of steel in sulfide environments. This study was performed to determine the effect of a cathodic potential of -950 mV on the activity of the biofilm formed and the production of sulfide within that biofilm. 50D mild steel corrosion coupons, both unprotected and protected with a sacrificial anode, were exposed in the estuarine waters of Aberdeen Harbor. The activities of the bacterial biofilms were determined using radiorespirometric methods.

S.C. Dexter, Corrosion in Marine and Natural Waters, in *Encyclopedia of Materials Science and Engineering*, Vol 2, Pergamon Press, Oxford, 1986. MetAbs No. 86-351933. **Abstract:** The most abundant and widespread corrosive electrolyte is water. The corrosiveness of fresh, brackish and seawaters to a variety of metals and alloys depends on many factors including water chemistry, temperature, velocity and biological growths (biofouling). Controlling corrosion on structures in natural waters is becoming increasingly difficult as the search for mineral and fossil-fuel resources is extended further offshore, and as more sophisticated technology demands increasing performance from existing structural materials.

S.C. Tjong, Aqueous Corrosion Properties of Austenitic Fe-8.7Al-29.7Mn-1.04C Alloy, *Surf. Coat. Technol.*, 28(2), 181-186, 1986. MetAbs No. 86-352088. **Abstract:** The aqueous corrosion behavior of the alloy Fe-8.7Al-29.7Mn-1.04C has been investigated by the anodic polarization technique.

S.P. Lynch and P. Trevena, Stress Corrosion Cracking and Liquid Metal Embrittlement in Pure Magnesium, *Corrosion*, 44(2), 113-124, 1988.

MetAbs No. 88-351089. **Abstract:** Metallographic and fractographic observations of crack growth in pure magnesium in dry air, aqueous, and liquid alkali metal environments are described.

S.R. Rao, G.M. Rao, R.V. Rama Rao, and G.J. Raju, Marine Fouling and Corrosion at Port Blair and Kamorta, *Corros. Maint.*, 8(1), 51-54, 1985. MetAbs No. 86-350492. **Abstract:** Microbiological corrosion and fouling of woods (six types) and metals (mild steel, brass and copper) in marine environment free of industrial effluent discharges are surveyed.

S.S. Jang, T. Shoji, H. Takahashi, and Y. Watanabe, Corrosion Fatigue of High Strength Steel in Flowing Sea Water, *Corros. Eng.*, 35(9), 503-508, 1986. MetAbs No. 87-351444. **Abstract:** To investigate the influence of flow rate on crack growth behavior in various corrosion potentials for HT80 steel, corrosion fatigue tests were conducted in synthetic seawater.

S.W. Smith Jr., N.D. Kackey, and R.M. Latanision, "Corrosion of Aluminum in Salt Water and Sea Water as Influenced by Magnesium and Copper," National Association of Corrosion Engineers, Houston, 1983. MetAbs No. 84-350479. **Abstract:** The chemical mechanisms by which magnesium and copper ions react with aluminum (5052) surfaces in seawater are discussed in terms of the fact that these ions are known to depolarize the cathodic half reactions occurring on aluminum surfaces.

Steels for the Salt Solution, *Iron Steel Int.*, 58(1), 9-13, 1985. MetAbs No. 85-351269. **Abstract:** A comprehensive account is given of the microstructure, physical and corrosion properties of a newly developed duplex stainless steel Zeron 100.

T. Nagoya, T. Yoshii, and T. Kanamaru, Effect of Various Factors on Corrosion Resistance of 20Cr-25Ni-6Mo Stainless Steels for Seawater, *Trans. Iron Steel Inst. Jpn.*, 25(1), B-32, 1985. MetAbs No. 86-350140. **Abstract:** Plate specimens of 20Cr-25Ni-6Mo austenitic stainless steels containing varying levels of alloying elements were solution treated at 1150 °C for 10 min, finished by wet polishing, and then subjected to electrochemical and immersion studies to determine their pitting, crevice and general corrosion resistances.

T. Okada, S. Hattori, and S. Yamagishi, The Notch Effect on Corrosion—Fatigue Strength of High-Strength Steels, *Bull. Jpn. Soc. Mech. Eng.*, 29(255), 2765-2770, 1986. MetAbs No. 87-350970. **Abstract:** The notch effect on corrosion-fatigue strength was investigated with high-strength steels of HT50 and HT80 in ion-exchanged seawater.

T. Okada and S. Hattori, Relation Between Concentration of Salt Water and Corrosion Fatigue Strength on 0.37% Carbon Structural Steel, *J. Eng. Mater. Technol. (Trans. ASME)*, 107(3), 235-239, 1985. MetAbs No. 85-352055. **Abstract:** The corrosion fatigue properties of 0.37% carbon structural steel (AISI 1035) were studied in salt water having concentrations from 0 wt% (ion exchanged water) to 10 wt%.

T. Peev, B. Mandjukova, and I. Mandjukova, Mossbauer Analysis of Corrosion Products Obtained on Steel in a Low-Magnetic Field, *Corrosion*, 43(12), 739-742, 1987. MetAbs No. 88-350653. **Abstract:** The corrosion products of steel plate obtained in aqueous solution in the presence or absence of an external magnetic field of 40 Oe were studied.

T.R. Vaidnath and T.R. Nagarajan, Corrosion in a High Pressure Boiler—A Case Study, *Trans. SAEST*, 21(4), 201-206, 1986. MetAbs No. 87-352806. **Abstract:** A case study on the failure analysis of a seawater-cooled high-pressure utility boiler is presented. The failure is attributed to the severe pitting corrosion of the radiative heat transfer surface of plain carbon steel caused due to the weight loading of up to 40% Cu on the protective magnetic layer, generated from the low-pressure heaters (made up of Cu alloy) in the preboiler circuit. Adequate

protection and maintenance procedures of the key system components through mechanical and chemical deaeration and chemically treating the feedwater and boiler water and the role of pH, dissolved oxygen and airtight condenses are stressed.

Th. Skoulikidis and Ath. Karageorgos, Protection of Aluminium Alloys Against Stress Corrosion Cracking in Saline Water by Properly Oriented Anodic Coating. III, *Br. Corros. J.*, 15(1), 41-43, 1980. MetAbs No. 81-350089. **Abstract:** A method was suggested for protecting Al-2.5 wt.% Mg alloy specimens against stress-corrosion cracking in saline water by using suitably oriented (in a direction normal to the future stress direction) anodic films of gamma $1-Al_2O_3$ and its hydrate in the thickness range 27.1 to 3.4 micrometers. The study has now been extended to cover thickness between 27.1 and 51.0 and 3.4 and 1.7 micrometers.

V. Scotto, R. DiCintio, and G. Marcenaro, The Influence of Marine Aerobic Microbial Film on Stainless Steel Corrosion Behavior, *Corros. Sci.*, 25(3), 185-194, 1985. MetAbs No. 85-351836. **Abstract:** An investigation was carried out, through laboratory experiments, into the corrosion behavior of stainless steels immersed in natural and sterile seawater to determine whether the observed ennoblement of the free corrosion potentials in sea-immersed stainless steels can be explained as due to the settlement of living microbiological slime on the metal surface.

V.A. Callcut, Expanding Markets for 90/10 Copper-Nickel Alloys, *Met. Mater.*, 1(8), 489-494, 1985. MetAbs No. 85-352452. **Abstract:** The 90/10 copper-nickel alloy has a unique combination of properties in resistance to marine corrosion and biofouling. It has adequate strength for many structural purposes and has been widely adopted as the material for seawater services in ships, desalination plant and on offshore structures.

W. Fairhurst, High Molybdenum Stainless Steels in Power Station Condensers, *Met. Mater.*, 2(1), 13-17, 1986. MetAbs No. 86-351234. **Abstract:** This article examines the role of high Mo stainless steels with particular reference to seawater-cooled power station condensers. The corrosion behavior of both austenitic and ferritic grades is described and particular reference is made to testing procedures and conditions. Finally, comparisons are made not only between alloy grades but also between stainless steel and competing nonferrous alloys.

W.J. Tomlinson, F.T. Moule, and G.N. Blount, Cavitation Erosion of a Nitrided Steel in Salt Water and Emulsion, *J. Mater. Sci. Lett.*, 6(8), 877-878, 1987. MetAbs No. 87-352851. **Abstract:** An investigation was made of cavitation erosion of a nitrided steel (Fe-0.3C-0.45Mn-3Cr-0.3Ni-0.4Mo) in distilled water, water containing 1.0% NaCl and a 5% emulsion containing 1.0% NaCl. The erosion damage as a function of time was shown for the three erosion fluids.

Y.J. Kim and R.A. Oriani, Electrochemical Behavior of Ti-30Mo in a Gamma Radiolysis Environment, *Corrosion*, 43(1), 56-58, 1987. **Abstract:** The corrosion behavior of Ti-30Mo was examined in brine under gamma radiation. The amounts of hydrogen take-up by Ti-30Mo alloy were measured by hot vacuum extraction. X-ray diffraction and scanning electron microscopy were applied to investigate the oxide layers and morphology of the surfaces after free immersion in the brine solution at 108 °C, both with and without radiation. In situ measurements of the open circuit potential and polarization behavior were conducted to study the corrosion properties of Ti-30Mo in brine at 25 °C, both with and without radiation. Hydrogen peroxide was added to brine to discover what effects are produced by H_2O_2 without radiation.

Y.W. Cheng, The Fatigue Crack Growth of a Ship Steel in Seawater Under Spectrum Loading, *Int. J. Fatigue*, 7(2), 95-100, 1985. MetAbs No. 85-351563. **Abstract:** Fatigue crack growth of ABS EH36 steel under spectrum loading intended to simulate sea loading of offshore structures in the North Sea was studied using fracture mechanics. A digital simulation technique was used to generate samples of load/time histories from a power spectrum characteristic of the North Sea environment.

Z. Ahmad, Development of New Materials for Desalination, *Anti-Corros. Methods Mater.*, *33*(1), 4-13, 1986. MetAbs No. 86-351181. **Abstract:** In multistage flash distillation type desalination plants, the colossal amount of heat exchanger surface required makes it mandatory to investigate new condenser materials. The development of modified Al alloys for use in desalination plants is being researched at the University of Petroleum and Minerals, Dhahran, Saudi Arabia. Alloys have been tested in both strain hardened and annealed forms.

Z. Ahmad, The Effect of Velocity on the Open Circuit Potential and Corrosion Rate of Aluminium Alloys, *Metaux-Corros.-Ind.*, *60*(722), 289-296, 1985. MetAbs No. 86-351206. **Abstract:** A study of the effect of velocity on the corrosion of aluminium and its alloys has been made. In particular, an overview of the effect of seawater velocity on the recently developed Al alloys has been presented.

Corrosion Behavior of Various Metals and Alloys in Seawater

Material	Condition, other factors, comments	Concentration, %	Temperature, °C (°F)	Duration	Corrosion rate, mm/yr (mils/yr) or other	Ref
Irons and steels						
0.3% Cu steel	(a)	...	...	1 yr	0.150 (5.9)	149
0.3% Cu steel	(a)	...	...	8 yr	0.090 (3.5)	149
0.3% Cu steel	(a)	...	...	16 yr	0.080 (3.1)	149
0.3% Cu steel	(b)	...	...	1 yr	0.915 (36)	149
0.3% Cu steel	(b)	...	...	8 yr	1.6 (63)	149
0.3% Cu steel	(b)	...	...	16 yr	2.16 (85)	149
0.3 Cu steel	(b)	...	...	1.5 yr	0.135 (5.3)	149
1.8Ni-0.81Cu	(c)	...	...	2.5 yr	0.115 (4.5)	149
1.8Ni-0.81Cu	(c)	...	...	4.5 yr	0.090 (3.5)	149
1.8Ni-0.81Cu	(c)	...	...	8.5 yr	0.080 (3.2)	149
1.8Ni-0.81Cu	(c)	...	...	1 yr	0.190 (7.4)	149
2 Ni steel	(a)	...	...	8 yr	0.10 (4)	149
2 Ni steel	(a)	...	...	16 yr	0.085 (3.3)	149
2 Ni steel	(a)	...	...	1 yr	0.840 (33)	149
2 Ni steel	(b)	...	...	8 yr	2.39 (94)	149
2 Ni steel	(b)	...	...	16 yr	...	149
2 Ni steel	Specimen corroded through. (b)	...	...	1 yr	0.07 (2.7)	149
5 Cr steel	(a)	...	...	8 yr	0.10 (4)	149
5 Cr steel	(a)	...	...	16 yr	0.085 (3.5)	149
5 Cr steel	(a)	...	...	1 yr	0.685 (27)	149
5 Cr steel	(b)	...	...	8 yr	1.6 (63)	149
5 Cr steel	(b)	...	...	16 yr	1.75 (69)	149
5 Cr steel	(b)	...	...	1 yr	0.160 (6.3)	149
5 Ni steel	(a)	...	...	8 yr	0.10 (4)	149
5 Ni steel	(a)	...	...	16 yr	0.085 (3.3)	149
5 Ni steel	(a)	...	...	1 yr	0.735 (29)	149
5 Ni steel	(b)	...	...	8 yr	2.97 (117)	149
5 Ni steel	(b)	...	...	16 yr	...	149
5 Ni steel	Specimen corroded through. (b)	...	...	1.5 yr	0.105 (4.2)	149
ASTM A242	Type 1. USS Cor-Ten A. (c)	...	...	2.5 yr	0.110 (4.3)	149
ASTM A242	Type 1. USS Cor-Ten A. (c)	...	...	4.5 yr	0.095 (3.8)	149
ASTM A242	Type 1. USS Cor-Ten A. (c)	...	...	8.5 yr	0.080 (3.1)	149
ASTM A242	Type 1. USS Cor-Ten A. (c)	...	...	1 yr	0.150 (5.9)	149
Carbon steel	(d)	...	...	8 yr	0.08 (3.2)	149
Carbon steel	(d)	...	...	16 yr	0.075 (2.9)	149
Carbon steel	(d)	...	...	1 yr	1.04 (41)	149
Carbon steel	(e)	...	...	8 yr	1.68 (66)	149
Carbon steel	(e)	...	...	16 yr	2.29 (90)	149
Carbon steel	(e)	...	...	...	34 mg/dm^2/d	171
Carbon steel	(f)	...	...	...	72 mg/dm^2/d	171
Carbon steel	(g)	...	...	...	254 mg/dm^2/d	171
Carbon steel	(h)	...	...	...	45 mg/dm^2/d	171
Cast iron	(f)	...	...	...	270 mg/dm^2/d	171
Cast iron	(h)	...	...	193 d	0.15 (6)	175
Low-carbon steel	Uncoupled. At half tide	...	...	56 months	0.156 (6.1)	175
Low-carbon steel	Uncoupled. In sea air	...	...			

(Continued)

Corrosion Behavior of Various Metals and Alloys in Seawater (Continued)

Material	Condition, other factors, comments	Concentration, %	Temperature, °C (°F)	Duration	Corrosion rate, mm/yr (mils/yr) or other	Ref
Structural carbon steel	(c)	...	...	1.5 yr	0.120 (4.8)	149
Structural carbon steel	(c)	...	...	2.5 yr	0.105 (4.1)	149
Structural carbon steel	(c)	...	...	4.5 yr	0.085 (3.3)	149
Structural carbon steel	(c)	...	...	8.5 yr	0.070 (2.7)	149
Mn-0.75Ni-0.45Cu	USS Tri-Ten. (c)	...	...	1.5 yr	0.110 (4.4)	149
Mn-0.75Ni-0.45Cu	USS Tri-Ten. (c)	...	...	2.5 yr	0.095 (3.8)	149
Mn-0.75Ni-0.45Cu	USS Tri-Ten. (c)	...	...	4.5 yr	0.075 (3.0)	149
Mn-0.75Ni-0.45Cu	USS Tri-Ten. (c)	...	...	8.5 yr	0.065 (2.6)	149
Stainless steels						
5Cr-1.5 Mo	1.93% Cl⁻, 690 kPa (100 psig). Plus CO_2, no H_2S	...	175 (350)	...	0.330 (13)	172
5Cr-1.5 Mo	1.92% Cl⁻, 690 kPa (100 psig). Plus CO_2 and 0.1% H_2S	...	175 (350)	...	1.016 (40)	172
13% Cr	1.92% Cl⁻, 690 kPa (100 psig). Plus CO_2 and 0.1% H_2S	...	175 (350)	...	0.025 (1.0)	172
2.6Cr-0.52Mo	(c)	...	...	1.5 yr	0.035 (1.4)	149
2.6Cr-0.52Mo	(c)	...	...	2.5 yr	0.040 (1.6)	149
2.6Cr-0.52Mo	(c)	...	...	4.5 yr	0.040 (1.6)	149
2.6Cr-0.52Mo	(c)	...	...	8.5 yr	0.033 (1.3)	149
Type 302 stainless steel	Uncoupled. At half tide	...	...	193 d	0.002 (0.08)	175
Type 302 stainless steel	Uncoupled. In sea air	...	...	56 months	nil	175
Type 304 stainless steel	Localized attack: perforated. Weight loss due to localized attack only: 16.8 g. Crevice corrosion under barnacles and at sheared edges. (j)	...	...	...	...	44
Type 304 stainless steel	Localized attack: 3.02 mm (119 mils) maximum; 1.07 mm (42 mils); average of five deepest areas. Weight loss due to localized attack only: 17.4 g. Crevice corrosion under barnacles and at sheared edges. (j)	...	...	...	...	44
Type 316 stainless steel	Localized attack: 1.83 mm (72 mils); 1.27 mm (50 mils) average of five deepest areas. Weight loss due to localized attack only: 4.0 g. Crevice corrosion under barnacles and at sheared edges. (j)	...	...	...	...	44
Type 316 stainless steel	Localized attack: 1.52 mm (60 mils) maximum; 1.14 mm (45 mils) average of five deepest areas. Weight loss due to localized attack only: 4.8 g. Crevice corrosion under barnacles and at sheared edges. (j)	...	...	...	...	44
Type 316 stainless steel	81% crevices initiated. (k)	...	14 (57)	29 d	1.2 (47)	60
Type 316 stainless steel	28% crevices initiated. (k)	...	30 (86)	30 d	1.9 (75)	60
Type 316 stainless steel	28% crevices initiated. (k)	...	52 (126)	30 d	0.10 (4)	60
Type 316 stainless steel	(f)	...	...	...	1 mg/dm²/d	171
Type 316 stainless steel	(g)	...	...	...	nil	171
Type 316 stainless steel	(h)	...	...	...	<1 mg/dm²/d	171
Type 316 stainless steel	Uncoupled. At half tide	...	...	193 d	nil	175
Type 316 stainless steel	Uncoupled. In sea air	...	...	56 months	nil	175
Type 316 stainless steel	Exposed to stagnant seawater. Maximum pit depth: 1.575 mm (62 mils)	...	...	3 yr	...	183
Type 317 stainless steel	76% crevices initiated. (k)	...	30 (86)	30 d	1.9 (75)	60
Type 317LM stainless steel	97% crevices initiated. (k)	...	30 (86)	30 d	1.1 (43)	60
Type 329 stainless steel	Mill-finished panels exposed to filtered seawater flowing at <0.1 m/s (<0.33 ft/s); crevice washers tightened to 2.8 or 8.5 N·m (25 or 75 in. · lb). Maximum pit depth: 1.6 mm (63 mils)	...	30 (86)	30, 60, 90 d	...	184
Type 410 stainless steel	1.93% Cl⁻, 690 kPa (100 psig). Plus CO_2, no H_2S	...	175 (350)	...	0.036 (1.4)	172
Type 410 stainless steel	1.92% Cl⁻, 690 kPa (100 psig). Plus CO_2 and 0.1% H_2S	...	175 (350)	...	0.030 (1.2)	172
Type 4130 stainless steel	1.92% Cl⁻, 690 kPa (100 psig). Plus CO_2 and 0.1% H_2S	...	175 (350)	...	2.565 (101)	172
Type 4130 stainless steel	1.93% Cl⁻, 690 kPa (100 psig). Plus CO_2, no H_2S	...	175 (350)	...	0.890 (35)	172

(Continued)

Corrosion Behavior of Various Metals and Alloys in Seawater (Continued)

Material	Condition, other factors, comments	Concentration, %	Temperature, °C (°F)	Duration	Corrosion rate, mm/yr (mils/yr) or other	Ref
AL-29-4C	Mill-finished panels exposed to filtered seawater flowing at <0.1 m/s (<0.33 ft/s); crevice washers tightened to 2.8 or 8.5 N·m (25 or 75 in. · lb). Maximum pit depth: nil	...	30 (86)	30, 60, 90 d	...	184
MONIT	Mill-finished panels exposed to filtered seawater flowing at <0.1 m/s (<0.33 ft/s); crevice washers tightened to 2.8 or 8.5 N·m (25 or 75 in. · lb). Maximum pit depth: 0.01 mm (0.4 mils)	...	30 (86)	30, 60, 90 d	...	184
254SMO	Mill-finished panels exposed to filtered seawater flowing at <0.1 m/s (<0.33 ft/s); crevice washers tightened to 2.8 or 8.5 N·m (25 or 75 in. · lb). Maximum pit depth: 0.19 mm (7.5 mils)	...	30 (86)	30, 60, 90 d	...	184
Sea-Cure	Mill-finished panels exposed to filtered seawater flowing at <0.1 m/s (<0.33 ft/s); crevice washers tightened to 2.8 or 8.5 N·m (25 or 75 in. · lb). Maximum pit depth: 0.11 mm (4.3 mils)	...	30 (86)	30, 60, 90 d	...	184
AL-6X	Mill-finished panels exposed to filtered seawater flowing at <0.1 m/s (<0.33 ft/s); crevice washers tightened to 2.8 or 8.5 N·m (25 or 75 in. · lb). Maximum pit depth: 0.34 mm (13.4 mils)	...	30 (85)	30, 60, 90 d	...	184
Nitronic 50	Mill-finished panels exposed to filtered seawater flowing at <0.1 m/s (<0.33 ft/s); crevice washers tightened to 2.8 or 8.5 N·m (25 or 75 in. · lb). Maximum pit depth: 1.2 mm (47.2 mils)	...	30 (86)	30, 60, 90 d	...	184
Aluminum						
1199	Maximum depth of attack: 0.039 mils. Average depth of attack: 0.003 mils. Change in tensile strength: 0%. (m)	...	...	10 yr	0.0009 (0.036)	150
1199	Change in tensile strength: 0%. (n)	...	...	10 yr	0.0002 (0.061)	150
5083-O	Maximum depth of attack: 0.038 mils. Average depth of attack: 0.012 mils. Change in tensile strength: 0%. (p)	...	...	10 yr	0.0009 (0.036)	150
5083-O	Maximum depth of attack: 0.024 mils. Average depth of attack: 0.001 mils. Change in tensile strength: 0%. (q)	...	...	10 yr	0.0015 (0.059)	150
5086-O	Maximum depth of attack: 0.027 mils. Average depth of attack: 0.002 mils. Change in tensile strength: -2.7%. (r)	...	...	10 yr	0.0009 (0.035)	150
5086-O	Change in tensile strength: -3.7%. (s)	...	...	10 yr	0.0015 (0.057)	150
5144-H38	Maximum depth of attack: 0.020 mils. Average depth of attack: 0.005 mils. Change in tensile strength: -2.1%. (m)	...	...	10 yr	0.0009 (0.037)	150
5154-H38	Change in tensile strength: -5.1%. (n)	...	...	10 yr	0.0014 (0.055)	150
5447-H34	Maximum depth of attack: 0.022 mils. Average depth of attack: 0.001 mils. Change in tensile strength: -4.2%. (t)	...	...	10 yr	0.0009 (0.036)	150
5454-H34	Maximum depth of attack: 0.015 mils. Average depth of attack: 0.003 mils. Change in tensile strength: -0.7%. (u)	...	...	10 yr	0.0010 (0.041)	150
5454-H34	Maximum depth of attack: 0.020 mils. Average depth of attack: 0.004 mils. Change in tensile strength: -0.5%. (v)	...	...	10 yr	0.0015 (0.059)	150
5456-H321	Maximum depth of attack: 0.072 mils. Average depth of attack: 0.013 mils. Change in tensile strength: -4.5%. (w)	...	...	10 yr	0.0013 (0.051)	150
5456-H321	Maximum depth of attack: 0.044 mils. Average depth of attack: 0.012 mils. Change in tensile strength: -1.1%. (x)	...	...	10 yr	0.0016 (0.064)	150
5456-O	Maximum depth of attack: 0.069 mils. Average depth of attack: 0.013 mils. Change in tensile strength: -0.4%. (w)	...	...	10 yr	0.0004 (0.014)	150
5456-O	Maximum depth of attack: 0.131 mils. Average depth of attack: 0.040 mils. Change in tensile strength: -3.0%. (x)	...	...	10 yr	0.0029 (0.116)	150
5457-H34	Change in tensile strength: -5.2%. (y)	...	...	10 yr	0.0014 (0.056)	150
Al-Mg₂Si alloys	...	...	...	...	Restricted applications	92
Alclad 2024-T3	Uncoupled. At half tide	...	...	193 d	0.015 (0.6)	175

(Continued)

Corrosion Behavior of Various Metals and Alloys in Seawater (Continued)

Material	Condition, other factors, comments	Concentration, %	Temperature, °C (°F)	Duration	Corrosion rate, mm/yr (mils/yr) or other	Ref
Alclad 2024-T3	Uncoupled. In sea air	...	...	56 months	0.001 (0.04)	175
Aluminum (99.0-99.5%)	...	...	...	...	Satisfactory	92
Aluminum-copper alloys	Clad	...	...	...	Satisfactory	92
Aluminum-magnesium alloys	...	...	...	...	Satisfactory	92
Aluminum-manganese alloys	..	...	...	...	Satisfactory	92
Aluminum-silicon alloys	...	...	...	...	Satisfactory	92
Coppers						
70-30 cupronickel	...	...	...	...	Suitable	93
70Cu-30Ni (0.5% Fe)	(f)	...	...	...	<1 mg/dm^2/d	171
70Cu-30Ni (0.5% Fe)	(g)	...	...	...	<1 mg/dm^2/d	171
70Cu-30Ni (0.5% Fe)	(h)	...	...	...	39 mg/dm^2/d	171
90-10 cupronickel	...	...	...	...	Suitable	93
90Cu-10Ni (0.8% Fe)	(f)	...	...	...	5 mg/dm^2/d	171
90Cu-10Ni (0.8% Fe)	(h)	...	...	...	99 mg/dm^2/d	171
Admiralty brass	...	...	...	...	Suitable	93
Admiralty brass	(f)	...	...	...	2 mg/dm^2/d	171
Admiralty brass	(g)	...	...	...	20 mg/dm^2/d	171
Admiralty brass	(h)	...	...	...	170 mg/dm^2/d	171
Aluminum brass	(f)	...	...	...	2 mg/dm^2/d	171
Aluminum brass	(h)	...	...	...	105 mg/dm^2/d	171
Aluminum bronze	(z)	...	...	...	Good	93
Aluminum bronze (10%)	(f)	...	...	...	5 mg/dm^2/d	171
Aluminum bronze (10%)	(h)	...	...	...	236 mg/dm^2/d	171
Architectural bronze	...	...	...	...	Fair	93
Brass	...	...	...	...	Suitable	93
C44300	(aa)	...	10-26 (50-80)	1-2 months	1.8-4.8 (71-189)	173
C68700	(aa)	...	10-26 (50-80)	1-2 months	0.36-3 (14.2-118)	173
C70600	(aa)	...	10-26 (50-80)	1-2 months	0.12-2.16 (4.7-85)	173
C70600	(bb)	...	10-26 (50-80)	1-2 months	0.36-1.56 (14.2-61.4)	173
C70600	(cc)	...	10-26 (50-80)	1-2 months	1.56 (61.4)	173
C71500	(aa)	...	10-26 (50-80)	1-2 months	0.12-1.08 (4.7-42.5)	173
C71500	(bb)	...	10-26 (50-80)	1-2 months	0.36-6.84 (14.2-269)	173
C71500	(cc)	...	10-26 (50-80)	1-2 months	1.68-2.04 (66-80.3)	173
C71900	(bb)	...	10-26 (50-80)	1-2 months	0.12-0.36 (4.7-14.2)	173
C71900	(aa)	...	10-26 (50-80)	1-2 months	No attack	173
C71900	(cc)	...	10-26 (50-80)	1-2 months	1.08-1.44 (42.5-56.7)	173
C72200	(aa)	...	10-26 (50-80)	1-2 months	No attack	173
C72200	(bb)	...	10-26 (50-80)	1-2 months	0.12 (4.7)	173
C72200	(cc)	...	10-26 (50-80)	1-2 months	No attack	173
Cartridge brass	...	...	...	...	Fair	93
Commercial bronze	(z)	...	...	...	Good	93

(Continued)

Corrosion Behavior of Various Metals and Alloys in Seawater (Continued)

Material	Condition, other factors, comments	Concentration, %	Temperature, °C (°F)	Duration	Corrosion rate, mm/yr (mils/yr) or other	Ref
Copper	Uncoupled. At half tide	...	...	193 d	0.013 (0.5)	175
Copper	Uncoupled. In sea air	...	...	56 months	0.002 (0.08)	175
Electrolytic copper	(z)	...	...	...	Good	93
Free-cutting brass	...	...	...	...	Fair	93
G bronze	(f)	...	...	...	7 mg/dm^2/d	171
G bronze	(g)	...	...	...	2 mg/dm^2/d	171
G bronze	(h)	...	...	...	280 mg/dm^2/d	171
Hydraulic bronze	(f)	...	...	...	4 mg/dm^2/d	171
Hydraulic bronze	(g)	...	...	...	1 mg/dm^2/d	171
Hydraulic bronze	(h)	...	...	...	339 mg/dm^2/d	171
Muntz metal	...	...	...	...	Fair	93
Naval brass	(z)	...	...	...	Good	93
Nickel silver	...	18	...	...	Suitable	93
Phosphor bronze	5% Sn. (z)	...	...	...	Good	93
Phosphor bronze	8% Sn	...	...	...	Suitable	93
Phosphor copper	(z)	...	...	...	Good	93
Red brass	(z)	...	...	...	Good	93
Silicon bronze	Low. (z)	...	...	...	Good	93
Silicon bronze	High. (z)	...	...	...	Good	93
Silicon bronze	(f)	...	...	...	1 mg/dm^2/d	171
Silicon bronze	(g)	...	...	...	2 mg/dm^2/d	171
Silicon bronze	(h)	...	...	...	343 mg/dm^2/d	171
Titanium						
Ti-6Al-4V	Ocean depth: 2 to 2070 m (6.5 to 6800 ft). (dd)	...	...	...	$<2.5 \times 10^{-4}$ (<0.01)	174
Ti-6Al-4V	Ocean depth: 1720 m (5640 ft). (dd)	...	...	...	8×10^{-6} (0.0003)	174
Ti-6Al-4V	Ocean depth: 1720 m (5640 ft)	...	Ambient	...	8×10^{-6} (0.0003)	185
Ti-6Al-4V	Ocean depth: 1720 m (5640 ft)	...	Ambient	...	$<1 \times 10^{-3}$ (<0.04)	185
Ti-6Al-4V	Ocean depth: 1720 m (5640 ft). (dd)	...	...	...	$<1 \times 10^{-3}$ (<0.04)	174
Ti-6Al-4V	Ocean depth: 2 to 2070 m (6.5 to 6800 ft)	...	Ambient	...	$<2.5 \times 10^{-4}$ (<0.01)	185
Titanium	(f)	...	...	...	0.0 mg/dm^2/d	171
Titanium	(h)	...	...	...	0.0 mg/dm^2/d	171
Titanium	Ocean depth: shallow. (dd)	...	...	...	8×10^{-7} (0.00003)	174
Titanium	Ocean depth: 720 to 2070 m (2360 to 6800 ft). (dd)	...	...	...	$<2.5 \times 10^{-4}$ (<0.1)	174
Titanium	Ocean depth: 2 to 2070 m (6.5 to 6800 ft). (dd)	...	...	...	nil	174
Titanium	Ocean depth: 1720 m (5640 ft). (dd)	...	...	...	4×10^{-5} (0.0015)	174
Titanium	Grade 9	...	Boiling	...	nil	33
Titanium	...	...	24 (75)	...	nil	90
Titanium	...	...	Ambient	4½ yr	nil	90
Titanium	Unalloyed. Ocean depth: shallow	...	Ambient	...	8×10^{-7} (0.00003)	185
Titanium	Unalloyed. Ocean depth: 720 to 2070 m (2360 to 6800 ft)	...	Ambient	...	$<2.5 \times 10^{-4}$ (<0.1)	185
Titanium	Unalloyed. Ocean depth: 2 to 2070 m (6.5 to 6800 ft)	...	Ambient	...	nil	185
Titanium	Unalloyed. Ocean depth: 1720 m (5640 ft)	...	Ambient	...	4×10^{-5} (0.0015)	185
Heat- and corrosion-resistant alloys						
Alloy 400	Exposed to stagnant seawater. Maximum pit depth: 1.067 mm (42 mils)	...	...	3 yr	...	183
Alloy K-500	Exposed to stagnant seawater. Maximum pit depth: 0.864 mm (34 mils)	...	...	3 yr	...	183
Alloy 625	Exposed to stagnant seawater. Maximum pit depth: nil	...	...	3 yr	...	183
Alloy 825	Exposed to stagnant seawater. Maximum pit depth: 0.025 mm (0.98 mils)	...	...	3 yr	...	183

(Continued)

Corrosion Behavior of Various Metals and Alloys in Seawater (Continued)

Material	Condition, other factors, comments	Concentration, %	Temperature, °C (°F)	Duration	Corrosion rate, mm/yr (mils/yr) or other	Ref
Alloy 904L	Mill-finished panels exposed to filtered seawater flowing at <0.1 m/s (<0.33 ft/s); crevice washers tightened to 2.8 or 8.5 N·m (25 or 75 in. · lb). Maximum pit depth: 0.37 mm (14.6 mils)	...	30 (86)	30, 60, 90 d	...	184
20Cb-3	41% crevices initiated. (k)	...	30 (86)	30 d	3.1 (122)	60
Cabot alloy No. 625	(ee)	...	20 (68)	96 h	nil	67
Cabot alloy No. 625	(ee)	...	35 (95)	96 h	nil	67
Cabot alloy No. 625	(ee)	...	50 (122)	96 h	<0.003 (0.1)	67
Cabot alloy No. 625	(ee)	...	65 (149)	96 h	<0.003 (0.1)	67
Cabot alloy No. 625	(ee)	...	80 (176)	96 h	nil	67
Cabot alloy No. 625	(ee)	...	90 (194)	96 h	nil	67
Ferralium 255	...	...	20 (68)	...	nil	60
Ferralium 255	...	...	35 (95)	...	nil	60
Ferralium 255	...	...	50 (122)	...	<0.01 (<0.1)	60
Ferralium 255	...	...	65 (149)	...	<0.01 (<0.1)	60
Ferralium 255	...	...	80 (176)	...	nil	60
Ferralium 255	...	...	90 (194)	...	nil	60
Ferralium 255	Saturated with Cl gas. (ff)	...	20 (68)	96 h	0.05 (2)	60
Ferralium 255	Saturated with Cl gas. (ff)	...	35 (95)	96 h	0.02 (0.8)	60
Ferralium 255	Saturated with Cl gas. (ff)	...	65 (149)	96 h	0.18 (7)	60
Ferralium 255	Seawater saturated with SO_2 gas	...	66 (150)	...	nil	60
Ferralium 255	No crevices initiated. (k)	...	14 (57)	29 d	<0.01 (0.4)	60
Ferralium 255	1.6% crevices initiated. (k)	...	30 (86)	30 d	<0.08 (3.1)	60
Ferralium 255	0.8% crevices initiated. (k)	...	52 (126)	30 d	<0.01 (0.4)	60
Ferralium 255	Mill-finished panels exposed to filtered seawater flowing at <0.1 m/s (<0.33 ft/s); crevice washers tightened to 2.8 or 8.5 N·m (25 or 75 in. · lb). Maximum pit depth: 0.09 mm (3.5 mils)	...	30 (86)	30, 60, 90 d	...	184
Hastelloy C	(f)	...	...	...	<1 mg/dm²/d	171
Hastelloy C	(h)	...	...	...	3 mg/dm²/d	171
Incoloy 825	Localized attack: 0.18 mm (7 mils) maximum; 0.03 mm (1 mil) average of five deepest areas. Weight loss due to localized attack only: 0.2 g. Crevice corrosion under barnacles. (j)	...	...	...	0.003 (0.1)	44
Incoloy 825	Localized attack: 0.03 mm (1 mil) maximum; 0.03 mm (1 mil) average of five deepest areas. Weight loss due to localized attack only: 0.2 g. (j)	...	...	...	0.003 (0.1)	44
Inconel 600	Uncoupled. At half tide	...	...	193 d	nil	175
Inconel 600	Uncoupled. In sea air	...	...	56 months	nil	175
Inconel 625	None of the specimens failed. Weight loss: 0.02 g. (gg)	...	...	180 d	...	64
Inconel 625	None of the specimens failed. Weight loss: 0.01 g. (gg)	...	...	365 d	...	64
Inconel 625	None of the specimens failed. Immersion in quiet seawater. Plain specimen. Crevice indicates 1¼-in. fiber washer bolted to center of panel face. No localized attack occurred. Weight loss: 0.05 g. (gg)	...	...	180 d	...	64
Inconel 625	None of the specimens failed. Immersion in quiet seawater. Crevice specimen. Crevice indicates 1¼-in. fiber washer bolted to center of panel face. No localized attack occurred. Weight loss: 0.05 g. (gg)	...	...	180 d	...	64
Inconel 625	None of the specimens failed. Immersion in quiet seawater. Plain specimen. Crevice indicates 1¼-in. fiber washer bolted to center of panel face. No localized attack occurred. Weight loss: 0.02 g. (gg)	...	...	365 d	...	64
Inconel 625	None of the specimens failed. Immersion in quiet seawater. Crevice specimen. Crevice indicates 1¼-in. fiber washer bolted to center of panel face. No localized attack occurred. Weight loss: 0.04 g. (gg)	...	...	365 d	...	64

(Continued)

Corrosion Behavior of Various Metals and Alloys in Seawater (Continued)

Material	Condition, other factors, comments	Concentration, %	Temperature, °C (°F)	Duration	Corrosion rate, mm/yr (mils/yr) or other	Ref
Inconel 625	None of the specimens failed. Immersion in flowing seawater (2 ft/s). Plain specimen. Crevice indicates 1¼-in. fiber washer bolted to center of panel face. No localized attack occurred. Weight loss: 0.04 g. (gg)	...	...	180 d	...	64
Inconel 625	None of the specimens failed. Immersion in flowing seawater (2 ft/s). Crevice specimen. Crevice indicates 1¼-in. fiber washer bolted to center of panel face. No localized attack occurred. Weight loss: 0.05 g. (gg)	...	...	180 d	...	64
Inconel 625	None of the specimens failed. Immersion in flowing seawater (2 ft/s). Plain specimen. Crevice indicates 1¼-in. fiber washer bolted to center of panel face. No localized attack occurred. Weight loss: 0.01 g. (gg)	...	...	365 d	...	64
Inconel 625	None of the specimens failed. Immersion in flowing seawater (2 ft/s). Crevice specimen. Crevice indicates 1¼-in. fiber washer bolted to center of panel face. No localized attack occurred. Weight loss: 0.02 g. (gg)	...	...	365 d	...	64
Monel 400	(f)	...	...	...	<1 mg/dm^2/d	171
Monel 400	(g)	...	...	...	<1 mg/dm^2/d	171
Monel 400	(h)	...	...	...	4 mg/dm^2/d	171
Monel 400	Uncoupled. At half tide	...	...	193 d	0.025 (1)	175
Monel 400	Uncoupled. In sea air	...	...	56 months	nil	175
Monel K-500	1.93% Cl⁻, 690 kPa (100 psig). Plus CO_2, no H_2S	...	175 (350)	...	0.003 (0.12)	172
Monel K-500	1.92% Cl⁻, 690 kPa (100 psig). Plus CO_2 and 0.1% H_2S	...	175 (350)	...	0.043 (2.7)	172
Zirconium						
Zr702	...	...	Boiling	...	Weight gain	62
Zr702	Pacific ocean	...	Boiling	...	nil	15
Zr702	Pacific ocean, pH 7.6	...	200 (390)	...	nil	15
Zr705	...	...	Boiling	...	Weight gain	62
Zr705	Pacific ocean	...	Boiling	...	nil	15
Lead, tin, and zinc						
Babbitt alloy (Sn-7.4Sb-3.7Cu)	Cast plate. Converted from weight loss data, assuming cast densities of 7.39 g/cm^3. Total immersion in seawater at Kure Beach, NC	...	...	1.4 yr	0.060 (2.4)	176
Lead	Bristol Channel. Immersion 93% of test period	...	...	...	0.0127 (0.50)	13
Lead	Southhampton docks. Half tide level	...	...	...	0.0027 (0.11)	13
Lead	Fort Amador, CZ. Tropical Pacific Ocean. Immersion. Flowing agitation at 150 mm/s (0.5 ft/s)	...	...	...	0.009 (0.36)	13
Lead	Fort Amador, CZ. Tropical Pacific Ocean. Mean tide level. Flowing agitation at 150 mm/s (0.5 ft/s)	...	...	...	0.005 (0.20)	13
Lead	San Francisco Harbor. Mean tide level. Flowing agitation	...	...	...	0.010 (0.42)	13
Lead	Port Hueneme Harbor, CA. Immersion. Flowing agitation at 60 mm/s (0.2 ft/s)	...	...	...	0.005 (0.22)	13
Lead	Kure Beach, NC. Immersion	...	...	...	0.015 (0.60)	13
Lead	Bristol Channel. Immersion 93% of the time	...	...	...	0.012 (0.5)	178
Lead	Southhampton docks. Half tide level	...	...	...	0.003 (0.11)	178
Lead	Gatun Lake, CZ. Tropical fresh water. Immersion. Agitation: still	...	...	...	0.002 (0.08)	178
Lead	Fort Amador, CZ. Tropical Pacific Ocean. Immersion. Agitation: 0.5 ft/s. Flow: 150 mm/s	...	...	...	0.009 (0.36)	178
Lead	Fort Amador, CZ. Tropical Pacific Ocean. Mean tide level. Agitation: 0.5 ft/s. Flow: 150 mm/s	...	...	...	0.005 (0.02)	178
Lead	San Francisco harbor. Seawater. Mean tide level. Agitation: flowing	...	...	...	0.01 (0.42)	178
Lead	Port Hueneme harbor, CA. Immersion. Agitation: 0.2 ft/s; 60 mm/s maximum	...	...	...	0.005 (0.22)	178
Lead	Kure Beach, NC. Immersion	...	...	...	0.015 (0.6)	178

(Continued)

Corrosion Behavior of Various Metals and Alloys in Seawater (Continued)

Material	Condition, other factors, comments	Concentration, %	Temperature, °C (°F)	Duration	Corrosion rate, mm/yr (mils/yr) or other	Ref
Solder (Sn-50Pb)	Sheet. Converted from weight loss data, assuming cast densities of 8.90 g/cm³. Total immersion in seawater at Bogue Inlet, NC	...	...	0.5 yr	0.075 (2.95)	176
Solder (Sn-60Pb on Cu)	Plate. Converted from weight loss data, assuming cast densities of 9.28 g/cm³. Total immersion in seawater at Kure Beach, NC	...	...	2.1 yr	0.011 (0.43)	176
Tin	...	...	...	...	...	...
Tin	...	...	20 (68)	...	Resistant	94
Tin	...	...	60 (140)	...	Resistant	94
Tin	...	...	100 (212)	...	Unsuitable	94
Tin (99.2)	Cast bar. Converted from weight loss data, assuming cast densities of 7.29 g/cm³. Total immersion in seawater at Bristol Channel	...	...	4 yr	0.0008 (0.03)	176
Tin (99.75)	Cast bar. Converted from weight loss data, assuming cast densities of 7.29 g/cm³. Total immersion in seawater at Bristol Channel	...	...	4 yr	0.0022 (0.087)	176
Tantalum and hafnium						
Hafnium	...					
Hafnium	...	...	...	10 d	nil	11
Tantalum	...	...	...	10 d	nil	11
Others	...	...	25(76)	...	nil	42
Magnesium	...	100	Room	...	Unsuitable	119

(a) Average penetration rate. (b) Average depth of 20 deepest pits. (c) Test location, Wrightsville Beach, NC. Average penetration rate for service life of material. (d) Pacific Ocean, near Panama Canal Zone. Pickled. Average depth of 20 deepest pits. (f) Immersed in tidal current. Agitation: 0.3 m/s (1 ft/s). (g) Immersed in seawater flume. Agitation: 1.2 m/s (4 ft/s). (h) Attached to immersed rotating disk. Agitation: 8.2 m/s (27 ft/s). (j) Results of 3-yr tests in quiet seawater. Specimen size: 3.18 mm x 102 mm x 305 mm (0.125 in. x 4.0 in. x 12.0 in.). (k) 120 crevices possible. (m) Half-tide exposure at Wrightsville Beach, NC. Thickness: 1.27 mm (0.050 in.). (n) Full-immersion at Wrightsville Beach, NC. Thickness: 1.27 mm (0.050 in.). (p) Half-tide exposure at Wrightsville Beach, NC. 4.5% Mg. Thickness: 6.35 mm (0.250 in.). (q) Full-immersion at Wrightsville Beach, NC. 4.5% Mg. Thickness: 6.35 mm (0.250 in.). (r) Half-tide exposure at Wrightsville Beach, NC. 4.0% Mg. Thickness: 2.03 mm (0.080 in.). (s) Full-immersion at Wrightsville Beach, NC. 4.0% Mg. Thickness: 2.03 mm (0.080 in.). (t) Half-tide exposure at Wrightsville Beach, NC. 1.0% Mg. Thickness: 1.02 mm (0.040 in.). (u) Half-tide exposure at Wrightsville Beach, NC. 2.7% Mg. Thickness: 6.35 mm (0.250 in.). (v) Full-immersion at Wrightsville Beach, NC. 2.7% Mg. Thickness: 6.35 mm (0.250 in.). (w) Half-tide exposure at Wrightsville Beach, NC. 5.1% Mg. Thickness: 6.17 mm (0.243 in.). (x) Full-immersion at Wrightsville Beach, NC. 5.1% Mg. Thickness: 6.17 mm (0.243 in.). (y) Full-immersion at Wrightsville Beach, NC. 1.0% Mg. Thickness: 1.02 mm (0.04 in.). (z) May be considered in place of a copper metal when some property, other than corrosion resistance, governs its use. (aa) Impingement attack at velocity of 4.6 m/s (15 ft/s). (bb) Impingement attack at velocity of 6.8 m/s (22 ft/s). (cc) Impingement attack at velocity of 9.8 m/s (32 ft/s). (dd) Unalloyed titanium. Ambient seawater. (ee) ASTM synthetic seawater. (ff) Average of duplicate, smooth specimens. (gg) Stress-corrosion tests on 102 mm x 305 mm x 6 mm (4 in. x 12 in. x ¼ in.) specimens with 50-mm (2-in.) circular welds; material annealed at 982 °C (1800 °F).

Corrosion of Stainless Steels in Flowing Seawater

Type(a)	Original surface condition	Test period, days	Weight loss, g	Depth of pitting								Condition of edge
				Surface				Under Bakelite washers				
				Maximum		Average(b)		Maximum		Average(b)		
				mm	in.	mm	in.	mm	in.	mm	in.	
405	Hot rolled, No. 4 finish	755(c)	135	2.5	0.100	1.5	0.059	4.75(d)	0.187(d)	2.6	0.103	Badly pitted
403	Hot rolled, No. 4 finish	388(c)	118	1.9	0.075	1.0	0.038	1.2(e)	0.046(e)	1.0	0.040	Badly pitted
430	Hot rolled, pickled	568(c)	109	3.4	0.135	1.45	0.057	1.85(e)	0.072(e)	1.55	0.061	Badly pitted
308	Hot rolled, No. 4 finish	755(c)	28	5.2	0.205	2.1	0.083	3.6	0.141	1.7	0.066	Badly pitted
347	Hot rolled, No. 4 finish	755(c)	26	3.8	0.148	1.5	0.59	1.55	0.061	1.2	0.046	Badly pitted
	Hot rolled, pickled	755(c)	30	2.0	0.079	1.4	0.054	1.2	0.047	1.0	0.038	Few pits
321	Hot rolled, welded, ½ pickled, ½ No. 4 finish	944	...	1.35(f)	0.053(f)	0.38	0.015	1.4	0.056	0.6	0.024	No pitting
316	Hot rolled, welded, ½ pickled, ½ No. 4 finish	944	...	0.18	0.007	1 pit	1 pit	0.25	0.010	0.08	0.003	No pitting
	Hot rolled, pickled	1255	3	1.3	0.050	0.56	0.022	4.3	0.170	1.2	0.046	No pitting

(Continued)

Corrosion of Stainless Steels in Flowing Seawater (Continued)

				Depth of pitting								
				Surface				Under Bakelite washers				
				Maximum		Average(b)		Maximum		Average(b)		
Type(a)	Original surface condition	Test period, days	Weight loss, g	mm	in.	mm	in.	mm	in.	mm	in.	Condition of edge
317	Hot rolled, No. 4 finish	1075	5	0.58	0.023	0.30(g)	0.012(g)	1.1	0.045	0.7	0.027	Pitted
304	Pickled in HNO$_3$-HF	320	12	0.89	0.035	0.56	0.022	0.9	0.036	0.6	0.024	No pitting
309	Pickled in HNO$_3$-HF	320	11	0.51	0.020	0.30	0.012	1.4(d)	0.055(d)	1.4(d)	0.055(d)	No pitting
310	Pickled in HNO$_2$-HF	320	4	0.15	0.006	0.08	0.003	0.6(d)	0.024(d)	0.6(d)	0.024(d)	No pitting
325	Hot rolled, pickled, No. 4 finish	106	15	0.81	0.032	0.18	0.007	None	None	None	None	Grooved to 1.3 mm (0.05 in.)
	Hot rolled, pickled, No. 1 finish	106	60	1.4	0.056	1 pit	1 pit	None	None	None	None	Grooved to 2.5 mm (0.10 in.)
329	Hot rolled, pickled, No. 4 finish	106	0	0.0	0.000	0.0	0.000	0.25	0.010	2 pits	2 pits	No pitting
	Hot rolled, pickled, No. 1 finish	106	7	0.0	0.000	0.0	0.000	0.9	0.037	2 pits	2 pits	No pitting

(a) Panels 305 by 305 mm (12 by 12 in.) were completely immersed at Kure Beach, North Carolina, in seawater flowing at 0.3 to 0.6 m/s (1 to 2 ft/s). (b) These values are averages of the ten deepest pits. (c) Specimens withdrawn from test due to failure in period indicated. (d) Specimen became perforated. (e) Local attack directly under washer; holes were greatly enlarged. (f) One pit in weld, 3.2 mm (0.125 in.) deep. (g) Five pits.

Source: *Metals Handbook*, 9th ed., Vol 3, Properties and Selection: Stainless Steels, Tool Materials and Special-Purpose Metals, American Society for Metals, Metals Park, OH, 1980, 71.

Ratings of Some Metals for Resistance to Cavitation Erosion in Seawater

Group 1: Most resistant. Subject to little or no damage. Useful under extremely severe conditions

Stellite hardfacing alloys
Titanium alloys
Austenitic and precipitation-hardening stainless steels
Nickel-chromium alloys such as Inconel alloys 625 and 718
Nickel-molybdenum-chromium alloys such as Hastelloy C

Group II: These metals are commonly used where a high order of resistance to cavitation damage is required. They are subject to some metal loss under the most severe conditions of cavitation.

Nickel-copper-aluminum alloy Monel K-500
Nickel-copper alloy Monel 400
Copper alloy C95500 (nickel-aluminum bronze, cast)
Copper alloy C95700 (nickel-aluminum-manganese bronze, cast)

Group III: These metals have some degree of cavitation resistance. They are generally limited to low-speed low-performance applications.

Copper alloy C71500 (copper-nickel, 30% Ni)
Copper alloys C92200 and C92300 (leaded tin bronzes M and G, cast)
Manganese bronze, cast
Austenitic nickel cast irons

Group IV: These metals normally are not used in applications where cavitation damage may occur, except in cathodically inhibited solutions or when protected by elastomeric coatings.

Carbon and low-alloy steels
Cast irons
Aluminum and aluminum alloys

(a) Applies to normal cavitation-erosion intensities, at which corrosion resistance has a substantial influence on the resistance to damage.

Source: A.H. Tuthill and C.M. Schillmoler, Guidelines for Selection of Marine Materials, in *Ocean Science and Science Engineering Conference*, Marine Technology Society, Washington, June 1965.

Galvanic Series of Some Commercial Metals and Alloys in Seawater

Active or anodic (-)

Magnesium
Magnesium alloys
Zinc
Galvanized steel

Aluminum 1100

Aluminum 2024 (4.5% Cu, 1.5% Mg, 0.6% Mn)

Mild steel
Wrought iron
Cast iron

13% chromium stainless steel
Type 410 (active)
18-8 stainless steel
Type 304 (active)

Lead-tin solders
Lead
Tin

Muntz metal
Manganese bronze
Naval brass

Nickel (active)
76Ni-16Cr-7Fe alloy (active)

60Ni-30Mo-6Fe-1Mn

Yellow brass
Admiralty brass

Red brass
Copper
Silicon bronze

70-30 cupronickel
G-bronze
Silver solder
Nickel (passive)
76Ni-16Cr-7Fe
Alloy (passive)

13% chromium stainless steel
Type 410 (passive)
Titanium
18-8 stainless steel
Type 304 (passive)

Noble or cathodic (+)

Silver

Graphite

Gold

Platinum

Source: *NACE Corrosion Basics*, National Association of Corrosion Engineers, Houston, 1984.

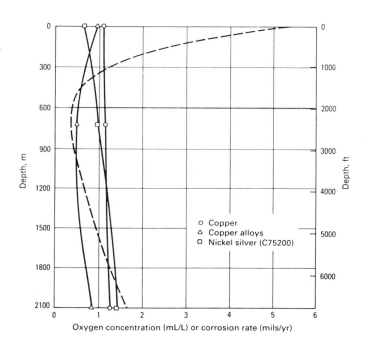

Copper. Corrosion of copper alloys vs. depth after 1 year of exposure compared to the shape of the dissolved oxygen profile (dashed line). Source: F.L. LaQue, *Marine Corrosion*, Wiley-Interscience, New York, 1975.

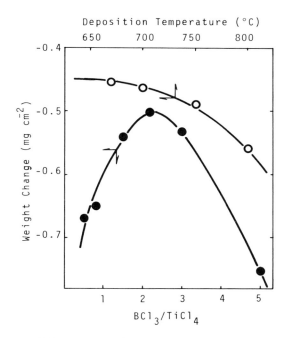

Copper. Effect of deposition temperature and gas-flow ratio (BCl$_3$/TiCl$_4$) on weight change of copper plate coated with CVD TiB$_2$ in seawater. Temperature of seawater, 33 °C; immersion time, 175 h. Open circle: gas-flow ratio (BCl$_3$/TiCl$_4$), 2.25; thickness of coated layer 1.0 μm. Closed circle: deposition temperature, 800 °C; thickness of coated layer, 0.7 μm. Source: S. Motojima and H. Kosaki, "Resistivities Against Seawater Corrosion and Sea-Sands Abrasion of TiB$_2$-Coated Copper Plate," *Journal of Materials Science Letters*, Vol 4, Nov 1985, 1351.

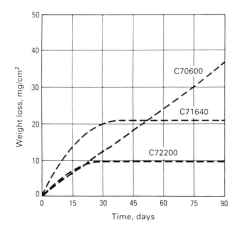

Copper. Weight loss vs. time curves for C70600, C71640, and C72200 exposed in seawater at a velocity of 9 m/s (40 ft/s). Source: C. Pearson, *British Corrosion Journal*, Vol 7, March 1972.

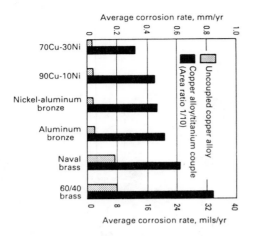

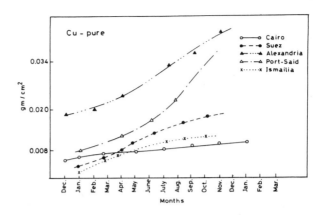

Copper. Corrosion of various copper alloys that were galvanically coupled to titanium in aerated seawater at 25 °C (77 °F). Source: T. Fukuzuka, K. Shimogori, H. Satoh, and F. Kamikubo, "Corrosion Problems and Countermeasures in MSF Desalination Plant Using Titanium Tube," Kobe Steel Ltd., 1985.

Copper. Weight loss vs. time of exposure for copper. Source: A.A. Ishmail, N.A. Khanem, *et al.*, "A Corrosion Map of Cairo and the Coastal Area of Egypt," *Corrosion Prevention and Control*, Vol 32, Aug 1985, 77.

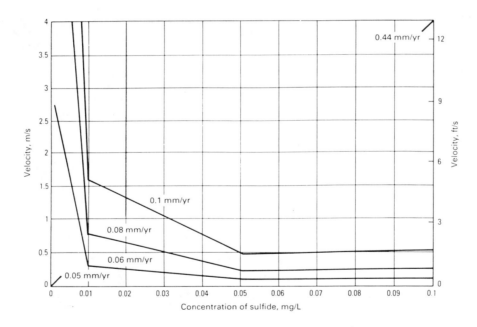

Copper. Corrosion rates of C70600 as a function of seawater velocity and sulfide content. Source: *Metals Handbook*, 9th ed., Vol 13, Corrosion, ASM International, Metals Park, OH, 1987, 625.

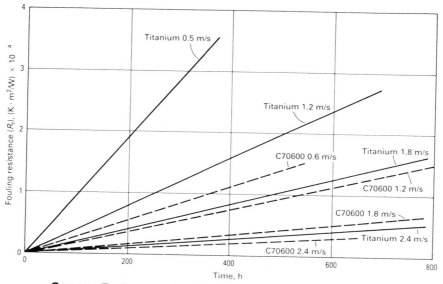

Copper. Fouling rates of C70600 and titanium as a function of seawater velocity. Source: R.B. Ritter and J.W. Suitor, "Fouling Research on Copper and Its Alloys—Seawater Studies," Progress Report, Project 214B, International Copper Research Association, March 1976 to Feb 1978.

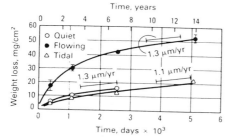

Copper. Chronogravimetric curves for C70600 in quiet, flowing, and tidal seawater. Source: K.D. Efird and D.B. Anderson, *Materials Performance*, Vol 14 (No. 11), 1975.

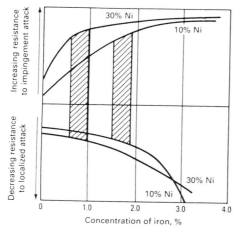

Copper-nickel alloys. Corrosion resistance of copper-nickel alloys as a function of iron content. Shaded areas indicate optimum iron contents for good balance between pitting resistance and impingement resistance. Source: C. Pearson, *British Corrosion Journal*, Vol 7, March 1972.

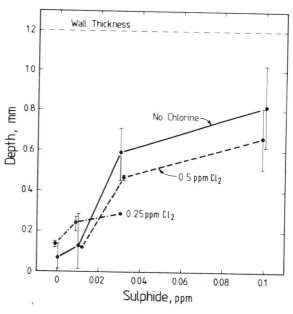

Copper alloy. Depth of impingement zone attack on 70Cu-30Ni as function of water chlorine and sulfide levels in seawater. Source: R. Francis, "Effect of Pollutants on Corrosion of Copper Alloys in Sea Water," *British Corrosion Journal*, Vol 20, July 1985, 178.

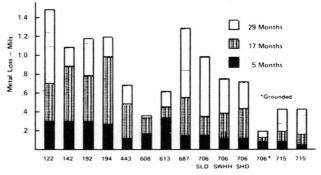

Copper alloys. Metal loss after 5, 17, and 29 months in a recycle brine exchanger. Source: A. Cohen, "Copper Alloys in Marine Environments," in *Source Book on Copper and Copper Alloys*, American Society for Metals, Metals Park, OH, 1979, 344.

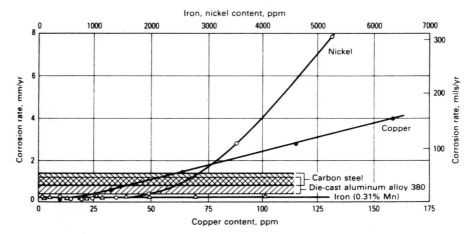

AZ91. Effect of nickel and copper contamination on the salt spray corrosion performance of die-cast AZ91 alloy. Source: J.E. Hillis and K.N. Reichek, Paper 860288, Society of Automotive Engineers, 1986.

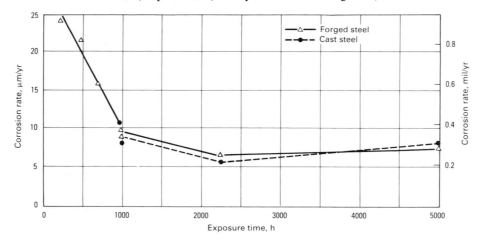

Low-alloy steels. Effect of time on the general corrosion of low-alloy steels in deaerated seawater at 90 °C (195 °F). Source: G.P. Marsh, "Influence of Temperature and Pressure on the Behaviour of High Level Waste and Canister Materials Under Marine Disposal Conditions," Part 2, Report S.P. 1.07.C2.85.51, Commission of European Communities, Dec 1985, 1, 15-27.

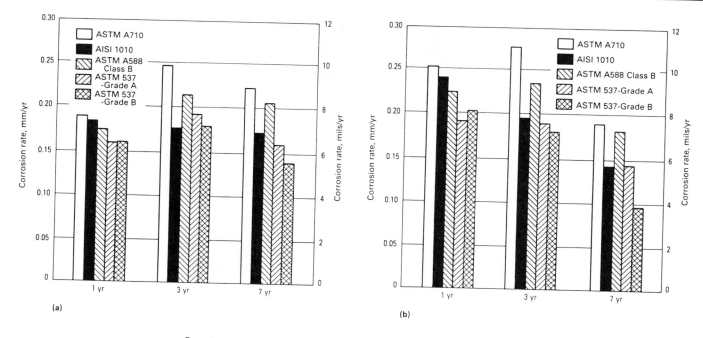

Steel. Corrosion results for ASTM A710 and other steels exposed to (a) low velocity (0.5 m/s or 1.6 ft/s) seawater and (b) quiet (still) seawater. Source: D.G. Melton and D.G. Tipton, Corrosion Behavior of A710 Grade A Steel in Marine Environments, LaQue Center for Corrosion Technology Inc., Wrightsville Beach, NC, June 1983.

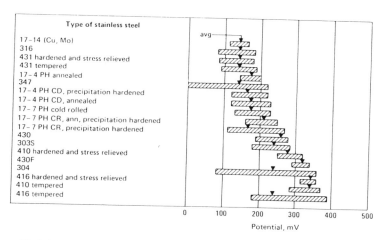

Stainless steels. Corrosion potentials of stainless steels in flowing seawater. Corrosion potentials vs. saturated calomel electrode in seawater flowing at 4 m/s (13 ft/s) vary with composition and condition of the stainless steels. Temperature for these tests was 18 to 29 °C (64 to 84 °F). Source: *Metals Handbook*, 9th ed., Vol 3, Properties and Selection: Stainless Steels, Tool Materials and Special-Purpose Metals, American Society for Metals, Metals Park, OH, 1980, 74.

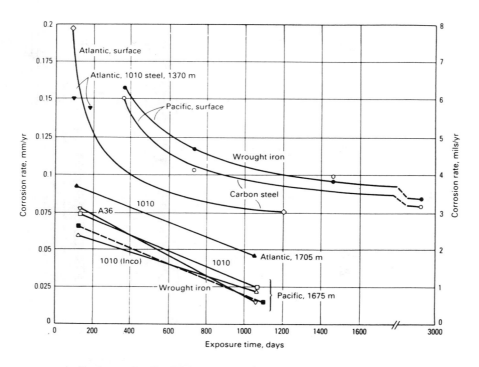

Carbon steels. Splash-zone and tidal-zone corrosion of carbon steel and two Ni-Cu-P steels. Source: C.V. Brouillette and A.E. Hanna, "Second Corrosion Survey of Steel Sheet Piling," U.S. Naval Civil Engineering Laboratory, 1965.

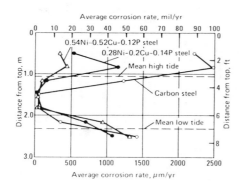

Carbon steel and wrought iron. Corrosion rates of carbon steel and wrought iron in the Atlantic and Pacific Oceans at various depths. Source: F.W. Fink and W.K. Boyd, Corrosion of Metals in Marine Environments, MCIC Report No. 78-37, Metals and Ceramics Information Center, Battelle Columbus Laboratories, Columbus, OH, 1978.

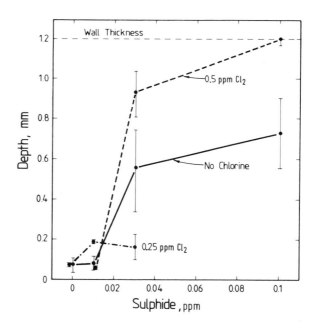

Aluminum brass. Depth of impingement zone attack on aluminum brass as a function of water chlorine and sulfide levels in seawater. Source: R. Francis, "Effect of Pollutants on Corrosion of Copper Alloys in Sea Water," *British Corrosion Journal*, Vol 20, July 1985, 177.

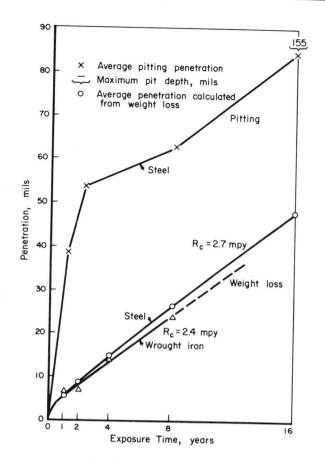

Carbon steel and wrought iron. Corrosion of carbon steel and wrought iron continuously immersed in seawater. Source: F.W. Fink and W.K. Boyd, *The Corrosion of Metals in Marine Environments* (DMIC Report 245), Defense Metals Information Center (Battelle), Columbus, OH, 1970, 14.

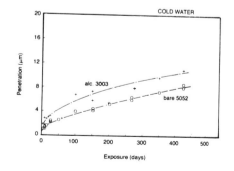

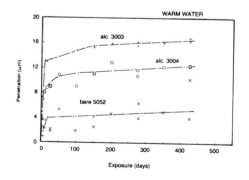

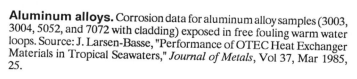

Aluminum alloys. Corrosion data for aluminum alloy samples (3003, 3004, 5052, and 7072 with cladding) exposed in free fouling warm water loops. Source: J. Larsen-Basse, "Performance of OTEC Heat Exchanger Materials in Tropical Seawaters," *Journal of Metals*, Vol 37, Mar 1985, 25.

Aluminum alloy. Corrosion data for aluminum alloy samples (3003, 3004, 5052, and 7072 with cladding) exposed in the cold, deep ocean water, calculated as uniform wall loss. Source: J. Larsen-Basse, "Performance of OTEC Heat Exchanger Materials in Tropical Seawaters," *Journal of Metals*, Vol 37, Mar 1985, 26.

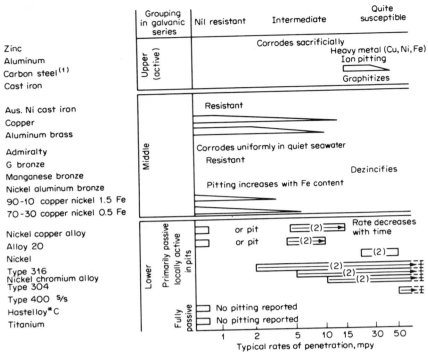

Grouping in galvanic series

| | | Nil resistant | Intermediate | Quite susceptible |

Upper (active)

Zinc
Aluminum
Carbon steel[1]
Cast iron

Corrodes sacrificially
Heavy metal (Cu, Ni, Fe) Ion pitting
Graphitizes

Middle

Aus. Ni cast iron
Copper
Aluminum brass

Resistant

Admiralty
G bronze
Manganese bronze
Nickel aluminum bronze
90-10 copper nickel 1.5 Fe
70-30 copper nickel 0.5 Fe

Corrodes uniformly in quiet seawater
Resistant
Dezincifies
Pitting increases with Fe content

Lower — Primarily passive locally active in pits

Nickel copper alloy
Alloy 20
Nickel
Type 316
Nickel chromium alloy
Type 304
Type 400 S/s
Hastelloy* C
Titanium

or pit — (2) Rate decreases with time
or pit — (2)
(2)
(2)
(2)
(2)

Fully passive

No pitting reported
No pitting reported

1 2 5 10 15 30 50
Typical rates of penetration, mpy

(1) Shallow round-bottom pits
(2) As velocity increases above 3 fps, pitting decreases. When continuously exposed to 5 fps and higher velocities these metals, except series 400 S/s, tend to remain passive without any pitting over the full surface in the absence of crevices.

* Trademark Union Carbide Corporation

Various alloys. Pitting in quiet seawater. Source: M.G. Fontana and N.D. Greene, *Corrosion Engineering*, McGraw-Hill, New York, 1967, 270.

Sodium

Sodium, Na, melts at 97.8 °C and boils at 892 °C. It is silver-white in color, is soft and malleable, and oxidizes in air. It occurs naturally only in the forms of its salts. The most important mineral that contains sodium is sodium chloride (NaCl), or common salt. Sodium is used as a chemical intermediate, and in pharmaceuticals, petroleum refining, and metallurgy. Sodium vapor is used in electric lamps.

Material Summaries

The following material summaries were compiled from a survey of the available literature. Inclusion of a material description under a given environment does not imply that it is the most appropriate material for corrosion service in that environment. Likewise, exclusion of a given material does not imply that it is not suitable for corrosion service applications in that environment.

Aluminum. Aluminum alloy trays have been used for heating sodium in the preparation of sodium products.

Additional Reading

H.-J. Heuvel, P. Holler, and P. Donner, Absorber Material Cladding Chemical Interaction in Vented Fast Breeder Reactor Absorber Pins. B₄C/Stainless Steel Chemical Interaction in Sodium Environment and Effect of Metallic Niobium and Chromium Layers, *J. Nucl. Mater.*, 130, 517-523, 1985. MetAbs No. 85-350837. **Abstract:** Out-of-pile tests were performed to study the chemical interaction between B₄C and cladding material (stainless steel) in a sodium environment as components of a "fast breeder" absorber pin.

K.J.L. Iyer, S. Ramakrishna Iyer, and V.M. Radhakrishnan, Role of Sodium in Hot Stress Corrosion of AISI 304 Stainless Steel, *Corrosion*, 41(6), 333-338, 1985. MetAbs No. 85-351732. **Abstract:** The effect of sodium in combustion gases on the crack propagation character of AISI 304 stainless steel at 550 °C was studied. The sodium level in the base fuel varied from 0 to 40 ppm.

K.B. Sarangapani, V. Balaramachandran, V. Kapali, S.V. Iyer, and M.G. Potdar, Aluminium as the Anode in Primary Alkaline Batteries, *Surf. Technol.*, 26(1), 67-76, 1985. MetAbs No. 86-350406. **Abstract:** Self-corrosion and the anodic behavior of commercially pure Al (Al-2S) have been studied in sodium and potassium hydroxide solutions. The effects of calcium hydroxide and sodium or potassium citrate on the corrosion and anodic behavior of 2S Al have been investigated.

T. Suzuki, I. Mutoh, T. Yagi, and Y. Ikenaga, Sodium Corrosion Behavior of Austenitic Alloys and Selective Dissolution of Chromium and Nickel,

J. Nucl. Mater., 139(2), 97-105, 1986. MetAbs No. 86-352058. **Abstract:** The corrosion behavior of six austenitic alloys and Type 316 stainless steel has been examined in a flowing sodium environment at 700 °C for up to approximately 4000 h. The corrosion loss of the alloys at zero downstream position and the concentrations of Cr, Ni and Fe in the surface region were determined as a function of corrosion time.

Corrosion Behavior of Various Metals and Alloys in Sodium

Material	Condition, other factors, comments	Concentration, %	Temperature, °C (°F)	Duration	Corrosion rate, mm/yr (mils/yr) or other	Ref
Aluminum (99.0-99.5%)	Plus K. Dry solid	...	...	...	Satisfactory	92
Titanium	...	100	Up to 593 (up to 1100)	...	Good	90

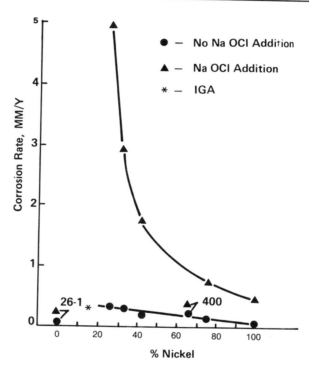

Nickel alloys. Effect of nickel content on static corrosion rate of various materials in simulated first-effect plant liquor environments involving quadruple-effect caustic evaporators at 185 °C for 720 h. Source: J.R. Crum and W.G. Lipscomb, "Performance of Nickel 200 and E-Brite 26-1 in First Effect Caustic Environments," *Materials Performance*, Vol 25, Apr, 1986, 10.

Sodium Bicarbonate

Sodium bicarbonate, NaHCO₃, also known as sodium acid carbonate and baking soda, is a white water-soluble crystalline solid. It has an alkaline taste, loses carbon dioxide at 270 °C (518 °F), and is used in food preparation. Sodium bicarbonate also finds use as a medicine, a butter preservative, in ceramics, and to prevent timber mold.

Material Summaries

The following material summaries were compiled from a survey of the available literature. Inclusion of a material description under a given environment does not imply that it is the most appropriate material for corrosion service in that environment. Likewise, exclusion of a given material does not imply that it is not suitable for corrosion service applications in that environment.

Iridium. Iridium is slightly attacked by sodium bicarbonate.

Additional Reading

M. Akkaya and J.R. Ambrose, The Effect of Ammonium Chloride and Fluid Velocity on the Corrosion Behavior of Copper in Sodium Bicarbonate Solutions, *Corrosion, 41*(12), 707-714, 1985. MetAbs No. 86-350430. **Abstract:** The effect of ammonium chloride additions on the corrosion behavior of copper in $1N$ sodium bicarbonate solutions has been characterized using a rotating ring-ring linear cyclic voltammetry technique. The experimentation and solution compositions used were selected to account for an unusually high incidence of pitting found to occur on interior surfaces of copper cold-water plumbing fixtures in the vicinity of neutral soldering flux residues.

G.K. Glass and V. Ashworth, The Corrosion Behaviour of the Zinc-Mild Steel Galvanic Cell in Hot Sodium Bicarbonate Solution, *Corros. Sci., 25*(11), 971-983, 1985. MetAbs No. 86-350701. **Abstract:** The electrochemical behavior of zinc and mild steel has been studied in 0.01M $NaHCO_3$ solution saturated with oxygen containing 1% CO_2 at 65 °C.

G.K. Glass, The Effect of a Change in Surface Conditions Produced by Anodic and Cathodic Reactions on the Passivation of Mild Steel, *Corros. Sci., 26*(6), 441-454, 1986. MetAbs No. 86-352707. **Abstract:** The corrosion of mild steel in oxygen saturated 0.01M $NaHCO_3$ at 65 °C depends strongly on the change in surface conditions produced by the anodic or cathodic reactions. This results in clearly distinguishable attacked and unattacked surface areas which can be generated separately on different electrodes using potentiostatic polarization methods.

Corrosion Behavior of Various Metals and Alloys in Sodium Bicarbonate

Material	Condition, other factors, comments	Concentration, %	Temperature, °C (°F)	Duration	Corrosion rate, mm/yr (mils/yr) or other	Ref
Stainless steels						
Type 304 stainless steel	Chemical processing; field or pilot plant test; strong aeration; no agitation. Plus ammonium chloride, remainder sodium chloride, ammonium bicarbonate, hydrogen sulfide, water (liquid); and air, sodium-carbonate dust, ammonia, hydrogen sulfide, water (vapors)	98	28 (82)	36 d	<0.0001 in./yr	89
Type 304 stainless steel	Chemical processing; field or pilot plant test; no aeration; rapid agitation. Sodium-bicarbonate slurry in solution of ammonium chloride, sodium chloride, and free ammonia 35 titer (carbonating tower)	...	29 (84)	3102 d	0.0001 in./yr	89
Type 304 stainless steel	Chemical processing; field or pilot plant test; strong aeration; rapid agitation. Slurry saturated with sodium chloride, sodium bicarbonate, ammonium chloride, ammonium bicarbonate, free ammonia and free carbon dioxide (bicarbonating tower). Slight pitting (maximum depth of pits from incipient to 0.005 in.). Crevice attack (tendency to concentration-cell corrosion)	...	27 (81)	90 d	0.0003 in./yr	89
Type 316 stainless steel	Chemical processing; field or pilot plant test; strong aeration; no agitation. Plus ammonium chloride, remainder sodium chloride, ammonium bicarbonate, hydrogen sulfide, water (liquid); and air, sodium-carbonate dust, ammonia, hydrogen sulfide, water (vapors)	98	28 (82)	36 d	<0.0001 in./yr	89
Type 316 stainless steel	Chemical processing; field or pilot plant test; strong aeration; rapid agitation. Slurry saturated with sodium chloride, sodium bicarbonate, ammonium chloride, ammonium bicarbonate, free ammonia and free carbon dioxide (bicarbonating tower). Crevice attack (tendency to concentration-cell corrosion)	...	27 (81)	90 d	0.0004 in./yr	89
Type 316 stainless steel	Chemical processing; field or pilot plant test; no aeration; rapid agitation. Sodium-bicarbonate slurry in solution of ammonium chloride, sodium chloride, and free ammonia 35 titer (carbonating tower)	...	29 (84)	3102 d	0.0001 in./yr	89
Type 316 stainless steel	Chemical processing; field or pilot plant test; strong aeration; rapid agitation. Plus trace sodium sulfide (carbonating tower), 1% solid ammonium bicarbonate, 1.2% free ammonia, 2% dissolved carbon dioxide, 5% sodium chloride, 15% ammonium chloride, soda-ash draw liquor	20	29 (85)	280 d	0.0001 in./yr	89

(Continued)

Corrosion Behavior of Various Metals and Alloys in Sodium Bicarbonate (Continued)

Material	Condition, other factors, comments	Concentration, %	Temperature, °C (°F)	Duration	Corrosion rate, mm/yr (mils/yr) or other	Ref
Type 317 stainless steel	Chemical processing; field or pilot plant test; strong aeration; rapid agitation. Plus trace sodium sulfide (carbonating tower), 1% solid ammonium bicarbonate, 1.2% free ammonia, 2% dissolved carbon dioxide, 5% sodium chloride, 15% ammonium chloride, soda-ash draw liquor	20	29 (85)	280 d	0.0001 in./yr	89
Aluminum						
Aluminum (99.0-99.5%)	Solution	...	20 (68)	...	Satisfactory	92
Aluminum-manganese alloys	Solution	...	20 (68)	...	Satisfactory	92
Coppers						
70-30 cupronickel	...	...	...	...	Suitable	93
90-10 cupronickel	...	...	...	...	Suitable	93
Admiralty brass	(a)	...	...	...	Good	93
Aluminum bronze	(a)	...	...	...	Good	93
Ampco 8, aluminum bronze	Generally suitable	...	...	...	<0.05 (<2)	96
Architectural bronze	...	...	...	...	Fair	93
Brass	(a)	...	...	...	Good	93
Cartridge brass	...	...	...	...	Fair	93
Commercial bronze	(a)	...	...	...	Good	93
Electrolytic copper	(a)	...	...	...	Good	93
Free-cutting brass	...	...	...	...	Fair	93
Muntz metal	...	...	...	...	Fair	93
Naval brass	...	...	...	...	Fair	93
Nickel silver	...	18	...	...	Suitable	93
Phosphor bronze	5% Sn. (a)	...	...	...	Good	93
Phosphor bronze	8% Sn. (a)	...	...	...	Good	93
Phosphor copper	(a)	...	...	...	Good	93
Red brass	(a)	...	...	...	Good	93
Silicon bronze	Low. (a)	...	...	...	Good	93
Silicon bronze	High. (a)	...	...	...	Good	93
Heat- and corrosion-resistant alloys						
Carpenter 20	Chemical processing; field or pilot plant test; strong aeration; rapid agitation. Plus trace sodium sulfide (carbonating tower), 1% solid ammonium bicarbonate, 1.2% free ammonia, 2% dissolved carbon dioxide, 5% sodium chloride, 15% ammonium chloride, soda-ash draw liquor	20	29 (85)	280 d	0.0001 in./yr	89
Lead, tin, and zinc						
Lead	Practically resistant; Pb recommended for use	10	24 (75)	...	<500 μm/yr (<20)	95

(a) May be considered in place of a copper metal when some property, other than corrosion resistance, governs its use.

Sodium Borate

Sodium borate, $Na_2B_4O_7 \cdot 10H_2O$, also known as sodium tetraborate and sodium pyroborate, is a white crystalline powder that melts at 120 °C (248 °F). Sodium borate in its natural impure form is also known as borax. Sodium borate is used in glass and ceramic enamel mixes, detergents, fertilizers, pharmaceuticals, and photography.

Additional Reading

J. Flis and D.J. Duquette, Effect of Phosphorus on Anodic Dissolution and Passivation of Nickel in Near-Neutral Solutions, *Corrosion*, 41(12), 700-706, 1985. MetAbs No. 86-350429. **Abstract:** Anodic dissolution of nickel, electroless nickel deposits with 2.9 and 12.3 wt% phosphorus and amorphous $Ni_{81}P_{19}$ alloy was examined in sodium hydroxide, sulfate, borate, and chloride solutions at 25 °C.

Corrosion Behavior of Various Metals and Alloys in Sodium Borate

Material	Condition, other factors, comments	Concentration, %	Temperature, °C (°F)	Duration	Corrosion rate, mm/yr (mils/yr) or other	Ref
Aluminum (>99.5%)	Solution	...	...	...	Satisfactory	92
Aluminum-manganese alloys	Solution	..	...	...	Satisfactory	92

Sodium Bromide

Sodium bromide, NaBr, is a white, hygroscopic, crystalline solid with a bitter, saline taste. It is water soluble, with a melting point of 758 °C (1400 °F). Sodium bromide is used in medicine as a sedative and in photography in the preparation of silver bromide emulsion on photographic plates or films.

Corrosion Behavior of Various Metals and Alloys in Sodium Bromide

Material	Condition, other factors, comments	Concentration, %	Temperature, °C (°F)	Duration	Corrosion rate, mm/yr (mils/yr) or other	Ref
Type 410 stainless steel	Highly susceptible to pitting in NaBr and other halides	...	Room	...	Slightly attacked	121
Magnesium	...	...	Room	...	Unsuitable	119
Magnesium alloy AZ61A	Specimen size, 75 x 25 x 1.5 mm (3 x 1 x 0.06 in.); surface preparation, HNO$_3$ pickling; volume of testing solution, 100 ml. Specimens were alternately immersed 30 s in solution and held 2 min in air	3	35 (95)	7 d	0.6 g/m^2/d (0.4 mg/in.^{2}/d)	12

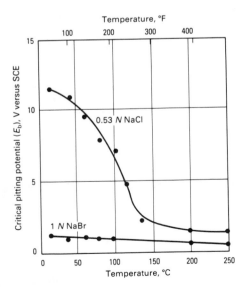

Titanium. Effect of temperature on the anodic pitting potential of grade 2 titanium in dilute NaCl and NaBr solutions. Source: *Metals Handbook*, 9th ed., Vol 13, Corrosion, ASM International, Metals Park, OH, 1987, 688.

Sodium Carbonate

Sodium carbonate, Na_2CO_3, also known as soda or soda ash, is the most important of the industrial alkalis. It is a white or grayish-white, lumpy, water-soluble powder that loses its water of crystallization when heated. It decomposes at a temperature of about 852 °C.

Soda ash is used in glassmaking, in production of sodium chemicals (such as sodium chromates, phosphates, and silicates), in the wood pulp industry, in production of soaps and detergents, in oil refining, in water softening, and in refining of nonferrous metals. In its hydrous crystallized form ($Na_2CO_3 \cdot 10H_2O$), it is known as sal soda, washing soda, or soda crystals, not to be confused with baking soda, which is sodium hydrogen carbonate or sodium bicarbonate ($NaHCO_3$). Its monohydrate form ($Na_2CO_3 \cdot H_2O$) is the standard compound for scouring solutions.

When in solution, sodium carbonate creates less alkalinity than the hydroxides. A 0.1% solution creates a pH of 11; a fully saturated solution is 35%, which has a pH of 12.5.

The safety requirements for sodium carbonate, because of its lower alkalinity, can be considered less demanding than those for the related bicarbonates.

Sodium carbonate is found in large quantities in a number of states located in the western United States.

Material Summaries

The following material summaries were compiled from a survey of the available literature. Inclusion of a material description under a given environment does not imply that it is the most appropriate material for corrosion service in that environment. Likewise, exclusion of a given material does not imply that it is not suitable for corrosion service applications in that environment.

Carbon Steels. Carbon steels have good resistance to sodium carbonate and are used extensively in sodium carbonate solutions up to boiling temperatures.

Stainless Steels. Stainless steels perform very effectively in sodium carbonate service. Rates of stress-corrosion cracking are similar to those in caustic solutions, but at considerably elevated temperatures.

Aluminum. In laboratory tests conducted at 100% relative humidity and ambient temperature, solid sodium carbonate was very corrosive to aluminum alloy 3003. Other tests showed that aqueous solutions of sodium carbonate (1 to 10%) were corrosive to aluminum alloy 1100. However, this corrosive action was effectively inhibited by the addition of silicates. Sodium carbonate has been transported in aluminum alloy hopper cars.

Zinc. Zinc and zinc brasses are attacked by sodium carbonate, but exhibit beneficial results from various inhibitors.

Additional Reading

V.R. Iyer and O.F. Devereux, Liquid-Line Corrosion of Nickel in Molten Sodium Carbonate, *J. Electrochem. Soc.*, 132(5), 1098-1105, 1985. MetAbs No. 85-351429. **Abstract:** Liquid-line corrosion of Ni in molten sodium carbonate at 1000 °C under reduced air pressures was measured as a function of time and air pressure.

J. Rechberger, D. Tromans, and A. Mitchell, Stress Corrosion Cracking of Conventional and Super-Clean 3.5NiCrMoV Rotor Steels in Simulated Condensates, *Corrosion*, 44(2), 79-87, 1988. MetAbs No. 88-351085. **Abstract:** The stress-corrosion cracking behavior of two bainitic 3.5NiCrMoV low-pressure rotor steels has been studied at 95 °C in environments containing species that are possible contaminants in steam condensates. The environments were 3.5M NaOH, 1M Na_2CO_3 + 1M $NaHCO_3$ and a saturated CO_2/H_2O solution.

Corrosion Behavior of Various Metals and Alloys in Sodium Carbonate

Material	Condition, other factors, comments	Concentration, %	Temperature, °C (°F)	Duration	Corrosion rate, mm/yr (mils/yr) or other	Ref
Stainless steels						
AM-363 stainless steel	...	...	Room	...	Unattacked	120
Type 304 stainless steel	Chemical processing; field or pilot plant test; strong aeration; rapid agitation. Plus 8% sodium chloride, 8% sodium borate, and 2.5% sodium sulfate. Severe pitting: maximum depth of pits over 0.010 in.	25.4	66 (150)	60 d	0.016 in./yr	89
Type 410 stainless steel	...	...	Room	...	Unattacked	121
Type 410 stainless steel	...	10	0-93 (0-200)	...	Unattacked	121
Type 410 stainless steel	...	50	0-93 (0-200)	...	Unattacked	121
Coppers						
70-30 cupronickel	...	...	...	...	Suitable	93
90-10 cupronickel	...	...	...	...	Suitable	93
Admiralty brass	...	...	...	...	Suitable	93
Aluminum bronze	...	...	...	...	Suitable	93
Ampco 8, aluminum bronze	Generally suitable. Conditions such as aeration or temperature could restrict use	...	...	...	<0.5 (<20)	96
Architectural bronze	(a)	...	...	...	Good	93

(Continued)

Corrosion Behavior of Various Metals and Alloys in Sodium Carbonate (Continued)

Material	Condition, other factors, comments	Concentration, %	Temperature, °C (°F)	Duration	Corrosion rate, mm/yr (mils/yr) or other	Ref
Brass	...	...	...	...	Suitable	93
Cartridge brass	(a)	...	...	...	Good	93
Commercial bronze	...	...	...	...	Suitable	93
Copper-nickel	...	...	...	...	2.5-40 (0.1-1.5)	76
Copper-tin	...	...	...	...	<50 (<2)	76
Copper-zinc	...	...	...	...	50-125 (2-5)	76
Electrolytic copper	...	...	...	...	Suitable	93
Free-cutting brass	(a)	...	...	...	Good	93
Muntz metal	(a)	...	...	...	Good	93
Naval brass	(a)	...	...	...	Good	93
Nickel silver	...	18	...	...	Suitable	93
Phosphor bronze	5% Sn	...	...	...	Suitable	93
Phosphor bronze	8% Sn	...	...	...	Suitable	93
Phosphor copper	...	...	...	...	Suitable	93
Red brass	...	...	...	...	Suitable	93
Silicon bronze	Low	...	...	...	Suitable	93
Silicon bronze	High	...	...	...	Suitable	93
Titanium						
Titanium	...	20	Boiling	...	nil	1
Titanium	...	20	Boiling	...	nil	1
Titanium	...	25	Boiling	...	nil	90
Heat- and corrosion-resistant alloys						
Incoloy 800	Solutions were prepared with reagent-grade chemicals. Test specimens were cold-rolled, annealed sheet, 2.84 mm (0.112 in.) thick. No pitting	...	80 (176)	7 d	nil	44
Inconel 601	...	10	80 (176)	7 d	nil	64
Inconel 690	...	10	80 (176)	...	<0.03 (<1)	57
Lead, tin, and zinc						
Tin	...	...	20 (68)	...	Resistant	94
Tin	...	...	60 (140)	...	Unsuitable	94
Tin	...	...	100 (212)	...	Unsuitable	94
Lead	...	...	8 (46)	...	0.015 (0.6)	49
Tin	(b)	0.005	60 (140)	...	0.030 (1.2)	75
Tin	(b)	0.02	60 (140)	...	0.045 (1.8)	75
Tin	(b)	0.05	60 (140)	...	0.24 (9.4)	75
Tin	(b)	0.10	60 (140)	...	0.26 (10.2)	75
Tin	(b)	0.15	60 (140)	...	0.27 (10.6)	75
Tin	(b)	0.20	60 (140)	...	0.27 (10.6)	75
Tin	(b)	0.25	60 (140)	...	0.27 (10.6)	75
Noble metals						
Silver	...	...	Boiling	...	<0.05 (<2)	9
Platinum	...	All	Boiling	...	<0.05 (<2)	5
Platinum	Melt	...	860 (1580)	...	<0.05 (<2)	5
Others						
Magnesium	...	All	Room	...	Suitable	119
Niobium	...	10	Room	...	0.025 (1.0)	2

(a) May be considered in place of a copper metal when some property, other than corrosion resistance, governs its use. (b) Converted from weight loss data, assuming a tin density of 7.29 g/cm³.

Sodium Chloride

Sodium chloride, NaCl, also known as common salt and halite, is a white crystalline solid. It is soluble in water, slightly soluble in alcohol, and melts at 804 °C (1480 °F). Sodium chloride is the most important sodium mineral and occurs naturally in seawater, underground deposits, and brine wells. Sodium chloride is a basic raw material for the production of chlorine, sodium hypochlorite, sodium bisulfate, soda ash, and hydrogen chloride. Sodium chloride is also used in food preparation, fertilizers, and by highway departments to control icy road conditions.

Material Summaries

The following material summaries were compiled from a survey of the available literature. Inclusion of a material description under a given environment does not imply that it is the most appropriate material for corrosion service in that environment. Likewise, exclusion of a given material does not imply that it is not suitable for corrosion service applications in that environment.

Aluminum. Aluminum alloys are used to ship, store, and handle sodium chloride either as a solid, as an aqueous solution, or as a brine in refrigeration systems. Sodium chloride is a standard testing medium to determine the corrosion and stress-corrosion cracking resistance of aluminum alloys. Aqueous solutions of 0.1 to 25% sodium chloride mildly attacked (0.05 mm/yr, or 2 mils/yr) alloy 1100 and produced localized pitting in tests run at ambient temperature. The presence of heavy metals in the solutions will increase the corrosion attack.

Amorphous Metals. Amorphous metals showed a sharp decrease in corrosion rate with increased chromium content and no sign of pitting in a $1N$ sodium chloride solution. Stress-corrosion cracking of a $Ni_{49}Fe_{29}P_{14}B_6Al_2$ glassy alloy was observed in a $3.5N$ sodium chloride solution, although one researcher suggested that the fracture was hydrogen induced.

Copper. Sodium chloride solutions reduce the service life of copper alloys under cyclic stress. Aluminum bronzes are generally suitable for service in sodium chloride.

Nickel. Nickel alloys have good resistance to solid sodium chloride.

Titanium. Titanium alloys are susceptible to crevice corrosion in hot, low pH, concentrated sodium chloride solutions. Crevice corrosion does not generally occur at temperatures below 70 °C (160 °F) or at pH values above 10. Grade 12 provides the greatest crevice corrosion resistance in solutions with pH values of 3 to 11 with temperatures as high as 300 °C (570 °F). Titanium alloys containing at least 4 wt% molybdenum (Ti-3-8-6-4-4 alloy) revealed no crevice corrosion in low pH, high-temperature tests. The addition of dissolved oxidizing species and imposing an anodic potential can reduce attack time and increase the attack rate of sodium chloride solutions on titanium alloys.

Zirconium. Zirconium resists stress-corrosion cracking in sodium chloride.

Powder/Metallurgy Alloys. Aluminum-magnesium alloys IN-9052 and IN-9021 were tested by alternate immersion in a sodium chloride solution (ASTM G 44). IN-9052 had a corrosion rate two magnitudes lower than that of the conventional 7075-T73. Another study involving short-term exposure in a 3.5% sodium chloride solution showed IN-9021 to be very susceptible to pitting, with a corrosion rate three times greater than that of the conventional 7075 alloy.

Low-Alloy Steel. Low-alloy sintered steel exhibited poor corrosion resistance to a 3% sodium chloride solution at high and low oxidation temperatures.

Sintered Stainless Steels. The corrosion resistance of sintered stainless steels in a chloride environment depends on the iron contamination and on the carbon, nitrogen, oxygen, and sintered part density.

Additional Reading

L.A. Luini, Stress Corrosion Cracking of an Aluminum-Zinc-Magnesium Alloy, *Diss. Abstr. Int.,* *41*(8), 68, 1981. MetAbs No. 81-351276. **Abstract:** The stress-corrosion cracking of a high-strength Al-Zn-Mg type 7039 alloy has been studied as a function of heat treatment, test temperature, and environment. For each of four heat treatments, plots of crack velocity vs stress intensity were obtained for testing in both distilled water and 3.5% NaCl and water.

M. Khobaib, C.T. Lynch, and F.W. Vahldiek, Inhibition of Corrosion Fatigue in High-Strength Aluminum Alloys, *Corrosion,* 37(5), 285-292, 1981. MetAbs No. 81-351962. **Abstract:** The effects of environment on the crack growth rate of several high-strength aluminum alloys such as 7075-T6, 7075-T73, and 2024-T3 have been investigated. The environments studied were distilled water, tap water, aqueous sodium chloride, aqueous inhibitors with and without sodium chloride and ambient air. Low-cycle corrosion fatigue studies were conducted at 0.1 Hz and R = 0.1 on compact-tension specimens.

P.H. Gimenez, J.J. Rameau, and M.C. Reboul, Experimental pH Potential Diagram of Aluminum for Sea Water, *Corrosion,* 37(12), 673-682, 1981. MetAbs No. 82-350772. **Abstract:** The theoretical Pourbaix diagram for the $Al-H_2O$ system does not take into account pitting corrosion. To obtain a practical representation of aluminum corrosion usable in seawater, pitting potentials, protection potentials and uniform attack potentials have been measured with 5086 AA specimens in 3% NaCl solutions buffered within the 4 to 9 pH range.

W. Chu, Y. Wang, and C. Hsiao, Research of Hydrogen-Induced Cracking and Stress Corrosion Cracking in an Aluminum Alloy, *Corrosion,* 38(11), 561-570, 1982. MetAbs No. 83-350292. **Abstract:** For a high-strength aluminum alloy (7075, LC4), the dynamic processes of nucleation and propagation of hydrogen-induced delayed cracking of a charged and modified WOL specimen were followed metallographically.

W.-T. Tsai, A. Moccari, and D.D. MacDonald, Effect of Silicate and Phosphate on the Fatigue Crack Growth Rates in Type 403 Stainless Steel in Concentrated Sodium Chloride and Sodium Hydroxide Solutions, *Corrosion,* 39(1), 1-12, 1983. MetAbs No. 83-350732. **Abstract:** Corrosion fatigue crack growth rates of a quenched and tempered 403 stainless steel were measured in concentrated sodium hydroxide and sodium chloride solutions, with and without the addition of sodium silicate and sodium phosphate as potential inhibitors, using compact tension specimens. All tests were performed at 100 °C.

L. Schra and J. Faber, "Influence of Environments on Constant Displacement Stress Corrosion Crack Growth in High-Strength Aluminum Alloys," National Aerospace Laboratory, Amsterdam, 48, 1981. MetAbs No. 83-351306. **Abstract:** An experimental investigation was carried out into the applicability of various corrosive environments for stress-corrosion crack propagation testing of high-strength aluminum alloys (7075, 7175, AZ74.61) using double cantilever beam specimens. Testing under atmospheric conditions was used as a reference.

L. Schra and R.J.H. Wanhill, The Influence of Different Environments on Stress Corrosion Cracking of High-Strength Aluminum Alloy Forgings, *Aluminium, 59*(3), 191-194, 1983. MetAbs No. 83-351476. **Abstract:** Several high-strength aluminum alloy (7075, 7175, 7050, AZ74.61) forgings have been used to evaluate accelerated methods of stress-corrosion testing with respect to atmospheric exposure. These methods were alternate immersion or periodic moistening using a 3.5% aqueous NaCl or synthetic seawater, and continuous immersion in 3.5% aqueous NaCl with additions of Na_2CrO_4.

M.A. Cavanaugh, J.A. Kargol, J. Nickerson, and N.F. Fiore, The Anodic Dissolution of a Nickel-Base Superalloy, *Corrosion, 39*(4), 144-150, 1983. MetAbs No. 83-351495. **Abstract:** A single-phase Ni-base superalloy, Hastelloy Alloy C-276, was anodically polarized in $0.5N$ NaCl at 70 °C and the concentrations of metal-ion complexes in solution were determined. Relative dissolution rates of alloying elements were obtained and selectivity coefficients were calculated.

D. Tromans and L. Frederick, Electrochemical Studies of Crevice Corrosion Rates on Stainless Steels, *Corrosion, 39*(8), 305-312, 1983. MetAbs No. 83-352517. **Abstract:** A crevice corrosion cell was designed to utilize electrochemical techniques for the quantitative determination of crevice corrosion rates in three commercial austenitic stainless steels—AISI 304, 316L and UHB 904L. Studies were conducted on Teflon/metal crevices exposed to 1M NaCl at 22 and 55 °C.

Y. Choi, H.-C. Kim, and S.-I. Pyun, Stress Corrosion Cracking of Al-Zn-Mg Alloy AA-7039 by Slow Strain-Rate Method, *J. Mater. Sci., 19*(5), 1517-1521, 1984. MetAbs No. 84-312725. **Abstract:** The stress-corrosion behavior of Al-Zn-Mg alloy AA-7039 in an aqueous 3.5 wt% NaCl solution (pH 1) was studied with the specimens under constant strain rate as a function of aging state and cold working. The tests were carried out at 30 and 45 °C and strain rates between 7.6 x 10^{-7} and 7.6 x 10^{-6} s^{-1}, and the apparent activation energy for mechanical deformation in oil and stress-corrosion cracking process in NaCl solution were determined.

F.D. Bogar and T.W. Crooker, Fatigue Testing in Natural and Marine Corrosion Environments Substitute Ocean Waters, *Mater. Perform., 22*(8), 37, 1983. MetAbs No. 84-350006. **Abstract:** Alloy AA 5083-H116 aluminum was tested by rotating beam fatigue in three different flowing, fully oxygenated environments: fresh natural seawater; ASTM substitute ocean water with heavy metals, and 3.5% NaCl solution.

P. Gopalan, T.S. Panchapagesan, T. Kishore, and E.S. Dwarakadasa, Stress Corrosion Cracking of Aged Al-5Zn-4Mg Alloy in 3.5% NaCl Solution, *J. Electrochem. Soc. India, 32*(1), 17-21, 1983. MetAbs No. 84-350041. **Abstract:** Specimens of high-strength Al-5Zn-4Mg alloy have been subjected to dynamic stress-corrosion cracking under constant strain rate tensile loading in 3.5% NaCl solution.

A.H. Le and R.T. Foley, Stress Corrosion Cracking of AA 7075-T651 in Various Electrolytes—Statistical Treatment of Data Obtained Using DCB Precracked Specimens, *Corrosion, 39*(10), 379-383, 1983. MetAbs No. 84-350291. **Abstract:** Double cantilever beam specimens were employed to measure the rate of stress-corrosion crack growth of AA 7075-T651 in $1N$ NaClO$_4$, $1N$ NaCl, $1N$ Na$_2$SO$_4$ and $1N$ NaNO$_3$ solutions.

A.V. Karlashov, A.D. Gnatyouk, and A.B. Kardash, Corrosion Fatigue Strength of Aluminium Alloys, in *Corrosion Fatigue*, The Metals Society, London, 101-111, 1983. MetAbs No. 84-350322. **Abstract:** Studies at the Liev Institute of Civil Aviation on the corrosion-fatigue of the D1T, D16T, D16AT, D16ATV, V95T, V92T, and V93 aluminum construction alloys in NaCl are reported. Factors discussed include the velocity and nature of the corrosion process, effects of temperature, and oxygen

solubility of the media, and influences of loading frequency, specimen size, and surface deformation.

Y.-S. Kim and S.-I. Pyun, Contribution to the Mechanism of Stress Corrosion Cracking in a Welded Al-Zn-Mg Alloy, *Br. Corros. J., 18*(2), 71-75, 1983. MetAbs No. 84-350385. **Abstract:** The stress-corrosion cracking of Al-Zn-Mg welds in an aqueous solution of 3.5 wt% NaCl (pH 1) was studied with specimens under constant load as a function of the applied anodic potential and the postweld heat treatment. Various theories of stress-corrosion cracking in high-strength Al-base alloys (Al-Zn-Mg, Al-Cu-Mg, Al-Zn-Mg-Cu) are reviewed.

N. Bui, A. Irhzo, R. Dabosi, and Y. Limouzin-Maire, On the Mechanism for Improved Passivation by Additions of Tungsten to Austenitic Stainless Steels, *Corrosion, 39*(12), 491-496, 1983. MetAbs No. 84-350836. **Abstract:** To elucidate the role of tungsten in improving the passivity of austenitic stainless steels, anodic polarization curves and X-ray photoelectron spectra have been obtained for pure tungsten and tungsten-containing steels passivated in $1N$ HCl, $0.1M$ NaCl and in Cl⁻ containing H_3PO_4.

E.I. Meletis and R.F. Hochman, Crystallography of Stress Corrosion Cracking in Pure Magnesium, *Corrosion, 40*(1), 39-45, 1984. MetAbs No. 84-351095. **Abstract:** A crystallographic characterization study has been made of the transgranular stress-corrosion cracking in pure magnesium tested at room temperature in aqueous NaCl-K$_2$CrO. Selected area electron channeling and photogrammetry were used to determine the cracking orientation.

S.M. El-Raghy, H. Abd-El-Kader, and M.E. Abou-El-Hassan, Electrochemistry of Abrasion Corrosion of Low-Alloy Steel in 1% NaCl Solution, *Corrosion, 40*(2), 60-61, 1984. MetAbs No. 84-351160. **Abstract:** Abrasion corrosion experiments with several chromium steel specimens are presented, using a Wenking potentiostat and with abrasion by a 103-mm disk of silicon carbide rotating at 350 or 650 rpm.

J. Blain, J. Masounave, and J.I. Dickson, A Study of Stress Corrosion Crack Propagation in 2024-T351 Aluminum Alloy by Acoustic Emission, *Can. Metall. Q., 23*(1), 51-57, 1984. MetAbs No. 84-352158. **Abstract:** The acoustic emission associated with stress-corrosion cracking of 2024-T351 aluminum alloy for SL and ST orientations in 3% NaCl solution was studied in parallel with measurements of stress-corrosion cracking velocities.

I.V. Riskin, V.B. Torshin, Ya.B. Skuratnik, and M.A. Dembrovsky, Corrosion of Titanium by Cathodic Currents in Chloride Solutions, *Corrosion, 40*(6), 266-271, 1984. MetAbs No. 84-352374. **Abstract:** Corrosion and hydrogenation of commercial-purity titanium (0.9% impurity) have been studied under cathodic polarization in Cl-saturated sodium chloride solutions. The mechanism of corrosion failure, conditions for inhibition of hydrogenation and corrosion have been elucidated.

R. Wang and M.D. Merz, Corrosion Resistance of Amorphous FeNiCrW Alloys, *Corrosion, 40*(6), 272-280, 1984. MetAbs No. 84-352375. **Abstract:** The corrosion resistance of amorphous FeNiCrW alloys prepared by cosputtering 304 stainless steel and tungsten was studied in chloride solutions by potentiodynamic polarization methods in neutral and acidic solutions.

S.I. Pyun, The Stress Corrosion Behavior of Al-Zn-Mg Alloy AA-7039, *Metall, 38*(3), 229-231, 1984. MetAbs No. 84-352517. **Abstract:** Time-to-failure of Al-Zn-Mg alloy AA-7039 in an aqueous 3.5 wt% NaCl solution (pH 1) at 30 °C was measured with specimens under constant load as a function of aging time with/without an applied anodic potential of 300 mV. The temperature dependence was also observed from 20 to 35 °C in the absence of applied anodic potentials.

A. Poznansky and D.J. Duquette, The Effect of Sensitization Heat Treatment on the Stress Corrosion Cracking of AISI 304 Stainless Steel, *Corrosion, 40*(7), 375-381, 1984. MetAbs No. 84-352607. **Abstract:** Constant extension rate experiments at controlled potentials have been performed in aqueous solutions containing 100 ppm NaCl and 100 ppm Na_2SO_4 at 290 °C on 304 stainless steel specimens that were heat treated at 620, 670, and 820 °C for different time periods.

K. Komai and K. Minoshima, Influences of Stress Ratios and Cycle Frequencies on Dynamic SCC Crack Growth in Aluminum Alloy, in *International Congress on Metallic Corrosion,* Vol 1, National Research Council of Canada, Ottawa, 167-173, 1984. MetAbs No. 84-352733. **Abstract:** Stress ratio and cycle frequency effects on transition behavior between dynamic, cyclic and static stress-corrosion cracking were investigated on a high-strength aluminum alloy in 3.5% NaCl solution. Loading variables that controlled threshold values are discussed.

R. Nishimura, M. Araki, and K. Kudo, Breakdown of Passive Film on Iron, *Corrosion, 40*(9), 465-470, 1984. MetAbs No. 84-353066. **Abstract:** The breakdown of passive films potentiostatically formed on iron in borate and phosphate solutions of pH 8.42 and 11.50 is investigated in NaCl solution at a constant potential of -0.195 V (SHE) higher than a critical pitting potential of -0.295 V in the same solution.

M.A. Pao and E. Klar, Corrosion Phenomena in Regular and Tin-Modified P/M Stainless Steels, in *Progress in Powder Metallurgy 1983,* Vol 39, Metal Powder Industries Federation, Princeton, 431-443, 1984. MetAbs No. 84-540899. **Abstract:** The corrosion behavior of P/M parts is dependent on processing. Corrosion data for three different corrosive media, including sodium chloride, are summarized.

D. Tromans and L. Frederick, Effect of Thiosulfate on Crevice Corrosion of Stainless Steels, *Corrosion, 40*(12), 633-639, 1984. MetAbs No. 85-350467. **Abstract:** Crevice corrosion studies were conducted on AISI 304, AISI 316L, and UHB 904L stainless steels using Teflon/metal crevices exposed to aqueous solutions of $1M$ NaCl and $1M$ NaCl + $0.01M$ $Na_2S_2O_3$. Tests were conducted at 22 °C, except for some additional tests at 55 °C on the more crevice-resistant 904L.

S.A. Lindqvist, Theory of Dielectric Properties of Heterogeneous Substances Applied to Water in a Paint Film, *Corrosion, 41*(2), 69-75, 1985. MetAbs No. 85-350638. **Abstract:** The water content of 12 paints on steel substrate, exposed to $0.1M$ sodium chloride at 25 °C for 24 h, was calculated from impedance measurements and compared with gravimetric determinations.

Y. Yoshino and A. Ikegaya, Pitting and Stress Cracking of 12Cr-Ni-Mo Martensitic Stainless Steels in Chloride and Sulfide Environments, *Corrosion, 41*(2), 105-113, 1985. MetAbs No. 85-350645. **Abstract:** Laboratory-melted 12Cr-Ni-Mo steels were tested in chloride/sulfide solutions at 60 °C and at room temperature to evaluate their resistance to pitting and stress cracking in connection with environmental and metallurgical factors.

R. Fratesi, Statistical Estimate of the Pitting Potential of AISI 316L Stainless Steel in 3.5% NaCl Measured by Means of Two Electrochemical Methods, *Corrosion, 41*(2), 114-117, 1985. MetAbs No. 85-350646. **Abstract:** The anodic behavior of the passive surfaces of an austenitic 18Cr-11Ni-2Mo stainless steel in 3.5% NaCl solution was studied by means of the potentiokinetic technique and the scratch method under potentiostatic polarization.

F. Mansfeld, M.W. Kendig, and W.J. Lorenz, Corrosion Inhibition in Neutral, Aerated Media, *J. Electrochem. Soc., 132*(2), 290-296, 1985. MetAbs No. 85-350787. **Abstract:** Experimental results of interphase inhibition have been obtained for a 4340 steel rotating cylinder electrode by impedance measurements during exposure over 48 h in aerated, neutral $0.5M$ Na_2SO_4, $0.5M$ NaCl, tap water and deionized water containing 10 mM $NaNO_2$, and mixtures of phosphonic acid/fatty amine or polyacrylic acid/fatty amine.

W.J.D. Shaw, Surface Corrosion Comparisons of Some Aluminum Alloys in 3.5% NaCl Solution, in *Microstructural Science,* Vol 12, American Society for Metals, Metals Park, OH, 243-262, 1985. MetAbs No. 85-350802. **Abstract:** The short-term corrosive effect of an aerated 3.5% NaCl solution on the surface of a number of different Al alloys (7075-T6, 2024-T4, 6061-T6511, and IN-9021-T452) is documented as a function of time.

W.R. Cieslak and D.J. Duquette, An Electrochemical Study of the Pit Initiation Resistance of Ferritic Stainless Steels, *J. Electrochem. Soc., 132*(3), 533-537, 1985. MetAbs No. 85-350861. **Abstract:** A variety of electrochemical techniques has been used to study the resistance of ferritic stainless steels to pit initiation in $1M$ NaCl at 80 °C. Critical pitting potentials have been measured by potentiodynamic anodic polarization and by the "scratch" technique. The effectiveness of passivation potential and alloy content to promote formation of a film that is resistant to breakdown has been studied by pit induction time measurements using steels with 18 and 28 wt% Cr.

M. Duprat, M.C. Lafont, and F. Dabosi, Study of the Corrosion and Inhibition Processes of a Carbon Steel in a Low Conductivity Medium by Electrochemical Methods, *Electrochim. Acta, 30,* 353-365, 1985. MetAbs No. 85-351090. **Abstract:** Ohmic drop corrected steady-state current-voltage curves and electrochemical impedance diagrams have been obtained for carbon steel (XC35) rotating disc electrodes in NaCl solutions with and without addition of the association of oleylaminopropylene and amino-tri(methyl-phosphonic) acid.

L. Felloni, R. Fratesi, O. Ruggeri, and G. Sambogna, Pitting and Crevice Corrosion Potentials of Solar Panel Stainless Steels in Seawater and 0.6M NaCl, *Corrosion, 41*(3), 169-177, 1985. MetAbs No. 85-351102. **Abstract:** The cyclic potentiokinetic polarization method (scanning rate 10 mV/min), starting at the free corrosion potential and going up to 100 μA/cm^2 (surface area), and microscopic observation of the surface were used to evaluate the susceptibility of commercial stainless steels (types 304, 316, and 430) to localized corrosion for their possible application in solar panels.

J.D. Redmond, Solving Brewery Stress Corrosion Cracking Problems. II, *Stainless Steel Ind., 13*(71), 8-9, 1985. MetAbs No. 85-351312. **Abstract:** The second generation of duplex stainless steels, particularly Alloy 2205 (22Cr-5Ni-3Mo-0.15N), are considered. The stress-corrosion cracking resistance in boiling 25% NaCl of Types 304, 316 and 444 and Alloy 2205 are compared, as are the corrosion rates for Alloy 2205 in various corrosive media.

M.G.S. Ferreira and J.L. Dawson, Electrochemical Studies of the Passive Film on 316 Stainless Steel in Chloride Media, *J. Electrochem. Soc., 132*(4), 760-765, 1985. MetAbs No. 85-351342. **Abstract:** The kinetics of passive film growth on 316 stainless steel in 3% sodium chloride solution have been studied by dc and ac electrochemical measurements.

N.J.H. Holroyd and G.M. Scamans, Slow-Strain-Rate Stress Corrosion Testing of Aluminum Alloys, *Environment-Sensitive Fracture: Evaluation and Comparison of Test Methods,* ASTM, 202-241, 1984. MetAbs No. 85-351410. **Abstract:** An extensive program of slow-strain-rate stress-corrosion testing of Al alloys in a wide variety of susceptibility conditions and environments is discussed. Tests were conducted both on laboratory alloys in sheet form and on commercial alloys in wire, sheet, and plate forms; the systems studied included Al-Zn-Mg, Al-Zn-Mg-Cu, Al-

Cu-Mg, and Al-Mg. Suitable strain rate regimes for testing, standard environments, and optimum stress-corrosion susceptibility parameters were established.

R. Alkire, T. Tomasson, and K. Hebert, The Critical Geometry for Initiation of Crevice Corrosion, *J. Electrochem. Soc.*, *132*(5), 1027-1031, 1985. MetAbs No. 85-351427. **Abstract:** The critical crevice dimensions for which initiation of crevice corrosion occurs spontaneously was determined experimentally for Al 99.9% in 0.05*M* NaCl.

H.P. Dhar, Corrosion Behavior of 70Cu-30Ni Alloy in 0.5M NaCl and in Synthetic Seawater, *Corrosion*, *41*(4), 193-196, 1985. MetAbs No. 85-351434. **Abstract:** Electrochemical corrosion rates of 70Cu-30Ni alloy have been measured in oxygenated 0.5*M* NaCl and in synthetic seawater by the Tafel extrapolation procedure using a rotating disk electrode system. The rotation rate was varied from 500 to 6000 rpm.

P.P. Corso Jr., R.M. German, and H.D. Simmons Jr., Corrosion Evaluation of Gold-Based Dental Alloys, *J. Dent. Res.*, *64*(5), 854-859, 1985. MetAbs No. 85-351470. **Abstract:** Three commercial Au-based dental alloys and three constant-nobility ternary alloys (Au-Ag-Cu) were evaluated for corrosion using a quantitative test battery. Integration of the current density, in a deaerated solution of 1% NaCl, yields a quantitative rank ordering of the test alloys. The results are combined with prior findings on other commercial alloys to demonstrate the interaction of nobility and microstructure.

H.P. Dhar, Corrosion of Cu and Cu-Ni Alloys in 0.5M NaCl and in Synthetic Seawater, *Corrosion*, *41*(6), 317-323, 1985. MetAbs No. 85-351730. **Abstract:** Electrochemical corrosion rates of Cu and Cu-Ni alloys have been measured in oxygenated 0.5*M* NaCl and in synthetic seawater using the Tafel extrapolation procedure. Copper corrosion has been measured with the linear polarization procedure. A rotating disk electrode system was used in the measurements with rotation rate varying from 500 to 6000 rpm.

G.P. Ray, R.A. Jarman, and J.G.N. Thomas, The Influence of Non-Metallic Inclusions on the Corrosion Fatigue of Mild Steel, *Corros. Sci.*, *25*(3), 171-184, 1985. MetAbs No. 85-351835. **Abstract:** A study has been made of the effect of sulfide inclusions on the corrosion fatigue of mild steel in 0.6*M* NaCl solutions.

T. Magnin and L. Coudreuse, The Effects of Strain Rate on the Corrosion Fatigue Behavior of B.C.C. Fe-26Cr-1Mo Stainless Steels, *Mater. Sci. Eng.*, *72*(2), 125-134, 1985. MetAbs No. 85-352106. **Abstract:** The corrosion fatigue damage mechanisms leading to crack initiation were studied in high-purity ferritic stainless steels in a 3.5% NaCl solution at 300 K and at the imposed corrosion potential. Particular attention was paid to the influence of strain rate on both the plastic deformation mechanisms and the dissolution characteristics that govern the crack initiation process.

A. Mance, D. Cerovic, and A. Mihajloviavc, The Effect of Gallium and Phosphorus on the Corrosion Behavior of Aluminium in Sodium Chloride Solution, *J. Appl. Electrochem.*, *15*(3), 415-420, 1985. MetAbs No. 85-352128. **Abstract:** To cause shifting of the potential in the negative direction and to simultaneously control dissolution in sodium chloride solutions, aluminium alloys used as anodes in electrochemical power sources contain small additions of alloying elements. This can be achieved with highly pure aluminum alloys.

W.Y. Chu, C.M. Hsiao, and J.W. Wang, Stress Corrosion Cracking of an Aluminum Alloy Under Compressive Stress, *Metall. Trans. A*, *16A*(9), 1663-1670, 1985. MetAbs No. 85-352301. **Abstract:** Stress-corrosion cracking of 7075 Al alloy in a 3.5% NaCl aqueous solution under compressive stress was investigated using modified WOL notched specimens.

S. Tosto, O. DiTollo, and M. Guerzoni, Corrosion Kinetics of HSLA and Low Carbon Steels in the Presence of Cl- Ions, *Corrosion*, *41*(8), 458-465, 1985. MetAbs No. 85-352335. **Abstract:** The corrosion kinetics of HSLA and mild steels in the presence of Cl- have been investigated. The dissolution rate was expressed by a logarithmic regression of weight loss per unit surface as a function of the residence time in the aggressive solution.

Y.G. Kim, G.W. Yoon, and N.S. Stoloff, Effect of Boron on the Corrosion Behavior of Polycrystalline Ni_3Al, *Metall. Trans. A*, *16A*(11), 2072-2073, 1985. MetAbs No. 85-352341. **Abstract:** The effects of boron additions on the corrosion behavior of Ni_3Al in HCl, H_2SO_4, NaCl, and H_3PO_4 electrolytes were studied.

A. McMinn, F.F. Lyle Jr., and G.R. Leverant, Stress Corrosion Crack Growth in NiCrMoV Turbine Disc Steels, *Corrosion*, *41*(9), 493-503, 1985. MetAbs No. 85-352342. **Abstract:** The effects of metallurgical and environmental variables on stress-corrosion cracking propagation rates in NiCrMoV turbine disc steels were studied. Constant displacement tests, using wedge-opening-load specimens, were performed on steels with yield strengths in the range of 627 to 1124 MPa.

J. Gluszek, G.B. Freeman, J. Baron, and J. Kubicki, Effect of Composition Modification of Passive Films Formed on Ferritic Stainless Steel on Resistance to Pitting, *Corrosion*, *41*(9), 527-532, 1985. MetAbs No. 85-352346. **Abstract:** The compositions of air-formed passive films on ferritic stainless steel were modified by exposure to corrosive solutions. The pitting resistance in 3% NaCl was studied by measuring the pitting nucleation potential. Auger electron spectroscopy of the prepared films was conducted, and a correlation was made between composition and resistance to the Cl- ions.

P.R. Shibad and K.N. Adhe, Effect of Addition Agents on the Corrosion Behavior of Copper Base Alloys in Salt Waters, *Trans. Indian Inst. Met.*, *38*(1), 17-22, 1985. MetAbs No. 85-352350. **Abstract:** Corrosion studies on Al brass, admiralty brass, Sn bronze, and Cu-Ni alloys in 3% NaCl solution and synthetic seawater have been carried out with and without the addition of inhibitors such as $FeSO_4$ (1 and 5 ppm), Na_2CrO_4 (5 ppm) + NaH_2PO_4 (1:9), Na_2MoO_4 (20 ppm) and addition of NH_4OH (10 ppm) as pollutants. Electrochemical measurements such as potential-time and potential-current have been carried out.

Y. Hirose and T. Mura, Crack Nucleation and Propagation of Corrosion Fatigue in High-Strength Steels, *Eng. Fract. Mech.*, *22*(5), 859-870, 1985. MetAbs No. 86-350057. **Abstract:** Crack nucleation and growth behavior of corrosion fatigue are investigated experimentally and theoretically for 200 °C tempered AISI 4340 steel in 3.5% NaCl solution. The crack nucleation at notch roots is determined by the electrical potential method.

H.G. Wheat and Z. Eliezer, Some Electrochemical Aspects of Corrosion of Steel in Concrete, *Corrosion*, *41*(11), 640-645, 1985. MetAbs No. 86-350206. **Abstract:** Because of the variation in composition and steel surface conditions in steel-reinforced concrete samples immersed in sodium chloride solutions, E_{corr} is a better indicator of corrosive behavior than the time of exposure.

M.R.G. de Chialvo, R.C. Salvarezza, D.Vasquez Moll, and A.J. Arvia, Kinetics of Passivation and Pitting Corrosion of Polycrystalline Copper in Borate Buffer Solutions Containing Sodium Chloride, *Electrochim. Acta*, *30*(11), 1501-1511, 1985. MetAbs No. 86-350223. **Abstract:** The pitting corrosion of Cu in borate buffer containing sodium chloride is studied by using potentiostatic and potentiodynamic techniques complemented with scanning electron microscopy and EDAX.

H.M. Shalaby and V.K. Gouda, Effect of Chloride Concentration and pH on Fatigue Crack Initiation Morphology of Type 403 Stainless Steel, *Br. Corros. J.*, *20*(3), 125-132, 1985. MetAbs No. 86-350262. **Abstract:**

Corrosion fatigue studies have been conducted on martensitic Type 403 turbine blade alloy in air, deaerated distilled water, and deaerated 0.01 and 1M NaCl solutions at pH 2, 7, and 10 at 100 °C.

R. Padmanabhan and W.E. Wood, Stress Corrosion Cracking Behavior of 300M Steel Under Different Heat Treated Conditions, *Corrosion*, *41*(12), 688-699, 1985. MetAbs No. 86-350428. **Abstract:** The resistance of 300M steel to stress-corrosion cracking in a 3.5% NaCl solution was studied as a function of heat treatment. Threshold stress intensity was affected by microstructural features, including prior austenite grain size, amounts of retained austenite, and twins, in addition to grain boundary segregation and fracture toughness of the steel.

J. Flis and D.J. Duquette, Effect of Phosphorus on Anodic Dissolution and Passivation of Nickel in Near-Neutral Solutions, *Corrosion*, *41*(12), 700-706, 1985. MetAbs No. 86-350429. **Abstract:** Anodic dissolution of Ni, electroless Ni deposits with 2.9 and 12.3 wt.% phosphorus, and amorphous $Ni_{81}P_{19}$ alloy was examined in sodium hydroxide, sulfate, borate, and chloride solutions at 25 °C.

E.F. Smith and D.J. Duquette, The Effect of Cathodic Polarization on the Corrosion Fatigue Behavior of a Precipitation Hardened Aluminum Alloy, *Metall. Trans. A*, *17A*(2), 339-347, 1986. MetAbs No. 86-350476. **Abstract:** Fatigue experiments were conducted on polycrystalline and monocrystalline samples of a high-purity Al-5.5Zn-2.5Mg-1.5Cu alloy in the peak-hardened heat treated condition. These experiments were conducted in dry laboratory air and in 0.5N NaCl solutions at the corrosion potential and at applied potentials cathodic to the corrosion potential.

D.P. Harvey, T.S. Sudarshan, M.R. Louthan Jr., and R.E. Swanson, Corrosion Fatigue Behavior of 90/10 Copper-Nickel Cladding for Marine Structures, *J. Mater. Energy Syst.*, *7*(3), 269-275, 1985. MetAbs No. 86-350483. **Abstract:** Tension-tension fatigue experiments on annealed Cu-Ni-Fe alloy (CA-706) tested in 3.5% NaCl solution showed that the fatigue life decreased with an increase in applied anodic current. A fracture mode transition from predominantly transgranular to intergranular also occurred as the applied current was increased. These results are explained by a dissolution mechanism that involves the preferential attack of the Fe-rich second phase particles along the grain boundaries.

M. Magrini, P. Matteazzi, and A. Frignani, Structural Characterization and Electrochemical Behavior of Fe-Ni-Mo-B Amorphous Alloys, *Mater. Chem. Phys.*, *13*(1), 71-83, 1985. MetAbs No. 86-350502. **Abstract:** A series of amorphous alloys obtained by the "melt-spinning" technique, with variable nickel and molybdenum contents, have been examined. Potentiodynamic anodic and cathodic polarization curves have been obtained in various environments. Electrochemical properties were correlated with the amorphous structure and composition and characterized by means of X-ray diffraction and Mossbauer spectroscopy.

J.L. Wendt and D.T. Chin, The A.C. Corrosion of Stainless Steel. I. The Breakdown of Passivity of SS304 in Neutral Aqueous Solutions, *Corros. Sci.*, *25*(10), 889-900, 1985. MetAbs No. 86-350522. **Abstract:** The effect of alternating current on the corrosion of Type 304 stainless steel in aqueous solutions of Na_2SO_4, $NaNO_3$, and NaCl has been investigated with an alternating voltage modulation technique, using 60-Hz square wave alternating voltage. The anodic and cathodic polarization curves were measured for a range of alternating voltage from 0 to 1000 mV and the surfaces of specimens after a potentiostatic coulometry experiment were examined under a scanning electron microscope.

R.D.K. Misra and R. Sivakumar, Effect of NaCl Vapor on the Oxidation of Ni-Cr Alloys, *Oxid. Met.*, *25*(1-2), 83-92, 1986. MetAbs No. 86-350874. **Abstract:** Ni-Cr alloys (Ni-5Cr, Ni-10Cr, Ni-15Cr, Ni-25Cr) are known for their resistance to high-temperature oxidation. The kinetics of scale formation and the nature of the scale in these alloys are affected by NaCl liquid or vapor. In this investigation, Ni-Cr alloys with Cr varying from 0 to 25 wt% were exposed to NaCl vapor at 850 °C for a few minutes. The surface chemistry of these alloys along with the unattacked specimens was analyzed by Auger electron spectroscopy.

S.K. Mukherjee, A. Kumar, and G.S. Upadhyaya, Anodic Polarization Study of Sintered 434L Ferritic Stainless Steel and Its Particulate Composites, *Powder Metall. Int.*, *17*(4), 172-175, 1985. MetAbs No. 86-350978. **Abstract:** A potentiodynamic study of sintered 434L ferritic stainless steel and its particulate composites with Al_2O_3 (2 to 8 vol%) was undertaken in 5% NaCl and 1N H_2SO_4 electrolytes.

C.J. Thomas, R.G.J. Edyvean, R. Brook, and W.G. Ferguson, Environmentally Assisted Crack Growth in a Martensitic Stainless Steel, *Mater. Sci. Eng.*, *78*(1), 55-63, 1986. MetAbs No. 86-351021. **Abstract:** The response of a martensitic stainless steel, En56C, to environmental stress cracking as a function of heat treatment has been examined. The as-quenched, 400, 550 and 650 °C temper conditions were studied. The threshold stress intensity for stress-corrosion cracking was determined in dry H_2S gas and the crack growth rate measured in distilled water and in acidified 3.5% NaCl solution at pH 3 (NACE solution).

B.E. Wilde, The Influence of Silicon on the Pitting Corrosion Resistance of an 18Cr-8Ni Stainless Steel, *Corrosion*, *42*(3), 147-151, 1986. MetAbs No. 86-351025. **Abstract:** The effect of Si additions to an 18Cr-8Ni stainless steel on the resistance to pit initiation in halide media is described in terms of electrochemical polarization measurements conducted in aerated 3.5 wt.% sodium chloride at 25 °C.

D.J. Stephenson, J.R. Nicholls, and P. Hancock, The Erosion of Gas Turbine Blade Materials by Solid Sea Salt, *Corros. Sci.*, *25*(12), 1181-1192, 1985. MetAbs No. 86-351118. **Abstract:** A single impact technique has been used to study the erosion of turbine blade materials IN738C, IN739, and IN792 mod 5A, by sea salt particles.

G.B. Evans, Design Against Corrosion, *Aerospace*, *12*(9), 23-28, 31-34, 1985. MetAbs No. 86-351178. **Abstract:** The selection of materials, types of corrosion, and measures to counter corrosion are described with reference to aircraft. Fatigue crack growth rates of Al alloys 2024-T3 and 7075-T6 in dry air, wet air, distilled water, and 3.5% NaCl solution are given.

A.M. Beccaria and G. Poggi, Effect of Some Surface Treatments on Kinetics of Aluminium Corrosion in NaCl Solutions at Various Hydrostatic Pressures, *Br. Corros. J.*, *21*(1), 19-22, 1986. MetAbs No. 86-351183. **Abstract:** The effect of various surface treatments (grinding, polishing, and pickling) and of prefilming (anodizing and passivation) on the susceptibility of Al to pitting in 0.5M NaCl solution at 20 °C under various hydrostatic pressures has been studied.

C. Andrade and C.L. Page, Pore Solution Chemistry and Corrosion in Hydrated Cement Systems Containing Chloride Salts: A Study of Cation Specific Effects, *Br. Corros. J.*, *21*(1), 49-53, 1986. MetAbs No. 86-351187. **Abstract:** The free chloride and hydroxyl ion concentrations of the pore electrolyte phase present in mature, hydrated cement pastes containing equivalent quantities of chloride ion, introduced into the mix water as NaCl or $CaCl_2$, have been determined for two commercial cements. The corrosion rates of mild steel electrodes embedded in these materials have also been monitored by the method of linear polarization.

S.C. Tjong, Stress Corrosion Cracking Behavior of the Duplex Fe-10Al-29Mn-0.4C Alloy in 20% NaCl Solution at 100 °C, *J. Mater. Sci.*, *21*(4), 1166-1170, 1986. MetAbs No. 86-351254. **Abstract:** The stress-corrosion cracking behavior of the duplex Fe-10Al-29Mn-0.4C alloy having two phases (alpha and gamma) in an aqueous 20% NaCl solution (100 °C) has been investigated using both the static constant load and dynamic slow strain rate tests.

N.B. De Cristofaro, C.A. Acosta, R.C. Salvarezza, and H.A. Videla, The Effect of Sulfides on the Electrochemical Behavior of AISI 304 Stainless Steel in Neutral Buffered Solutions, *Corrosion*, 42(4), 240-242, 1986. MetAbs No. 86-351333. **Abstract:** The electrochemical behavior of AISI 304 in buffered neutral media containing sodium sulfide and mixtures of sodium chloride and sodium sulfide is studied using potentiodynamic techniques complemented with scanning electron microscopy and energy dispersive X-ray analysis to obtain information on the pitting process of the metal.

I. Sekine and Y. Hirakawa, Effect of 1-Hydroxyethylidene-1,1-Diphosphonic Acid on the Corrosion of SS 41 Steel in 0.3% Sodium Chloride Solution, *Corrosion*, 42(5), 272-277, 1986. MetAbs No. 86-351364. **Abstract:** The effectiveness of 1-hydroxyethylidene-1,1-diphosphonic acid (HEDP) as a corrosion inhibitor was investigated by measuring corrosion weight losses and polarization curves of SS 41 steel in 0.3% NaCl.

N.S. Berke, Corrosion Rates of Steel in Concrete. Why Worry?, *ASTM Stand. News*, 14(3), 57-61, 1986. MetAbs No. 86-351489. **Abstract:** The alkaline environments of concrete are adversely affected by Cl ions that result in corrosion of the steel. Two nondestructive electrochemical techniques to determine corrosion rates of steel in concrete—polarization resistance and alternating-current impedance—are discussed.

F. Mancia and A. Tamba, Slow Strain Rate Stress Corrosion Cracking of AISI 304 Stainless Steel in NaCl Solution and Its Prevention by Controlled Cathodic Protection, *Corrosion*, 42(6), 362-367, 1986. MetAbs No. 86-351502. **Abstract:** The slow strain rate test technique was applied to AISI 304 stainless steel in neutral and acidic NaCl solutions to define the laboratory test conditions suitable for inducing transgranular stress-corrosion cracking.

E. McCafferty and P.G. Moore, Corrosion Behavior of Laser-Surface Melted and Laser-Surface Alloyed Steels, *J. Electrochem. Soc.*, 133(6), 1090-1096, 1986. MetAbs No. 86-351703. **Abstract:** Fe-Cr surface alloys of 100 μm thickness and containing 5 to 80% Cr were formed by laser-surface alloying Cr into underlying steel substrates.

W.J.D. Shaw, Stress Corrosion Cracking Behavior of IN-9021 Aluminum Alloy, *Metallography*, 19(2), 227-233, 1986. MetAbs No. 86-351704. **Abstract:** The fracture mechanism during stress-corrosion cracking in 3.5% NaCl solution of IN-9021-T452 is described. IN-9021 is a mechanically alloyed Al alloy of high strength and toughness. The results of the fracture toughness tests are shown.

M.G. Figueroa, R.C. Salvarezza, and A.J. Arvia, The Influence of Temperature on the Pitting Corrosion of Copper, *Electrochim. Acta*, 31(6), 665-669, 1986. MetAbs No. 86-352054. **Abstract:** The influence of temperature on pitting corrosion of Cu in borate-boric acid buffer + sodium chloride is studied in the 0 to 50 °C range, through the change in the breakdown potential determined at a low sweep rate and the passivity current measured at a constant potential.

S. Kameswari, The Role of NaCl in the Hot-Corrosion Behavior of Nimonic Alloy 90, *Oxid. Met.*, 26(1-2), 33-44, 1986. MetAbs No. 86-352123. **Abstract:** The influence of sodium chloride on the hot corrosion behavior of Nimonic alloy 90 has been investigated by employing the half-immersion crucible test. Nimonic 90 samples were hot corroded in the presence of NaCl between 700 to 900 °C.

P. Bruuesch, K. Muller, A. Atrens, and H. Neff, Corrosion of Stainless Steels in Chloride Solution: An XPS Investigation of Passive Films, *Appl.*

Phys. A, A38(1), 1-18, 1985. MetAbs No. 86-352154. **Abstract:** Five commercial steels ranging from the martensitic stainless steel containing 12% Cr to the superferrite containing 29% Cr, 4% Mo, and 2% Ni have been studied by XPS.

C.H. Huang, Corrosion Protection of Copper With Benzotriazole, *Plat. Surf. Finish.*, 73(6), 96-100, 1986. MetAbs No. 86-352189. **Abstract:** It is suggested that the mechanism of Fe phosphating and the protection of Cu with benzotriazole are similar. For maximum tarnish resistance in air, a pH of approximately 5 is best for benzotriazole solutions used to pretreat Cu.

A.K. Bhattamishra and R. Kumar, Influence of the Modification of Environments on the Stress Corrosion/Exfoliation Behavior of Al-Zn-Mg Alloy, in "International Conference on Aluminium-85 (INCAL),'' Indian Institute of Metals, Calcutta, 609-621, 1985. MetAbs No. 86-352215. **Abstract:** Al-Zn-Mg alloys (Al-4.3Zn-1.8Mg-0.3Fe-0.2Si and Al-4Zn-2Mg-0.31Fe-0.19Si sheet) are used for applications that need high strength-to-weight ratios with good forming and welding characteristics. However, the alloy is prone to stress-corrosion cracking and exfoliation corrosion. The stress-corrosion cracking testing was a four-point bend test at 75% of the proof stress.

C. Tjong and C.S. Wu, The Microstructure and Stress Corrosion Cracking Behavior of Precipitation-Hardened Fe-8.7Al-29.7Mn-1.04C Alloy in 20% NaCl Solution, *Mater. Sci. Eng.*, 80(2), 203-211, 1986. MetAbs No. 86-352233. **Abstract:** The microstructure of Fe-8.7Al-29.7Mn-1.04C alloy (approximate weight percent) was examined by transmission electron microscopy after various aging treatments.

W.M.M. Huijbregts, Oxygen and Corrosion Potential Effects on Chloride Stress Corrosion Cracking, *Corrosion*, 42(8), 456-462, 1986. MetAbs No. 86-352257. **Abstract:** Constant extension rate test experiments have been performed on AISI 304 at 200 °C in a 0.001M NaCl solution. During straining, the specimens were kept at constant potentials in the range of -400 to 425 normal hydrogen electrode.

A.M. Beccaria and G. Poggi, Influence of Hydrostatic Pressure and Salt Concentration on Aluminum Corrosion in NaCl Solutions, *Corrosion*, 42(8), 470-475, 1986. MetAbs No. 86-352258. **Abstract:** The effect of hydrostatic pressure on the corrosion kinetics of 99.99% Al in NaCl solutions at different concentrations at pH 8.2 at 20 °C, and with a dissolved oxygen concentration near saturation (approximately 5 ppm), has been examined.

E.U. Lee, Corrosion Fatigue and Stress Corrosion Cracking of 7475-T7351 Aluminum Alloy, in *Corrosion Cracking*, American Society for Metals, Metals Park, OH, 1986, 123-128. MetAbs No. 86-352601. **Abstract:** The corrosion fatigue and stress-corrosion cracking of 7475-T7351 Al alloy were characterized. Fatigue tests were performed under constant and variable amplitude loadings in a controlled laboratory atmosphere and in a 3.5% NaCl aqueous solution. Stress-corrosion cracking tests were conducted under sustained tension in a 3.5% NaCl aqueous solution.

D.E. Gordon, S.D. Manning, and R.P. Wei, Effects of Salt Water Environment and Loading Frequency on Crack Initiation in 7075-T7651 Aluminum Alloy and Ti-6Al-4V, in *Corrosion Cracking*, American Society for Metals, Metals Park, OH, 1986, 157-165. MetAbs No. 86-352606. **Abstract:** Strain-controlled experiments were conducted on 7075-T7651 Al alloy and beta annealed Ti-6Al-4V in both dry air and salt solution. A new method for acquiring crack initiation data was used.

E.I. Meletis, Stress Corrosion Cracking Properties of 2090 Al-Li Alloy, in *Corrosion Cracking*, American Society for Metals, Metals Park, OH, 1986, 315-326. MetAbs No. 86-352620. **Abstract:** The stress-corrosion cracking properties of 2090 Al-Li alloy (Al-2.9Cu-2.2Li-0.12Zr) were investigated in 3.5% NaCl solution. The alloy was tested in the peak-strength condition and in two overaged tempers.

K. Ramakrishnaiah, Role of Some Biologically Important Compounds on the Corrosion of Mild Steel and Copper in Sodium Chloride Solutions, *Bull. Electrochem.*, 2(1), 7-10, 1986. MetAbs No. 86-352700. **Abstract:** The performance of amino acids and carboxylic acids of biological importance on the corrosion of mild steel and copper in sodium chloride solutions was investigated.

C.F. Clarke, D. Hardie, and P. McKay, The Cracking of Titanium in Hot Aqueous Sodium Chloride Solutions, *Corros. Sci.*, 26(6), 425-440, 1986. MetAbs No. 86-352706. **Abstract:** The results of slow tensile straining of ASTM Grade 2 and Grade 12 Ti in 3.5% aqueous sodium chloride are discussed.

A. Kawashima and K. Hashimoto, The Pitting Corrosion Behavior of Rapidly Solidified Fe-Cr Alloys in 0.5M NaCl Solution, *Corros. Sci.*, 26(6), 467-478, 1986. MetAbs No. 86-352709. **Abstract:** The pitting corrosion resistance of rapidly solidified Fe-Cr alloys was compared with that of conventionally processed counterparts.

E. Bilgram and P.J. Winkler, "Stress Corrosion Behavior of Welded Aluminium Alloy AlMg4.5Mn (5083)," in *Aluminium Weldments III*, Vol 7, Aluminium-Verlag GmbH, Dusseldorf, 1985, 14. MetAbs No. 86-550026. **Abstract:** Stress-corrosion cracking of TIG-welded AlMg4.5Mn (5083) in the sensitized and non-sensitized condition was studied by constant load testing in 3.5% sodium chloride solution according to ASTM G44, "Alternate Immersion Stress Corrosion Testing." Failure analysis was made by micrographs and scanning electron microscopy.

D. Tromans, Effect of Organic Adsorbants on the Aqueous Stress Corrosion Cracking of AA 7075-T651 Aluminum Alloy, *Corrosion*, 42(10), 601-608, 1986. MetAbs No. 87-350022. **Abstract:** The effect of eight different organic adsorbants on the stress-corrosion cracking behavior of the Aluminum Association 7075-T651 alloy in 3.5 wt% NaCl was studied by fracture mechanics testing techniques, using self-loaded double cantilever beam specimens.

W.J.D. Shaw, Aspects of Accelerated SCC Tests on Aluminum Alloys in 3.5% NaCl Solution, in *Corrosion, Failure Analysis, and Metallography*, American Society for Metals, Metals Park, OH, 1986. 565-581. MetAbs No. 87-350064. **Abstract:** Using a constant rate of crack-opening displacement, an evaluation of susceptibility to stress-corrosion cracking in aerated 3.5% NaCl solution was made for Al alloys (7075-T6, 2024-T4, 6061-T651, and IN 9021-T452). Based upon variations in K_{IC} and K_C between air and salt environment tests, the alloys are grouped in order of sensitivity.

C. Pallotta, N. de Cristofano, R.C. Salvarezza, and A.J. Arvia, The Influence of Temperature and the Role of Chromium in the Passive Layer in Relation to Pitting Corrosion of 316 Stainless Steel in NaCl Solution, *Electrochim. Acta*, 31(10), 1265-1270, 1986. MetAbs No. 87-350069. **Abstract:** The electrochemical behavior of 316 stainless steel was studied in nearly neutral electrolytes containing NaCl in the -3 to 50 °C temperature range, using potentiostatic and potentiodynamic techniques. Special attention was paid to both the current fluctuations previous to the irreversible breakdown of the passive film and to the breakdown potential.

T. Magnin, C. Dubessy, and P. Rieux, A Comparison Between the Corrosion Fatigue and the Stress Corrosion Cracking Properties of Al-Zn-Mg and Al-Li Alloys in a 3.5% NaCl Solution, in *Aluminum Alloys: Their Physical and Mechanical Properties*, Vol II, Engineering Materials

Advisory Services Ltd., W. Midlands, UK, 1986, 1177-1188. MetAbs No. 87-350144. **Abstract:** An attempt was made to analyze and compare the stress-corrosion cracking and the corrosion fatigue mechanisms of smooth specimens of Al-5Zn-1.2Mg alloys (7020) and Al-2.5Li-0.25Mn alloys in an aerated 3.5% NaCl solution.

P.P. Pizzo and D.L. Daeschner, Aqueous Sodium Chloride Induced Intergranular Corrosion of Al-Li-Cu Alloys, in *Aluminum Alloys: Their Physical and Mechanical Properties*, Vol II, Engineering Materials Advisory Services Ltd., W. Midlands, UK, 1986, 1197-1226. MetAbs No. 87-350145. **Abstract:** Two methods have been explored to assess the susceptibility of Al-Li-Cu alloys to intergranular corrosion in aqueous sodium chloride solution: (1) constant extension rate testing with and without alternate-immersion pre-exposure and (2) metallographic examination after exposure to a NaCl-H$_2$O$_2$ corrosive solution/Mil-H-6088F.

J.K. Gregory, P.J. Meschter, and J.E. O'Neal, Corrosion of RSP Aluminum-High-Lithium Alloys in Aqueous 3.5% NaCl Solution, *Aluminum Alloys: Their Physical and Mechanical Properties*, Vol II, Engineering Materials Advisory Services Ltd., W. Midlands, UK, 1986, 1227-1235. MetAbs No. 87-350146. **Abstract:** The corrosion behavior of several P/M high-lithium aluminum alloys, as measured by weight loss rates, corrosion potential, and potentiodynamic scans, is assessed.

A. Raharinaivo, P. Brevet, G. Pannier, and G. Grimaldi, The Influence of Concrete Deterioration on Reinforcement Rusting, *Corros. Prev. Control*, 33(4), 83-87, 1986. MetAbs No. 87-350279. **Abstract:** An experimental study was undertaken to develop information on rusting of the reinforcing bar with the condition of the concrete. Steel wires were embedded into concrete samples after 10 months in air or carbon dioxide followed by 1 week in sodium chloride solutions. The composite examples were examined at the end of 3 months following the immersion in chloride solutions.

G.R. Wallwork, Pitting in Welds and Welded Mild Steels—AWRA Document P11-7-85, AWRA Contract 56, *Aust. Weld. Res.*, 14, 69-82, 1985. MetAbs No. 87-350291. **Abstract:** A study of pitting corrosion in mild steel and welded mild steels was carried out. The experimental technique chosen was a scanning microprobe potentiometric method. The electrolyte was sodium chloride. The experiments were designed to evaluate the relationship between sulfide inclusions and pitting corrosion in steels and weld metal of various manganese and sulfur concentrations.

D.R. MacFarlane and S.I. Smedley, The Dissolution Mechanism of Iron in Chloride Solutions, *J. Electrochem. Soc.*, 133(11), 2240-2248, 1986. MetAbs No. 87-350363. **Abstract:** The polarization curve and the electrochemical impedance for the dissolution of Fe in sodium chloride solutions of varying pH of were measured.

Z.S. Tong, B.X. Feng, M.Q. Li, and Y. Shi, Investigation of Transient Polarization Currents During the Corrosion Fatigue of Mild Steel in 3.5% NaCl Solution, *Corrosion*, 42(11), 669-678, 1986. MetAbs No. 87-350381. **Abstract:** The corrosion fatigue behavior of mild steel in aqueous 3.5% NaCl solution has been investigated. The corrosion fatigue crack growth rate and the variation of transient polarization currents have been studied simultaneously under anodic and cathodic polarization conditions and at open circuit potential.

J.M. Lardon, T. Magnin, C. Amzallag, and A. Desestret, The Corrosion Fatigue Behavior of a Duplex Stainless Steel in a 30 g/l NaCl Solution, *Bull. Cercle Etud. Metaux*, 15(11), 21-23, 1986. MetAbs No. 87-350690. **Abstract:** The problems of initiation of cracks in fatigue-corrosion in an austeno-ferritic stainless steel with 50% ferrite are studied by analyzing the influence of both mechanical and electrochemical coupling between the two phases. Theoretical aspects of fatigue-corrosion are examined and the servo-controlled electrohydraulic apparatus for plastic deformation studies under potentiostatic control is described. Results are presented for steel of the Uranus 50 type.

S.C. Tjong, Stress Corrosion Cracking of the Austenitic Fe-Al-Mn Alloy in Chloride Environment, *Werkst. Korros.*, 37(8), 444-447, 1986. MetAbs No. 87-350762. **Abstract:** The stress-corrosion cracking behavior of Fe-8.7Al-29.7Mn-1.04C alloy in a 20% sodium chloride solution (100 °C) has been investigated by the slow strain rate method.

B. Pawlowski, Effect of Microstructure on Stress Corrosion Cracking of Cr-Mn-Si-Ni Steel, *Werkst. Korros.*, 37(8), 448-451, 1986. MetAbs No. 87-350763. **Abstract:** The susceptibility to stress-corrosion cracking of Cr-Mn-Si-Ni steel in 3.5% aqueous sodium chloride solution was determined. The K_{ISCC} values for specimens with two different microstructures and comparable mechanical properties were obtained.

K.P. Sherif and R. Narayan, Corrosion of Aluminium in 1M NaCl—An Impedance Study, *Bull. Electrochem.*, 2(5), 453-456, 1986. MetAbs No. 87-350963. **Abstract:** Bode plots are constructed for air-formed oxide-covered Al electrode in 1M NaCl at pH 7 as a function of time of immersion.

G. Radhakrishnan, S. Birlasekaran, K. Balakrishnan, and P. Subramanian, Microprocessor Based Electrochemical Protection Set Up, *Bull. Electrochem.*, 2(5), 499-501, 1986. MetAbs No. 87-350968. **Abstract:** The design details of an automated multielectrochemical protection setup for laboratory study is described. Four bare mild steel cylindrical tanks of 0.6 m diameter and 0.9 m height of approximately 25 m^2 surface area containing 3% NaCl solution were tested for 2 months.

Y.S. Chang and J.C. Lin, Pitting Corrosion Behavior and Mechanism on Carbon Steel Induced by Aluminium Cations, *Mater. Chem. Phys.*, 16(1), 31-44, 1987. MetAbs No. 87-350988. **Abstract:** A series of tests indicated that the corrosion of steel in a 3.5% NaCl solution could be effectively inhibited by Al ions. However, a detrimental side effect of pitting corrosion occurred in longer duration tests. This particular pitting corrosion behavior is induced by adding Al ions which are originally considered to be an inhibitor. A tentative mechanism for the system based on various evidences is proposed.

D.J. Stephenson, J.R. Nicholls, and P. Hancock, The Interaction Between Corrosion and Erosion During Simulated Sea Salt Compressor Shedding in Marine Gas Turbines, *Corros. Sci.*, 26(10), 757-767, 1986. MetAbs No. 87-351014. **Abstract:** The erosion-corrosion behavior of IN738C has been examined under conditions simulating compressor shedding of sea salt particles in a marine gas turbine.

H. Yoshioka, S. Yoshida, A. Kawashima, K. Asami, and K. Hashimoto, The Pitting Corrosion Behavior of Rapidly Solidified Aluminum Alloys, *Corros. Sci.*, 26(10), 795-812, 1986. MetAbs No. 87-351015. **Abstract:** The effects of rapid solidification and alloying on the pitting corrosion resistance of binary and ternary aluminum alloys containing Mg, Ti, Mn, Cr, Fe, Ni, Cu, Zn, Zr, Nb and/or Si in deaerated 0.5N NaCl at 30 °C have been investigated.

J.L. Dawson and M.G.S. Ferreira, Electrochemical Studies of the Pitting of Austenitic Stainless Steel, *Corros. Sci.*, 26(12), 1009-1026, 1986. MetAbs No. 87-351231. **Abstract:** Electrochemical impedance and noise measurements have been obtained both below and above the pitting potential on 316 stainless steel immersed in 3% NaCl solutions. The data are interpreted using an extended model of film rupture and repassivation which incorporates both stochastic processes and modified kinetics of film formation and metal dissolution.

J.L. Dawson and M.G.S. Ferreira, Crevice Corrosion on 316 Stainless Steel in 3% Sodium Chloride Solution, *Corros. Sci.*, 26(12), 1027-1040, 1986. MetAbs No. 87-351232. **Abstract:** The kinetics of the electrochemical reactions occurring during the initiation and propagation of crevice corrosion have been investigated using electrochemical impedance measurements. Two types of crevices formed were employed and comparable results obtained.

T. Notoya, Inhibition of 70/30 Brass Dezincification by Water-Soluble Organic Inhibitors, *Boshoku Gijutsu (Corros. Eng.)*, 35(9), 515-520, 1986. MetAbs No. 87-351446. **Abstract:** Five different types of copper complexing agents as water-soluble dezincification inhibitors for 70/30 brass were tested by using a potentiostatic acceleration technique in 0.5M NaCl solution containing an acetic acid-sodium acetate buffer solution of pH 4.43 at 60 °C.

W. Koehler, Influence of Different Peening Media on the Stress Corrosion and Corrosion Fatigue Behavior of a Welded AlZnMg-Alloy, in *Advances in Surface Treatments: Technology—Applications—Effects*, Vol 3, Pergamon Press, Oxford, 1986, 221-227. MetAbs No. 87-351476. **Abstract:** Using the alloy AlZn4.5Mg2 as an example, the influence of shot peening on the stress-corrosion resistance and corrosion fatigue behavior was investigated. Welded tensile test samples of alloy were shot peened with glass, steel and ceramic beads as well as granulated aluminium material. The samples were tested in 2 and 3.5% NaCl solution for stress-corrosion resistance.

I.B. Singh, R.S. Chaudhary, and T.K.G. Namboodhiri, Corrosion Resistance of Two Magnetic Metallic Glasses in Acidic and Neutral Aqueous Solutions, *J. Electrochem. Soc. India*, 35(4), 279-282, 1986. MetAbs No. 87-351508. **Abstract:** The corrosion resistance of two magnetic metallic glasses was evaluated in H_2SO_4 and NaCl solutions by weight loss measurement and electrochemical techniques.

R. Kerr, F. Solana, I.M. Bernstein, and A.W. Thompson, Microstructural Effects on the Stress Corrosion Cracking Behavior of Medium and High Strength Steels, *Metall. Trans. A*, 18A(6), 1011-1022, 1987. MetAbs No. 87-351660. **Abstract:** The effects of variations in microstructure and strength level on the stress-corrosion cracking susceptibility of three media to high-strength steels (H13, 300M, and HY-130) in 3.5% NaCl have been studied.

A.M.P. Simoes and M.G.S. Ferreira, Crevice Corrosion Studies on Stainless Steel Using Electrochemical Noise Measurements, *Br. Corros. J.*, 22(1), 21-25, 1987. MetAbs No. 87-351700. **Abstract:** Potential noise and current noise measurements were carried out on an AISI 304 stainless steel specimen with an artificial crevice, immersed in 3% NaCl solution.

E. Lunarska, E. Trela, and Z. Szklarska-Smialowska, Pitting Corrosion of Powder Metallurgy AlZnMg Alloys, *Corrosion*, 43(4), 219-228, 1987. MetAbs No. 87-351995. **Abstract:** Pitting susceptibility in 3.5% NaCl was compared for three AlZnMg alloys containing 2.5% magnesium and 8.8, 9.0, and 12.5% Zn. Pit nucleation potentials were determined using electrochemical techniques. The distribution, size, and density of second-phase precipitates in the alloy microstructures were evaluated by scanning electron microscopy.

F. Mancia and A. Tamba, Electrochemical Prevention and Control of Localized Corrosion and SCC of AISI 304 Stainless Steels in NaCl Solutions, *Mater. Sci. Forum*, 8, 189-199, 1986. MetAbs No. 87-352156. **Abstract:** The conditions for preventing and controlling localized corrosion of AISI 304 stainless steels in chloride-containing water are defined by means of experimental electrode potential versus NaCl concentration diagrams. The validity of the diagrams was checked by means of long-term tests carried out under controlled conditions (in a laboratory loop and in neutral seawater) on precorroded and non-precorroded specimens provided with crevice geometry.

M. Duprat, A. Shiri, Y. Derbali, and N. Pebere, An Electrochemical Impedance Approach to the Corrosion Inhibition of a Carbon Steel in Neutral Media, *Mater. Sci. Forum*, 8, 267-279, 1986. MetAbs No. 87-352163. **Abstract:** Coupling of the steady-state (plotting of the current-voltage curves) and transient (determination of the impedance) electrochemical measurements based on a rotating disc electrode were used to study the corrosion inhibition process of a carbon steel in 3% NaCl solutions containing various organic compounds.

P.D.W. Bottomley, J.R. Gill, and J.L. Dawson, Hot Corrosion Investigation by Electrochemical Methods, *Mater. Sci. Forum*, 8, 509-518, 1986. MetAbs No. 87-352184. **Abstract:** The corrosion of nickel and Ni-20Cr alloy in molten Na_2SO_4-NaCl has been investigated at 700 to 950 °C in laboratory air by means of various electrochemical techniques, potential and current noise, ac impedance and cyclic voltammetry using platinum wire as a reference electrode.

S. Kameswari and R.D.K. Misra, Corrosion Behavior of Nimonic-75 and Ni-19.4Cr-1.25Al in NaCl and Na_2SO_4, *Werkst. Korros.*, 38(1), 20-25, 1987. MetAbs No. 87-352229. **Abstract:** The corrosion behavior of Nimonic-75 and Ni-Cr-Al alloys has been investigated in NaCl and Na_2SO_4 by employing the half-immersion crucible test. Weight loss results were obtained as a function of temperature (700 to 800 °C) and concentration of NaCl in the mixture.

W.J. Tomlinson, R. Rushton, C. Cindeny, and S. Palmer, Anodic Polarization and Corrosion of Vanadium, and V-Ta, V-W, V-Cr, and V-Cr-W Alloys in 110% H_2SO_4 and 3% NaCl in Water, *J. Less-Common Met.*, 132(1), L1-L4, 1987. MetAbs No. 87-352314. **Abstract:** Vanadium, V-22Ta, V-7.1W, V-13.6Cr, and V-12.6Cr-7.5W specimens were subjected to accelerated corrosion testing by anodic polarization in 10% sulfuric acid and in 3% salt water.

O. Seri and K. Tagashira, Effect of Dissolved Oxygen on Corrosion Behavior of Al-Fe Alloys in NaCl Solution, *J. Jpn. Inst. Light Met.*, 37(2), 103-108, 1987. MetAbs No. 87-352321. **Abstract:** Differences in corrosion weight loss of Al-Fe alloys as a function of the degree of presence of dissolved oxygen were studied using the 10^3 h immersion corrosion test and electrochemical methods in NaCl solution.

T. Ohnishi and K. Yoshimura, Corrosion Fatigue of 7075 Aluminum Alloy, *J. Jpn. Inst. Light Met.*, 37(2), 127-133, 1987. MetAbs No. 87-352322. **Abstract:** Fatigue tests of 7075-T651 Al alloy were carried out in laboratory air and in aerated 3.5% NaCl aqueous solution.

K. Ogino, A. Hida, S. Kishima, and S. Kumanomido, Susceptibility of Type 431 Stainless Steel to Erosion-Corrosion by Vibratory Cavitation in Corrosive Media, *Wear*, 116(3), 299-307, 1987. MetAbs No. 87-352329. **Abstract:** The structural characteristics of 431 type stainless steel were used to reveal a wide range of strength and corrosion resistance with tempering after quenching; its susceptibility to erosion-corrosion was investigated as a function of tempering temperature. As a preliminary investigation, the mechanical properties and corrosion resistance, in the same solutions as the cavitation media, were also determined as a function of the tempering temperature.

M.P. Muller, A. Atrens, and J.E. Allison, Effect of Cold Work on the Corrosion Fatigue and Stress Corrosion Cracking Properties of the Duplex Stainless Steel A905, *Mater. Tech.*, 15(1), 3-8, 1987. MetAbs No. 87-352362. **Abstract:** A study of the effect of cold work on the susceptibility to stress-corrosion cracking and the corrosion fatigue behavior of the duplex stainless steel (A905) in air and in a 4*N* NaCl solution, at 80

°C and a pH of 5, is discussed. The corrosion fatigue behavior has been determined after an 8% reduction in area and compared with the solution treated material. Constant extension rate tests were performed on material having 8, 17, 31 and 56% reduction in area.

H. Shaikh, H.S. Khatak, and J.B. Gnanamoorthy, Stress Corrosion Cracking of Weldments of AISI Type 316 Stainless Steel, *Werkst. Korros.*, 38(4), 183-187, 1987. MetAbs No. 87-352409. **Abstract:** The weldments of AISI Type 316 stainless steel prepared by the TIG and MMA welding processes were tested in a boiling solution of 5*M* NaCl + 0.15*M* Na_2SO_4 (pH 1.3) at an initial stress level of 200 MPa under the open circuit potential and the impressed potential conditions using the constant load technique.

E. Lunarska and Z. Szklarska-Smialowska, Surface Degradation of Powder Metallurgy AlZnMg Alloys in NaCl Solutions at Different Applied Potentials, *Corrosion*, 43(6), 353-359, June 1987. MetAbs No. 87-352497. **Abstract:** Changes in morphology and chemical composition of corrosion products on the surface of three P/M AlZnMg alloys containing 8.8 to 12.5% Zn, 2.4 to 2.5% Mg, and 1.2 to 1.5% Cu were studied after exposure to deaerated 3.5% NaCl solutions of pH 1, 7, and 13 at room temperature in a wide range of applied potentials, using scanning electron microscopy and energy dispersive spectroscopy techniques.

L.E. Kanary, W.F. Caley, H.A. Hancock, and R.S. Hollingshead, Effect of Zinc Additions to NaCl-Na_2SO_4 Molten Salt Mixture on Hot Corrosion of Nimocast 713, High-Temperature Corrosion of Superalloys, *Mater. Sci. Technol.*, 3(7), 571-575, 1987. MetAbs No. 87-352607. **Abstract:** Hot corrosion studies were conducted at 900 °C in a simulated combustion gas atmosphere containing sulfur trioxide at a partial pressure of 750 Pa on a Ni-base superalloy (Nimocast 713) partially immersed in various ZnSO_4-10 wt.% NaCl-Na_2SO_4 molten salt mixtures. Weight changes were measured thermogravimetrically with time.

T. Magnin and L. Coudreuse, Corrosion Fatigue Mechanisms in B.C.C. Stainless Steels, *Acta Metall.*, 35(8), 2105-2113, 1987. MetAbs No. 87-352653. **Abstract:** The influence of a 3.5% NaCl solution on the cyclic plastic deformation a b.c.c. Fe-26Cr-1Mo ferritic stainless steel is analyzed as a function of the applied electrochemical potential, taking into account the dislocation behavior, the formation of microcracks and the evolution of the cyclic corrosion current transients.

R.C. Salvarezza, N. de Cristofaro, C. Pallotta, and A.J. Arvia, Stochastic and Deterministic Behaviours of 316 Stainless Steel Pitting Corrosion in Phosphate-Borate Buffer Containing Sodium Chloride, *Electrochim. Acta*, 32(7), 1049-1055, 1987. MetAbs No. 87-352693. **Abstract:** The pitting corrosion of 316 stainless steel in phosphate-borate buffer (pH 8.00) containing 0.5*M* NaCl at 25 °C is studied through current transients run under a constant potential step, potentiodynamic runs and scanning electron microscopy.

T. Magnin and P. Rieux, The Relation Between Corrosion Fatigue and Stress Corrosion Cracking in Al-Zn-Mg Alloys, *Scr. Metall.*, 21(7), 907-911, 1987. MetAbs No. 87-352709. **Abstract:** A comparison is made of the stress-corrosion cracking and the corrosion fatigue behavior of smooth specimens of a weldable 7020 Al-Zn-Mg alloy deformed at an imposed strain rate in a 3.5% NaCl solution.

E. Lunarska and Z. Szklarska-Smialowska, Stress Corrosion Cracking of Powder Metallurgy (P/M) AlZnMg Alloys in Deaerated 3.5% NaCl, *Corrosion*, 43(7), 414-424, 1987. MetAbs No. 87-352750. **Abstract:** Stress-corrosion cracking of three wrought P/M AlZnMg alloys differing in Zn content and heat treatment was studied in deaerated 3.5% NaCl solution over a wide range of applied potentials, using the slow strain rate tensile technique. Hydrogen absorption measurements, fractographic and metallographic observations, and energy dispersive spectroscopy analyses of corrosion products were performed.

G.S. Frankel, L. Stockert, F. Hunkeler, and H. Boehni, Metastable Pitting of Stainless Steel, *Corrosion*, 43(7), 429-436, 1987. MetAbs No. 87-352752. **Abstract:** Current transients resulting from metastable pitting events on stainless steel in sodium chloride at potentials below the pitting potential are studied. Metastable pits are covered during growth and exhibit a constant current density.

I.B. Singh, T.K.G. Namboodhiri, and R.S. Chaudhary, On the Corrosion Characteristics of Some Commercial Magnetic Metallic Glasses in NaCl Solution, *J. Mater. Sci.*, 22(8), 2723-2728, 1987. MetAbs No. 87-352771. **Abstract:** The corrosion characteristics of six commercial magnetic metallic glasses in which Fe and B are common base elements have been studied by immersion tests and potentiostatic techniques in various concentrations of NaCl solutions at room temperature.

H. Farzammehr, Ch. Dehghanian, and C.E. Locke, Study of the Effects of Cations on Chloride Caused Corrosion of Steel in Concrete, *Rev. Tech.*, 10(1), 33-40, 1987. MetAbs No. 87-352824. **Abstract:** An electrochemical study has been combined with a pore solution analysis study to determine the effects of cations on chloride caused corrosion of steel in concrete. The effects of $CaCl_2$ and NaCl (mixed in Type I Portland cement concrete) on corrosion of steel in concrete was investigated.

J.C. Lin and H.C. Shih, The Dual Character of an Aluminium-Thiourea Mixture in an NaCl Aqueous Solution—An Inhibitor and an Accelerator of Corrosion for Low Carbon Steel, *Corros. Sci.*, 27(8), 839-858, 1987. MetAbs No. 87-352918. **Abstract:** The effect of temperature on the corrosion inhibition of low-carbon steel in 31.3 g/L NaCl solution has been investigated.

Z. Szklarska-Smialowska, D. Grimes, and J. Park, The Kinetics of Pit Growth on Alloy 600 in Chloride Solutions at High Temperatures, *Corros. Sci.*, 27(8), 859-567, 1987. MetAbs No. 87-352919. **Abstract:** Alloy 600 tube specimens were subjected to corrosion in deaerated 0.1M NaCl solution at applied potentials more positive than the respective pit nucleation potentials, and in deaerated 200 ppm $CuCl_2$ solution at 150 and 280 °C under open circuit conditions.

M. Barteri, F. Mancia, A. Tamba, and R. Bruno, Microstructural Study and Corrosion Performance of Duplex and Superaustenitic Steels in Sour Well Environment, *Centro Sviluppo Materiali Corrosion*, 43(9), 518-525, 1987. MetAbs No. 88-350048. **Abstract:** A study has been made of mill-annealed and cold-worked duplex Dalmine D22 and D25 stainless steels (75 and 140 ksi) and of cold-worked superaustenitic Dalmine D28-32 steel (110 ksi). The materials have been tested under conditions typical of oil and natural gas wells operating in a severe environment. The effect of environmental variables and cold-working on corrosion properties, particularly sulfide stress-corrosion cracking, has been investigated.

M. Drogowska, L. Brossard, and H. Menard, Anodic Copper Dissolution in the Presence of Chlorine$^-$ Ions at pH 12, *Corrosion*, 43(9), 549-552, 1987. MetAbs No. 88-350051. **Abstract:** The dissolution of Cu has been investigated in an alkaline aqueous solution at pH 12 (0.01M NaOH) containing up to 1M NaCl at 25 °C.

K. Komai, K. Minoshima, and M. Yasumura, SCC Crack Growth Behavior in Aluminum Alloy Under Dynamic Mixed Mode Loading Conditions, in "FANUC, Thirtieth Japan Congress on Materials Research," Society of Materials Science, Kyoto, Japan, 1987, 77-83. MetAbs No. 88-350057. **Abstract:** Stress-corrosion crack growth behavior under dynamic mixed mode loading conditions (Mode II dynamic loads with superposition of Mode I static loads) has been investigated in a high-strength Al-Zn-Mg alloy (ZK141) in 3.5% NaCl solution.

K. Ogino, A. Hida, and S. Kishima, Effects of pH on Cavitation Corrosion of Medium Carbon Steel in Distilled Water and Sodium Chloride Solutions, *Corrosion*, 43(11), 652-655, 1987. MetAbs No. 88-350469. **Abstract:** Effects of pH on cavitation corrosion of 0.23% carbon steel in distilled water and in NaCl solutions with a concentration in the range of 3 to 20% were investigated. The pH was controlled with HCl and KOH in the range of 1 to 12. Tests were conducted for 2.0 h, including four periods of 0.5 h each.

S.C. Srivastava and M.B. Ives, Dissolutions of Inclusions in Low-Alloy Steel Exposed to Chloride-Containing Environments, *Corrosion*, 43(11), 687-692, 1987. MetAbs No. 88-350475. **Abstract:** The role played by nonmetallic inclusions in the nucleation of pitting corrosion in low-alloy steels is determined by the detailed analysis of the inclusions in an AISI 1536 steel and their behavior on exposure to ferric chloride and sodium chloride solutions at various pH values.

W.J. Tomlinson and D.R. Brearey, Cathodic Polarization and Corrosion of Zinc and ZnAl in 3% NaCl Solution, *Corrosion*, 44(1), 62-63, 1988. MetAbs No. 88-350931. **Abstract:** The cathodic polarization of pure ZnAl alloys when polished or thermally oxidized in deaerated and aerated 3% NaCl solution was investigated.

I. Suzuki, The Behavior of Corrosion Products on Zinc in Sodium Chloride Solution, *Corros. Sci.*, 25(11), 1029-1034, 1985. MetAbs No. 86-350705. **Abstract:** The behavior of corrosion products on Zn was examined by cathodic polarization in sodium chloride solution. The type and amount of Zn compound contained in corrosion products were determined from cyclic cathodic polarization curves. To evaluate the barrier effect of the corrosion product layer, a new function of compactness of the corrosion layer was introduced.

Corrosion Behavior of Various Metals and Alloys in Sodium Chloride

Material	Condition, other factors, comments	Concentration, %	Temperature, °C (°F)	Duration	Corrosion rate, mm/yr (mils/yr) or other	Ref
Cast irons						
Ductile iron (1.5% Ni)	As-cast with pearlitic matrix. (a)	3.5	30 (86)	...	145 mg/dm^2/d (0.029 in./yr)	167
Ductile iron (1.5% Ni)	Annealed with ferritic matrix. (a)	3.5	30 (86)	...	155 mg/dm^2/d (0.031 in./yr)	167
Gray cast iron (1.5% Ni)	As-cast with pearlitic matrix. (a)	3.5	30 (86)	...	135 mg/dm^2/d (0.027 in./yr)	167

(Continued)

Corrosion Behavior of Various Metals and Alloys in Sodium Chloride (Continued)

Material	Condition, other factors, comments	Concentration, %	Temperature, °C (°F)	Duration	Corrosion rate, mm/yr (mils/yr) or other	Ref
Gray cast iron (1.5% Ni)	Annealed with ferritic matrix. (a)	3.5	30 (86)	...	130 mg/dm^2/d (0.026 in./yr)	167
Unalloyed gray cast iron	As-cast with pearlitic matrix. (a)	3.5	30 (86)	...	180 mg/dm^2/d (0.036 in./yr)	167
Unalloyed gray cast iron	Annealed with ferritic matrix. (a)	3.5	30 (86)	...	140 mg/dm^2/d (0.028 in./yr)	167
Stainless steels						
AL 2205 stainless steel	...	3	Boiling	...	<0.01 (0.1)	169
AM-363 stainless steel	...	...	Room	...	Attacked	120
Type 304 stainless steel	Average metal affected (metal loss + internal penetration): 3.2 mils	...	845 (1550)	100 h	...	166
Type 304 stainless steel	Chemical processing; field or pilot plant test; strong aeration; slight to moderate agitation. Purified sodium chloride slurry from vacuum pans with approximately 75% brine, and approximately 25% salt crystals. Slight pitting: maximum depth of pits from incipient to 0.005 in. Crevice attack (tendency to concentration-cell corrosion)	...	32-38 (90-100)	90 h	<0.0001 in./yr	89
Type 304 stainless steel	Chemical processing; field or pilot plant test; slight to moderate aeration; slight to moderate agitation. With carbon over the standard maximum. Saturated sodium chloride brine, some oxidizing materials from products of combustion of gas flame. Severe pitting: maximum depth of pits over 0.010 in. Crevice attack (tendency to concentration-cell corrosion)	...	82 (180)	52 d	0.0004 in./yr	89
Type 304 stainless steel	Chemical processing; field or pilot plant test; slight to moderate aeration; slight to moderate agitation. Saturated sodium chloride brine, some oxidizing materials from products of combustion of gas flame. Severe pitting: maximum depth of pits from over 0.010 in. Crevice attack (tendency to concentration-cell corrosion)	...	82 (180)	52 d	0.0007 in./yr	89
Type 304 stainless steel	Chemical processing; field or pilot plant test; slight to moderate aeration; rapid agitation. Saturated sodium chloride solution (Oliver vacuum filter). Severe pitting: maximum depth of pits over 0.010 in. Crevice attack (tendency to concentration-cell corrosion)	...	32 (90)	90 d	0.0012 in./yr	89
Type 304 stainless steel	Metal processing; field or pilot plant test; slight to moderate aeration; slight to moderate agitation. Saturated to 15.3% sodium chloride solution (alternate immersion). Crevice attack (tendency to concentration-cell corrosion)	...	16-27 (60-80)	160 d	0.0002 in./yr	89
Type 304 stainless steel	Chemical processing; field or pilot plant test; no aeration; rapid agitation. With carbon over the standard maximum. Vapors from boiling saturated sodium chloride solution (evaporator). Severe pitting: maximum depth of pits over 0.010 in. Crevice attack (tendency to concentration-cell corrosion)	...	99 (210)	210 d	0.0001 in./yr	89
Type 304 stainless steel	Air conditioning; field or pilot plant test; no aeration; no agitation. Sodium chloride solution, pH 8.5. Severe pitting: maximum depth of pits over 0.010 in. Crevice attack (tendency to concentration-cell corrosion)	...	8 (17)	90 d	0.00015 in./yr	89
Type 304 stainless steel	Air conditioning; field or pilot plant test; no aeration; no agitation; low-carbon grade: 0.03% maximum. Sodium chloride solution, pH 8.5. Severe pitting: maximum depth of pits over 0.010 in. Crevice attack (tendency to concentration-cell corrosion)	...	8 (17)	90 d	0.0001 in./yr	89
Type 304 stainless steel	Refrigeration; field or pilot plant test; slight to moderate aeration; rapid agitation. Sodium chloride spray, pH 8.5. Severe pitting: maximum depth of pits over 0.010 in. Crevice attack (tendency to concentration-cell corrosion)	...	8 (17)	90 d	0.00013 in./yr	89
Type 304 stainless steel	Refrigeration; field or pilot plant test; slight to moderate aeration; rapid agitation; low-carbon grade: 0.03% C maximum. Sodium chloride spray, pH 8.5. Severe pitting: maximum depth of pits over 0.010 in. Crevice attack (tendency to concentration-cell corrosion)	...	8 (17)	90 d	0.00011 in./yr	89

(Continued)

Corrosion Behavior of Various Metals and Alloys in Sodium Chloride (Continued)

Material	Condition, other factors, comments	Concentration, %	Temperature, °C (°F)	Duration	Corrosion rate, mm/yr (mils/yr) or other	Ref
Type 304 stainless steel	Soap processing; field or pilot plant test; strong aeration; slight to moderate agitation; welded. Sodium chloride and 13-17% sodium sulfate, 10-12% glycerine, spent soap lye treated with ferric chloride and sulfuric acid to pH 4.5, mud and water. Severe pitting: maximum depth of pits over 0.010 in. Crevice attack (tendency to concentration-cell corrosion)	...	29 (85)	105 d	0.001 in./yr	89
Type 304 stainless steel	Soap processing; field or pilot plant test; slight to moderate aeration; slight to moderate agitation; welded. Sodium chloride and 13-16% sodium sulfate, acid lye treated with alkali to pH 9, 10-12% glycerine, mud and water. Severe pitting: maximum depth of pits over 0.010 in. Crevice attack (tendency to concentration-cell corrosion)	...	29 (85)	105 d	0.006 in./yr	89
Type 304 stainless steel	Soap processing; field or pilot plant test; slight to moderate aeration; slight to moderate agitation; welded. Sodium chloride and 13-16% sodium sulfate, acid lye treated with alkali to pH 9, 10-12% glycerine, mud and water. Severe pitting: maximum depth of pits over 0.010 in.	...	29 (85)	105 d	0.004 in./yr	89
Type 304 stainless steel	Soap processing; field or pilot plant test; slight to moderate aeration; slight to moderate agitation; welded. Sodium chloride and 13-16% sodium sulfate, acid lye treated with alkali to pH 9, 10-12% glycerine, mud and water. Moderate pitting: maximum depth of pits from 0.005 to 0.010 in. Crevice attack (tendency to concentration-cell corrosion)	...	29 (85)	105 d	0.0001 in./yr	89
Type 304 stainless steel	Chemical processing; field or pilot plant test; strong aeration; rapid agitation. With carbon over the standard maximum. Plus sodium chloride and potassium chloride. Crevice attack (tendency to concentration-cell corrosion)	...	54 (130)	45 d	0.0022 in./yr	89
Type 304 stainless steel	Chemical processing. Sodium chloride with 3% water, and 0.7% ferrous chloride. Slight pitting: maximum depth of pits from incipient to 0.005 in. Crevice attack (tendency to concentration-cell corrosion)	...	...	147 d	0.0002 in./yr	89
Type 304 stainless steel	Chemical processing; field or pilot plant test; strong aeration. Sodium chloride bittern (heat-exchanger head). Severe pitting: maximum depth of pits over 0.010 in. Stress corrosion cracking	...	76 (169)	168 d	0.0006 in./yr	89
Type 304 stainless steel	Tanning; field or pilot plant test; Sodium chloride plus sodium sulfate	...	...	180 d	0.0002 in./yr	89
Type 304 stainless steel	Soap processing; field or pilot plant test; slight to moderate aeration; rapid agitation. Plus sodium chloride, sodium sulfate, glycerine, pH 6-10 (vertical tube evaporator). Severe pitting: maximum depth of pits over 0.010 in. Crevice attack (tendency to concentration-cell corrosion)	...	60-66 (140-150)	1235 d	<0.0001 in./yr	89
Type 304 stainless steel	Soap processing; field or pilot plant test; no aeration; no agitation. Saturated salt solution of glycerine and water, with 1-80% gylcerine (Wooster-Sanger evaporator, vapors). Severe pitting: maximum depth of pits over 0.010 in. Crevice attack (tendency to concentration-cell corrosion)	...	60-104 (140-220)	91 d	0.0003 in./yr	89
Type 304 stainless steel	Soap processing; field or pilot plant test; Plus salt and crude glycerine, 7-25% solids, water vapor, pH 7-9	...	88 (190)	24 d	nil	89
Type 304 stainless steel	Mining; field or pilot plant test; strong aeration; slight to moderate agitation. Spent brine mine water from Frasch process with 500-1000 ppm calcium carbonate, 150-200 ppm hydrogen sulfide, 75-100 ppm polysulfides, 4-10 ppm thiosulfates as hydrogen sulfide, pH 6-6.8. Severe pitting: maximum depth of pits over 0.010 in.	~1.6	49 (120)	67 d	0.0001 in./yr	89
Type 304 stainless steel	Chemical processing; field or pilot plant test; slight to moderate aeration; no agitation. Plant-waste effluent with 4-5% solids, chlorides, carbonates, sulfates, sulfides and organic salts, water remainder, pH 10	2	16 (60)	105 d	<0.0001 in./yr	89

(Continued)

Corrosion Behavior of Various Metals and Alloys in Sodium Chloride (Continued)

Material	Condition, other factors, comments	Concentration, %	Temperature, °C (°F)	Duration	Corrosion rate, mm/yr (mils/yr) or other	Ref
Type 304 stainless steel	Research; laboratory test; strong aeration; no agitation. Moderate pitting: maximum depth of pits from 0.005 to 0.010 in.	4	91 (195)	1 d	0.0146 in./yr	89
Type 304 stainless steel	Agriculture (fertilizer); field or pilot plant test; no aeration; slight to moderate agitation. Plus 3.5% hydrofluosilicic acid. Severe pitting: maximum depth of pits over 0.010 in. Crevice attack (tendency to concentration-cell corrosion)	4.7	27 (80)	35 d	0.0026 in./yr	89
Type 304 stainless steel	Chemical (distillation) processing; field or pilot plant test; no aeration; rapid agitation. Plus 1% sodium hydroxide (bottom of column). Crevice attack (tendency to concentration-cell corrosion)	5-4	104 (220)	58 d	<0.0001 in./yr	89
Type 304 stainless steel	Chemical processing; field or pilot plant test; strong aeration; rapid agitation. Plus 4.5% potassium chloride	5	19 (67)	35 d	<0.0001 in./yr	89
Type 304 stainless steel	Tanning; field or pilot plant test. Plus pickle liquor with 0.25-0.5% sulfuric acid	~7	16-21 (60-70)	180 d	0.0022 in./yr	89
Type 304 stainless steel	Tanning; field or pilot plant test. Plus pickle liquor with 0.25-0.5% sulfuric acid (above liquor level)	~7	16-21 (60-70)	180 d	<0.0001 in./yr	89
Type 304 stainless steel	Textile processing; laboratory test; rapid agitation	10	66 (150)	4 d	0.0007 in./yr	89
Type 304 stainless steel	Mining; field or pilot plant test; no aeration; no agitation. Plus acidic salt stripping solution with 70 g/L chloride, 50 g/L sulfate, 20-25 g/L nitrate, 4-5 g/L thorium, 1 g/L ferric ion, sulfuric acid 0.1N, and pH approximately 0.5. Slight pitting: maximum depth of pits from incipient to 0.005 in.	10.5	31 (86)	21 d	0.018 in./yr	89
Type 304 stainless steel	Tanning; field or pilot plant test; slight to moderate agitation. Acidified with sulfuric acid, petroleum solvent added, pH 2.5 (sheepskin degreasing drum)	12	...	180 d	0.0001 in./yr	89
Type 304 stainless steel	Mining (sulfur); field or pilot plant test; strong aeration; rapid agitation. Waste brine with 1 g/L calcium chloride, and 250 ppm hydrogen sulfide (line). Severe pitting: maximum depth of pits over 0.010 in. Crevice attack (tendency to concentration-cell corrosion)	~12	44 (112)	17 d	0.156 in./yr	89
Type 304 stainless steel	Chemical processing; field or pilot plant test; slight to moderate aeration; slight to moderate agitation. Sodium chloride slurry with approximately 12% potassium chloride (Dorr thickener, center well). Slight pitting: maximum depth of pits from incipient to 0.005 in.	~14	25 (77)	38 d	0.0003 in./yr	89
Type 304 stainless steel	Chemical processing; field or pilot plant test; no aeration; rapid agitation. Sodium chloride bittern plus chloride ion 5N, 55 g/L sulfate ion, 41 g/L magnesium ion, sodium and potassium ions balance of cations, and pH 2-5 (heat exchanger). Stress corrosion cracking	~14	77 (170)	90 d	0.0036 in./yr	89
Type 304 stainless steel	Soap processing; field or pilot plant test; strong aeration; rapid agitation. Residual soap with 0.25% aluminum chloride hydrate (filter). Severe pitting: maximum depth of pits over 0.010 in.	18	71 (160)	65 d	0.0007 in./yr	89
Type 304 stainless steel	Soap processing; field or pilot plant test; strong aeration; rapid agitation. Residual soap with 0.25% aluminum chloride hydrate	18	74 (165)	65 d	<0.0001 in./yr	89
Type 304 stainless steel	Soap processing; field or pilot plant test; strong aeration; rapid agitation. Residual soap with approximately 0.03% total sodium oxide, and approximately 0.0003% free sodium oxide. Crevice attack (tendency to concentration-cell corrosion)	18	74 (165)	65 d	0.0002 in./yr	89
Type 304 stainless steel	Soap processing; field or pilot plant test; strong aeration; rapid agitation. Residual soap with approximately 0.03% total sodium oxide, and approximately 0.003% free sodium oxide. Crevice attack (tendency to concentration-cell corrosion)	18	60 (140)	65 d	0.0004 in./yr	89
Type 304 stainless steel	Soap processing; field or pilot plant test; strong aeration; rapid agitation. Plus approximately 0.25% aluminum chloride hydrate, 110 psi	18	74 (165)	65 d	<0.0001 in./yr	89

(Continued)

Corrosion Behavior of Various Metals and Alloys in Sodium Chloride (Continued)

Material	Condition, other factors, comments	Concentration, %	Temperature, °C (°F)	Duration	Corrosion rate, mm/yr (mils/yr) or other	Ref
Type 304 stainless steel	Soap processing; field or pilot plant test; strong aeration; rapid agitation. Plus approximately 0.25% aluminum chloride hydrate. Severe pitting: maximum depth of pits over 0.010 in.	18	71 (160)	65 d	0.00064 in./yr	89
Type 304 stainless steel	Soap processing; field or pilot plant test; strong aeration; rapid agitation. Plus approximately 0.03% total sodium oxide, approximately 0.003% free sodium oxide, pressure 110 psi. Slight pitting: maximum depth of pits from incipient to 0.005 in. Crevice attack (tendency to concentration-cell corrosion)	18	71 (160)	46 d	0.0004 in./yr	89
Type 304 stainless steel	Soap processing; field or pilot plant test; strong aeration; rapid agitation. Plus approximately 0.03% total sodium oxide, approximately 0.003% free sodium oxide, pressure 110 psi. Crevice attack (tendency to concentration-cell corrosion)	18	60 (140)	46 d	0.00084 in./yr	89
Type 304 stainless steel	Research; laboratory test. Sodium chloride spray. Severe pitting: maximum depth of pits over 0.010 in.	20	35 (95)	84 d	0.00036 in./yr	89
Type 304 stainless steel	Chemical processing; field or pilot plant test; strong aeration; rapid agitation. Sodium chloride solution with 39 g/L free ammonia, 1.5 g/L fixed ammonia as ammonium chloride, 19 g/L carbon dioxide, and 0.5 g/L hydrogen sulfide (piping). Severe pitting: maximum depth of pits over 0.010 in.	~21.2	63 (145)	174 d	<0.0001 in./yr	89
Type 304 stainless steel	Chemical processing; field or pilot plant test; no aeration; rapid agitation. Sodium chloride solution, with 60 g/L sodium sulfate, and 7 g/L sodium hydroxide (crystallizer tank)	~22	9 (48)	119 d	<0.0001 in./yr	89
Type 304 stainless steel	Research; laboratory test. Remainder water. Slight pitting: maximum depth of pits from incipient to 0.005 in.	25	60 (140)	4 d	nil	89
Type 304 stainless steel	Chemical processing; laboratory test. Remainder water (vapors, liquid). Slight pitting: maximum depth of pits from incipient to 0.005 in.	25	60 (140)	4.5 d	nil	89
Type 304 stainless steel	Chemical processing; field or pilot plant test; slight to moderate aeration; rapid agitation. With carbon over the standard maximum. Sodium chloride brine with oxidizing materials from combustion products of gas flame (open evaporator). Moderate pitting: maximum depth of pits from 0.005 to 0.010 in. Crevice attack (tendency to concentration-cell corrosion)	<50	93 (200)	14 d	0.009 in./yr	89
Type 304 stainless steel	Chemical processing; field or pilot plant test; slight to moderate aeration; rapid agitation; low-carbon grade: 0.03 % C maximum. Sodium chloride brine with oxidizing materials from combustion products of gas flame (open evaporator). Moderate pitting: maximum depth of pits from 0.005 to 0.010 in. Crevice attack (tendency to concentration-cell corrosion)	<50	93 (200)	14 d	0.0215 in./yr	89
Type 304 stainless steel	Chemical processing; field or pilot plant test; no aeration; rapid agitation. Plus 8% sodium hydroxide, 1% sodium chlorate; 1% ammonia, and the remainder water (ammonia still)	50	204 (400)	27 d	0.004 in./yr	89
Type 310 stainless steel	Average metal affected (metal loss + internal penetration): 4.2 mils	...	845 (1550)	100 h	...	166
Type 316 stainless steel	Average metal affected (metal loss + internal penetration): 3.2 mils	...	845 (1550)	100 h	...	166
Type 316 stainless steel	Chemical processing; field or pilot plant test; strong aeration; slight to moderate agitation. Purified sodium chloride slurry from vacuum pans with approximately 75% brine, and approximately 25% salt crystals	...	32-38 (90-100)	90 h	<0.0001 in./yr	89
Type 316 stainless steel	Chemical processing; field or pilot plant test; slight to moderate aeration; slight to moderate agitation. Saturated sodium chloride brine, some oxidizing materials from products of combustion of gas flame. Severe pitting: maximum depth of pits over 0.010 in. Crevice attack (tendency to concentration-cell corrosion)	...	82 (180)	52 d	0.0022 in./yr	89

(Continued)

Corrosion Behavior of Various Metals and Alloys in Sodium Chloride (Continued)

Material	Condition, other factors, comments	Concentration, %	Temperature, °C (°F)	Duration	Corrosion rate, mm/yr (mils/yr) or other	Ref
Type 316 stainless steel	Chemical processing; field or pilot plant test; slight to moderate aeration; rapid agitation. Saturated sodium chloride solution (Oliver vacuum filter). Slight pitting: maximum depth of pits from incipient to 0.005 in.	...	32 (90)	90 d	0.0001 in./yr	89
Type 316 stainless steel	Metal processing; field or pilot plant test; slight to moderate aeration; slight to moderate agitation. Saturated to 15.3% sodium chloride solution (alternate immersion). Crevice attack (tendency to concentration-cell corrosion)	...	16-27 (60-80)	160 d	0.0001 in./yr	89
Type 316 stainless steel	Chemical processing; field or pilot plant test; no aeration; rapid agitation. Vapors from boiling saturated sodium chloride solution (evaporator). Moderate pitting: maximum depth of pits from 0.005 to 0.010 in. Crevice attack (tendency to concentration-cell corrosion)	...	99 (210)	210 d	<0.0001 in./yr	89
Type 316 stainless steel	Air conditioning; field or pilot plant test; no aeration; no agitation. Sodium chloride solution, pH 8.5. Severe pitting: maximum depth of pits over 0.010 in. Crevice attack (tendency to concentration-cell corrosion)	...	8 (17)	90 d	<0.0001 in./yr	89
Type 316 stainless steel	Refrigeration; field or pilot plant test; slight to moderate aeration; rapid agitation. Sodium chloride spray, pH 8.5. Crevice attack (tendency to concentration-cell corrosion)	...	8 (17)	90 d	<0.0001 in./yr	89
Type 316 stainless steel	Chemical processing; field or pilot plant test; strong aeration; rapid agitation. Saturated salt brine, hydrogen sulfide 0.15 g/L, pH 6.7. Severe pitting: maximum depth of pits over 0.010 in.	...	38 (100)	393 d	0.0001 in./yr	89
Type 316 stainless steel	Soap processing; field or pilot plant test; strong aeration; slight to moderate agitation; welded. Sodium chloride and 13-17% sodium sulfate, 10-12% glycerine, spent soap lye treated with ferric chloride and sulfuric acid to pH 4.5, mud and water. Severe pitting: maximum depth of pits over 0.010 in. Crevice attack (tendency to concentration-cell corrosion)	...	29 (85)	105 d	0.001 in./yr	89
Type 316 stainless steel	Soap processing; field or pilot plant test; slight to moderate aeration; slight to moderate agitation; welded. Sodium chloride and 13-16% sodium sulfate, acid lye treated with alkali to pH 9, 10-12% glycerine, mud and water. Severe pitting: maximum depth of pits over 0.010 in. Crevice attack (tendency to concentration-cell corrosion)	...	29 (85)	105 d	0.003 in./yr	89
Type 316 stainless steel	Soap processing; field or pilot plant test; slight to moderate aeration; slight to moderate agitation; welded. Sodium chloride and 13-16% sodium sulfate, acid lye treated with alkali to pH 9, 10-12% glycerine, mud and water	...	29 (85)	105 d	0.003 in./yr	89
Type 316 stainless steel	Soap processing; field or pilot plant test; slight to moderate aeration; slight to moderate agitation; welded. Sodium chloride and 13-16% sodium sulfate, acid lye treated with alkali to pH 9, 10-12% glycerine, mud and water. Crevice attack (tendency to concentration-cell corrosion)	...	29 (85)	105 d	<0.0001 in./yr	89
Type 316 stainless steel	Chemical processing; field or pilot plant test; strong aeration; rapid agitation. Sodium chloride plus potassium chloride. Crevice attack (tendency to concentration-cell corrosion)	...	54 (130)	45 d	0.0022 in./yr	89
Type 316 stainless steel	Salt processing; field or pilot plant test; no aeration; rapid agitation. Purified sodium chloride brine, acidified with hydrochloric acid to pH 3.5-4.5	...	109 (228)	18 d	0.263 in./yr	89
Type 316 stainless steel	Chemical processing. Sodium chloride with 3% water, and 0.7% ferrous chloride. Slight pitting: maximum depth of pits from incipient to 0.005 in. Crevice attack (tendency to concentration-cell corrosion)	...	...	147 d	0.0001 in./yr	89
Type 316 stainless steel	Chemical processing; field or pilot plant test; strong aeration. Sodium chloride bittern (heat-exchanger head). Severe pitting: maximum depth of pits over 0.010 in.	...	76 (169)	168 d	0.0006 in./yr	89

(Continued)

Corrosion Behavior of Various Metals and Alloys in Sodium Chloride (Continued)

Material	Condition, other factors, comments	Concentration, %	Temperature, °C (°F)	Duration	Corrosion rate, mm/yr (mils/yr) or other	Ref
Type 316 stainless steel	Tanning; field or pilot plant test; Sodium chloride plus sodium sulfate	...	...	180 d	0.0001 in./yr	89
Type 316 stainless steel	Soap processing; field or pilot plant test; slight to moderate aeration; rapid agitation. Sodium chloride plus sodium sulfate, glycerine, pH 6-10 (vertical tube evaporator)	...	60-66 (140-150)	1235 d	<0.0001 in./yr	89
Type 316 stainless steel	Soap processing; field or pilot plant test; no aeration; no agitation. Saturated salt solution of glycerine and water, with 1-80% gylcerine (Wooster-Sanger evaporator, vapors). Slight pitting: maximum depth of pits from incipient to 0.005 in. Crevice attack (tendency to concentration-cell corrosion)	...	60-104 (140-220)	91 d	<0.0001 in./yr	89
Type 316 stainless steel	Soap processing; field or pilot plant test; Plus salt and crude glycerine, 7-25% solids, water vapor, pH 7-9	...	88 (190)	24 d	nil	89
Type 316 stainless steel	Chemical processing; field or pilot plant test; strong aeration; rapid agitation. Plus oil-field brine, 10% calcium and magnesium chlorides, 0.4% bromine, pH 6. Severe pitting: maximum depth of pits over 0.010 in.	0.15	65 (149)	144 d	0.016 in./yr	89
Type 316 stainless steel	Mining; field or pilot plant test; strong aeration; slight to moderate agitation. Spent brine mine water from Frasch process with 500-1000 ppm calcium carbonate, 150-200 ppm hydrogen sulfide, 75-100 ppm polysulfides, 4-10 ppm thiosulfates as hydrogen sulfide, pH 6-6.8. Severe pitting: maximum depth of pits over 0.010 in.	~1.6	49 (120)	67 d	0.0001 in./yr	89
Type 316 stainless steel	Chemical processing; field or pilot plant test; slight to moderate aeration; no agitation. Plant-waste effluent with 4-5% solids, chlorides, carbonates, sulfates, sulfides and organic salts, water remainder, pH 10	2	16 (60)	105 d	<0.0001 in./yr	89
Type 316 stainless steel	...	3	Boiling	...	0.005 (0.2)	51
Type 316 stainless steel	Plus 20 ppm Cu^{2+}	3	Room	...	0.025 (1.0)	51
Type 316 stainless steel	Research; laboratory test; strong aeration; no agitation	4	91 (195)	1 d	<0.0001 in./yr	89
Type 316 stainless steel	Chemical (distillation) processing; field or pilot plant test; no aeration; rapid agitation. Plus 1% sodium hydroxide (bottom of column). Crevice attack (tendency to concentration-cell corrosion)	4-5	104 (220)	58 d	<0.0001 in./yr	89
Type 316 stainless steel	Agriculture (fertilizer); field or pilot plant test; no aeration; slight to moderate agitation. Plus 3.5% hydrofluosilicic acid. Slight pitting: maximum depth of pits from incipient to 0.005 in. Crevice attack (tendency to concentration-cell corrosion)	4.7	27 (80)	35 d	0.0007 in./yr	89
Type 316 stainless steel	Chemical processing; field or pilot plant test; strong aeration; rapid agitation. Plus 4.5% potassium chloride	5	19 (67)	35 d	<0.0001 in./yr	89
Type 316 stainless steel	Tanning; field or pilot plant test. Plus pickle liquor with 0.25-0.5% sulfuric acid	~7	16-21 (60-70)	180 d	0.0012 in./yr	89
Type 316 stainless steel	Tanning; field or pilot plant test. Plus pickle liquor with 0.25-0.5% sulfuric acid (above liquor level)	~7	16-21 (60-70)	180 d	<0.0001 in./yr	89
Type 316 stainless steel	Textile processing; laboratory test; rapid agitation	10	66 (150)	4 d	<0.0001 in./yr	89
Type 316 stainless steel	Mining; field or pilot plant test; no aeration; no agitation. Acidic salt stripping solution with 70 g/L chloride, 50 g/L sulfate, 20-25 g/L nitrate, 4-5 g/L thorium, 1 g/L ferric ion, sulfuric acid 0.1N, and pH approximately 0.5. Severe pitting: maximum depth of pits over 0.010 in. Crevice attack (tendency to concentration-cell corrosion)	10.5	31 (86)	21 d	0.016 in./yr	89
Type 316 stainless steel	Tanning; field or pilot plant test; slight to moderate agitation. Acidified with sulfuric acid, petroleum solvent added, pH 2.5 (sheepskin degreasing drum)	12	...	180 d	0.0001 in./yr	89

(Continued)

Corrosion Behavior of Various Metals and Alloys in Sodium Chloride (Continued)

Material	Condition, other factors, comments	Concen-tration, %	Temperature, °C (°F)	Duration	Corrosion rate, mm/yr (mils/yr) or other	Ref
Type 316 stainless steel	Mining (sulfur); field or pilot plant test; strong aeration; rapid agitation. Waste brine with 1 g/L calcium chloride, and 250 ppm hydrogen sulfide (line). Severe pitting: maximum depth of pits over 0.010 in. Crevice attack (tendency to concentration-cell corrosion)	~12	44 (112)	17 d	0.047 in./yr	89
Type 316 stainless steel	Chemical processing; field or pilot plant test; slight to moderate aeration; slight to moderate agitation. Sodium chloride slurry with approximately 12% potassium chloride (Dorr thickener, center well)	~14	25 (77)	38 d	0.0003 in./yr	89
Type 316 stainless steel	Chemical processing; field or pilot plant test; no aeration; rapid agitation. Sodium chloride bittern plus chloride ion 5N, 55 g/L sulfate ion, 41 g/L magnesium ion, sodium and potassium ions balance of cations, and pH 2-5 (heat exchanger). Severe pitting: maximum depth of pits over 0.010 in.	~14	77 (170)	90 d	0.006 in./yr	89
Type 316 stainless steel	Chemical processing; laboratory test; slight to moderate aeration; slight to moderate agitation. Plus 240 g/L ammonium perchlorate, 78 g/L sodium perchlorate, 2 g/L sodium chlorate, trace ammonium chloride, and pH 4.8. Severe pitting: maximum depth of pits over 0.010 in. Crevice attack (tendency to concentration-cell corrosion)	~15.3	68-77 (155-170)	98 d	0.0002 in./yr	89
Type 316 stainless steel	Soap processing; field or pilot plant test; strong aeration; rapid agitation. Residual soap with 0.25% aluminum chloride hydrate (filter). Severe pitting: maximum depth of pits over 0.010 in.	18	71 (160)	65 d	0.0004 in./yr	89
Type 316 stainless steel	Soap processing; field or pilot plant test; strong aeration; rapid agitation. Residual soap with 0.25% aluminum chloride hydrate	18	74 (165)	65 d	<0.0001 in./yr	89
Type 316 stainless steel	Soap processing; field or pilot plant test; strong aeration; rapid agitation. Residual soap with approximately 0.03% total sodium oxide, and approximately 0.0003% free sodium oxide	18	74 (165)	65 d	0.0001 in./yr	89
Type 316 stainless steel	Soap processing; field or pilot plant test; strong aeration; rapid agitation. Residual soap with approximately 0.03% total sodium oxide, and approximately 0.003% free sodium oxide	18	60 (140)	65 d	0.0002 in./yr	89
Type 316 stainless steel	Soap processing; field or pilot plant test; strong aeration; rapid agitation. Plus approximately 0.25% aluminum chloride hydrate, 110 psi	18	74 (165)	65 d	<0.0001 in./yr	89
Type 316 stainless steel	Soap processing; field or pilot plant test; strong aeration; rapid agitation. Plus approximately 0.25% aluminum chloride hydrate. Severe pitting: maximum depth of pits over 0.010 in. Crevice attack (tendency to concentration-cell corrosion)	18	71 (160)	65 d	0.00036 in./yr	89
Type 316 stainless steel	Soap processing; field or pilot plant test; strong aeration; rapid agitation. Plus approximately 0.03% total sodium oxide, approximately 0.003% free sodium oxide, pressure 110 psi	18	71 (160)	46 d	0.00014 in./yr	89
Type 316 stainless steel	Soap processing; field or pilot plant test; strong aeration; rapid agitation. Plus approximately 0.03% total sodium oxide, approximately 0.003% free sodium oxide, pressure 110 psi	18	60 (140)	46 d	0.00038 in./yr	89
Type 316 stainless steel	Chemical processing; field or pilot plant test; no aeration; rapid agitation. Sodium chloride brine with 30-50 g/L sodium chlorate, 1-1.5 ppm iron, 1-1.5 ppm mercury, and 0.2% sodium hypochlorite as chlorine. Severe pitting: maximum depth of pits over 0.010 in. Crevice attack (tendency to concentration-cell corrosion)	~19	10 (50)	90 d	0.003 in./yr	89
Type 316 stainless steel	Research; laboratory test. Sodium chloride spray. Slight pitting: maximum depth of pits from incipient to 0.005 in.	20	35 (95)	84 d	<0.0001 in./yr	89
Type 316 stainless steel	Chemical processing; field or pilot plant test; strong aeration; rapid agitation. Sodium chloride solution with 39 g/L free ammonia, 1.5 g/L fixed ammonia as ammonium chloride, 19 g/L carbon dioxide, and 0.5 g/L hydrogen sulfide (piping). Severe pitting: maximum depth of pits over 0.010 in.	~21.2	63 (145)	174 d	<0.0001 in./yr	89

(Continued)

Corrosion Behavior of Various Metals and Alloys in Sodium Chloride (Continued)

Material	Condition, other factors, comments	Concentration, %	Temperature, °C (°F)	Duration	Corrosion rate, mm/yr (mils/yr) or other	Ref
Type 316 stainless steel	Chemical processing; field or pilot plant test; no aeration; rapid agitation. Sodium chloride solution, with 60 g/L sodium sulfate, and 7 g/L sodium hydroxide (crystallizer tank)	~22	9 (48)	119 d	<0.0001 in./yr	89
Type 316 stainless steel	Brine production; field or pilot plant test; strong aeration; slight to moderate agitation. Sodium chloride brine, with 18 g/L sodium sulfate, 18 g/L sodium carbonate, and 1 g/L sodium hydroxide	~23.5	Room-71 (room-160)	225 d	nil	89
Type 316 stainless steel	Chemical processing; field or pilot plant test; strong aeration; no agitation. Sodium chloride brine with 3 g/L calcium sulfate, 0.5 g/L sodium chlorate, and traces of sodium hypochlorite and mercury	~23.6	65 (149)	31 d	0.002 in./yr	89
Type 316 stainless steel	Research; laboratory test. Remainder water	25	60 (140)	4 d	nil	89
Type 316 stainless steel	Chemical processing; laboratory test. Remainder water (vapors, liquid). Slight pitting: maximum depth of pits from incipient to 0.005 in.	25	60 (140)	4.5 d	nil	89
Type 316 stainless steel	Chemical processing; field or pilot plant test; strong aeration; slight to moderate agitation. Saturated sodium chloride solution with 10 g/L calcium chloride, 2 g/L calcium sulfate, pH 6.5	26	10 (50)	180 d	0.0003 in./yr	89
Type 316 stainless steel	Chemical processing; field or pilot plant test; slight to moderate aeration; slight to moderate agitation. Sodium chloride slurry with 17.8% calcium chloride, 3.2% magnesium chloride, solid salt in suspension, pH 6.3 (limed); pH 5.3 (unlimed). Severe pitting: maximum depth of pits over 0.010 in. Crevice attack (tendency to concentration-cell corrosion)	45.6	54 (129)	215 d	0.0011 in./yr	89
Type 316 stainless steel	Chemical processing; field or pilot plant test; slight to moderate aeration; rapid agitation. Sodium chloride brine with oxidizing materials from combustion products of gas flame (open evaporator). Moderate pitting: maximum depth of pits from 0.005 to 0.010 in. Crevice attack (tendency to concentration-cell corrosion)	<50	93 (200)	14 d	0.0418 in./yr	89
Type 316 stainless steel	Chemical processing; field or pilot plant test; no aeration; rapid agitation. Plus 8% sodium hydroxide, 1% sodium chlorate; 1% ammonia, and the remainder water (ammonia still)	50	204 (400)	27 d	0.0023 in./yr	89
Type 317 stainless steel	Salt processing; field or pilot plant test; no aeration; rapid agitation. Purified sodium chloride brine, acidified with hydrochloric acid to pH 3.5-4.5	...	109 (228)	18 d	0.189 in./yr	89
Type 317 stainless steel	Mining; field or pilot plant test; no aeration; no agitation. Acidic salt stripping solution with 70 g/L chloride, 50 g/L sulfate, 20-25 g/L nitrate, 4-5 g/L thorium, 1 g/L ferric ion, sulfuric acid 0.1N, and pH approximately 0.5. Slight pitting: maximum depth of pits from incipient to 0.005 in. Crevice attack (tendency to concentration-cell corrosion)	10.5	31 (86)	21 d	0.0051 in./yr	89
Type 317 stainless steel	Chemical processing; field or pilot plant test; strong aeration; no agitation. Sodium chloride brine with 3 g/L calcium sulfate, 0.5 g/L sodium chlorate, and traces of sodium hypochlorite and mercury	~23.6	65 (149)	31 d	0.0007 in./yr	89
Type 317L stainless steel	...	3	Boiling	...	0.03 (1.0)	169
Type 446 stainless steel	Average metal affected (metal loss + internal penetration): 3.2 mils	...	845 (1550)	100 h	...	166
Aluminum						
IN-9021-T452	Mean value. Aerated	3.5	20 (68)	3 d	0.226 (8.9)	168
IN-9021-T452	Mean value. Aerated	3.5	20 (68)	7 d	0.577 (23.1)	168
IN-9021-T452	Mean value. Aerated	3.5	20 (68)	14 d	0.27 (10.9)	168
IN-9021-T452	Mean value. Aerated	3.5	20 (68)	28 d	0.22 (8.8)	168
Coppers						
70-30 cupronickel	...	...	...	...	Suitable	93
90-10 cupronickel	...	...	...	...	Suitable	93
Admiralty brass	(b)	...	...	...	Good	93

(Continued)

Corrosion Behavior of Various Metals and Alloys in Sodium Chloride (Continued)

Material	Condition, other factors, comments	Concentration, %	Temperature, °C (°F)	Duration	Corrosion rate, mm/yr (mils/yr) or other	Ref
Aluminum bronze	(b)	...	...	...	Good	93
Ampco 8, aluminum bronze	Generally suitable	...	...	...	<0.05 (<2)	96
Architectural bronze	...	...	...	...	Not suitable	93
Brass	(b)	...	...	...	Good	93
Cartridge brass	...	...	...	...	Not suitable	93
Commercial bronze	(b)	...	...	...	Good	93
Electrolytic copper	(b)	...	...	...	Good	93
Free-cutting brass	...	...	...	...	Not suitable	93
Muntz metal	...	...	...	...	Not suitable	93
Naval brass	...	...	...	...	Fair	93
Nickel silver	...	18	...	...	Suitable	93
Phosphor bronze	5% Sn. (b)	...	...	...	Good	93
Phosphor bronze	8% Sn	...	...	...	Suitable	93
Phosphor copper	(b)	...	...	...	Good	93
Red brass	(b)	...	...	...	Good	93
Silicon bronze	Low. (b)	...	...	...	Good	93
Silicon bronze	High. (b)	...	...	...	Good	93
Titanium						
Ti-3Al-2.5V	ASTM Grade 9. Plus 0.5% CH_3COOH + saturated H_2S	5	Room	...	nil	91
Ti-3Al-2.5V	ASTM Grade 9. Plus 0.5% CH_3COOH + 0.1% S + saturated H_2S	25	Room	...	nil	91
Titanium	...	Saturated	Room	...	nil	90
Titanium	pH 7	23	Boiling	...	nil	90
Titanium	pH 1.5	23	Boiling	...	nil	90
Titanium	pH 1.2	23	Boiling	...	0.71 (28.4)	90
Titanium	pH 1.2; some dissolved Cl_2	23	Boiling	...	nil	90
Titanium	Grade 9; pH 1	Saturated	93 (200)	...	nil	33
Titanium	Plus 0.5% CH_3COOH + saturated H_2S	5	Room	...	nil	91
Titanium	Plus 0.5% CH_3COOH + 0.1% S + saturated H_2S	25	Room	...	nil	91
Heat- and corrosion-resistant alloys						
Alloy 825	Chemical processing; field or pilot plant test; slight to moderate aeration; slight to moderate agitation. Saturated sodium chloride brine. Crevice attack (tendency to concentration-cell corrosion)	...	71 (160)	204 d	<0.0001 in./yr	89
Alloy 825	Soap processing; field or pilot plant test; no aeration; no agitation. Saturated salt solution of glycerine and water, with 1-80% gylcerine (Wooster-Sanger evaporator, vapors). Crevice attack (tendency to concentration-cell corrosion)	...	60-104 (140-220)	91 d	<0.0001 in./yr	89
Alloy 825	Chemical processing; field or pilot plant test; strong aeration; rapid agitation. Oil-field brine, 10% calcium and magnesium chlorides, 0.4% bromine, pH 6. Severe pitting: maximum depth of pits over 0.010 in.	0.15	65 (149)	144 d	0.012 in./yr	89
Alloy 825	Chemical (distillation) processing; field or pilot plant test; no aeration; rapid agitation. Plus 1% sodium hydroxide (bottom of column). Crevice attack (tendency to concentration-cell corrosion)	5-4	104 (220)	58 d	<0.0001 in./yr	89
Alloy 825	Mining; field or pilot plant test; no aeration; no agitation. Acidic salt stripping solution with 70 g/L chloride, 50 g/L sulfate, 20-25 g/L nitrate, 4-5 g/L thorium, 1 g/L ferric ion, sulfuric acid 0.1N, and pH approximately 0.5. Severe pitting: maximum depth of pits over 0.010 in. Crevice attack (tendency to concentration-cell corrosion)	10.5	31 (86)	21 d	0.006 in./yr	89

(Continued)

Corrosion Behavior of Various Metals and Alloys in Sodium Chloride (Continued)

Material	Condition, other factors, comments	Concentration, %	Temperature, °C (°F)	Duration	Corrosion rate, mm/yr (mils/yr) or other	Ref
Alloy 825	Chemical processing; laboratory test; slight to moderate aeration; slight to moderate agitation. Plus 240 g/L ammonium perchlorate, 78 g/L sodium perchlorate, 2 g/L sodium chlorate, trace ammonium chloride, and pH 4.8. Slight pitting: maximum depth of pits from incipient to 0.005 in.	~15.3	68-77 (155-170)	98 d	0.0001 in./yr	89
Alloy 825	Brine production; field or pilot plant test; strong aeration; slight to moderate agitation. Sodium chloride brine, with 18 g/L sodium sulfate, 18 g/L sodium carbonate, and 1 g/L sodium hydroxide	~23.5	Room-71 (Room-160)	225 d	nil	89
Alloy 825	Metal processing; field or pilot plant test; slight to moderate aeration; slight to moderate agitation. Sodium chloride solution saturated to 15.3% (alternate immersion)	...	16-27 (60-80)	160 d	<0.0001 in./yr	89
Cabot alloy No. 625	With crevice	3	Room	96 h	nil	67
Cabot alloy No. 625	With crevice	3	50 (122)	96 h	nil	67
Cabot alloy No. 625	With crevice	3	70 (158)	96 h	nil	67
Cabot alloy No. 625	...	4	Room	24 h	nil	67
Cabot alloy No. 625	...	4	70 (158)	24 h	nil	67
Cabot alloy No. 625	...	4	Boiling	24 h	nil	67
Carpenter 20	Chemical processing; field or pilot plant test; slight to moderate aeration; slight to moderate agitation. Saturated sodium chloride brine. Crevice attack (tendency to concentration-cell corrosion)	...	71 (160)	204 d	<0.0001 in./yr	89
Carpenter 20	Chemical processing; field or pilot plant test; slight to moderate aeration; slight to moderate agitation; cast specimens. Saturated sodium chloride brine. Crevice attack (tendency to concentration-cell corrosion)	...	71 (160)	204 d	<0.0001 in./yr	89
Carpenter 20	Chemical processing; field or pilot plant test; strong aeration. Sodium chloride bittern (heat-exchanger head). Severe pitting: maximum depth of pits over 0.010 in.	...	76 (169)	168 d	0.0002 in./yr	89
Carpenter 20	Soap processing; field or pilot plant test; slight to moderate aeration; rapid agitation. Plus sodium chloride, sodium sulfate, glycerine, pH 6-10 (vertical tube evaporator)	...	60-66 (140-150)	1235 d	<0.0001 in./yr	89
Carpenter 20	Soap processing; field or pilot plant test; no aeration; no agitation. Saturated salt solution of glycerine and water, with 1-80% gylcerine (Wooster-Sanger evaporator, vapors). Crevice attack (tendency to concentration-cell corrosion)	...	60-104 (140-220)	91 d	<0.0001 in./yr	89
Carpenter 20	Chemical (distillation) processing; field or pilot plant test; no aeration; rapid agitation. Plus 1% sodium hydroxide (bottom of column). Crevice attack (tendency to concentration-cell corrosion)	4-5	104 (220)	58 d	<0.0001 in./yr	89
Carpenter 20	Mining; field or pilot plant test; no aeration; no agitation. Acidic salt stripping solution with 70 g/L chloride, 50 g/L sulfate, 20-25 g/L nitrate, 4-5 g/L thorium, 1 g/L ferric ion, sulfuric acid 0.1N, and pH approximately 0.5. Slight pitting: maximum depth of pits from incipient to 0.005 in.	10.5	31 (86)	21 d	0.0074 in./yr	89
Carpenter 20	Chemical processing; field or pilot plant test; no aeration; rapid agitation. Sodium chloride bittern plus chloride ion 5N, 55 g/L sulfate ion, 41 g/L magnesium ion, sodium and potassium ions balance of cations, pH 2-5 (heat exchanger). Severe pitting: maximum depth of pits over 0.010 in. Crevice attack (tendency to concentration-cell corrosion)	~14	77 (170)	90 d	0.0038 in./yr	89
Carpenter 20	Chemical processing; laboratory test; slight to moderate aeration; slight to moderate agitation. Plus 240 g/L ammonium perchlorate, 78 g/L sodium perchlorate, 2 g/L sodium chlorate, trace ammonium chloride, pH 4.8. Slight pitting: maximum depth of pits from incipient to 0.005 in.	~15.3	68-77 (155-170)	98 d	0.0001 in./yr	89

(Continued)

Corrosion Behavior of Various Metals and Alloys in Sodium Chloride (Continued)

Material	Condition, other factors, comments	Concen-tration, %	Temperature, °C (°F)	Duration	Corrosion rate, mm/yr (mils/yr) or other	Ref
Carpenter 20	Chemical processing; field or pilot plant test; no aeration; rapid agitation. Sodium chloride brine with 30-50 g/L sodium chlorate, 1-1.5 ppm iron, 1-1.5 ppm mercury, and 0.2% sodium hypochlorite as chlorine. Severe pitting: maximum depth of pits over 0.010 in. Crevice attack (tendency to concentration-cell corrosion)	~19	10 (50)	90 d	0.0006 in./yr	89
Carpenter 20	Chemical processing; field or pilot plant test; strong aeration; rapid agitation. Sodium chloride solution with 39 g/L free ammonia, 1.5 g/L fixed ammonia as ammonium chloride, 19 g/L carbon dioxide, and 0.5 g/L hydrogen sulfide (piping)	~21.2	63 (145)	174 d	0.0001 in./yr	89
Ferralium	...	3	Boiling	...	0.01 (0.4)	51
Ferralium	Plus 20 ppm Cu^{++}	3	Room	...	0.01 (0.4)	51
Ferralium 255	...	3	Boiling	...	0.01 (0.4)	169
Hastelloy alloy S	Average metal affected (metal loss + internal penetration): 6.6 mils	...	845 (1550)	100 h	...	166
Hastelloy alloy X	Average metal affected (metal loss + internal penetration): 3.8 mils	...	845 (1550)	100 h	...	166
Haynes alloy 188	Average metal affected (metal loss + internal penetration): 2.0 mils	...	845 (1550)	100 h	...	166
Haynes alloy 214	Average metal affected (metal loss + internal penetration): 3.1 mils	...	845 (1550)	100 h	...	166
Haynes alloy 230	Average metal affected (metal loss + internal penetration): 5.5 mils	...	845 (1550)	100 h	...	166
Haynes alloy 556	Average metal affected (metal loss + internal penetration): 2.6 mils	...	845 (1550)	100 h	...	166
Inco alloy G	3.18 mm (0.125 in.) sheet in 35,000-ppm chloride as NaCl (pH 5.0) simulated SO_2 scrubber environment. Duplicate specimens, maximum crevice pit depth <0.05 mm (<2 mils), 26% of crevice area attacked	...	58 (135)	30 d	<0.025 (<1)	40
Inco alloy G-3	3.18 mm (0.125 in.) sheet in 35,000-ppm chloride as NaCl (pH 5.0) simulated SO_2 scrubber environment. Maximum crevice pit depth <0.05 mm (<2 mils); 33% of crevice area attacked; 40 crevices per specimen	...	58 (135)	30 d	<0.025 (<1)	40
Incoloy 800	Solutions were prepared with reagent-grade chemicals. Test specimens were cold-rolled, annealed sheet, 2.84 mm (0.112 in.) thick. Incipient pits	10	80 (176)	42 d	<0.003 (<0.1)	44
Incoloy 800	Solutions were prepared with reagent-grade chemicals. Test specimens were cold-rolled, annealed sheet, 2.84 mm (0.112 in.) thick. Pitting occurred after 7 d	20	80 (176)	42 d	0.008 (0.3)	44
Incoloy 800H	Average metal affected (metal loss + internal penetration): 4.3 mils	...	845 (1550)	100 h	...	166
Inconel 600	Average metal affected (metal loss + internal penetration): 7.7 mils	...	845 (1550)	100 h	...	166
Inconel 601	Pitting attack	10	80 (176)	30 d	0.005 (0.2)	64
Inconel 601	Pitting attack	20	80 (176)	30 d	0.008 (0.3)	64
Inconel 617	Average metal affected (metal loss + internal penetration): 4.8 mils	...	845 (1550)	100 h	...	166
Inconel 625	Average metal affected (metal loss + internal penetration): 4.4 mils	...	845 (1550)	100 h	...	166
RA330	Average metal affected (metal loss + internal penetration): 4.6 mils	...	845 (1550)	100 h	...	166
RA333	Average metal affected (metal loss + internal penetration): 7.5 mils	...	845 (1550)	100 h	...	166
Zirconium						
Zr702	Saturated concentration, adjusted to pH 1	Saturated	Boiling	...	0.025 (1.0)	62
Zr705	Saturated concentration, adjusted to pH 1	Saturated	Boiling	...	0.025 (1)	62
Zr702	...	3 to saturated	35 to boiling (95 to boiling)	...	<0.025 (<1)	15
Zr702	...	29	Boiling	...	<0.025 (<1)	15
Zr702	...	Saturated	Room	...	<0.025 (<1)	15

(Continued)

Corrosion Behavior of Various Metals and Alloys in Sodium Chloride (Continued)

Material	Condition, other factors, comments	Concentration, %	Temperature, °C (°F)	Duration	Corrosion rate, mm/yr (mils/yr) or other	Ref
Zr702	Adjusted to pH 1	Saturated	Boiling	...	<0.025 (<1)	15
Zr702	Adjusted to pH 0	Saturated	107 (225)	...	nil	15
Zr702	Plus saturated SO_2	3.5	80 (175)	...	nil	15
Zr702	Plus saturated SO_2	25	80 (175)	...	nil	15
Zr702	Plus saturated SO_2	Saturated	80 (175)	...	nil	15
Zr702	Plus 0.5% acetic acid, 1% S, saturated H_2S	25	215 (420)	...	nil	15
Zr704	Plus 0.5% acetic acid, 1% S, saturated H_2S	25	215 (420)	...	nil	15
Zr705	...	3 to saturated	35 to boiling (95 to boiling)	...	<0.025 (<1)	15
Zr705	Adjusted to pH 1	Saturated	Boiling	...	<0.025 (<1)	15
Zr705	Plus 0.5% acetic acid, 1% S, saturated H_2S	25	215 (420)	...	nil	15
Lead, tin, and zinc						
Lead	...	0.25-6	8 (46)	...	0.005-0.03 (0.2-1.2)	49
Lead	...	0.5-24	25 (77)	...	<50 μm/yr (<2)	95
Lead	Negligible corrosion; Pb recommended for use	...	20 (68)	...	Resistant	94
Tin	Pitting possible in stagnant solutions	...	60 (140)	...	Unsuitable	94
Tin	...	...	100 (212)	...	Unsuitable	94
Tin	...					
Noble metals						
Platinum	...	All	Boiling	...	<0.05 (<2)	5
Platinum	Melt. Provided no ammonia is present	...	800 (1470)	...	<0.05 (<2)	5
Silver	...	All	Boiling	...	<0.05 (<2)	9
Magnesium						
AZ31B	As-cast, as-extruded, or as-rolled; sheet, extrusion. (c)	3	...	14 d	3 g/m²/d (1.9 mg/in.²/d)	170
AZ61A	Specimen size, 75 x 25 x 1.5 mm (3 x 1 x 0.06 in.); surface preparation, HNO_3 pickling; volume of testing solution, 100 ml. Specimens were alternately immersed 30 s in solution and held 2 min in air	3	35 (95)	7 d	1.4 g/m²/d (0.9 mg/in.²/d)	12
AZ61A	Strain hardened and partially annealed; sheet. (c)	3	...	14 d	2 g/m²/d (1.29 mg/in.²/d)	170
AZ63A	As-cast, as-extruded, or as-rolled; sand casting. (c)	3	...	14 d	15 g/m²/d (9.67 mg/in.²/d)	170
AZ63A	Solution heat treated; sand casting. (c)	3	...	14 d	40 g/m²/d (25.1 mg/in.²/d)	170
AZ63A	Solution heat treated and artificially aged; sand casting. (c)	3	...	14 d	20 g/m²/d (12.9 mg/in.²/d)	170
AZ92A	As-cast, as-extruded, or as-rolled; sand casting. (c)	3	...	14 d	40 g/m²/d (25.1 mg/in.²/d)	170
AZ92A	Solution heat treated; sand casting. (c)	3	...	14 d	100 g/m²/d (64.5 mg/in.²/d)	170
AZ92A	Solution heat treated and artificially aged; sand casting. (c)	3	...	14 d	60 g/m²/d (38.7 mg/in.²/d)	170
HK31A	Strain hardened, artificially annealed; sheet. (c)	3	...	14 d	2 g/m²/d (1.29 mg/in.²/d)	170
HM21A	Solution heat treated, strain hardened, and artificially aged; sheet. (c)	3	...	14 d	2 g/m²/d (1.29 mg/in.²/d)	170
M1A	As-cast, as-extruded, or as-rolled; extrusion. (c)	3	...	14 d	4 g/m²/d (2.5 mg/in.²/d)	170
Magnesium	...	All	Room	...	Unsuitable	119
ZK60A	Artificially aged; extrusion. (c)	3	...	14 d	8 g/m²/d (5.16 mg/in.²/d)	170
Others						
Hafnium	Saturated solution (pH 1)	Saturated	...	21 d	<0.025 (<1)	11
Hafnium	pH 1	Saturated	...	21 d	<0.025 (<1)	11
Niobium	Saturated solution (pH 1)	Saturated	Boiling	...	0.025 (1.0)	2

(a) Air saturated; specimens moved at 16 ft/min for 7 d. (b) May be considered in place of a copper metal when some property, other than corrosion resistance, governs its use. (c) Alternate immersion 14 d, specimen surface ground with Al_2O_3.

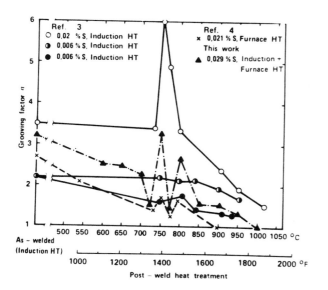

Low-alloy steel. Effect of annealing temperature on the susceptibility of grooving corrosion in electric resistance welded pipe. (Summary of the Masamura and Matsushima and Williams findings and findings established in cited source). Short-run test conditions involve welded specimens exposed to a 3.5% sodium chloride solution at 30 °C (86 °F) and anodically polarized to E_H = -0.3 V for 6 days. This susceptibility to grooving corrosion can be quantitatively described by a grooving factor (alpha). Source: C. Duran, E. Treiss, *et at.,* "The Resistance of High Frequency Inductive Welded Pipe to Grooving Corrosion in Salt Water," *Materials Performance,* Vol 25, 1986, 46.

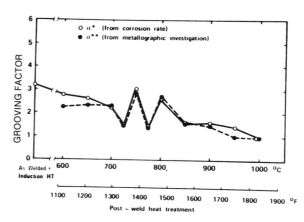

Low-alloy steel. Effect of post-weld heat treatment (annealing time, 30 min) on grooving corrosion in steel with a 0.029% sulfur content. Source: C. Duran, E. Treiss, *et al.,* "The Resistance of High Frequency Inductive Welded Pipe to Grooving Corrosion in Salt Water," in *Materials Performance,* Vol 25, 1986, 46.

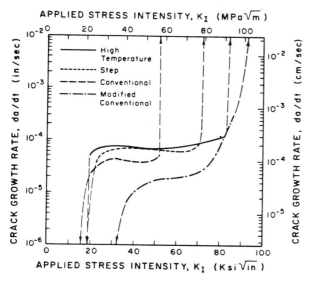

Low-alloy steel. Comparison of crack growth rates for various heat treatments of 300M steel in 3.5% sodium chloride. Source: R. Padmanabhan and W.E. Wood, "Stress Corrosion Cracking Behavior of 300M Steel Under Different Heat Treated Conditions," *Corrosion,* Vol 41, Dec 1985, 691.

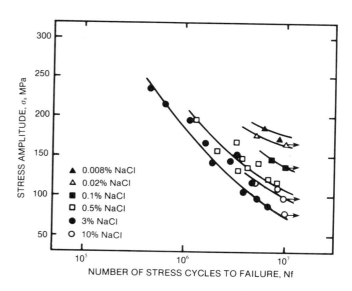

Steel. S-N curves (rotating bending test, 30 Hz) for AISI 1035 steel. Source: T. Okada and S. Hattori, "Relation Between Concentration of Salt Water and Corrosion Fatigue Strength on 0.37% Carbon Structural Steel," *Journal of Engineering Materials Technology,* Vol 107, July 1985, 236.

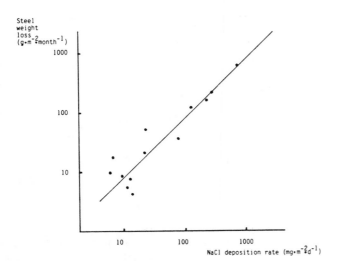

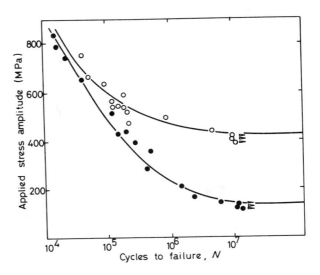

Steel. Corrosion vs. sodium chloride deposition rate. Corrosion on a painted steel surface generally begins at a defect in the coating with an initial loss of coating adhesion through cathodic delamination. Exposure to sodium chloride, a common corrosion stimulator that occurs in coastal and salt road areas, tends to give an alkaline subcoating liquid. Source: L. Igetoft, "Reactions on Painted Steel Under the Influence of Sulfur Dioxide, Sodium Chloride, and Combinations Thereof," *Industrial Engineering Chemistry, Product Research and Development*, Vol 24, Sept 1985, 376.

Maraging steel. S-N curves for 18 Ni maraging steel (yield strength 930 MPa) in air and 3.5 wt% sodium chloride solution. Open circle: air. Closed circle: sodium chloride. Source: T. Alp, Z. Husain, *et al.*, "Corrosion Fatigue Crack Initiation and Growth in 18 Ni Maraging Steel," *Journal of Material Science*, Vol 21, Sept 1986, 3265.

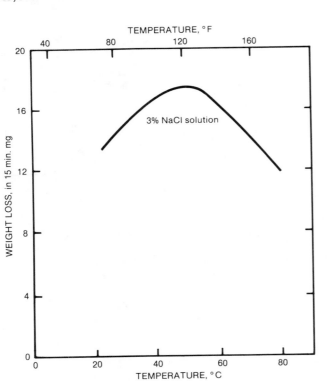

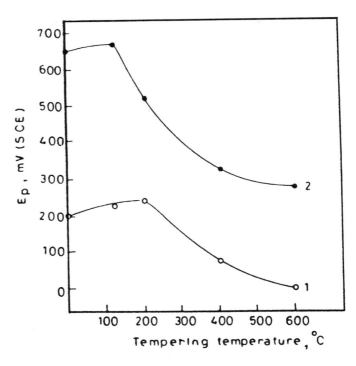

Carbon steel. Influence of temperature on the erosion rate of plain carbon steel in a vibratory cavitation device. Source: *Metals Handbook*, 9th ed., Vol 13, Corrosion, ASM International, Metals Park, OH, 1987, 313.

Carbon steel. Dependence of pitting corrosion potential on tempering temperature. Curve 1: 1×10^{-2} M sodium hydroxide, 1×10^{-2} sodium chloride. Curve 2: 1×10^{-1} M sodium hydroxide, 2×10^{-2} M sodium chloride. Source: S.M. Abd El-Haleem, S.S. Abd El Rehim, *et al.*, "Anodic Behavior and Pitting Corrosion of Plain Carbon Steel in NaOH Solutions Containing Chlorine Ions," *Surface Coating Technology*, Vol 27, Feb 1986, 172.

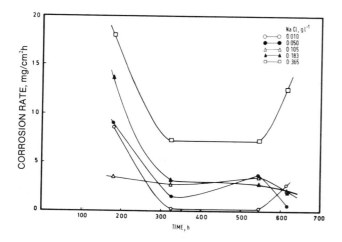

Carbon steel. Corrosion rate vs. time for carbon steel in 0.43 g/L calcium hydroxide solutions containing various concentrations of sodium chloride. Source: A.P. Akolzin, P. Ghosh, *et al.*, "Application and Peculiarity of Ca(OH)₂ as Inhibitor in the Presence of Corrosion Activators," *British Corrosion Journal*, Vol 20, Jan 1985, 33.

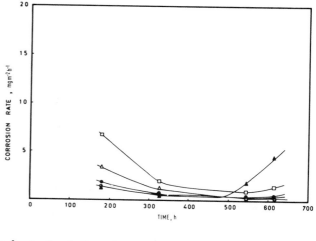

Carbon steel. Corrosion rate vs. time for carbon steel in 0.76 g/L calcium hydroxide solutions containing various concentrations of sodium chloride. Open circle: air. Closed circle: sodium chloride. Source: A.P. Akolzin, P. Ghosh, *et al.*, "Application and Peculiarity of Ca(OH)₂ as Inhibitor in the Presence of Corrosion Activators," *British Corrosion Journal*, Vol 20, Jan 1985, 33.

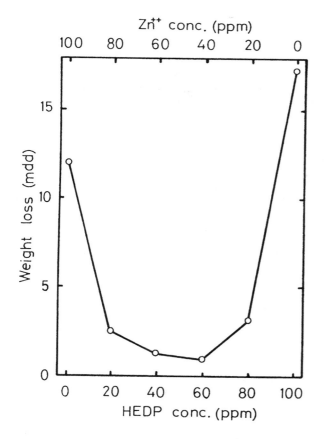

Stainless steel. Corrosion weight loss vs. concentration of HEDP and the Zn^{2+} ion in 0.3% sodium chloride solution. Source: I. Sekine and Y. Hirakawa, "Effect of 1-Hydorxyethylidene-1, 1-Diphosphonic Acid on the Corrosion of SS 41 Steel in 0.3% Sodium Chloride Solution," *Corrosion*, Vol 42, May 1986, 275.

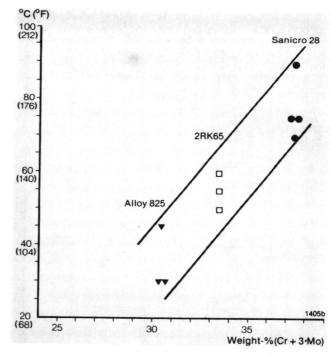

Stainless steel. Critical crevice temperatures at 200 mV SCE in a 3% sodium chloride aqueous solution, pH about 6, 15 min at each testing temperature. Sanicro 28 (Sweden) = ASTM B668; 2RK65 (Sweden) = ASTM B677; Alloy 825 = ASTM B423. Source: S. Bernhardsson, R. Mellstrom, *et al.*, "Performance of a Highly Alloyed Stainless Steel in Marine Environments," *Anti-Corrosion Methods and Materials*, Vol 32, April 1985, 11.

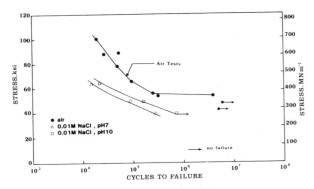

Stainless steel. S-N curves for type 403 stainless steel tested in air and in 0.01*M* sodium chloride solutions at pH 7 and 10. Source: H.M. Shalaby and V.K. Gouda, "Effect of Chloride Concentration and pH on Fatigue Crack Initiation Morphology of Type 403 Stainless Steel," *British Corrosion Journal*, Vol 20, June 1983, 126.

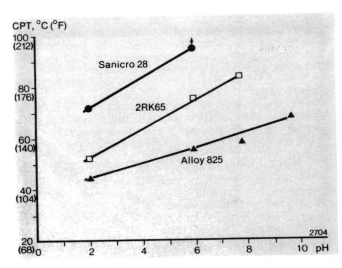

Stainless steel. Influence of pH on CPT at 400 mV SCE in 3% sodium chloride solutions. Sanicro 28 (Sweden) = ASTM B668. 2RK65 (Sweden) = ASTM B677. Alloy 825 = ASTM B423. Source: S. Bernhardsson, R. Mellstrom, *et al.*, "Performance of a Highly Alloyed Stainless Steel in Marine Environments," *Anti-Corrosion Methods and Materials*, Vol 32, April 1985, 8.

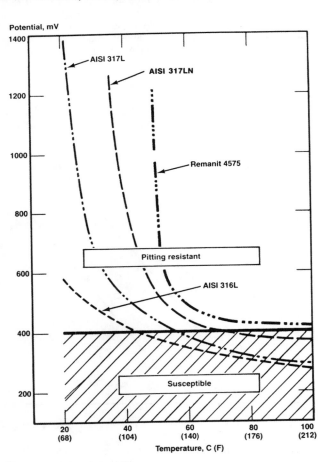

Stainless steel. Pitting potential of alloy 4575 and three standard austenitic stainless steels as a function of temperature in aerated 3% sodium chloride solution. Alloy 4575 is a ferritic stainless steel of nominal 28Cr-2.5Mo-4Ni composition. Source: H.E. Chandler, "Ferritic Stainless Steel Combats Chloride Corrosion," *Metal Progress*, Vol 128, Oct 1985, 63-66.

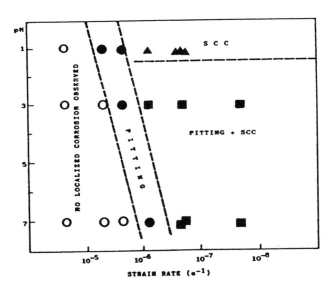

Stainless steel. Localized corrosion morphology of AISI 304 steel at 110 °C in 5*M* sodium chloride solution. Source: F. Mancia and A. Tamba, "Slow Strain Rate Stress Corrosion Cracking of AISI 304 Stainless Steel in NaCl Solution and Its Prevention by Controlled Cathodic Protection," *Corrosion*, Vol 42, June 1986, 365.

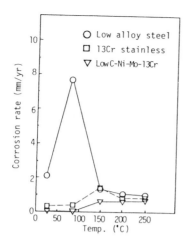

Stainless steel. Corrosion rate in 3.5% sodium chloride solution at 30 atm P_{CO_2}. Source: T. Kurisu, M. Kimura, *et al,* "Corrosion Resistance of Low C-Ni-13Cr Stainless Steels in CO_2/H_2O Environments," *Transactions of the Iron and Steel Institute of Japan*, Vol 25, April 1985, B-133.

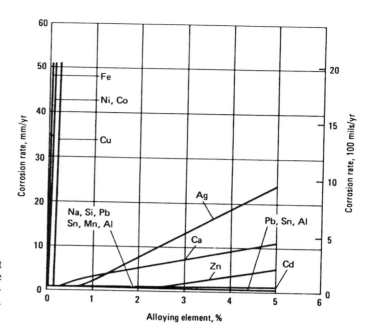

Magnesium. Effect of alloy content on corrosion rates of magnesium-base binary alloys tested in 3% sodium chloride solution. Source: *Metals Handbook*, 9th ed., Vol 2, Properties and Selection: Nonferrous Alloys and Pure Metals, American Society for Metals, Metals Park, OH, 1979, 597.

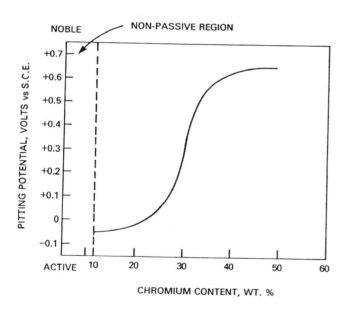

Stainless steel. Effect of chromium content on pitting potential of iron-chromium alloys in deaerated 0.1N sodium chloride at 25 °C. Source: A.J. Sedriks, "Effects of Alloy Composition and Microstructure on the Passivity of Stainless Steels," *Corrosion*, Vol 42, July 1986, 379.

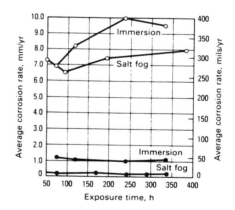

Analysis of die-cast plates, %		
	AM60A (○)	AZ91D (●)
Aluminum	6.2	9.7
Zinc	0.09	0.74
Manganese	0.22	0.19
Nickel	0.003	0.0018
Iron	0.005	0.006
Copper	0.03	0.0067

Magnesium. Corrosion rates of die cast magnesium in 5% sodium chloride salt spray and continuous-immersion exposure. Source: AMAX Magnesium.

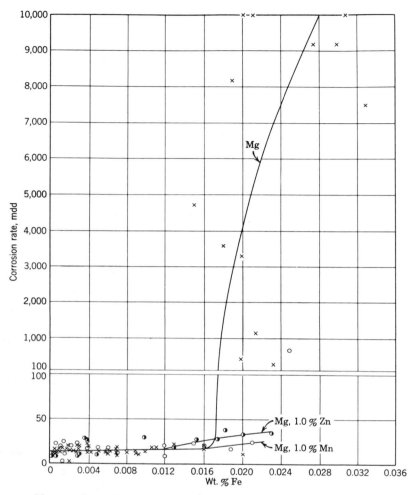

Magnesium. Corrosion of magnesium in 3% sodium chloride, alternate immersion, 16 weeks, showing tolerance limit for iron and beneficial effect of alloyed zinc and manganese. Source: Herbert H. Uhlig, *Corrosion and Corrosion Control: An Introduction to Corrosion Science and Engineering*, John Wiley & Sons, New York, 1963, 308.

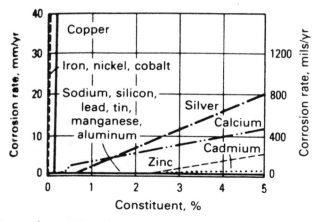

Magnesium. Effect of alloying and contaminant metals on the corrosion rate of magnesium as determined by alternate immersion in 3% sodium chloride solution. Source: J.D. Hanawalt, C.E. Nelson, and J.A. Peloubet, *Transactions of the AIME*, Vol 147, 1942, 273.

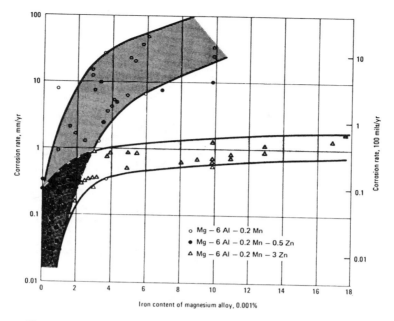

Magnesium. Effect of zinc content on relationship between iron content and corrosion rate for Mg-6Al-0.2Mn alloys in 3% sodium chloride solution. Source: *Metals Handbook*, 9th ed., Vol 2, Properties and Selection: Nonferrous Alloys and Pure Metals, American Society for Metals, Metals Park, OH, 1979, 597.

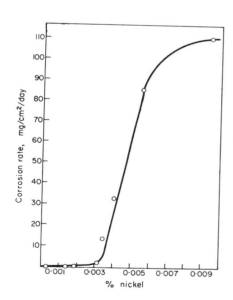

Magnesium. Tolerance limit for nickel shown by Mg-0.6% Zr alloy (ZA) when tested in 3% sodium chloride solution (total immersion conditions). Source: E.F. Emley, *Principles of Magnesium Technology*, Pergamon Press, Oxford, 1966, 685.

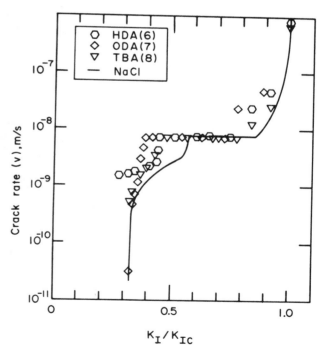

Aluminum. Normalized stress-corrosion cracking behavior of 7075-T651 alloy in 3.5 wt% sodium chloride and alkyl amine (HDA, ODA, and TBA, with the hexadecyl-, octadecyl-, and tributyl- groups, respectively). Solid line represents behavior in 3.5 wt% sodium chloride alone. Source: D. Tromans, "Effect of Organic Adsorbants on the Aqueous Stress Corrosion Cracking of AA 7075-T651 Aluminum Alloy," *Corrosion*, Vol 42, Oct 1986, 604.

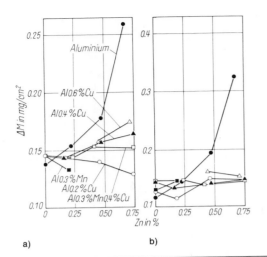

a)   b)

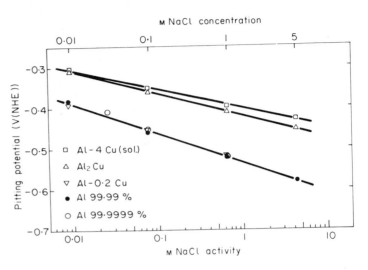

	Corrosion loss in mg/cm²	Pit density in 1/cm²	Maximum pit depth in mm
Aluminum	1.7 · 10⁻²	135	0.06
− 0.25% Zn	2.7 · 10⁻²	95	0.03
− 0.75% Zn	2.8 · 10⁻²	72	0.29
Al − 0.2% Cu	4.1 · 10⁻²	43	0.07
− 0.2% Cu − 0.5% Zn	3.9 · 10⁻²	50	<0.02
Al − 0.4% Cu	7.5 · 10⁻²	23	0.13
− 0.4% Cu − 0.25% Zn	4.6 · 10⁻²	23	0.07
Al − 0.3% Mn	1.1 · 10⁻²	57	<0.02
− 0.3% Mn − 0.25% Zn	1.8 · 10⁻²	105	<0.02

Aluminum. Effect of chloride concentration on the pitting potential of pure aluminum and various aluminum-copper alloys in deaerated sodium chloride solutions. Source: J.R. Galvele, "Pitting Corrosion," in *Treatise on Materials Science and Technology*, Vol 23, J.C. Scully, Ed., Academic Press, New York, 1983, 17.

Aluminum. Effect of zinc content on corrosion mass loss after immersion for 100 h in 1*M* sodium chloride solution at 40 °C. (a) pH 6. (b) pH 3. Source: K. Tohma, N. Takahashi, *et al.*, "Compound Effects of Additions of Zn, Cu, and Mn on the Electrochemical Properties and Corrosion Resistance of Aluminum," *Aluminum*, Vol 61, April 1985, 278.

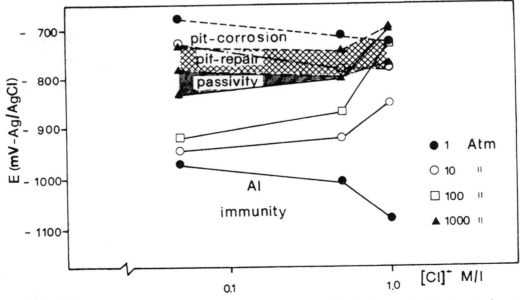

Aluminum. E_{corr} (solid line), E_p (broken line), and E_{pp} (dash-dot-dash line) potentials for aluminum corrosion in sodium chloride at different hydrostatic pressures. Source: A.M. Beccaria and G. Poggi, "Influence of Hydrostatic Pressure and Salt Concentration on Aluminum Corrosion in NaCl Solutions," *Corrosion*, Vol 42, Aug 1986, 475.

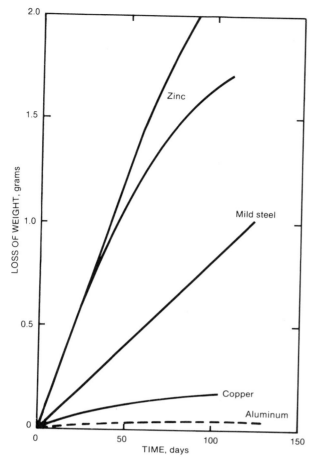

Various metals. Corrosion resistance of common metals in sodium chloride solutions. The specimen was 2.5 cm in diameter, 0.6 cm thick, with 4.35 cm² surface area. The corrosion loss in centimeters can be calculated by dividing weight loss by 4.35 and multiplying by the specific gravity of the metal. Source: *Guidelines for the Use of Aluminum with Food and Chemicals: Compatibility Data on Aluminum in the Food and Chemical Process Industries*, 5th ed., The Aluminum Association, Washington, DC, 1984, 54.

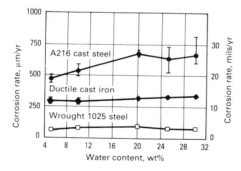

Cast iron. Effect of low levels of magnesium containing brine in sodium chloride on the general corrosion rate of cast irons and steel at 150 °C (300 °F). Test duration: 13 weeks. Source: R.E. Westerman and S.G. Pittman, "Corrosion of Candidate Iron-Base Waste Package Structural Barrier Materials in Moist Salt Environments," *Materials Research Society*, Vol 44, 1985, 282-285.

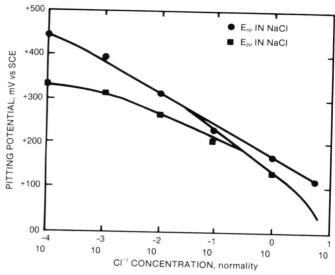

Zirconium. Variation of nucleation and pit passivation potentials for zirconium as a function of chloride ion concentration in sodium chloride. Source: G.C. Palit and H.S. Gadiyar, "Pitting Corrosion of Zirconium in Chloride Solution," *Corrosion*, Vol 43, March 1987, 144.

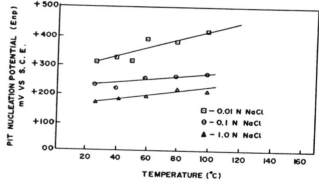

Zirconium. Pit nucleation potential of zirconium as a function of temperature in various concentrations of sodium chloride solutions. Source: G.C. Palit and H.S. Gadiyar, "Pitting Corrosion of Zirconium in Chloride Solution," *Corrosion*, Vol 43, March 1987, 144.

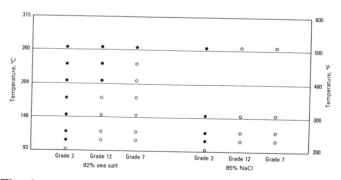

Titanium. Temperature guidelines for avoiding localized attack of grades 2, 7, and 12 titanium in pressure-bled tests in concentrated sea salt and sodium chloride slurries in the absence of crevices. Closed circle denotes susceptibility to localized attack. Source: *Metals Handbook*, 9th ed., Vol 13, Corrosion, ASM International, Metals Park, OH, 1987, 684.

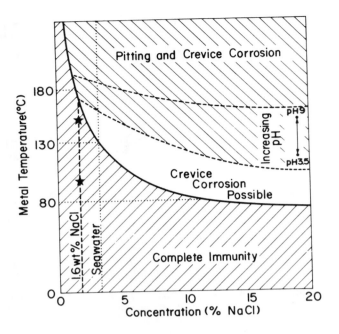

Titanium. Effect of temperature, chloride concentration, and pH on the localized corrosion of unalloyed titanium. Data on crevice corrosion of grade 2 titanium in 1.6 wt% sodium chloride are included for comparison. Source: P. McKay and D.B. Mitton, "An Electrochemical Investigation of Localized Corrosion on Titanium in Chloride Environments," *Corrosion*, Vol 41, Jan 1985, 61.

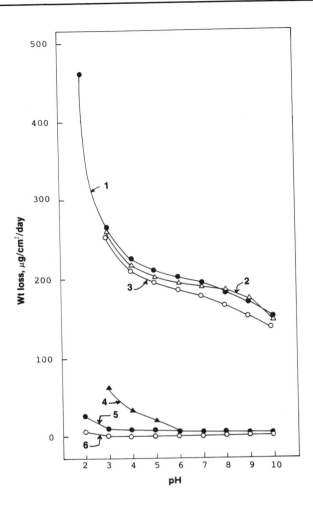

Copper. Effect of pH on corrosion rate of copper (as measured by weight loss) during 1 week of immersion in aerated solutions containing 3% sodium chloride and/or 0.2% benzotriazole at 60 °C. Curve 1: Copper sheet was immersed in 3% sodium chloride. Curve 2: Pretreated for 4 s in 0.2% benzotriazole at pH 10, then immersed in 3% sodium chloride. Curve 3: Pretreated for 5 s in 0.2% benzotriazole at pH 4, then immersed in 3% sodium chloride. Curve 4: Immersed in 3% sodium chloride and 0.2% benzotriazole and pH adjusted with acetic acid. Curve 5: Immersed in 3% sodium chloride and 0.2% benzotriazole. Curve 6: Immersed in 0.2% benzotriazole. The pH of all solutions (except that used to produce Curve 4) was adjusted with hydrochloric acid or potassium hydroxide. Source: C.H. Huang, "Corrosion Protection of Copper with Benzotriazole," *Plating and Surface Finishing*, Vol 73, June 1986, 99.

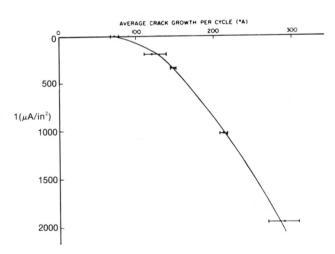

Copper. Average crack growth per cycle as a function of applied current in 3.5% sodium chloride for (90-10 cupronickel, CA 706). Source: D.P. Harvey, T.S. Sudarshan, *et al.*, "Corrosion Fatigue Behavior of 90/10 Copper-Nickel Cladding for Marine Structures," *Journal of Materials for Energy Systems*, Vol 7, Dec 1985, 272.

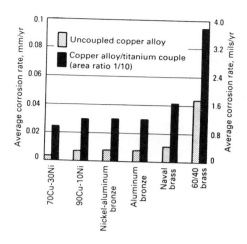

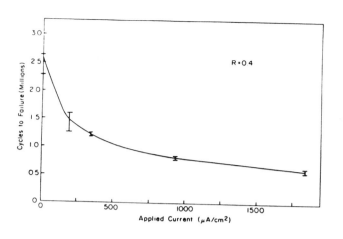

Copper. Corrosion of copper alloys that were galvanically coupled to titanium in boiling, deaerated 6% sodium chloride at 100 °C (212 °F). Source: T. Fukuzuka, K. Shimogori, H. Satoh, and F. Kamikubo, "Corrosion Problems and Countermeasures in MSF Desalination Plant Using Titanium Tube," Kobe Steel, Ltd., 1985.

Copper. Cycles to failure as a function of applied current in 3.5% sodium chloride for (90-10 cupronickel, CA 706). Source: D.P. Harvey, T.S. Sudarshan, *et al.*, "Corrosion Fatigue Behavior of 90/10 Copper-Nickel Cladding for Marine Structures," *Journal of Materials for Energy Systems*, Vol 7, Dec 1985, 272.

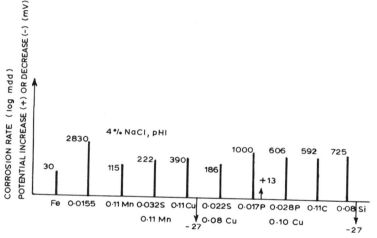

Iron. Corrosion rate (mdd) for iron, pure and alloyed, with stated percentages of sulfur, manganese, copper, phosphorus, carbon and silicon in acid sodium chloride solution. In three cases, the change in corrosion potential is also shown. Source: G. Wranglen, *An Introduction to Corrosion and Protection of Metals*, Chapman Hall, New York, 1985, 74.

Sodium Fluoride

Sodium fluoride, NaF, also known as villiaumite, is a white, poisonous, crystalline powder that melts at 980 °C (1796 °F). Sodium fluoride is formed by the reaction of sodium carbonate and hydrofluoric acid. It is soluble in water and is used in dentistry to prevent tooth decay. Sodium fluoride is used in agriculture as a fungicide and an insecticide, in the preparation of ceramic enamels and fluxes, and as a preservative for food, wood, and adhesives.

Material Summaries

The following material summaries were compiled from a survey of the available literature. Inclusion of a material description under a given environment does not imply that it is the most appropriate material for corrosion service in that environment. Likewise, exclusion of a given

material does not imply that it is not suitable for corrosion service applications in that environment.

Aluminum. During laboratory tests at ambient temperature and 100% relative humidity, aluminum alloy 3003 was attacked by solid sodium fluoride. Other tests disclosed that aqueous solutions (0.1 to 4%) of sodium fluoride attacked aluminum alloy 1100 at a moderate (0.25 mm/yr, or 10 mils/yr) rate that varied with concentration.

Zirconium. Although zirconium has good resistance in sodium fluoride at low temperatures, resistance decreases rapidly with increasing temperature.

Additional Reading

V.D. Vasquez Moll, C.A. Acosta, R.C. Salvarezza, H.A. Videla, and A.J. Arvia, The Kinetics and Mechanism of the Localized Corrosion of Mild Steel in Neutral Phosphate—Borate Buffer Containing Sodium Fluoride, *Corros. Sci.*, 25(4), 239-252, 1985. MetAbs No. 85-351893.

Abstract: The localized corrosion of mild steel in neutral buffered solutions containing NaF is studied using potentiostatic and potentiodynamic techniques, complemented by scanning electron microscopy. The results obtained are similar to those reported for the pitting of mild steel in the presence of other aggressive anions.

Corrosion Behavior of Various Metals and Alloys in Sodium Fluoride

Material	Condition, other factors, comments	Concentration, %	Temperature, °C (°F)	Duration	Corrosion rate, mm/yr (mils/yr) or other	Ref
Stainless steels						
Type 317 stainless steel	Metal processing; no aeration; no agitation. Plus aluminum fluoride, sodium sulfate, sodium carbonate, sodium bicarbonate, air, water, aluminum oxide, pH 9	...	30 (87)	69 d	<0.0001 in./yr	89
Type 410 stainless steel	...	...	Room	...	Slightly attacked	121
Titanium						
Titanium	...	Saturated	Room	...	0.008(0.32)	90
Titanium		1	Boiling	...	0.001 (0.04)	90
Titanium	pH 7	1	Boiling	...	0.001 (0.04)	90
Titanium	pH 10	1	204 (399)	...	0.000	90
Titanium	pH 7	1	Boiling	...	0.001 (0.039)	33
Titanium	Grade 12; pH 7	1	Boiling	...	0.002 (0.07)	33
Titanium	Grade 7; pH 7					
Heat- and corrosion-resistant alloys						
Alloy 825	Metal processing; no aeration; no agitation. Plus aluminum fluoride, sodium sulfate, sodium carbonate, sodium bicarbonate, air, water, aluminum oxide, pH 9	...	30 (87)	69 d	<0.00011 in./yr	89
Carpenter 20	Metal processing; no aeration; no agitation. Plus aluminum fluoride, sodium sulfate, sodium carbonate, sodium bicarbonate, air, water, aluminum oxide, pH 9	...	30 (87)	69 d	<0.0001 in./yr	89
Zirconium						
Zr702	...	Saturated	28 (82)	...	nil	15
Zr702	...	Saturated	90 (195)	...	>1.3 (>50)	15
Others						
Magnesium	...	All	Room	...	Suitable	119
Magnesium alloy AZ61A	Specimen size, 75 x 25 x 1.5 mm (3 x 1 x 0.06 in.); surface preparation, HNO3 pickling; volume of testing solution, 100 ml. Specimens were alternately immersed 30 s in solution and held 2 min in air	3	35 (95)	7 d	0.3 g/m²/d (0.2 mg/in.²/d)	12

Sodium Hydroxide

Sodium hydroxide, NaOH, also referred to as caustic soda or sodium hydrate (and formerly known as lye), is a white, massive, deliquescent crystalline solid that is soluble in water, alcohol, and glycerol. It melts at 318 °C and is the most widely used and available alkaline chemical. Most sodium hydroxide is produced as a coproduct of chlorine through the use of electrolytic cells; the cells are of the diaphragm, mercury, or membrane type. Some sodium hydroxide is marketed as produced in the cells; most is evaporated and sold as 50 and 73% solutions or as anhydrous beads. Most caustic end uses require solutions of relatively low concentrations. Caustic soda is used as an analytical reagent and chemical intermediate, in scouring and cleaning baths, in rubber reclaiming and petroleum refining, in quenching baths for heat treating of steel, in cutting and soluble oils, in soaps and detergents, and in a wide variety of other applications.

Material Summaries

The following material summaries were compiled from a survey of the available literature. Inclusion of a material description under a given environment does not imply that it is the most appropriate material for corrosion service in that environment. Likewise, exclusion of a given material does not imply that it is not suitable for corrosion service applications in that environment.

Cast Irons. Unalloyed cast irons exhibit generally good resistance to alkali solutions (caustic solutions) such as sodium hydroxide, with the resistance being approximately equivalent to that of steel. These cast irons are not attacked by dilute alkalis at any temperature. Hot alkalis at concentrations exceeding 30% attack unalloyed iron. Temperatures should not exceed 80 °C (175 °F) for concentrations up to 70% if corrosion rates of less than 0.25 mm/yr (10 mils/yr) are desired. Ductile and gray iron exhibit about equal resistance to alkalis; however, ductile iron is susceptible to cracking in highly alkaline solutions, but gray iron is not. Alloying with 3 to 5% nickel substantially improves the resistance of cast irons to alkalis. High-nickel austenitic cast irons offer even better resistance to alkalis than unalloyed or low-nickel cast irons.

High-silicon cast irons exhibit good resistance to relatively dilute solutions of sodium hydroxide at moderate temperatures, but should not be applied for more concentrated conditions at elevated temperatures. High-silicon cast irons are usually economical over unalloyed and nickel cast irons in alkaline solutions only when other corrosives are involved for which the lesser alloys are unsuitable. High-chromium cast irons have inferior resistance to alkaline solutions and are generally not recommended for alkaline service.

Austenitic cast irons (Ni-Resist types) show superior resistance to caustic solutions up to 70% concentration and approaching boiling temperatures; corrosion rates are generally less than 0.25 mm/yr (10 mils/yr). Nickel-containing cast irons generally benefit by additional nickel alloying as long as sulfur or sulfur compounds are not present.

Stress-corrosion cracking is not a problem for cast irons.

Carbon and Alloy Steels. The possibilities of product contamination and stress-corrosion cracking (often called caustic embrittlement) are primary restrictions to the use of iron and steel in caustic service. These problems limit applications, yet low-carbon steel remains the most frequently used material. It is effective in caustic solutions of up to 50% concentration and at temperatures up to 90 °C (190 °F).

Effective use is made of bare steel tanks storing 50% caustic at temperatures from ambient to 65 °C (150 °F). Iron contamination is frequently a concern because many caustic applications must limit the presence of iron to only a few parts per million. Where iron contamination of the product is of concern, spray-applied neoprene latex or phenolic-epoxy linings are used. If iron contamination is not a problem, the next limiting factor is stress-corrosion cracking.

Stainless Steels. All stainless steels resist general corrosion by all concentrations of sodium hydroxide up to about 65 °C (150 °F). Types 304 and 316 stainless steels exhibit low rates of general corrosion in boiling sodium hydroxide up to nearly 20% concentration. Stress-corrosion cracking of these grades can occur at about 100 °C (212 °F). Good resistance to general corrosion and stress-corrosion cracking in 50% sodium hydroxide at 135 °C (275 °F) is provided by E-Brite and 7-Mo stainless steels.

Although the austenitic stainless steels crack readily in neutral and acid chlorides above 60 °C (140 °F), the effect of chlorides in an alkaline solution seems to be nil. As long as the solution remains alkaline, the mode of stress cracking is that of caustic embrittlement and continues to occur only in a limited range. A solution of 0.5 g/L sodium hydroxide with a pH of 12 is sufficiently alkaline. The concern for chloride contaminations in caustic when using stainless steel equipment is not well founded.

More important concerns are those extraneous to the caustic solution. Failures resulting from such factors as external exposure, faulty insulation, contaminated test water, and improper cleaning and storage have produced more problems than handling caustic.

Because chloride pitting and/or chloride stress cracking are often primary concerns, alloy selection should consider relative performance in these areas. Although types 304 and 316 stainless steel perform comparably in caustic and in standard stress-cracking tests, type 316 shows improved overall performance because of its pitting resistance. The role of dissolved oxygen may be significant in this effect. In addition, the low-carbon grades perform marginally better because of their resistance to sensitization. This suggests that type 316L (molybdenum-containing, low-carbon type 316) should be used unless significant controls are to be placed on the total exposure of the equipment.

Applications of stainless steel for caustic service include piping, valves, pumps, and equipment. Transfer piping applications are quite common. Problems rarely occur whenever 10 to 20% solutions are involved, because clean-out and freezing considerations are minimal.

Cast stainless pumps and valves have performed very well in caustic applications. The nature of cast surfaces minimizes stress-corrosion cracking problems, and castings are usually acceptable in situations considerably beyond the capabilities of wrought products. Corrosion rates are similar to those of the wrought products.

One other practical application of stainless steel in caustic service is in evaporation processes, in which high-purity alloy 26-1 (a low-carbon version of type 446 stainless steel containing niobium and molybdenum) heat-exchanger tubing has been used. Some high-temperature applications have proven effective where corrosion rates on nickel are excessive. This is probably due to the presence of hypochlorite or chlorate contaminants. The debate between nickel and ferrous alloys continues, yet both materials have shown satisfactory performance. The 26-1 alloy is useful up to 175 °C (350 °F), depending on the caustic, chloride, and contaminant concentrations. When 26-1 is attacked, the normal failure mode seems to be intergranular. At this time, there are no specific criteria to provide recommendations regarding the use of ferritic stainless steel. There probably are suitable applications for the new ferritic and duplex steels; however, little testing has been completed.

Aluminum. Aluminum alloys exhibited poor resistance to sodium hydroxide solutions in laboratory tests at all concentrations and all temperatures. Additions of inhibitors, such as potassium dichromate, ammonium metavanadate, or ammonium persulfate, to dilute solutions of sodium hydroxide have repressed corrosion.

Copper. Copper and some copper-base alloys (aluminum bronzes and copper-nickel alloys) are generally suitable for service in sodium hydroxide. Higher nickel content in copper-nickel alloys indicates better resistance. Alloy 70-30 (CDA 71500) has been used where copper contamination can be tolerated. Zinc-containing brasses and bronzes are not suitable for sodium hydroxide service.

Nickel. Nickel and nickel-base alloys are used extensively in sodium hydroxide service. Their very low corrosion rates also ensure low metal ion contamination. Nickel has the lowest corrosion rates, even in molten anhydrous sodium hydroxide at temperatures up to 540 °C (1000 °F) and is essentially immune to caustic stress-corrosion cracking.

A major use for Nickel 200 is in the production of sodium hydroxide. Nickel 200 exhibits outstanding corrosion resistance to sodium hydroxide at concentrations up to anhydrous at boiling or molten temperatures. Caustic soda is normally produced at 11 to 15% concentration and further concentrated by evaporation to 50% or higher. As sodium hydroxide concentration and temperature increase during the evaporation process or during other chemical-processing conditions, the corrosivity increases dramatically. Similarly, increasing the nickel content of nickel-base alloys produces increasing resistance to general corrosion and stress-corrosion cracking in caustic. Thus, a number of nickel-base alloys can be used for handling sodium hydroxide, depending on solution concentration and temperature.

At temperatures above 315 °C (600 °F), Nickel 200 is replaced by Nickel 201 because of its low carbon content. This material was specifically designed to avoid potential intergranular corrosion, which may occur in Nickel 200 (0.15% carbon maximum). In areas of high stress, this type of attack has resulted in cracking after intergranular corrosion, but is mechanically driven.

In some caustic applications where higher strength or resistance to other corrodents is required, Monel 400, Inconel 600, Hastelloy C-276, and other nickel alloys are used. These alloys are highly resistant to general corrosion and stress-corrosion cracking, but can be attacked at high caustic concentrations and temperatures. In the handling of brines in sodium hydroxide production as well as the commercial production of salt, Monel 400 has performed well in a variety of components, such as heat exchangers, vacuum pans, heater tubes, rotary dryers, and transfer piping. Inconel 600 and Incoloy 800 have been used extensively in nuclear steam generator service at about 300 °C (570 °F). In this service, resistance to caustic, which can be formed and concentrated at tube sheets, is of concern. The higher chromium alloy Inconel 690 is more resistant to stress-corrosion cracking under some conditions.

Niobium. In ambient aqueous alkaline solutions, niobium has corrosion rates of less than 0.025 mm/yr (1 mil/yr). At higher temperatures, even though the corrosion rate does not seem excessive, niobium is embrittled even at low concentrations (5%) of sodium hydroxide.

Silver. Although it is attacked by most fused bisulfates, cyanides, halides, phosphates, and peroxides, silver is not attacked by sodium hydroxide at temperatures below 500 °C (930 °F).

Tantalum. Sodium hydroxide solutions do not dissolve tantalum, but tend to destroy the metal by formation of successive layers of surface scale. The rate of the destruction increases with concentration and temperature. Damage to tantalum equipment has been experienced unexpectedly when strong alkaline solutions have been used during cleaning and maintenance.

In a study using change in electrical resistivity to measure corrosion rates, tantalum wire totally immersed in 10% sodium hydroxide solution at room temperature for 210 days corroded at the rate of 0.24 μm/yr. A similar rate occurred in 10% sodium hydroxide at 100 °C (212 °F). In the latter case, there was some local effect at the points where the wire left the solution and entered submerged rubber stoppers in the sides of the corrosion vessel; this accounted for most of the weight loss.

In tests conducted on unalloyed tantalum and a Ta-10W alloy in 5% sodium hydroxide solution at 100 °C (212 °F), both metals suffered considerable weight losses, and the difference, if any, between their corrosion rates was small. In this study, the sodium hydroxide corrosion test was conducted because tantalum is known to be susceptible to caustic embrittlement; therefore, it was desired to determine whether the Ta-10W alloy suffered embrittlement also. Unalloyed tantalum showed approximately a 25% increase in yield strength and a 10% increase was attributed to a pickup of interstitial elements (oxygen, nitrogen, and hydrogen), although chemical analyses of the materials before and after exposure were not conducted. With the Ta-10W alloy, the exposure to 5% sodium hydroxide at 100 °C (212 °F) produced embrittlement, as evidenced by the premature fracture in the tensile test. Reportedly, such embrittlement was not evident on the sample of the Ta-10W alloy to which a platinum spot had been welded before the test.

Titanium. Titanium alloys are generally very resistant to alkaline media, including sodium hydroxide. Titanium exhibits low corrosion rates in sodium hydroxide at sub-boiling temperatures. However, significant increases in corrosion are noted as sodium hydroxide concentration increases at higher temperatures.

Although corrosion rates are relatively low in alkaline media, titanium alloys may experience excessive hydrogen pickup and eventual embrittlement under certain conditions. For alpha and near-alpha alloys, hydrogen embrittlement is possible when temperatures exceed 80 °C (175 °F) and pH is 12 or more. The presence of dissolved oxidizing species in hot caustic solutions, such as chlorate, hypochlorite, or nitrate compounds, can extend resistance to hydrogen uptake to somewhat higher temperatures.

Zirconium. Zirconium is very resistant to corrosion by molten sodium hydroxide at temperatures above 1000 °C (1830 °F). Zirconium U-bend specimens were tested in boiling concentrated sodium hydroxide. During the test period, the concentration changed from 50 to about 85%, and temperature increased from 150 to 300 °C (300 to 570 °F). The PTFE washers and tubes used to make the U-bends dissolved. However, the zirconium U-bend specimens remained ductile and did not show any cracks after 20 days. Zirconium is resistant to stress-corrosion cracking in sodium hydroxide.

Additional Reading

W.-T. Tsai, A. Moccari, and D.D. Macdonald, Effect of Silicate and Phosphate on the Fatigue Crack Growth Rates in Type 403 Stainless Steel in Concentrated Sodium Chloride and Sodium Hydroxide Solutions, *Corrosion*, 39(1), 1-12, 1983. MetAbs No. 83-350732. **Abstract:** Corrosion fatigue crack growth rates of a quenched and tempered 403 stainless steel were measured in concentrated sodium hydroxide and sodium chloride solutions, with and without the addition of sodium silicate and sodium phosphate as potential inhibitors, using compact tension specimens. All tests were performed at 100 °C.

M. Yasuda, F. Takeya, and F. Hine, Corrosion Behavior of Nickel in Concentrated NaOH Solutions Under Heat Transfer Conditions, *Corrosion*, 39(10), 399-405, 1983. MetAbs No. 84-350294. **Abstract:** The electrochemical behavior of a Ni specimen heated in boiling NaOH solutions under atmospheric pressure was investigated.

Z. Szklarska-Smialowska and W. Kozlowski, The Behavior of Armco Iron in Its Passive and Transpassive States in NaOH and Na_2SiO_3 Solutions, *Corrosion*, 40(11), 595-597, 1984. MetAbs No. 85-350446. **Abstract:** In an earlier work, pits were found on Fe specimens immersed in a borate buffer solution containing 0.15M H_3BO_3 + 0.0375M $Na_2B_4O_7$ (pH 8.45). It was found by ellipsometry that the surfaces of pitted specimens were covered with a film composed of two layers, one on top of the other, having different optical properties. The aim of this study was to ascertain if Fe would also suffer pitting in the transpassive region in other halide-free solutions and if some correlation could be found between the propensity to undergo pitting and the optical properties of surface films; 0.1M Na_2SiO_3 and 0.05M NaOH solutions were used.

R. Bandy, R. Roberge, and D. van Rooyen, Intergranular Failures of Alloy 600 in High Temperature Caustic Environments, *Corrosion, 41*(3), 142-150, 1985. MetAbs No. 85-351101. **Abstract:** The results of an investigation of two commonly observed modes of failure of Inconel 600 in a high-temperature caustic environment—intergranular stress-corrosion cracking and intergranular attack—are described. Specimens were C-rings under constant deflection, wires with and without any externally applied load, and straining electrodes.

T.C. Tan and D.-T. Chin, Polarization of Aluminum During AC Corrosion in Sulfate Solutions, *J. Electrochem. Soc., 132*(4), 766-772, 1985. MetAbs No. 85-351343. **Abstract:** An experimental study has been made of the effect of alternating voltage on the corrosion of Al (6061) in aqueous solutions of $1N$ H_2SO_4, $1N$ Na_2SO_4, $1N$ NaOH, and $1N$ Na_2SO_4 containing 0 to 5010 ppm Cl⁻ ions. The polarization curves were measured with an alternating voltage modulation technique using sinusoidal waves, and the pitting behavior of Al was examined with constant potentiostatic coulometry and SEM photomicrography.

A. Moccari and D.D. MacDonald, Electrochemical Screening of Organic and Inorganic Inhibitors for the Corrosion of ASTM A-470 Steel in Concentrated Sodium Hydroxide Solution, *Corrosion, 41*(5), 264-273, 1985. MetAbs No. 85-351573. **Abstract:** The corrosion of ASTM A-470 turbine disk steel in concentrated sodium hydroxide solution (10 mol/kg) containing sodium silicate, sodium dihydrogen phosphate, sodium chromate, aniline and some of its derivatives, tannic acid, L-(-)-phenylalanine (aminopropionic acid) and octadecylamine as potential inhibitors has been studied using the potentiodynamic, AC impedance, and Tafel extrapolation techniques.

N. Bandyopadhyay and C.L. Briant, Caustic Stress Corrosion Cracking of Low Alloy Iron Base Materials, *Corrosion, 41*(5), 274-280, 1985. MetAbs No. 85-351574. **Abstract:** A study of stress-corrosion cracking of Fe-3Ni, Fe-3Ni-0.5Mo, and Fe-3Ni-0.06P alloys in $9M$ NaOH is reported.

D. Moll, de.C. Vasquez, R.C. Salvarezza, and A.J. Arvia, Corrosion and Passivity of Copper in Solutions Containing Sodium Sulfide. Analysis of Potentiostatic Current Transients, *Electrochim. Acta, 30*(8), 1011-1016, 1985. MetAbs No. 85-352071. **Abstract:** The electrochemical behavior of Cu electrodes in NaOH solutions with the addition of Na_2S was studied through the analysis of current transients under constant potential and complementary voltammetric and scanning electron microscopy data including energy dispersive X-ray analysis.

R. Sriram and D. Tromans, Stress Corrosion Cracking of Carbon Steel in Caustic Aluminate Solutions—Slow Strain Rate Studies, *Corrosion, 41*(7), 381-385, 1985. MetAbs No. 85-352103. **Abstract:** Stress-corrosion cracking susceptibility of 0.18% carbon steel (ASME SA516 Grade 70) in hot (92 °C) caustic aluminate solutions was studied by potentiostatically controlled slow strain rate testing techniques.

S.M. Abd El Haleem, A.A. Abdel Fattah, and W. Tayor, Inhibition of Pitting Corrosion of Zinc Using Some Organic Amines, *Res. Mech., 15*(2), 87-98, 1985. MetAbs No. 85-352250. **Abstract:** Potentiodynamic anodic polarization curves were constructed for a Zn electrode in 0.01, 0.05 and $0.1M$ NaOH solutions containing different additions of Cl⁻ ions.

A. McMinn, F.F. Lyle Jr., and G.R. Leverant, Stress Corrosion Crack Growth in NiCrMoV Turbine Disc Steels, *Corrosion, 41*(9), 493-503, 1985. MetAbs No. 85-352342. **Abstract:** A study was made of the effects of metallurgical and environmental variables on stress-corrosion cracking propagation rates in NiCrMoV turbine disc steels.

K.H. Lee, G. Cragnolino, and D.D. MacDonald, Effect of Heat Treatment Applied Potential on the Caustic Stress Corrosion Cracking of

Inconel 600, *Corrosion, 41*(9), 540-553, 1985. MetAbs No. 85-352348. **Abstract:** The stress-corrosion cracking behavior of heat treated specimens of Inconel 600 in 25 molal NaOH solution at 140 °C was studied as a function of potential by using the slow strain rate technique.

J. Flis and D.J. Duquette, Effect of Phosphorus on Anodic Dissolution and Passivation of Nickel in Near-Neutral Solutions, *Corrosion, 41*(12), 700-706, 1985. MetAbs No. 86-350429. **Abstract:** Anodic dissolution of Ni, electroless Ni deposits with 2.9 and 12.3 wt% phosphorus and amorphous $Ni_{81}P_{19}$ alloy was examined in sodium hydroxide, sulfate, borate, and chloride solutions at 25 °C.

T. Zakroczymski, C.-J. Fan, and Z. Szklarska-Smialowska, Kinetics and Mechanism of Passive Film Formation on Iron in $0.05M$ NaOH, *J. Electrochem. Soc., 132*(12), 2862-2867, 1985. MetAbs No. 86-350435. **Abstract:** Simultaneous electrochemical and ellipsometric studies of the anodic film growth on Fe in $0.05M$ NaOH have revealed that passivation occurs in two stages. This phenomenon is discussed.

X. Liu, J. Shao, G. Cragnolino, and D.D. MacDonald, Selective Grain-Boundary Dissolution of Alloy 600 in a Concentrated Caustic Solution at 140 °C, *J. Mater. Energy Syst., 7*(3), 223-236, 1985. MetAbs No. 86-350479. **Abstract:** Selective dissolution of grain boundaries was observed on Alloy 600 after exposure to a 25 molal (50 wt%) NaOH solution at 140 °C under applied anodic potentials. Three heat treatment conditions were investigated in addition to the original mill annealed material (carbon content 0.04%): solution annealed, sensitized (700 °C/1 h), and thermally treated (700 °C/16 h).

R. Bandy and D. van Rooyen, Mechanisms of Stress Corrosion Cracking and Intergranular Attack in Alloy 600 in High Temperature Caustic and Pure Water, *J. Mater. Energy Syst., 7*(3), 237-245, 1985. MetAbs No. 86-350480. **Abstract:** In recent years, several studies have been conducted on the intergranular stress-corrosion cracking and intergranular attack of Alloy 600. A combination of attack has been observed in Alloy 600 tubing on the hot leg of some operating steam generators in pressurized water reactor nuclear power plants, and sodium hydroxide along with several other chemical species have been implicated in the tube degradations.

M. Magrini, P. Matteazzi, and A. Frignani, Structural Characterization and Electrochemical Behavior of Fe-Ni-Mo-B Amorphous Alloys, *Mater. Chem. Phys., 13*(1), 71-83, 1985. MetAbs No. 86-350502. **Abstract:** A series of amorphous alloys obtained by the "melt-spinning" technique, with variable nickel and molybdenum contents, have been examined. Potentiodynamic anodic and cathodic polarization curves have been obtained for each of these amorphous alloys in various environments ($1N$ HCl, $1N$ H_2SO_4, 3% NaCl, and $1N$ NaOH).

D. Tromans, S. Ramakrishna, and E.B. Hawbolt, Stress Corrosion Cracking of ASTM A516 Steel in Hot Caustic Sulfide Solutions—Potential and Weld Effects, *Corrosion, 42*(2), 63-70, 1986. MetAbs No. 86-350809. **Abstract:** A combination of slow strain rate (tensile) testing and double cantilever beam fracture mechanics testing techniques have been used to study the stress-corrosion cracking behavior of welded and unwelded pressure vessel quality steel plate (ASTM A516 Grade 70) in hot (92 °C) caustic sulfide solutions ($3.35M$ NaOH + $0.42M$ Na_2S) of general relevance to the pulp and paper industry.

S.M. Abd El Haleem, S.S. Abd El Rehim, and M.Sh. Shalaby, Anodic Behavior and Pitting Corrosion of Plain Carbon Steel in NaOH Solutions Containing Chlorine Ions, *Surf. Coat. Technol., 27*(2), 167-173, 1986. MetAbs No. 86-351033. **Abstract:** The anodic behavior of hot-rolled and hardened carbon steel (1.05% C) was investigated potentiodynamically in NaOH solutions with and without NaCl as a pitting corrodent.

W.A. Badawy, A.G. Gad-Allah, H.A. Abed El-Rahman, and M.M. Abouromia, Kinetics of the Passivation of Molybdenum in Acids and Alkali Solutions as Inferred From Impedance and Potential Measurements, *Surf. Coat. Technol.*, 27(2), 187-196, 1986. MetAbs No. 86-351035. **Abstract:** The electrochemical behavior of mechanically polished Mo electrodes in different acid and alkali solutions was investigated using open-circuit potential and impedance measurements. The effect of the concentration of acid (HCl) and alkali (NaOH) on the electrochemical behavior of the Mo electrodes was also studied.

N.A. Darwish, A.A. Razik, E.M. Khairy, and T.H. Hussein, Formation and Electrochemical Behavior of Some Tin-Antimony Alloys in Various pH Media, *Corros. Prev. Control*, 32(6), 127-132, 1985. MetAbs No. 86-351058. **Abstract:** Five Sn-Sb alloys were prepared to compositions involving eutectic, under-eutectic and over eutectic states. D-spacing relative-intensity diagrams were prepared. Electrochemical measurements were made.

D.C. Crowe and D. Tromans, The Silver Sulfide Reference Electrode for Use in Alkaline Sulfide Solutions, *Corrosion*, 42(7), 409-415, 1986. MetAbs No. 86-351727. **Abstract:** The high-temperature behavior of the Ag-Ag$_2$S electrode has been investigated in aqueous solutions of NaOH + Na$_2$S, the compositions of which were of particular relevance to the kraft pulping process.

A.S. Fouda, H.A. Mostafa, and A.A. El-Asmy, Efficiency of Some Phenylthiosemicarbazide Derivatives in Retarding the Dissolution of Aluminium in NaOH Solution, *Indian J. Technol.*, 24(4), 201-204, 1986. MetAbs No. 86-352717. **Abstract:** Five derivatives of phenylthiosemicarbazide were prepared and treated as inhibitors for the corrosion of Al in 2*M* sodium hydroxide. All the five substances afford 98.5 to 75% protection to aluminium in sodium hydroxide.

P. Skeldon, Environment-Assisted Cracking of 2.25Cr-1Mo Steel in Fused Sodium Hydroxide at 623 K, 1 atm. II. Results of Slow Strain Rate and Constant Strain Tests, *Corros. Sci.*, 26(7), 507-523, 1986. MetAbs No. 87-350535. **Abstract:** Slow strain rate tests have shown that quench-hardened 2.25Cr-1Mo steel is susceptible to cracking in fused caustic at 623 K and 1 atm in acidic and basic melts.

L.M. Al-Shama, J. Saleh, J. Mohammed, and N.A. Hikmat, Potentiostatic Studies of the Corrosion of Gray Cast Iron in Sulfuric Acid and Sodium Hydroxide Solutions, *Corros. Sci.*, 27(3), 221-228, 1987. MetAbs No. 87-351481. **Abstract:** A potentiostatic investigation of the corrosion behavior of two gray cast iron specimens has been performed in 2.5M H$_2$SO$_4$ and 1.0*M* NaOH solutions at 303 to 333 K. A similar determination was also made with specimens in 5.0*M* solutions of both HCl and NHO$_3$ at 303 K.

A. Kassab, Kh.M. Kamel, T. Hamid, and E. Abdel, Effect of Molybdate Ion on the Corrosion Behavior of Aluminium in NaOH Solutions, *J. Electrochem. Soc. India*, 36(1), 27-30, 1987. MetAbs No. 87-352799. **Abstract:** The corrosion rate and potential of Al were measured in 0.01 to 0.2*M* NaOH solution.

M. Yasuda, K. Fukumoto, H. Koizumi, Y. Ogata, and F. Hine, On the Active Dissolution of Metals and Alloys in Hot Concentrated Caustic Soda, *Corrosion*, 43(8), 492-498, 1987. MetAbs No. 87-352845. **Abstract:** The corrosion behavior of carbon steel, austenitic stainless steels (304, 316, 305J1, 310), Ni-base alloys (Inconel 600, Incoloy 825, Monel 400), and Ni (Ni200) in hot, concentrated caustic soda solutions at the active potential range was investigated.

J. Rechberger, D. Tromans, and A. Mitchell, Stress Corrosion Cracking of Conventional and Super-Clean 3.5NiCrMoV Rotor Steels in Simulated Condensates, *Corrosion*, 44(2), 79-87, 1988. MetAbs No. 88-351085. **Abstract:** The stress-corrosion cracking behavior of two bainitic 3.5NiCrMoV low-pressure rotor steels has been studied at 95 °C in environments containing species that are possible contaminants in steam condensates.

Corrosion Behavior of Various Metals and Alloys in Sodium Hydroxide

Material	Condition, other factors, comments	Concentration, %	Temperature, °C (°F)	Duration	Corrosion rate, mm/yr (mils/yr) or other	Ref
Cast irons						
3% nickel-iron	(a)	...	510 (950)	4 d	1.8 (71)	115
Austenitic cast iron	Type 1. Pit depth 1.5 mm (60 mils). (a)	...	510 (950)	4 d	15.9 (628)	115
Austenitic cast iron	Type 2. Pit depth 1.8 mm (70 mils). (a)	...	510 (950)	4 d	24.2 (954)	115
Austenitic cast iron	Type 3. (a)	...	510 (950)	4 d	2.2 (87)	115
Austenitic cast iron	Type 4. Pit depth 1.0 mm (40 mils). (a)	...	510 (950)	4 d	13.6 (534)	115
Cast iron	NaCl concentration, 12%. (b)	10	88 (190)	24-29 d	0.102 (4)	112
Cast iron	First effect of a multi-effect evaporator	14	90 (190)	90 d	0.21 (8.2)	112
Cast iron	NaCl concentration, 7-8%. (b)	23	93 (200)	24-29 d	0.254 (2)	112
Cast iron	Test in single-effect evaporator	30-50	80 (180)	16 d	0.18 (7)	113
Cast iron	NaCl concentration, 6-7%. (b)	35-40	116 (240)	24-29 d	1.245 (49)	112
Cast iron	(c)	50	35-90 (95-190)	...	0.11 (4.2)	114
Cast iron	(d)	50	40-80 (100-180)	...	0.08 (3.3)	114
Cast iron	...	50	55-75 (130-165)	30 d	0.27 (10.5)	112
Cast iron	NaCl concentration, 10-15%. (b)	50	93 (200)	24-29 d	0.152 (6)	112
Cast iron	0% nickel. (e)	50-65	...	81 d	1.9 (73)	112
Cast iron	0% nickel. (e)	50-65	...	81 d	2.2 (86)	112
Cast iron	0% nickel. (e)	50-65	...	81 d	1.2 (47)	112
Cast iron	3.5% nickel. (e)	50-65	...	81 d	2.3 (91)	112
Cast iron	0% nickel. (e)	50-65	...	81 d	1.24 (49)	112
Cast iron	5% nickel. (e)	50-65	...	81 d	0.8 (30)	112
Cast iron	15% nickel. (e)	50-65	...	81 d	0.08 (3.3)	112
Cast iron	20% nickel. (e)	50-65	...	81 d	0.08 (3.3)	112

(Continued)

Corrosion Behavior of Various Metals and Alloys in Sodium Hydroxide (Continued)

Material	Condition, other factors, comments	Concen-tration, %	Temperature, °C (°F)	Duration	Corrosion rate, mm/yr (mils/yr) or other	Ref
Cast iron	20% nickel plus 2% chromium. (e)	50-65	...	81 d		112
Cast iron	30% nickel. (e)	50-65	...	81 d	0.15 (6)	112
Cast iron	NaCl concentration unknown. (b)	72	121 (250)	24-29 d	0.01 (0.4)	112
Cast iron	(c)	73	100-125 (212-260)	...	0.406 (16)	114
Cast iron	(d)	73	115 (240)	...	1.06 (41.7)	114
Cast iron	Plant test. NaOH concentrated to anhydrous. Batch shaded with sulfur and Na$_2$NO$_3$	73	540 (1000)	2.5 d	2.1 (82)	114
		73	540 (1000)	2.5 d	5.3 (210)	114
Cast iron	Laboratory test. NaOH concentrated to anhydrous	75	480 (900)	...	3.3 (130)	114
Ductile austenitic cast iron	Type 2. Pit depth 1.5 mm (60 mils). (a)	...	510 (950)	4 d	11.8 (466)	115
Ductile cast iron	(c)	50	35-90 (95-190)	...	0.1 (3.9)	114
Ductile cast iron	(c)	73	100-125 (212-260)	...	1.7 (65.7)	114
Ductile cast iron	(d)	50	40-80 (100-180)	...	0.06 (2.4)	114
Ductile cast iron	(d)	73	115 (240)	...	2.6 (103)	114
Ductile iron	(a)	...	510 (950)	4 d	5.3 (207)	115
Gray iron	Pit depth 0.13 mm (5 mils). (a)	...	510 (950)	4 d	2.5-3.4 (97-135)	115
Ni-Resist type 2	Laboratory test. NaOH concentrated to anhydrous	75	480 (900)	...	3.8 (150)	114
Ni-Resist Type 2	(p)	20	127 (293)	15 h	2.388 (94)	112
Ni-Resist Type 2	(p)	40	127 (293)	15 h	0.152 (6)	112
Ni-Resist Type 2	(p)	60	127 (293)	15 h	0.432 (17)	112
Ni-Resist Type 2	(p)	80	127 (293)	15 h	0.711 (28)	112
Ni-Resist type 3	(c)	50	35-90 (95-190)	...	0.0064 (0.25)	114
Ni-Resist type 3	(c)	73	100-125 (212-260)	...	0.094 (3.7)	114
Ni-Resist type 3	(d)	50	40-80 (100-180)	...	0.0025 (0.1)	114
Ni-Resist type 3	(d)	73	115 (240)	...	0.03 (1.2)	114
Ni-Resist type 3	Laboratory test. NaOH concentrated to anhydrous	75	480 (900)	...	3.3 (130)	114
Ni-Resist Type 3	NaCl concentration unknown. (b)	72	121 (250)	24-29 d	0.127 (5)	112
Ni-Resist Type 3	NaCl concentration, 12%. (b)	10	88 (190)	24-29 d	0.005 (0.2)	112
Ni-Resist Type 3	NaCl concentration, 7-8%. (b)	23	93 (200)	24-29 d	0.025 (1)	112
Ni-Resist Type 3	NaCl concentration, 6-7%. (b)	35-40	116 (240)	24-29 d	0.076 (3)	112
Ni-Resist Type 3	NaCl concentration, 10-15%. (b)	50	93 (200)	24-29 d	0.102 (0.4)	112
White iron	Pit depth 0.5 mm (20 mils). (a)	...	510 (950)	4 d	3.8 (151)	115
Irons and steels						
Chromium steel (14Cr)	Test in single-effect evaporator	30-50	80 (180)	16 d	0.84 (33)	113
Chromium steel (18.5% Cr)	Laboratory test. NaOH concentrated to anhydrous	75	480 (900)	...	68.6 (2700)	114
Iron	Metal pickup, none. (e)	...	360 (680)	4 h	...	112
Iron	Metal pickup, 0.426 g. (e)	...	400 (752)	4 h	...	112
Iron	Metal pickup, 0.2-0.3 g. (e)	...	450 (842)	4 h	...	112
Iron	Metal pickup, 0.2-0.3 g. (e)	...	500 (932)	4 h	...	112
Iron	Metal pickup, 0.4-0.48 g. (e)	...	550 (1022)	4 h	...	112
Iron	Metal pickup, 0.13-0.3 g. (e)	...	600 (1112)	4 h	...	112
Iron	Plus 5% sodium peroxide. Metal pickup, 0.024 g. (e)	...	350 (662)	4 h	...	112
Iron	Plus 5% sodium peroxide. Metal pickup, 0.25 g. (e)	...	400 (752)	4 h	...	112
Iron	Plus 5% sodium peroxide. Metal pickup, 0.11 g. (e)	...	450 (842)	4 h	...	112
Iron	Metal pickup, 0.4 g. (e)	...	350 (662)	4 h	...	112
Low-carbon steel	Slight pitting attack	5-10	21 (70)	124 d	0.1 (4)	112
Low-carbon steel	Exposure to effluent from an electrolytic chlorine cell containing 15% NaCl; slight attack under spacer	10	80 (180)	207 d	0.015 (0.6)	111
Low-carbon steel	First effect of a multi-effect evaporator	14	90 (190)	90 d	0.21 (8.2)	112
Low-carbon steel	Test in single-effect evaporator	30-50	80 (180)	16 d	0.09 (3.7)	113
Low-carbon steel	(c)	50	35-90 (95-190)	...	0.12 (4.7)	114
Low-carbon steel	(d)	50	40-80 (100-180)	...	0.09 (3.4)	114
Low-carbon steel	...	50	40 (100)	162 d	0.018 (0.7)	111

(Continued)

Corrosion Behavior of Various Metals and Alloys in Sodium Hydroxide (Continued)

Material	Condition, other factors, comments	Concentration, %	Temperature, °C (°F)	Duration	Corrosion rate, mm/yr (mils/yr) or other	Ref
Low-carbon steel	...	50	55-75 (130-165)	30 d	0.2 (8)	112
Low-carbon steel	...	50	60 (135)	135 d	0.13 (5)	111
Low-carbon steel	...	73	100-125 (212-260)	...	>0.87 (>34.2)	114
Low-carbon steel	(c)	73	115 (240)	...	1.8 (71)	114
Low-carbon steel	(d)	73	540 (1000)	2.5 d	12.7 (500)	114
Low-carbon steel	Plant test. NaOH concentrated to anhydrous. Batch shaded with sulfur and Na_2NO_3					
Mild steel	NaCl concentration, 7-8%. (b)	23	93 (200)	24-29 d	0.229 (9)	112
Mild steel	NaCl concentration, 6-7%. (b)	35-40	116 (240)	24-29 d	1.169 (46)	112
Mild steel	NaCl concentration, 10-15%. (b)	50	93 (200)	24-29 d	0.127 (5)	112
Mild steel	NaCl concentration unknown. (b)	72	121 (250)	24-29 d	0.102 (4)	112
Mild steel	NaCl concentration, 12%. (b)	10	88 (190)	24-29 d	0.127 (5)	112
Steel	...	0.0 g/L	Room	22 d	0.05 (2)	117
Steel	...	0.001 g/L	Room	22 d	0.05 (2)	117
Steel	...	0.01 g/L	Room	22 d	0.05 (2)	117
Steel	...	1.0 g/L	Room	22 d	0.018 (0.7)	117
Steel	...	10 g/L	Room	22 d	nil	117
Steel	...	100 g/L	Room	22 d	0.0025 (0.1)	117
Steel	...	540 g/L	Room	22 d	nil	117
Steel	...	70-73	110 (230)	126 d	0.99 (39)	111
Steel	...	70-73	90-115 (190-240)	90 d	1.45 (57)	112
Steel	Duplicate specimens consumed during test	70-73	130 (265)	200 d	>2 (>80)	113
Stainless steels						
AL-6XN	Welded sample	50	Boiling	...	0.437 (17.22)	120
AL 29-4-2 stainless steel	Plus 5% NaCl	45	177 (350)	4 d	0.19 (7.4)	81
AL 29-4-2 stainless steel	Plus 9% NaCl	26	Boiling	4 d	0.00 (0.0)	81
AL 29-4-2 stainless steel	Plus 14% NaCl	16	Boiling	4 d	0.00 (0.0)	81
AL 29-4-2 stainless steel	Plus 5% NaCl	45	149 (300)	4 d	0.04 (1.5)	81
AL 29-4-2 stainless steel	Plus 23% NaCl, 0.1% Na_2CO_3, 0.15% $NaClO_3$, 0.01% Na_2SO_4	45	177 (350)	4 d	0.14 (5.6)	81
AL 29-4-2 stainless steel	Plus 5% NaCl	45	Boiling	4 d	0.00 (0.0)	81
AL 29-4-2 stainless steel	Plain and welded U-bent samples showed no stress-corrosion cracking in 264-h tests	50	Boiling	5 d	0.00 (0.1)	81
AL 29-4-2 stainless steel	...	60	Boiling	4 d	0.02 (0.8)	81
AL 29-4-2 stainless steel	...	70	Boiling	4 d	0.10 (3.8)	81
AL 29-4C stainless steel	...	20	121 (250)	...	0.015 (0.6)	80
AL 29-4C stainless steel	...	40	121 (250)	...	0.002 (0.1)	80
AL 29-4C stainless steel	...	60	121 (250)	...	0.007 (0.3)	80
AL 29-4C stainless steel	...	60	157 (315)	...	0.04 (1.6)	80
AL 29-4C stainless steel	...	70	121 (250)	...	0.005 (0.2)	80
AL 29-4C stainless steel	...	70	177 (350)	...	0.048 (1.9)	80
AL 904L	...	50	Boiling	...	0.24 (9.6)	120
AM-363 stainless steel	...	...	Room	...	Unattacked	120
AM-363 stainless steel	...	50	Room	...	Unattacked	120
Cast alloy 20	(c)	50	35-90 (95-190)	...	<0.0025 (<0.1)	114
Cast alloy 20	(c)	73	100-125 (212-260)	...	0.09 (3.5)	114
Cast alloy 20	(d)	50	40-80 (100-180)	...	<0.0025 (<0.1)	114
Cast alloy 20	(d)	73	115 (240)	...	0.01 (0.4)	114
E-Brite	...	7.5	102 (215)	5 d	0.000 (0.01)	80
E-Brite	...	15	104 (220)	5 d	0.001 (0.04)	80
E-Brite	Plus 10% NaCl	20	104 (220)	...	0.015 (0.6)	80
E-Brite	...	25	110 (230)	7 d	0.000 (0.01)	80
E-Brite	...	30	116 (240)	5 d	0.001 (0.05)	80
E-Brite	Plus 5% NaCl	45	143 (290)	...	0.041 (1.6)	80
E-Brite	...	50	143 (290)	...	0.003 (0.1)	80
E-Brite	Plus 5% NaCl	50	152 (305)	...	0.076 (3.0)	80
E-Brite	Plus 5% NaCl and 0.1% $NaClO_3$	50	152 (305)	...	0.069 (2.7)	80
E-Brite	Plus 5% NaCl and 0.2% $NaClO_3$	50	152 (305)	...	0.028 (1.1)	80

(Continued)

Corrosion Behavior of Various Metals and Alloys in Sodium Hydroxide (Continued)

Material	Condition, other factors, comments	Concen-tration, %	Temperature, °C (°F)	Duration	Corrosion rate, mm/yr (mils/yr) or other	Ref
E-Brite	Plus 5% NaCl and 0.4% NaClO₃	50	152 (305)	...	0.028 (1.1)	80
E-Brite	...	50	143 (290)	5 d	0.003 (0.11)	80
E-Brite	...	60	157 (315)	4 d	0.084 (3.3)	80
E-Brite	...	70	177 (350)	4 d	0.152-0.381 (6-15)	80
Type 302 stainless steel	...	20	50-60 (120-140)	134 d	<0.0025 (<0.1)	115
Type 302 stainless steel	No aeration	73	100-120 (210-245)	88 d	0.97 (38)	115
Type 302 stainless steel	Laboratory test. NaOH concentrated to anhydrous	75	480 (900)	...	45.7 (1800)	114
Type 304 stainless steel	Chemical processing; field or plant test; slight to moderate aeration; slight to moderate agitation. Plus 99.5% water, traces of butane and kerosene	0.5	160 (320)	275 d	nil	89
Type 304 stainless steel	Chemical processing; field or plant test; slight to moderate aeration; rapid agitation. Plus 12% amine salt, 8% methanol, 7% sodium chloride	1.5-15	28 (85)	20 d	0.0001 in./yr	89
Type 304 stainless steel	Chemical processing; field or plant test; no aeration; slight to moderate agitation; Plus 10% sulfuric acid, 0.1% sulfur dioxide, pH 4.3	2	52 (125)	104 d	<0.0001 in./yr	89
Type 304 stainless steel	Chemical processing; field or plant test; slight to moderate aeration; rapid agitation; sensitized. Plus 12% organic salt, 8% methanol, 7% sodium chloride, liquid line	2-17	29 (85)	37 d	0.0001 in./yr	89
Type 304 stainless steel	Chemical processing; field or plant test; no aeration; rapid agitation. Plus 12% organic salt, 8% methanol, 7% sodium chloride	2-17	29 (85)	37 d	<0.0001 in./yr	89
Type 304 stainless steel	Chemical processing; field or plant test; no aeration; rapid agitation; sensitized. Plus 12% organic salt, 8% methanol, 7% sodium chloride	2-17	29 (85)	37 d	0.0001 in./yr	89
Type 304 stainless steel	Chemical processing; field or plant test; slight to moderate aeration; rapid agitation. Plus 12% organic salt, 8% methanol, 7% sodium chloride, liquid line	2-17	29 (85)	37 d	<0.0001 in./yr	89
Type 304 stainless steel	Research; laboratory test; rapid agitation. Plus occasionally some sulfuric acid. Slight pitting: maximum depth of pits from incipient to 0.005 in.	3-10	87 (190)	300 d	0.03 in./yr	89
Type 304 stainless steel	...	5	Room	...	0.0025 (0.1)	116
Type 304 stainless steel	Petrochemical processing; field or plant test; no aeration; no agitation; with carbon over the standard maximum. Plus <1% sodium hypochlorite, gas scrubber. Severe pitting: depth of pits over 0.010 in., crevice attack (tendency to concentration-cell corrosion)	6	27-32 (80-90)	138 d	0.024 in./yr	89
Type 304 stainless steel	Chemical processing; field or plant test; slight to moderate aeration; slight to moderate agitation. Caustic cell liquor, plus 12% salt	10	87 (190)	279 d	0.0002 in./yr	89
Type 304 stainless steel	...	10	21 (70)	...	Very good	121
Type 304 stainless steel	NaCl concentration, 12%. (b)	10	88 (190)	24-29 d	0.005 (0.2)	112
Type 304 stainless steel	NaCl concentration, 12%. (b)	10	88 (190)	24-29 d	<0.0025 (<0.1)	112
Type 304 stainless steel	Chemical processing; field or plant test; no aeration; no agitation. Multiple effect evaporator	14	87 (190)	90 d	<0.0001 in./yr	89
Type 304 stainless steel	...	15	Room	...	<0.0025 (<0.1)	116
Type 304 stainless steel	Petroleum processing; field or plant test; slight to moderate aeration; rapid agitation. Plus mercaptans, cresolates	18-22	37-104 (100-220)	30 d	0.0001 in./yr	89
Type 304 stainless steel	Petroleum processing; field or plant test; slight to moderate aeration; rapid agitation; with carbon over the standard maximum. Plus mercaptans, cresolates	18-22	37-104 (100-220)	30 d	0.0001 in./yr	89
Type 304 stainless steel	Petroleum processing; field or plant test; no aeration; slight to moderate agitation. Plus naphthenic acid, cresols, phenols, 0.04% mercaptan sulfur, tower	18	107 (225)	660 d	0.0001 in./yr	89
Type 304 stainless steel	Petroleum processing; field or plant test; no aeration; slight to moderate agitation. Plus naphthenic acid, cresols, phenols, 0.04% mercaptan sulfur, tower	18	107 (225)	564 d	0.0001 in./yr	89
Type 304 stainless steel	Plastic distillation; field or plant test; no aeration; rapid agitation. Plus 2-7% potassium hydroxide, still pot in cracking column	20	152 (305)	60 d	<0.0001 in./yr	89

(Continued)

Corrosion Behavior of Various Metals and Alloys in Sodium Hydroxide (Continued)

Material	Condition, other factors, comments	Concentration, %	Temperature, °C (°F)	Duration	Corrosion rate, mm/yr (mils/yr) or other	Ref
Type 304 stainless steel	Field or plant test; no aeration; rapid agitation. Approximately 20% suspended crystalline salt, evaporator	20	60 (140)	196 d	0.0014 in./yr	89
Type 304 stainless steel	...	22	50-60 (120-140)	133 d	<0.0025 (<0.1)	115
Type 304 stainless steel	Chemical processing; field or plant test; no aeration; slight to moderate agitation	22	55 (131)	133 d	<0.0001 in./yr	89
Type 304 stainless steel	Chemical processing; field or plant test; no aeration; slight to moderate agitation; with carbon over the standard maximum	22	55 (131)	133 d	<0.0001 in./yr	89
Type 304 stainless steel	Soap processing; field or plant test; rapid agitation. Caustic soda lye, plus 10-15% sodium chloride, tallow, coconut oil, glycerine removed with sodium chloride, 0.05-0.15% sodium hydrosulfite added in alkaline solution. Severe pitting: maximum depth of pits over 0.010 in., crevice attack (tendency to concentration-cell corrosion)	23	87 (190)	64 d	<0.0001 in./yr	89
Type 304 stainless steel	Soap processing; field or plant test; rapid agitation. Caustic soda lye, plus 10-15% sodium chloride, tallow, coconut oil, glycerine removed with sodium chloride, 0.05-0.15% sodium hydrosulfite added in alkaline solution. Moderate pitting: maximum depth of pits from 0.005 to 0.010 in.	23	87 (190)	64 d	0.0001 in./yr	89
Type 304 stainless steel	Soap processing; field or plant test; rapid agitation; with carbon over the standard maximum. Caustic soda lye, plus 10-15% sodium chloride, tallow, coconut oil, glycerine removed with sodium chloride, 0.05-0.15% sodium hydrosulfite added in alkaline solution. Slight pitting: maximum depth of pits from incipient to 0.005 in.	23	87 (190)	64 d	0.0001 in./yr	89
Type 304 stainless steel	Soap processing; field or plant test; rapid agitation: with carbon over the maximum standard. Caustic soda lye, plus 10-15% sodium chloride, tallow, coconut oil, glycerine removed with sodium chloride, 0.05-0.15% sodium hydrosulfite added in alkaline solution. Severe pitting: maximum depth of pits over 0.010 in., crevice attack (tendency to concentration-cell corrosion)	23	87 (190)	64 d	<0.0001 in./yr	89
Type 304 stainless steel	Chemical processing; field or plant test; slight to moderate aeration; slight to moderate agitation. Approximately 23%, plus 7-8% salt	23	93 (200)	48 d	0.0004 in./yr	89
Type 304 stainless steel	NaCl concentration, 7-8%. (b)	23	93 (200)	24-29 d	0.01 (0.4)	112
Type 304 stainless steel	NaCl concentration, 7-8%. (b)	23	93 (200)	24-29 d	0.051 (2)	112
Type 304 stainless steel	...	25	Room	...	<0.0025 (<0.1)	116
Type 304 stainless steel	No activation	25	100 (212)	24 h	0.0275 (1.1)	52
Type 304 stainless steel	Petroleum processing; field or plant test	30	20 (68)	30 d	<0.0001 in./yr	89
Type 304 stainless steel	Intergranular plus grain detachment. Sensitized (650 °C for 10 h, air cooled)	30	100 (212)	72 h	...	148
Type 304 stainless steel	...	35	Room	...	<0.0025 (<0.1)	116
Type 304 stainless steel	No activation	35	100 (212)	24 h	0.044 (2.2)	52
Type 304 stainless steel	Atomic energy; laboratory test; no aeration; no agitation. Plus 3 ppm chloride ion, vapors. Stress-corrosion cracking	35	260 (500)	21 d	...	89
Type 304 stainless steel	Chemical processing; field or plant test; slight to moderate aeration; slight to moderate agitation. Approximately 35-40%, plus 6-7% salt, salt settler	35-40	115 (240)	24 d	0.001 in./yr	89
Type 304 stainless steel	NaCl concentration, 6-7%. (b)	35-40	115 (240)	24-29 d	0.025 (1)	112
Type 304 stainless steel	NaCl concentration, 6-7%. (b)	35-40	115 (240)	24-29 d	0.051 (2)	112
Type 304 stainless steel	NaCl concentration, 6-7%. (b)	35-40	115 (240)	24-29 d	0.0229 (0.9)	112
Type 304 stainless steel	Selective dissolution. General corrosion. As-received	40	90 (194)	72 h	...	148
Type 304 stainless steel	Uniform corrosion. As-received	40	110 (230)	72 h	...	148
Type 304 stainless steel	...	45	Room	...	<0.0025 (<0.1)	116
Type 304 stainless steel	Chemical processing; field or pilot plant test; no aeration; no agitation	49-51	65 (150)	30 d	0.0001 in./yr	89
Type 304 stainless steel	Chemical processing; field or plant test; slight to moderate aeration; slight to moderate agitation	50	58 (136)	167 d	<0.0001 in./yr	89
Type 304 stainless steel	(c)	50	35-90 (95-190)	...	0.005 (0.2)	114

(Continued)

Corrosion Behavior of Various Metals and Alloys in Sodium Hydroxide (Continued)

Material	Condition, other factors, comments	Concen-tration, %	Temperature, °C (°F)	Duration	Corrosion rate, mm/yr (mils/yr) or other	Ref
Type 304 stainless steel	(d)	50	40-80 (100-180)	...	0.019 (0.75)	114
Type 304 stainless steel	...	50	55-75 (130-165)	30 d	0.0025 (0.1)	112
Type 304 stainless steel	NaCl concentration, 10-15%. (b)	50	93 (200)	24-29 d	0.005 (0.2)	112
Type 304 stainless steel	Chemical processing; slight to moderate aeration; slight to moderate agitation. Plus 10-15% sodium chloride	50	93 (200)	119 d	0.0002 in./yr	89
Type 304 stainless steel	NaCl concentration, 10-15%. (b)	50	93 (200)	24-29 d	0.102 (0.4)	112
Type 304 stainless steel	Laboratory test	50	150 (300)	...	1.2 (47)	113
Type 304 stainless steel	No activation	60	100 (212)	24 h	0.06 (3.0)	52
Type 304 stainless steel	...	70-73	90-115 (190-240)	90 d	0.69 (27)	112
Type 304 stainless steel	...	70-73	120 (240)	180 d	0.26 (10.2)	113
Type 304 stainless steel	Chemical processing; field or plant test; no aeration; no agitation	70	90-143 (194-239)	90 d	0.0268 in./yr	89
Type 304 stainless steel	Chemical processing; field or plant test; slight to moderate aeration; slight to moderate agitation	72	121 (250)	119 d	0.0037 in./yr	89
Type 304 stainless steel	Solution moderately agitated	72	120-125 (245-255)	119 d	0.09 (3.7)	115
Type 304 stainless steel	NaCl concentration unknown. (b)	72	121 (250)	24-29 d	0.102 (4)	112
Type 304 stainless steel	NaCl concentration unknown. (b)	72	121 (250)	24-29 d	0.0076 (0.3)	112
Type 304 stainless steel	(c)	73	100-125 (212-260)	...	0.4 (15.8)	114
Type 304 stainless steel	(d)	73	115 (240)	...	0.38 (15)	114
Type 304 stainless steel	No aeration	73	100-120 (210-245)	88 d	1.1 (45)	115
Type 304 stainless steel	Chemical processing; field or pilot plant test; no aeration; no agitation	73	120-160 (248-320)	34 d	0.113 in./yr	89
Type 304 stainless steel	Chemical processing; field or pilot plant test; no aeration; slight to moderate agitation	73	110 (230)	88 d	0.045 in./yr	89
Type 304 stainless steel	Chemical processing; field or pilot plant test; no aeration; slight to moderate agitation; with carbon over the standard maximum	73	110 (230)	88 d	0.038 in./yr	89
Type 304 stainless steel	Chemical processing; field or plant test; no aeration; slight to moderate agitation	73	110 (230)	52 d	0.0093 in./yr	89
Type 304 stainless steel	Chemical processing; field or plant test; no aeration; slight to moderate agitation; with carbon over the standard maximum	73	110 (230)	52 d	0.0093 in./yr	89
Type 304 stainless steel	Chemical processing; field or pilot plant test; no aeration; no agitation. Slight pitting: maximum depth of pits from incipient to 0.005 in.	75	135 (275)	35 d	0.005 in./yr	89
Type 304 stainless steel	Chemical processing; field or pilot plant test; no aeration; no agitation; with carbon over the standard maximum. Slight pitting: maximum depth of pits from incipient to 0.005 in.	75	135 (275)	35 d	0.007 in./yr	89
Type 304 stainless steel	Chemical processing; field or plant test; slight to moderate aeration; rapid agitation. Plus sulfur dioxide, normally acid solution	...	54-60 (130-140)	99 d	<0.0001 in./yr	89
Type 304 stainless steel	Chemical processing; field or plant test; slight to moderate aeration; rapid agitation. Plus sulfur dioxide, normally alkaline solution	...	54-60 (130-140)	99 d	<0.0001 in./yr	89
Type 304 stainless steel	Chemical processing; field or plant test; slight to moderate aeration; rapid agitation. Plus sodium hydrosulfide, sodium sulfide, intermittent exposure to air, steam, and hydrogen sulfide (gas absorption column)	...	75 (167)	15 d	0.00015 in./yr	89
Type 304 stainless steel	Chemical processing; field or plant test; slight to moderate aeration; slight to moderate agitation. Plus organic material, sulfuric acid, arsenious acid (in resin of ion exchanger)	...	76 (167)	30 d	0.0001 in./yr	89
Type 304 stainless steel	Chemical processing; field or plant test; slight to moderate aeration; rapid agitation. Dilute caustic soda, plus sodium formate, methanol, nitrogen compounds	...	30-120 (86-248)	75 d	<0.0001 in./yr	89
Type 304 stainless steel	Chemical processing; field or plant test; slight to moderate aeration; rapid agitation. Dilute caustic soda, plus sodium formate, methanol, nitrogen compounds	...	30-120 (86-248)	75 d	0.0003 in./yr	89
Type 309 stainless steel	...	20	50-60 (120-140)	134 d	<0.0025 (<0.1)	115
Type 310 stainless steel	...	20	50-60 (120-140)	134 d	<0.0025 (<0.1)	115

(Continued)

Corrosion Behavior of Various Metals and Alloys in Sodium Hydroxide (Continued)

Material	Condition, other factors, comments	Concentration, %	Temperature, °C (°F)	Duration	Corrosion rate, mm/yr (mils/yr) or other	Ref
Type 316 stainless steel	Chemical processing; field or plant test; slight to moderate aeration; slight to moderate agitation. Plus 99.5% water, traces of butane and kerosene	0.5	160 (320)	275 d	nil	89
Type 316 stainless steel	Chemical processing; field or plant test; slight to moderate aeration; rapid agitation; low-carbon grade (0.03% carbon maximum). Plus 12% amine salt, 8% methanol, 7% sodium chloride	1.5-15	28 (85)	20 d	0.0002 in./yr	89
Type 316 stainless steel	Chemical processing; field or plant test; no aeration; slight to moderate agitation; Plus 10% sulfuric acid, 0.1% sulfur dioxide, pH 4.3	2	52 (125)	104 d	<0.0001 in./yr	89
Type 316 stainless steel	Chemical processing; field or plant test; slight to moderate aeration; rapid agitation; sensitized. Plus 12% organic salt, 8% methanol, 7% sodium chloride, liquid line	2-17	29 (85)	37 d	0.0001 in./yr	89
Type 316 stainless steel	Chemical processing; field or plant test; no aeration; rapid agitation. Plus 12% organic salt, 8% methanol, 7% sodium chloride	2-17	29 (85)	37 d	<0.0001 in./yr	89
Type 316 stainless steel	Chemical processing; field or plant test; no aeration; rapid agitation; sensitized. Plus 12% organic salt, 8% methanol, 7% sodium chloride	2-17	29 (85)	37 d	0.0001 in./yr	89
Type 316 stainless steel	Chemical processing; field or plant test; slight to moderate aeration; rapid agitation. Plus 12% organic salt, 8% methanol, 7% sodium chloride, liquid line	2-17	29 (85)	37 d	<0.0001 in./yr	89
Type 316 stainless steel	Research; laboratory test; rapid agitation. Plus occasionally some sulfuric acid	3-10	87 (190)	300 d	0.0083 in./yr	89
Type 316 stainless steel	Petrochemical processing; field or plant test; no aeration; no agitation; with carbon over the standard maximum. Plus <1% sodium hypochlorite, gas scrubber. Severe pitting: depth of pits over 0.010 in., crevice attack (tendency to concentration-cell corrosion)	6	27-32 (80-90)	138 d	0.022 in./yr	89
Type 316 stainless steel	Chemical processing; field or plant test; slight to moderate aeration; slight to moderate agitation. Caustic cell liquor, plus 12% salt	10	87 (190)	279 d	<0.0001 in./yr	89
Type 316 stainless steel	...	10	21 (70)	...	Very good	121
Type 316 stainless steel	Chemical distillation; field or plant test; no aeration; slight to moderate agitation. Plus 2% chlorine-saturated monochlorotoluene, and approximately 2% hydrochloric acid, batch still. Severe pitting: depth of pits over 0.010 in., crevice attack (tendency to concentration-cell corrosion)	15	100 (212)	33 d	0.023 in./yr	89
Type 316 stainless steel	Petroleum processing; field or plant test; slight to moderate aeration; rapid agitation. Plus mercaptans, cresolates	18-22	37-104 (100-220)	30 d	0.0004 in./yr	89
Type 316 stainless steel	Petroleum processing; field or plant test; no aeration; slight to moderate agitation. Plus naphthenic acid, cresols, phenols, 0.04% mercaptan sulfur, tower	18	107 (225)	660 d	0.0002 in./yr	89
Type 316 stainless steel	Petroleum processing; field or plant test; no aeration; slight to moderate agitation. Plus naphthenic acid, cresols, phenols, 0.04% mercaptan sulfur, tower	18	107 (225)	660 d	0.0001 in./yr	89
Type 316 stainless steel	Plastic distillation; field or plant test; no aeration; rapid agitation. Plus 2-7% potassium hydroxide, still pot in cracking column	20	152 (305)	60 d	<0.0001 in./yr	89
Type 316 stainless steel	Field or plant test; no aeration; rapid agitation. Approximately 20% suspended crystalline salt, evaporator	20	60 (140)	196 d	0.0036 in./yr	89
Type 316 stainless steel	Soap processing; field or plant test; rapid agitation. Caustic soda lye, plus 10-15% sodium chloride, tallow, coconut oil, glycerine removed with sodium chloride, 0.05-0.15% sodium hydrosulfite added in alkaline solution. Slight pitting: maximum depth of pits from incipient to 0.005 in.	23	87 (190)	64 d	<0.0001 in./yr	89
Type 316 stainless steel	Soap processing; field or plant test; rapid agitation. Caustic soda lye, plus 10-15% sodium chloride, tallow, coconut oil, glycerine removed with sodium chloride, 0.05-0.15% sodium hydrosulfite added in alkaline solution	23	87 (190)	64 d	0.0003 in./yr	89

(Continued)

Corrosion Behavior of Various Metals and Alloys in Sodium Hydroxide (Continued)

Material	Condition, other factors, comments	Concentration, %	Temperature, °C (°F)	Duration	Corrosion rate, mm/yr (mils/yr) or other	Ref
Type 316 stainless steel	Chemical processing; field or plant test; slight to moderate aeration; slight to moderate agitation. Approximately 23%, plus 7-8% salt	23	93 (200)	48 d	0.0023 in./yr	89
Type 316 stainless steel	Scratches remained. As-received	25	95 (203)	72 h	...	148
Type 316 stainless steel	No activation	25	100 (212)	24 h	0.0475 (1.9)	52
Type 316 stainless steel	No activation	35	100 (212)	24 h	0.04 (1.6)	52
Type 316 stainless steel	Chemical processing; field or plant test; slight to moderate aeration; slight to moderate agitation. Approximately 35-40%, plus 6-7% salt, salt settler	35-40	115 (240)	24 d	0.0015 in./yr	89
Type 316 stainless steel	(c)	50	35-90 (95-190)	...	0.017 (0.65)	114
Type 316 stainless steel	(d)	50	40-80 (100-180)	...	0.0025 (0.1)	114
Type 316 stainless steel	Chemical processing; slight to moderate aeration; slight to moderate agitation. Plus 10-15% sodium chloride	50	93 (200)	119 d	0.0002 in./yr	89
Type 316 stainless steel	Base metal sample	50	Boiling	...	3.12 (123)	120
Type 316 stainless steel	...	50	Boiling	...	>2.5 (>100)	120
Type 316 stainless steel	Welded sample	50	Boiling	...	3.45 (136)	120
Type 316 stainless steel	Intergranular corrosion. As-received	50	130 (266)	72 h	...	148
Type 316 stainless steel	No activation	60	100 (212)	24 h	0.0675 (2.7)	52
Type 316 stainless steel	Solution moderately agitated	72	120-125 (245-255)	119 d	0.08 (3.1)	115
Type 316 stainless steel	Chemical processing; field or plant test; slight to moderate aeration; slight to moderate agitation	72	121 (250)	119 d	0.0031 in./yr	89
Type 316 stainless steel	(c)	73	100-125 (212-260)	...	0.24 (9.3)	114
Type 316 stainless steel	(d)	73	115 (240)	...	0.25 (10)	114
Type 316 stainless steel	Chemical processing; field or pilot plant test; no aeration; no agitation	73	120-160 (248-320)	34 d	0.105 in./yr	89
Type 316 stainless steel	Chemical processing; field or pilot plant test; rapid agitation. Tank car	74	129 (265)	88 d	0.0084 in./yr	89
Type 316 stainless steel	Chemical processing; field or pilot plant test; no aeration; no agitation. Slight pitting; maximum depth of pits from incipient to 0.005 in.	75	135 (275)	35 d	0.007 in./yr	89
Type 316 stainless steel	Chemical processing; field or plant test; slight to moderate aeration; rapid agitation. Plus sulfur dioxide, normally acid solution	...	54-60 (130-140)	99 d	<0.0001 in./yr	89
Type 316 stainless steel	Chemical processing; field or plant test; slight to moderate aeration; rapid agitation. Plus sulfur dioxide, normally alkaline solution	...	54-60 (130-140)	99 d	<0.0001 in./yr	89
Type 316 stainless steel	Chemical processing; field or plant test; slight to moderate aeration; rapid agitation. Plus sodium hydrosulfide, sodium sulfide, intermittent exposure to air, steam, and hydrogen sulfide (gas absorption column)	...	75 (167)	15 d	0.0004 in./yr	89
Type 316 stainless steel	Chemical processing; field or plant test; slight to moderate aeration; slight to moderate agitation. Plus organic material, sulfuric acid, arsenious acid (in resin of ion exchanger)	...	76 (167)	30 d	0.0001 in./yr	89
Type 316 stainless steel	Chemical processing; field or plant test; slight to moderate aeration; rapid agitation. Dilute caustic soda, plus sodium formate, methanol, nitrogen compounds	...	30-120 (86-248)	75 d	<0.0001 in./yr	89
Type 316 stainless steel	Chemical processing; field or plant test; slight to moderate aeration; rapid agitation. Dilute caustic soda, plus sodium formate, methanol, nitrogen compounds	...	30-120 (86-248)	75 d	0.0003 in./yr	89
Type 316L stainless steel	Stress-corrosion cracking: no failure in 1000 h. (f)	50	143 (290)	...	...	60
Type 317L stainless steel	Stress-corrosion cracking: no failure in 1000 h. (f)	50	143 (290)	...	...	60
Type 317L stainless steel	Stress-corrosion cracking: duplicate specimens tested at 1031 h. (f)	70	177 (350)	...	...	60
Type 316L stainless steel	Stress-corrosion cracking: duplicate specimens tested at 200 and 648 h. (f)	70	177 (350)	...	...	60
Type 329 stainless steel	Solution moderately agitated	72	120-125 (245-255)	119 d	0.0025 (0.1)	115
Type 410 stainless steel	...	20	50-60 (120-140)	134 d	0.0025 (0.1)	115
Type 410 stainless steel	Solution moderately agitated	72	120-125 (245-255)	119 d	0.8 (32)	115

(Continued)

Corrosion Behavior of Various Metals and Alloys in Sodium Hydroxide (Continued)

Material	Condition, other factors, comments	Concentration, %	Temperature, °C (°F)	Duration	Corrosion rate, mm/yr (mils/yr) or other	Ref
		10	21 (70)	...	Very good	121
Type 410 stainless steel	...	10	21 (70)	...	Very good	121
Type 430 stainless steel	...	20	50-60 (120-140)	134 d	0.0025 (0.1)	115
Type 430 stainless steel	...	50	35-90 (95-190)	...	0.01 (0.4)	114
Type 430 stainless steel	(c)	73	100-125 (212-260)	...	>0.97 (>38)	114
Type 430 stainless steel	(c)	50	40-80 (100-180)	...	>0.14 (>5.4)	114
Type 430 stainless steel	(d)	73	115 (240)	...	1.5 (60)	114
Type 430 stainless steel	(d)	25	100 (212)	24 h	0.19 (7.6)	52
Type 444 stainless steel	No activation	35	100 (212)	24 h	0.5 (20)	52
Type 444 stainless steel	No activation	60	100 (212)	24 h	0.6 (24)	52
Type 444 stainless steel	No activation	20	132 (270)	19 h	0.102 (4)	112
Worthite	Solution quenched. (p)	20	156 (345)	20 h	0.356 (14)	112
Worthite	Solution quenched. (p)	20	171 (340)	19 h	0.635 (25)	112
Worthite	Solution quenched. Two tests. (p)				1.753 (69)	
Worthite	Solution quenched. (p)	40	132 (270)	19 h	0.229 (9)	112
Worthite	Solution quenched. (p)	40	156 (345)	20 h	0.432 (17)	112
Worthite	Solution quenched. Two tests. (p)	40	171 (340)	19 h	0.914 (36)	112
					0.711 (28)	
Worthite	Solution quenched. (p)	60	132 (270)	19 h	0.025 (1)	112
Worthite	Solution quenched. (p)	60	156 (345)	20 h	0.838 (33)	112
Worthite	Solution quenched. Two tests. (p)	60	171 (340)	19 h	0.051 (2)	112
					0.965 (38)	
Worthite	Solution quenched. (p)	80	132 (270)	19 h	nil	112
Worthite	Solution quenched. Two tests. (p)	80	171 (340)	19 h	nil	112
Worthite	Solution quenched. (p)	80	156 (345)	20 h	0.025 (1)	112
Coppers						
60-40 cupronickel	Laboratory test in glass bottle	5	15-20 (59-68)	21 d	nil	112
60-40 cupronickel	Diaphragm cell liquor-coupons in distributor box to settlers	11	Hot	25 d	0.012 (0.5)	112
70-30 cupronickel	...	50	55-75 (130-165)	30 d	0.0013 (0.05)	112
70-30 cupronickel	...	...	...	...	Suitable	93
70-30 cupronickel (CA 715)	Laboratory test in glass bottle	5	15-20 (59-68)	21 d	nil	112
70-30 cupronickel (CA 715)	Diaphragm cell liquor-coupons in distributor box to settlers	11	Hot	25 d	0.109 (4.3)	112
70-30 cupronickel (CA 715)	Velocity 1.8 ft/s. Salt saturated	50	95 (203)	67 d	0.02 (0.8)	112
70-30 cupronickel (CA 715)	In storage tank	50	65 (149)	30 d	nil	112
70-30 cupronickel (CA 715)	...	73	105 (221)	118 d	0.03 (1.2)	112
70-30 cupronickel (CA 715)	In evaporator concentrating from 60-75%	60-75	150-175 (302-347)	0.5 d	0.11 (4.4)	112
70-30 cupronickel (CA 715)	In evaporator concentrating from 60% to anhydrous	60-100	150-260 (302-500)	2 d	0.533 (21)	112
70-30 cupronickel (CA 715)	In anhydrous melt	100	400-410 (752-770)	1 d	1.77 (70)	112
80-20 cupronickel (CA 710)	Laboratory test in glass bottle	5	15-20 (59-68)	21 d	nil	112
80-20 cupronickel (CA 710)	In evaporator concentrating from 60-75%	60-75	150-175 (302-347)	0.5 d	0.205 (8.1)	112
80-20 cupronickel (CA 710)	In evaporator concentrating from 60% to anhydrous	60-100	150-260 (302-500)	2 d	0.711 (28)	112
80-20 cupronickel (CA 710)	In anhydrous melt	100	400-410 (752-770)	1 d	2.28 (90)	112
90-10 cupronickel	...	...	...	...	Suitable	93
90-10 cupronickel (CA 706)	Velocity 1.8 ft/s. Salt saturated	50	95 (203)	67 d	0.045 (1.8)	112
90-10 cupronickel (CA 706)	...	73	105 (221)	118 d	0.05 (2)	112
Admiralty brass	(g)	...	...	...	Good	93

(Continued)

Corrosion Behavior of Various Metals and Alloys in Sodium Hydroxide (Continued)

Material	Condition, other factors, comments	Concen-tration, %	Temperature, °C (°F)	Duration	Corrosion rate, mm/yr (mils/yr) or other	Ref
Aluminum bronze	...	70-73	110 (230)	126 d	0.023 (0.9)	111
Aluminum bronze	...	70-73	120 (240)	180 d	0.15 (6.1)	113
Aluminum bronze	...	5	Room	...	0.09 (3.8)	116
Aluminum bronze	...	15	Room	...	0.018 (0.7)	116
Aluminum bronze	...	25	Room	...	0.008 (0.3)	116
Aluminum bronze	...	35	Room	...	0.01 (0.4)	116
Aluminum bronze	...	45	Room	...	0.005 (0.2)	116
Aluminum bronze	Laboratory test	50	60 (135)	135 d	0.025 (1)	111
Aluminum bronze	(g)	50	150 (300)	...	0.08 (3)	113
Ampco 8, aluminum bronze	Generally suitable	...	...	...	Good	93
Architectural bronze	...	...	...	...	<0.05 (<2)	96
Brass	(g)	...	...	...	Fair	93
Cartridge brass	...	...	...	...	Good	93
Commercial bronze	(g)	...	...	...	Fair	93
Copper	Test in single-effect evaporator	30-50	80 (180)	16 d	Good	93
Copper	Metal pickup, strongly attacked. (e)	...	360 (680)	4 h	0.06 (2.3)	113
Copper	Metal pickup, strongly attacked. (e)	...	400 (752)	4 h	...	112
Copper	Metal pickup, strongly attacked. (e)	...	450 (842)	4 h	...	112
Copper	Metal pickup, strongly attacked. (e)	...	500 (932)	4 h	...	112
Copper	Metal pickup, strongly attacked. (e)	...	550 (1022)	4 h	...	112
Copper	Metal pickup, strongly attacked. (e)	...	600 (1112)	4 h	...	112
Copper	Plus 5% sodium peroxide. Metal pickup, trace. (e)	...	350 (662)	4 h	...	112
Copper	Plus 5% sodium peroxide. Metal pickup, 0.013 g. (e)	...	400 (752)	4 h	...	112
Copper	Plus 5% sodium peroxide. Metal pickup, 0.08. (e)	...	450 (842)	4 h	...	112
Copper	Metal pickup, strongly attacked. (e)	...	350 (662)	4 h	...	112
Copper-nickel-zinc (75Cu-20Ni-5Zn)	Test in single-effect evaporator	30-50	80 (180)	16 d	0.013 (0.5)	113
Deoxidized copper	...	5	Room	...	0.086 (3.4)	116
Deoxidized copper	...	15	Room	...	0.008 (0.3)	116
Deoxidized copper	...	25	Room	...	0.008 (0.3)	116
Deoxidized copper	...	35	Room	...	0.025 (1)	116
Deoxidized copper	...	45	Room	...	0.005 (0.2)	116
Deoxidized copper	Laboratory test	50	150 (300)	...	0.14 (5.5)	113
Electrolytic copper	(g)	...	...	...	Good	93
Free-cutting brass	...	...	...	...	Fair	93
Muntz metal	...	...	...	...	Fair	93
Naval brass	...	...	...	...	Fair	93
Nickel silver	...	18	...	...	Suitable	93
Phosphor bronze	5% Sn. (g)	...	...	...	Good	93
Phosphor bronze	8% Sn. (g)	...	...	...	Good	93
Phosphor copper	(g)	...	...	...	Good	93
Red brass	(g)	...	...	...	Good	93
Silicon bronze	Low. (g)	...	...	...	Good	93
Silicon bronze	High. (g)	...	...	...	Good	93
Titanium						
Ti-3Al-2.5V	ASTM Grade 9	50	150 (302)	...	0.48 (19.4)	91
Titanium	...	5-10	21 (70)	124 d	0.001 (0.04)	112
Titanium	...	5-10	21 (70)	...	0.001 (0.04)	90
Titanium	...	10	Boiling	...	0.02 (0.8)	1
Titanium	Exposure to effluent from an electrolytic chlorine cell containing 15% NaCl	10	80 (180)	207 d	nil	111
Titanium	...	10	Boiling	...	0.021 (0.84)	90
Titanium	...	10	Boiling	...	0.02 (0.8)	1
Titanium	...	28	25 (75)	...	0.003 (0.12)	1

(Continued)

Corrosion Behavior of Various Metals and Alloys in Sodium Hydroxide (Continued)

Material	Condition, other factors, comments	Concentration, %	Temperature, °C (°F)	Duration	Corrosion rate, mm/yr (mils/yr) or other	Ref
Titanium	...	28	Room	...	0.003 (0.12)	90
Titanium	...	40	66 (150)	...	0.038 (1.5)	1
Titanium	...	40	80 (176)	...	0.127 (5.08)	90
Titanium	...	40	93 (200)	...	0.064 (2.5)	1
Titanium	...	40	121 (250)	...	0.13 (5)	1
Titanium	...	50	57 (135)	...	0.013 (0.52)	90
Titanium	...	50	38 (100)	...	0.023 (0.92)	90
Titanium	...	50	66 (150)	...	0.018 (0.7)	1
Titanium	Grade 9	50	150 (302)	...	0.49 (19.2)	33
Titanium	...	50	150 (302)	...	0.05 (2.2)	91
Titanium	...	50	40 (100)	162 d	0.00025 (0.01)	111
Titanium	...	50	60 (135)	135 d	0.013 (0.5)	111
Titanium	...	50	Boiling	...	0.051 (2.04)	90
Titanium	...	50-73	188 (370)	...	>1.1 (>43.3)	1
Titanium	...	50-73	188 (370)	...	>1.09 (>43.6)	90
Titanium	...	50-73	188 (370)	...	>1.1 (>43.3)	1
Titanium	...	73	110 (230)	...	0.05 (2)	1
Titanium	...	73	Boiling	...	0.13 (5)	1
Titanium	...	73	129 (265)	...	0.178 (7.12)	90
Titanium	...	73	110 (230)	...	0.05 (2)	1
Titanium	...	73	Boiling	...	0.13 (5)	1
Titanium	...	70-73	110 (230)	126 d	0.05 (2)	111
Titanium	...	70-73	130 (265)	200 d	0.18 (7)	113
Heat- and corrosion-resistant alloys						
20Cb-3	(c)	50	35-90 (95-190)	...	<0.0025 (<0.1)	114
20Cb-3	(d)	50	40-80 (100-180)	...	<0.0025 (<0.1)	114
20Cb-3	(c)	73	100-125 (212-260)	...	0.02 (0.8)	114
20Cb-3	(d)	73	115 (240)	...	0.01 (0.4)	114
21Cr-4Ni-0.5Cu	Solution moderately agitated	72	120-125 (245-255)	119 d	0.15 (6)	115
44Co-31Cr-13W	(h)	50	65 (150)	...	0.0007 (0.3)	53
44Co-31Cr-13W	Heat treated 4 h at 899 °C (1650 °F) and furnace cooled. (h)	50	65 (150)	...	0.015 (0.6)	53
50Co-20Cr-15W-10Ni	...	50	65 (150)	...	nil	53
53Co-30Cr-4.5W	(h)	50	65 (150)	...	0.007 (0.3)	53
53Co-30Cr-4.5W	Heat treated 4 h at 899 °C (1650 °F). (h)	50	65 (150)	...	0.01 (0.4)	53
ACI CN-7M	Cast	20	150 (334)	18 h	0.254 (10)	112
ACI CN-7M	Cast	20	183 (394)	15 h	nil	112
ACI CN-7M	Cast	40	150 (334)	18 h	0.025 (1)	112
ACI CN-7M	Cast	60	152 (336)	19 h	0.305 (12)	112
ACI CN-7M	Cast	60	183 (394)	15 h	3.835 (151)	112
ACI CN-7M	Cast	80	183 (394)	15 h	0.051 (2)	112
Alloy 825	Chemical processing; field or plant test; slight to moderate aeration; rapid agitation. Plus 12% organic salt, 8% methanol, 7% sodium chloride, liquid line	2-17	29 (85)	37 d	<0.0001 in./yr	89
Alloy 825	Chemical processing; no aeration; rapid agitation. Plus 12% organic salt, 8% methanol, 7% sodium chloride	2-17	29 (85)	37 d	<0.0001 in./yr	89
Alloy 825	Research; laboratory test; rapid agitation. Plus occasionally some sulfuric acid	3-10	87 (190)	300 d	0.0001 in./yr	89
Alloy 825	Chemical distillation; no aeration; slight to moderate agitation. Plus 2% chlorine-saturated monochlorotoluene, approximately 2% hydrochloric acid, batch still. Severe pitting: maximum depth of pits over 0.010 in., crevice attack (tendency to concentration-cell corrosion)	15	100 (212)	33 d	0.018 in./yr	89
Alloy 825	Chemical processing; field or plant test; rapid agitation. Tank car	74	129 (265)	88 d	0.0003 in./yr	89
Alloy 825	Chemical processing; field or plant test; slight to moderate aeration; rapid agitation. Dilute caustic soda, plus sodium formate, methanol, nitrogen compounds	...	30-120 (86-248)	75 d	<0.0001 in./yr	89

(Continued)

Corrosion Behavior of Various Metals and Alloys in Sodium Hydroxide (Continued)

Material	Condition, other factors, comments	Concentration, %	Temperature, °C (°F)	Duration	Corrosion rate, mm/yr (mils/yr) or other	Ref
Cabot alloy No. 625	...	10	66 (151)	96 h	nil	67
Cabot alloy No. 625	...	10	93 (199)	96 h	nil	67
Cabot alloy No. 625	...	10	Boiling	96 h	<0.003 (0.1)	67
Cabot alloy No. 625	...	30	66 (151)	96 h	nil	67
Cabot alloy No. 625	...	30	93 (199)	96 h	nil	67
Cabot alloy No. 625	...	30	Boiling	96 h	nil	67
Cabot alloy No. 625	...	50	66 (151)	96 h	<0.003 (0.1)	67
Cabot alloy No. 625	...	50	93 (199)	96 h	0.01 (0.4)	67
Cabot alloy No. 625	...	50	Boiling	96 h	0.06 (2.4)	67
Carpenter 20	Chemical processing; field or plant test; slight to moderate aeration; rapid agitation. Plus 12% organic salt, 8% methanol, 7% sodium chloride, liquid line	2-17	29 (85)	37 d	<0.0001 in./yr	89
Carpenter 20	Chemical processing; no aeration; rapid agitation. Plus 12% organic salt, 8% methanol, 7% sodium chloride	2-17	29 (85)	37 d	<0.0001 in./yr	89
Carpenter 20	Research; laboratory test; rapid agitation; cast. Plus occasionally some sulfuric acid	3-10	87 (190)	300 d	0.0006 in./yr	89
Carpenter 20	Chemical distillation; no aeration; slight to moderate agitation. Plus 2% chlorine-saturated monochlorotoluene, approximately 2% hydrochloric acid, batch still. Severe pitting: maximum depth of pits over 0.010 in., crevice attack (tendency to concentration-cell corrosion)	15	100 (212)	33 d	0.022 in./yr	89
Carpenter 20	Chemical processing; field or plant test; rapid agitation. Tank car	74	129 (265)	88 d	0.0009 in./yr	89
Carpenter 20	Chemical processing; field or plant test; slight to moderate aeration; rapid agitation. Dilute caustic soda, plus sodium formate, methanol, nitrogen compounds	...	30-120 (86-248)	75 d	<0.0001 in./yr	89
Duranickel alloy 301	Molten	...	400 (750)	...	0.0432 (1.7)	112
Duranickel alloy 301	Molten	..	500 (932)	...	0.081 (3.2)	112
Duranickel alloy 301	Molten	...	580 (1076)	...	0.264 (10.4)	112
Duranickel alloy 301	Molten	...	680 (1256)	...	1.034 (40.7)	112
Ferralium alloy 255	Stress-corrosion cracking: no failure in 1000 h. (f)	50	143 (290)	...	...	60
Ferralium alloy 255	Stress-corrosion cracking: no failure in 1000 h. (f)	70	177 (350)	...	...	60
Hastelloy alloy C	Molten	...	400 (750)	...	...	112
Hastelloy alloy C	Molten	..	500 (932)	...	2.55 (100.5)	112
Hastelloy alloy C	Molten. Gained weight. Swollen outside surface largely oxide—heavily corroded	...	580 (1076)	...	...	112
Hastelloy alloy C	Molten	...	680 (1256)	...	...	112
Hastelloy alloy D	Molten	...	400 (750)	...	0.0178 (0.7)	112
Hastelloy alloy D	Molten	..	500 (932)	...	0.056 (2.2)	112
Hastelloy alloy D	Molten	...	580 (1076)	...	0.252 (9.9)	112
Hastelloy alloy D	Molten. Gained weight. Swollen outside surface largely oxide—heavily corroded	...	680 (1256)	...	...	112
Haynes alloy 6B	...	50	Boiling	...	2.74 (108)	23
Haynes alloy No. 25	...	50	Boiling	...	0.53 (21)	23
Haynes alloy No. 25	(j)	5	Room	24 h	nil	68
Haynes alloy No. 25	(j)	5	66 (150)	24 h	nil	68
Haynes alloy No. 25	(j)	5	Boiling	24 h	nil	68
Haynes alloy No. 25	(j)	25	Room	24 h	nil	68
Haynes alloy No. 25	(j)	25	66 (150)	24 h	nil	68
Haynes alloy No. 25	(j)	50	66 (150)	24 h	nil	68
Haynes alloy No. 25	(j)	50	Room	24 h	nil	68
Haynes alloy 188	...	50	Boiling	...	0.43 (17)	23
Incoloy 800	(c)	50	35-90 (95-190)	...	<0.0025 (<0.1)	114
Incoloy 800	(c)	73	100-125 (212-260)	...	0.04 (1.6)	114
Incoloy 800	(d)	50	40-80 (100-180)	...	<0.0025 (<0.1)	114
Incoloy 800	(d)	73	115 (240)	...	0.008 (0.3)	114

(Continued)

Corrosion Behavior of Various Metals and Alloys in Sodium Hydroxide (Continued)

Material	Condition, other factors, comments	Concentration, %	Temperature, °C (°F)	Duration	Corrosion rate, mm/yr (mils/yr) or other	Ref
Incoloy 800	NaCl concentration, 6-7%. (b)	35-40	116 (240)	24-29 d	0.015 (0.6)	112
Incoloy 800	NaCl concentration, 10-15%. (b)	50	93 (200)	24-29 d	<0.0025 (<0.1)	112
Incoloy 800	NaCl concentration unknown. (b)	72	121 (250)	24-29 d	0.0025 (0.1)	112
Incoloy 800	NaCl concentration, 12%. (b)	10	88 (190)	24-29 d	<0.0025 (<0.1)	112
Incoloy 800	NaCl concentration, 7-8%. (b)	23	93 (200)	24-29 d	0.005 (0.2)	112
Inconel	...	5-10	21 (70)	124 d	0.0013 (0.05)	112
Inconel	Exposure to effluent from an electrolytic chlorine cell containing 15% NaCl	10	80 (180)	207 d	nil	111
Inconel	First effect of a multi-effect evaporator	14	90 (190)	90 d	0.0008 (0.03)	112
Inconel	...	50	40 (100)	162 d	0.0002 (0.008)	111
Inconel	...	50	60 (135)	135 d	0.0005 (0.02)	111
Inconel	...	50	55-75 (130-165)	30 d	0.0008 (0.03)	112
Inconel	...	70-73	110 (230)	126 d	0.0025 (0.1)	111
Inconel	...	70-73	90-115 (190-240)	90 d	0.008 (0.3)	112
Inconel	...	70-73	120 (240)	180 d	0.005 (0.2)	113
Inconel	...	70-73	130 (265)	200 d	0.025 (1)	113
Inconel	Plant test. NaOH concentrated to anhydrous. Batch shaded with sulfur and Na2NO3	73	540 (1000)	2.5 d	49 (1930)	114
Inconel 600	Test coupons removed, cleaned and dried each day for 30 d. Aeration: none. Agitation: none. Corrosion rate less than 0.005 mils/yr	0.7	30 (86)	27 d	nil	112
Inconel 600	Average of tests run at eight separate laboratories. Aeration: none. Agitation: none	4	30 (86)	1 & 2 d	...	112
Inconel 600	Average of tests run at eight separate laboratories. Aeration: air agitated. Agitation: air agitated	4	30 (86)	1 & 2 d	...	112
Inconel 600	Storage tank. Aeration: extensive. Agitation: due to filling tank	5-10	21-32 (70-90)	124 d	0.0013 (0.05)	112
Inconel 600	NaCl concentration, 12%. (b)	10	88 (190)	24-29 d	<0.0025 (<0.1)	112
Inconel 600	Stress-corrosion cracking, acceptable. (k)	10	200 (390)	7 d	...	112
Inconel 600	Stress-corrosion cracking, acceptable. (k)	10	300 (570)	7 d	...	112
Inconel 600	Stress-corrosion cracking, acceptable. (k)	10	300 (570)	7 d	...	112
Inconel 600	Storage tank coupons immersed 95% of time. Aeration: none. Agitation: due to filling tank	22	50-60 (120-140)	133 d	0.00025 (0.01)	112
Inconel 600	NaCl concentration, 7-8%. (b)	23	93 (200)	24-29 d	0.0025 (0.1)	112
Inconel 600	Single-effect evaporator. Rates are average of three tests. Aeration: none. Agitation: none	30-50	81 (178)	16 d	...	112
Inconel 600	Storage tank in which air was bubbled through from bottom. Aeration: extensive. Agitation: mild	34	65 (150)	37 d	0.00076 (0.03)	112
Inconel 600	NaCl concentration, 6-7%. (b)	35-40	116 (240)	24-29 d	0.0127 (0.5)	112
Inconel 600	Storage tank coupons fully immersed. Aeration: none. Agitation: due to filling tank	49-51	55-75 (131-167)	30 d	0.0005 (0.02)	112
Inconel 600	Storage tank. Aeration: none. Agitation: due to filling tank	50	55-61 (131-142)	135 d	0.0005 (0.02)	112
Inconel 600	Transfer piping, at pump discharge. Agitation: moderate. Agitation: by 100 gal/min flow from pump	50	60-70 (140-158)	393 d	0.00076 (0.03)	112
Inconel 600	Laboratory test on tubing; average of four coupons. Aeration: none. Agitation: none.	50	150 (302)	14 d	0.0064 (0.25)	112
Inconel 600	(c)	50	35-90 (95-190)	...	<0.0025 (<0.1)	114
Inconel 600	(d)	50	40-80 (100-180)	...	<0.0025 (0.1)	114
Inconel 600	NaCl concentration, 10-15%. (b)	50	93 (200)	24-29 d	<0.0025 (<0.1)	112
Inconel 600	Stress-corrosion cracking, acceptable. (k)	50	200 (390)	7 d	...	112
Inconel 600	Stress-corrosion cracking, stress-cracked. (k)	50	300 (570)	7 d	...	112
Inconel 600	NaCl concentration unknown. (b)	72	121 (250)	24-29 d	<0.0025 (<0.1)	112
Inconel 600	Storage tank. Aeration: none. Agitation: due to filling tank.	72-73	116 (273)	183 d	0.0102 (0.4)	112
Inconel 600	Storage tank. Aeration: moderate. Agitation: due to filling tank	72	121 (282)	119 d	0.0025 (0.10)	112
Inconel 600	Test tank, simulating action of tank car. Aeration: none. Agitation: by rocking of tank	73	95-100 (203-212)	111 d	0.0036 (0.14)	112

(Continued)

Corrosion Behavior of Various Metals and Alloys in Sodium Hydroxide (Continued)

Material	Condition, other factors, comments	Concen-tration, %	Temperature, °C (°F)	Duration	Corrosion rate, mm/yr (mils/yr) or other	Ref
Inconel 600	Storage tank coupons immersed 95% of time. Aeration: none. Agitation: due to filling tank	73	100-120 (212-248)	52 d	0.0015 (0.06)	112
Inconel 600	(c)	73	100-125 (212-260)	...	0.005 (0.2)	114
Inconel 600	(d)	73	115 (240)	...	0.005 (0.2)	114
Inconel 600	Storage tank coupons fully immersed. Aeration: none. Agitation: due to filling tank.	73	104-116 (244-251)	126	0.00025 (0.01)	112
Inconel 600	Coupons in railroad tank car. Aeration: not specified. Agitation: by movement of tank car. Eleven trips of 7-9 days	74	130 (266)	7-9 d	...	112
Inconel 600	Storage tank between evaporator and finishing pots. Ammonia soda process. Aeration: not specified. Agitation: due to filling tank	75	135 (271)	35 d	0.0330 (1.3)	112
Inconel 600	Stress-corrosion cracking, stress-cracked. (k)	90	300 (570)	7 d	...	112
Inconel 600	Stress-corrosion cracking, acceptable. (k)	90	250 (480)	7 d	...	112
Inconel 600	Stress-corrosion cracking, acceptable. (k)	90	300 (570)	7 d	...	112
Inconel 600	Molten	...	400 (750)	...	0.0279 (1.1)	112
Inconel 600	Molten	..	500 (932)	...	0.061 (2.4)	112
Inconel 600	Molten	...	580 (1076)	...	0.129 (5.1)	112
Inconel 600	Molten	...	680 (1256)	...	1.687 (66.4)	112
Inconel 600	Concentration in caustic evaporator. Concentration: 60 to nearly anhydrous. Aeration: none. Agitation: none	...	150-260 (302-500)	2 d	...	112
Inconel 601	(m)	10	80 (176)	672 h	<0.002 (<0.1)	64
Inconel 601	(m)	10	Boiling	168 h	<0.002 (<0.1)	64
Inconel 601	(m)	20	80 (176)	672 h	<0.002 (<0.1)	64
Inconel 601	(m)	20	Boiling	168 h	0.005 (0.2)	64
Inconel 601	(m)	30	80 (176)	672 h	0.005 (0.2)	64
Inconel 601	(m)	30	Boiling	168 h	0.018 (0.7)	64
Inconel 601	(m)	40	80 (176)	672 h	0.010 (0.4)	64
Inconel 601	(m)	40	Boiling	168 h	<0.002 (<0.1)	64
Inconel 601	(m)	50	80 (176)	672 h	0.002 (0.1)	64
Inconel 601	(m)	50	Boiling	168 h	<0.002 (<0.1)	64
Inconel 601	(m)	60	80 (176)	672 h	0.008 (0.3)	64
Inconel 601	(m)	60	Boiling	168 h	<0.002 (<0.1)	64
Inconel 601	(m)	70	80 (176)	672 h	0.018 (0.7)	64
Inconel 601	(m)	70	Boiling	168 h	0.005 (0.2)	64
Inconel 601	(m)	98	Molten	168 h	0.076 (3.0)	64
Monel	...	50	40 (100)	162 d	0.0005 (0.02)	111
Monel	...	50	60 (135)	135 d	0.0005 (0.02)	111
Monel	...	50	55-75 (130-165)	30 d	0.0008 (0.03)	112
Monel	Laboratory test	50	150 (300)	...	0.013 (0.5)	113
Monel	Test in single-effect evaporator	30-50	80 (180)	16 d	0.005 (0.2)	113
Monel	...	70-73	110 (230)	126 d	0.0025 (0.1)	111
Monel	...	70-73	90-115 (190-240)	90 d	0.028 (1.1)	112
Monel	...	70-73	120 (240)	180 d	0.013 (0.5)	113
Monel	...	70-73	130 (265)	200 d	0.023 (0.9)	113
Monel	Laboratory test. NaOH concentrated to anhydrous	75	480 (900)	...	6.6 (260)	114
Monel	Plant test. NaOH concentrated to anhydrous. Batch shaded with sulfur and Na_2NO_3	73	540 (1000)	2.5 d	9.7 (380)	114
Monel	...	5	Room	...	<0.0025 (<0.1)	116
Monel	...	15	Room	...	<0.0025 (<0.1)	116
Monel	...	25	Room	...	<0.0025 (<0.1)	116
Monel	...	35	Room	...	<0.0025 (<0.1)	116
Monel	...	45	Room	...	<0.0025 (<0.1)	116
Monel	..	5-10	21 (70)	124 d	0.008 (0.3)	112
Monel	Exposure to effluent from an electrolytic chlorine cell containing 15% NaCl	10	80 (180)	207 d	nil	111
Monel	First effect of a multi-effect evaporator	14	90 (190)	90 d	0.0013 (0.05)	112
Monel 400	Molten	...	400 (750)	...	0.0457 (1.8)	112

(Continued)

Corrosion Behavior of Various Metals and Alloys in Sodium Hydroxide (Continued)

Material	Condition, other factors, comments	Concentration, %	Temperature, °C (°F)	Duration	Corrosion rate, mm/yr (mils/yr) or other	Ref
Monel 400	Molten	..	500 (932)	...	0.129 (5.1)	112
Monel 400	Molten	...	580 (1076)	...	0.447 (17.6)	112
Monel 400	Molten	...	680 (1256)	...	...	112
Monel 400	Test coupons removed, cleaned and dried each day for 30 d. Aeration: none. Agitation: none	0.7	30 (86)	27 d	0.00025 (0.01)	112
Monel 400	Average of tests run at eight separate laboratories. Aeration: none. Agitation: none	4	30 (86)	1 & 2 d	0.0041 (0.16)	112
Monel 400	Average of tests run at eight separate laboratories. Aeration: air agitated. Agitation: air agitated	4	30 (86)	1 & 2 d	0.0053 (0.21)	112
Monel 400	Storage tank. Aeration: extensive. Agitation: due to filling tank	5-10	21-32 (70-90)	124 d	0.00789 (0.31)	112
Monel 400	NaCl concentration, 12%. (b)	10	88 (190)	24-29 d	<0.0025 (<0.1)	112
Monel 400	First effect of multiple-effect evaporator. Aeration: none. Agitation: none.	14	88 (190)	90 d	0.0013 (0.05)	112
Monel 400	Laboratory tests	20	149 (332)	19 h	nil	112
Monel 400	Storage tank coupons immersed 95% of time. Aeration: none. Agitation: due to filling tank	22	50-60 (120-140)	133 d	0.00025 (0.01)	112
Monel 400	NaCl concentration, 7-8%. (b)	23	93 (200)	24-29 d	0.0076 (0.3)	112
Monel 400	Storage tank in which air was bubbled through from bottom. Aeration: extensive. Agitation: mild	34	65 (150)	37 d	nil	112
Monel 400	Single-effect evaporator. Rates are average of 3 tests. Aeration: none. Agitation: none	30-50	81 (178)	16 d	0.0049 (0.19)	112
Monel 400	NaCl concentration, 6-7%. (b)	35-40	116 (240)	24-29 d	0.025 (1)	112
Monel 400	Laboratory tests	40	149 (332)	19 h	0.076 (3)	112
Monel 400	(c)	50	35-90 (95-190)	...	<0.0025 (<0.1)	114
Monel 400	(d)	50	40-80 (100-180)	...	0.0025 (<0.1)	114
Monel 400	Storage tank. Aeration: none. Agitation: due to filling tank	50	55-61 (131-142)	135 d	0.0005 (0.02)	112
Monel 400	Transfer piping, at pump discharge. Agitation: moderate. Agitation: by 100 gal/min flow from pump	50	60-70 (140-158)	393 d	0.0025 (0.10)	112
Monel 400	NaCl concentration, 10-15%. (b)	50	93 (200)	24-29 d	0.005 (0.2)	112
Monel 400	Laboratory test on tubing; average of four coupons. Aeration: none. Agitation: none.	50	150 (302)	14 d	...	112
Monel 400	Laboratory tests	60	149 (332)	19 h	0.025 (1)	112
Monel 400	Storage tank. Aeration: none. Agitation: due to filling tank.	72-73	116 (273)	183 d	0.0178 (0.7)	112
Monel 400	Storage tank. Aeration: moderate. Agitation: due to filling tank	72	121 (282)	119 d	0.0076 (0.3)	112
Monel 400	NaCl concentration unknown. (b)	72	121 (250)	24-29 d	0.0076 (0.3)	112
Monel 400	(c)	73	100-125 (212-260)	...	0.01 (0.4)	114
Monel 400	(d)	73	115 (240)	...	0.013 (0.5)	114
Monel 400	Test tank, simulating action of tank car. Aeration: none. Agitation: by rocking of tank	73	95-100 (203-212)	111 d	0.0041 (0.16)	112
Monel 400	Storage tank coupons immersed 95% of time. Aeration: none. Agitation: due to filling tank	73	100-120 (212-248)	52 d	0.0010 (0.04)	112
Monel 400	Storage tank coupons fully immersed. Aeration: none. Agitation: due to filling tank.	73	104-116 (244-251)	126	0.0025 (0.10)	112
Monel 400	Coupons in railroad tank car. Aeration: not specified. Agitation: by movement of tank car. Eleven trips of 7-9 days	74	130 (266)	7-9 d	0.0102 (0.4)	112
Monel 400	Storage tank between evaporator and finishing pots. Ammonia soda process. Aeration: not specified. Agitation: due to filling tank	75	135 (271)	35 d	0.0432 (1.7)	112
Monel 400	Concentration in caustic evaporator. Concentration: 60 to nearly anhydrous. Aeration: none. Agitation: none	...	150-260 (302-500)	2 d	0.340 (13.4)	112
Monel 400	Cold-drawn. No heat treatment. Stress-corrosion cracking, coarse intergranular cracks visible to naked eye. (n)	...	300 (570)	...	...	112
Monel 400	850 °C (1562 °F), 1/4 h, water quenched. Stress-corrosion cracking, no cracks. (n)	...	300 (570)	...	...	112

(Continued)

Corrosion Behavior of Various Metals and Alloys in Sodium Hydroxide (Continued)

Material	Condition, other factors, comments	Concentration, %	Temperature, °C (°F)	Duration	Corrosion rate, mm/yr (mils/yr) or other	Ref
Monel 400	Stress relieved 540 °C (1004 °F), ½ h. Stress-corrosion cracking, specimen fractured with intergranular cracks. (n)	...	300 (570)	...	...	112
Monel 400	Work annealed at 950 °C (1742 °F), ½ h. Stress-corrosion cracking, no cracks. (n)	...	300 (570)	...	...	112
Monel 600	Storage tank coupons fully immersed. Aeration: none. Agitation: due to filling tank	49-51	55-75 (131-167)	30 d	0.00076 (0.03)	112
Monel K-500	Cold-drawn. No heat treatment. Stress-corrosion cracking, deep intergranular and transgranular cracks visible under microscope. (n)	...	300 (570)	...	...	112
Monel K-500	870 °C (1598 °F), 5 min, water quenched. Stress-corrosion cracking, no cracks. (n)	...	300 (570)	...	...	112
Monel K-500	580 °C (1076 °F), 8 h, furnace-cooled at about 10 °C (18 °F)/h to 480 °C (896 °F) then air-cooled to room temperature. Stress-corrosion cracking, shallow transgranular cracks visible under microscope. (n)	...	300 (570)	...	...	112
Monel K-500	870 °C (1598 °F), 5 min, water quenched, plus 580 °C (1076 °F), 16 h, furnace-cooled at about 10 °C (18 °F)/h to 480 °C (896 °F) then air-cooled to room temperature. Stress-corrosion cracking, specimen fractured with transgranular cracks. (n)	...	300 (570)	...	...	112
Monel K-500	Cold-drawn. No heat treatment. Stress-corrosion cracking, shallow cracks visible under microscope. Type of cracking not identified—cracks very short. (n)	...	300 (570)	...	...	112
Monel K-500	870 °C (1598 °F), 5 min, water quenched. Stress-corrosion cracking, no cracks. (n)	...	300 (570)	...	...	112
Monel K-500	580 °C (1076 °F), 8 h, furnace-cooled at about 10 °C (18 °F)/h to 480 °C (896 °F) then air-cooled to room temperature. Stress-corrosion cracking, specimen fractured with intergranular cracks. (n)	...	300 (570)	...	...	112
Monel K-500	870 °C (1598 °F), 5 min, water quenched, plus 580 °C (1076 °F), 16 h, furnace-cooled at about 10 °C (18 °F)/h to 480 °C (896 °F) then air-cooled to room temperature. Stress-corrosion cracking, specimen fractured with intergranular cracks. (n)	...	300 (570)	...	...	112
Multimet	(j)	5	Room	24 h	nil	68
Multimet	(j)	5	66 (150)	24 h	nil	68
Multimet	(j)	5	Boiling	24 h	nil	68
Multimet	(j)	25	Room	24 h	nil	68
Multimet	(j)	25	66 (150)	24 h	nil	68
Multimet	(j)	50	Room	24 h	nil	68
Multimet	(j)	50	66 (150)	24 h	nil	68
Ni-Resist I	...	50	55-75 (130-165)	30 d	0.05 (2)	112
Ni-Resist I	First effect of a multi-effect evaporator	14	90 (190)	90 d	0.074 (2.9)	112
Nickel	...	50	40 (100)	162 d	0.00023 (0.009)	111
Nickel	...	50	60 (135)	135 d	0.0005 (0.02)	111
Nickel	...	50	55-75 (130-165)	30 d	0.0005 (0.02)	112
Nickel	(p)	50	150 (300)	...	0.013 (0.5)	113
Nickel	Test in single-effect evaporator	30-50	80 (180)	16 d	0.0025 (0.1)	113
Nickel	...	70-73	110 (230)	126 d	0.0025 (0.1)	111
Nickel	...	70-73	90-115 (190-240)	90 d	0.0025 (0.1)	112
Nickel	...	70-73	120 (240)	180 d	0.005 (0.2)	113
Nickel	...	70-73	130 (265)	200 d	0.025 (1)	113
Nickel	Laboratory test. NaOH concentrated to anhydrous	75	480 (900)	...	1.3-1.8 (52-72)	114
Nickel	Plant test. NaOH concentrated to anhydrous. Batch shaded with sulfur and Na_2NO_3	73	540 (1000)	2.5 d	6.6 (260)	114
Nickel	...	5	Room	...	<0.0025 (<0.1)	116
Nickel	...	15	Room	...	<0.0025 (<0.1)	116
Nickel	...	25	Room	...	<0.0025 (<0.1)	116
Nickel	...	35	Room	...	<0.0025 (<0.1)	116
Nickel	...	45	Room	...	<0.0025 (<0.1)	116
Nickel	...	5-10	21 (70)	124 d	0.005 (0.2)	112

(Continued)

Corrosion Behavior of Various Metals and Alloys in Sodium Hydroxide (Continued)

Material	Condition, other factors, comments	Concen-tration, %	Temperature, °C (°F)	Duration	Corrosion rate, mm/yr (mils/yr) or other	Ref
Nickel	Exposure to effluent from an electrolytic chlorine cell containing 15% NaCl	10	80 (180)	207 d	8 x 10⁻5 (0.003)	111
Nickel	First effect of a multi-effect evaporator	14	90 (190)	90 d	0.0005 (0.02)	112
Nickel	Metal pickup, none. (e)	...	350 (662)	4 h	...	112
Nickel	Metal pickup, 0.01-0.02 g. (e)	...	360 (680)	4 h	...	112
Nickel	Metal pickup, trace-0.02 g. (e)	...	400 (752)	4 h	...	112
Nickel	Metal pickup, 0.01-0.02 g. (e)	...	450 (842)	4 h	...	112
Nickel	Metal pickup, 0.005-0.015 g. (e)	...	500 (932)	4 h	...	112
Nickel	Metal pickup, none. (e)	...	550 (1022)	4 h	...	112
Nickel	Metal pickup, none. (e)	...	600 (1112)	4 h	...	112
Nickel	Plus 5% sodium peroxide. Metal pickup, 0.0024 g. (e)	...	350 (662)	4 h	...	112
Nickel	Plus 5% sodium peroxide. Metal pickup, 0.0135 g. (e)	...	400 (752)	4 h	...	112
Nickel	Plus 5% sodium peroxide. Metal pickup, 0.0131 g. (e)	...	450 (842)	4 h	...	112
Nickel	Wrought. (a)	...	510 (950)	4 d	0.23 (9)	115
Nickel 200	Laboratory test in caustic soda. Quiet immersion	4	Room	...	0.001 (0.05)	44
Nickel 200	Laboratory test in caustic soda. Air-agitated immersion	4	Room	...	0.001 (0.05)	44
Nickel 200	Laboratory test in caustic soda. Continuous alternate immersion	4	Room	...	0.012 (0.50)	44
Nickel 200	Laboratory test in caustic soda. Intermittent alternate immersion	4	Room	...	0.015 (0.60)	44
Nickel 200	Laboratory spray test in caustic soda	4	Room	...	0.001 (0.05)	44
Nickel 200	Plant test in first effect of multiple-effect evaporator with caustic soda	14	88 (190)	...	0.0005 (0.02)	44
Nickel 200	Plant test in tank receiving liquor from evaporator with caustic soda	23	104 (220)	...	0.004 (0.16)	44
Nickel 200	Plant test in single-effect evaporator with caustic soda	30-50	81 (179)	...	0.0025 (0.1)	44
Nickel 200	Plant test in evaporator with caustic soda	50	...	...	0.0025 (0.1)	44
Nickel 200	Laboratory test in caustic soda. Vacuum, 640-685 mm mercury	32-52	84-91 (185-196)	...	0.03 (1.3)	44
Nickel 200	Tests in storage tank with caustic soda	49-51	55-75 (131-167)	...	0.0005 (0.02)	44
Nickel 200	Laboratory test in caustic soda	75	121 (250)	...	0.025 (1)	44
Nickel 200	Plant test in electrolytic solution of caustic soda in receiving tank	70	90-115 (194-239)	...	0.0025 (0.1)	44
Nickel 200	In caustic soda at atmospheric pressure	50	30 (86)	120 h	0.0015 (0.06)	44
Nickel 200	In caustic soda at atmospheric pressure	50	30 (86)	24 h	0.007 (0.3)	44
Nickel 200	In caustic soda at atmospheric pressure; velocity 15 ft/min	50	90 (195)	24 h	0.013 (0.55)	44
Nickel 200	In caustic soda. Pressure, 610 mm	50	100 (212)	24 h	0.017 (0.7)	44
Nickel 200	In caustic soda. Pressure, 610 mm	50	100 (212)	240 h	0.0017 (0.07)	44
Nickel 200	In caustic soda. Pressure, 620 mm	50	100 (212)	264 h	0.012 (0.5)	44
Nickel 200	In caustic soda at atmospheric pressure	50	130 (266)	720 h	0.027 (1.1)	44
Nickel 200	In caustic soda at atmospheric pressure	50	150 (302)	336 h	0.010 (0.4)	44
Nickel 200	In caustic soda at atmospheric pressure	50	154 (310)	672 h	0.012 (0.5)	44
Nickel 200	In caustic soda. Pressure, 5 psi; velocity, 75 ft/min	50	154 (310)	20 h	0.03 (1.2)	44
Nickel 200	(c)	50	35-90 (95-190)	...	<0.0025 (<0.1)	114
Nickel 200	(c)	73	100-125 (212-260)	...	<0.005 (<0.2)	114
Nickel 200	(d)	50	40-80 (100-180)	...	<0.0025 (<0.1)	114
Nickel 200	(d)	73	115 (240)	...	0.008 (0.3)	114
Nickel 200	Test coupons removed, cleaned and dried each day for 30 d. Aeration: none. Agitation: none	0.7	30 (86)	27 d	0.00025 (0.01)	112
Nickel 200	Average of tests run at eight separate laboratories. Aeration: none. Agitation: none	4	30 (86)	1 & 2 d	0.0013 (0.05)	112
Nickel 200	Average of tests run at eight separate laboratories. Aeration: air agitated. Agitation: air agitated	4	30 (86)	1 & 2 d	0.0013 (0.05)	112
Nickel 200	Storage tank. Aeration: extensive. Agitation: due to filling tank	5-10	21-32 (70-90)	124 d	0.0038 (0.15)	112

(Continued)

Corrosion Behavior of Various Metals and Alloys in Sodium Hydroxide (Continued)

Material	Condition, other factors, comments	Concentration, %	Temperature, °C (°F)	Duration	Corrosion rate, mm/yr (mils/yr) or other	Ref
Nickel 200	First effect of multiple-effect evaporator. Aeration: none. Agitation: none.	14	88 (190)	90 d	0.0005 (0.02)	112
Nickel 200	First effect of multiple-effect evaporator. Aeration: none. Agitation: none.	14	88 (190)	90 d	0.00076 (0.03)	112
Nickel 200	Storage tank coupons immersed 95% of time. Aeration: none. Agitation: due to filling tank	22	50-60 (120-140)	133 d	nil	112
Nickel 200	Storage tank in which air was bubbled through from bottom. Aeration: extensive. Agitation: mild	34	65 (150)	37 d	0.00076 (0.03)	112
Nickel 200	Single-effect evaporator. Rates are average of three tests. Aeration: none. Agitation: none	30-50	81 (178)	16 d	0.0023 (0.09)	112
Nickel 200	Storage tank coupons fully immersed. Aeration: none. Agitation: due to filling tank	49-51	55-75 (131-167)	30 d	0.0005 (0.02)	112
Nickel 200	Storage tank. Aeration: none. Agitation: due to filling tank	50	55-61 (131-142)	135 d	0.0005 (0.02)	112
Nickel 200	Transfer piping, at pump discharge. Agitation: moderate. Agitation: by 100 gal/min flow from pump	50	60-70 (140-158)	393 d	0.00178 (0.07)	112
Nickel 200	Laboratory test on tubing; average of four coupons. Aeration: none. Agitation: none.	50	150 (302)	14 d	...	112
Nickel 200	Storage tank. Aeration: none. Agitation: due to filling tank.	72-73	116 (273)	183 d	0.0076 (0.3)	112
Nickel 200	Storage tank. Aeration: moderate. Agitation: due to filling tank	72	121 (282)	119 d	0.0025 (0.10)	112
Nickel 200	Test tank, simulating action of tank car. Aeration: none. Agitation: by rocking of tank	73	95-100 (203-212)	111 d	0.0033 (0.13)	112
Nickel 200	Storage tank coupons immersed 95% of time. Aeration: none. Agitation: due to filling tank	73	100-120 (212-248)	52 d	0.0013 (0.05)	112
Nickel 200	Storage tank coupons fully immersed. Aeration: none. Agitation: due to filling tank.	73	104-116 (244-251)	126	0.0005 (0.02)	112
Nickel 200	Coupons in railroad tank car. Aeration: not specified. Agitation: by movement of tank car. Eleven trips of 7-9 days	74	130 (266)	7-9 d	0.0076 (0.3)	112
Nickel 200	Storage tank between evaporator and finishing pots. Ammonia soda process. Aeration: not specified. Agitation: due to filling tank	75	135 (271)	35 d	0.0406 (1.6)	112
Nickel 200	Concentration in caustic evaporator. Concentration: 60 to nearly anhydrous. Aeration: none. Agitation: none	...	150-260 (302-500)	2 d	0.0991 (3.9)	112
Nickel 200	Chemically pure	75	130 ± 5 (266 ±9)	...	0.015 (0.6)	112
Nickel 200	Plus 0.75% sodium sulfide	75	130 ± 5 (266 ±9)	...	0.579 (22.8)	112
Nickel 200	Plus 0.75% sodium thiosulfate	75	130 ± 5 (266 ±9)	...	0.201 (7.9)	112
Nickel 200	Plus 0.75% sodium sulfite	75	130 ± 5 (266 ±9)	...	0.132 (5.2)	112
Nickel 200	Plus 0.75% sodium sulfate	75	130 ± 5 (266 ±9)	...	0.015 (0.6)	112
Nickel 200	Commercial. Sulfur content at start, calculated as H_2S, 0.009%	50-75	130 ± 5 (266 ±9)	...	0.0432 (1.7)	112
Nickel 200	(p)	20	110 (262)	15 h	nil	112
Nickel 200	(p)	20	115 (272)	19 h	nil	112
Nickel 200	(p)	40	110 (262)	15 h	nil	112
Nickel 200	(p)	40	115 (272)	19 h	nil	112
Nickel 200	(p)	60	110 (262)	15 h	nil	112
Nickel 200	(p)	60	115 (272)	19 h	nil	112
Nickel 200	(p)	80	110 (262)	15 h	nil	112
Nickel 200	(p)	80	115 (272)	19 h	nil	112
Nickel 200	(p)	20	162 (355)	19 h	nil	112
Nickel 200	(p)	40	162 (355)	19 h	nil	112
Nickel 200	(p)	60	162 (355)	19 h	nil	112
Nickel 200	(p)	80	162 (355)	19 h	nil	112
Nickel 200	NaCl concentration, 12%. (b)	10	88 (190)	24-29 d	<0.0025 (<0.1)	112
Nickel 200	NaCl concentration, 7-8%. (b)	23	93 (200)	24-29 d	0.0025 (0.1)	112
Nickel 200	NaCl concentration, 6-7%. (b)	35-40	116 (240)	24-29 d	0.0102 (0.4)	112
Nickel 200	NaCl concentration, 10-15%. (b)	50	93 (200)	24-29 d	<0.0025 (<0.1)	112
Nickel 200	NaCl concentration unknown. (b)	72	121 (250)	24-29 d	<0.0025 (<0.1)	112
Nickel 201	Molten	...	400 (750)	...	0.0229 (0.9)	112

(Continued)

Corrosion Behavior of Various Metals and Alloys in Sodium Hydroxide (Continued)

Material	Condition, other factors, comments	Concen-tration, %	Temperature, °C (°F)	Duration	Corrosion rate, mm/yr (mils/yr) or other	Ref
Nickel 201	Molten	..	500 (932)	...	0.033 (1.3)	112
Nickel 201	Molten	...	580 (1076)	...	0.064 (2.5)	112
Nickel 201	Molten	...	680 (1256)	...	0.960 (37.8)	112
Nimonic alloy 75	Molten	...	400 (750)	...	0.0279 (1.1)	112
Nimonic alloy 75	Molten	..	500 (932)	...	0.363 (14.3)	112
Nimonic alloy 75	Molten. Pitted	...	580 (1076)	...	0.528 (20.8)	112
Nimonic alloy 75	Molten	...	680 (1256)	...	1.209 (47.6)	112
Zirconium						
Zirconium		50	40 (100)	162 d	0.0023 (0.09)	111
Zirconium	...	50	60 (135)	135 d	0.002 (0.08)	111
Zirconium	...	70-73	110 (230)	126 d	0.02 (0.8)	111
Zirconium	...	70-73	130 (265)	200 d	0.05 (2)	113
Zirconium	Plant test. NaOH concentrated to anhydrous. Batch shaded with sulfur and Na_2NO_3	73	540 (1000)	2.5 d	2.8 (110)	114
Zirconium	Slight pitting attack	5-10	21 (70)	124 d	0.005 (0.2)	112
Zirconium	Exposure to effluent from an electrolytic chlorine cell containing 15% NaCl	10	80 (180)	207 d	0.0018 (0.07)	111
Zr702	...	5-10	21 (70)	...	<0.025 (<1)	15
Zr702	...	28	Room	...	<0.025 (<1)	15
Zr702	...	10-25	Boiling	...	<0.025 (<1)	15
Zr702	...	40	100 (212)	...	<0.025 (<1)	15
Zr702	...	50	38-57 (100-135)	...	<0.025 (<1)	15
Zr702	...	50-73	188 (370)	...	0.5-1.3 (20-50)	15
Zr702	...	73	110-129 (230-265)	...	<0.05 (<2)	15
Zr702	Concentrated to anhydrous	73	212-538 (415-1000)	...	0.5-1.3 (20-50)	15
Zr702	Plus 15% NaCl	9-11	82 (180)	...	<0.025 (<1)	15
Zr702	Plus 10% NaCl, wet $CaCl_2$	10	10-32 (50-90)	...	<0.025 (<1)	15
Zr702	Plus 2% $NaClO_3$, and a trace of NH_3	0.6%	129 (265)	...	<0.025 (<1)	15
Zr702	Plus 53% NaCl, 7% $NaClO_3$, 80-100 ppm NH_3	7	191 (375)	...	<0.025 (<1)	15
Zr702	Plus 16% NH_3	52	138 (280)	...	<0.13 (<5)	15
Zr702	Suspended salt, violent boiling	20	60 (140)	...	0.25-015.5 (10-20)	15
Zr702	Plus 750 ppm free Cl_2	50	38 (100)	...	<0.025 (<1)	15
Zr702	Plus 750 ppm free Cl_2	50	38-57 (100-135)	...	<0.025 (<1)	15
Lead, tin, and zinc						
Lead	Practically resistant; Pb recommended for use	0-30	26 (79)	...	<500 μm/yr (<20)	95
Tin	(q)	0.005	60 (140)	...	0.21 (8.3)	75
Tin	(q)	0.02	60 (140)	...	0.24 (9.4)	75
Tin	(q)	0.05	60 (140)	...	0.21 (8.3)	75
Tin	(q)	0.10	60 (140)	...	0.20 (7.9)	75
Tin	(q)	0.15	60 (140)	...	0.20 (7.9)	75
Tin	(q)	0.20	60 (140)	...	0.21 (8.3)	75
Tin	(q)	0.25	60 (140)	...	0.24 (9.4)	75
Tantalum and hafnium						
Hafnium	...	50	...	2 d	0.39 (15.3)	11
Hafnium	...	50	...	2 d	0.39 (15.3)	11
Tantalum	...	5	21 (70)	...	nil	42
Tantalum	...	5	100 (212)	...	0.0178 (0.7)	42
Tantalum	...	10	100 (212)	...	0.0254 (1)	42
Tantalum	...	40	80 (176)	...	Rapid	42
Noble metals						
Platinum	...	<90	Boiling	...	<0.05 (<2)	5
Platinum	Melt	...	350 (660)	...	<0.05 (<2)	5
Silver	Laboratory test. NaOH concentrated to anhydrous	75	480 (900)	...	0.13 (5.3)	114
Silver	...	<95	Boiling	...	<0.05 (<2)	9
Silver	Melt. Air must be excluded. Mass transfer possible above 600 °C (1110 °F)	...	500 (930)	...	<0.05 (<2)	9

(Continued)

Corrosion Behavior of Various Metals and Alloys in Sodium Hydroxide (Continued)

Material	Condition, other factors, comments	Concentration, %	Temperature, °C (°F)	Duration	Corrosion rate, mm/yr (mils/yr) or other	Ref
Others						
Cobalt	Static	10	25 (77)	...	0.02 (0.8)	54
Magnesium	...	All	Room	...	Suitable	119
Niobium	...	1-40	Room	...	0.125 (5.0)	2
Niobium	...	1-10	98 (208)	...	Embrittlement	2
TaC-4Co-3Ni-1Cr	Weight loss	5	50 (120)	72 h	0.71 mg/cm^2/d	147
TaC-4Co-3Ni-1Cr	Weight loss	10	50 (120)	72 h	0.68 mg/cm^2/d	147
WC-2TaC-3TiC	Weight loss	5	50 (120)	72 h	0.87 mg/cm^2/d	147
WC-2TaC-3TiC	Weight loss	10	50 (120)	72 h	0.90 mg/cm^2/d	147
WC-5TaC	Weight loss	5	50 (120)	72 h	0.89 mg/cm^2/d	147
WC-5TaC	Weight loss	10	50 (120)	72 h	0.92 mg/cm^2/d	147
WC-6Co	Weight loss	5	50 (120)	72 h	0.75 mg/cm^2/d	147
WC-6Co	Weight loss	10	50 (120)	72 h	0.85 mg/cm^2/d	147
WC-8Ni-2Mo-3Cr	Weight loss	5	50 (120)	72 h	0.09 mg/cm^2/d	147
WC-8Ni-2Mo-3Cr	Weight loss	10	50 (120)	72 h	0.11 mg/cm^2/d	147
WC-9Co	Weight loss	5	50 (120)	72 h	0.83 mg/cm^2/d	147
WC-9Co	Weight loss	10	50 (120)	72 h	0.88 mg/cm^2/d	147

(a) Test in molten, anhydrous NaOH, plus 0.5% NaCl, 0.5% Na$_2$CO$_3$, 0.03% Na$_2$SO$_4$. (b) Average test temperature. (c) Diaphragm cell corrosion rate. (d) Mercury cell corrosion rate. (e) In each test, 5 g of the substance were fused for 4 h in a laboratory crucible of the given metal and analyzed for metal pick-up. (f) Saturated with NaCl. All tests were run on duplicate specimens. (g) May be considered in place of a copper metal when some property, other than corrosion resistance, governs its use. (h) As cast, based on five 24-h test periods with cast specimens 38 mm x 25 mm x 6 mm (1.5 in. x 1 in. x 0.25 in.), 120-grit abrasive finish. (j) Laboratory tests on 12-gage, solution heat-treated sheet; minimum of five 24-h test periods. (k) U-bend specimens. Testing performed in autoclaves under static conditions without replenishment of air or argon. (m) Average rate for duplicate specimens. (n) Specimens were coated in condensing steam after being coated with NaOH. (p) Laboratory tests. (q) Converted from weight loss data, assuming a tin density of 7.29 g/cm^3.

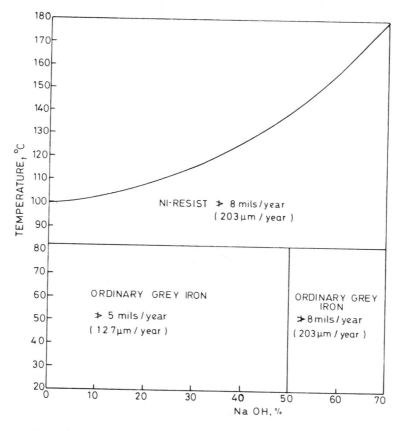

Cast irons. Corrosion rates of cast irons in sodium hydroxide. Source: H.T. Angus, *Cast Iron: Physical and Engineering Properties*, 2nd ed., Butterworths, London, 1976, 314.

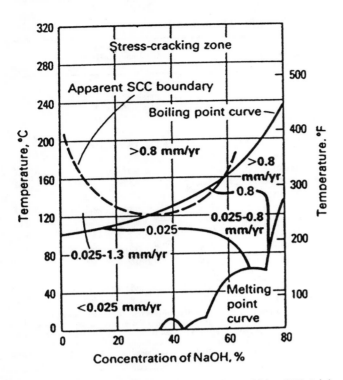

Stainless steel. Isocorrosion diagram for type 304 or 316 stainless steels in sodium hydroxide. Source: *Metals Handbook*, 9th ed., Vol 13, Corrosion, ASM International, Metals Park, OH 1987, 1178.

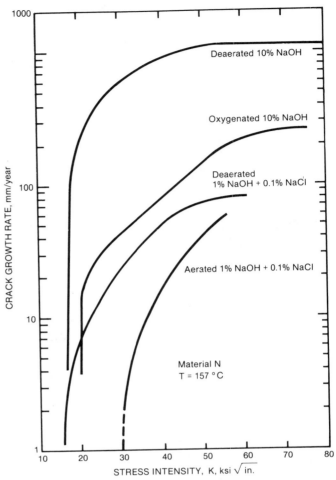

Steel. Typical crack growth data for 3.5Ni-1.7Cr-0.4Mo steel. Source: A. McMinn, F.F. Lyle, *et al.*, "Stress Corrosion Crack Growth in NiCr-MoV Turbine Disc Steels," *Corrosion*, Vol 41, Sept 1985, 493.

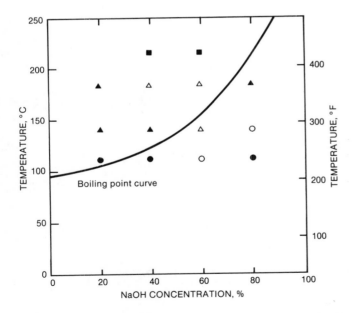

ACI CF-8. Isocorrosion diagram for ACI CF-8 in sodium hydroxide solutions. (a) Test performed in a closed container at equilibrium pressure. (b) Tested at atmospheric pressure. Source: *Metals Handbook*, 9th ed., Vol 13, Corrosion, ASM International, Metals Park, OH, 1987, 579.

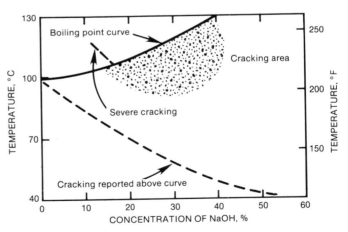

Steel. Temperature and concentration of sodium hydroxide required to cause cracking of steel. Source: H.W. Schmidt, P.J. Gegner, G. Heinemann, C.F. Pogacar, and E.H. Wyche, *Corrosion*, Vol 7, 1951, 295 and A.A. Berk and W.F. Waldeck, *Chemical Engineering*, Vol 57 (No. 6), 1950, 235.

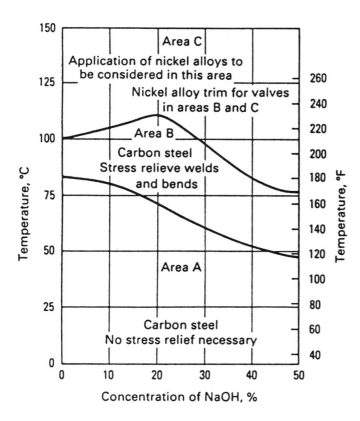

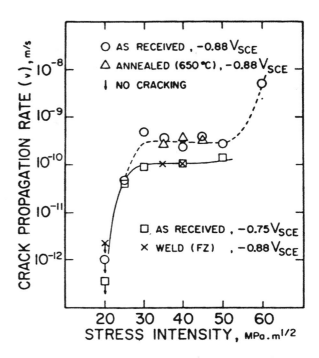

ASTM A516 steel. Effect of stress intensity and potential on stress-corrosion crack propagation in 3.35m sodium hydroxide and 0.42m sodium sulfide at 92 °C. Source: D. Tromans, E.G. Hawbolt, *et al.*, "Stress Corrosion Cracking of ASTM A516 Steel in Hot Caustic Sulfide Solutions: Potential and Weld Effects," *Corrosion*, Vol 42, Feb 1986, 66.

Carbon steels. Temperature and concentration limits for stress-corrosion cracking susceptibility of carbon steels in caustic soda. Source: Corrosion Data Survey — Metals Selection, 6th ed., National Association of Corrosion Engineers, Houston, 1985, 176.

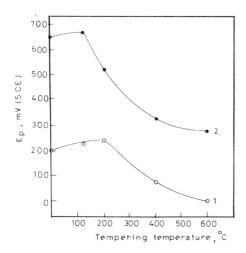

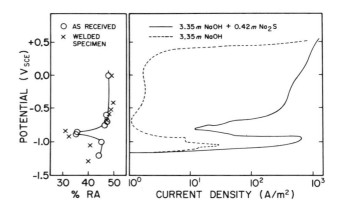

ASTM A516 steel. Effect of electrochemical potential on reduction in area of slow strain rate specimens tested at 92 °C in 3.35m sodium hydroxide and 42m sodium sulfide. Also shown are anodic polarization curves for the as-received steel in the sulfide solution and 3.35m sodium hydroxide at 92 °C. Source: D. Tromans, E.B. Hawbolt, *et al.*, "Stress Corrosion Cracking of ASTM A516 Steel in Hot Caustic Sulfide Solutions: Potential and Weld Effects," *Corrosion*, Vol 42, Feb 1986, 65.

Carbon steels. Dependence of the pitting corrosion potential on the tempering temperature. Curve 1: 0.01M sodium hydroxide and 0.01M sodium chloride. Curve 2: 0.1M sodium hydroxide and 0.02M sodium chloride. Source: S.M. Abd El-Haleem, S.S. Abd El Rehim, *et al.*, "Anodic Behavior and Pitting Corrosion of Plain Carbon Steel in NaOH Solutions Containing Chlorine Ions," *Surface Coating Technology*, Vol 27, Feb 1986, 172.

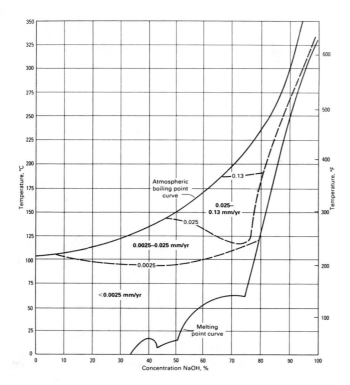

Nickel alloys. Isocorrosion chart for Nickel 200 and Nickel 201 in sodium hydroxide. Only at high caustic concentration near the boiling point does the corrosion rate exceed 1 mil/yr. This isocorrosion chart is intended only as a guide; there are specific conditions under which higher or possibly lower corrosion rates can prevail. Source: *"Corrosion Resistance of Nickel and Nickel-containing Alloys in Caustic Soda and Other Alkalies,"* The International Nickel Company, 1973.

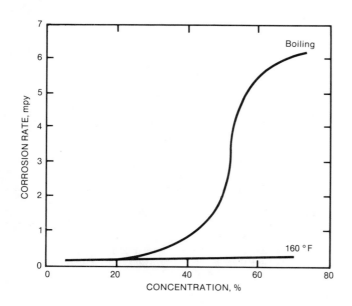

Nickel 201. Corrosion of Nickel 201 in sodium hydroxide. Source: Inco Alloys International, 1979.

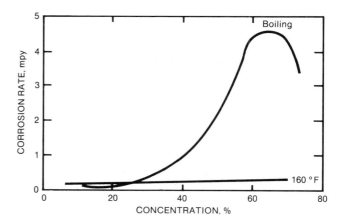

Nickel 270. Corrosion of Nickel 270 in sodium hydroxide. Source: Inco Alloys International, 1979.

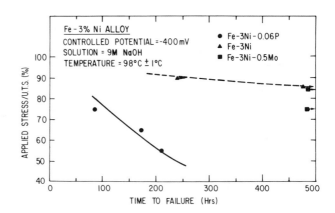

Iron-nickel alloys. Time to failure for various iron-nickel alloys. The vertical axis shows the initial applied stress normalized to the ultimate tensile strength; the horizontal axis shows time to failure. Data points with horizontal arrows indicate that the test was stopped at the time indicated with no failure having occurred. Source: N. Bandyopadhay and C.L. Briant, "Caustic Stress Corrosion Cracking of Low Alloy Iron Base Materials," *Corrosion*, Vol 41, May 1985, 275.

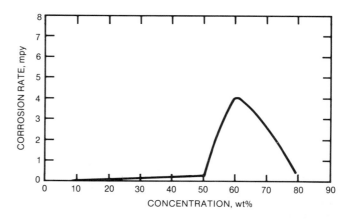

Inconel 600. Corrosion rates in boiling sodium hydroxide. Source: Inco Alloys International, 1962.

Sodium Hypochlorite

Sodium hypochlorite, NaOCl, is an air-unstable, pale green crystalline solid that is soluble in cold water, decomposes in hot water, and has a sweet aroma. It generally is available in one of two strengths. The household liquid bleach contains about 5.25 wt% NaClO. The commercial product (sometimes called 15% bleach) contains 150 g/L available chlorine. This is equivalent to about 13 wt% sodium hypochlorite. Sodium hypochlorite is used as a bleaching agent for paper pulp and textiles, as an oxidizing reagent, as a disinfectant, as a chemical intermediate, and in medicines.

The hypochlorite ion (OCl^-) is similar to wet chlorine gas in its effects on materials. Not many metals exhibit good resistance even at low temperatures and concentrations. Because hypochlorite solutions are unstable at neutral and lower pHs, they normally contain excess alkali, which modifies the aggressiveness somewhat.

Material Summaries

The following material summaries were compiled from a survey of the available literature. Inclusion of a material description under a given environment does not imply that it is the most appropriate material for corrosion service in that environment. Likewise, exclusion of a given material does not imply that it is not suitable for corrosion service applications in that environment.

Stainless Steels. Some of the newer super stainless steel materials exhibit useful resistance in certain sodium hypochlorite solutions. Successful performance of a high-alloy duplex stainless steel (Ferralium Alloy 255) in a sodium hypochlorite scrubber was recently reported. When stainless steels are attacked in sodium hypochlorite, the mode is usually pitting and/or crevice corrosion.

Aluminum. Generally, hypochlorites promptly destroy the protective oxide films on aluminum and aluminum alloys and cause rapid attack. In laboratory tests, aqueous solutions of sodium hypochlorite caused corrosion that varied with concentration. Alloy 1100 was resistant to dilute solutions of sodium hypochlorite at ambient temperature, whereas more concentrated solutions were very corrosive. Silicates have been used as inhibitors for corrosion of aluminum alloys by sodium hypochlorite.

Copper. In sodium hypochlorite, copper is normally attacked by localized pitting, with corrosion rates exceeding 0.5 mm/yr (20 mils/yr).

Nickel. Nickel and some nickel alloys can be protected from corrosion by sodium hypochlorite by the use of alkaline inhibitors, such as Na_2SiO_3 and Na_3PO_4. The corrosion rates are significantly reduced, and the mode of corrosion becomes more uniform. However, nickel finds few successful applications in sodium hypochlorite service, contrary to its dominance in sodium hydroxide.

Wrought and cast nickel-base iron-chromium-molybdenum alloys (Hastelloy Alloy C-276 wrought, Chlorimet 3, for example) exhibit good resistance in various solutions. The high iron-chromium-nickel alloys such as 20Cb-3 have also been used, especially as pump materials, in less aggressive environments. Many of these materials have shown unpredictable performance in seemingly similar applications.

Osmium is dissolved fairly rapidly in sodium hypochlorite at room temperature.

Rhodium, although resistant to corrosion by nearly all aqueous solutions at room temperature, is slowly attacked by solutions of sodium hypochlorite.

Ruthenium is attacked fairly rapidly by sodium hypochlorite.

Tantalum. Tantalum is very resistant to sodium hypochlorite, but its use is limited because of its relatively high cost.

Titanium. Titanium is the only metal that provides consistently good performance in sodium hypochlorite. Although special titanium alloys are available, the commercial grade 2 is usually suitable for a full range of concentrations and temperatures. Although titanium has been known to suffer crevice corrosion in hot wet chlorine, it apparently has not shown the same susceptibility in hypochlorite solutions. A wide variety of titanium products are used, including piping, pumps, valves, heat exchangers, fans, and vessels.

Additional Reading

G. Daufin, J. Pagetti, J.P. Labbe, and F. Michel, Pitting Initiation on Stainless Steels: Electrochemical and Micrographic Aspects, *Corrosion,* 41(9), 533-539, 1985. MetAbs No. 85-352347. **Abstract:** Pitting initiation has been studied on several austenitic (Z3CN18 10) and ferritic stainless steels (Z5CDT18 1) in contact with an oxidizing chloride solution (sodium hypochlorite at 70 °C). Systematic micrographic inspection of the stainless steel surface has been performed after recording electrochemical curves vs. time (free potential and current intensity under potentiostatic control).

Corrosion Behavior of Various Metals and Alloys in Sodium Hypochlorite

Material	Condition, other factors, comments	Concentration, %	Temperature, °C (°F)	Duration	Corrosion rate, mm/yr (mils/yr) or other	Ref
Stainless steels						
2Mo-0.4Cu stainless steel	(a)	...	50 (120)	...	0.00025 (0.01)	45
Remanit 2800	(a)	...	50 (120)	...	0.000025 (0.001)	45
Type 304 stainless steel	(a)	...	50 (120)	...	0.025 (1.0)	45
Type 316 stainless steel	(b)	...	65-95 (150-200)	72 d	>2.5 (>100 consumed)	46
Type 316 stainless steel	(a)	...	50 (120)	...	0.008 (0.3)	45
Type 317 stainless steel	(a)	...	50 (120)	...	0.00025 (0.01)	45
Type 410 stainless steel	...	...	Room	...	Attacked	121
		(Continued)				

Corrosion Behavior of Various Metals and Alloys in Sodium Hypochlorite (Continued)

Material	Condition, other factors, comments	Concen-tration, %	Temperature, °C (°F)	Duration	Corrosion rate, mm/yr (mils/yr) or other	Ref
Type 410 stainless steel	Slight alkaline	Saturated	0-93 (0-200)	...	Slightly attacked	121
Irons and steels						
Duriron	(b)	...	65-95 (150-200)	72 d	0.3 (12)	46
Low-carbon steel	(b)	...	65-95 (150-200)	72 d	>5 (>200 consumed)	46
Low-carbon steel	(a)	...	50 (120)	...	0.025 (1.0)	45
Coppers						
70-30 cupronickel	May be considered in place of a copper metal when some property, other than corrosion resistance, governs its use	...	...	...	Good	93
90-10 cupronickel	...	...	...	...	Fair	93
Admiralty brass	...	...	...	...	Fair	93
Aluminum bronze	...	...	...	...	Fair	93
Architectural bronze	...	...	...	...	Not suitable	93
Brass	...	...	...	...	Fair	93
Cartridge brass	...	...	...	...	Not suitable	93
Commercial bronze	...	...	...	...	Fair	93
Electrolytic copper	...	...	...	...	Fair	93
Free-cutting brass	...	...	...	...	Not suitable	93
Muntz metal	...	...	...	...	Not suitable	93
Naval brass	...	...	...	...	Not suitable	93
Nickel silver	May be considered in place of a copper metal when some property, other than corrosion resistance, governs its use	18	...	...	Good	93
Phosphor bronze	5% Sn	...	...	...	Fair	93
Phosphor bronze	8% Sn	...	...	...	Fair	93
Phosphor copper	...	...	...	...	Fair	93
Red brass	...	...	...	...	Fair	93
Silicon bronze	Low	...	...	...	Fair	93
Silicon bronze	High	...	...	...	Fair	93
Titanium						
Titanium	Repeated exposures	16	20 (70)	170 d	<0.0025 (<0.1)	3
Titanium	...	6	Room	...	nil	90
Titanium	Plus 15% NaCl + 1% NaOH	1.5-4	66-93 (151-200)	...	0.030 (1.2)	90
Titanium	...	6	25 (77)	...	nil	27
Titanium	(b)	...	65-95 (150-200)	72 d	0.0025 (0.1)	46
Titanium	(a)	...	50 (120)	...	0.000025 (0.001)	45
Heat- and corrosion-resistant alloys						
Chlorimet 3	Repeated exposures	16	20 (70)	170 d	0.008 (0.3)	3
Durachlor	Repeated exposures	16	20 (70)	170 d	0.02 (0.8)	3
Durichlor	(b)	...	65-95 (150-200)	72 d	0.18 (7)	46
E-Brite	(a)	...	50 (120)	...	0.00025 (0.01)	45
Hastelloy C	Repeated exposures	16	20 (70)	170 d	0.0025 (0.1)	3
Hastelloy C	(b)	...	65-95 (150-200)	72 d	1.2 (46)	46
Hastelloy C	(a)	...	50 (120)	...	0.005 (0.2)	45
Incoloy 800	Solutions were prepared with reagent-grade chemicals. Test specimens were cold-rolled, annealed sheet, 2.84 mm (0.112 in.) thick. Pitting occurred after 7 d	1	80 (176)	42 d	0.13 (5.0)	44
Incoloy 800	Solutions were prepared with reagent-grade chemicals. Test specimens were cold-rolled, annealed sheet, 2.84 mm (0.112 in.) thick. Pitting occurred after 7 d	5	80 (176)	42 d	0.20 (8.0)	44
Incoloy 825	(a)	...	50 (120)	...	0.005 (0.2)	45
Inconel 600	(a)	...	50 (120)	...	0.005 (0.02)	45
Inconel 600	(g)	6.5 g/L	40 (105)	16 h	0.3 (12)	118

(Continued)

Corrosion Behavior of Various Metals and Alloys in Sodium Hypochlorite (Continued)

Material	Condition, other factors, comments	Concen-tration, %	Temperature, °C (°F)	Duration	Corrosion rate, mm/yr (mils/yr) or other	Ref
Inconel 600	(c)	6.5 g/L	40 (105)	16 h	0.08 (3)	118
Inconel 600	(d)	6.5 g/L	40 (105)	16 h	0.08 (3)	118
Inconel 600	(e)	6.5 g/L	40 (105)	16 h	0.025 (1)	118
Inconel 600	(f)	6.5 g/L	40 (105)	16 h	0.025 (1)	118
Inconel 600	(g)	3.3 g/L	40 (105)	16 h	0.13 (5)	118
Inconel 600	(c)	3.3 g/L	40 (105)	16 h	0.025 (1)	118
Inconel 600	(d)	3.3 g/L	40 (105)	16 h	0.025 (1)	118
Inconel 600	(g)	0.1 g/L	40 (105)	16 h	0.05 (2)	118
Inconel 600	(c)	0.1 g/L	40 (105)	16 h	0.018 (0.7)	118
Inconel 600	(d)	0.1 g/L	40 (105)	16 h	0.018 (0.7)	118
Inconel 601	Pitting attack. Average of two tests	1	80 (176)	7 d	0.089 (3.5)	64
Inconel 601	Pitting attack. Average of two tests	5	80 (176)	7 d	0.175 (6.9)	64
Monel 400	(g)	6.5 g/L	40 (105)	16 h	2.9 (113)	118
Monel 400	(c)	6.5 g/L	40 (105)	16 h	0.46 (18)	118
Monel 400	(d)	6.5 g/L	40 (105)	16 h	0.2 (8)	118
Monel 400	(e)	6.5 g/L	40 (105)	16 h	0.05 (2)	118
Monel 400	(f)	6.5 g/L	40 (105)	16 h	0.08 (3)	118
Monel 400	(g)	3.3 g/L	40 (105)	16 h	1.0 (40)	118
Monel 400	(c)	3.3 g/L	40 (105)	16 h	0.025 (1)	118
Monel 400	(d)	3.3 g/L	40 (105)	16 h	0.1 (4)	118
Monel 400	(g)	0.1 g/L	40 (105)	16 h	0.1 (4)	118
Monel 400	(c)	0.1 g/L	40 (105)	16 h	0.008 (0.3)	118
Monel 400	(d)	0.1 g/L	40 (105)	16 h	0.033 (1.3)	118
Nickel 200	(g)	6.5 g/L	40 (105)	16 h	1.3 (52)	118
Nickel 200	(c)	6.5 g/L	40 (105)	16 h	0.25 (10)	118
Nickel 200	(d)	6.5 g/L	40 (105)	16 h	0.5 (20)	118
Nickel 200	(e)	6.5 g/L	40 (105)	16 h	0.025 (1)	118
Nickel 200	(f)	6.5 g/L	40 (105)	16 h	0.23 (9)	118
Nickel 200	(g)	3.3 g/L	40 (105)	16 h	0.8 (30)	118
Nickel 200	(c)	3.3 g/L	40 (105)	16 h	0.1 (4)	118
Nickel 200	(d)	3.3 g/L	40 (105)	16 h	0.15 (6)	118
Nickel 200	(g)	0.1 g/L	40 (105)	16 h	0.1 (4)	118
Nickel 200	(c)	0.1 g/L	40 (105)	16 h	0.013 (0.5)	118
Nickel 200	(d)	0.1 g/L	40 (105)	16 h	0.015 (0.6)	118
Nickel 200	35 ppm available chlorine	...	25 (77)	...	0.0025 (0.1)	44
Nickel 200	100 ppm available chlorine	...	25 (77)	...	0.0075 (0.3)	44
Nickel 200	500 ppm available chlorine	...	25 (77)	...	0.02 (0.8)	44
Zirconium						
Zirconium	(b)	...	65-95 (150-200)	72 d	0.1 (4)	46
Zirconium	Repeated exposures	16	20 (70)	170 d	<0.0025 (<0.1)	3
Zr702	...	6	100 (212)	...	<0.13 (<5)	15
Zr702	...	6	50 (120)	...	nil	15
Zr705	...	6	50 (120)	...	nil	15
Noble metals						
Iridium	(h)	Saturated	100 (212)	...	<0.25 (<10)	18
Osmium	(h)	Saturated	Room	...	Rapid dissolution	26
Palladium	(h)	Saturated	Room	...	1.8 (71)	17
Palladium	(h)	Saturated	100 (212)	...	14.9 (587)	17
Platinum	...	All	100 (212)	...	<0.05 (<2)	5
Rhodium	(h)	Saturated	Room	...	<0.25 (<10)	29
Ruthenium	Plus NaCl, saturated solution	Saturated	100 (212)	...	Moderate attack	18
Ruthenium	(h)	Saturated	100 (212)	..	Moderate attack	18
Silver	...	All	Room	...	<0.05 (<2)	9
Silver	(h)	Saturated	Room	...	<0.05 (<2)	9

(Continued)

Corrosion Behavior of Various Metals and Alloys in Sodium Hypochlorite (Continued)

Material	Condition, other factors, comments	Concentration, %	Temperature, °C (°F)	Duration	Corrosion rate, mm/yr (mils/yr) or other	Ref
Others						
Magnesium alloy AZ61A	Specimen size, 75 x 25 x 1.5 mm (3 x 1 x 0.06 in.); surface preparation, HNO3 pickling; volume of testing solution, 100 ml. Specimens were alternately immersed 30 s in solution and held 2 min in air	3	35 (95)	7 d	0.5 g/m^2/d (0.3 mg/in.^{2}/d)	12
Niobium	...	6	50 (120)	...	1.25 (50)	2

(a) NaOCl solution (pH 9) with 500 ppm active chlorine and 1.2% NaCl. (b) In 1.5 to 4% NaOCl with 12-15% NaCl and 1% NaOH. (c) Plus 0.5 g/L Na2SiO3, beaker test, no agitation. (d) Plus 0.5 g/L Na3PO4, beaker test, no agitation. (e) Plus 2.0 g/L Na2SiO3, beaker test, no agitation. (f) Plus 2.0 g/L Na3PO4, beaker test, no agitation. (g) Beaker test, no agitation. (h) Plus NaCl.

Sodium Nitrate

Sodium nitrate, NaNO3, also known as soda niter and Chile saltpeter, is a fire-hazardous, transparent, colorless and odorless crystalline solid. It is soluble in glycerol and water, decomposes when heated, and melts at 308 °C. Sodium nitrate is used in making nitric and sulfuric acids, in the manufacture of glass and pottery enamel, as a fertilizer, as a food preservative, in explosives, and as a welding flux.

Material Summaries

The following material summaries were compiled from a survey of the available literature. Inclusion of a material description under a given environment does not imply that it is the most appropriate material for corrosion service in that environment. Likewise, exclusion of a given material does not imply that it is not suitable for corrosion service applications in that environment.

Aluminum. Aluminum alloy 3003 was resistant to solid sodium nitrate in laboratory tests conducted under conditions of 100% relative humidity at ambient temperature. In other laboratory tests, alloy 1100 was resistant to aqueous solutions of sodium nitrate (0.1 to 43%) at ambient temperature. Sodium nitrate has been used in combination with sodium nitrite as an inhibitor to retard the corrosion of aluminum alloys.

Copper. Transgranular cracking was observed on specimens of copper alloy C44300 immersed in naturally aerated 1N sodium nitrate at pH 8 and a potential of 0.15 V versus standard hydrogen electrode (SHE). The fracture stress relative to air was 0.34.

Copper alloy (Cu-23Zn-12Ni) wires measuring 0.6 mm (0.023 in.) in diameter and normally under a 6-g load and a positive potential in telephone equipment were observed to undergo stress-corrosion cracking within 2 years. Laboratory tests suggested that nitrate salts were the cause. Wires of Cu-20Ni did not crack under similar conditions.

Corrosion Behavior of Various Metals and Alloys in Sodium Nitrate

Material	Condition, other factors, comments	Concentration, %	Temperature, °C (°F)	Duration	Corrosion rate, mm/yr (mils/yr) or other	Ref
Stainless steels						
Type 304 stainless steel	...	10	21 (70)	...	Good	121
Type 304 stainless steels	Chemical processing; field or pilot plant test; no aeration; rapid agitation. Plus crude sodium-nitrate solution (evaporator). Severe pitting (maximum depth of pits from 0.005 to 0.010 in.)	~12-68	111 (232)	30 d	0.0007 in./yr	89
Type 316 stainless steels	Chemical processing; field or pilot plant test; no aeration; rapid agitation. Plus crude sodium-nitrate solution (evaporator)	~12-68	111 (232)	30 d	0.0006 in./yr	89
Type 316 stainless steel	...	10	21 (70)	...	Good	121
Type 410 stainless steel	...	10	21 (70)	...	Good	121
Type 430 stainless steel	...	10	21 (70)	...	Good	121
Coppers						
70-30 cupronickel	...	...	...	...	Suitable	93
90-10 cupronickel	...	...	...	...	Suitable	93
Admiralty brass	(a)	...	...	...	Good	93
Aluminum bronze	(a)	...	...	...	Good	93
Ampco 8, aluminum bronze	Generally suitable. Conditions such as aeration or temperature could restrict use	...	...	...	<0.5 (<20)	96
Architectural bronze	...	...	...	...	Fair	93

(Continued)

Corrosion Behavior of Various Metals and Alloys in Sodium Nitrate (Continued)

Material	Condition, other factors, comments	Concentration, %	Temperature, °C (°F)	Duration	Corrosion rate, mm/yr (mils/yr) or other	Ref
Brass	(a)	...	...	...	Good	93
Cartridge brass	...	...	...	...	Fair	93
Commercial bronze	(a)	...	...	...	Good	93
Electrolytic copper	(a)	...	...	...	Good	93
Free-cutting brass	...	...	...	...	Fair	93
Muntz metal	...	...	...	...	Fair	93
Naval brass	...	...	...	...	Fair	93
Nickel silver	...	18	...	...	Suitable	93
Phosphor bronze	5% Sn. (a)	...	...	...	Good	93
Phosphor bronze	8% Sn. (a)	...	...	...	Good	93
Phosphor copper	(a)	...	...	...	Good	93
Red brass	(a)	...	...	...	Good	93
Silicon bronze	Low. (a)	...	...	...	Good	93
Silicon bronze	High. (a)	...	...	...	Good	93
Titanium						
Titanium	...	Saturated	Room	...	nil	90
Heat- and corrosion-resistant alloys						
Carpenter 20	Chemical processing; field or pilot plant test; no aeration; rapid agitation. Plus crude sodium-nitrate solution (evaporator). Severe pitting (maximum depth of pits from 0.005 to 0.010 in.)	~12-68	111 (232)	30 d	0.0006 in./yr	89
Lead, tin, and zinc						
Lead	Corrosion rate too high to merit any consideration of lead	10	24 (75)	...	>1270 μm/yr (>50)	95
Tin	...	...	20 (68)	...	Resistant	94
Tin	...	...	60 (140)	...	Resistant	94
Tin	...	...	100 (212)	...	Resistant	94
Noble metals						
Platinum	...	All	Boiling	...	<0.05 (<2)	5
Silver	...	All	Boiling	...	<0.05 (<2)	9

(a) May be considered in place of a copper metal when some property, other than corrosion resistance, governs its use.

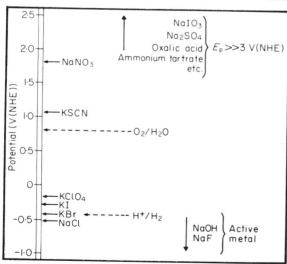

Aluminum. Pitting potentials of aluminum in various electrolytes. Solutions of 1*M* concentration were used, except for KClO$_4$, for which a 0.1*M* solution was used. The standard potentials for hydrogen evolution and for oxygen reduction in neutral solutions have been included as a reference. Source: J.R. Galvele, Pitting Corrosion, in *Treatise on Materials Science and Technology*, Vol 23, J.C. Scully, Ed., Academic Press, New York, 1983, 16.

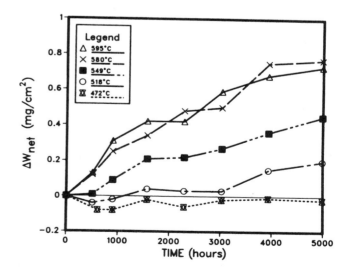

Incoloy 800. Net weight changes vs. time for Incoloy 800 exposed at various temperatures to 60% NaNO$_3$ + 40% KNO$_3$. Source: R.W. Bradshaw, "Thermal Convection Loop Study of the Corrosion of Incoloy 800 in Molten NaNO$_3$/KNO$_3$," *Corrosion*, Vol 43, Mar 1987, 174.

Sodium Nitrite

Sodium nitrite, $NaNO_2$, is a fire-hazardous, air-sensitive, yellowish-white powder that is soluble in water and decomposes at temperatures above 320 °C. Sodium nitrite is used as an intermediate for dyestuffs and for pickling of meat, in dyeing of textiles, in rustproofing, in medicine, and as a reagent in organic chemistry.

Material Summaries

The following material summaries were compiled from a survey of the available literature. Inclusion of a material description under a given environment does not imply that it is the most appropriate material for corrosion service in that environment. Likewise, exclusion of a given material does not imply that it is not suitable for corrosion service applications in that environment.

Copper. Copper, 99.9 and 99.996% pure, exhibited transgranular cracking when subjected to a strain rate of 10^{-6} s^{-1} while immersed in 1M sodium nitrite at a pH of 8.2. The 99.9% copper tested in solution exhibited an ultimate tensile strength of 160 MPa (23 ksi) and 25% elongation, as opposed to the 196 MPa (28.5 ksi) and 55% elongation obtained in air. Cracking in 1M sodium nitrite was also observed in alloy C26000, in admiralty brasses, and in alloy C70600.

Additional Reading

J. Yu and R.N. Parkins, Stress Corrosion Crack Propagation in Alpha-Brass and Copper Exposed to Sodium Nitrite Solutions, *Corros. Sci.*, 27(2), 159-182, 1987. MetAbs No. 87-351238. **Abstract:** Crack growth in alpha-brass and 99.99% copper exposed to $NaNO_2$ solutions has been studied as a function of solution composition, potential, temperature and strain rate.

Corrosion Behavior of Various Metals and Alloys in Sodium Nitrite

Material	Condition, other factors, comments	Concentration, %	Temperature, °C (°F)	Duration	Corrosion rate, mm/yr (mils/yr) or other	Ref
Irons and steels						
Mild steel	(a)	0.0	Room	14 d	0.11 (2.794)	140
Mild steel	(a)	0.02	Room	14 d	0.08 (2.032)	140
Mild steel	(a)	0.04	Room	14 d	0.02 (0.508)	140
Mild steel	(a)	0.06	Room	14 d	0.0	140
Mild steel	(a)	0.10	Room	14 d	0.0	140
Stainless steels						
AM-363 stainless steel	...	...	Room	...	Unattacked	120
Type 304 stainless steel	Textile processing; laboratory test; no aeration; rapid agitation. Plus 0.9% sodium chloride, diazoting bath	0.3-0.4	82 (180)	0.2 d	0.0056 in./yr	89
Type 304 stainless steel	Textile processing; laboratory test; no aeration; rapid agitation; low-carbon grade specimens (0.03% C max). Plus 0.9% sodium chloride, diazoting bath	0.3-0.4	82 (180)	0.2 d	0.0058 in./yr	89
Type 316 stainless steel	Textile processing; laboratory test; no aeration; rapid agitation. Plus 0.9% sodium chloride, diazoting bath	0.3-0.4	82 (180)	0.2 d	0.0044 in./yr	89
Type 410 stainless steel	...	...	Room	...	Unattacked	121
Others						
Magnesium alloy AZ61A	Specimen size, 75 x 25 x 1.5 mm (3 x 1 x 0.06 in.); surface preparation, HNO_3 pickling; volume of testing solution, 100 ml. Specimens were alternately immersed 30 s in solution and held 2 min in air	3	35 (95)	7 d	0.5 g/m^2/d (0.3 mg/in.^{2}/d)	12

(a) Rotating bottle tests using pipeline water, pH 9, and regular gasoline.

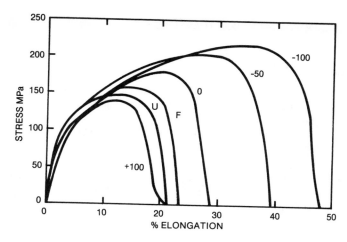

Copper. Stress-elongation curves obtained from slow strain rate testing of copper (Cu-OF) in aerated 0.6M sodium nitrite solution at room temperature. The figures on the curves indicate applied potential in mV, saturated calomel electrode (SCE); F = free corrosion potential, and U = +50 mV; the strain rate = 2.6 x 10^{-6} s^{-1}. Source: E. Mattisson, "Focus on Copper in Modern Corrosion Research," *Materials Performance*, Vol 26, April 1987, 15.

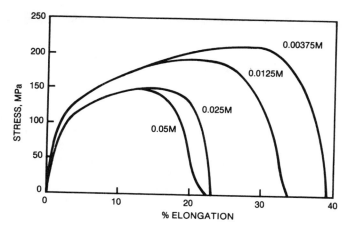

Copper. Stress-elongation curves obtained from slow strain rate testing of copper (Cu-OF) in aerated solutions of sodium nitrite at room temperature and an electrode potential of +100 mV (SCE) at a strain rate of 2.6 x 10^{-6} s^{-1}. Source: E. Mattisson, "Focus on Copper in Modern Corrosion Research," *Materials Performance*, Vol 26, April 1987, 15.

Sodium Perchlorate

Sodium perchlorate, $NaClO_4$, is a flammable, white crystalline deliquescent solid that melts at 482 °C (899.6 °F). Soluble in water and alcohol, it is used as an analytical reagent. Sodium perchlorate is explosive in nature when in contact with concentrated sulfuric acid and finds use in explosives and jet fuels.

Additional Reading

A.H. Le and R.T. Foley, Stress Corrosion Cracking of AA 7075-T651 in Various Electrolytes—Statistical Treatment of Data Obtained Using DCB Precracked Specimens, *Corrosion*, 39(10), 379-383, 1983. MetAbs No. 84-350291. **Abstract:** Double cantilever beam specimens were employed to measure the rate of stress-corrosion crack growth of AA 7075-T651 in 1N $NaClO_4$, 1N NaCl, 1N Na_2SO_4 and 1N $NaNO_3$ solutions. The data were treated statistically to arrive at a measure of the reliability of the test using double cantilever beam specimens.

R.C. Newman, Pitting of Stainless Alloys in Sulfate Solutions Containing Thiosulfate Ions, *Corrosion*, 41(8), 450-453, 1985. MetAbs No. 85-352333. **Abstract:** A scratch test was used to study the pitting of an Fe-19Cr-10Ni alloy in a solution containing 0.25M Na_2SO_4 and 0.025M $Na_2S_2O_3$.

Z.Y. Zhu, G.C. Farrington, and C. Laird, Fatigue Crack Initiation and Propagation in AISI 4130 Steel Exposed to Neutral Perchlorate Solution, *Mater. Sci. Eng.*, 91(1-2), 125-135, 1987. MetAbs No. 87-352467. **Abstract:** To check whether recent results on the corrosion fatigue of copper single crystals may apply to a commercial metal, corrosion fatigue crack initiation and propagation in normalized AISI 4130 steel have been studied in air, in 0.1M $NaClO_4$ solution in free corrosion and in the same solution but at an imposed anodic potential of -0.555 V with respect to a saturated calomel electrode.

Corrosion Behavior of Various Metals and Alloys in Sodium Perchlorate

Material	Condition, other factors, comments	Concentration, %	Temperature, °C (°F)	Duration	Corrosion rate, mm/yr (mils/yr) or other	Ref
Gold	Melt	...	480 (900)	...	Attacked	9
Platinum	...	All	Boiling	...	<0.05 (<2)	5
Platinum	Melt	...	480 (900)	...	Attacked	5
Silver	...	All	Boiling	...	<0.05 (<2)	9
Titanium	...	900 g/L	50 (122)	...	0.003 (0.12)	90

Sodium Peroxide

Sodium peroxide, Na_2O_2, is a fire-hazardous white powder that yellows when heated and causes ignition when in contact with water. Sodium peroxide is decomposed by heating, although this is not easily accomplished. It is stable in dry air; however, in moist air, or when acted on by water, it decomposes readily. It can be a powerful oxidizer and a powerful reducing agent, depending on conditions. Sodium peroxide is also used as a bleach, in medicinal soap, and in the decomposition of minerals.

Material Summaries

The following material summaries were compiled from a survey of the available literature. Inclusion of a material description under a given environment does not imply that it is the most appropriate material for corrosion service in that environment. Likewise, exclusion of a given material does not imply that it is not suitable for corrosion service applications in that environment.

Aluminum. Solid sodium peroxide was very corrosive to alloys 3003 and 5154 in laboratory tests under conditions of 100% relative humidity at ambient temperature.

Ruthenium. Ruthenium is attacked rapidly by fused sodium peroxide.

Corrosion Behavior of Various Metals and Alloys in Sodium Peroxide

Material	Condition, other factors, comments	Concen- tration, %	Temperature, °C (°F)	Duration	Corrosion rate, mm/yr (mils/yr) or other	Ref
Coppers						
70-30 cupronickel	(a)	...	...	...	Good	93
90-10 cupronickel	(a)	...	...	...	Good	93
Admiralty brass	...	...	...	...	Fair	93
Aluminum bronze	...	...	...	...	Fair	93
Ampco 8, aluminum bronze	Generally not suitable	...	...	...	>0.5 (>20)	96
Architectural bronze	...	...	...	...	Not suitable	93
Brass	...	...	...	...	Fair	93
Cartridge brass	...	...	...	...	Not suitable	93
Commercial bronze	...	...	...	...	Fair	93
Electrolytic copper	...	...	...	...	Fair	93
Free-cutting brass	...	...	...	...	Not suitable	93
Muntz metal	...	...	...	...	Not suitable	93
Naval brass	...	...	...	...	Not suitable	93
Nickel silver	(a)	18	...	...	Good	93
Phosphor bronze	5% Sn	...	...	...	Fair	93
Phosphor bronze	8% Sn	...	...	...	Fair	93
Phosphor copper	...	...	...	...	Fair	93
Red brass	...	...	...	...	Fair	93
Silicon bronze	Low	...	...	...	Fair	93
Silicon bronze	High	...	...	...	Fair	93
Zirconium						
Zr702	...	0-100	Room to 100 (room to 212)	...	<0.025 (<2)	15
Lead, tin, and zinc						
Tin	...	...	20 (68)	...	Resistant	94
Tin	...	...	60 (140)	...	Resistant	94
Tin	...	...	100 (212)	...	Resistant	94
Noble metals						
Platinum	...	All	Boiling	...	<0.05 (<2)	5
Platinum	Melt	...	400 (750)	...	<0.05 (<2)	5
Silver	Melt	...	400 (750)	...	Attacked	9

(a) May be considered in place of a copper metal when some property, other than corrosion resistance, governs its use.

Sodium Silicate

Sodium silicate, Na_2SiO_3, also known as liquid glass, silicate of soda, sodium metasilicate, and soluble glass, is a grayish-white crystalline powder that has a melting point of 1088 °C (1990 °F). It is soluble in water and has strong detergent and emulsifying properties. Sodium silicate is used to fireproof textiles, insulate electric wire, protect wood and porous stone, greaseproof paper containers, and as a catalyst in refining high-octane gasoline.

Material Summaries

The following material summaries were compiled from a survey of the available literature. Inclusion of a material description under a given environment does not imply that it is the most appropriate material for corrosion service in that environment. Likewise, exclusion of a given material does not imply that it is not suitable for corrosion service applications in that environment.

Aluminum. The resistance to corrosion of aluminum alloys by sodium silicates depends on the weight ratio of SiO_2/Na_2O. Commercial sodium silicates with a weight ratio of 2 have been used as inhibitors of corrosion of aluminum alloys in alkaline solutions. In laboratory tests, sodium metasilicate with a weight ratio of 1 was very corrosive to alloy 1100 at ambient temperature.

Additional Reading

Z. Szklarska-Smialowska and W. Kozlowski, The Behavior of Armco Iron in Its Passive and Transpassive States in NaOH and Na_2SiO_3 Solutions, *Corrosion, 40*(11), 595-597, 1984. MetAbs No. 85-350446. **Abstract:** In an earlier work, pits were found on iron specimens immersed in a borate buffer solution containing $0.15M$ H_3BO_3 + $0.0375M$ $Na_2B_4O_7$ (pH 8.45) and subjected to anodic polarization for 1 h. The aim was to ascertain if iron would also suffer pitting in the transpassive region in other halide-free solutions and if some correlation could be found between the propensity to undergo pitting and the optical properties of surface films; $0.1M$ Na_2SiO_3 and $0.05M$ NaOH solutions were chosen for this study. Other experimental details and the results are presented and compared with the earlier results on iron in borate buffer solution.

C.R. Bergen, Sodium Silicates—Stress Corrosion Cracking Agents for Alloys 600 and 690 at 315 °C, *Corrosion, 41*(2), 85-88, 1985. MetAbs No. 85-350641. **Abstract:** Thirteen compositions were selected from the phases known to exist at 300 °C, and U-bends of welded Alloy 600 were tested to determine which compositions caused the most rapid stress-corrosion cracking.

Corrosion Behavior of Various Metals and Alloys in Sodium Silicate

Material	Condition, other factors, comments	Concentration, %	Temperature, °C (°F)	Duration	Corrosion rate, mm/yr (mils/yr) or other	Ref
Aluminum						
Aluminum (99.0-99.5%)	...	...	...	...	Restricted applications	92
Aluminum-silicon alloys	...	...	...	...	Restricted applications	92
Coppers						
70-30 cupronickel	...	...	...	...	Suitable	93
90-10 cupronickel	...	...	...	...	Suitable	93
Admiralty brass	...	...	...	...	Suitable	93
Aluminum bronze	...	...	...	...	Suitable	93
Ampco 8, aluminum bronze	Generally suitable	...	...	...	<0.05 (<2)	96
Architectural bronze	(a)	...	...	...	Good	93
Brass	...	...	...	...	Suitable	93
Cartridge brass	(a)	...	...	...	Good	93
Commercial bronze	...	...	...	...	Suitable	93
Copper nickel	...	...	...	...	Suitable	93
Copper tin	...	...	..	...	2.5-40 (0.1-1.5)	76
Copper zinc	...	...	...	...	<50 (<2)	76
Electrolytic copper	...	...	...	....	50-125 (2-5)	76
Free-cutting brass	(a)	...	...	...	Suitable	93
Muntz metal	(a)	...	...	...	Good	93
Naval brass	(a)	...	...	...	Good	93
Nickel silver	...	...	...	...	Good	93
Phosphor bronze	5% Sn	18	...	...	Suitable	93
Phosphor bronze	8% Sn	...	...	...	Suitable	93
Phosphor copper	...	...	...	...	Suitable	93
Red brass	...	...	...	...	Suitable	93
Silicon bronze	Low	...	...	...	Suitable	93
Silicon bronze	High	...	...	...	Suitable	93
Titanium						
Titanium	...	25	Boiling	...	nil	90

(Continued)

Corrosion Behavior of Various Metals and Alloys in Sodium Silicate (Continued)

Material	Condition, other factors, comments	Concen-tration, %	Temperature, °C (°F)	Duration	Corrosion rate, mm/yr (mils/yr) or other	Ref
Zirconium						
Zr702	...	0-100	Room to 100 (room to 212)	...	<0.025 (<2)	15
Lead, tin, and zinc						
Tin	(b)	0.005	60 (140)	...	0.030 (1.2)	75
Tin	(b)	0.02	60 (140)	...	0.045 (1.8)	75
Tin	(b)	0.05	60 (140)	...	nil	75
Tin	(b)	0.10	60 (140)	...	0.015 (0.6)	75
Tin	(b)	0.15	60 (140)	...	0.075 (2.95)	75
Tin	(b)	0.20	60 (140)	...	0.090 (3.5)	75
Tin	(b)	0.25	60 (140)	...	0.12 (4.7)	75
Tin	...	...	20 (68)	...	Resistant	94
Tin	...	...	60 (140)	...	Resistant	94
Tin	...	...	100 (212)	...	Resistant	94
Noble metals						
Platinum	...	All	Boiling	...	<0.05 (<2)	5
Silver	...	All	Boiling	...	<0.05 (<2)	9
Others						
Magnesium	...	All	Room	...	Suitable	119
Magnesium alloy AZ61A	Specimen size, 75 x 25 x 1.5 mm (3 x 1 x 0.06 in.); surface preparation, HNO3 pickling; volume of testing solution, 100 ml. Specimens were alternately immersed 30 s in solution and held 2 min in air	3	35 (95)	7 d	0.07 g/m²/d (0.04 mg/in.²/d)	12

(a) May be considered in place of a copper metal when some property, other than corrosion resistance, governs its use. (b) Converted from weight loss data, assuming a tin density of 7.29 g/cm³.

Sodium Sulfate

Sodium sulfate, Na₂SO₄, also known as thenardite and salt cake, is a crystalline compound that melts at 888 °C (1632 °F). Sodium sulfate is found in natural form (thenardite) in Chile and Spain. It is used in the manufacture of paperboard, glass, and freezing mixtures. The hydrate, Na₂SO₄·10H₂O, also known as "Glauber's salt," is a white water-soluble solid formed by heating sodium chloride and sulfuric acid. It is used in dyeing, manufacturing glass, and in the preparation of sodium bisulfate.

Material Summaries

The following material summaries were compiled from a survey of the available literature. Inclusion of a material description under a given environment does not imply that it is the most appropriate material for corrosion service in that environment. Likewise, exclusion of a given material does not imply that it is not suitable for corrosion service applications in that environment.

Aluminum. Aluminum alloy 3003 resisted solid sodium sulfate under laboratory conditions of 100% relative humidity and ambient temperature. In other tests run at ambient temperature, aqueous solutions of sodium sulfate in concentrations of 0.1 to 14% mildly attacked (0.05 mm/yr, or 2 mils/yr) aluminum alloy 1100. Sodium sulfate has been handled in aluminum alloy tote bins.

P/M Superalloys. Pure sodium sulfate heavily corroded P/M LC Astroloy and isostatically pressed IN-100 samples. The addition of a heat treatment and coarse powder lowered the susceptibility to catastrophic corrosion.

Copper. A sample of C26000 that was polarized at a potential of 0.25 V versus SHE, subjected to constant strain, and immersed in a solution of 1N sodium sulfate and 0.01N sulfuric acid, was found to suffer stress-corrosion cracking.

Lead. Although acid sodium sulfate rapidly attacks lead when dilute, it has little effect at strengths of 52 to 70%.

Nickel. In hot corrosion tests for automotive applications, a weight loss of 5% was recorded when a sample of Inconel alloy X-750 was exposed for 100 h in a 90% sodium sulfate and 10% sodium chloride air mixture.

Titanium. Although unalloyed titanium was attacked by concentrated sodium sulfate solutions, crevice attack was dependent on the combination of pH and temperature. Grade 2 titanium alloy resisted crevice attack by a simulated acid sulfate galvanizing solution (pH 1.3) at temperatures below 100 °C (212 °F); grades 7 and 12 resisted attack under all conditions. Results indicate that threshold temperatures for crevice corrosion in sulfate solution are much higher than those for chloride solutions.

Additional Reading

A.H. Le and R.T. Foley, Stress Corrosion Cracking of AA 7075-T651 in Various Electrolytes–Statistical Treatment of Data Obtained Using DCB Precracked Specimens, *Corrosion, 39*(10), 379-383, 1983. MetAbs No. 84-350291. **Abstract:** Double cantilever beam specimens were employed to measure the rate of stress-corrosion crack growth of AA 7075-T651 in $1N$ NaClO$_4$, $1N$ NaCl, $1N$ Na$_2$SO$_4$ and $1N$ NaNO$_3$ solutions.

C.A. Caramihas and D.F. Taylor, Constant Extension Rate Tensile (CERT) Tests of Creviced Alloy 600 Specimens in Aqueous Environments at 288 °C, *Corrosion, 40*(7), 382-385, 1984. MetAbs No. 84-352608. **Abstract:** Constant extension rate tensile tests on creviced tubular Alloy 600 specimens containing 0.1M Na$_2$SO$_4$ demonstrated that overaging could restore resistance to intergranular stress-corrosion cracking in solution-annealed material after furnace sensitization had dramatically increased this susceptibility.

G.A. Fuller and D.D. MacDonald, The Effect of Fluid Flow on the Stress Corrosion Cracking of AISI 304 Stainless Steel in 0.01M Na$_2$SO$_4$ Solution at 280 °C, *Corrosion, 40*(9), 474-477, 1984. MetAbs No. 84-353068. **Abstract:** The stress-corrosion cracking of sensitized AISI 304 stainless steel in high-temperature (280 °C) 0.01M Na$_2$SO$_4$ solution has been studied as a function of flow velocity and applied potential over a range that spans the critical potential for intergranular stress-corrosion cracking.

W.-T. Tsai, A. Moccari, Z. Szklarska-Smialowska, and D.D. MacDonald, Effect of Potential on the Corrosion Fatigue Crack Growth Rate in AISI 304 Stainless Steel in Sodium Sulfate Solution at 250 °C, *Corrosion, 40*(11), 573-583, 1984. **Abstract:** The corrosion fatigue-crack growth behavior of sensitized AISI 304 stainless steel was studied in 0.1M Na$_2$SO$_4$ solution at 250 °C. Crack growth rates at different frequencies ranging from 1.0 to 8×10^{-3} Hz, and at different electrochemical potentials, were measured with a sinusoidal loading waveform at a load ratio of 0.5.

F. Mansfeld, M.W. Kendig, and W.J. Lorenz, Corrosion Inhibition in Neutral, Aerated Media, *J. Electrochem. Soc., 132*(2), 290-296, 1985. MetAbs No. 85-350787. **Abstract:** The concepts of interface and interphase inhibition as two different types of corrosion inhibition mechanisms are discussed briefly. Experimental results of interphase inhibition have been obtained for a 4340 steel rotating cylinder electrode. An optimized approach for collecting impedance data for high R_p values and a low frequency limit between 0.4 to 5 mHz has been applied.

M.B. Hintz, L.J. Nettleton, and L.A. Heldt, Stress Corrosion Cracking of Alpha-Beta Brass in Distilled Water and Sodium Sulfate Solutions, *Metall. Trans. A, 16A*(5), 971-978, 1985. MetAbs No. 85-351019. **Abstract:** Specimens of a Cu-42 wt% zinc alpha-beta alloy have been tested to failure in uniaxial tension at constant extension rates in a variety of environments. The electrochemical potentials of the specimens have been monitored and/or controlled during testing.

F. Di Quarto, S. Piazza, and C. Sunseri, Photoelectrochemical Study of the Corrosion Product Layers on Copper in Weakly Acidic Solutions, *Electrochim. Acta, 30*(3), 315-324, 1985. MetAbs No. 85-351089. **Abstract:** The nature of the surface layers grown on copper electrodes in free corrosion conditions in unbuffered aerated Na$_2$SO$_4$ solutions (pH 3.0 to 6.0) was investigated by photoelectrochemical methods.

T.C. Tan and D.-T. Chin, Polarization of Aluminum During AC Corrosion in Sulfate Solutions, *J. Electrochem. Soc., 132*(4), 766-772, 1985. MetAbs No. 85-351343. **Abstract:** An experimental study has been made of the effect of alternating voltage on the corrosion of Al (6061) in aqueous solutions of $1N$ H$_2$SO$_4$, $1N$ Na$_2$SO$_4$, $1N$ NaOH, and $1N$ Na$_2$SO$_4$ containing 0 to 5010 ppm Cl$^-$ ions. The polarization curves were measured with an alternating voltage modulation technique using sinusoidal waves, and the pitting behavior of Al was examined with constant potentiostatic coulometry and SEM photomicrography. The measurements were made over a range of alternating voltage magnitudes from 0 to 1500 mV rms, and alternating voltage frequencies from 20 to 600 Hz.

S.K. Somuah and D.D. MacDonald, Performance of Ni-Cr-Mo-V Turbine Rotor Steels in Na$_2$SO$_4$ Solution, *Br. Corros. J., 20*(1), 45-50, 1985. MetAbs No. 85-351887. **Abstract:** The stress-corrosion cracking susceptibility of different heats of steels from three turbine rotors in Na$_2$SO$_4$ solution was investigated as a function of applied potential and heat treatment. The electrochemical reactivity of the steels was studied by generating potentiodynamic polarization curves to determine the possible potential ranges for stress-corrosion cracking.

C.A. Acosta, R.C. Salvarezza, H.A. Videla, and A.J. Arvia, The Pitting of Mild Steel in Phosphate-Borate Solutions in the Presence of Sodium Sulphate, *Corros. Sci., 25*(5), 291-303, 1985. MetAbs No. 85-351901. **Abstract:** The localized corrosion of mild steel in neutral solutions containing Na$_2$SO$_4$ was studied using potentiostatic and potentiodynamic techniques complemented by scanning electron microscopy.

R.C. Newman, Pitting of Stainless Alloys in Sulfate Solutions Containing Thiosulfate Ions, *Corrosion, 41*(8), 450-453, 1985. MetAbs No. 85-352333. **Abstract:** A scratch test was used to study the pitting of an Fe-19Cr-10Ni alloy in a solution containing 0.25M Na$_2$SO$_4$ and 0.025M Na$_2$S$_2$O$_3$.

J.M. Bastidas and J.D. Scantlebury, Photopotentials and the Corrosion of Mild Steel in Sodium Sulphate Solution, *Corros. Sci., 25*(6), 377-382, 1985. MetAbs No. 85-352380. **Abstract:** Experiments were carried out to observe the effect of light on the photopotential of mild steel in a neutral sodium sulfate solution.

V. Lemoine, P. Steinmetz, and B. Roques, The Influence of Reducing Conditions on the Sodium Sulfate-Induced Corrosion of Pure and Alloyed beta NiAl, *Corros. Sci., 25*(6), 431-447, 1985. MetAbs No. 85-352384. **Abstract:** This study concerns the corrosion of the beta NiAl phase (pure or with additions of Co and Cr) by Na$_2$SO$_4$ in reducing atmospheres at 850 °C.

S.S. Abd El Rehim, S.M. Abd El Haleem, and M.S. Shalaby, Electrochemical Behaviour and Corrosion of 18-8 Austenitic Stainless Steel in Sulphate Solutions, *Surf. Technol., 26*(1), 77-85, 1985. MetAbs No. 86-350407. **Abstract:** The electrochemical behavior and corrosion of a commercial Egyptian 18-8 austenitic stainless steel was investigated in sulfuric acid and in sodium sulfate solutions using the potentiodynamic technique.

R. Sivakumar, P.K. Sagar, and M.L. Bhatia, On the Electrochemical Nature of Hot-Corrosion Attack in Ni-Cr Alloys, *Oxid. Met., 24*(5-6), 315-330, 1985. MetAbs No. 86-350423. **Abstract:** Hot-corrosion attack on gas-turbine components has been a problem of practical importance for over two decades. An attempt has been made to investigate the role of Al and Ti in influencing the hot-corrosion attack of Ni-20Cr alloys (Ni-19.3Cr, Ni-19.4Cr-1.95Ti, and Ni-19.4Cr-1.25Al) in molten Na$_2$SO$_4$-NaCl mixtures.

J. Flis and D.J. Duquette, Effect of Phosphorus on Anodic Dissolution and Passivation of Nickel in Near-Neutral Solutions, *Corrosion, 41*(12), 700-706, 1985. MetAbs No. 86-350429. **Abstract:** Anodic dissolution of nickel, electroless nickel deposits with 2.9 and 12.3 wt% phosphorus and amorphous $Ni_{81}P_{19}$ alloy was examined in sodium hydroxide, sulfate, borate, and chloride solutions at 25 °C.

J.L. Wendt and D.-T. Chin, The A.C. Corrosion of Stainless Steel. I. The Breakdown of Passivity of SS304 in Neutral Aqueous Solutions, *Corros. Sci.*, 25(10), 889-900, 1985. MetAbs No. 86-350522. **Abstract:** The effect of alternating current on the corrosion of Type 304 stainless steel in aqueous solutions of Na_2SO_4, $NaNO_3$ and $NaCl$ has been investigated with an alternating voltage modulation technique, using 60 Hz square wave alternating voltage. The anodic and cathodic polarization curves were measured for a range of alternating voltage from 0 to 1000 mV and the surfaces of specimens after a potentiostatic coulometry experiment were examined under a scanning electron microscope.

A.K. Misra, Studies on the Hot Corrosion of a Nickel-Base Superalloy, Udimet 700, *Oxid. Met.*, 25(3-4), 129-161, 1986. MetAbs No. 86-351048. **Abstract:** The hot corrosion of a nickel-base superalloy, Udimet 700, has been studied at 900 to 950 °C. The effect of the amount of Na_2SO_4 on the corrosion kinetics was determined.

I.A. Ammar, S. Darwish, M.W. Khalil, and A. Galal, Investigation of the Passivity of Tin in Neutral Media by Cyclic Galvanostatic Polarization, *Z. Werkstofftech.*, 16(12), 413-421, 1985. MetAbs No. 86-351232. **Abstract:** To understand the passivity of tin in neutral media, open-circuit measurements and cyclic galvanostatic polarization measurements have been performed in aerated unstirred KCl, Na_2SO_4 solutions (0.1, 0.5, 1.0 and 2.0M) and in phosphate buffer (pH 6.6 to 6.7).

T.A. Mozhi, K. Nishimoto, B.E. Wilde, and W.A.T. Clark, The Effect of Nitrogen on Stress Corrosion Cracking of AISI 304 Stainless Steel in High-Temperature Sulfate Solution, *Corrosion*, 42(4), 197-203, 1986. MetAbs No. 86-351328. **Abstract:** Slow strain rate tests were conducted on solution annealed and sensitized AISI 304 stainless steels with varying nitrogen and carbon contents to study their susceptibility to stress-corrosion cracking. The tests were conducted in deaerated 0.1M Na_2SO_4 at 250 °C at a strain rate of 2 x 10^{-6}/s.

M.B. Hintz, W.K. Blanchard, P.K. Brindley, and L.A. Heldt, Further Observations of SCC in Alpha-Beta Brass: Considerations Regarding the Appearance of Crack Arrest Markings During SCC, *Metall. Trans. A*, 17A(6), 1081-1086, 1986. MetAbs No. 86-351451. **Abstract:** A series of constant displacement and constant extension rate stress-corrosion cracking tests was performed on an alpha-beta brass alloy (Cu-42Zn) in 1N Na_2SO_4 solutions.

E. McCafferty and P.G. Moore, Corrosion Behavior of Laser-Surface Melted and Laser-Surface Alloyed Steels, *J. Electrochem. Soc.*, 133(6), 1090-1096, 1986. MetAbs No. 86-351703. **Abstract:** Fe-Cr surface alloys of 100 μm thickness and containing 5 to 80% Cr were formed by laser-surface alloying Cr into underlying steel substrates.

A.K. Misra, Mechanism of Na_2SO_4-Induced Corrosion of Molybdenum Containing Nickel-Base Superalloys at High Temperatures. I. Corrosion in Atmospheres Containing Oxygen Only, *J. Electrochem. Soc.*, 133(5), 1029-1038, 1986. MetAbs No. 86-352068. **Abstract:** The corrosion of nickel-base superalloys containing molybdenum (B-1900, Udimet 700) has been studied at 750 to 950 °C in the presence of a Na_2MoO_4 deposit. The corrosion kinetics were determined and the corrosion products were characterized by metallography, scanning electron microscope, and chemical analysis. The results obtained in the present study have been analyzed according to various hot corrosion models.

A.K. Misra, Mechanism of Na_2SO_4-Induced Corrosion of Molybdenum Containing Nickel-Base Superalloys at High Temperatures. II. Corrosion in Oxygen + SO_2 Atmospheres, *J. Electrochem. Soc.*, 133(5), 1038-1042, 1986. MetAbs No. 86-352069. **Abstract:** The effect of SO_2 content in

the atmosphere on the Na_2SO_4-induced corrosion of a molybdenum-containing nickel-base superalloy, Udimet 700, has been studied at 950 °C. Based on transport considerations, a mechanism is proposed to explain the rapid rate of corrosion in the presence of MoO_3 in the melt.

E.I. Sokolova, S.N. Raicheva, and M.R. Goulamali, Effect of Functional Groups in the Inhibitor on Its Protective Action, *C.R. Acad. Bulg. Sci.*, 39(4), 55-58, 1986. MetAbs No. 86-352499. **Abstract:** Gravimetric and galvanometric methods were used to study the effects of selected inhibitors on the corrosion of low-carbon steel in 0.5M Na_2SO_4 solution and copper in 0.1N KCl. Inhibitors studied were piperazine, morpholine, ethylamine, ethylenediamine and monoethanolamine for steel and quinoline, 8-oxyquinoline and 2-methyl-oxyquinoline for copper.

K. Tanno, S. Ishizuka, S. Higuchi, and N. Ohnaka, Stress Corrosion Cracking of Sensitized AISI 304 Stainless Steel in High-Temperature Sodium Sulfate Solutions, *Corrosion*, 42(9), 559-564, 1986. MetAbs No. 86-352582. **Abstract:** The susceptibility of sensitized AISI 304 stainless steel to intergranular stress-corrosion cracking was studied in 0.01M Na_2SO_4 solution at 100 to 250 °C under constant load conditions.

Y. Okanda, M. Fukusumi, K. Mizuuchi, and S. Nenno, Effect of Cerium Additions on the Microstructure and High Temperature Corrosion Behavior of Fe-30Cr-5Al Alloys, *Trans. Jpn. Inst. Met.*, 27(9), 680-692, 1986. MetAbs No. 87-351209. **Abstract:** The microstructures of two alloys, Fe-27Cr-4Al-0.25Ce and Fe-29Cr-4Al-0.76Ce were examined using optical microscopy, X-ray diffraction, electron probe microanalysis and transmission electron microscopy. High-temperature corrosion tests in 80% Na_2SO_4-20% NaCl were made on both the cerium-containing alloys used for the metallographic examinations.

A.M. Beccaria, E.D. Mor, G. Poggi, and F. Mazza, A Study of the Corrosion Products of Aluminum Brass Formed in Sodium Sulfate Solution in the Presence of Chlorides, *Corros. Sci.*, 27(4), 363-372, 1987. MetAbs No. 87-351683. **Abstract:** The surface film forming on aluminum brass specimens immersed in stagnant Na_2SO_4 solutions containing chlorides at pH 3.0 to 7.25 was examined by using chemical, electrochemical and X-ray techniques.

A.M. Beccaria and G. Poggi, Aluminum Corrosion in Slightly Alkaline Sodium Sulfate Solutions at Different Hydrostatic Pressures, *Corrosion*, 43(3), 153-158, 1987. MetAbs No. 87-351815. **Abstract:** The effect of variable SO_4 concentrations in slightly alkaline solutions (pH 8.2) on aluminum corrosion has been studied at different hydrostatic pressures (1, 100, and 300 atm). The solution temperature was 20 °C, and it contained approximately 8 ppm of dissolved oxygen.

S.H. Shim and Z. Szklarska-Smialowska, Effect of Fluid Flow Rate on the Intergranular Stress Corrosion Cracking of AISI 304 Stainless Steel, *Corrosion*, 43(5), 280-286, 1987. MetAbs No. 87-351916. **Abstract:** The effect of fluid flow on stress-corrosion cracking of sensitized AISI 304 stainless steel has been studied in air-saturated and deaerated 0.01M Na_2SO_4 solution at 250 °C using slow strain rate tensile tests.

S.H. Shim and Z. Szklarska-Smialowska, Effect of Fluid Flow on the Stress Corrosion Cracking of AISI 304 Stainless Steel in Pure Water and 0.01N Na_2SO_4 Solutions Differing in pH, *Corrosion*, 43(5), 286-290, 1987. MetAbs No. 87-351917. **Abstract:** The effect of fluid flow on stress-corrosion cracking of sensitized AISI 304 stainless steel was studied in air-saturated pure water and in air-saturated acidified and alkaline 0.01M Na_2SO_4 solutions under open circuit conditions at 250 °C, using slow strain rate tensile tests.

K. Tanno, Y. Yuasa, and H. Yashiro, Stress Corrosion Cracking of Sensitized AISI 304 Stainless Steel in Oxygenated Na_2SO_4 Solution at High Temperature, *Corrosion*, 43(4), 248-250, 1987. MetAbs No.

87-351997. **Abstract:** Experimental conditions for measurement of the effects of temperature on intergranular stress-corrosion cracking of AISI 304 stainless steel sensitized at 650 °C are detailed. Cathodic reactions are discussed. Stress-corrosion cracking test results at 150 and 250 °C are tabulated and discussed for creviced and uncreviced specimens. Comparisons are made to tests performed under controlled potential.

S. Kameswari and R.D.K. Misra, Corrosion Behaviour of Nimonic-75 and Ni-19.4Cr-1.25Al in NaCl and Na2SO4, *Werkst. Korros., 38*(1), 20-25, 1987. MetAbs No. 87-352229. **Abstract:** The corrosion behavior of Nimonic-75 and Ni-Cr-Al alloys has been investigated in NaCl and Na2SO4 by employing the half-immersion crucible test. Weight loss results obtained as a function of temperature (700 to 800 °C) and concentration of NaCl in the mixture (1 to 30 wt%) are given.

L.E. Kanary, W.F. Caley, H.A. Hancock, and R.S. Hollingshead, Effect of Zinc Additions to NaCl-Na2SO4 Molten Salt Mixture on Hot Corrosion of Nimocast 713, *Mater. Sci. Technol., 3*(7), 571-575, 1987. MetAbs No. 87-352607. **Abstract:** Hot corrosion studies were conducted at 900 °C in a simulated combustion gas atmosphere containing sulfur trioxide at a partial pressure of 750 Pa on a nickel-base superalloy (Nimocast 713) partially immersed in various ZnSO4-10 wt% NaCl-Na2SO4 molten salt mixtures. Weight changes were measured thermogravimetrically with time.

M. Wang, Z. Jin, and W. Wu, Hot Corrosion Behaviour of Nickel-Based Superalloy Irradiated With a Laser Beam, *Mater. Sci. Eng., 92*(1-2), 145-151, 1987. MetAbs No. 87-352790. **Abstract:** The structure and hot corrosion behavior of cast nickel-based superalloy M38 irradiated with a CO_2 laser beam of 1.3 kW output have been studied using optical microscopy, X-ray diffraction, scanning electron microscopy and electron probe microanalysis and compared with the structure and hot corrosion behavior of the unirradiated alloy. The hot corrosion tests were carried out in a crucible filled with 75 mol% Na2SO4 plus 25 mol% NaCl at 900 °C for 15, 35, 55, 80 and 100 h.

W.C. Moshier, G.D. Davis, and J.S. Ahearn, The Corrosion and Passivity of Aluminum Exposed to Dilute Sodium Sulfate Solutions, *Corros. Sci., 27*(8), 785-801, 1987. MetAbs No. 87-352914. **Abstract:** The composition and thickness of the oxide/hydroxide film that forms on pure aluminum surfaces that are polarized in $0.05M$ Na2SO4 in acidic, near-neutral, and alkaline solutions have been characterized using XPS. The results of this effort have been plotted on surface behavior diagrams to follow the evolution of the surface film during polarization.

Corrosion Behavior of Various Metals and Alloys in Sodium Sulfate

Material	Condition, other factors, comments	Concentration, %	Temperature, °C (°F)	Duration	Corrosion rate, mm/yr (mils/yr) or other	Ref
Stainless steels						
AM-363 stainless steel	...	...	Room	...	Unattacked	120
Type 304 stainless steel	...	10	21 (70)	...	Good	121
Type 304 stainless steel	Rayon processing; field or plant test; slight to moderate aeration; rapid agitation. Saturated sodium sulfate solution, 20% crystals	Saturated	76 (170)	48 d	0.0001 in./yr	89
Type 304 stainless steel	Chemical processing; field or plant test; no aeration; rapid agitation. Sodium sulfate saturated slurry, plus 1% zinc sulfate, sodium hydroxide, pH 8.5-9, evaporator	Saturated	110 (230)	193 d	0.0001 in./yr	89
Type 304 stainless steel	Paper processing; field or plant test; strong aeration; rapid agitation. Top waters from organic yellow pigment, plus 3% sodium acetate, 1.6% sodium chloride. Slight pitting: maximum depth of pits from incipient to 0.005 in., crevice attack (tendency to concentration-cell corrosion)	20-25	70-80 (158-176)	7.5 d	0.0006 in./yr	89
Type 304 stainless steel	Pharmaceutical processing; field or plant test; slight to moderate aeration; rapid agitation. Plus 4% chloride ion, 4% ferric ion, 1% phosphate ion, pH 1-2.5. Severe pitting: maximum depth of pits over 0.010 in., crevice attack (tendency to concentration-cell corrosion)	14.8	52 (125)	20 d	0.0028 in./yr	89
Type 316 stainless steel	...	10	21 (70)	...	Very good	121
Type 316 stainless steel	Rayon processing; field or plant test; slight to moderate aeration; rapid agitation. Saturated sodium sulfate solution, 20% crystals	Saturated	76 (170)	48 d	0.0001 in./yr	89
Type 316 stainless steel	Chemical processing; field or plant test; no aeration; rapid agitation. Sodium sulfate saturated slurry, plus 1% zinc sulfate, sodium hydroxide, pH 8.5-9, evaporator	Saturated	110 (230)	193 d	0.0001 in./yr	89
Type 316 stainless steel	Paper processing; field or plant test; strong aeration; rapid agitation. Top waters from organic yellow pigment, plus 3% sodium acetate, 1.6% sodium chloride. Crevice attack (tendency to concentration-cell corrosion)	20-25	70-80 (158-176)	7.5 d	0.0003 in./yr	89
Type 316 stainless steel	Pharmaceutical processing; field or plant test; slight to moderate aeration; rapid agitation. Plus 4% chloride ion, 4% ferric ion, 1% phosphate ion, pH 1-2.5. Severe pitting: maximum depth of pits over 0.010 in., crevice attack (tendency to concentration-cell corrosion)	14.8	52 (125)	20 d	0.001 in./yr	89

(Continued)

Corrosion Behavior of Various Metals and Alloys in Sodium Sulfate (Continued)

Material	Condition, other factors, comments	Concentration, %	Temperature, °C (°F)	Duration	Corrosion rate, mm/yr (mils/yr) or other	Ref
Type 317 stainless steel	Rayon processing; field or plant test; slight to moderate aeration; rapid agitation. Saturated sodium sulfate solution, 20% crystals	Saturated	76 (170)	48 d	0.0001 in./yr	89
Type 317 stainless steel	Chemical processing; field or plant test; no aeration; rapid agitation. Sodium sulfate saturated slurry, plus 1% zinc sulfate, sodium hydroxide, pH 8.5-9, evaporator	Saturated	110 (230)	193 d	0.0001 in./yr	89
Type 410 stainless steel	...	10	21 (70)	...	Fair	121
Type 410 stainless steel	...	...	Room	...	Practically unattacked	121
Type 430 stainless steel	...	10	21 (70)	...	Good	121
Coppers						
Ampco 8, aluminum bronze	Generally suitable	...	...	...	<0.05 (<2)	96
Titanium						
Titanium		10-20	Boiling	...	nil	90
Titanium	...	Saturated	Room	...	nil	90
Titanium	...	10	Boiling	...	nil	33
Titanium	Grade 7; pH 1					
Heat- and corrosion-resistant alloys						
Incoloy 800	Solutions were prepared with reagent-grade chemicals. Test specimens were cold-rolled, annealed sheet, 2.84 mm (0.112 in.) thick. No pitting	5	80 (176)	7 d	nil	44
Incoloy 800	Solutions were prepared with reagent-grade chemicals. Test specimens were cold-rolled, annealed sheet, 2.84 mm (0.112 in.) thick. No pitting	10	80 (176)	7 d	<0.003 (<0.1)	44
Inconel 601	...	5	80 (176)	7 d	nil	64
Inconel 601	...	10	80 (176)	7 d	<0.002 (<0.1)	64
Inconel 690	...	5	80 (176)	...	<0.03 (<1)	57
Inconel 690	...	10	80 (176)	...	<0.03 (<1)	57
Zirconium						
Zr702	...	0-20	Room to 100 (room to 212)	...	<0.05 (<2)	15
Lead, tin, and zinc						
Lead	...	Saturated	24 (75)	...	0.025 (1)	49
Lead	Negligible corrosion; Pb recommended for use	2-20	24 (75)	...	<50 μm/yr (<2)	95
Tin	...	...	20 (68)	...	Resistant	94
Tin	...	...	60 (140)	...	Unsuitable	94
Tin	...	...	100 (212)	...	Unsuitable	94
Noble metals						
Platinum	...	All	Boiling	...	<0.05 (<2)	5
Silver	...	All	Boiling	...	<0.05 (<2)	9
Others						
Magnesium alloy AZ61A	Specimen size, 75 x 25 x 1.5 mm (3 x 1 x 0.06 in.); surface preparation, HNO$_3$ pickling; volume of testing solution, 100 ml. Specimens were alternately immersed 30 s in solution and held 2 min in air	3	35 (95)	7 d	0.8 g/m^2/d (0.5 mg/in.^{2}/d)	12

Weight Loss and Corrosion Product Analysis After 120-h Exposure of Aluminum in Sodium Sulfate Solutions

Na$_2$SO$_4$ (Molarity)	p (atm)	Al Solution (μg·cm^{-2})	Corrosion Product Analysis				Al Total Dissolution (μg·cm^{-2})
			Al^{+++} (μg·cm^{-2})	Na$^+$ (μg·cm^{-2})	SO$_4^{--}$ (μg·cm^{-2})	X-ray Diffractometry	
10^{-2}	1	157 ± 10	92 ± 8	8.5 ± 0.3	22 ± 2.0	Al$_{10}$O$_{15}$·H$_2$O (22-1119) Al(OH)$_3$ (7-324)	249 ± 12
	300	210 ± 18	76 ± 7	3.0 ± 0.2	5.7 ± 0.3	5Al$_2$O$_3$·H$_2$O (15-740)	286 ± 19
5 × 10^{-2}	1	88 ± 7	71 ± 6	4.1 ± 0.3	5.1 ± 0.4	α Al$_2$O$_3$ (10-173) Al(OH)$_3$ (20-11)	159 ± 9
	300	50 ± 6	80 ± 8	3.0 ± 0.2	6.8 ± 0.4	α Al$_2$O$_3$ (10-173)	130 ± 10
10^{-1}	1	35 ± 4	69 ± 7	3.4 ± 0.2	1.7 ± 0.3	α Al$_2$O$_3$ (10-173) Al$_{10}$O$_{15}$·H$_2$O (22-1119)	104 ± 8
	300	19 ± 3	97 ± 10	1.2 ± 0.1	2.1 ± 0.2	α Al$_2$O$_3$ (10-173)	116 ± 10
Not corroded	—	—	0.5 ± 0.1	—	—		

Source: A.M. Beccaria and G. Poggi, "Aluminum Corrosion in Slightly Alkaline Sodium Sulfate Solutions at Different Hydrocaustic Pressures," *Corrosion*, Vol 43, Mar 1987, 154.

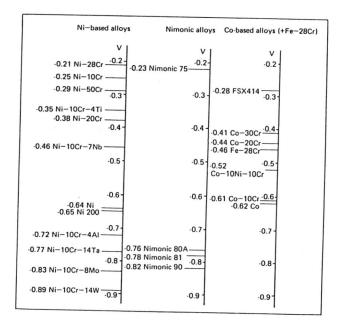

Various alloys. Half-immersion tests: galvanic series in equimolar Na$_2$SO$_4$/NaCl melts at 700 °C (against a Pt wire reference electrode). Source: P.D.W. Bottomley, J.L. Dawson, *et al.*, "Semi-immersed Galvanic Series in Na$_2$SO$_4$/NaCl Melts and a Comparison with Full-Immersion Potentials," *High Temperature Technology*, Vol 4, Feb 1986, 37-45.

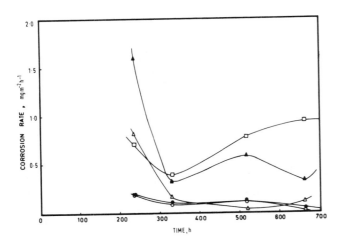

Carbon steel. Variation with time of corrosion rate of carbon steel in 0.76 g/L Ca(OH)$_2$ solutions containing various concentrations of Na$_2$SO$_4$. Source: A.P. Akolzin, P. Ghosh, *et al.*, "Application and Peculiarity of Ca(OH)$_2$ as Inhibitor in Presence of Corrosion Activators," *British Corrosion Journal*, Vol 20, Jan 1985, 34.

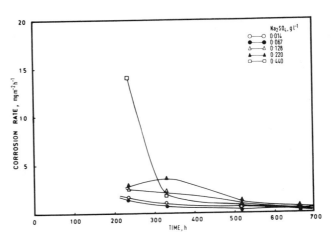

Carbon steel. Variation with time of corrosion rate of carbon steel in 0.43 g/L Ca(OH)$_2$ solutions containing various concentrations of Na$_2$SO$_4$. Source: A.P. Akolzin, P. Ghosh, *et al.*, "Application and Peculiarity of Ca(OH)$_2$ as Inhibitor in Presence of Corrosion Activators," *British Corrosion Journal*, Vol 20, Jan 1985, 34.

Sodium Sulfide

Sodium sulfide, Na$_2$S, also known as sodium sulfuret, is an irritating, water-soluble, yellowish to reddish, deliquescent powder that melts at 1180 °C. Sodium sulfide is used as a chemical intermediate and solvent, in conversion of wood into paper pulp, as a photographic and analytical reagent, as a source of sulfide, as a reducing agent, in organic reactions, as a depilatory, and in sheep dips.

Material Summaries

The following material summaries were compiled from a survey of the available literature. Inclusion of a material description under a given environment does not imply that it is the most appropriate material for corrosion service in that environment. Likewise, exclusion of a given material does not imply that it is not suitable for corrosion service applications in that environment.

Aluminum. Solid sodium sulfide was very corrosive to 3003 and 5154 alloys in laboratory tests conducted under conditions of 100% relative humidity at ambient temperature.

Additional Reading

D. Moll, Vasquez, R.C. Salvarezza, H.A. Videla, and A.J. Arvia, Localized Corrosion of Mild Steel in Base Solutions Containing Sodium Sulfide. Influence of pH and Sodium Acetate Addition, *Corrosion*, 40(8), 414-417, 1984. MetAbs No. 84-352699. **Abstract:** Mild steel (1020 SAE steel) specimens in alkaline solutions containing 10^{-2} M sodium sulfide subjected to a slow potential sweep show no pitting at pH greater than 12.0. Conversely, if the pH is lowered by the addition of acetic acid, pitting corrosion and the simultaneous formation of ferrous sulfide are observed when the potential is raised above the breakdown potential. The role played by sulfide, hydroxyl and acetate ions in solution to explain pit initiation and growth on mild steel is presented.

P.P. Corso Jr., R.M. German, and H.D. Simmons Jr., Tarnish Evaluation of Gold-Based Dental Alloys, *J. Dent. Res.*, 64(5), 848-853, 1985. MetAbs No. 85-351469. **Abstract:** Three commercial Au dental alloys and three ternary (Au-Ag-Cu) alloys of constant nobility were subjected to a standardized test battery for tarnish. The tests included sodium sulfide and artificial saliva solutions, both at 37 °C, in sealed containers. Quantitative measurements of tarnish were made from the alloy color change during a three-day exposure.

L. Niemi and H. Hero, Structure, Corrosion, and Tarnishing of Ag-Pd-Cu Alloys, *J. Dent. Res.*, 64(9), 1163-1169, 1985. MetAbs No. 85-352099. **Abstract:** The structure of Ag-Pd-Cu-Au-Zn alloys can be expected to have an influence on their corrosion and tarnish resistance. Four experimental Ag-base alloys (I-IV) with varying Pd/Ag ratios were studied by scanning electron microscopy, microprobe analyses, and X-ray diffraction analyses.

E. Suoninen, H. Hero, and E. Minni, Effect of Palladium on Sulfide Tarnishing of Noble Metal Alloys, *J. Biomed. Mater. Res.*, 19(8), 917-934, 1985. MetAbs No. 86-350166. **Abstract:** Electron spectroscopic studies of Au-Ag-Cu alloys of the type used for dental castings show that small additions (<3 wt%) of Pd reduce the thickness of the sulfide layer formed on surfaces of samples treated in aqueous Na$_2$S solutions.

N.B. De Cristofaro, C.A. Acosta, R.C. Salvarezza, and H.A. Videla, The Effect of Sulfides on the Electrochemical Behavior of AISI 304 Stainless Steel in Neutral Buffered Solutions, *Corrosion*, 42(4), 240-242, 1986. MetAbs No. 86-351333. **Abstract:** The electrochemical behavior of AISI 304 in buffered neutral media containing sodium sulfide and mixtures of sodium chloride and sodium sulfide is studied using potentiodynamic techniques complemented with scanning electron microscopy and energy dispersive X-ray analysis to obtain information on the pitting process of the metal.

Corrosion Behavior of Various Metals and Alloys in Sodium Sulfide

Material	Condition, other factors, comments	Concentration, %	Temperature, °C (°F)	Duration	Corrosion rate, mm/yr (mils/yr) or other	Ref
Stainless steels						
Type 304 stainless steel	Chemical processing; field or pilot plant test; no aeration; rapid agitation. Evaporator	10	85 (185)	21 d	0.0005 in./yr	89
Type 304 stainless steel	Chemical processing; field or pilot plant test; no aeration; rapid agitation. With carbon over the standard maximum. Evaporator	10	85 (185)	21 d	0.0001 in./yr	89
Type 304 stainless steel	Chemical processing; field or pilot plant test; no aeration; rapid agitation. Evaporator, vapors	15	85 (185)	30 d	0.0001 in./yr	89
Type 304 stainless steel	Chemical processing; field or pilot plant test; no aeration; rapid agitation. With carbon over the standard maximum. Evaporator, vapors	15	85 (185)	30 d	0.0001 in./yr	89
Type 304 stainless steel	(a)	30	54 (130)	...	0.230 (9.1)	19
Type 304 stainless steel	Chemical processing; field or pilot plant test; no aeration; rapid agitation. Evaporator, vapors	30	124 (255)	30 d	0.0075 in./yr	89
Type 304 stainless steel	(a)	40	Boiling	...	0.038 (1.5)	19
Type 304 stainless steel	Chemical processing; field or pilot plant test; no aeration; slight to moderate agitation. Concentration 40% initially, 45% sodium hydrosulfide final concentration	40	90 (194)	160 d	0.0026 in./yr	89
Type 304 stainless steel	Chemical processing; field or pilot plant test; no aeration; no agitation	60	171 (340)	28 d	0.036 in./yr	89
Type 316 stainless steel	Chemical processing; field or pilot plant test; no aeration; rapid agitation. Evaporator	10	85 (185)	21 d	0.0001 in./yr	89
Type 316 stainless steel	(a)	30	54 (130)	...	0.530 (21)	19
Type 316 stainless steel	(a)	40	Boiling	...	0.064 (2.5)	19
Type 316 stainless steel	Chemical processing; field or pilot plant test; no aeration; slight to moderate agitation. Concentration 40% initially, 45 % sodium hydrosulfide final concentration	40	90 (194)	160 d	0.0039 in./yr	89
Type 316 stainless steel	Chemical processing; field or pilot plant test; no aeration; no agitation	60	171 (340)	28 d	0.038 in./yr	89
Type 317 stainless steel	Chemical processing; field or pilot plant test; no aeration; rapid agitation. Evaporator, vapors	15	85 (185)	30 d	0.0001 in./yr	89
Type 317 stainless steel	Chemical processing; field or pilot plant test; no aeration; rapid agitation. Evaporator, vapors	30	124 (255)	30 d	0.019 in./yr	89
Type 410 stainless steel	...	...	Room	...	Unattacked	121
Coppers						
70-30 cupronickel	(b)	...	...	...	Good	93
90-10 cupronickel	...	...	...	...	Fair	93
Admiralty brass	(b)	...	...	...	Good	93
Aluminum bronze	...	...	...	...	Fair	93
Ampco 8, aluminum bronze	Generally not suitable	...	...	...	>0.5 (>20)	96
Architectural bronze	(b)	...	...	...	Good	93
Brass	(b)	...	...	...	Good	93
Cartridge brass	(b)	...	...	...	Good	93
Commercial bronze	...	...	...	...	Good	93
Electrolytic copper	...	...	...	...	Fair	93
Free-cutting brass	(b)	...	...	...	Fair	93
Muntz metal	(b)	...	...	...	Good	93
Naval brass	(b)	...	...	...	Good	93
Nickel silver	(b)	...	...	...	Good	93
Phosphor bronze	5% Sn	18	...	...	Good	93
Phosphor bronze	8% Sn	...	...	...	Fair	93
Phosphor copper	...	...	...	...	Fair	93
Red brass	...	...	...	...	Fair	93
Silicon bronze	Low	...	...	...	Fair	93
Silicon bronze	High	...	...	...	Fair	93
Titanium						
Titanium	...	10	Boiling	...	0.027 (1.08)	90
Titanium	...	Saturated	Room	...	nil	90

(Continued)

Corrosion Behavior of Various Metals and Alloys in Sodium Sulfide (Continued)

Material	Condition, other factors, comments	Concentration, %	Temperature, °C (°F)	Duration	Corrosion rate, mm/yr (mils/yr) or other	Ref
Heat- and corrosion-resistant alloys						
Carpenter 20	Chemical processing; field or pilot plant test; no aeration; slight to moderate agitation. Concentration 40% initially, 45% sodium hydrosulfide final concentration	40	90 (194)	160 d	0.0015 in./yr	89
Carpenter 20	Chemical processing; field or pilot plant test; no aeration; no agitation; cast specimens	60	171 (340)	28 d	0.081 in./yr	89
Alloy 825	Chemical processing; field or pilot plant test; no aeration; slight to moderate agitation. Concentration 40% initially, 45% sodium hydrosulfide final concentration	40	90 (194)	160 d	0.0005 in./yr	89
Zirconium						
Zr702	...	33	Boiling	...	nil	15
Zr705	...	33	Boiling	...	nil	15
Lead, tin, and zinc						
Lead	...	10	24 (75)	...	0.025 (1)	49
Tin	...	...	20 (68)	...	Unsuitable	94
Tin	...	...	60 (140)	...	Unsuitable	94
Tin	...	...	100 (212)	...	Unsuitable	94
Noble metals						
Platinum	...	All	Boiling	...	<0.05 (<2)	5
Platinum	Melt	...	700 (1290)	...	<0.05 (<2)	5
Silver	...	All	Room	...	Slight attack	9
Others						
Magnesium	...	3	Room	...	Suitable	119

(a) Annealed. All solutions from CP chemicals. Tests made in the laboratory. (b) May be considered in place of a copper metal when some property, other than corrosion resistance, governs its use.

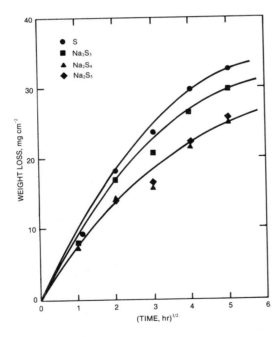

Nickel. Corrosion behavior of nickel plotted as weight loss due to corrosion vs. the square root of the time of corrosion at 350 °C. Source: A.P. Brown and J.E. Battles, Corrosion of Nickel-200 and AISI-1008 Steel in Sodium Polysulfides and Sulfur at 350 °C, *Journal of the Electrochemical Society*, Vol 133, July 1986, 1322.

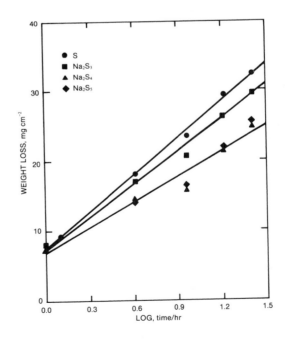

Nickel. Corrosion behavior of nickel plotted as weight loss vs. the logarithm of time at 350 °C. Source: A.P. Brown and J.E. Battles, Corrosion of Nickel-200 and AISI-1008 Steel in Sodium Polysulfides and Sulfur at 350 °C, *Journal of the Electrochemical Society*, Vol 133, July 1986, 1323.

Sodium Sulfite

Sodium sulfite, Na_2SO_3, is a white, water-soluble, crystalline solid with a sulfurous, salty taste. It decomposes when heated. Sodium sulfite is used as a source of sulfite, as a chemical intermediate and food preservative, in medicine and paper manufacturing, in photographic developing, and as a bleaching agent in the textile industry. Most boiler operators use sodium sulfite for chemical scavenging of oxygen in the feedwater. Because it decomposes into acidic gases at the high temperatures that accompany high pressures, sodium sulfite should not be used for this purpose at pressures above 122 atm (12.4 MPa, or 1.8 ksi).

Material Summaries

The following material summaries were compiled from a survey of the available literature. Inclusion of a material description under a given environment does not imply that it is the most appropriate material for corrosion service in that environment. Likewise, exclusion of a given material does not imply that it is not suitable for corrosion service applications in that environment.

Aluminum. In laboratory tests conducted at 100% relative humidity and ambient temperature, aluminum alloys 3003 and 5154 resisted solid sodium sulfite. Alloy 1100 resisted aqueous solutions (0.1 to 15%) of sodium sulfite in tests run at ambient temperature.

Corrosion Behavior of Various Metals and Alloys in Sodium Sulfite

Material	Condition, other factors, comments	Concen-tration, %	Temperature, °C (°F)	Duration	Corrosion rate, mm/yr (mils/yr) or other	Ref
Stainless steels						
AM-363 stainless steel	...	...	Room	...	Unattacked	120
Type 304 stainless steel	Pulp and paper processing; field or pilot plant test; no aeration; no agitation. Plus sodium bicarbonate, pH 7.5	~6.84	24 (75)	28 d	<0.0001 in./yr	89
Type 304 stainless steel	Tanning; field or pilot plant test; rapid agitation; with carbon over the standard maximum. Plus organic acids, sulfurous acid, tannins (under false bottom of quebracho bisulfiting tank)	3	...	180 d	0.0001 in./yr	89
Type 316 stainless steel	Tanning; field or pilot plant test; rapid agitation. Plus organic acids, sulfurous acid, tannins (under false bottom of quebracho bisulfiting tank)	3	...	180 d	0.0001 in./yr	89
Type 316 stainless steel	Pulp and paper processing; field or pilot plant test; no aeration; no agitation. Plus sodium bicarbonate, pH 7.5	~6.84	24 (75)	28 d	<0.0001 in./yr	89
Type 410 stainless steel	...	...	Room	...	Unattacked	121
Type 410 stainless steel	...	Saturated	Room	...	Unattacked	121
Aluminum						
Aluminum (99.0-99.5%)	Solution	...	20 (68)	...	Excellent	92
Aluminum-manganese alloys	Solution	...	20 (68)	...	Excellent	92
Coppers						
70-30 cupronickel	(a)	...	...	...	Good	93
90-10 cupronickel	(a)	...	...	...	Good	93
Admiralty brass	(a)	...	...	...	Good	93
Aluminum bronze	(a)	...	...	...	Good	93
Architectural bronze	...	...	...	...	Not suitable	93
Brass	(a)	...	...	...	Good	93
Cartridge brass	...	...	...	...	Not suitable	93
Commercial bronze	(a)	...	...	...	Good	93
Electrolytic copper	(a)	...	...	...	Good	93
Free-cutting brass	...	...	...	...	Not suitable	93
Muntz metal	...	...	...	...	Not suitable	93
Naval brass	...	...	...	...	Not suitable	93
Nickel silver	(a)	18	...	...	Good	93
Phosphor bronze	5% Sn. (a)	...	...	...	Good	93
Phosphor bronze	8% Sn. (a)	...	...	...	Good	93
Phosphor copper	(a)	...	...	...	Good	93
Red brass	(a)	...	...	...	Good	93
Silicon bronze	Low. (a)	...	...	...	Good	93
Silicon bronze	High. (a)	...	...	...	Good	93

(Continued)

Corrosion Behavior of Various Metals and Alloys in Sodium Sulfite (Continued)

Material	Condition, other factors, comments	Concentration, %	Temperature, °C (°F)	Duration	Corrosion rate, mm/yr (mils/yr) or other	Ref
Titanium						
Titanium	...	Saturated	Boiling	...	nil	90
Zirconium						
Zr705	...	10	Boiling	...	Weight gain	62
Noble metals						
Platinum	...	All	Boiling	...	<0.05 (<2)	5
Others						
Magnesium alloy AZ61A	Specimen size, 75 x 25 x 1.5 mm (3 x 1 x 0.06 in.); surface preparation, HNO_3 pickling; volume of testing solution, 100 ml. Specimens were alternately immersed 30 s in solution and held 2 min in air.	3	35 (95)	7 d	0.2 g/m^2/d (0.1 mg/in.^{2}/d)	12

(a) May be considered in place of a copper metal when some property, other than corrosion resistance, governs its use.

Sodium Thiosulfate

Sodium thiosulfate, $Na_2S_2O_3 \cdot 5H_2O$, also known as sodium hyposulfite, hypo, and sodium subsulfite, is a white crystalline solid that has a melting point of 48 °C (118 °F). Water soluble, it is used as a fixing agent for photographic films, plates, and papers. Sodium thiosulfate is used in medicine, as a germicide, in manufacturing leather, as a mordant in dyeing, and for extracting silver from ore.

Additional Reading

R. Bandy and R.L. Sabatini, Relationship Between Chromium Depletion in Sensitized Alloy 600 and U-Bend Cracking in Sodium Thiosulfate Solution, *Corrosion, 41*(4), 242-244, 1985. MetAbs No. 85-351438. **Abstract:** The U-bend cracking of sensitized Inconel 600 in sodium thiosulfate solution was investigated.

Corrosion Behavior of Various Metals and Alloys in Sodium Thiosulfate

Material	Condition, other factors, comments	Concentration, %	Temperature °C (°F)	Duration	Corrosion rate, mm/yr (mils/yr) or other	Ref
Aluminum						
Aluminum (99.0-99.5%)	Solution	...	20 (68)	...	Excellent	92
Coppers						
70-30 cupronickel	(a)	...	...	...	Good	93
90-10 cupronickel	...	...	...	...	Fair	93
Admiralty brass	(a)	...	...	...	Good	93
Aluminum bronze	...	...	...	...	Fair	93
Architectural bronze	(a)	...	...	...	Good	93
Brass	(a)	...	...	...	Good	93
Cartridge brass	(a)	...	...	...	Good	93
Commercial bronze	...	...	...	...	Fair	93
Electrolytic copper	...	...	...	...	Fair	93
Free-cutting brass	(a)	...	...	...	Good	93
Muntz metal	(a)	...	...	...	Good	93
Naval brass	(a)	...	...	...	Good	93
Nickel silver	(a)	18	...	...	Good	93
Phosphor bronze	5% Sn	...	...	...	Fair	93
Phosphor bronze	8% Sn	...	...	...	Fair	93
Phosphor copper	...	...	...	...	Fair	93
Red brass	...	...	...	...	Fair	93

(Continued)

Corrosion Behavior of Various Metals and Alloys in Sodium Thiosulfate (Continued)

Material	Condition, other factors, comments	Concen-tration, %	Temperature °C (°F)	Duration	Corrosion rate, mm/yr (mils/yr) or other	Ref
Silicon bronze	Low	...	...	...	Fair	93
Silicon bronze	High	...	...	...	Fair	93
Titanium						
Titanium	...	25	Boiling	...	nil	90
Titanium	Plus 20% $CH_3 \cdot COOH$	20	Room	...	nil	90
Noble metals						
Platinum	...	All	Boiling	...	<0.05 (<2)	5
Silver	...	All	Room	...	<0.05 (<2)	9

(a) May be considered in place of a copper metal when some property, other than corrosion resistance, governs its use.

Steam

The corrosive properties of the steam that will be used in a plant are seldom considered, particularly if the steam will be supplied by a public utility or power plant in which boiler water treatment is sufficient to prevent condensate corrosion. However, the impurities in steam can cause corrosion problems.

At one site, for example, high-pressure steam was purchased from a central power station, and there were no problems for 15 years. Within a few months after routine work, however, cracks and resulting leaks appeared adjacent to and across the welded joints in the new piping. Metallographic examination showed that the cracking was the result of caustic embrittlement. The deionized water contained 10 ppm sodium, which formed concentrated sodium hydroxide (NaOH) as the water evaporated. The older piping did not crack, because it had been stress relieved by the superheated steam over a period of years before cooling of the steam was initiated.

In the majority of cases, it is not necessary to treat steam condensate before it is reused, and boiler feedwater is prepared simply by adding makeup water to the condensate. However, condensate is sometimes contaminated by corrosion products or by the leaking in of cooling water or other undesirable substances. In such cases, the corrosion must be reduced, or the unwanted contaminants removed, before the condensate can be recycled. When steam contains acidic gases such as carbon dioxide and oxygen, its condensate will be acidic and as a result will cause corrosion of metal surfaces.

Material Summaries

The following material summaries were compiled from a survey of the available literature. Inclusion of a material description under a given environment does not imply that it is the most appropriate material for corrosion service in that environment. Likewise, exclusion of a given material does not imply that it is not suitable for corrosion service applications in that environment.

Copper. Copper and copper alloys resist attack by pure steam, but if much carbon dioxide, oxygen, or ammonia is present, the condensate is corrosive. Even though wet steam at high velocities can cause severe impingement attack, copper alloys are used extensively in condensers and heat exchangers. Copper alloys are also used for feedwater heaters, although their use in such applications is somewhat limited because of their rapid decline in strength and creep resistance at moderately elevated temperatures. Copper nickels are the preferred copper alloys for the higher temperatures and pressures.

Use of copper in systems handling hot water and steam is limited by the working pressures of tubes and joints. A few copper alloys have shown a tendency to fail by stress-corrosion cracking when they are highly stressed and exposed to steam. Alpha aluminum bronzes that do not contain tin are among the alloys susceptible to this type of failure. Copper-silicon alloys, which generally have the same corrosion resistance as copper, appear to be much more resistant to stress-corrosion cracking than the common brasses. Silicon bronzes are susceptible to embrittlement by high-pressure steam and should be tested for suitability in the service environment before being specified for components to be used at elevated temperature.

Steam condensate that has been properly treated so that it is relatively free of gases, as in a power-generating station, is relatively noncorrosive to copper and copper alloys. Rates of attack in such exposures are less than 2.5 μm/yr (0.1 mil/yr). Copper and its alloys are not attacked by condensate that contains a significant amount of oil, such as condensate from a reciprocating steam engine.

Dissolved carbon dioxide, oxygen, or both significantly increase the rate of attack. For example, condensate with 4.6 ppm oxygen, and 14 ppm carbon dioxide, and a pH of 5.5 at 68 °C (155 °F) caused an average penetration of 175 to 350 μm/yr (6.9 to 13.8 mils/yr) when in contact with C12200 (phosphorus-deoxidized copper), C14200 (arsenical copper), C23000 (red brass), C44300 to C44500 (admiralty metal), and C71000 (copper nickel, 20%). Steel tested under the same conditions was penetrated at about twice the rate given for the copper alloys listed above, but tin-coated copper proved to be much more resistant and was attacked at a rate of less than 25 μm/yr (1 mil/yr). To attain the optimum service life in condensate systems, it is necessary to ensure that the tubes are installed with enough slope to allow proper drainage, to reduce the quantity of corrosive gases (usually carbon dioxide and oxygen) at the source by mechanical or chemical treatment of the feedwater, or to treat the steam chemically.

Modern power utility boiler feedwater treatments commonly include the addition of organic amines and oxygen scavengers to inhibit the corrosion of iron components in the system by scavenging oxygen and increasing the pH of the feedwater. Chemicals, such as morpholine and hydrazine, decompose in service to yield ammonia, which can be quite corrosive toward some copper alloys. In the main body of well-monitored operating condensers, oxygen and ammonia levels are quite low, and corrosion is usually mild. More aggressive conditions exist in the air removal section. Abnormal operating conditions, tube leakage, and shutdown-startup cycles may also increase the corrosivity of the steam-side environment by raising the oxygen concentration. Laboratory corrosion tests were performed on a number of copper alloys and on low-carbon steel in both aerated (8 to 12 ppm oxygen) and deaerated (100 to 200 ppb oxygen) ammonia solutions. In these tests, ammonia enhanced the corrosion resistance of the copper-nickel alloys, modifying surface oxides by increasing nickel content. Elevated oxygen levels are generally more deleterious than elevated ammonia levels. However, C71500 was minimally affected by the elevated oxygen content.

Nickel. The nickel-chromium-iron alloys are very popular materials for critical applications in pressurized and boiling water reactors, because of their excellent corrosion resistance in steam and water environments and because of their resistance to chloride stress-corrosion cracking. The age-hardenable alloy Inconel X-750 is used as a spring material for fuel pellet hold-down springs, fuel element divider plates, and reactor scram springs, and for bolting. Another age-hardenable alloy, Inconel 718, because of its high strength and spring characteristics, is also used for fuel assembly divider plates. It also has demonstrated excellent wear resistance in sodium fast breeder reactor environments.

In steam-hot water systems such as condensers, appreciable corrosion of Nickel 200 and Monel 400 may occur if noncondensables (carbon dioxide and air) in the steam exist in certain proportions. Deaeration of the feedwater or venting of the noncondensable gases will prevent this attack.

The single most significant application of nickel-base alloys in the nuclear industry has been the use of Inconel 600 for steam generator tubing in pressurized water reactors. Inconel 600 is resistant to all mixtures of steam, air, and carbon dioxide and thus is particularly useful in contact with steam at high temperatures. An alternative material for this application is Inconel 690.

Silver. Silver is resistant to corrosion attack by steam at temperatures up to 600 °C (1110 °F).

Tantalum. No failures caused by exposure of tantalum to steam condensate have ever been recorded. Tantalum is used in many cases at saturated steam pressures above 1035 kPa (150 psi) at temperatures of 185 °C (365 °F) and is considered resistant to saturated steam below 250 °C (480 °F) at a pressure of 3.9 MPa (560 psi). In addition, although few published data have been found on the attack of steam on tantalum at high temperatures, it is known from industrial practice that tantalum is not affected adversely when heated with steam at pressures to 1380 kPa (200 psig), corresponding to a temperature of 200 °C (390 °F). It has been reported that at temperatures above 1125 °C (2240 °F) water is decomposed by tantalum, with adsorption of oxygen by the metal and evolution of hydrogen. At 925 °C (1700 °F) and lower temperatures, the reaction is negligibly slow.

Titanium. Extensive erosion-corrosion testing of titanium alloys Ti-6Al-4V, Ti-5Al-2.5Sn, and Ti-7Al-4Mo has been conducted in high-velocity wet steam environments for application in low-pressure steam turbine blading in power plants. These alloys have demonstrated superior resistance to type 403 stainless steel (12 to 13% Cr steel) in operating turbines and in water droplet erosion and water jet impingement tests. Full erosion resistance of Ti-6Al-4V blades to velocities of 440 to 530 m/s (1450 to 1740 ft/s) at 10% steam moisture has been noted in turbines. In fact, these studies suggest useful erosion resistance of Ti-6Al-4V in approximately 8% steam moisture up to 549 m/s (1800 ft/s) and in 11% steam moisture up to 488 m/s (1600 ft/s). Single-shot water jet impingement testing has shown that annealed Ti-7Al-4Mo alloy is significantly more erosion resistant than 12% Cr steel, type 303 stainless steel, or Stellite alloy 6 at jet velocities of 610 and 915 m/s (2000 and 3000 ft/s).

Zirconium. Corrosion and oxidation of unalloyed zirconium in water and steam are reported to be irregular. This behavior is probably caused by variations in the impurity content in the metal. Nitrogen and carbon impurities are particularly harmful. The corrosion rate of zirconium increases markedly when nitrogen and carbon concentrations exceed 40 and 300 ppm, respectively.

The irregular corrosion behavior of unalloyed zirconium can be seen in the curves for corrosion at 315 and 360 °C (600 and 680 °F). The data for corrosion resistance at 315 °C (600 °F) must be plotted as a band because there is too much scatter in the data. The curve at 360 °C (680 °F) has three bands extending upward from it; each band represents a change in corrosion rate from the basic rate indicated by the single line and represents data from a different set of test specimens.

Zircaloy-2, Zircaloy-4, Zr-2.5Nb, and Zr-1Nb are the most important alloys used in water-cooled nuclear reactors, because they have the most reliable corrosion resistance in high-temperature water and steam. Zircaloy-2 is superior to unalloyed zirconium in high-temperature water and steam.

Zircaloy-4 differs in composition from Zircaloy-2 only in having no nickel and a slightly greater iron content. Both variations are intended to reduce hydrogen pickup in reactor operation. The corrosion behavior of Zircaloy-4 is very similar to that of Zircaloy-2. However, hydrogen pickup for Zircaloy-4 is significantly lower, particularly when the alloy is exposed to water at 360 °C (680 °F). At this temperature, hydrogen pickup for Zircaloy-4 is about 25% of theoretical, or less than half that for Zircaloy-2. In addition, hydrogen pickup for Zircaloy-4 is less sensitive to hydrogen overpressure than that for Zircaloy-2. For both Zircaloys, hydrogen pickup is markedly decreased when dissolved oxygen is present in the corrosion medium.

Alloy Zr-2.5Nb is considered to be somewhat less resistant to corrosion than the Zircaloys. Nevertheless, Zr-2.5Nb is acceptable for many applications. An example is the use of Zr-2.5Nb pressure tubes in the primary loops of some reactors. The corrosion resistance of Zr-2.5Nb can be substantially improved by heat treatment. Also, Zr-2.5Nb is superior to Zircaloys in steam at temperatures above 400 °C (750 °F).

Hafnium. The resistance of hafnium to corrosion by steam is superior to that of zirconium and Zircaloy alloys.

Additional Reading

G.P. Airey and F.W. Pement, A Comparison of Intergranular Attack in Inconel Alloy 600 Observed in the Laboratory and in Operating Steam Generators, *Corrosion*, 39(2), 46-55, 1983. MetAbs No. 83-351055. **Abstract:** Intergranular attack has been observed in Inconel 600 tubing on the hot leg of some operating steam generators. Attack has also been reproduced in the laboratory in high-temperature (316 to 343 °C) sodium hydroxide solutions and environments containing sulfur compounds such as polythionic acid and sodium tetrathionate. The degradation morphology and associated chemical species were compared in tubing from two steam generators and tubing exposed to the above laboratory environments.

R.K. Conrad, J.P. Carter, and S.D. Cramer, "Corrosion of Selected Metals and a High-Temperature Thermoplastic in Hypersaline Geothermal Brine," U.S. Department of Interior, Bureau of Mines, 1983. MetAbs No. 83-352445. **Abstract:** Corrosion research has been conducted to determine suitable construction materials for geothermal resource recovery plants. Weight loss, pitting and crevice corrosion, U-bend stress corrosion and electrochemical polarization measurements were made on selected metals in brine and steam.

S.J. Lennon, F.P.A. Robinson, and G.G. Garrett, The Influence of Applied Stress and Surface Finish on the Pitting Susceptibility of Low-Alloy Turbine Disk Steels in Wet Steam, *Corrosion*, 40(8), 409-413, 1984. MetAbs No. 84-352698. **Abstract:** The effects of applied tensile and compressive stresses and surface finish on the pitting susceptibility, and hence stress-corrosion crack initiation, of 34CrNiMo6 and 26NiCr-MoV145 steam turbine disk steels were studied. In an attempt to simulate actual conditions, all tests were conducted in an aerated wet steam environment.

G.P. Sheldon and N.W. Polan, Field Testing of Power Utility Condenser Tube Alloys, *J. Mater. Energy Syst.*, 6(4), 313-319, 1985. MetAbs No. 85-351443. **Abstract:** The performances of various Cu alloys (C71500, C70600, C19400, C443) after four years exposure in condenser stream-side and cooling water environments of three operating power utility plants are described.

C. Buchalet, Framatome's Continuous Efforts to Improve Steam Generator Corrosion Resistance, *Nucl. Eng. Des.*, 86(3), 341-344, 1985. MetAbs No. 85-352065. **Abstract:** Corrosion of steam generator tubes has been observed in a large number of operating steam generators, especially in the United States. Construction of the French PWR nuclear program started in the early 1970s. Modifications have been made on the first units to improve steam generator resistance to corrosion. These developments are discussed.

Some Features of Zircaloy Behavior in Nodular Corrosion, *J. Nucl. Mater.*, 132(3), 291-292, 1985. MetAbs No. 85-352110. **Abstract:** The nodular corrosion behavior of Zircaloy is evaluated in high-temperature steam. Most common tests parameters used are 500 °C, 24 h and 10.2 MPa.

F. Abe, H. Araki, H. Yoshida, and M. Okada, Corrosion Behavior of Nickel Base Heat Resisting Alloys for Nuclear Steelmaking System in High-Temperature Steam, *Trans. Iron Steel Inst. Jpn.*, 25(5), 424-432, 1985. MetAbs No. 86-350256. **Abstract:** The corrosion behavior of nickel-base heat-resisting alloys is investigated in steam at 800 °C and 40 atm, simulating the superheated steam of the nuclear steelmaking system. The alloys tested are five new alloys developed for the nuclear steelmaking system and Inconel 617.

K.-Y. Huang and C.-H. Tsai, The Effect of Heat Treatment on the Microstructure and the Corrosion Resistance of Zircaloy-4 in 450 °C Steam, *J. Nucl. Mater.*, 136(1), 16-29, 1985. MetAbs No. 86-350381. **Abstract:** The effect of beta treatment and the subsequent cold work and alpha annealing on the microstructure and corrosion resistance of Zircaloy-4 in 450 °C steam was investigated.

J.C. Thrackray, Progress Report on Sea-Cure Tubing, *Stainless Steel Ind.*, 14(78), 4-5, 1986. MetAbs No. 86-351629. **Abstract:** Sea-Cure (27.5% Cr, 3.4% Mo, 1.7% Ni ferritic stainless steel stabilized with 0.5% Ti) tubing was developed and has proved highly successful for use in steam surface condensers. Mechanical and physical properties that make it applicable for use in feedwater heaters and other heat exchangers are described.

R. Kuwae, T. Hatanaka, J. Kawashima, and S. Shima, Hafnium Corrosion Behavior in High-Temperature Steam, *J. Nucl. Mater.*, 139(1), 42-47, 1986. MetAbs No. 86-351688. **Abstract:** Corrosion properties for three Hf alloys have been examined in 10.5 MPa steam at 773 K.

A.J. Sedriks, Corrosion of Nickel Alloys, in *Encyclopedia of Materials Science and Engineering*, Vol 2, Pergamon Press, Oxford, 1986. MetAbs No. 86-351945. **Abstract:** Nickel alloys are important corrosion-resistant materials in aggressive environments and are indicated to replace aluminium alloys and stainless steels as service temperature or environmental corrosivity increases. The largest family of Ni alloys is that based on the Ni-Cr system, with Inconel alloy 600 at 15% Cr being the prototype. These alloys are discussed.

P.A. Coulon, Erosion-Corrosion in Steam Turbines. II. A Problem Largely Resolved, *Lubr. Eng.*, 42(6), 357-362, 1986. MetAbs No. 86-352057. **Abstract:** The effects of mixed erosion and/or corrosion have been quantified. On-site observations have confirmed laboratory tests which relate the rate of erosion-corrosion primarily to the chemical composition of the steel used, but also to the temperature and to the conditions of flow. For steels containing a high enough proportion of certain alloying elements (Cr is the most important, but cobalt, tungsten, Cu and Mo are also effective), weight loss for corrosion and/or erosion is characterized by a very long incubation period and a drastically reduced rate.

G. Frederick and P. Hernalsteen, Comparative Evaluation of Preventive Measures Against Primary Side Stress Corrosion Cracking of Mill Annealed Inconel 600 Steam Generator Tubes, *Int. J. Pressure Vessels Piping*, 25(1-4), 47-67, 1986. MetAbs No. 87-350336. **Abstract:** Significant amounts of primary side cracking have been reported in the mechanically expanded area of the tubes of PWR steam generators in Europe, in Japan and to a lesser extent in the United States. The Belgian utilities are faced with the same problem. A Belgian program coordinated by the Electric Power Research Institute is discussed.

L. Hunyadi, Ringhals No. 2—Steam Generator Repair/Replacement Options, *Int. J. Pressure Vessels Piping*, 25(1-4), 75-87, 1986. MetAbs No. 87-350337. **Abstract:** Steam generator operational experience is reported for Ringhals No. 2 PWR nuclear power plant. A study carried out to find the cause of corrosion and to evaluate steam generator performance is presented.

S.J. Green, Methods for Preventing Steam Generator Failure or Degradation, *Int. J. Pressure Vessels Piping*, 25(1-4), 359-391, 1986. MetAbs No. 87-350340. **Abstract:** PWR steam generators have suffered from a variety of degradation phenomena. The corrosion-related defects and their probable causes are identified and approaches to correct and prevent corrosive activity suggested.

R. Kuwae, K. Sato, J. Kawashima, and E. Higashinakagawa, Influence of Some Factors on Nodular Corrosion Behavior of Zircaloy-2, *J. Nucl. Sci. Technol. (Jpn.)*, 23(7), 661-663, 1986. MetAbs No. 87-350508. **Abstract:** The corrosion mechanisms of various boiling water reactor fuel cladding plates made from Zircaloy-2 are examined.

R.E. Gold and L. Van Hulle, SCC of Mill Annealed Inconel 600 in Pure and Primary Water Environments and Accelerated SCC of Alloy 600 in 400 °C Superheated Steam, *ATB Metall.*, 26(1-2), 17-21, 1986. MetAbs No. 87-350814. **Abstract:** Degradation of mill annealed alloy 600 steam generator tubing in service due to primary water stress corrosion cracking both in the roll transition area and the U-bend area has gained increasing attention in recent years. In 1985, Westinghouse attempted to identify test media which could lead to intergranular stress corrosion cracking in mill annealed alloy 600 at rates that significantly exceeded the conventional thermally accelerated pressurized water tests at 360 °C by raising the temperature to 400 °C above the critical point of water into the regime of superheated steam.

S.P. Cooper and G.H. Whitley, Titanium in the Power Generation Industry, *Mater. Sci. Technol.*, *3*(2), 91-96, 1987. MetAbs No. 87-351168. **Abstract:** The role and construction of steam condensers are reviewed and the factors affecting materials selection are outlined. Comparisons are made between the behavior of Cu-base alloys and commercial pure titanium tubing under test and in service. The implications of a change in tube material on condenser design are reviewed.

J. Daret and G. Santarini, Intergranular Attack of Alloy 600 in Pressurized Water Reactor Steam Generator Tubes, *Mater. Perform.*, *26*(3), 18-23, 1987. MetAbs No. 87-351343. **Abstract:** In some steam generators, intergranular attack has been detected on Alloy 600 tubes within or near the tubesheet crevice region. A study was undertaken to reproduce attack in an experimental device simulating steam generator conditions. Chemical parameters and test procedures were adjusted to obtain a high concentration of alkalies in the tubesheet crevices and a representative corrosion attack of tubing materials.

H. Shaban, Stress Corrosion Cracking of Tube of a Vacuum Residue Steam Generator: A Case Study, *Rev. Tech.*, *10*(1), 40-47, 1987. MetAbs No. 87-352825. **Abstract:** Causes of failure of vacuum residue steam generator tubes were investigated using visual, microscopic and chemical methods. It was found that the main cause of such failure was stress corrosion cracking. Suggestions were made to control causes of such failure.

N. Totsuka, E. Lunarska, and G. Cragnolino, Effect of Hydrogen on the Intergranular Stress Corrosion Cracking of Alloy 600 in High Temperature Aqueous Environments, *Corrosion*, *43*(8), 505-514, 1987. MetAbs No. 87-352847. **Abstract:** Slow strain rate tests on differently shaped tensile specimens machined from two heats of Alloy 600 tubing were conducted at 350 °C in deaerated aqueous solutions containing small amounts of lithium hydroxide and boric acid at different partial pressures of hydrogen, using a recirculating autoclave system.

G. Economy, R.J. Jacko, and F.W. Pement, IGSCC Behavior of Alloy 600 Steam Generator Tubing in Water or Steam Tests Above 360 °C, *Corrosion*, *43*(12), 727-734, 1987. MetAbs No. 88-350651. **Abstract:** Laboratory testing to produce intergranular stress-corrosion cracking of Alloy 600 steam generator tubing in primary water environments can require lengthy exposure times, even at a temperature of 360 °C. Recent testing of Alloy 600 in hydrogen-containing steam at 400 °C has shown the characteristic attack, but with about a tenfold decrease. The role of microstructural variables, including grain boundary carbide precipitation and heat treatment, is similar in water and steam.

Corrosion Behavior of Various Metals and Alloys in Steam

Material	Condition, other factors, comments	Concentration, %	Temperature, °C (°F)	Duration	Corrosion rate, mm/yr (mils/yr) or other	Ref
Irons and steels						
5Cr-Mo	Composition: 0.22% carbon, 5.07% chromium, 0.47% molybdenum	...	650 (1200)	570 h	0.1 (4)	107
5Cr-Mo	Composition: 0.27% carbon, 5.49% chromium, 0.43% molybdenum	...	650 (1200)	570 h	0.1 (4)	107
7Cr-Mo	Composition: 0.11% carbon, 7.33% chromium, 0.59% molybdenum. Not a cast steel	...	650 (1200)	570 h	0.05 (2)	107
9Cr-1.5Mo	Composition: 0.23% carbon, 9.09% chromium, 1.56% molybdenum	...	650 (1200)	570 h	0.025 (1)	107
Carbon-molybdenum	Composition: 0.21% carbon, 0.49% molybdenum	...	650 (1200)	570 h	0.3 (12)	107
Carbon-molybdenum	Composition: 0.20% carbon, 0.49% molybdenum	...	650 (1200)	570 h	0.25 (10)	107
Carbon steel	Composition: 0.24% carbon	...	650 (1200)	570 h	0.3 (12)	107
Carbon steel	Composition: 0.25% carbon	...	650 (1200)	570 h	0.28 (11)	107
Nickel-chromium-molybdenum	Composition: 0.35% carbon, 0.64% chromium, 2.13% nickel, 0.26% molybdenum	...	650 (1200)	570 h	0.25 (10)	107
Nickel-chromium-molybdenum	Composition: 0.28% carbon, 0.73% chromium, 2.25% nickel, 0.26% molybdenum	...	650 (1200)	570 h	0.25 (10)	107
Stainless steels						
Type 410 stainless steel	Plus air, refluxed	...	...	...	Very slightly attacked	121
Titanium						
Titanium	Plus air	...	82 (197)	...	nil	90
Titanium	Plus 7.65% H_2S	...	93-110 (200-230)	...	nil	90
Lead, tin, and zinc						
Chemical lead	Condensed with traces of acid. No aeration, slow agitation	...	21-38 (70-100)	...	0.021 (0.85)	13
Noble metals						
Gold	...	...	800 (1470)	...	<0.05 (<2)	8
Gold	...	...	800 (1470)	...	<0.05 (<2)	8
Platinum	...	...	600 (1110)	...	<0.05 (<2)	6
Silver	Without pressure	Pure	600 (1110)	...	<0.05 (<2)	8

(Continued)

Corrosion Behavior of Various Metals and Alloys in Steam (Continued)

Material	Condition, other factors, comments	Concentration, %	Temperature, °C (°F)	Duration	Corrosion rate, mm/yr (mils/yr) or other	Ref
Others						
Magnesium	...	100	...	...	Unsuitable	119
Uranium	(a)	...	200 (392)	...	5.5 cm/h x 10⁻³	106
Uranium	(a)	...	250 (482)	...	31.25 cm/h x 10⁻³	106
Uranium	(a)	...	300 (572)	...	27.5 cm/h x 10⁻³	106
Uranium	(a)	...	350 (662)	...	35 cm/h x 10⁻³	106
Uranium	(a)	...	400 (752)	...	31.25 cm/h x 10⁻³	106
Uranium	(a)	...	450 (842)	...	20 cm/h x 10⁻³	106
Uranium	(a)	...	500 (932)	...	20 cm/h x 10⁻³	106
Uranium	(a)	...	600 (1112)	...	17.5 cm/h x 10⁻³	106

(a) Penetration.

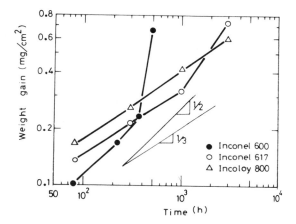

Heat-resisting alloys. Log-log plots of weight gain curves of Inconel 600, Inconel 617, and Incoloy 800 in steam at 800 °C and 40 atm. Source: F. Abe and H. Yoshida, Corrosion Behaviours of Heat Resisting Alloys in Steam at 800 °C and 40 atm Pressure, *Zeitschrift für Metallkunde*, Vol 76, Mar 1985, 219-225.

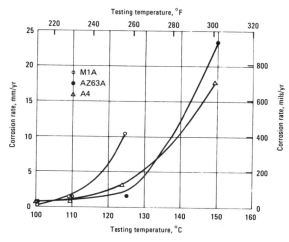

Magnesium. Effects of temperature on corrosion rates of magnesium alloys M1A, AZ63A, and A4 in steam. Source: *Metals Handbook*, 9th ed., Vol 2, Properties and Selection: Nonferrous Alloys and Pure Metals, American Society for Metals, Metals Park, OH, 1979, 602.

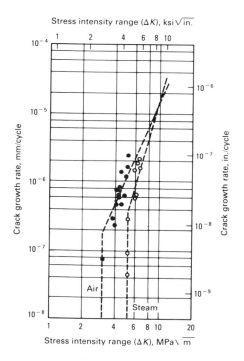

Steel. Corrosion fatigue crack propagation in ASTM A471 steel exposed to moist air and steam. Temperature: 100 °C (212 °F); frequency: 100 Hz; stress ratio: $R = 0.35$. Source: L.K.L. Tu and B.B. Seth, Threshold Corrosion Fatigue Crack Growth in Steels, *Journal of Testing and Evaluation*, Vol 6, 1978, 66-74.

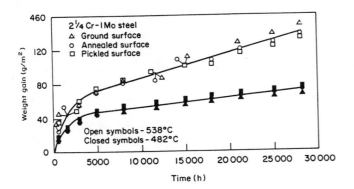

Steel. Weight gains for 2.25Cr-1Mo steel exposed to superheated steam at 10.5 MPa. Source: J. Stringer, Performance Limitations in Electric Power Generating Systems Imposed by High-Temperature Corrosion, *High Temperature Technology*, Vol 3, Aug 1985, 129.

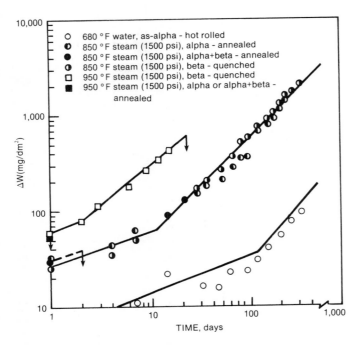

Zirconium. Corrosion of nickel-free Zircaloy-2. Source: Stanley Kass, The Development of the Zircaloys, in *Corrosion of Zirconium Alloys* (STP 368), ASTM, Philadelphia, 1964, 19.

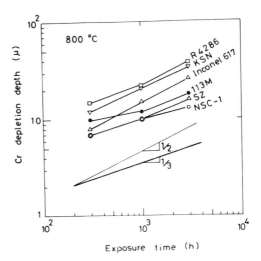

Nickel alloys. Depth of chromium-depleted zone beneath the Cr_2O_3 scale of nickel alloys in steam at 800 °C and 40 atm, as a function of exposure time. Source: F. Abe, H. Araki, *et al.*, Corrosion Behavior of Nickel Base Heat Resisting Alloys for Nuclear Steelmaking System in High-Temperature Steam, *Transactions of the Iron and Steel Institute of Japan*, Vol 25, May 1985, 427.

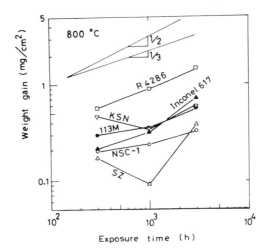

Nickel alloys. Weight gain curves for nickel alloys in steam at 800 °C and 40 atm. Also shown are reference lines with slopes of 1/2 and 1/3, corresponding to parabolic and cubic rate laws, respectively. Source: F. Abe, H. Araki, *et al.*, Corrosion Behavior of Nickel Base Heat Resisting Alloys for Nuclear Steelmaking System in High-Temperature Steam, *Transactions of the Iron and Steel Institute of Japan*, Vol 25, May 1985, 426.

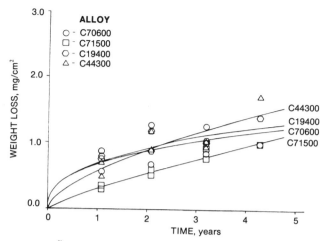

Copper. Weight loss vs. time curves for various copper alloys exposed to the steam-side environment of a condenser. The plant is located on Lake Michigan. The condenser pH averaged 9.15 to 9.30, and the average hot well oxygen concentration was approximately 25 to 50 ppb. The water temperature of the hot well was approximately 78 to 80 °F. Source: G.P. Sheldon and N.W. Polan, Field Testing of Power Utility Condenser Tube Alloys, *Journal of Material for Energy Systems*, Vol 6, Mar 1986, 314.

Stearic Acid

Stearic acid, $CH_3(CH_2)_{16}COOH$, is a white or colorless, waxlike solid with a melting point of 70 °C and a boiling point of 383 °C. It is soluble in alcohol, ether, and chloroform, and is insoluble in water. Stearic acid, nature's most common fatty acid, is derived from natural animal and vegetable fats. Also known as *n*-octadecanoic acid, stearic acid is used in the preparation of metallic stearates, as a lubricant, and in pharmaceuticals, cosmetics, candles, and food packaging.

Material Summaries

The following material summaries were compiled from a survey of the available literature. Inclusion of a material description under a given environment does not imply that it is the most appropriate material for corrosion service in that environment. Likewise, exclusion of a given material does not imply that it is not suitable for corrosion service applications in that environment.

Aluminum. Aluminum alloy equipment has been used for steam distillation, filtration, and storage of stearic acid. In laboratory tests conducted in 100% relative humidity and ambient temperature, aluminum alloys 3003 and 5154 resisted solid stearic acid.

Copper. In the presence of moisture and air, stearic acid, like all other fatty acids, attacks copper and copper alloys. The rate of attack is also influenced by temperature and the presence of impurities. Tests made at 25 to 100 °C (75 to 212 °F) in stearic acid showed corrosion rates of C11000, C26000, and C65500 to be in the range of 500 to 1250 μm/yr (20 to 50 mils/yr).

Additional Reading

J.V. Dobson and B.R. Chapman, Electrode Kinetic Behaviour of 18Cr-8Ni Stainless Steels in Aqueous Stearic Acid Salt Media From 20 to 210 °C, *Br. Corros. J.*, *22*(1), 17-20, 1987. MetAbs No. 87-351699. **Abstract:** An experimental study of the electrode kinetic behavior of 18Cr-8Ni stainless steels in aqueous stearic acid salt media at 20 to 210 °C is reported.

Corrosion Behavior of Various Metals and Alloys in Stearic Acid

Material	Condition, other factors, comments	Concentration, %	Temperature, °C (°F)	Duration	Corrosion rate, mm/yr (mils/yr) or other	Ref
Stainless steels						
Type 410 stainless steel	...	...	Room	...	Unattacked	121
Coppers						
70-30 cupronickel	(a)	...	...	...	Good	93
90-10 cupronickel	(a)	...	...	...	Good	93
		(Continued)				

Corrosion Behavior of Various Metals and Alloys in Stearic Acid (Continued)

Material	Condition, other factors, comments	Concentration, %	Temperature, °C (°F)	Duration	Corrosion rate, mm/yr (mils/yr) or other	Ref
Admiralty brass	(a)	...	...	...	Good	93
Aluminum bronze	(a)	...	...	...	Good	93
Architectural bronze	...	...	...	...	Fair	93
Brass	(a)	...	...	...	Good	93
Cartridge brass	...	...	...	...	Fair	93
Commercial bronze	(a)	...	...	...	Good	93
Electrolytic copper	(a)	...	...	...	Good	93
Free-cutting brass	...	...	...	...	Fair	93
Muntz metal	...	...	...	...	Fair	93
Naval brass	...	...	...	...	Fair	93
Nickel silver	(a)	18	...	...	Good	93
Phosphor bronze	5% Sn. (a)	...	...	...	Good	93
Phosphor bronze	8% Sn. (a)	...	...	...	Good	93
Phosphor copper	(a)	...	...	...	Good	93
Red brass	(a)	...	...	...	Good	93
Silicon bronze	Low. (a)	...	...	...	Good	93
Silicon bronze	High. (a)	...	...	...	Good	93
Titanium						
Titanium	Molten	100	180 (356)	...	0.003 (0.12)	90
Heat- and corrosion-resistant alloys						
Ferralium 255	Plus 3% NaCl	...	100 (212)	...	<0.01 (0.3)	60
Ferralium 255	Plus 1% H$_2$SO$_4$	...	100 (212)	...	0.21 (8.3)	60
Ferralium 255	Plus 1% H$_2$SO$_4$ and 3% NaCl	...	100 (212)	...	0.01 (0.4)	60
Noble metals						
Gold	...	Pure	Boiling	...	<0.05 (<2)	8
Silver	...	Pure	160 (320)	...	<0.05 (<2)	4
Silver	...	Pure	160 (320)	...	<0.05 (<2)	4
Others						
Magnesium	Dry	100	Room	...	Suitable	119

(a) May be considered in place of a copper metal when some property, other than corrosion resistance, governs its use.

Succinic Acid

Succinic acid, CO$_2$H(CH$_2$)$_2$CO$_2$H, also known as butanedioic acid, butane diacid, and amber acid, is a colorless crystalline solid that melts at 185 °C (364 °F). Soluble in water and alcohol, it is used as a chemical intermediate. Succinic acid is used in lacquers, medicine, dyes, and as a taste modifier.

Material Summaries

The following material summaries were compiled from a survey of the available literature. Inclusion of a material description under a given environment does not imply that it is the most appropriate material for corrosion service in that environment. Likewise, exclusion of a given material does not imply that it is not suitable for corrosion service applications in that environment.

Aluminum. Under laboratory conditions of ambient temperature and 100% relative humidity, aluminum alloys 3003 and 5154 resisted solid succinic acid. Aqueous solutions of succinic acid (0.25 to 50%) caused attack of alloy 1100 that increased with concentration and temperature. In laboratory tests at 100 °C (212 °F), the attack was moderate (~6 mils/yr) at 0.25% concentration, whereas at 50% it was corrosive.

Additional Reading

M.A. Elmorsi, E.M. Mabrouk, R.M. Issa, and M.M. Ghoneim, Electrochemical Studies of the Corrosion of Some Cu-Zn Alloys in Organic Acids, *Surf. Coat. Technol.*, *30*(3), 277-287, 1987. MetAbs No. 87-351667. **Abstract:** The electrochemical corrosion parameters (e.g., corrosion current density, corrosion rate and polarization resistance) of 63Cu-37Zn, 70Cu-30Zn and 58.81Cu-39.53Zn-1.66Pb alloys were measured in aqueous solutions of weak organic acids (oxalic, tartaric and succinic acid). Potentiodynamic, Tafel plot and polarization resistance techniques were used with the model 350A-PARC corrosion measurement system. The effect of acid concentration and temperature on the corrosion parameters of such alloys is discussed.

Corrosion Behavior of Various Metals and Alloys in Succinic Acid

Material	Condition, other factors, comments	Concen-tration, %	Temperature, °C (°F)	Duration	Corrosion rate, mm/yr (mils/yr) or other	Ref
Aluminum (>99.5%)	Solution	...	20-100 (68-212)	...	Satisfactory	92
Aluminum-manganese alloys	Solution	...	20-100 (68-212)	...	Satisfactory	92
Titanium	...	100	185 (366)	...	nil	90
Titanium	...	Saturated	Room	...	nil	90
Zr702	...	0-50	100 (212)	...	<0.05 (<2)	15
Zr702	...	100	150 (300)	...	<0.05 (<2)	15

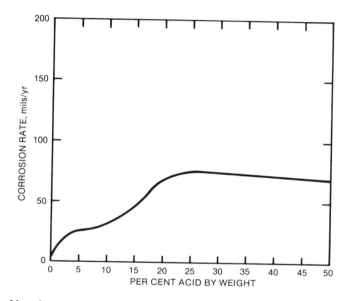

Aluminum. Effects of succinic acid on alloy 1100 at 100 °C (212 °F). Source: *Guidelines for the Use of Aluminum with Food and Chemicals: Compatibility Data on Aluminum in the Food and Chemical Process Industries*, 5th ed., The Aluminum Association, Washington, DC, 1984, 33.

Sulfur

Sulfur, S, is a nonmetallic element that exists in a crystalline or amorphous form and in four stable isotopes. Sulfur melts at temperatures ranging from 112.8 °C for the rhombic form to 120.0 °C for amorphous sulfur, and all forms boil at 444.7 °C.

Sulfur occurs as free sulfur in many volcanic areas and is often associated with gypsum and limestone. It is used as a chemical intermediate and fungicide and in the vulcanization of rubber.

Material Summaries

The following material summaries were compiled from a survey of the available literature. Inclusion of a material description under a given environment does not imply that it is the most appropriate material for corrosion service in that environment. Likewise, exclusion of a given material does not imply that it is not suitable for corrosion service applications in that environment.

Carbon steel. Sulfur in the presence of water causes severe localized corrosion of steels at ambient temperature.

Aluminum. In laboratory tests, 1100 and 3003 alloys were resistant to liquid sulfur at 135 to 154 °C (275 to 310 °F). Aluminum alloy equipment has been used for the recovery and purification of sulfur, in sulfur mining equipment, buildings, freight cars, hopper cars, and conveyors.

Osmium burns in the vapor of sulfur.

Rhodium in its massive form is attacked slowly by molten sulfur, but the finely divided metal may react violently.

Platinum is resistant to sulfurous gases, even at elevated temperatures.

Tantalum reacts with sulfur or H_2S at red heat to form tantalum sulfide (Ta_2S_4). Tantalum sulfide is also formed when Ta_2O_5 is heated in H_2S or carbon disulfide (CS_2).

Additional Reading

J.L. Jones, D.B. Nordman, and S.T. Gadomski, Sulfation of Y_2O_3 and HfO_2 in Relation to MCrAl Coatings, *Metall. Trans. A, 16A*(2), 303-306, 1985. MetAbs No. 85-350459. **Abstract:** The sulfation of yttrium (as Y_2O_3) and Hf (as HfO_2) is compared to determine which may potentially be used in low-temperature hot corrosion-resistant MCrAl coatings on Ni-base superalloy turbine blades. The sulfation mechanisms of both oxides are detailed.

P.K. Datta, K.N. Strafford, and A.L. Dowson, Environment/Mechanical Interaction Processes and Hydrogen Embrittlement of Titanium, *Mech. Corros. Prop. A, Key Eng. Mater., A8*, 203-216, 1985. MetAbs No. 86-350055. **Abstract:** Although extensive studies have been carried out to characterize the degradation behavior of Ti in complex H-O-S environments, little attention has been given to the contamination and embrittlement of the metal substrate. The degradation of Ti (IMI115, IMI130, IMI155) in hydrogen, oxygen and/or sulfur-containing environments at 300 to 500 °C has been studied and has been shown to involve the simultaneous occurrence of oxidation, H absorption and hydride precipitation reactions.

A.P. Brown and J.E. Battles, Corrosion of Nickel-200 and AISI-1008 Steel in Sodium Polysulfides and Sulfur at 350 °C, *J. Electrochem. Soc., 133*(7), 1321-1325, 1986. MetAbs No. 86-352060. **Abstract:** Tests were conducted to determine the corrosion behavior of Ni-200 and AISI-1008 steel in sulfur and Na polysulfides (Na_2S_5, Na_2S_4, and Na_2S_3) at 350 °C for times between 1 to 25 h. Both the corrosion kinetics and the morphology of the corrosion scale formed on these metals are described.

V.B. Rajan and G.S. Was, The Anodic Dissolution Behavior of NiSCr9Fe in Sulfur Containing Solutions, *Corrosion, 43*(5), 305-308, 1987. MetAbs No. 87-351921. **Abstract:** The effect of sulfur and sulfur-containing compounds on the anodic dissolution behavior of a Ni-5Cr-9Fe alloy (which simulates the grain boundary composition of sensitized Inconel 600) was studied. The study was conducted under controlled potential and pH conditions to establish, on a thermodynamic foundation, the effect of one or more of the species on the dissolution behavior.

Corrosion Behavior of Various Metals and Alloys in Sulfur

Material	Condition, other factors, comments	Concentration, %	Temperature, °C (°F)	Duration	Corrosion rate, mm/yr (mils/yr) or other	Ref
Stainless steels						
AM-363 stainless steel	...	...	Room	...	Unattacked	120
Type 304 stainless steel	Metal processing (distillation); field or pilot plant test; no aeration. Liquid, plus selenium	...	454 (850)	7.8 d	0.015 in./yr	89
Type 304 stainless steel	Chemical processing; field or pilot plant test; no aeration; rapid agitation. With carbon over the standard maximum. Liquid, plus iron and aluminum chlorides, approximately 600 ppm, hydrochloric acid trace possible; filter. Severe pitting: maximum depth of pits over 0.010 in. Crevice attack (tendency to concentration-cell corrosion)	...	135 (275)	83 d	0.0037 in./yr	89
Type 304 stainless steel	Mining; field or pilot plant test; strong aeration; rapid agitation. Liquid, plus small amounts of sulfuric acid and iron sulfate (air-sulfur interface)	...	138 (280)	13 d	0.015 in./yr	89
Type 304 stainless steel	Chemical processing; field or pilot plant test; no aeration; no agitation. Liquid, with traces of moisture and hydrochloric acid. Severe pitting: maximum depth of pits over 0.010 in. Crevice attack (tendency to concentration-cell corrosion)	...	150 (302)	105 d	0.0048 in./yr	89
Type 304 stainless steel	Chemical processing; field or pilot plant test; no aeration; no agitation. Liquid, water saturated, pressure 25 psig. Severe pitting: maximum depth of pits over 0.010 in.	...	120 (248)	8.5 d	0.088 in./yr	89
Type 304 stainless steel	Chemical processing; field or pilot plant test; rapid agitation. Vapors	...	571 (1060)	54 d	0.027 in./yr	89
Type 316 stainless steel	Metal processing (distillation); field or pilot plant test; no aeration. Liquid, plus selenium	...	454 (850)	7.8 d	0.008 in./yr	89
Type 316 stainless steel	Chemical processing; field or pilot plant test; no aeration; rapid agitation. Liquid plus iron and aluminum chlorides, approximately 600 ppm, hydrochloric acid trace possible; filter	...	135 (275)	83 d	0.0024 in./yr	89
Type 316 stainless steel	Mining; field or pilot plant test; strong aeration; rapid agitation. Liquid, plus small amounts of sulfuric acid and iron sulfate (air-sulfur interface)	...	138 (280)	13 d	0.018 in./yr	89
Type 316 stainless steel	Chemical processing; field or pilot plant test; no aeration; no agitation. Liquid with traces of moisture and hydrochloric acid. Severe pitting: maximum depth of pits over 0.010 in. Crevice attack (tendency to concentration-cell corrosion)	...	150 (302)	105 d	0.0033 in./yr	89

(Continued)

Corrosion Behavior of Various Metals and Alloys in Sulfur (Continued)

Material	Condition, other factors, comments	Concentration, %	Temperature, °C (°F)	Duration	Corrosion rate, mm/yr (mils/yr) or other	Ref
Type 316 stainless steel	Chemical processing; field or pilot plant test; no aeration; no agitation. Liquid, water saturated, pressure 25 psig. Severe pitting: maximum depth of pits over 0.010 in.	...	120 (248)	8.5 d	0.058 in./yr	89
Type 316 stainless steel	Chemical processing; field or pilot plant test; rapid agitation. Vapors	...	571 (1060)	54 d	0.0311 in./yr	89
Type 317 stainless steel	Chemical processing; field or pilot plant test; no aeration; rapid agitation. Liquid plus iron and aluminum chlorides, approximately 600 ppm, hydrochloric acid trace possible; filter	...	135 (275)	83 d	0.0033 in./yr	89
Type 317 stainless steel	Mining; field or pilot plant test; strong aeration; rapid agitation. Liquid plus small amounts of sulfuric acid and iron sulfate (air-sulfur interface)	...	138 (280)	13 d	0.017 in./yr	89
Aluminum						
Aluminum (99.0-99.5%)	...	...	...	...	Excellent	92
Coppers						
70-30 cupronickel	Dry	...	...	...	Suitable	93
70-30 cupronickel	Molten	...	...	...	Not suitable	93
90-10 cupronickel	Dry. (a)	...	...	...	Good	93
90-10 cupronickel	Molten	...	...	...	Not suitable	93
Admiralty brass	Dry	...	...	...	Suitable	93
Admiralty brass	Molten	...	...	...	Not suitable	93
Aluminum bronze	Dry. (a)	...	...	...	Good	93
Aluminum bronze	Molten	...	...	...	Not suitable	93
Ampco 8, aluminum bronze	Molten. Generally not suitable	...	...	...	>0.5 (>20)	96
Architectural bronze	Dry	...	...	...	Suitable	93
Architectural bronze	Molten	...	...	...	Not suitable	93
Brass	Dry. (a)	...	...	...	Good	93
Brass	Molten	...	...	...	Not suitable	93
Cartridge brass	Dry	...	...	...	Suitable	93
Cartridge brass	Molten	...	...	...	Not suitable	93
Commercial bronze	Dry. (a)	...	...	...	Good	93
Commercial bronze	Molten	...	...	...	Not suitable	93
Electrolytic copper	Dry. (a)	...	...	...	Good	93
Electrolytic copper	Molten	...	...	...	Not suitable	93
Free-cutting brass	Dry	...	...	...	Suitable	93
Free-cutting brass	Molten	...	...	...	Not suitable	93
Muntz metal	Dry	...	...	...	Suitable	93
Muntz metal	Molten	...	...	...	Not suitable	93
Naval brass	Dry	...	...	...	Suitable	93
Naval brass	Molten	...	...	...	Not suitable	93
Nickel silver	Dry. (a)	18	...	...	Good	93
Nickel silver	Molten	18	...	...	Not suitable	93
Phosphor bronze	5% Sn. Dry. (a)	...	...	...	Good	93
Phosphor bronze	8% Sn. Dry. (a)	...	...	...	Good	93
Phosphor bronze	5% Sn. Molten	...	...	...	Not suitable	93
Phosphor bronze	8% Sn. Molten	...	...	...	Not suitable	93
Phosphor copper	Molten	...	...	...	Not suitable	93
Phosphor copper	Dry. (a)	...	...	...	Good	93
Red brass	Dry. (a)	...	...	...	Good	93
Red brass	Molten	...	...	...	Not suitable	93
Silicon bronze	Low. Dry. (a)	...	...	...	Good	93
Silicon bronze	High. Dry. (a)	...	...	...	Good	93
Silicon bronze	Low. Molten	...	...	...	Not suitable	93
Silicon bronze	High. Molten	...	...	...	Not suitable	93
Titanium						
Titanium	Molten	100	240 (464)	...	nil	90

(Continued)

Corrosion Behavior of Various Metals and Alloys in Sulfur (Continued)

Material	Condition, other factors, comments	Concentration, %	Temperature, °C (°F)	Duration	Corrosion rate, mm/yr (mils/yr) or other	Ref
Heat- and corrosion-resistant alloys						
Carpenter 20	Metal processing (distillation); field or pilot plant test; no aeration. Plus selenium	Liquid	454 (850)	7.8 d	0.028 in./yr	89
Carpenter 20	Chemical processing; field or pilot plant test; no aeration; rapid agitation; cast specimens. Plus iron and aluminum chlorides, approximately 600 ppm, hydrochloric acid trace possible; filter	Liquid	135 (275)	83 d	0.004 in./yr	89
Carpenter 20	Mining; field or pilot plant test; strong aeration; rapid agitation. Plus small amounts of sulfuric acid and iron sulfate (air-sulfur interface)	Liquid	138 (280)	13 d	0.015 in./yr	89
Others						
Magnesium	...	100	Room	...	Suitable	119

(a) May be considered in place of a copper metal when some property, other than corrosion resistance, governs its use.

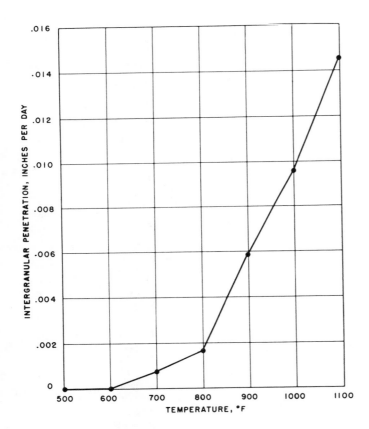

Nickel. Effect of temperature on the intergranular penetration of nickel by sulfur from Ni₃S₂ vapor. Based on 23-h tests. Source: W.Z. Friend, *Corrosion of Nickel and Nickel-Base Alloys*, John Wiley & Sons, New York, 1980, 72.

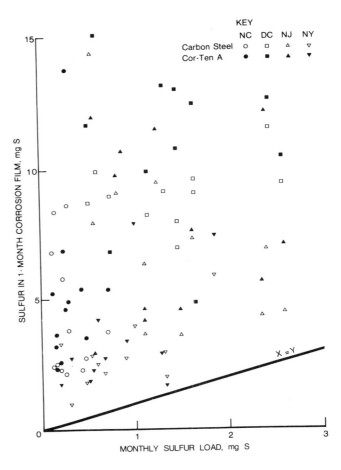

Carbon steel. Total amount of sulfur in 1-month corrosion films formed on carbon steel and Cor-Ten A compared to the amount of sulfur delivered to the samples by wet deposition during the exposure period. Exposures were made at four sites in 1983. Source: D.R. Flinn, S.D. Cramer, *et al.*, Field Exposure Study for Determining the Effects of Acid Deposition on the Corrosion and Deterioration of Materials: Description of the Program and Preliminary Results, in *Durability of Building Materials,* Vol 3, 1985, 171.

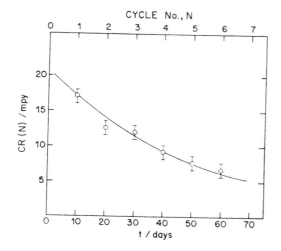

Carbon steel. Plot of the integral corrosion rate, CR(N), as a function of time and cycle number for the cyclical exposure of carbon steel to wet elemental sulfur (4 days) and the atmosphere (6 days). Source: D.D. MacDonald, B. Roberts, and J.B. Hyne, Corrosion of Carbon Steel During Cyclical Exposure to Wet Elemental Sulfur and the Atmosphere, *Corrosion Science*, Vol 18, 501, 1978.

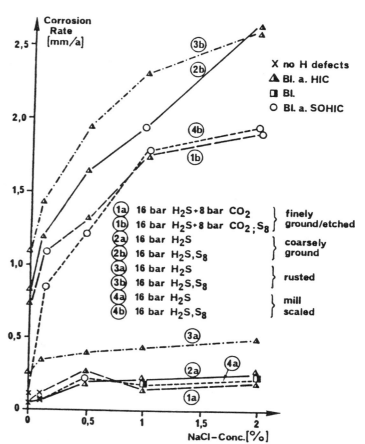

Steel. Effect of sodium chloride concentration and presence of solid elemental sulfur on corrosion behavior of stressed coupons of steel with different surface status, filmed with triethylene glycol solutions (10% water) and exposed to 16 bar H_2S + 8 bar CO_2 at 25 °C. Bl = visible blisters on surface areas of the specimens exposed to the liquid and to the gas phase of the corrosive environment. HIC = surface-parallel internal hydrogen-induced cracks observed in metallographic sections. SOHIC = stress-oriented hydrogen-induced cracks (combination of HIC and HSCC). Source: W. Bruckhoff, O. Geier, K. Hofbauer, G. Schmitt, and D. Steinmetz, "Rupture of a Sour Gas Line Due to Stress Oriented Hydrogen Induced Cracking Failure Analyses, Experimental Results and Corrosion Prevention," *Corrosion 85*, National Association of Corrosion Engineers, Houston, March 1985.

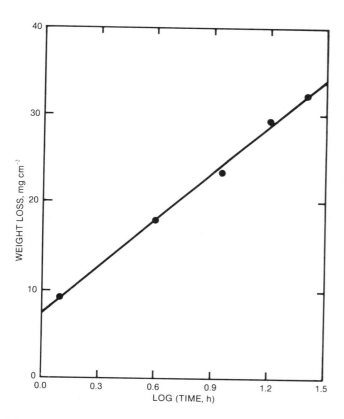

Nickel. The corrosion behavior of nickel in sulfur plotted as weight loss vs. the logarithm of time at 350 °C. Source: A.P. Brown and J.E. Battles, Corrosion of Nickel-200 and AISI-1008 Steel in Sodium Polysulfides and Sulfur at 350 °C, *Journal of the Electrochemical Society*, Vol 133, 1986, 1323.

Sulfur Dioxide

Sulfur dioxide, SO_2, also known as sulfurous acid anhydride, is a toxic, irritating, colorless gas. It is soluble in water, alcohol, and ether, and boils at -10 °C. Sulfur dioxide is used as a chemical intermediate, in artificial ice, in paper pulping, in ore refining, and as a solvent.

Material Summaries

The following material summaries were compiled from a survey of the available literature. Inclusion of a material description under a given environment does not imply that it is the most appropriate material for corrosion service in that environment. Likewise, exclusion of a given material does not imply that it is not suitable for corrosion service applications in that environment.

Stainless Steels. Conventional austenitic stainless steels have been used in sulfite digestors, and types 316 and 317 stainless steels, 20Cb-3, and ACI CF-8M and CN-7M have seen service in wet sulfur dioxide and H_2SO_3 environments.

Aluminum. In laboratory tests, sulfur dioxide saturated with water was corrosive to all aluminum alloys at ambient temperature. Aluminum alloy equipment has been used for refrigeration systems containing sulfur dioxide, for heat exchangers in cooling sulfur dioxide, and for reactors converting sulfur dioxide to sulfur trioxide.

Copper. Gases containing sulfur dioxide attack copper in a manner similar to oxygen. The dry gas does not corrode copper or copper alloys, but the moist gas reacts to produce a mixture of oxide and sulfide scale. Brass is susceptible to stress-corrosion cracking in moist air containing 0.05 to 0.5 vol% sulfur dioxide.

Magnesium. Dry, gaseous sulfur dioxide causes no attack of magnesium at ordinary temperatures. If water vapor is present, some corrosion may occur. Wet (below dew point) sulfur dioxide gas is severely corrosive to magnesium due to the formation of sulfurous and sulfuric acids.

It has been shown that the effects of sulfur dioxide pollution on the atmospheric corrosion of alloys ZK61A and AZ80A may cause corrosion rates of these alloys in industrial atmospheres to be somewhat higher than those found in marine atmospheres.

Niobium. At 100 °C (212 °F), niobium is inert in sulfur dioxide (wet or dry).

Gold is resistant to sulfur dioxide (wet or dry) at temperatures up to 600 °C (1110 °F).

Iridium is resistant to wet or dry gaseous sulfur dioxide up to 1000 °C (1830 °F) if elemental sulfur is not present.

Rhodium is resistant to wet or dry gaseous sulfur dioxide vapors up to 1000 °C (1830 °F) if elemental sulfur is not present.

Silver. At red heat, sulfur dioxide (and sulfur trioxide) rapidly attacks silver. This attack becomes progressively worse with temperatures beginning at or near room temperature.

Tantalum. In spite of the scarcity of published data, it is to be expected that tantalum would react at some elevated temperature with oxygen-containing gaseous compounds such as sulfur dioxide.

Tin. Materials containing sulfur dioxide as a preservative produce sulfide stains on tin, but the rate of metal loss is low.

Titanium. The oxide film on titanium alloys provides an effective barrier to attack by most gases in wet or dry conditions, including sulfur dioxide. This protection extends to temperatures in excess of 150 °C (300 °F).

Zinc. Sulfur dioxide has a corrosive action on zinc because water-soluble and hygroscopic salts are formed.

Zirconium is stable in sulfur dioxide at temperatures as high as 300 to 400 °C (570 to 750 °F).

Additional Reading

S.J. Ketcham and E.J. Jankowsky, Shipboard Exposure Tests of Aluminum Alloys, Tri-Service Conference on Corrosion, US Air Force Academy, AFWAL-TR-81-4019, Vol I, Air Force Wright Aeronautical Laboratory, Wright-Patterson AFB, 1980. MetAbs No. 82-350485. **Abstract:** A program is underway to quantitatively determine the corrosivity of the aircraft carrier environment by exposing a variety of materials on a carrier deck. The environment of a conventionally powered aircraft carrier that uses diesel fuel includes stack gas exhaust products in addition to sea spray. One of these products is sulfur dioxide.

I.J.M. Lefever and S.R.J. Saunders, Corrosion Behavior of Porous Sintered Metal Fibre Structures, *Bull. Cercle Etud. Metaux*, *14*(19), 8-1 to 8-10, 1982. MetAbs No. 83-350508. **Abstract:** Synopsis of paper presented at the 21st Journees des Aciers Speciaux, St-Etienne, France, Apr. 1982. Porous sheets made from 12- to 22-μm diameter fibers of a stainless steel or some nickel-base alloys were exposed to combustion gases containing SO_2 and HCl.

M.Da Cunha Belo, C. Bombart, and Ph. Berge, Intergranular Corrosion of Type 304 Stainless Steel and Alloy 600 in Aqueous Solutions Containing SO_2, *Corrosion*, *39*(7), 279-284, 1983. MetAbs No. 83-352124. **Abstract:** The susceptibility to intergranular corrosion of 304 stainless steel and Alloy 600 has been investigated in aqueous solutions containing SO_2.

D.W. Deberry, G.R. Peyton, and W.S. Clark, Evaluation of Corrosion Inhibitors in SO_2 Scrubber Solutions, *Corrosion*, *40*(5), 250-256, 1984. MetAbs No. 84-351929. **Abstract:** Twenty-six compounds were screened via electrochemical measurements to detect any corrosion inhibition properties on carbon steel and AISI 304 and 316 stainless steels in simulated SO_2 scrubber solutions.

N.S. Berke and H.E. Townsend, Comparison of the Kesternich Sulfur Dioxide Atmospheric Corrosion Tests of Zinc-, Aluminum-, and Al-Zn-Coated Steel Sheet, *ASTM J. Test. Eval.*, *13*(1), 74-76, 1985. MetAbs No. 85-350636. **Abstract:** Results of the Deutsches Institute fur Normung (DIN) Kesternich sulfur dioxide test (DIN 50018) are compared with those of long-term industrial atmospheric exposure tests of sheet steels coated with Zn, Al, and Al-Zn alloy coatings.

W. Bogaerts, A. van Haute, and P. Weisgerber, Corrosion Studies on Collector Materials, EUR No. 9597, 47, Commission of the European Communities, Luxembourg, 1985. MetAbs No. 85-351724. **Abstract:** A synopsis of the results of two previously reported literature studies on "Absorber Surfaces and Durability of Solar Heat Collectors" and on "Atmospheric Corrosion and Degradation of Construction Materials for Solar Collectors" is presented.

K. Przybylski and A. Wojtowicz, Oxidation of Cobalt and Cobalt-Chromium Alloys in SO_2-O_2 Atmosphere at 1073K, *Bull. Pol. Acad. Sci., Chem.*, *33*(3-4), 169-179, 1985. MetAbs No. 85-352378. **Abstract:** Cobalt and cobalt-chromium alloys (0.8-33% Cr) have been oxidized in SO_2 atmosphere containing 0.15 vol% O_2 at 1 atm and 1073 K.

M.G. Hocking and V. Vasantasree, Evaluation of Additive Effects on Hot Corrosion of Ni-Cr and Co-Cr Alloys, Protective Coating Systems for High-Temperature Gas Turbine Components, *Mater. Sci. Technol.*, *2*(3), 318-321, 1986. MetAbs No. 86-351608. **Abstract:** A general report is given on the relative performances of Ni and Co alloys and of the effect of varying Hf additions.

G.H. Koch and N.G. Thompson, Localized Attack of Nickel-Containing Alloys in SO_2 Scrubber Environments, *J. Mater. Energy Syst.*, *8*(2), 197-210, 1986. MetAbs No. 86-352626. **Abstract:** A review of SO_2 scrubber environments and their effect on corrosion of alloys is presented. Field experiments on nickel-containing alloys (Hastelloy C276, C22, G, G3, and G30; Inconel 625 and 825; Alloy 904L, Alloy 700, 20Mo-6, and types 317L, 317L4, and 316L stainless steels) in an aggressive outlet duct environment of a limestone SO_2 scrubber are described.

S. Yajima, Y. Togawa, S. Matsushita, and T. Kanbe, Outdoor Exposure and Accelerated Tests of Electroless Nickel Plating, *Plat. Surf. Finish.*, *74*(8), 66-71, 1987. MetAbs No. 87-352754. **Abstract:** A cyclic accelerated corrosion test that includes exposure to high humidity, neutral salt spray, and SO_2 was evaluated to simulate the effects of outdoor exposure on electroless nickel.

Corrosion Behavior of Various Metals and Alloys in Sulfur Dioxide

Material	Condition, other factors, comments	Concentration, %	Temperature, °C (°F)	Duration	Corrosion rate, mm/yr (mils/yr) or other	Ref
Stainless steels						
Type 304 stainless steel	Chemical processing; field or plant test; no aeration; rapid agitation. Plus 20% nitrogen, saturated water vapor	80	15 (60)	94 d	0.0001 in./yr	89
Type 304 stainless steel	Pulp and paper processing; field or plant test. Plus moisture, small amount of sulfur trioxide, tower. Slight pitting: maximum depth of pits from incipient to 0.005 in.	13-17	38 (100)	37 d	<0.0001 in./yr	89
Type 304 stainless steel	Sulfuric acid processing; field or plant test; strong aeration; rapid agitation. With carbon over the standard maximum. Approximately 10%, water saturated, recycle liquor contains 0.3-0.75% sulfuric acid, Peabody scrubber	10	29-32 (85-95)	20 d	0.0001 in./yr	89
Type 304 stainless steel	Sulfuric acid processing; field or plant test; strong aeration; rapid agitation. Approximately 10%, water saturated, recycle liquor contains 0.7-2.5% sulfuric acid. Slight pitting: maximum depth of pits from incipient to 0.005 in.	10	52-57 (125-135)	20 d	0.002 in./yr	89
Type 304 stainless steel	Sulfuric acid processing; field or plant test; strong aeration; rapid agitation. Approximately 10%, water saturated, recycle liquor contains 0.7-2.5% sulfuric acid. Slight pitting: maximum depth of pits from incipient to 0.005 in.	10	52-57 (125-135)	20 d	0.254 in./yr	89
Type 304 stainless steel	Chemical processing; field or plant test; rapid agitation. Plus 30-80% water, 5-7% sulfur trioxide	7-10	82-93 (180-200)	4.5 d	0.02 in./yr	89
Type 304 stainless steel	Plus air, 6% moisture, 1% sulfur trioxide	5	218 (425)	68 d	0.002 in./yr	89
Type 316 stainless steel	Chemical processing; field or plant test; no aeration; rapid agitation. Plus 20% nitrogen, saturated water vapor	80	15 (60)	94 d	0.00025 in./yr	89
Type 316 stainless steel	Chemical processing; field or plant test; strong aeration; rapid agitation. Small amount of sulfur trioxide and moisture, sulfur burner, discharge line	18	260-371 (500-700)	90 d	0.0002 in./yr	89
Type 316 stainless steel	Pulp and paper processing; field or plant test. Plus moisture, small amount of sulfur trioxide, tower	13-17	38 (100)	37 d	<0.0001 in./yr	89
Type 316 stainless steel	Sulfuric acid processing; field or plant test; strong aeration; rapid agitation. Approximately 10%, water saturated, recycle liquor contains 0.3-0.75% sulfuric acid, Peabody scrubber	10	29-32 (85-95)	20 d	0.0001 in./yr	89
Type 316 stainless steel	Sulfuric acid processing; field or plant test; strong aeration; rapid agitation. Approximately 10%, water saturated, recycle liquor contains 0.7-2.5% sulfuric acid	10	52-57 (125-135)	20 d	0.052 in./yr	89
Type 316 stainless steel	Chemical processing; field or plant test; rapid agitation. Plus 30-80% water, 5-7% sulfur trioxide	7-10	82-93 (180-200)	4.5 d	0.021 in./yr	89
Type 316 stainless steel	Plus air, 6% moisture, 1% sulfur trioxide	5	218 (425)	68 d	0.002 in./yr	89
Type 317 stainless steel	Chemical processing; field or plant test; strong aeration; rapid agitation. Small amount of sulfur trioxide and moisture, sulfur burner, discharge line	18	260-371 (500-700)	90 d	0.0003 in./yr	89

(Continued)

Corrosion Behavior of Various Metals and Alloys in Sulfur Dioxide (Continued)

Material	Condition, other factors, comments	Concen-tration, %	Temperature, °C (°F)	Duration	Corrosion rate, mm/yr (mils/yr) or other	Ref
Type 317 stainless steel	Pulp and paper processing; field or plant test. Plus moisture, small amount of sulfur trioxide, tower	13-17	38 (100)	37 d	<0.0001 in./yr	89
Type 317 stainless steel	Sulfuric acid processing; field or plant test; strong aeration; rapid agitation. Approximately 10%, water saturated, recycle liquor contains 0.3-0.75% sulfuric acid, Peabody scrubber	10	29-32 (85-95)	20 d	0.0001 in./yr	89
Type 317 stainless steel	Sulfuric acid processing; field or plant test; strong aeration; rapid agitation. Approximately 10%, water saturated, recycle liquor contains 0.7-2.5% sulfuric acid	10	52-57 (125-135)	20 d	0.006 in./yr	89
Aluminum						
Aluminum (99.0-99.5%)	Dry gas	...	...	...	Excellent	92
Aluminum-manganese alloys	Dry gas	...	...	...	Excellent	92
Coppers						
70-30 cupronickel	Dry	...	...	...	Suitable	93
70-30 cupronickel	Moist	...	...	...	Fair	93
90-10 cupronickel	Dry	...	...	...	Suitable	93
90-10 cupronickel	Moist	...	...	...	Fair	93
Admiralty brass	Dry	...	...	...	Suitable	93
Admiralty brass	Moist. (a)	...	...	...	Good	93
Aluminum bronze	Dry	...	...	...	Suitable	93
Aluminum bronze	Moist. (a)	...	...	...	Good	93
Aluminum bronze (C61800)	Plus 1-2% oxygen	17-18	200-220 (390-430)	30 d	26.4 g/m^2/d	110
Ampco 8, aluminum bronze	Dry. Generally suitable. Conditions such as aeration or temperature could restrict use	...	...	...	<0.5 (<20)	96
Ampco 8, aluminum bronze	Wet. Generally not suitable	...	...	...	>0.5 (>20)	96
Architectural bronze	Dry	...	...	...	Suitable	93
Architectural bronze	Moist	...	...	...	Not suitable	93
Brass	Dry	...	...	...	Suitable	93
Brass	Moist. (a)	...	...	...	Good	93
Bronze (90Cu-10Sn)	Plus 1-2% oxygen	17-18	200-220 (390-430)	30 d	22.0 g/m^2/d	110
Cartridge brass	Dry	...	...	...	Suitable	93
Cartridge brass	Moist	...	...	...	Not suitable	93
Commercial bronze	Dry	...	...	...	Suitable	93
Commercial bronze	Moist. (a)	...	...	...	Good	93
Electrolytic copper	Dry	...	...	...	Suitable	93
Electrolytic copper	Moist. (a)	...	...	...	Good	93
Free-cutting brass	Dry	...	...	...	Suitable	93
Free-cutting brass	Moist	...	...	...	Not suitable	93
Muntz metal	Dry	...	...	...	Suitable	93
Muntz metal	Moist	...	...	...	Not suitable	93
Naval brass	Dry	...	...	...	Suitable	93
Naval brass	Moist	...	...	...	Not suitable	93
Nickel bronze (88.5Cu-5Sn-5Ni-1.5Si)	Plus 1-2% oxygen	17-18	200-220 (390-430)	30 d	70.5 g/m^2/d	110
Nickel silver	Dry	18	...	...	Suitable	93
Nickel silver	Moist	18	...	...	Fair	93
Nickel silver 75-20 (C73200)	Plus 1-2% oxygen	17-18	200-220 (390-430)	30 d	35.6 g/m^2/d	110
Nickel silver 55-18 (C77000)	Plus 1-2% oxygen	17-18	200-220 (390-430)	30 d	63.8 g/m^2/d	110
Nickel silver 65-18 (C75200)	Plus 1-2% oxygen	17-18	200-220 (390-430)	30 d	67.4 g/m^2/d	110
Phosphor bronze	5% Sn. Dry	...	...	...	Suitable	93
Phosphor bronze	8% Sn. Dry	...	...	...	Suitable	93
Phosphor bronze	5% Sn. Moist. (a)	...	...	...	Good	93
Phosphor bronze	8% Sn. Moist. (a)	...	...	...	Good	93

(Continued)

Corrosion Behavior of Various Metals and Alloys in Sulfur Dioxide (Continued)

Material	Condition, other factors, comments	Concentration, %	Temperature, °C (°F)	Duration	Corrosion rate, mm/yr (mils/yr) or other	Ref
Phosphor bronze (C51100)	Plus 1-2% oxygen	17-18	200-220 (390-430)	30 d	28.6 g/m²/d	110
Phosphor bronze (C52100)	Plus 1-2% oxygen. 8% carbon	17-18	200-220 (390-430)	30 d	39.4 g/m²/d	110
Phosphor copper	Dry	...	...	...	Suitable	93
Phosphor copper	Moist. (a)	...	...	...	Good	93
Red brass	Dry	...	...	...	Suitable	93
Red brass	Moist. (a)	...	...	...	Good	93
Silicon bronze	Low. Dry	...	...	...	Suitable	93
Silicon bronze	High. Dry	...	...	...	Suitable	93
Silicon bronze	Low. Moist. (a)	...	...	...	Good	93
Silicon bronze	High. Moist. (a)	...	...	...	Good	93
Silicon bronze (C65800)	Plus 1-2% oxygen	17-18	200-220 (390-430)	30 d	50.2 g/m²/d	110
Titanium						
Titanium	Dry	...	21 (70)	...	nil	90
Titanium	Water saturated	Near 100	Room	...	0.003 (0.12)	90
Titanium	Gas + small amount SO₃ and approx 3% oxygen	18	316 (601)	...	0.006 (0.24)	90
Heat- and corrosion-resistant alloys						
Alloy 825	Chemical processing; field or plant test; strong aeration; rapid agitation. Small amount of sulfur trioxide and moisture, sulfur burner, discharge line	18	260-371 (500-700)	90 d	0.0001 in./yr	89
Alloy 825	Sulfuric acid processing; field or plant test; strong aeration; rapid agitation. Approximately 10%, water saturated, recycle liquor contains 0.3-0.75% sulfuric acid, Peabody scrubber	10	29-32 (85-95)	20 d	<0.0001 in./yr	89
Alloy 825	Sulfuric acid processing; field or plant test; strong aeration; rapid agitation. Approximately 10%, water saturated, recycle liquor contains 0.7-2.5% sulfuric acid	10	52-57 (125-135)	20 d	0.002 in./yr	89
Alloy 825	Chemical processing; field or plant test; rapid agitation. Plus 30-80% water, 5-7% sulfur trioxide	7-10	82-93 (180-200)	4.5 d	0.02 in./yr	89
Carpenter 20	Chemical processing; field or plant test; strong aeration; rapid agitation. Small amount of sulfur trioxide and moisture, sulfur burner, discharge line	18	260-371 (500-700)	90 d	0.0002 in./yr	89
Carpenter 20	Sulfuric acid processing; field or plant test; strong aeration; rapid agitation. Approximately 10%, water saturated, recycle liquor contains 0.3-0.75% sulfuric acid, Peabody scrubber	10	29-32 (85-95)	20 d	0.0001 in./yr	89
Carpenter 20	Sulfuric acid processing; field or plant test; strong aeration; rapid agitation. Approximately 10%, water saturated, recycle liquor contains 0.7-2.5% sulfuric acid	10	52-57 (125-135)	20 d	0.003 in./yr	89
Inconel 600	(b)	...	127 (260)	96 h	0.015 (0.6)	109
Inconel 600	(b)	...	296 (565)	64 h	0.02 (0.8)	109
Inconel 600	(b)	...	352 (665)	66 h	0.3 (12)	109
Inconel 600	(b)	...	366 (690)	65 h	0.4 (16)	109
Inconel 600	(b)	...	446 (835)	48 h	2.2 (86)	109
Monel 400	(b)	...	127 (260)	96 h	0.04 (1.6)	109
Monel 400	(b)	...	260 (500)	96 h	0.07 (3)	109
Monel 400	(b)	...	296 (565)	64 h	0.91 (36)	109
Monel 400	(b)	...	352 (665)	66 h	0.4 (16)	109
Monel 400	(b)	...	366 (690)	65 h	1.4 (57)	109
Monel 400	(b)	...	446 (835)	48 h	33.02 (1300)	109
Nickel 200	(b)	...	127 (260)	96 h	0.025 (1)	109
Nickel 200	(b)	...	260 (500)	96 h	0.304 (12)	109
Nickel 200	(b)	...	296 (565)	64 h	0.33 (13)	109
Nickel 200	(b)	...	352 (665)	66 h	8.4 (330)	109
Nickel 200	(b)	...	366 (690)	65 h	17.78 (700)	109
Nickel 200	(b)	...	446 (835)	48 h	30.7 (1210)	109

(Continued)

Corrosion Behavior of Various Metals and Alloys in Sulfur Dioxide (Continued)

Material	Condition, other factors, comments	Concen- tration, %	Temperature, °C (°F)	Duration	Corrosion rate, mm/yr (mils/yr) or other	Ref
Noble metals						
Gold	Dry and wet	...	600 (1110)	...	<0.05 (<2)	8
Gold	Dry and wet	...	600 (1110)	...	<0.05 (<2)	8
Platinum	Dry and wet	...	600 (1110)	...	<0.05 (<2)	6
Silver	...	Pure	Red heat	...	Attacked	8
Others						
Magnesium	Dry	100	Room	...	Suitable	119

(a) May be considered in place of a copper metal when some property, other than corrosion resistance, governs its use. (b) Molten sulfur.

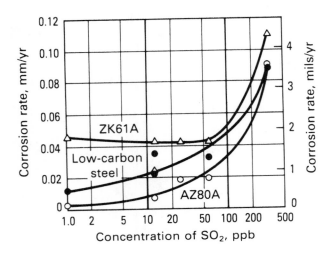

Magnesium. Corrosion rates vs. sulfur dioxide pollution levels at six exposure sites. Rainfall at the sites ranged from 533 to 965 mm/yr (21 to 38 in./yr). Source: *Metals Handbook,* 9th ed., Vol 13, Corrosion, ASM International, Metals Park, OH, 1987, 747.

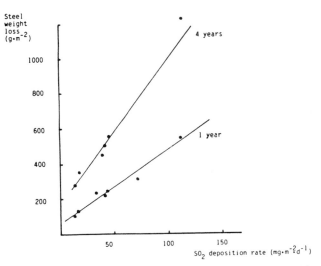

Steel. Corrosion vs. sulfur dioxide deposition rate. Corrosion on a painted steel surface generally begins at a defect in the coating with an initial loss of coating adhesion through cathodic delamination. Exposure to sulfur dioxide, a common corrosion stimulator that occurs in industrial and dense population areas, tends to give a neutral-to-acid subcoating liquid. Source: L. Igetoft, Reactions on Painted Steel Under the Influence of Sulfur Dioxide, Sodium Chloride and Combinations Thereof, *Industrial and Engineering Chemistry, Product Research and Development,* Vol 24, 1985, 376.

Sulfur Trioxide

Sulfur trioxide, SO_3, also known as sulfuric anhydride, exists in a number of modifications that differ in molecular species and crystalline form. It has a white, ice-like modification that melts at 16 °C (61 °F) and two other asbestos-like forms that melt at the higher temperatures of 33 and 62 °C (90 and 144 °F). The colorless liquid or gas form has irritating, toxic fumes and boils at 45 °C (112 °F). Sulfur trioxide is a highly reactive substance, a strong oxidizing agent, and a fire hazard. It reacts with metallic oxides to form sulfates and with water to form sulfuric acid. Sulfur trioxide is used for sulfonation.

Material Summaries

The following material summaries were compiled from a survey of the available literature. Inclusion of a material description under a given environment does not imply that it is the most appropriate material for corrosion service in that environment. Likewise, exclusion of a given material does not imply that it is not suitable for corrosion service applications in that environment.

Aluminum. Aluminum alloy reactors have been used for converting sulfur dioxide to sulfur trioxide.

Tantalum. Tantalum is attacked, even at room temperature, by free sulfur trioxide (as in fuming sulfuric acid).

Silver. Sulfur trioxide attacks silver at room temperature. The attack becomes progressively worse with rising temperatures.

Additional Reading

R.F. Littlejohn, D.M. Lloyd, and D.M. Willis, Experience in Coal-Fired Industrial Boilers, in *Dewpoint Corrosion*, Ellis Horwood, West Sussex, 35-49, 1985. MetAbs No. 86-350939. **Abstract:** Measurements of SO_3 concentration, dewpoints, and corrosion on several commercially operating plants have generally shown dewpoints and corrosion rates to be lower than might be expected from the direct measurements of SO_3. This phenomenon is discussed.

Corrosion Behavior of Various Metals and Alloys in Sulfur Trioxide

Material	Condition, other factors, comments	Concentration, %	Temperature, °C (°F)	Duration	Corrosion rate, mm/yr (mils/yr) or other	Ref
Coppers						
70-30 cupronickel	Dry	...	...	...	Suitable	93
90-10 cupronickel	Dry	...	...	...	Suitable	93
Admiralty brass	Dry	...	...	...	Suitable	93
Aluminum bronze	Dry	...	...	...	Suitable	93
Architectural bronze	Dry	...	...	...	Suitable	93
Brass	Dry	...	...	...	Suitable	93
Cartridge brass	Dry	...	...	...	Suitable	93
Commercial bronze	Dry	...	...	...	Suitable	93
Electrolytic copper	Dry	...	...	...	Suitable	93
Free-cutting brass	Dry	...	...	...	Suitable	93
Muntz metal	Dry	...	...	...	Suitable	93
Naval brass	Dry	...	...	...	Suitable	93
Nickel silver	Dry	18	...	...	Suitable	93
Phosphor bronze	5% Sn. Dry	...	...	...	Suitable	93
Phosphor bronze	8% Sn. Dry	...	...	...	Suitable	93
Phosphor copper	Dry	...	...	...	Suitable	93
Red brass	Dry	...	...	...	Suitable	93
Silicon bronze	Low. Dry	...	...	...	Suitable	93
Silicon bronze	High. Dry	...	...	...	Suitable	93
Noble metals						
Silver	...	Pure	Red heat	...	<0.05 (<2)	8

Sulfuric Acid

Sulfuric acid, H_2SO_4, also known as oil of vitriol and dipping acid, is a colorless, toxic, oily liquid. A great deal of heat is released when concentrated sulfuric acid and water are mixed; therefore, acid should always be added to water with sufficient stirring to prevent splattering and boiling. Sulfuric acid has a strong attraction for water and forms four crystalline hydrates. This affinity for water makes sulfuric acid an efficient drying agent for gases such as hydrogen, oxygen, nitrogen, and carbon dioxide, but results in the charring of organic compounds containing carbon, hydrogen, and oxygen such as cellulose, sugar, paper, and wood. Sulfuric acid participates in two types of oxidation reactions. One is the typical reaction of a strong acid that depends on the oxidizing power of the hydrogen ion, for example, the reaction of an active metal with the dilute acid to produce hydrogen. Sulfuric acid is a strong electrolyte and is used in electroplating baths, for pickling, and for other operations in the production of iron and steel. In the second type of oxidation reaction, the sulfate portion of the molecule reacts to form acid sulfates or bisulfates and the normal sulfates. Sulfuric acid is used in the manufacture of fertilizers, organic pigments, explosives, rayon, and film. Sulfuric acid has low volatility, a feature utilized in the manufacture of volatile acids such as nitric, hydrochloric, and hydrofluoric, where the volatile acid is vaporized when one of its salts is heated with the sulfuric acid.

Sulfuric acid is manufactured by the catalytic oxidation of sulfur dioxide by either the contact process or the lead-chamber process, although the contact process is now the primary process used to manufacture sulfuric acid. Acid produced by the conversion of sulfur trioxide by the contact process is concentrated (98 to 99%) and pure. Because anhydrous sulfuric acid is difficult to ship on account of its high freezing point, 10.5 °C (50 °F), sulfuric acid is ordinarily shipped at the 93.19% concentration, which is designated as oil of vitriol. This concentration has a low freezing point of -34 °C (-29 °F) and does not corrode steel containers at ordinary temperatures.

In the lead-chamber process, sulfur dioxide, oxygen, water vapor, and oxides of nitrogen are mixed in large, lead-lined chambers, and the liquid product as run off from the floor of the chambers is called chamber acid. Chamber acid has a concentration of 60 to 70% sulfuric acid by weight and contains considerable impurities. It reacts with steel shipping containers and is rarely shipped in quantity. Although more dilute acids are prepared, they must be shipped in expensive glass bottles. Chamber acid may be concentrated to 77% by evaporation in lead-lined pans and shipped in areas where its freezing point of -10.8 °C (12.6 °F) is acceptable. In cold climates, the concentration may be diluted to 76% to lower the freezing point. Sulfuric acid at the 76 to 78% concentration level is not seriously corrosive to steel tank cars and is an economical supply for the production of superphosphate by the fertilizer industry.

Temperature, concentration, and the presence of impurities affect the corrosiveness of sulfuric acid. Below 85% by weight at room temperature or about 65% at higher temperatures, sulfuric acid is a reducing acid and can best be handled by materials resistant to reducing conditions. In higher concentrations, it becomes an oxidizing acid and materials resistant to oxidizing agents are required. Selection of a metal or alloy for a particular application depends on the reducing or oxidizing nature of the solution, velocity, film formation, continuity of exposure, and physical properties of the alloy. Of the common metals, only lead is acceptably resistant to cold sulfuric acid in concentrations up to 100% and hot sulfuric acid in concentrations up to 70%. Cast iron resists both hot and cold sulfuric acid because of the formation of a protective scale layer. This resistance is very dependent on the concentration, which must be over 70% for cold acid and over 90% for hot acid. Cast iron may crack with explosive violence in the presence of sulfur trioxide gas and therefore should not be used as container material for oleum unless acid-resistant linings are used. Mild steel forms the same protective layer as cast iron, but is not as resistant and should not be used at temperatures over 49 °C (120 °F). In general, cast steel and malleable iron are available for specific concentrations, temperatures, and applications. Care must be exercised to exclude moisture from any iron or steel containers to prevent dilution and subsequent rapid corrosion. Other common alloys used to service sulfuric acid are Ni-Mo (Hastelloy B), Ni-Mo-Cr (Alloy C-276), Duriron, and Durimet 20. Duriron has the necessary corrosion resistance for use in concentrated sulfuric acid at very high temperatures (up to 400 °F).

Material Summaries

The following material summaries were compiled from a survey of the available literature. Inclusion of a material description under a given environment does not imply that it is the most appropriate material for corrosion service in that environment. Likewise, exclusion of a given material does not imply that it is not suitable for corrosion service applications in that environment.

Alloy Steel. Steel tanks are used to store sulfuric acid at ambient temperatures at concentrations of 65 to 100%. Corrosion can rapidly become catastrophic at these concentrations and at temperatures above 25 °C (75 °F).

Aluminum. Because the rate of attack is very low, aluminum alloys may be used to handle both dilute (below 10%) and concentrated (above 98%) sulfuric acid solutions. However, rapid attack occurs in the concentration range of 40 to 95%, with the maximum corrosion occurring at 80% concentration. In laboratory tests at ambient temperature, aluminum alloy 3003 suffered mild attack by fuming acids containing 101, 103, 107, and 115% sulfuric acid. Aluminum alloy 1100 pipe carries 99.5% acid at 45 °C (113 °F) in one plant. In another plant, 98% acid is transported in alloy 1100-H112 pipe at 200 °C (392 °F). Dilute solutions also utilize aluminum. For example, aluminum is used to process a thin aqueous slurry containing 1% sulfuric acid at room temperature, and an aluminum condenser cools sludge vapors from coking pots. Although the dilute sulfuric acid condensate causes some corrosion, aluminum has proved economical.

Carbon Steel. Steel has long been used in handling concentrated sulfuric acid at ambient temperatures under static and low-velocity conditions (<0.9 m/s, or 3 ft/s). A soft sulfate film forms that is highly protective unless physically disturbed. The actual corrosion rate of steel depends on temperature, acid concentration, iron content, and flow, because these parameters determine the dissolution rate of the protective sulfate film. Carbon steel corrodes in the active state at all concentrations up to 100% sulfuric acid. At concentrations below 50%, the iron sulfate corrosion product readily goes into solution, and corrosion rates are high at any temperature. At higher concentrations, the initial corrosion rate is high, but it is quickly reduced by the accumulation of iron sulfate corrosion product. It has been shown that the dissolution and diffusion of the ferrous sulfate away from the surface is the rate-limiting step. The effects of velocity, concentration, and temperature on the corrosion process in piping and storage tanks have been modeled. High velocity increases corrosion; therefore, steel is unsuitable for pump construction. At concentrations from 65 to 100% and at ambient temperatures, the sulfate layer diffuses into solution sufficiently slowly for the use of steel as a material of construction. Corrosion rates are typically 0.15 to 1.0 mm/yr (5.9 to 39 mils/yr). Storage tanks, pipelines, tank cars, and shipping drums made of ordinary carbon steel routinely handle sulfuric acid in concentrations of 78, 93, and 98%. In the oleum range above 101% sulfuric acid concentration (4% free SO_3), steel corrodes in the passive region because of the oxidizing effect of the SO_3. The passive film contains iron ions oxidized to the ferric state. Corrosion rates are typically 0.1 mm/yr (3.9 mils/yr) at ambient temperature. In the 100 to 101% concentration range, the steel goes through an active-passive transition state, and measured corrosion rates are erratic and excessive above 25 °C (75 °F). Steel is generally unsuitable in temperatures above 78 °C (175 °F).

Powder Metallurgy. In one study, potentiostatic anodic polarization measurements of steam-treated carbon steel in dilute (0.5%) sulfuric acid and aqueous sodium chloride solutions (400 ppm chloride ion) revealed significant reduction of corrosion rates for the chloride ion environment, whereas sulfuric acid testing showed an increase in corrosion rate. The latter was attributed to the solubility of the oxides in dilute sulfuric acid and their increased attack compared to the unoxidized steel.

Cast Irons. Cast iron alloys containing approximately 14.5% silicon have the best overall corrosion resistance to sulfuric acid in the 0 to 100% concentration range. Rapid attack occurs at concentrations over 100% and in service environments containing sulfur trioxide. It demonstrates good corrosion resistance (<5 mils/yr) to concentrated sulfuric acid at temperatures up to and including boiling. The resistance of high-silicon iron derives from the formation of a strong silicon-rich abrasion-resistant film that allows it to handle even the most abrasive slurries. High-silicon cast iron has been used at temperatures as high as 538 °C (1000 °F), when the temperature was raised and lowered slowly to prevent thermal shock. Duriron, a high-silicon cast iron alloy, is widely used for pumps, valves, heat exchangers, fans, tower sections, spargers, and sulfuric acid concentrator heating tubes.

High-nickel austenitic cast irons containing molybdenum exhibit acceptable corrosion resistance at room temperature and at slightly elevated temperatures. They are adequate over the entire range of sulfuric acid concentrations, but are a second choice compared to high-silicon cast irons.

Use of unalloyed and low-alloyed cast iron is limited to low-velocity, low-temperature concentrated (>70%) sulfuric acid service. In a low flow velocity, concentrated sulfuric acid may form a protective coating of insoluble iron sulfate film. If the acid is diluted to concentrations below 60%, the iron sulfate becomes soluble and rapid corrosion occurs. Therefore, unalloyed cast iron is rarely used in dilute or intermediate concentrations. Ductile iron is generally considered superior to gray iron, and ferritic matrix irons are superior to pearlitic matrix irons. The graphite flakes in cast iron are detrimental in oleum service. The acid can penetrate along the graphite flakes, and the corrosion product will build up sufficient pressure to split the iron. Interconnecting graphite is believed to be necessary to cause this form of cracking; therefore, ductile and malleable irons are generally acceptable for this service. In tests at room or moderate temperatures, iron demonstrates excellent resistance to mixtures of concentrated nitric and sulfuric acids with up to 20% water. The corrosion rate of iron in a mixture of 60% nitric and 10% sulfuric acids was 0.1 mm/yr (5 mils/yr). The iron-base superalloy Pyromet RN-155 (AISI 661, UNS R30155) has better resistance than stainless steel to dilute solutions of sulfuric acid.

Cemented Carbides. Sulfuric acid vigorously attacks the basic cemented carbides. The experimental grade 7 (WC-40TaC-3NiCoCr) provides excellent corrosion resistance. The straight WC-Co compositions experience rapid attack in warm (50 °C, or 120 °F) dilute sulfuric acid, but little attack in concentrated sulfuric acid. The TiC-6.5Ni-5Mo composition is quite good in warm sulfuric acid. Because sulfuric acid attacks the binders in cemented carbides, several of the binderless compositions and the TaC-base cemented carbides exhibit very acceptable corrosion resistance in warm sulfuric acid.

Copper Alloys. Copper and copper alloys are generally not suited for service in sulfuric acid because of their strong oxidation potentials. Brass can suffer dezincification in sulfuric acid. Normal copper-tin-bronzes may be used in concentrations below 60% at 79 °C (174 °F). Silicon bronzes such as C65500 can be used in solutions containing 3 to 70% by weight sulfuric acid at temperatures of 25 to 70 °C (75 to 160 °F). Aluminum bronzes are generally suitable for service in dilute (10 to 20%) sulfuric acid, especially in steel-pickling acids and in handling oil refinery sludges.

Zinc. The corrosion rate of zinc in sulfuric acid depends on the concentration of the acid and the impurities present in the metal. Zinc is slowly dissolved by dilute sulfuric acid, a reaction that releases hydrogen. Impurities in commercial zinc, such as aluminum, retard corrosion by the formation of a protective film. Other impurities, such as copper, reprecipitate in the form of a black metallic sponge, which may accelerate the attack by providing increased surface area. Tin and lead initially retard the corrosion rate, but after a few hours, they are deposited as metallic sponge and the corrosion rate is the same as in commercial zinc.

Lead. Lead exhibits high corrosion resistance to sulfuric acid and is used extensively in applications using concentrations below 70%. Lead has a protective film of lead sulfate that is soluble in concentrated sulfuric acid. This film is easily damaged by erosion or abrasion even at low velocities. For this reason, lead is rarely used for pumps or valves. Chemical lead, which contains 0.06% copper, is used in aggressive corrosion applications. Tellurium lead resists hot concentrated acid, but is inferior to chemical lead in all other conditions according to laboratory tests and plant data. Hard lead (4 to 15% antimony) is used when superior strength is required in dilute acid conditions. Lead is used as a pan material to catch acid drippings and as a membrane behind brick in sulfuric acid concentrating and scrubbing units.

Metallic Glasses. Copper-zirconium alloys have excellent resistance to sulfuric acid when they are devitrified to a single-phase or a multiphase equilibrium microstructure. However, the glassy state was about 20% more corrosion resistant than the devitrified state. The corrosion rates of the glassy alloy system containing phosphorus as the major metalloid were two orders of magnitude lower than those of the alloy system with boron as the major metalloid. In addition, the corrosion rate of the glassy iron-chromium alloy progressively decreased by the addition of silicon,

boron, carbon, and phosphorus in 0.1N sulfuric acid. The addition of chromium without phosphorus to glassy alloys is relatively ineffective in reducing corrosion rates.

Nickel. Nickel 200 can be used in sulfuric acid solutions at low or moderate temperatures. Aeration, increasing temperature, and the presence of oxidizing salts increase corrosion rates. The corrosion rate of Nickel 200 in boiling 5% sulfuric acid is 34 mils/yr, whereas in 10% boiling sulfuric acid it is 120 mils/yr. These corrosion rates could be lowered by either boiling under vacuum where the temperatures would be reduced or by the addition of inhibitors.

Nickel-Base Alloys. The corrosion rates of nickel-base alloys, in general, increase with acid concentrations up to about 90 wt%. However, the determining factor is the molybdenum and chromium content in the alloy composition. Higher concentrations of the acid are generally less corrosive. At low acid concentrations, the nickel-chromium-molybdenum alloys, such as Alloy C-276, show a significantly higher resistance than type 316 stainless steel. Alloy 20, a high-nickel stainless steel, shows similar behavior. These high nickel-chromium-molybdenum alloys can be used only at moderate temperatures in intermediate and high concentrations of sulfuric acid. The nickel-molybdenum Alloy B-2 performs well in pure, deaerated sulfuric acid; however, in the presence of oxidizing species (ferric ions) and oxygen (air), it suffers serious corrosion.

The presence of oxidizing impurities can be beneficial to nickel-chromium-molybdenum alloys because these impurities can aid in the formation of passive films that retard corrosion. Another important consideration is the presence of chlorides. Chlorides generally accelerate the attack. Therefore, high-molybdenum alloys are used in the production of mineral acids when the acid is contaminated with halides. These alloys are also specified when sulfuric acid is used in the production of other chemicals and for the construction of radioactive waste disposal evaporators.

Some nickel-base alloys have superior resistance to corrosion in sulfuric acid up to 95% concentration because of their high alloy content, e.g., Alloy C-276 and Alloy 625. Frequently, low corrosion rates occur in both the active and passive states. Thus, reliable corrosion behavior is achieved over a wide range of concentrations, temperatures, and impurity levels.

Nickel-copper alloys, for example Monel 400, are used to handle sulfuric acid under reducing conditions. This alloy offers an alternative to stainless steels and other alloys exhibiting active-passive behavior when the sulfuric acid solutions are nonoxidizing such as deaerated dilute acid. Monel 400 has low corrosion rates in air-free sulfuric acid up to 85% concentration at 30 °C (85 °F) and up to 60% concentration at 95 °C (205 °F). In air-saturated acid, increasing the temperature or the velocity accelerates the corrosion rate considerably.

Inconel 600, because of its high chromium content, has better resistance to sulfuric acid under oxidizing conditions than either Nickel 200 or Monel 400. Although Inconel 600 may be passivated by the addition of oxidizing salts, it should not be subjected to hot sulfuric acid except in low concentrations. When aeration is combined with high temperature, corrosion rates are high. Both Chlorimet 3 and Hastelloy C are useful in all concentrations of sulfuric acid. They exhibit good resistance to hot dilute acids under reducing conditions and, because of their high chromium contents, are not affected by oxidizing conditions. Alloy 617 is resistant to sulfuric acid in concentrations of 30% at 80 °C (175 °F) and 10% at boiling.

Nickel-base iron-chromium-molybdenum-copper alloys, such as Incoloy 825, provide excellent service in applications where chlorides are present. Incoloy 825 is highly resistant to all concentrations of sulfuric acid at temperatures below 65 °C (150 °F). Its corrosion resistance is enhanced by the presence of oxidizing salts; therefore, it is suitable for use in mixtures containing nitric acid, ferric sulfate, and cupric sulfate. Incoloy 800 is only useful at low concentrations of sulfuric acid at ambient temperatures.

Nickel-base chromium-iron-cobalt-silicon alloys are proprietary alloys developed specifically for hot concentrated sulfuric acid pump and valve applications. Alloy 55 is one such cast alloy. Alloy 66 is a ductile cast alloy that can also be made in the wrought form. Both forms have excellent corrosion resistance in the 0 to 60% and 80 to 90% ranges, but performance is erratic in the 60 to 80% range.

Nickel-base chromium-molybdenum-copper alloys are proprietary alloys designed to resist sulfuric acid concentrations up to 98% at temperatures up to 100 °C (212 °F). Illium 98 is a weldable, machinable cast alloy.

Niobium. Niobium is resistant to sulfuric acid under oxidizing conditions, for example, in concentrated sulfuric acid containing cupric or ferric ions. Niobium is also resistant at room temperature to all concentrations of sulfuric acid up to 95%.

Gold. Gold exhibits excellent resistance to sulfuric acid up to 250 °C (480 °F) and is used when no corrosion or contamination can be tolerated.

Silver. Silver is rapidly attacked by hot concentrated (60%) sulfuric acid and by 95% sulfuric acid at room temperature.

Platinum. Platinum resists sulfuric acid in all concentrations and temperatures.

Palladium. Palladium is generally resistant to corrosion by most single acids, but when air is present, hot sulfuric acid attacks palladium.

Osmium. Osmium is resistant to sulfuric acid.

Rhodium. In wrought or cast form, rhodium is attacked slowly at 100 °C (212 °F) by concentrated sulfuric acid.

Stainless Steels. The conventional austenitic grades exhibit good resistance in very dilute or highly concentrated sulfuric acid at slightly elevated temperatures. Acid in the intermediate concentration is more aggressive; thus conventional grades have very limited use. Aeration or the addition of an oxidizing species stabilizes the chromium-rich passive oxide film that protects the stainless steel and reduces the corrosive action of sulfuric acid. Cations that are easily reduced, such as ferric, cupric, and stannic ions, are oxidizing agents that can inhibit corrosion. Nitric acid concentrations as low as 1.5% were found to inhibit the corrosion of stainless steel over a wide range of concentrations at ambient and elevated temperatures. Concentrated sulfuric acid (above 97%) and oleum are strongly oxidizing and corrosion is reduced dramatically. Most stainless steels and nickel-based alloys experience similar reductions in corrosion rates with increasing concentration.

The resistance of austenitic stainless steels to sulfuric acid is complex due to the active-passive nature of the alloys. Stable passivity is achieved at ambient temperatures in the very low concentrations, very high concentrations, and in oleum. In the oleum range, stainless steels are free from the concerns about minor concentration variations, and corrosion resistance is extended well in excess of 100 °C (212 °F). At ambient temperature, austenitic stainless steels, for example type 304, exhibit passivity in 93% sulfuric acid and are used for piping and tankage where product purity is desirable. Anodic protection by an impressed current can extend the useful temperature and concentration range by holding the stainless steel component in the passive condition. For example, stainless steel may be protected in 93% sulfuric acid up to 70 °C (160 °F) and in 98% sulfuric acid up to 120 °C (250 °F). If a stainless steel is solidly

in the passive state, velocity has little effect. However, if the alloy drops to active-passive behavior, usually due to increasing temperature, velocity has a major effect. Abrasive conditions can force active-passive behavior even in 96% sulfuric acid at ambient temperature.

The performance of stainless steel in sulfuric acid depends on the composition of the grade. For example, the presence of nickel and copper in some austenitic grades greatly enhances resistance to sulfuric acid compared to the resistance of ferritic grades. Conventional ferritic grades, such as type 430, have limited use in sulfuric acid. Stainless steels have poor resistance to deaerated dilute solutions. Type 310 stainless steel with 25% chromium and no intentionally added molybdenum is more resistant than the molybdenum-bearing grades when oxidizing agents are present. Type 316 and type 317 are more resistant than any of the other chromium-nickel types to sulfuric acid solutions. They resist solutions up to 5% concentration at temperatures as high as 49 °C (120 °F), and higher concentrations at temperatures under 38 °C (100 °F).

Like the austenitic stainless steels, the corrosion resistance of the higher austenitic stainless steels is also complex. However, the range of passivity and corrosion resistance is extended because of the higher alloy content. Like the stainless steels, active and active-passive behavior are the modes of corrosion. The class of alloys with an iron base and approximately 25% nickel, 20% chromium, and 4.5% molybdenum have higher resistance than type 316 stainless steel as a result of the higher alloy content. Copper, titanium, and niobium are sometimes added as stabilizing agents. The copper-bearing alloys are more resistant than the copper-free alloys over the entire range of sulfuric acid concentrations at ambient temperature.

An alloy that was originally developed for sulfuric acid service, but is used for many other environments, is generally known as Alloy 20. Improved resistance to general corrosion and stress-corrosion cracking has been obtained by increasing the nickel and chromium and molybdenum content of type 316 and 317 stainless steels and adding copper. Its counterpart, cast ACI CN-7M, has equivalent resistance to sulfuric acid and is suitable up to 80 °C (175 °F) at concentrations up to 50%. For higher concentrations, good corrosion resistance is expected up to 65 °C (150 °F). This alloy is fully austenitic and must be solution annealed for maximum corrosion resistance. Although foundries have their own trade names, the alloy is always identified with the number 20, for example, Carpenter 20 (wrought form), FA-20 (austenitic and ductile), Durimet 20, Esco 20, CH-20, and CK-20. This alloy is suitable in all concentrations, with the largest corrosion rates occurring at 78%. The oxidizing agents ferric sulfate and copper sulfate added to the acid act as inhibitors and decrease attack. Alloy 20 is used in contact-process acid plants for pumps and valves. An improved version of the alloy is known as 20Cb-3. This alloy has higher nickel and is stabilized against chromium carbide precipitation. Alloy 20Cb-3, for instance, is used for valve springs in sulfuric acid service.

Austenitic stainless steels containing 5 to 6% silicon, available in either cast or wrought versions, have interesting corrosion characteristics. Corrosion protection is obtained by the formation of a tenacious silicon-rich film produced on the surface during the initial days of corrosion. These alloys resist corrosion in 99% sulfuric acid up to 120 °C (250 °F) without anodic protection and are used for piping and vessels for hot, concentrated sulfuric acid.

Cast stainless steels have the same corrosion resistance to sulfuric acid as their wrought equivalents. In general, Alloy 20 castings outperform the other cast stainless steels, except in high concentrations and in oleum service. Because the cast versions contain second-phase ferrite for castability, proper heat treatment must be undertaken to ensure maximum corrosion resistance. The alloy CD-4MCu, which does not have a wrought counterpart, resists sulfuric acid in all concentrations at ambient temperature and is suitable for oleum service at temperatures above 100 °C (212 °F). The CE-30 cast alloy is resistant to sulfurous acid, sulfites, and mixtures of sulfurous and sulfuric acids. The high-chromium CC-50 cast alloy is used as castings in contact with acid mine waters, sulfuric and nitric acid mixtures, alkaline liquors, and sulfurous liquors.

Corrosion studies of sintered austenitic stainless steels have shown that the corrosion resistance improves with increasing density in dilute sulfuric acid. Stainless steel parts made by extrusion from rapidly solidified powders have superior oxidation resistance, no surface pitting, low pit density within the material, and the lowest corrosion rate at the corrosion potential in $1M$ sulfuric acid. This superior oxidation and corrosion resistance is attributed to the elevated temperature grain growth inhibiting effect of uniformly dispersed manganese sulfide particles.

Tantalum. Tantalum is highly resistant to corrosion by sulfuric acid in all concentrations up to about 98%. It is inert to dilute acid even at boiling temperatures and is not attacked by concentrated acids at temperatures below 150 °C (300 °F). A slow, uniform attack by concentrated sulfuric acid begins on tantalum at about 175 °C (345 °F). However, the corrosion by hot, concentrated sulfuric acid is uniform, and at a temperature as high as 200 °C (390 °F), tantalum can be successfully used with 98% sulfuric acid.

Fuming sulfuric acid (oleum) attacks the metal much more rapidly than the concentrated acid, but the attack is uniform over the entire surface. The presence of impurities does not increase the corrosion rate. Although no failures due to hydrogen embrittlement have been reported for tantalum chemical-processing equipment used in sulfuric acid service, hydrogen embrittlement in tantalum has been produced under special laboratory test conditions.

In applications where a material harder and stronger than the pure metal is desired, Ta-10W binary solid-solution alloy, also known as Fansteel 60 Metal, has been used. For example, Ta-10W alloy is used as an insert in the plug of a tantalum-lined split-body valve to give a hard plug to a soft seat and also to repair glass-lined steel equipment. Tests run at 205 and 230 °C (400 and 450 °F) indicate that either unalloyed tantalum or Ta-10W can be used at 230 °C (450 °F) to handle sulfuric acid in concentrations below 90%. However, the corrosion weight loss of Ta-10W is about twice that of unalloyed tantalum at 230 °C (450 °F) in sulfuric acid over the concentration range of 70 to 90%.

Corrosion tests run in both hot and cold concentrated sulfuric acid on alloys with various proportions of tantalum and niobium showed the corrosion rates increased roughly in proportion to the niobium content of the alloy. Even though the 95Ta-5Nb alloy showed excellent resistance in all exposures, the attack was three times that obtained on pure tantalum. Tests on the materials were carried out in 75% sulfuric acid at 185 °C (360 °F), in 70% at 165 °C (330 °F), and in 75% at room temperature. The tantalum-niobium alloys containing approximately 60% or more tantalum appeared promising for boiling 70% sulfuric acid. The addition of zirconium, hafnium, chromium, and vanadium lowered the corrosion resistance.

Alloy WC-640 was developed for corrosion-resistant applications. It exhibited excellent resistance to all test environments except concentrated sulfuric acid at 200 °C (390 °F). The chemical composition of the alloy corresponded to a ternary tantalum-niobium-tungsten alloy, Ta-40Nb-0.5W, and its tensile strength was similar to that of Tantaloy 63.

Tin. The corrosion rate of tin in sulfuric acid varies with concentration and temperature. At ordinary temperatures, concentrated sulfuric acid has slight action on tin, but as the temperature is increased sulfur dioxide and a little hydrogen sulfide are evolved along with a separation of sulfur. In a more dilute acid (1:3), the reaction occurs at a lower temperature, with more hydrogen sulfide and less sulfur dioxide being formed. In a diluted (1:5) acid, no reaction occurs at 25 °C (75 °F), but at 100 °C (212 °F), hydrogen with a trace of hydrogen sulfide is evolved.

Titanium. Unalloyed titanium is rapidly attacked by all concentrations of sulfuric acid except very dilute solutions at low temperatures. Impurities in the form of oxidizing agents may act as inhibitors; for example, titanium resists 0 to 50% concentrations of sulfuric acid saturated with chlorine. Titanium has also been used in the sulfuric acid leaching of nickel ores, for example, the leaching of a nickel-cobalt ore by a 10% sulfuric acid solution at 246 °C (475 °F). The acid contained 32 to 35% solids that added abrasion to the corrosive environment. Resistance is attributed to the presence of heavy-metal oxidizing agents, such as ferric, cupric, and chromate ions.

Another method of reducing the attack on titanium by sulfuric acid is to use an anodic passivation technique. This consists of coupling the titanium to the positive pole of a DC source and applying a potential of between 1.5 and 12 V. This reinforces the oxide film, which allows the material to withstand attack by 60% sulfuric acid at temperatures up to 90 °C (208 °F). Titanium has been used for electrolyte refining in copper sulfate solutions and for steam coils in 25 to 30% sulfuric acid in pigment processes.

The titanium-palladium alloy, Titanium 260, is significantly more resistant than unalloyed titanium in pure sulfuric acid solutions and is suitable for use in a 4% solution at the boiling point, 10% at 70 °C (158 °F), and 25% at room temperature. After slight initial corrosion, the palladium redeposits on the surface to provide efficient cathodic areas for passivating the anode reaction. The palladium alloys were developed to eliminate crevice and deposit corrosion problems.

Moderate additions of molybdenum to titanium can provide excellent resistance to strong reducing acid environments. The grade 12 alloy, Ti-0.8Ni-0.3Mo, has better resistance to dilute reducing acid solutions than unalloyed titanium and is a less expensive alternative to palladium alloys in services where crevice or deposit attack is a concern. Molybdenum is more efficient than tantalum, niobium, or zirconium in this role.

Hafnium. Hafnium is soluble in concentrated sulfuric acid. It is resistant to dilute sulfuric acid.

Zirconium. Zirconium has excellent resistance to sulfuric acid up to 50% concentration at temperatures to boiling and above. The corrosion resistance of zirconium depends on the formation of the passive film, zirconium dioxide, which is highly ordered and corrosion resistant. Electrochemical measurements show the corrosion potential of zirconium in sulfuric acid to be located solidly in the passive region when it is resisting corrosion. However, as temperature and/or concentration increases, the transpassive potential (breakdown) decreases, and there is less tolerance for oxidizing agents. At high temperatures in concentrations exceeding 50%, sufficient quantities of oxidizing agents, such as ferric, cupric, and nitrate ions, deplete the passive region, causing zirconium to corrode actively. However, in 20% or less, zirconium can tolerate a great deal of strong oxidizing agents. Consequently, zirconium equipment is often used in steel pickling processes.

Zirconium weld material may corrode preferentially when sulfuric acid concentration is 55% and higher; therefore, zirconium is seldom used in the welded condition unless it has been heat treated to maximize corrosion resistance. Zirconium finds use in the concentration range of 0 to 50% and in dilute sulfuric acid at elevated temperatures. In these two regions, iron- and nickel-base alloys corrode rapidly, or their resistance depends strongly on concentration, temperature, or aeration. Another important application for zirconium is in processes that cycle between sulfuric acid and alkaline solutions. One company replaced a lead- and brick-lined carbon steel reactor vessel with zirconium because the reaction alternated between hot sulfuric acid and caustic. The vessel has been in use for several years with no corrosion problems.

Zirconium is used in sulfuric acid recovery and recycle systems in which fluorides are not present and the acid concentration does not exceed 65%. Zirconium can tolerate only very small amounts of fluoride ions in sulfuric acid even at low acid concentrations. When heavy-metal ions and halide ions coexist in sulfuric acid (for example, when ferric chloride is present), the optimum acid concentration range for zirconium is 60 to 65%.

The earliest application for zirconium was in the production of hydrogen peroxide using sulfuric acid. Zirconium shell and tube heat exchangers replaced graphite exchangers at one plant where they were used to condense a 75% concentrated sulfuric acid medium. The average maintenance-free life of the heat exchanger was 12 years. The tubes were thinned at the liquid/gas interface area because of bubble collapse, but no other corrosion occurred. Because of this experience, the company used zirconium shell and tube exchangers in the manufacture of acrylic films and fibers. In this application, the sulfuric acid concentration was as high as 60% at 150 °C (300 °F). Acid concentration limit is very important when zirconium is used to handle sulfuric acid at elevated temperatures in the marginal concentration region, such as 60% or more. When the limit is exceeded, zirconium may corrode rapidly. Acid concentration may change significantly because of an imperfect seal, or when the system is under vacuum because the water vapor is continuously taken away.

Additional Reading

S.K. Brubecker, Materials of Construction for Sulfuric Acid, "Process Industries Corrosion," National Association of Corrosion Engineers, Houston, 1986. **Abstract:** Corrosion resistance of metals and nonmetals commonly used in sulfuric acid service is summarized. The corrosion protection of metals is explained in the context of electrochemical behavior. The effect of velocity, temperature, impurities and oxidants is discussed. Materials of construction for specific equipment are included.

"The Corrosion Resistance of Nickel-Containing Alloys in Sulfuric Acid and Related Compounds," International Nickel Co., 1983, 89 pages. **Abstract:** This publication gathers data from a variety of sources, including laboratory and field exposures, as well as the literature, technical bulletins of the alloy producers and actual plant experience.

W. Kamer, M.Y. Nazmy, and A. Arfaj, Phase Instability and Corrosion Behavior of AISI 316 P/M Stainless Steel, *Werkst. Korros.*, *31*(6), 446-452, 1980. MetAbs No. 81-350458. **Abstract:** The corrosion behavior of metal powder compacts of different densities, made from AISI 316 stainless steel prealloyed powder, heat treated at different temperatures and times, was investigated. Microcharacterization of polished and fracture surfaces was performed by scanning electron microscopy. Energy dispersive X-ray analysis was used to identify precipitated phases.

P. Millenbach and M. Givon, The Effect of Arsenic on the Active-Passive Transition of Titanium, *Corrosion*, *39*(1), 13-14, 1983. MetAbs No. 83-350733. **Abstract:** Anodic polarization experiments on Ti showed that the presence of arsenic markedly decreased the critical current and the primary passivation potential. These results indicate that As acts as an anticorrosive agent.

M. Hasegawa and M. Osawa, Anomalous Corrosion of Hydrogen-Containing Ferritic Steels in Aqueous Acid Solution, *Corrosion*, *39*(4), 115-120, 1983. MetAbs No. 83-351493. **Abstract:** The effect of dissolved hydrogen in soft Fe and ferritic low-alloy steel on general corrosion was investigated in acid solutions.

R.A. Mulford, E.L. Hall, and C.L. Briant, Sensitization of Austenitic Stainless Steels. II. Commercial-Purity Alloys, *Corrosion*, *39*(4), 132-143, 1983. MetAbs No. 83-351494. **Abstract:** The effects of nitrogen and Mo on the sensitization of commercial-purity 304 and 316 stainless steels were studied. The degree of sensitization of the steels and the chemistry of grain boundaries and the crystallography and chemistry of grain boundary phases are noted. Corrosion data from different alloys are considered in terms of effective Cr content.

T.L. Yau and R.T. Webster, The Effects of Iron on the Corrosion Resistance of Zirconium, *Corrosion*, *39*(6), 218-226, 1983. MetAbs No. 83-352024. **Abstract:** Zirconium is one of the few metals that resists attack by sulfuric acid up to 75% concentration. Selective corrosion may be found in welds at somewhat lower concentrations. It is generally believed that Fe in Zr plays an important role in degrading Zr corrosion resistance.

T.L. Walzak and J.S. Sheasby, The Effect of Heat Treatment Parameters on the Anodic Polarization Behavior of 440C Stainless Steel, *Corrosion*, *39*(12), 502-507, 1983. MetAbs No. 84-350838. **Abstract:** The consequences of varying the heat treatment for hardening 440C stainless steel on the anodic polarization behavior in dilute sulfuric acid were investigated by electrochemical methods.

K. Bilogan, Corrosion Cracking Phenomena Under Different Polarizing and Microstructural Conditions in a 304 Stainless Steel Tested in Low-Temperature Acid Solutions, *Corrosion*, *39*(12), 508-514, 1983. MetAbs No. 84-350839. **Abstract:** Experiments have shown that for the various microstructural conditions of 304 stainless steels (i.e., annealed, cold worked and dynamically recrystallized) there was no evidence of cracking in specimens tested under freely corroding conditions. At the more active potentials, an increased susceptibility to cracking was observed.

P. Gupta, R.S. Chaudhary, T.K.G. Namboodhiri, B. Prakash, and B.B. Prasad, Effect of Mixed Inhibitors on Dezincification and Corrosion of 63/37 Brass in 1% Sulfuric Acid, *Corrosion*, *40*(1), 33-36, 1984. MetAbs No. 84-351093. **Abstract:** Dezincification, pitting corrosion and grain boundary attack are some of the prevalent types of corrosion failures among brasses. Malachite green, congo red, crystal violet, alizarin, methyl orange and benzotriazole have been used as mixed inhibitors for minimizing the corrosion and the dezincification rate of 63/37 brass in 1% H_2SO_4 solution.

T. Ramchandran and T.K.G. Namboodhiri, A Potentiostatic Evaluation of the Corrosion of a Ni-Co Base Amorphous Alloy, *Corrosion*, *40*(2), 73-77, 1984. MetAbs No. 84-351162. **Abstract:** Corrosion of a $Ni_{40}Co_{20}Cr_{12}Mo_6Fe_6B_{16}$ amorphous alloy in deaerated H_2SO_4 was evaluated by potentiostatic polarization measurements. Effects of acid concentration, sequence of polarization and presence of Cl^- ions in the acid on the polarization curves were determined.

B.S. Covino Jr. and M. Rosen, Induction Time Studies of Fe18Cr and 430 SS Under Open-Circuit Conditions in Chloride-Containing Sulfuric Acid, *Corrosion*, *40*(4), 140-145, 1984. MetAbs No. 84-351889. **Abstract:** To promote the effective and efficient application of corrosion-resistant metals and alloys in mineral processing environments, the US Bureau of Mines has characterized the effect of aggressive ions on the corrosion and passive behavior of two stainless steels—Fe18Cr and AISI 430. Susceptibility to chloride ion attack was determined as a function of time in solution (film aging time), chloride ion concentration, and open-circuit potentials.

S. Wakefield, F.H. Beck, and G.W. Powell, The Anodic Polarization Characteristics of Fe-Si-Al Alloys in 1N H_2SO_4, *Corrosion*, 40(4), 190-195, 1984. MetAbs No. 84-351896. **Abstract:** The anodic polarization characteristics in 1N H_2SO_4 (25 °C) of Fe-8% Si, Fe-8Al and Fe-5Si-3Al alloys fabricated by conventional processing (ingot metallurgy) and of Fe-8Al fabricated by powder metallurgy were determined.

D. Itzhak and E. Aghion, An Anodic Behavior Study of an Analogical Sintered System of Austenitic Stainless Steel in H_2SO_4 Solution, *Corros. Sci.*, 24(2), 145-152, 1984. MetAbs No. 84-352032. **Abstract:** The anodic behavior of sintered austenitic stainless steel was investigated on an analogical system using wrought type 316 stainless steel plate. Potentiodynamic polarization measurements were carried out in an analogical concentration cell using a special method. The effect of carbide precipitation on the anodic behavior was investigated on carburized 316 wrought stainless steel containing an average carbon concentration of 0.06 and 0.15 wt%.

M. Hasegawa and M. Osawa, Corrosion Behavior of Ultrafine-Grained Austenitic Stainless Steel, *Corrosion*, 40(7), 371-374, 1984. MetAbs No. 84-352606. **Abstract:** Ultrafine-grained AISI 304 steel was produced by low-temperature recrystallization after subzero working and the corrosion behavior of these steels was investigated in various corrosive environments.

A.A. Aksut, The Corrosion Behavior of Cobalt and Nickel in Sulfuric Acid Solution Containing Propargylic Alcohol, *Corrosion*, 40(8), 418-420, 1984. MetAbs No. 84-352700. **Abstract:** The inhibiting effect of propargylic alcohol on the corrosion of analytically pure Co and Ni was studied.

J.B. Lee, J.F. Smith, A.L. Geiger, and D.H. Kah, An Analytical Electron Microscope Examination of Sensitized AISI 430 Stainless Steel, *Corrosion*, 41(2), 76-80, 1985. MetAbs No. 85-350639. **Abstract:** The microstructures of sensitized and nonsensitized AISI 430 stainless (17% Cr, 0.07% carbon) have been studied using analytical electron microscopy.

R.S. Glass, Passivation of Titanium by Molybdate Ion, *Corrosion*, 41(2), 89-93, 1985. MetAbs No. 85-350642. **Abstract:** The passivating effect of molybdate ion on the corrosion of Ti in deaerated, boiling 1N H_2SO_4 has been explored.

R. Kotz and S. Stucki, Oxygen Evolution and Corrosion on Ruthenium-Iridium Alloys, *J. Electrochem. Soc.*, 132(1), 103-107, 1985. MetAbs No. 85-350685. **Abstract:** The initial stages of oxygen evolution and anodic corrosion on Ru-Ir alloys have been investigated in 1N H_2SO_4 using voltammetry and X-ray photoelectron spectroscopy.

S. Berhnardsson, P. Norberg, H. Eriksson, and O. Forssell, Stainless Steels in the Petrochemical Industries, *Iron Steel Inst.*, 58(1), 7-9, 1985. MetAbs No. 85-351268. **Abstract:** The corrosion resistance of austenitic and duplex stainless steels is compared. Results of tests in neutral aerated aqueous chloride environments, critical pitting temperature and isocorrosion diagrams in stagnant H_2SO_4 in contact with air are described.

T.C. Tan and D.-T. Chin, Polarization of Aluminum During AC Corrosion in Sulfate Solutions, *J. Electrochem. Soc.*, 132(4), 766-772, 1985. MetAbs No. 85-351343. **Abstract:** An experimental study has been made on the effect of alternating voltage on the corrosion of Al (6061) in aqueous solutions of 1N H_2SO_4, 1N Na_2SO_4, 1N NaOH, and 1N Na_2SO_4 containing 0 to 5010 ppm Cl- ions. The polarization curves were measured with an alternating voltage modulation technique.

S.S. Abd El Rehim, M.Sh. Shalaby, and S.M. Abd El Haleem, Effect of Some Anions on the Anodic Dissolution of Delta-52 Steel in Sulfuric Acid Solutions, *Surf. Technol.*, 24(3), 241-251, 1985. MetAbs No. 85-351759. **Abstract:** The anodic dissolution of hot-rolled Delta-52 steel (an Egyptian product) was studied protentiodynamically in H_2SO_4 solutions of various concentrations.

B.A. Abd-El-Nabey, N. Khalil, and A. Mohamed, Inhibition by Amino Acids of the Corrosion of Steel in Acid, *Surf. Technol.*, 24(4), 383-389, 1985. MetAbs No. 85-351810. **Abstract:** Electrochemical measurements and corrosion tests were performed at room temperature using mild steel (0.09% carbon) specimens immersed in 1N H_2SO_4 solutions.

R.P. Singh, O.P. Modi, M.N. Mungole, and K.P. Singh, Corrosion of 2.25Cr-1Mo Ferritic Steel in Sulfuric Acid and Seawater, *Br. Corros. J.*, 20(1), 28-31, 1985. MetAbs No. 85-351883. **Abstract:** The corrosion behavior of 2.25Cr-1Mo ferritic steel in different concentrations (0.05-5N) of sulfuric acid and in seawater has been studied by potentiodynamic polarization measurements at scan rates of 45 mV/min. The experiments were performed on steels in two different conditions—cold worked and annealed at 850 °C for 2 h in vacuum (0.1 Pa), and the effect of microstructure was also analyzed.

S.K. Mukherjee, A. Kumar, and G.S. Upadhyaya, Effect of Fe_2P Additions on Corrosion Behavior of Ferritic Stainless Steel Composite Compacts Containing 6 vol% Al_2O_3, *Br. Corros. J.*, 20(1), 41-44, 1985. MetAbs No. 85-351886. **Abstract:** A potentiodynamic study has been made of sintered 434L ferritic stainless steel compacts containing 6 vol% Al_2O_3 and various amounts (0-3 wt%) of phosphorus, added as Fe_2P. The tests were carried out at room temperature in 1N H_2SO_4.

S.H. Sanad, H. Abbas, A.A. Ismail, and K.M. El-Sobki, Benzotriazole as a Corrosion Inhibitor for Brass, *Surf. Technol.*, 25(1), 39-48, 1985. MetAbs No. 85-352057. **Abstract:** The effect of benzotriazole on the corrosion of 67/33, 70/30, and 90/10 brasses in 0.1N HCl, 0.1N H_2SO_4 and 0.1N NH_4Cl was studied by means of immersion tests and galvanostatic measurements.

H. Bala, Effect of Stirring on Spontaneous Dissolution Rate of Iron in Sulfuric Acid Solutions, *Electrochim. Acta*, 30(8), 1043-1047, 1985. MetAbs No. 85-352072. **Abstract:** The effect of concentration of deaerated 0.5-11M sulfuric acid on corrosion rate of rotating discs made of pure Fe was investigated at 1-36 rps.

Y.-N. Chang, Corrosion of Steels in the Mixture of Sulfuric Acid and Activated Carbon, *Anti-Corros. Methods Mater.*, 32(5), 7-8, 1985. MetAbs No. 85-352210. **Abstract:** Corrosion of steels in a mixture of sulfuric acid and activated carbon has been investigated, and a "rolling ball" model is suggested to explain the corrosion-resistant characteristics of chromium steels.

J. Vehlow, Corrosion of Zircaloy-4 in H_2SO_4-NaF and Its Application for Measuring the Distribution Pattern of Fission Products in Zircaloy-4 Fuel Hulls, *Werkst. Korros.*, 36(5), 195-202, 1985. MetAbs No. 85-352244. **Abstract:** The corrosion behavior of Zircaloy-4 in 1N H_2SO_4 with small amounts of NaF was investigated by means of radionuclide technical and electrochemical methods.

Y.G. Kim, G.W. Yoon, and N.S. Stoloff, Effect of Boron on the Corrosion Behavior of Polycrystalline Ni_3Al, *Metall. Trans. A*, 16A(11), 2072-2073, 1985. MetAbs No. 85-352341. **Abstract:** The effects of boron additions on the corrosion behavior of Ni_3Al in HCl, H_2SO_4, NaCl and H_3PO_4 electrolytes were studied.

S.K. Mukherjee and G.S. Upadhyaya, Corrosion Behavior of Sintered 434L Ferritic Stainless Steel-Al_2O_3 Composites Containing Phosphorus, *Corros. Sci.*, 25(7), 463-470, 1985. MetAbs No. 85-352386. **Abstract:** The effect of phosphorus, either as Fe_3P or Fe_2P, on the corrosion behavior of sintered ferritic stainless steel-Al_2O_3 composites in 1N H_2SO_4 solution at room temperature has been studied.

D. Kelly, P. Niessen, and E.M.L. Valeriote, The Influence of Composition and Microstructure on the Corrosion Behavior of Pb-Ca-Sn Alloys in Sulfuric Acid Solutions, *J. Electrochem. Soc.*, 132(11), 2533-2538, 1985. MetAbs No. 86-350168. **Abstract:** The corrosion behavior of select Pb-Ca-Sn alloys after various thermal treatments has been studied.

S.S. Abd El Rehim, S.M. Abd El Haleem, and M.Sh. Shalaby, Electrochemical Behavior and Corrosion of 18-8 Austenitic Stainless Steel in Sulfate Solutions, *Surf. Technol.*, 26(1), 77-85, 1985. MetAbs No. 86-350407. **Abstract:** The electrochemical behavior and corrosion of a commercial Egyptian 18-8 austenitic stainless steel was investigated in sulfuric acid and in sodium sulfate solutions using the potentiodynamic technique.

M.M. Nerodenko, L.M. Onoprienko, V.A. Gorban, and A.B. Goncharov, Corrosion Resistance of Welded Joints of Zirconium Alloy With 2.5% Niobium in Hydrochloric, Sulfuric and Phosphoric Acids, *Avtom. Svarka*, (8), 53-56, 1985. MetAbs No. 86-350415. **Abstract:** Corrosion resistance of TIG welded samples from Zr-Nb alloy (2.5% Nb, 0.056% oxygen, 0.0006% hydrogen and 0.0067% nitrogen) was determined by weight loss in boiling solutions of HCl, H_2SO_4 and H_3PO_4 and also in 20% solution of HCl with addition of 1 g/L $CuCl_2$.

K.P. Soni and I.M. Bhatt, Inhibition of Copper, Brass and Aluminium in Nitric Acid, Sulfuric Acid and Trichloroacetic Acid, *J. Electrochem. Soc. India*, 34(1), 76-77, 1985. MetAbs No. 86-350473. **Abstract:** A number of workers have studied corrosion of 99.6% Cu, brass (36.7% Zn) and Al in acid, alkali and neutral solutions; various organic and inorganic substances have also been investigated as inhibitors. Corrosion of brass, Cu and Al in acid media and the inhibition by diphenyl thiourea and dithioglycolic acid were studied.

M. Magrini, P. Matteazzi, and A. Frignani, Structural Characterization and Electrochemical Behavior of Fe-Ni-Mo-B Amorphous Alloys, *Mater. Chem. Phys.*, 13(1), 71-83, 1985. MetAbs No. 86-350502. **Abstract:** A series of amorphous alloys obtained by the "melt-spinning" technique, with variable nickel and molybdenum contents, have been examined. Potentiodynamic anodic and cathodic polarization curves have been obtained for each of these amorphous alloys in various environments (1N HCl, 1N H_2SO_4, 3% NaCl, 1N NaOH). Their electrochemical properties were correlated with the amorphous structure and with composition.

D. Itzhak and S. Harush, The Effect of Tin Addition on the Corrosion Behavior of Sintered Stainless Steel in H_2SO_4, *Corros. Sci.*, 25(10), 883-888, 1985. MetAbs No. 86-350521. **Abstract:** The influence of Sn addition on the corrosion behavior of hot-pressed sintered stainless steel of type 316 in H_2SO_4 solutions was investigated.

N.S. Rawat, G. Udayabhanu, and R.K. Arora, Studies on the Effect of Chloride Ions on the Inhibition of Mild Steel Corrosion by Some Nitrogenous Aromatic Compounds in Sulfuric Acid Medium, *Trans. SAEST*, 20(2-3), 63-66, 1985. MetAbs No. 86-350548. **Abstract:** Dissolution of mild steel in dilute sulfuric acid of pH 1 was studied in the presence and absence of some nitrogenous inhibitors, like o-toluidine, p-toluidine, benzylamine, and benzotriazole.

S. Webster, P.J. Mitchell, N.A. Hampson, and J.I. Dyson, The Cycle Life of Various Lead Alloys in 5M H_2SO_4, *J. Electrochem. Soc.*, 133(1), 133-136, 1986. MetAbs No. 86-350555. **Abstract:** The electrochemical behavior of various Pb alloys (99.999 Pb, Pb-0.3Sn, Pb-0.1Ca, Pb-4.5Sb, Pb-1.8Sb-0.04Se) intended for battery electrodes was studied in sulfuric acid.

S. Webster, P.J. Mitchell, N.A. Hampson, and J.I. Dyson, Electroreduction Processes of Lead and Lead Alloys in 5M H_2SO_4, *J. Electrochem. Soc.*, 133(1), 137-139, 1986. MetAbs No. 86-350556. **Abstract:** In the Pb-acid battery, the behavior of the interface between the active mass and the supporting grid alloy of the positive plate is important in determining the cycle life of the battery. The purpose of this work was to elucidate the difference between the nucleation and growth mechanisms of $PbSO_4$ on the various Pb alloys and to determine whether or not these differences explain the effects observed in industrial practice.

H. Bala, The Effect of Sulfur Content of Steel on Its Corrosion in 2M H_2SO_4, *Corros. Sci.*, 25(11), 1057-1068, 1985. MetAbs No. 86-350708. **Abstract:** The corrosion mechanism and kinetics of low-carbon steels with various S content (0.015-0.35%) in deaerated 2.0M H_2SO_4 (pH 0) at 25 °C, subjected to various stirring rates, have been studied.

V.S. Muralidharan, M. Veerashanmugamani, G. Kalaignan, G. Paruthimal, and S. Arulraj, Mechanism of Corrosion of Pure Nickel in Sulfuric Acid Solutions, *Bull. Electrochem.*, 1(3), 241-244, 1985. MetAbs No. 86-350963. **Abstract:** The anodic behavior of Ni in acid baths in plating, electrowinning and pickling processes is of industrial concern. Potentiostatic measurements were carried out to find corrosion rates in different concentrations of sulfuric acid solutions.

S. Szymura and H. Bala, Polarization Curves of Fe-28% Cr-24% Co-1% Si Permanent Magnet Alloy in Sulfuric Acid Solution, *Mater. Chem. Phys.*, 14(2), 167-180, 1986. MetAbs No. 86-350975. **Abstract:** The potentiokinetic curves of anodic polarization of magnetically hard Fe-28Cr-24Co-1Si alloy in sulfuric acid of pH 0 were plotted. The Fe-Cr-Co-Si alloy was subjected to four different treatments that are usually used for generation of magnetic properties.

S.K. Mukherjee, A. Kumar, and G.S. Upadhyaya, Anodic Polarization Study of Sintered 434L Ferritic Stainless Steel and Its Particulate Composites, *Powder Metall. Int.*, 17(4), 172-175, 1985. MetAbs No. 86-350978. **Abstract:** A potentiodynamic study of sintered 434L ferritic stainless steel and its particulate composites with Al_2O_3 (2-8 vol%) was undertaken in 5% NaCl and 1N H_2SO_4 electrolytes.

N.A. Darwish, A.A. Razik, E.M. Khairy, and T.H. Hussein, Formation and Electrochemical Behavior of Some Tin-Antimony Alloys in Various pH Media, *Corros. Prev. Control*, 32(6), 127-132, 1985. MetAbs No. 86-351058. **Abstract:** Five Sn-Sb alloys were prepared to compositions involving eutectic, under-eutectic and over eutectic states. D-spacing relative-intensity diagrams were prepared and electrical measurements were made.

A. Kawashima, K. Asami, and K. Hashimoto, An XPS Study of Passive Films on Nickel and Alloy 600 in Acids, *Corros. Sci.*, 25(12), 1103-1114, 1985. MetAbs No. 86-351115. **Abstract:** Compositions of surface films formed on Ni and Alloy 600 in 1M HCl, 0.5M H_2SO_4 and 1/3M H_3PO_4 solutions were investigated as a function of polarization potential.

M. Studnicki, Syntheses of Derivatives of Alkylarylamines and Their Properties as Pickling Inhibitors of Carbon Steels and Stainless Steels, *Ind. Eng. Chem. Prod. Res. Dev.*, 25(1), 96-102, 1986. MetAbs No. 86-351260. **Abstract:** Derivatives of alkylarylamines have been found to be among the most effective inhibitors. Preparation and application of pickling inhibitor derivatives of alkylarylamines in hydrochloric acid and sulfuric acid are described.

V.S. Muralidharan, M. Veerashanmugamani, and G.P. Kalaignan, Ethanolamines as Corrosion Inhibitors for Pure Nickel in Sulfuric Acid Solutions, *Bull. Electrochem.*, 1(4), 373-375, 1985. MetAbs No. 86-351380. **Abstract:** Mono-, di- and tri-ethanolamines have been studied as inhibitors for pure Ni in sulfuric acid solutions. Potentiostatic polarization studies have been carried out to follow the corrosion rate in the presence and in the absence of these amines.

G.O. Davis, J. Kolts, and N. Sridhar, Polarization Effects in Galvanic Corrosion, *Corrosion*, 42(6), 329-336, 1986. MetAbs No. 86-351501. **Abstract:** Galvanic corrosion in couples of AISI 304 stainless steel, Ferralium Alloy 255, Hastelloy Alloys B-2 and G-3, grade 2 Ti, and graphite was examined in boiling 10% sulfuric and ambient temperature hydrochloric acids.

D. Itzhak and P. Peled, The Effect of Copper Addition on the Corrosion Behavior of Sintered Steel in H_2SO_4 Environment, *Corros. Sci.*, 26(1), 49-54, 1986. MetAbs No. 86-351577. **Abstract:** The influence of Cu addition on the corrosion behavior of hot pressed and sintered type 316 stainless steel in H_2SO_4 solution was investigated.

A.E.B. Mostafa, S.M. Abdel-Wahaab, and E.M. Mabrouk, The Corrosion Behavior of Zinc Metal in Acidic Solutions of Polyvinylpyrrolidones and Polyvinylpyridines, *Surf. Coat. Technol.*, 27(4), 317-324, 1986. MetAbs No. 86-351632. **Abstract:** The effect of polyvinylpyrrolidone of various average molecular weights, poly-2-vinylpyridine, and poly-4-vinylpyridine as inhibitors of the corrosion behavior of Zn in 1.0M H_2SO_4 solutions has been studied.

B.A. Abd-El-Nabey, A. El-Toukhy, M.Z. El-Gamal, and F. Mahgoob, 4-Amino-3-Substituted-5-Mercapto-1,2,4-Triazolines as Inhibitors for the Acid Corrosion of Steel, *Surf. Coat. Technol.*, 27(4), 325-334, 1986.

MetAbs No. 86-351633. **Abstract:** Corrosion inhibition by 4-amino-3-H-5-mercapto-1,2,4-triazoline and some related compounds on the dissolution of mild steel (Fe-0.27C-0.7Mn) in sulfuric acid solutions was measured using chemical and electrochemical methods.

Z.A. El-Hadi, Organic Corrosion Inhibitors for TA6V Alloy in Non-Oxidizing Acid Solutions, *J. Electrochem. Soc. India*, 35(1), 33-36, 1986. MetAbs No. 86-351635. **Abstract:** The efficiency of the azo compounds as corrosion inhibitors for TA6V alloy in aerated 10, 15 and 25N H_2SO_4 has been investigated.

B.A. Abd El-Nabey, E. Khamis, M.A.E. Shaban, G.E. Thompson, and J.L. Dawson, Impedance Studies of the Inhibition of the Corrosion of Mild Steel in 0.1M Sulfuric Acid With 10% Methanol by Thiosemicarbazide Derivatives, *Surf. Coat. Technol.*, 28(1), 67-82, 1986. MetAbs No. 86-351654. **Abstract:** Selected substituted thiosemicarbazides and thiosemicarbazones have been studied as corrosion inhibitors for mild steel (Fe-0.27C-0.07Mn-0.05S-0.05P-0.35Si) in sulfuric acid using electrochemical techniques.

B.A. Abd El-Nabey, E. Khamis, G.E. Thompson, and J.L. Dawson, Effect of Temperature on the Inhibition of the Acid Corrosion of Steel by Benzaldehyde Thiosemicarbazone: Impedance Measurements, *Surf. Coat. Technol.*, 28(1), 83-91, 1986. MetAbs No. 86-351655. **Abstract:** An impedance study has been carried out of the corrosion of steel (Fe-0.27C-0.70Mn-0.05P-0.05S-0.35Si) in sulfuric acid containing benzaldehyde thiosemicarbazone as an inhibitor, over the temperature range 25-60 °C.

K.R. Bullock and M.A. Butler, Corrosion of Lead in Sulfuric Acid at High Potentials, *J. Electrochem. Soc.*, 133(6), 1085-1089, 1986. MetAbs No. 86-351702. **Abstract:** The corrosion of Pb in sulfuric acid is studied in the potential region of 1.35 V and above, which corresponds to conditions on the positive electrode of a Pb-acid battery during overcharge.

M.J. Weinbaum and W.A. McGill, Elimination of High Temperature Scaling in the Modern Sulfuric Acid Plant, *Corros. Maint.*, 8(4), 261-267, 1985. MetAbs No. 86-352029. **Abstract:** In sulfur burning plants, chromium alloys and stainless steels are used in tubes with their inner tube surfaces Alonized. With respect to fabricating heat exchangers, Alonized components and carbon steel tubes are discussed.

T.K. Pal, S.C. Sircar, and G.L. Datta, Corrosion Behavior of 9% Nickel Steel Weldments, *Corros. Maint.*, 8(4), 271-275, 1985. MetAbs No. 86-352030. **Abstract:** In the welding processes, potentiostatic anodic polarization data of different regions of the weldments were recorded.

U. Heubner, M.B. Rockel, and E. Wallis, The Corrosion Behavior of Copper-Alloyed Stainless Steels in Reducing Acids, *ATB Metall.*, 25(3), 235-241, 1985. MetAbs No. 86-352047. **Abstract:** Additions of Cu to austenitic stainless steels improves their corrosion resistance in reducing acids. Tests on steels 20Cr25Ni4.7Mo1.5Cu (Cronifer 1925 LC, alloy 904 L), Cr28Ni2.8Mo2.8Cu (Cronifer 2328) and Ni-alloy 42Ni21Cr2.7Mo2.2Cu (Nicrofer 4221, alloy 825) in comparison to AISI 316 Ti as a reference in up to 20% sulfuric acid at 50 and 100 °C containing additional chloride ions exhibit optimum corrosion resistance for the high Cu-containing materials.

W.J. Tomlinson and S.A. Campbell, Passivity, Pitting and Corrosion of Anodically Polarized Fe-Ni Alloys in 0.5M H_2SO_4 Containing Cl^-, *J. Mater. Sci.*, 21(7), 2590-2596, 1986. MetAbs No. 86-352056. **Abstract:** Fe-Ni alloys have been anodically polarized in 0.5M H_2SO_4 containing Cl^-, and the conditions for passivity, pitting and corrosion with respect to alloy composition and Cl^- concentration are broadly defined.

K.E. Perumal, Solution of Severe Corrosion Problems in Chemical Process Industries With Special Stainless Steels, *Tool Alloy Steels*, 20(2), 53-61, 1986. MetAbs No. 86-352151. **Abstract:** In the application of stainless steels for process equipment in chemical industries the common stainless steels have some inherent limitations, including poor resistance to general corrosion in reducing and less oxidizing acids and susceptibility to pitting and stress corrosion cracking in sulfide and chloride-containing solutions. The economical solution to these problems is to upgrade the stainless steel with respect to its corrosion resistance by changing the alloy chemistry: increasing the Ni and Mo contents and adding elements like Cu. These applications are discussed.

J.P. Crousier, J. Crousier, M. Dubusc, and P.L. Bonora, Behavior of Nickel in Methanol-Water Sulfuric Acid Solution, *Mater. Chem. Phys.*, 14(6), 501-512, 1986. MetAbs No. 86-352420. **Abstract:** The electrochemical behavior of Ni in water-methanol-acid solutions has been investigated; the concentration of the three constituents of the solution have been varied extensively.

J.D. Rubio, R.R. Hart, and R.B. Griffin, Effects of BF^+_2 Ion Implantation on the Corrosion Resistance of Inconel 600, *Corrosion*, 42(9), 557-558, 1986. MetAbs No. 86-352581. **Abstract:** The results of this investigation indicate that the implantation of large doses of 100 keV BF^+_2 ions considerably reduces the corrosion rate of Inconel 600 in 1.0N H_2SO_4 solution.

R.H. Jones, M.J. Danielson, and D.R. Baer, Role of Segregated P and S in Intergranular Stress Corrosion Cracking of Ni, *J. Mater. Energy Syst.*, 8(2), 185-196, 1986. MetAbs No. 86-352625. **Abstract:** The effect of phosphorus and sulfur on the intergranular corrosion and stress corrosion of Ni has been evaluated with corrosion tests, crack tip corrosion modeling and stress corrosion tests, and modeling.

D. Mukherjee, C.O. Augustin, and G. Rajagopal, Stress Relieving as a Technique for Improving the Corrosion Resistance of Low Alloy Steels, *Bull. Electrochem.*, 2(1), 3-5, 1986. MetAbs No. 86-352699. **Abstract:** The corrosion behavior of a low-alloy steel in 18% H_2SO_4 solution, containing 1000 ppm chloride ion, after annealing and stress relieving, is reported.

D. Mukherjee, Heat Treatment of Carbon Steel for Better Corrosion Protection, *Tool Alloy Steels*, 20(4-5), 145-150, 1986. MetAbs No. 87-350111. **Abstract:** Preliminary results from an investigation of the effect of heat treatment on the corrosion resistance of carbon steels, in the presence of chloride ions, are reported. Carbon steel specimens were normalized, annealed, and stress relieved, and then immersed in an 18% H_2SO_4 solution.

R.T. Webster and T.L. Yau, Zircadyne Exhibits Superior Corrosion Resistance in Sulfuric Acid Media, *Outlook*, 7(3), 6-8, 1986. MetAbs No. 87-350147. **Abstract:** Zirconium has been used in industrial applications since 1950 because of its high resistance to corrosion by acids, caustics, water and salts. One of the applications has been in hot sulfuric acid producing plants. Its corrosion properties in sulfuric acid solutions are discussed, and comparative corrosion data of Zr vs. several Fe- and Ni-base alloys are given.

S.M. Roshdy, L.A. Kamel, and N.A. Accad, The Electrochemical Behavior of Molybdenum Alloyed Steel in Sulfate Solutions, *Indian J. Technol.*, 24(2), 83-88, 1986. MetAbs No. 87-350214. **Abstract:** Anodic polarization measurements were made for two types of molybdenum alloyed steel containing 3.15% Mo and 4.5% Mo to study their ability in attaining passivity in different sulfuric acid concentrations varying from 0.001 to 1M solutions.

I.H. Omar, F. Zucchi, and G. Trabanelli, Schiff Bases as Corrosion Inhibitors of Copper and Its Alloys in Acid Media, *Surf. Coat. Technol.*, 29(2), 141-151, 1986. MetAbs No. 87-350278. **Abstract:** The inhibiting action of some Schiff bases on the corrosion of Cu and its alloys in hydrochloric and sulfuric acid solutions has been studied. The Schiff bases were synthesized by reacting salicyl aldehyde with aliphatic or aromatic amines. The behaviors of electrolytic Cu, Al brass and cupronickels (90Cu-10Ni and 70Cu-30Ni with 0.4 wt% Fe) have been examined.

I.B. Singh, R.S. Chaudhary, and T.K.G. Namboodhiri, Effect of Alloying on the Corrosion Behavior of Fe-B Metallic Glasses in Sulfuric Acid, *Mater. Sci. Eng.*, 83(1), 123-133, 1986. MetAbs No. 87-350360. **Abstract:** The corrosion behavior of seven metallic glasses based on the Fe-B system, namely Vitrovac 0040, Metglas 2826MB, Vitrovac 4040, Metglas 2826, Metglas 2826A, Metglas 2605-S-2, and Metglas 2605Co, was investigated in H_2SO_4 solutions of various concentrations (0.001-0.1M) using mass loss and electrochemical techniques.

M.N. Singh and I. Singh, Polarization Studies on the Cold Rolled Mild Steel in Sulfuric Acid Containing Metallic Ions and an Inhibitor, *NML Tech. J.*, 27(1-2), 3-8, 1985. MetAbs No. 87-350785. **Abstract:** The influence of thiourea in association with Cu^{++}, Hg^{++} or Ce^{++++} on the open circuit potential, anodic and cathodic polarization of the cold rolled mild steel (0.1% carbon) in 2N H_2SO_4 has been studied at room temperature.

R.D.K. Misra and D. Akhtar, Effect of Cold Work on Hydrogen Embrittlement Susceptibility of $Ni_{60}Nb_{40}$ Glass, *Mater. Res. Bull.*, 21(12), 1473-1479, 1986. MetAbs No. 87-350793. **Abstract:** $Ni_{60}Nb_{40}$ glass ribbons were cold rolled to a reduction of approximately 25%. As-quenched and cold-rolled ribbons were embrittled by cathodic charging in 1.0N H_2SO_4.

A.R. Brooks, C.R. Clayton, K. Doss, and Y.C. Lu, On the Role of Chromium in the Passivity of Stainless Steel, *J. Electrochem. Soc.*, 133(12), 2459-2464, 1986. MetAbs No. 87-350811. **Abstract:** The nature of passive films formed on 304 stainless steel in deaerated solutions of 0.5M H_2SO_4 and 0.5M H_2SO_4 + 0.35M NaCl has been determined.

N.R. Sorensen, R.B. Diegle, and S.T. Picraux, Corrosion Behavior of Phosphorus-Implanted Fe-6Cr and Fe-18Cr Amorphous Alloys, *Cor-*

rosion, 43(1), 2-7, 1987. MetAbs No. 87-350837. **Abstract:** The passivation of phosphorus-implanted Fe-6Cr and Fe-18Cr alloys has been investigated in 0.1N H_2SO_4 with and without the addition of chloride ions.

M. Seo, G. Hultquist, C. Leygraf, and N. Sato, The Influence of Minor Alloying Elements (Nb, Ti and Cu) on the Corrosion Resistivity of Ferritic Stainless Steel in Sulfuric Acid Solution, *Corros. Sci.*, 26(11), 949-960, 1986. MetAbs No. 87-350974. **Abstract:** The effect of the minor alloying elements (Nb, Ti and Cu) and of Mo on the corrosion resistivity of ferritic stainless steel (Fe-26Cr alloy) was investigated in 1.0 mol/dm^3 sulfuric acid solution with or without 0.5 mol sodium chloride, based on potentiodynamic polarization, potential decay and reactivation potential measurements.

E. Angelini and F. Zucchi, Corrosion Behavior of Various Duplex Stainless Steels in the Welded Condition, *Br. Corros. J.*, 21(4), 257-213, 1986. MetAbs No. 87-351176. **Abstract:** A number of duplex stainless steels, whose ferrite content ranged from 25 to 70%, were studied for evidence of corrosion in the aged and welded conditions. Microstructural reasons for differences in corrosion properties have been investigated, together with the influence of base alloy composition.

C.R. Molock, R.P. Walters, and P.M. Fabis, Effect of Laser Processing on the Electrochemical Behavior of Fe-Cr Alloys, *J. Electrochem. Soc.*, 134(2), 289-294, 1987. MetAbs No. 87-351284. **Abstract:** Fe-Cr substrates (5 and 9 wt% Cr) electroplated with 1-3 μm of Cr were processed with an Nd-YAG pulsed laser to produce surface alloys with 25-35 μm melt depths. The corrosion resistance of laser-processed alloys in deaerated 1N H_2SO_4 solution was studied.

L.M. Al-Shama, J. Saleh, J. Mohammed, and N.A. Hikmat, Potentiostatic Studies of the Corrosion of Gray Cast Iron in Sulfuric Acid and Sodium Hydroxide Solutions, *Corros. Sci.*, 27(3), 221-228, 1987. MetAbs No. 87-351481. **Abstract:** A potentiostatic investigation of the corrosion behavior of two gray cast iron specimens has been performed in 2.5M H_2SO_4 and 1.0M NaOH solutions at 303 to 333 K. A similar determination was also made in 5.0M solutions of both HCl and NHO_3 at 303 K.

E.M.M. Sutter, A. Cornett, and J. Pagetti, The Inhibition of the Corrosion of Titanium in 10N Sulfuric Acid by Cupferron (N-Nitrosophenyl Hydroxylamine), *Corros. Sci.*, 27(3), 229-238, 1987. MetAbs No. 87-351482. **Abstract:** The mechanism of inhibition of cupferron (N-nitrosophenyl hydroxylamine) toward Ti in 10N sulfuric acid solutions is studied using electrochemical techniques.

V. Mitrovic-Scepanovic, B. MacDougall, and M.J. Graham, The Effect of Cl$^-$ Ions on the Passivation of Fe-26Cr Alloy, *Corros. Sci.*, 27(3), 239-247, 1987. MetAbs No. 87-351483. **Abstract:** Anodic oxide films formed on Fe-26Cr in pH 2.0 H_2SO_4 solution in the presence and absence of Cl$^-$ ions have been investigated using electrochemical techniques combined with ion sputtering.

I.B. Singh, R.S. Chaudhary, and T.K.G. Namboodhiri, Corrosion Resistance of Two Magnetic Metallic Glasses in Acidic and Neutral Aqueous Solutions, *J. Electrochem. Soc. India*, 35(4), 279-282, 1986. MetAbs No. 87-351508. **Abstract:** The corrosion resistance of two magnetic metallic glasses, $Fe_{40}Ni_{40}B_{20}$ and $Fe_{39}Ni_{39}Mo_2(SiB)_{20}$, was evaluated in H_2SO_4 and NaCl solutions by weight loss measurement and electrochemical techniques.

Y. Yahagi and Y. Mizutani, Corrosive Wear of Cast Iron in Sulfuric Acid, *J. Tribology (Trans. ASME)*, 109(2), 238-242, 1987. MetAbs No. 87-351666. **Abstract:** The wear rate of gray cast iron and the corrosion potential and current were measured in sulfuric acid to study the mechanism of corrosive wear of cast iron.

A. Frignani, M. Tassinari, C. Monticelli, and G. Trabanelli, Inhibition Mechanism of Sulfur-Containing Additives Towards Intergranular Corrosion of a Sensitized Stainless Steel, *Corros. Sci.*, 27(1), 75-81, 1987. MetAbs No. 87-351713. **Abstract:** The comparison of the polarization curves recorded on both pure Fe, Cr, Ni, and Fe-18Cr-8Ni, Fe-8Cr-8Ni alloys, and Fe-10Ni, Fe-17Cr alloys in 1N H_2SO_4 at 70 °C clarifies the mechanism of inhibition of intergranular corrosion on sensitized AISI 304 stainless steel by S-containing additives.

S.L.F.A. da Costa, S.M.L. Agostinho, H.C. Chagas, and J.C. Rubim, Inhibiting Action of Benzotriazole on Copper Corrosion in Deaerated Sulfuric Acid Containing Ferric Ions by the Rotating Disc Electrode, Fluorescence, and Raman Spectroscopies, *Corrosion*, 43(3), 149-153, 1987. MetAbs No. 87-351814. **Abstract:** The rate of Cu corrosion by ferric ions in 0.5M deaerated sulfuric acid in the presence and absence of benzotriazole has been studied. The rotating disk electrode has been used in weight loss experiments.

J.W. Schultze and K. Wippermann, Inhibition of Electrode Processes on Copper by AHT in Acid Solutions, *Electrochim. Acta*, 32(5), 823-831, 1987. MetAbs No. 87-351923. **Abstract:** 3-amino-5-heptyl-1,2,4-triazole (AHT) is a very effective inhibitor of Cu corrosion in neutral as well as acid solutions. The influence of AHT concentration is explained by the thickening of the layer, the conductivity of which differs for ions and electrons.

M. Asawa, Stress Corrosion Cracking Regions on Contour Maps of Dissolution Rates for AISI 304 Stainless Steel in Sulfuric Acid Solutions With Chloride, Bromide, or Iodide, *Corrosion*, 43(4), 198-203, 1987. MetAbs No. 87-351991. **Abstract:** Weight loss measurements and stress corrosion cracking tests were performed on AISI 304 stainless steel in sulfuric acid solutions with chloride, bromide, or iodide at different potentials near the corrosion potential and at different concentrations of each halide.

Y.J. Kim and R.A. Oriani, Effect of the Microstructure of Ti-5Mo on the Anodic Dissolution in H_2SO_4, *Corrosion*, 43(4), 239-243, 1987. MetAbs No. 87-351996. **Abstract:** The effect of microstructure of the Ti-5Mo alloy on its anodic dissolution rate in sulfuric acid solution at various temperatures has been investigated.

A.I. Al-Zanki, J.S. Gill, and J.L Dawson, Electrochemical Noise Measurements on Mild Steel in 0.5M Sulfuric Acid, *Mater. Sci. Forum*, 8, 463-476, 1986. MetAbs No. 87-352180. **Abstract:** The paper describes a series of experiments on a relatively simple corrosion system undergoing general corrosion. Analysis of the spontaneous fluctuation of the corrosion potential and the current measurements, made by coupling two similar mild steel electrodes together by means of a zero resistance ammeter, were monitored using a digital voltmeter controller by a microcomputer.

A. Frignani, G. Demertzis, and G. Trabanelli, Electrochemical Investigation of $Fe_{80}B_{20}$ Amorphous Alloy, *Mater. Chem. Phys.*, 16(5-6), 569-574, 1987. MetAbs No. 87-352197. **Abstract:** The behavior of $Fe_{80}B_{20}$ amorphous alloy is compared to that of crystalline iron (Armco iron) in 0.1N HBr, HCl, $HClO_4$ and H_2SO_4.

H. Bala, The Acid Corrosion of Fe-P Alloys, *Werkst. Korros.*, 38(1), 26-31, 1987. MetAbs No. 87-352230. **Abstract:** The effect of P content in iron (0.002-0.12% P) and the stirring rate on the corrosion rate of five Fe-P alloys in H_2SO_4 and HCl solutions (pH 0) has been investigated.

H. Bala and S. Szymura, Acid Corrosion Behavior of Amorphous and Crystalline $Ti_{75}Ni_{20}Si_5$ Alloys, *Thin Solid Films*, 149(2), 171-176, 1987. MetAbs No. 87-352233. **Abstract:** The corrosion resistance of amorphous and crystalline $Ti_{75}Ni_{20}Si_5$ alloy as well as that of pure crystalline titanium as a reference material were investigated in sulfuric and hydrochloric acids.

W.J. Tomlinson, R. Rushton, C. Cindeny, and S. Palmer, Anodic Polarization and Corrosion of Vanadium, and V-Ta, V-W, V-Cr, and V-Cr-W Alloys in 10% H_2SO_4 and 3% NaCl in Water, *J. Less-Common Met.*, 132(1), L1-L4, 1987. MetAbs No. 87-352314. **Abstract:** Vanadium, V-22Ta, V-7.1W, V-13.6Cr, and V-12.6Cr-7.5W specimens were subjected to accelerated corrosion testing by anodic polarization in 10% sulfuric acid and in 3% salt water.

K. Ogino, A. Hida, S. Kishima, and S. Kumanomido, Susceptibility of Type 431 Stainless Steel to Erosion-Corrosion by Vibratory Cavitation in Corrosive Media, *Wear*, 116(3), 299-307, 1987. MetAbs No. 87-352329. **Abstract:** By utilizing the structural characteristics of type 431 stainless steel, which reveals a wide range of strength and corrosion resistance with tempering after quenching, its susceptibility to erosion-corrosion was investigated as a function of tempering temperature.

N. Nigam and K. Srivastava, Role of Impurities on the Dissolution of Mild Steel in Acidic Media, *Anti-Corros. Methods Mater.*, 34(5), 4-5, 1987. MetAbs No. 87-352383. **Abstract:** Sulfates, chlorides, nitrates and oxidizing agents were studied as impurities in sulfuric acid and hydrochloric acid.

C. Fiaud, S. Bensarsa, I. des Aulnois, I. Demesy, and M. Tzinmann, Inhibiting Properties of Phosphines Against Zinc Corrosion in Acidic Media, *Br. Corros. J.*, 22(2), 109-112, 1987. MetAbs No. 87-352390. **Abstract:** A more uniform corrosion of zinc in aqueous deaerated sulfate solutions can be achieved by the use of organic phosphines and diphosphines. The inhibition mechanism in sulfuric acid solutions has been studied by conducting electrochemical and weight loss experiments.

G. Riedel, C. Voigt, H. Werner, K.P. Erkel, and M. Gunzel, The Influence of Acid Soluble Sulfide Inclusions on the Passivation Behavior of Austenitic Cr-Ni Stainless Steels, *Corros. Sci.*, 27(6), 533-544, 1987. MetAbs No. 87-352393. **Abstract:** The cathodic and anodic effects of acid soluble sulfide inclusions on the passivation behavior of unstabilized austenitic Cr-Ni-(Mo) stainless steels were studied by means of potentiodynamic polarization measurements in 0.1N H_2SO_4 acid solutions.

V. Jagannathan, T.A. Mozhi, W.A.T. Clark, and B.E. Wilde, The Simulation of Intergranular Attack of AISI 304 Stainless Steels in H_2SO_4, *Corros. Sci.*, 27(6), 555-559, 1987. MetAbs No. 87-352395. **Abstract:** Galvanic currents were measured when Fe-(8)Ni-(0-18)Cr alloys were coupled to AISI 304 stainless steel in 1N H_2SO_4. Anodic polarization curves were also measured.

A. Dhirendra, S. Gupta, G.N. Pandey, and B. Sanyal, "Water Line" and "Above Water Line" Corrosion of Stainless Steel (AISI 321) in H_2SO_4 and Its Inhibition, *Corros. Prev. Control*, 34(2), 58-59, 1987. MetAbs No. 87-352491. **Abstract:** Water-line corrosion was studied with stainless steel (AISI 321) and sulfuric acid as the fluid.

G. Rocchini, A Computerized Tool for Corrosion Rate Monitoring, *Corrosion*, 43(6), 326-331, 1987. MetAbs No. 87-352495. **Abstract:** Two variations of the INTER1 program for determination of the corrosion rate of a metal are presented that are valid from a mathematical viewpoint only when the overall electrochemical reaction is controlled by the activation energy and contains two processes (one cathodic and the other anodic).

Y.H. Yau and M.A. Streicher, Galvanic Corrosion of Duplex FeCr-10% Ni Alloys in Reducing Acids, *Corrosion*, 43(6), 366-373, 1987. MetAbs

No. 87-352499. **Abstract:** The effect on corrosion of composition and microstructure in a series of FeCr-10Ni alloys with increasing Cr content has been investigated in reducing acids.

A. Rauscher and Z. Lukacs, Effect of Hydrogen Sulfide on the Corrosion Behavior of Titanium, *Werkst. Korros.*, 38(6), 326-329, 1987. MetAbs No. 87-352649. **Abstract:** The effect of hydrogen sulfide on the electrochemical and corrosion behavior of VT1-0 commercial titanium has been studied in acidic solutions containing polarization and analytical methods.

O. Teschke, Interfacial Corrosion on Iron at the Passive Potential Range, *J. Electrochem. Soc.*, 134(7), 1865-1866, 1987. MetAbs No. 87-352704. **Abstract:** Interfacial corrosion on Fe electrodes at the liquid/electrode interface was investigated. Iron electrodes were suspended in solutions of various sulfuric acid concentrations.

I. Singh and M. Singh, Effect of Metallic Cations on the Corrosion and the Hydrogen Absorption by Cold-Rolled Mild Steel in Inhibited Sulfuric Acid, *Corrosion*, 43(7), 425-429, 1987. MetAbs No. 87-352751. **Abstract:** The effect of metallic cations, such as Cu^{++}, Hg^{++}, and Ce^{++++}, on the corrosion rate and hydrogen absorption by cold-rolled mild steel in 2N H_2SO_4 containing thiourea and allylthiourea at 30 °C has been studied.

I.B. Singh, R.D.K. Misra, R.S. Chaudhary, and D. Akhtar, Anodic Polarization Behavior of $Ni_{60}Nb_{40}$ and $Ni_{55}Cr_5Nb_{40}$ Glasses, *Mater. Sci. Eng.*, 92(1-2), 173-178, 1987. MetAbs No. 87-352791. **Abstract:** The corrosion behavior of $Ni_{60}Nb_{40}$ and $Ni_{55}Cr_5Nb_{40}$ metallic glass alloys in a 0.1M H_2SO_4 solution has been investigated.

R. Agrawal, R.S. Chaudhary, and T.K.G. Namboodhiri, Inhibitive of Piperidine on HSLA Steel Corrosion and Hydrogen Evolution Reaction in H_2SO_4 Media, *J. Electrochem. Soc. India*, 36(1), 31-36, 1987. MetAbs No. 87-352800. **Abstract:** A study of the corrosion behavior of HSLA steel in 1N H_2SO_4 solution suggests that piperidine acts as a good inhibitor for corrosion and hydrogen evolution reaction.

T.D. Burleigh and R.M. Latanision, The Effect of Phosphorus on the Corrosion of Glassy Copper-Zirconium Alloys, *Corrosion*, 43(8), 471-475, 1987. MetAbs No. 87-352841. **Abstract:** Glassy $Cu_{60}Zr_{40}$ and $Cu_{56}Zr_{42}P_2$ were melt-spun and tested in various corrosive solutions.

M.A. El Zeky, Z. Szklarska-Smialowska, and E. Lunarska, Electrochemical Behavior of Hastelloy C-276 in Sulfuric Acid Solutions in a Wide Range of Concentrations and Temperatures, *Corrosion*, 43(11), 656-660, 1987. MetAbs No. 88-350470. **Abstract:** Measurements of anodic and cathodic polarization and of potential time curves for Hastelloy C-276 in 30-96 wt% sulfuric acid solutions at temperatures ranging from 25-150 °C were made.

T.P. Moffat, W.F. Flanagan, and B.D. Lichter, Effects of Alloy Chemistry on the Corrosion of FeNi Metal-Metalloid Metallic Glasses, *Corrosion*, 43(10), 589-593, 1987. MetAbs No. 88-350600. **Abstract:** The polarization characteristics of $Fe_{40}Ni_{40}P_{14}B_6$ and $Fe_{40}Ni_{38}Mo_4B_{18}$ metallic glasses have been determined in 1N H_2SO_4 and 1N HCl. Results have been compared with those for metallic glasses of other compositions and with results for metalloid-free crystalline alloys.

M. Shirkhanzadeh, A Rotating Cylinder Electrode for Corrosion Studies Under Controlled Heat Transfer Conditions, *Corrosion*, 43(10), 621-623, 1987. MetAbs No. 88-350604. **Abstract:** A rotating cylinder electrode with internal heat transfer facilities is described for the study of controlled heat and mass transfer under turbulent flow conditions. A schematic of the apparatus and preliminary results are given.

M. Vajpeyi, S. Gupta, B. Dhirendra, and G.N. Pandey, Corrosion of Stainless Steel (AISI 304) in H_2SO_4 Contaminated With HCl and HNO_3, *Corros. Prev. Control*, 32(5), 102-104, 1985. MetAbs No. 86-351104. **Abstract:** The effects of contamination of hydrochloric and nitric acids in sulfuric acid on the passivity of stainless steel (AISI 304) under different operating conditions is discussed. Efforts have also been made to theoretically explain the experimental data obtained.

Corrosion Behavior of Various Metals and Alloys in Sulfuric Acid

Material	Condition, other factors, comments	Concentration, %	Temperature, °C (°F)	Duration	Corrosion rate, mm/yr (mils/yr) or other	Ref
Irons and steels						
Armco iron	1.5N	...	45 (115)	3 h	22 (866)	31
Armco iron	Dilute. 1.5N	...	45 (115)	3 h	22 (866)	31
ASTM A106 carbon steel	1.5N	...	45 (115)	3 h	20 (787)	31
ASTM A106 carbon steel	Dilute. 1.5N	...	45 (115)	3 h	20 (787)	31
ASTM A335	1.5N. Grade P11 (1.5Cr-0.25Mo)	...	45 (115)	3 h	41 (1.6 in./yr)	31
ASTM A335	1.5N. Grade P22 (2Cr-1Mo)	...	45 (115)	3 h	330 (13 in./yr)	31
ASTM A335	1.5N. Grade P5 (5Cr-0.5Mo)	...	45 (115)	3 h	94 (3.7 in./yr)	31
ASTM A335	1.5N. Grade P9 (10Cr-1Mo)	...	45 (115)	3 h	83 (3.27 in./yr)	31
Altemp A-286	Solution treated	10	Boiling	...	0.75 (29.5)	98
Stainless steels						
18-8 PLUS	Annealed. (a)	5	80 (176)	48 h	0.0508 (2)	145
18-8 PLUS	Annealed. (a)	10	80 (176)	48 h	0.0508 (2)	145
18Cr-2Ni-12Mn	Passive in 2nd and 3rd periods (i.e., <1 mil/yr). (a)	5	80 (176)	48 h	6.299 (248)	145
18Cr-2Ni-12Mn	Annealed. (a)	20	93 (200)	48 h	0.038 (1.5)	145
21Cr-6Ni-9Mn	Annealed. (b)	5	Room	48 h	nil	47
22Cr-13Ni-5Mn	Annealed. (a)	5	80 (176)	48 h	0.005 (0.2)	145
22Cr-13Ni-5Mn	Annealed. (a)	10	80 (176)	48 h	0.381 (15)	145
AL-6XN	Base metal sample	10	Boiling	...	2.14 (84.4)	120

(Continued)

Corrosion Behavior of Various Metals and Alloys in Sulfuric Acid (Continued)

Material	Condition, other factors, comments	Concentration, %	Temperature, °C (°F)	Duration	Corrosion rate, mm/yr (mils/yr) or other	Ref
AL-6XN	Welded sample	10	Boiling	...	2.34 (92.3)	120
AL-6XN	...	95	30 (86)	...	<0.01 (0.12)	120
AL 29-4-2	Dilute. Nonactivated. (b)	1	Boiling	48 h	0.005 (0.2)	39
AL 29-4-2	Dilute. Activated. Sample activated at start of each test period. (b)	1	Boiling	48 h	0.076 (3)	39
AL 29-4-2	Dilute. (c)	1	Boiling	...	0.07 (2.6)	98
AL 29-4-2	Dilute. Nonactivated. (b)	5	Boiling	48 h	0.025 (1)	39
AL 29-4-2	Dilute. Activated. Sample activated at start of each test period. (b)	5	Boiling	48 h	0.279 (11)	39
AL 29-4-2	Dilute. (c)	5	Boiling	...	0.27 (10.7)	98
AL 29-4-2	Dilute. (c)	10	Boiling	...	0.46 (18.2)	98
Alloy 20	...	60	50 (122)	...	0.1 (4.0)	120
Alloy C-276	...	60	50 (122)	...	0.12 (4.8)	120
Altemp 625	Dilute. (c)	1	Boiling	...	0.06 (2.2)	98
Altemp 625	Dilute. (c)	5	Boiling	...	0.23 (8.9)	98
Altemp 625	Dilute. (c)	10	Boiling	...	0.64 (25.3)	98
AM-363 stainless steel	...	...	Room	...	Attacked	120
E-Brite	Dilute. Nonactivated. (b)	1	Boiling	48 h	0.018 (0.7)	39
E-Brite	Dilute. Activated. Sample activated at start of each test period. (b)	1	Boiling	48 h	13.741 (541)	39
E-Brite	Dilute. Nonactivated. (b)	5	Boiling	48 h	0.356 (14)	39
E-Brite	Dilute. Activated. Sample activated at start of each test period. One period or less	5	Boiling	48 h	76.7 (3020)	39
Jessop JS700	...	30	Boiling	48 h	3.81 (0.150 in./yr)	97
Jessop JS700	...	50	Boiling	48 h	6.27 (0.247 in./yr)	97
Jessop JS700	Plus 0.5% HCl	50	Boiling	48 h	22.35 (0.880 in./yr)	97
Jessop JS700	...	70	Boiling	48 h	1463 (57.6 in./yr)	97
Type 304 stainless steel	Research; laboratory test; no aeration; no agitation	...	Boiling	...	16.5 in./yr	89
Type 304 stainless steel	...	0.25	60 (140)	1 d	0.036 in./yr	89
Type 304 stainless steel	Research; laboratory test; slight to moderate aeration; no agitation	0.5	38 (100)	0.08 d	0.037 in./yr	89
Type 304 stainless steel	...	0.5	40 (104)	1 d	0.025 in./yr	89
Type 304 stainless steel	Synthetic rubber processing; field or pilot plant test; strong aeration; slight to moderate agitation	0.5	27-43 (80-110)	9 d	0.021 in./yr	89
Type 304 stainless steel	...	0.5	60 (140)	1 d	0.047 in./yr	89
Type 304 stainless steel	Research; laboratory test; slight to moderate aeration; no agitation	0.5	66 (150)	0.08 d	0.0225 in./yr	89
Type 304 stainless steel	Research; laboratory test; slight to moderate aeration; no agitation	0.5	79 (175)	0.08 d	0.445 in./yr	89
Type 304 stainless steel	Research; laboratory test; slight to moderate aeration; no agitation	0.5	93 (200)	0.08 d	0.79 in./yr	89
Type 304 stainless steel	Synthetic rubber processing; field or pilot plant test; strong aeration; slight to moderate agitation. With carbon over the standard maximum	0.5	27-43 (80-110)	9 d	0.0056 in./yr	89
Type 304 stainless steel	...	1	Room	1 d	0.025 in./yr	89
Type 304 stainless steel	Research; laboratory test; slight to moderate aeration; no agitation	1	38 (100)	0.08 d	0.0575 in./yr	89
Type 304 stainless steel	...	1	40 (104)	1 d	0.028 in./yr	89
Type 304 stainless steel	...	1	60 (140)	1 d	nil	89
Type 304 stainless steel	Research; laboratory test; slight to moderate aeration; no agitation	1	66 (150)	0.08 d	0.22 in./yr	89
Type 304 stainless steel	Research; laboratory test; slight to moderate aeration; no agitation	1	79 (175)	0.08 d	0.38 in./yr	89
Type 304 stainless steel	Research; laboratory test; slight to moderate aeration; no agitation	1	93 (200)	0.08 d	0.79 in./yr	89
Type 304 stainless steel	Research; laboratory test; rapid agitation	1	Boiling	0.5 d	0.3161 in./yr	89
Type 304 stainless steel	Pulp and paper processing; field or pilot plant test	~2	...	90 d	nil	89

(Continued)

Corrosion Behavior of Various Metals and Alloys in Sulfuric Acid (Continued)

Material	Condition, other factors, comments	Concentration, %	Temperature, °C (°F)	Duration	Corrosion rate, mm/yr (mils/yr) or other	Ref
Type 304 stainless steel	...	2.5	Room	1 d	0.031 in./yr	89
Type 304 stainless steel	...	2.5	40 (104)	1 d	0.036 in./yr	89
Type 304 stainless steel	...	2.5	60 (140)	1 d	0.16 in./yr	89
Type 304 stainless steel	Research; laboratory test; slight to moderate aeration; no agitation	3	38 (100)	0.08 d	0.067 in./yr	89
Type 304 stainless steel	Research; laboratory test; slight to moderate aeration; no agitation	3	66 (150)	0.08 d	0.388 in./yr	89
Type 304 stainless steel	Research; laboratory test; slight to moderate aeration; no agitation	3	79 (175)	0.08 d	0.528 in./yr	89
Type 304 stainless steel	Research; laboratory test; slight to moderate aeration; no agitation	3	93 (200)	0.08 d	1.3 in./yr	89
Type 304 stainless steel	Passive in 2nd and 3rd periods. Annealed. (a)	5 wt%	80 (176)	48 h	2.1 (85)	47
Type 304 stainless steel	...	5	Room	1 d	0.047 in./yr	89
Type 304 stainless steel	Textile processing; field or pilot plant test; strong aeration; no agitation	5	Room	104 d	<0.0001 in./yr	89
Type 304 stainless steel	Research; laboratory test; strong aeration; no agitation	5	16 (60)	1 d	0.013 in./yr	89
Type 304 stainless steel	Textile processing; field or pilot plant test; slight to moderate aeration; slight to moderate agitation	5	27 (80)	106 d	nil	89
Type 304 stainless steel	Research; laboratory test; slight to moderate aeration; no agitation	5	38 (100)	0.08 d	0.222 in./yr	89
Type 304 stainless steel	...	5	40 (104)	1 d	0.058 in./yr	89
Type 304 stainless steel	Research; laboratory test; strong aeration; no agitation	5	40 (104)	1 d	0.0875 in./yr	89
Type 304 stainless steel	Research; laboratory test; slight to moderate aeration; no agitation	5	66 (150)	0.08 d	1.1 in./yr	89
Type 304 stainless steel	Research; laboratory test; slight to moderate aeration; no agitation	5	79 (175)	0.08 d	1.63 in./yr	89
Type 304 stainless steel	Research; laboratory test; slight to moderate aeration; no agitation	5	93 (200)	0.08 d	5.4 in./yr	89
Type 304 stainless steel	Annealed. Passive in 2nd and 3rd periods (i.e., <1 mil/yr). (a)	5	80 (176)	48 h	2.159 (85)	145
Type 304 stainless steel	Metal (pickling) processing; field or pilot plant test; no aeration; no agitation	8	54 (130)	47 d	0.0108 in./yr	89
Type 304 stainless steel	Metal (pickling) processing; field or pilot plant test; no aeration; no agitation	8	54 (130)	47 d	0.0504 in./yr	89
Type 304 stainless steel	Research; laboratory test	8.7	80 (176)	9-10 d	0.460 in./yr	89
Type 304 stainless steel	Sugar processing; field or pilot plant test. With carbon over the standard maximum	~10	20-67 (68-152)	97 d	<0.0001 in./yr	89
Type 304 stainless steel	Sugar processing; field or pilot plant test	~10	20-67 (68-152)	97 d	<0.0001 in./yr	89
Type 304 stainless steel	Sugar processing; field or pilot plant test	~10	20-67 (68-152)	97 d	0.0007 in./yr	89
Type 304 stainless steel	...	10	Boiling	...	>12 (>500)	98
Type 304 stainless steel	...	10	Room	1 d	0.065 in./yr	89
Type 304 stainless steel	Research; laboratory test; strong aeration; no agitation	10	15 (60)	1 d	0.0175 in./yr	89
Type 304 stainless steel	Research; laboratory test; slight to moderate aeration; no agitation	10	38 (100)	0.08 d	0.39 in./yr	89
Type 304 stainless steel	Research; laboratory test; strong aeration; no agitation	10	40 (104)	1 d	0.193 in./yr	89
Type 304 stainless steel	...	10	40 (104)	1 d	0.17 in./yr	89
Type 304 stainless steel	Research; laboratory test; no aeration; no agitation	10	Boiling	...	16.5 in./yr	89
Type 304 stainless steel	Research; laboratory test; slight to moderate aeration; no agitation	10	65 (150)	0.08 d	1.83 in./yr	89
Type 304 stainless steel	Research; laboratory test; slight to moderate aeration; no agitation	10	79 (175)	0.08 d	4.5 in./yr	89
Type 304 stainless steel	Research; laboratory test; slight to moderate aeration; no agitation	10	93 (200)	0.08 d	7.0 in./yr	89
Type 304 stainless steel	Metal (pickling) processing; strong aeration; rapid agitation. Slight pitting: maximum depth of pits from incipient to 0.005 in.	~12	85-90 (185-195)	14 d	0.0126 in./yr	89
Type 304 stainless steel	Research; laboratory test; strong aeration; no agitation	15	15 (60)	1 d	0.03 in./yr	89

(Continued)

Corrosion Behavior of Various Metals and Alloys in Sulfuric Acid (Continued)

Material	Condition, other factors, comments	Concentration, %	Temperature, °C (°F)	Duration	Corrosion rate, mm/yr (mils/yr) or other	Ref
Type 304 stainless steel	Coal by-product processing; field or pilot plant test; slight to moderate aeration; rapid agitation. Severe pitting: maximum depth of pits over 0.010 in.	15	15-30 (59-86)	212 d	0.024 in./yr	89
Type 304 stainless steel	Research; laboratory test; strong aeration; no agitation	15	40 (104)	1 d	0.292 in./yr	89
Type 304 stainless steel	Chemical processing; field or pilot plant test; strong aeration; no agitation	~20	<40 (<104)	8.5 d	0.0002 in./yr	89
Type 304 stainless steel	Chemical processing; field or pilot plant test; strong aeration; no agitation; low-carbon grade (0.03% C max)	~20	<40 (<104)	8.5 d	0.0001 in./yr	89
Type 304 stainless steel	...	20	Room	1 d	0.13 in./yr	89
Type 304 stainless steel	Research; laboratory test; strong aeration; no agitation	20	15 (60)	1 d	0.44 in./yr	89
Type 304 stainless steel	Research; laboratory test; strong aeration; no agitation	20	40 (104)	1 d	0.437 in./yr	89
Type 304 stainless steel	...	20	40 (104)	1 d	0.68 in./yr	89
Type 304 stainless steel	Research; laboratory test; slight to moderate aeration; no agitation	20	65 (150)	0.08 d	5.75 in./yr	89
Type 304 stainless steel	Research; laboratory test; slight to moderate aeration; no agitation	20	80 (175)	0.08 d	10.7 in./yr	89
Type 304 stainless steel	Research; laboratory test; slight to moderate aeration; no agitation	20	93 (200)	0.08 d	21.0 in./yr	89
Type 304 stainless steel	Annealed. (a)	20	93 (200)	48 h	0.028 (1.1)	145
Type 304 stainless steel	Research; laboratory test; slight to moderate aeration; no agitation	20	38 (100)	0.08 d	1.01 in./yr	89
Type 304 stainless steel	Research; laboratory test; strong aeration; no agitation	25	15 (60)	1 d	0.053 in./yr	89
Type 304 stainless steel	Research; laboratory test; strong aeration; no agitation	25	40 (104)	1 d	0.41 in./yr	89
Type 304 stainless steel	Research; laboratory test; strong aeration; no agitation	30	15 (60)	1 d	0.035 in./yr	89
Type 304 stainless steel	Research; laboratory test; strong aeration; no agitation	30	40 (104)	1 d	0.474 in./yr	89
Type 304 stainless steel	Metal (cleaning) processing; field or pilot plant test; strong aeration; rapid agitation	30	54 (130)	62 d	0.0001 in./yr	89
Type 304 stainless steel	...	35	Room	1 d	0.6 in./yr	89
Type 304 stainless steel	Research; laboratory test; strong aeration; no agitation	40	15 (60)	1 d	0.048 in./yr	89
Type 304 stainless steel	Research; laboratory test; slight to moderate aeration; no agitation	40	38 (100)	0.08 d	0.85 in./yr	89
Type 304 stainless steel	Research; laboratory test; strong aeration; no agitation	40	40 (104)	1 d	0.9 in./yr	89
Type 304 stainless steel	Research; laboratory test; slight to moderate aeration; no agitation	40	65 (150)	0.08 d	13.0 in./yr	89
Type 304 stainless steel	Research; laboratory test; strong aeration; no agitation	50	15 (50)	1 d	0.15 in./yr	89
Type 304 stainless steel	Research; laboratory test; no aeration; no agitation	50	32 (90)	...	0.217 in./yr	89
Type 304 stainless steel	Research; laboratory test; strong aeration; no agitation	50	40 (104)	1 d	4.4 in./yr	89
Type 304 stainless steel	Research; laboratory test; strong aeration; no agitation	60	15 (60)	1 d	0.306 in./yr	89
Type 304 stainless steel	Research; laboratory test; strong aeration; no agitation	60	40 (104)	1 d	0.346 in./yr	89
Type 304 stainless steel	Research; laboratory test; no aeration; no agitation	66	32 (90)	...	0.204 in./yr	89
Type 304 stainless steel	Research; laboratory test; strong aeration; no agitation	70	15 (60)	1 d	0.039 in./yr	89
Type 304 stainless steel	Research; laboratory test; strong aeration; no agitation	70	40 (104)	1 d	0.0875 in./yr	89
Type 304 stainless steel	Research; laboratory test; no aeration; no agitation	77.6	32 (90)	...	0.0001 in./yr	89
Type 304 stainless steel	Research; laboratory test; strong aeration; no agitation	80	15 (60)	60 d	0.002 in./yr	89

(Continued)

Corrosion Behavior of Various Metals and Alloys in Sulfuric Acid (Continued)

Material	Condition, other factors, comments	Concen-tration, %	Temperature, °C (°F)	Duration	Corrosion rate, mm/yr (mils/yr) or other	Ref
Type 304 stainless steel	Research; laboratory test; slight to moderate aeration; no agitation	80	38 (100)	0.08 d	0.736 in./yr	89
Type 304 stainless steel	Research; laboratory test; strong aeration; no agitation	80	40 (104)	1 d	0.022 in./yr	89
Type 304 stainless steel	Research; laboratory test; slight to moderate aeration; no agitation	80	65 (150)	0.08 d	1.26 in./yr	89
Type 304 stainless steel	Research; laboratory test; slight to moderate aeration; no agitation	80	79 (175)	0.08 d	2.1 in./yr	89
Type 304 stainless steel	Research; laboratory test; slight to moderate aeration; no agitation	80	93 (200)	0.08 d	7.05 in./yr	89
Type 304 stainless steel	Research; laboratory test; strong aeration; no agitation	90	40 (104)	1 d	0.017 in./yr	89
Type 304 stainless steel	Plastic processing; no aeration; no agitation	93.5	9-25 (49-77)	102 d	<0.0001 in./yr	89
Type 304 stainless steel	Research; laboratory test; slight to moderate aeration; no agitation	95	38 (100)	0.08 d	0.0042 in./yr	89
Type 304 stainless steel	Research; laboratory test; slight to moderate aeration; no agitation	95	65 (150)	0.08 d	0.15 in./yr	89
Type 304 stainless steel	Research; laboratory test; slight to moderate aeration; no agitation	95	79 (175)	0.08 d	0.138 in./yr	89
Type 304 stainless steel	Research; laboratory test; slight to moderate aeration; no agitation	95	93 (200)	0.08 d	0.177 in./yr	89
Type 304 stainless steel	...	95	30 (86)	...	0.28 (11)	120
Type 304 stainless steel	Research; laboratory test; strong aeration; no agitation	95	40 (104)	1 d	0.022 in./yr	89
Type 316 stainless steel	1N	...	Boiling	...	65 (2600)	51
Type 316 stainless steel	Hot H₂SO₄, pH 3.0, containing W and Mo salts with 2-3 g/L fluorides, moderate aeration	0-4	60 (140)	...	0.05-0.25 (2-10)	68
Type 316 stainless steel	0.057% HCl, pH 2 to 5, incineration of municipal waste	0.19	60 (140)	2360 h	<0.05 (<2)	68
Type 316	...	0.25	Boiling	1 d	0.0027 in./yr	89
Type 316 stainless steel	...	0.25	60 (140)	1 d	nil	89
Type 316 stainless steel	...	0.25	80 (176)	1 d	nil	89
Type 316 stainless steel	Research; laboratory test; slight to moderate aeration; no agitation	0.5	38 (100)	0.08 d	nil	89
Type 316 stainless steel	...	0.5	40 (104)	1 d	nil	89
Type 316 stainless steel	Synthetic rubber processing; field or pilot plant test; strong aeration; slight to moderate agitation	0.5	27-43 (80-110)	9 d	0.0011 in./yr	89
Type 316 stainless steel	...	0.5	60 (140)	1 d	nil	89
Type 316 stainless steel	Research; laboratory test; slight to moderate aeration; no agitation	0.5	66 (150)	0.08 d	nil	89
Type 316 stainless steel	Research; laboratory test; slight to moderate aeration; no agitation	0.5	79 (175)	0.08 d	nil	89
Type 316 stainless steel	...	0.5	80 (176)	1 d	nil	89
Type 316 stainless steel	Research; laboratory test; slight to moderate aeration; no agitation	0.5	93 (200)	0.08 d	0.0038 in./yr	89
Type 316 stainless steel	...	0.5	Boiling	1 d	0.054 in./yr	89
Type 316 stainless steel	...	1	Room	1 d	nil	89
Type 316 stainless steel	Research; laboratory test; slight to moderate aeration; no agitation	1	38 (100)	0.08 d	nil	89
Type 316 stainless steel	...	1	40 (104)	1 d	nil	89
Type 316 stainless steel	...	1	60 (140)	1 d	nil	89
Type 316 stainless steel	Research; laboratory test; slight to moderate aeration; no agitation	1	66 (150)	0.08 d	nil	89
Type 316 stainless steel	Research; laboratory test; slight to moderate aeration; no agitation	1	79 (175)	0.08 d	nil	89
Type 316 stainless steel	...	1	80 (176)	1 d	nil	89
Type 316 stainless steel	Research; laboratory test; slight to moderate aeration; no agitation	1	93 (200)	0.08 d	nil	89
Type 316 stainless steel	...	1	Boiling	1 d	0.14 in./yr	89
Type 316 stainless steel	Research; laboratory test; rapid agitation	1	Boiling	0.5 d	0.0489 in./yr	89
Type 316 stainless steel	Dilute. Nonactivated. (b)	1	Boiling	48 h	0.551 (21.7)	39

(Continued)

Corrosion Behavior of Various Metals and Alloys in Sulfuric Acid (Continued)

Material	Condition, other factors, comments	Concentration, %	Temperature, °C (°F)	Duration	Corrosion rate, mm/yr (mils/yr) or other	Ref
Type 316 stainless steel	Dilute. Activated. Sample activated at start of each test period. (b)	1	Boiling	48 h	0.660 (26)	39
Type 316 stainless steel	Dilute. (c)	1	Boiling	...	0.65 (25.8)	98
Type 316 stainless steel	Pulp and paper processing; field or pilot plant test	~2	...	90 d	nil	89
Type 316 stainless steel	...	2.5	Room	1 d	nil	89
Type 316 stainless steel	...	2.5	40 (104)	1 d	nil	89
Type 316 stainless steel	...	2.5	60 (140)	1 d	0.0036 in./yr	89
Type 316 stainless steel	...	2.5	80 (176)	1 d	0.036 in./yr	89
Type 316 stainless steel	Plus 0.8-5.3% AlSO$_4$, 0-0.3% KCr(SO$_4$)$_2$, H$_2$O, moderate aeration	2.8-9.3	28 (83)	...	<0.05 (<2)	68
Type 316 stainless steel	Research; laboratory test; slight to moderate aeration; no agitation	3	38 (100)	0.08 d	nil	89
Type 316 stainless steel	Research; laboratory test; slight to moderate aeration; no agitation	3	66 (150)	0.08 d	0.0082 in./yr	89
Type 316 stainless steel	Research; laboratory test; slight to moderate aeration; no agitation	3	79 (175)	0.08 d	0.04 in./yr	89
Type 316 stainless steel	Research; laboratory test; slight to moderate aeration; no agitation	3	93 (200)	0.08 d	0.094 in./yr	89
Type 316 stainless steel	...	5	Room	1 d	nil	89
Type 316 stainless steel	Textile processing; field or pilot plant test; strong aeration; no agitation	5	Room	104 d	<0.0001 in./yr	89
Type 316 stainless steel	Research; laboratory test; strong aeration; no agitation	5	16 (60)	1 d	nil	89
Type 316 stainless steel	Textile processing; field or pilot plant test; slight to moderate aeration; slight to moderate agitation	5	27 (80)	106 d	nil	89
Type 316 stainless steel	Research; laboratory test; slight to moderate aeration; no agitation	5	38 (100)	0.08 d	nil	89
Type 316 stainless steel	...	5	40 (104)	1 d	nil	89
Type 316 stainless steel	Research; laboratory test; strong aeration; no agitation	5	40 (104)	1 d	nil	89
Type 316 stainless steel	Research; laboratory test; slight to moderate aeration; no agitation	5	66 (150)	0.08 d	0.036 in./yr	89
Type 316 stainless steel	Research; laboratory test; slight to moderate aeration; no agitation	5	79 (175)	0.08 d	0.74 in./yr	89
Type 316 stainless steel	Research; laboratory test; slight to moderate aeration; no agitation	5	93 (200)	0.08 d	0.14 in./yr	89
Type 316 stainless steel	Dilute. Nonactivated. (b)	5	Boiling	48 h	2.489 (98)	39
Type 316 stainless steel	Dilute. Activated. Sample activated at start of each test period. (b)	5	Boiling	48 h	2.718 (107)	39
Type 316 stainless steel	Dilute. (c)	5	Boiling	...	2.72 (107)	98
Type 316 stainless steel	Annealed. (a)	5	80 (176)	48 h	0.839 (33)	145
Type 316 stainless steel	Plus 3-4% zirconyl sulfate	5	32 (90)	15 d	<0.05 (<2)	68
Type 316 stainless steel	Aeration, laboratory test	5	58-67 (137-153)	29.5 d	>0.51-1.27 (>20-50)	68
Type 316 stainless steel	Plus Cu, 10-60 g/L (40 avg); Ag, 0-12 g/L (3.5 avg). Solids consist of precious metals, silica, PbSO$_4$, and a few % or less of Se, Te, As, Sb and Bi	5-150 g/L	71 (160)	...	<0.05 (<2)	68
Type 316 stainless steel	Metal (pickling) processing; field or pilot plant test; no aeration; no agitation	8	54 (130)	47 d	0.0014 in./yr	89
Type 316 stainless steel	Research; laboratory test	8.7	80 (176)	9-10 d	0.0001 in./yr	89
Type 316 stainless steel	Sugar processing; field or pilot plant test	~10	20-67 (68-152)	97 d	0.0001 in./yr	89
Type 316 stainless steel	Research; laboratory test; no aeration; no agitation	10	Boiling	...	0.86 in./yr	89
Type 316 stainless steel	Research; laboratory test; slight to moderate aeration; no agitation	10	65 (150)	0.08 d	0.081 in./yr	89
Type 316 stainless steel	Research; laboratory test; no aeration; no agitation	10	Boiling	...	0.86 in./yr	89
Type 316 stainless steel	Metal (pickling) processing; no aeration; no agitation; low-carbon grade (0.03% C max)	10	48-71 (120-160)	23 d	nil	89
Type 316 stainless steel	Research; laboratory test; no aeration; no agitation	10	60 (140)	1 d	0.09 in./yr	89
Type 316 stainless steel	...	10	40 (104)	1 d	0.0036 in./yr	89

(Continued)

Corrosion Behavior of Various Metals and Alloys in Sulfuric Acid (Continued)

Material	Condition, other factors, comments	Concentration, %	Temperature, °C (°F)	Duration	Corrosion rate, mm/yr (mils/yr) or other	Ref
Type 316 stainless steel	Research; laboratory test; strong aeration; no agitation	10	40 (104)	1 d	nil	89
Type 316 stainless steel	Research; laboratory test; slight to moderate aeration; no agitation	10	38 (100)	0.08 d	0.0096 in./yr	89
Type 316 stainless steel	Research; laboratory test; strong aeration; no agitation	10	15 (60)	1 d	nil	89
Type 316 stainless steel	...	10	Room	1 d	nil	89
Type 316 stainless steel	Research; laboratory test; slight to moderate aeration; no agitation	10	79 (175)	0.08 d	0.15 in./yr	89
Type 316 stainless steel	...	10	80 (176)	1 d	0.18 in./yr	89
Type 316 stainless steel	Research; laboratory test; slight to moderate aeration; no agitation	10	93 (200)	0.08 d	0.207 in./yr	89
Type 316 stainless steel	...	10	Boiling	...	>5 (>200)	98
Type 316 stainless steel	Base metal sample	10	Boiling	...	9.45 (372)	120
Type 316 stainless steel	Welded sample	10	Boiling	...	9.42 (371)	120
Type 316 stainless steel	Dilute. (c)	10	Boiling	...	8.73 (344)	98
Type 316 stainless steel	Annealed. (a)	10	80 (176)	48 h	2.845 (112)	145
Type 316 stainless steel	3% chromic acid in deionized water	10	80 (175)	...	0.05-0.25 (2-10)	68
Type 316 stainless steel	3% chromic acid in deionized water	10	80-82 (175-180)	...	<0.05 (<2)	68
Type 316 stainless steel	Nickel sulfide impurities	10	107 (225)	240 h	>1.27 (>50)	68
Type 316 stainless steel	Reacts with Fe_2O_3 to produce $Fe_2(SO_4)_3$, field test, aeration, moderate agitation, 6 ft/s	10-15	112 (234)	10 d	>1.27 (>50)	68
Type 316 stainless steel	Plus 10% $CuSO_4$, 52 pp. Cl^-. Average Baume 28.7, pH 1	10-20	86 (186)	90 d	<0.05 (<2)	68
Type 316 stainless steel	Metal (pickling) processing; strong aeration; rapid agitation	~12	85-90 (185-195)	14 d	0.0027 in./yr	89
Type 316 stainless steel	Saturated with SO_2. Slight aeration	14-16	79 (175)	...	>1.27 (>50)	68
Type 316 stainless steel	Research; laboratory test; strong aeration; no agitation	15	40 (104)	1 d	nil	89
Type 316 stainless steel	Coal by-product processing; field or pilot plant test; slight to moderate aeration; rapid agitation	15	15-30 (59-86)	212 d	0.0014 in./yr	89
Type 316 stainless steel	Research; laboratory test; strong aeration; no agitation	15	15 (60)	1 d	nil	89
Type 316 stainless steel	To 5% (final before discarding), 0.09% (original) to 0.54% (final) $FeSO_4$. Inhibited with Acti-vol 3591	16	74 (165)	...	0.05-0.25 (2-10)	68
Type 316 stainless steel	Chemical processing; field or pilot plant test; strong aeration; no agitation; low-carbon grade (0.03% C max)	~20	<40 (<104)	8.5 d	0.0001 in./yr	89
Type 316 stainless steel	Research; laboratory test; slight to moderate aeration; no agitation	20	93 (200)	0.08 d	1.77 in./yr	89
Type 316 stainless steel	Research; laboratory test; slight to moderate aeration; no agitation	20	80 (175)	0.08 d	0.84 in./yr	89
Type 316 stainless steel	Research; laboratory test; slight to moderate aeration; no agitation	20	65 (150)	0.08 d	0.191 in./yr	89
Type 316 stainless steel	...	20	40 (104)	1 d	0.027 in./yr	89
Type 316 stainless steel	Research; laboratory test; strong aeration; no agitation	20	40 (104)	1 d	0.11 in./yr	89
Type 316 stainless steel	Research; laboratory test; slight to moderate aeration; no agitation	20	38 (100)	0.08 d	0.0745 in./yr	89
Type 316 stainless steel	Research; laboratory test; strong aeration; no agitation	20	15 (60)	1 d	nil	89
Type 316 stainless steel	...	20	Room	1 d	0.009 in./yr	89
Type 316 stainless steel	Plus 12% CO. Copper refining. Moderate aeration	20	52 (125)	90 d	<0.05 (<2)	68
Type 316 stainless steel	Plus 1-2% Cu, 7000 oz/ton Ag, 200 oz/ton Au, 0.5% Sb, 0.5% Co, 1.0% 12% Te, 2% Cu. Trace Ag, Au, Sb, Co	20	52 (125)	90 d	<0.05 (<2)	68
Type 316 stainless steel	Saturated with $CuSO_4$. Pickling copper and brass. Aeration, moderate agitation	20	60 (140)	120 d	<0.05 (<2)	68
Type 316 stainless steel	Plus 8% $CuSO_4$, 52 ppm Cl. Copper refining	20	63 (145)	90 d	<0.05 (<2)	68
Type 316 stainless steel	Research; laboratory test; strong aeration; no agitation	25	40 (104)	1 d	0.47 in./yr	89

(Continued)

Corrosion Behavior of Various Metals and Alloys in Sulfuric Acid (Continued)

Material	Condition, other factors, comments	Concen-tration, %	Temperature, °C (°F)	Duration	Corrosion rate, mm/yr (mils/yr) or other	Ref
Type 316 stainless steel	Research; laboratory test; strong aeration; no agitation	25	15 (60)	1 d	nil	89
Type 316 stainless steel	Metal (cleaning) processing; field or pilot plant test; strong aeration; rapid agitation	30	54 (130)	62 d	<0.0003 in./yr	89
Type 316 stainless steel	Research; laboratory test; strong aeration; no agitation	30	40 (104)	1 d	0.665 in./yr	89
Type 316 stainless steel	Research; laboratory test; strong aeration; no agitation	30	15 (60)	1 d	0.065 in./yr	89
Type 316 stainless steel	...	35	Room	1 d	0.072 in./yr	89
Type 316 stainless steel	Research; laboratory test; slight to moderate aeration; no agitation	40	65 (150)	0.08 d	6.4 in./yr	89
Type 316 stainless steel	Research; laboratory test; strong aeration; no agitation	40	40 (104)	1 d	6.5 in./yr	89
Type 316 stainless steel	Research; laboratory test; slight to moderate aeration; no agitation	40	38 (100)	0.08 d	0.825 in./yr	89
Type 316 stainless steel	Research; laboratory test; strong aeration; no agitation	40	15 (60)	1 d	0.18 in./yr	89
Type 316 stainless steel	Research; laboratory test; strong aeration; no agitation	50	40 (104)	1 d	6.5 in./yr	89
Type 316 stainless steel	Research; laboratory test; no aeration; no agitation	50	32 (90)	...	Corrosion	89
Type 316 stainless steel	Research; laboratory test; strong aeration; no agitation	50	15 (50)	1 d	0.258 in./yr	89
Type 316 stainless steel	Research; laboratory test; strong aeration; no agitation	60	40 (104)	1 d	1.08 in./yr	89
Type 316 stainless steel	Research; laboratory test; strong aeration; no agitation	60	15 (60)	1 d	0.43 in./yr	89
Type 316 stainless steel	Research; laboratory test; no aeration; no agitation	66	32 (90)	...	0.144 in./yr	89
Type 316 stainless steel	Research; laboratory test; strong aeration; no agitation	70	40 (104)	1 d	0.54 in./yr	89
Type 316 stainless steel	Research; laboratory test; strong aeration; no agitation	70	15 (60)	1 d	0.05 in./yr	89
Type 316 stainless steel	Research; laboratory test; no aeration; no agitation	77.6	32 (90)	...	0.0007 in./yr	89
Type 316 stainless steel	Research; laboratory test; slight to moderate aeration; no agitation	80	93 (200)	0.08 d	4.0 in./yr	89
Type 316 stainless steel	Research; laboratory test; slight to moderate aeration; no agitation	80	79 (175)	0.08 d	1.2 in./yr	89
Type 316 stainless steel	Research; laboratory test; slight to moderate aeration; no agitation	80	65 (150)	0.08 d	0.572 in./yr	89
Type 316 stainless steel	Research; laboratory test; strong aeration; no agitation	80	40 (104)	1 d	nil	89
Type 316 stainless steel	Research; laboratory test; slight to moderate aeration; no agitation	80	38 (100)	0.08 d	0.282 in./yr	89
Type 316 stainless steel	Research; laboratory test; strong aeration; no agitation	80	15 (60)	60 d	nil	89
Type 316 stainless steel	Plastic processing; no aeration; no agitation	93.5	9-25 (49-77)	102 d	nil	89
Type 316 stainless steel	Research; laboratory test; slight to moderate aeration; no agitation	95	93 (200)	0.08 d	0.338 in./yr	89
Type 316 stainless steel	Research; laboratory test; slight to moderate aeration; no agitation	95	79 (175)	0.08 d	0.0825 in./yr	89
Type 316 stainless steel	Research; laboratory test; slight to moderate aeration; no agitation	95	65 (150)	0.08 d	0.059 in./yr	89
Type 316 stainless steel	Research; laboratory test; strong aeration; no agitation	95	40 (104)	1 d	nil	89
Type 316 stainless steel	Research; laboratory test; slight to moderate aeration; no agitation	95	38 (100)	0.08 d	nil	89
Type 317 stainless steel	Research; laboratory test; slight to moderate aeration; no agitation	0.5	38 (100)	0.08 d	nil	89
Type 317 stainless steel	Research; laboratory test; slight to moderate aeration; no agitation	0.5	66 (150)	0.08 d	nil	89
Type 317 stainless steel	Research; laboratory test; slight to moderate aeration; no agitation	0.5	79 (175)	0.08 d	nil	89

(Continued)

Corrosion Behavior of Various Metals and Alloys in Sulfuric Acid (Continued)

Material	Condition, other factors, comments	Concen-tration, %	Temperature, °C (°F)	Duration	Corrosion rate, mm/yr (mils/yr) or other	Ref
Type 317 stainless steel	Research; laboratory test; slight to moderate aeration; no agitation	0.5	93 (200)	0.08 d	nil	89
Type 317 stainless steel	Research; laboratory test; slight to moderate aeration; no agitation	1	38 (100)	0.08 d	nil	89
Type 317 stainless steel	Research; laboratory test; slight to moderate aeration; no agitation	1	66 (150)	0.08 d	nil	89
Type 317 stainless steel	Research; laboratory test; slight to moderate aeration; no agitation	1	79 (175)	0.08 d	nil	89
Type 317 stainless steel	Research; laboratory test; slight to moderate aeration; no agitation	1	93 (200)	0.08 d	nil	89
Type 317 stainless steel	Research; laboratory test; slight to moderate aeration; no agitation	3	38 (100)	0.08 d	nil	89
Type 317 stainless steel	Research; laboratory test; slight to moderate aeration; no agitation	3	66 (150)	0.08 d	nil	89
Type 317 stainless steel	Research; laboratory test; slight to moderate aeration; no agitation	3	79 (175)	0.08 d	0.058 in./yr	89
Type 317 stainless steel	Research; laboratory test; slight to moderate aeration; no agitation	3	93 (200)	0.08 d	0.12 in./yr	89
Type 317 stainless steel	Research; laboratory test; slight to moderate aeration; no agitation	5	38 (100)	0.08 d	nil	89
Type 317 stainless steel	Research; laboratory test; slight to moderate aeration; no agitation	5	66 (150)	0.08 d	0.0038 in./yr	89
Type 317 stainless steel	Research; laboratory test; slight to moderate aeration; no agitation	5	79 (175)	0.08 d	0.09 in./yr	89
Type 317 stainless steel	Research; laboratory test; slight to moderate aeration; no agitation	5	93 (200)	0.08 d	0.23 in./yr	89
Type 317 stainless steel	Research; laboratory test	8.7	80 (176)	9-10 d	0.0252 in./yr	89
Type 317 stainless steel	Research; laboratory test; slight to moderate aeration; no agitation	10	65 (150)	0.08 d	0.078 in./yr	89
Type 317 stainless steel	Research; laboratory test; slight to moderate aeration; no agitation	10	38 (100)	0.08 d	nil	89
Type 317 stainless steel	Research; laboratory test; slight to moderate aeration; no agitation	10	79 (175)	0.08 d	0.197 in./yr	89
Type 317 stainless steel	Research; laboratory test; slight to moderate aeration; no agitation	10	93 (200)	0.08 d	0.55 in./yr	89
Type 317 stainless steel	Research; laboratory test; slight to moderate aeration; no agitation	20	80 (175)	0.08 d	0.576 in./yr	89
Type 317 stainless steel	Research; laboratory test; slight to moderate aeration; no agitation	20	93 (200)	0.08 d	1.06 in./yr	89
Type 317 stainless steel	Research; laboratory test; slight to moderate aeration; no agitation	20	65 (150)	0.08 d	0.198 in./yr	89
Type 317 stainless steel	Research; laboratory test; slight to moderate aeration; no agitation	20	38 (100)	0.08 d	0.024 in./yr	89
Type 317 stainless steel	Metal (cleaning) processing; field or pilot plant test; strong aeration; rapid agitation	30	54 (130)	62 d	0.0004 in./yr	89
Type 317 stainless steel	Research; laboratory test; slight to moderate aeration; no agitation	40	65 (150)	0.08 d	2.64 in./yr	89
Type 317 stainless steel	Research; laboratory test; slight to moderate aeration; no agitation	40	38 (100)	0.08 d	0.22 in./yr	89
Type 317 stainless steel	Research; laboratory test; slight to moderate aeration; no agitation	80	93 (200)	0.08 d	6.05 in./yr	89
Type 317 stainless steel	Research; laboratory test; slight to moderate aeration; no agitation	80	79 (175)	0.08 d	3.35 in./yr	89
Type 317 stainless steel	Research; laboratory test; slight to moderate aeration; no agitation	80	65 (150)	0.08 d	1.12 in./yr	89
Type 317 stainless steel	Research; laboratory test; slight to moderate aeration; no agitation	80	38 (100)	0.08 d	0.579 in./yr	89
Type 317 stainless steel	Plastic processing; no aeration; no agitation	93.5	9-25 (49-77)	102 d	<0.0001 in./yr	89
Type 317 stainless steel	Research; laboratory test; slight to moderate aeration; no agitation	95	93 (200)	0.08 d	0.551 in./yr	89
Type 317 stainless steel	Research; laboratory test; slight to moderate aeration; no agitation	95	79 (175)	0.08 d	0.26 in./yr	89
Type 317 stainless steel	Research; laboratory test; slight to moderate aeration; no agitation	95	65 (150)	0.08 d	0.084 in./yr	89

(Continued)

Corrosion Behavior of Various Metals and Alloys in Sulfuric Acid (Continued)

Material	Condition, other factors, comments	Concen-tration, %	Temperature, °C (°F)	Duration	Corrosion rate, mm/yr (mils/yr) or other	Ref
Type 317 stainless steel	Research; laboratory test; slight to moderate aeration; no agitation	95	38 (100)	0.08 d	nil	89
Type 317L stainless steel	...	5	66 (150)	...	nil	63
Type 317L stainless steel	...	5	Boiling	...	5.1 (200)	63
Type 317L stainless steel	...	10	66 (150)	...	0.23 (8.9)	63
Type 317L stainless steel	...	10	Boiling	...	12 (490)	63
Type 317L stainless steel	...	20	66 (150)	...	1.3 (50)	63
Type 317L stainless steel	Dissolved completely	50	Boiling	48 h	...	97
Type 317L stainless steel	Plus 0.5% HCl	50	Boiling	48 h	13.72 (0.540 in./yr)	97
Type 317L Plus stainless steel	Dissolved completely	50	Boiling	48 h	...	97
Type 317L Plus stainless steel	Plus 0.5% HCl	50	Boiling	48 h	24.43 (0.962 in./yr)	97
Type 410 stainless steel	...	Conc.	Room	...	Practically unattacked	121
Type 410 stainless steel	...	Dilute	Room	...	Attacked	121
Aluminum						
Aluminum (>99.5%)	Solution	...	20 (68)	...	Restricted applications	92
Coppers						
90-10 cupronickel	(d)	...	...	...	Good	93
Admiralty brass	...	...	...	...	Fair	93
Aluminum bronze	(d)	...	...	...	Good	93
Ampco 8, aluminum bronze	Generally suitable	To 50	...	...	<0.05 (<2)	96
Architectural bronze	...	...	...	...	Not suitable	93
Brass	...	...	...	...	Fair	93
C11000	Pressure of 13.3 kPa (100 torr)	30	Boiling	24-48 h	0.670-0.700 (26.4-27.6)	54
C11000	Solution agitated	30	...	16-24 h	0.060-0.245 (2.4-9.6)	54
C11000	Pressure of 13.3 kPa (100 torr)	40	Boiling	24-48 h	0.487-0.700 (19.2-27.6)	54
C11000	Solution agitated	40	...	16-24 h	0.018-0.060 (0.7-2.4)	54
C11000	Pressure of 13.3 kPa (100 torr)	50	Boiling	24-48 h	0.660-0.792 (26.0-31.2)	54
C11000	Solution agitated	50	...	16-24 h	0.060 (2.4)	54
C11000	Pressure of 13.3 kPa (100 torr)	60	Boiling	24-48 h	2.195-2.255 (86.4-88.8)	54
C11000	Solution agitated	60	...	16-24 h	0.060-0.092 (2.4-3.6)	54
C11000	Pressure of 13.3 kPa (100 torr)	70	Boiling	24-48 h	0.853-1.067 (33.6-42.0)	54
C11000	Solution agitated	70	...	16-24 h	1.830-2.745 (72.0-108.0)	54
C11000	Pressure of 13.3 kPa (100 torr)	80	Boiling	24-48 h	39.630-166.420 (1560-6552)	54
C11000	Solution agitated	80	...	16-24 h	39.370-40.890 (1550-1610)	54
C14200	Pressure of 13.3 kPa (100 torr)	30	Boiling	24-48 h	0.640-0.670 (25.2-26.4)	54
C14200	Solution agitated	30	...	16-24 h	0.092-0.335 (3.6-13.2)	54
C14200	Pressure of 13.3 kPa (100 torr)	40	Boiling	24-48 h	0.487-0.548 (19.2-21.6)	54
C14200	Solution agitated	40	...	16-24 h	nil	54
C14200	Pressure of 13.3 kPa (100 torr)	50	Boiling	24-48 h	0.610 (24.0)	54
C14200	Solution agitated	50	...	16-24 h	0.050-0.060 (2.0-2.4)	54
C14200	Pressure of 13.3 kPa (100 torr)	60	Boiling	24-48 h	2.285-2.377 (90.0-93.6)	54
C14200	Solution agitated	60	...	16-24 h	0.015-0.060 (0.6-2.4)	54

(Continued)

Corrosion Behavior of Various Metals and Alloys in Sulfuric Acid (Continued)

Material	Condition, other factors, comments	Concen-tration, %	Temperature, °C (°F)	Duration	Corrosion rate, mm/yr (mils/yr) or other	Ref
C14200	Pressure of 13.3 kPa (100 torr)	70	Boiling	24-48 h	0.945 (37.2)	54
C14200	Solution agitated	70	...	16-24 h	2.135 (84.0)	54
C14200	Pressure of 13.3 kPa (100 torr)	80	Boiling	24-48 h	67.310-527.300 (650-20760)	54
C14200	Solution agitated	80	...	16-24 h	39.370-50.550 (1550-1990)	54
C26000	Pressure of 13.3 kPa (100 torr)	30	Boiling	24-48 h	...	54
C26000	Pressure of 13.3 kPa (100 torr)	40	Boiling	24-48 h	...	54
C26000	Pressure of 13.3 kPa (100 torr)	50	Boiling	24-48 h	...	54
C26000	Pressure of 13.3 kPa (100 torr)	60	Boiling	24-48 h	...	54
C27000	Pressure of 13.3 kPa (100 torr)	70	Boiling	24-48 h	0.580-0.793 (22.8-31.2)	54
C28000	Pressure of 13.3 kPa (100 torr)	80	Boiling	24-48 h	72.850-206.050 (2868-8112)	54
C51000	Pressure of 13.3 kPa (100 torr)	30	Boiling	24-48 h	0.640 (25.2)	54
C51000	Pressure of 13.3 kPa (100 torr)	40	Boiling	24-48 h	0.395-0.457 (15.6-18.0)	54
C51000	Pressure of 13.3 kPa (100 torr)	50	Boiling	24-48 h	0.915 (36.0)	54
C51000	Pressure of 13.3 kPa (100 torr)	60	Boiling	24-48 h	2.957-3.385 (116.4-133.2)	54
C51000	Pressure of 13.3 kPa (100 torr)	70	Boiling	24-48 h	0.945-1.067 (37.2-42.0)	54
C51000	Pressure of 13.3 kPa (100 torr)	80	Boiling	24-48 h	60.660-62.080 (2388-2444)	54
Titanium						
Ti-3-8-6-4-4	Naturally aerated	1	Boiling	...	nil	33
Ti-3-8-6-4-4	Naturally aerated	5	Boiling	...	1.85 (72.8)	33
Ti-3-8-6-4-4	Plus 1 g/L FeCl$_3$	10	Boiling	...	0.15 (5.9)	33
Ti-3-8-6-4-4	Plus 50 g/L FeCl$_3$	10	Boiling	...	0.05 (1.96)	33
Ti-3-8-6-4-4	Plus 3% Fe$_2$(SO$_4$)$_3$	50	Boiling	...	<0.03 (<1.18)	33
Ti-3Al-2.5V	ASTM Grade 9	0.5	Boiling	...	0.35 (334)	91
Titanium	Grade 7. Plus 100 ppm Cu^{2+}, 1% thiourea (deaerated)	1	100 (212)	...	nil	33
Titanium	Grade 7. Naturally aerated	1.0	204 (400)	...	0.005 (0.19)	33
Titanium	Grade 7. Nitrogen saturated	1, 5	190 (375)	...	0.13 (5.1)	33
Titanium	Grade 7. Oxygen saturated	1-10	190 (375)	...	0.13 (5.1)	33
Titanium	Grade 7. Naturally aerated	2.0	204 (400)	...	nil	33
Titanium	Grade 7. Nitrogen saturated	5	70 (158)	...	0.15 (5.9)	33
Titanium	Grade 7. Chlorine saturated	10	190 (375)	...	0.051 (2.0)	33
Titanium	Grade 7. Nitrogen saturated	10	190 (375)	...	1.50 (59.0)	33
Titanium	Grade 7. Nitrogen saturated	10	25 (75)	...	0.025 (0.98)	33
Titanium	Grade 7. Aerated	10	70 (158)	...	0.10 (3.93)	33
Titanium	Grade 7. Plus 5 g/L Fe$_2$(SO$_4$)$_3$	10	Boiling	...	0.178 (7.00)	33
Titanium	Grade 7. Plus 16 g/L Fe$_2$(SO$_4$)$_3$	10	Boiling	...	<0.03 (<1.18)	33
Titanium	Grade 7. Nitrogen saturated	10	70 (158)	...	0.25 (9.84)	33
Titanium	Grade 7. Plus 15% CuSO$_4$	15	Boiling	...	0.64 (25.1)	33
Titanium	Grade 7. Plus 1000 ppm Cl$^-$	15	49 (120)	...	0.015 (0.59)	33
Titanium	Grade 7. Plus 16 g/L Fe$_2$(SO$_4$)$_3$	20	Boiling	...	0.15 (5.9)	33
Titanium	Grade 7. Chlorine saturated	20	190 (375)	...	0.38 (39.3)	33
Titanium	Grade 7. Plus 1% CuSO$_4$	30	Boiling	...	1.75 (68.8)	33
Titanium	Grade 7. Nitrogen saturated	40	25 (75)	...	0.23 (9.05)	33
Titanium	Grade 7. Aerated	40	70 (158)	...	0.94 (37.0)	33
Titanium	Grade 9. Naturally aerated	0.5	Boiling	...	8.48 (333.8)	33
Titanium	Grade 9. Aerated	5	35 (95)	...	0.025 (0.98)	33
Titanium	Grade 9. Nitrogen saturated	5	35 (95)	...	0.405 (15.9)	33
Titanium	Grade 12. Naturally aerated	0.75	Boiling	...	0.003 (0.11)	33
Titanium	Grade 12. Plus 100 ppm Cu^{2+}, 1% thiourea (deaerated)	1	100 (212)	...	0.23 (9.0)	33

(Continued)

Corrosion Behavior of Various Metals and Alloys in Sulfuric Acid (Continued)

Material	Condition, other factors, comments	Concen-tration, %	Temperature, °C (°F)	Duration	Corrosion rate, mm/yr (mils/yr) or other	Ref
Titanium	Grade 12. Naturally aerated	1.0	Boiling	...	0.91 (35.8)	33
Titanium	Grade 12. Naturally aerated	1.0	204 (400)	...	0.91 (35.8)	33
Titanium	Grade 12. Naturally aerated	2.75	66 (150)	...	0.015 (0.59)	33
Titanium	Grade 12. Naturally aerated	3.0	66 (150)	...	1.65 (64.9)	33
Titanium	Grade 12. Naturally aerated	3.5	52 (125)	...	0.013 (0.51)	33
Titanium	Grade 12. Naturally aerated	3.75	52 (125)	...	1.73 (68.1)	33
Titanium	Grade 12. Naturally aerated	9	24 (75)	...	0.003 (0.11)	33
Titanium	Grade 12. Naturally aerated	9.5	24 (75)	...	0.006 (0.23)	33
Titanium	Grade 12. Naturally aerated	10	24 (75)	...	0.38 (14.9)	33
Titanium	...	0.5	Boiling	...	>5.0 (>200)	91
Titanium	...	1	Boiling	...	17.8 (712)	90
Titanium	Aerated	1	60 (140)	...	0.008 (0.32)	90
Titanium	Aerated	1	100 (212)	...	0.005 (0.2)	90
Titanium	Aerated	1	100 (212)	...	7.16 (286.4)	90
Titanium	Aerated	3	60 (140)	...	0.013 (0.52)	90
Titanium	Aerated	3	100 (212)	...	23.4 (936)	90
Titanium	Aerated	3	100 (212)	...	21.1 (844)	90
Titanium	...	5	Boiling	...	25.4 (1016)	90
Titanium	Aerated	5	60 (140)	...	4.83 (193.2)	90
Titanium	Plus 0.25% $CuSO_4$	5	95 (204)	...	nil	90
Titanium	Plus 0.5% CrO_3	5	95 (204)	...	nil	90
Titanium	Plus 95% HNO_3	5	60 (140)	...	0.005 (0.2)	90
Titanium	Saturated with chlorine	5, 10	190 (374)	...	<0.025 (<1)	90
Titanium	Aerated	10	35 (95)	...	1.27 (50.8)	90
Titanium	Plus 90% HNO_3	10	Room	...	nil	90
Titanium	Plus 90% HNO_3	10	60 (140)	...	0.011 (0.44)	90
Titanium	Plus 0.25% $CuSO_4$	30	38 (100)	...	0.061 (2.44)	90
Titanium	Plus 0.25% $CuSO_4$	30	95 (204)	...	0.088 (3.52)	90
Titanium	Plus 0.5% $CuSO_4$	30	38 (100)	...	0.067 (2.68)	90
Titanium	Plus 0.5% $CuSO_4$	30	95 (204)	...	0.823 (32.92)	90
Titanium	Plus 1.0% $CuSO_4$	30	38 (100)	...	0.020 (0.8)	90
Titanium	Plus 1.0% $CuSO_4$	30	95 (204)	...	0.884 (35.36)	90
Titanium	Plus 0.5% CrO_3	30	95 (204)	...	nil	90
Titanium	Plus 1.0% $CuSO_4$	30	Boiling	...	1.65 (66)	90
Titanium	Plus 70% HNO_3	30	Room	...	0.102 (4.08)	90
Titanium	Aerated	40	35 (95)	...	8.64 (345.6)	90
Titanium	Plus 4 g/L Ti^{4+}	40	100 (212)	...	nil	90
Titanium	Saturated with chlorine	45	24 (75)	...	0.003 (0.12)	90
Titanium	...	50	19-26 (65-80)	35 d	0.053 (2.1)	74
Titanium	Plus 50% HNO_3	50	60 (140)	...	0.399 (15.96)	90
Titanium	Plus 50% HNO_3	50	Room	...	0.635 (25.4)	90
Titanium	Saturated with chlorine	62	16 (61)	...	0.002 (0.08)	90
Titanium	Aerated	75	35 (95)	...	1.07 (1.045)	90
Titanium	Aerated	75	Room	...	10.8 (432)	90
Titanium	Plus 20% HNO_3	80	60 (140)	...	1.59 (63.6)	90
Titanium	Saturated with chlorine	82	50 (122)	...	>1.19 (>47.6)	90
Titanium	Plus 10% HNO_3	90	Room	...	0.457 (18.28)	90
Titanium	Vapors	96	38 (100)	...	nil	90
Titanium	Vapors	96	66 (151)	...	nil	90
Titanium	Vapors	96	200-300 (392-572)	...	0.013 (0.52)	90
Titanium	...	98	19-26 (65-80)	36 d	1.2 (46.8)	74
Titanium	...	98	145 (295)	30 d	Very soluble	74
Titanium	Aerated	Conc	Room	...	1.57 (62.8)	90
Titanium	Aerated	Conc	Boiling	...	5.38 (215.2)	90
Heat- and corrosion-resistant alloys						
18Cr-2Ni-12Mn	Passive in 2nd and 3rd periods. (a)	5 wt%	80 (176)	48 h	6.2 (248)	47

(Continued)

Corrosion Behavior of Various Metals and Alloys in Sulfuric Acid (Continued)

Material	Condition, other factors, comments	Concen-tration, %	Temperature, °C (°F)	Duration	Corrosion rate, mm/yr (mils/yr) or other	Ref
44Co-31Cr-13W	(e)	25	65 (150)	...	>25.4 (>1000)	53
44Co-31Cr-13W	Heat treated 4 h at 899 °C (1650 °F) and furnace cooled. (e)	25	65 (150)	...	>25 (>1000)	53
44Co-31Cr-13W	(e)	25	66 (150)	24 h	>25.4 (>1000)	53
44Co-31Cr-13W	Heat treated 4 h at 899 °C (1650 °F) and furnace cooled. (e)	25	66 (150)	24 h	>25.4 (>1000)	53
44Co-31Cr-13W	(e)	77	Room	...	nil	53
44Co-31Cr-13W	(e)	77	Room	24 h	nil	53
44Co-31Cr-13W	Heat treated 4 h at 899 °C (1650 °F) and furnace cooled. (e)	77	Room	24 h	...	53
44Co-31Cr-13W	(e)	96	Room	...	nil	53
44Co-31Cr-13W	Heat treated 4 h at 899 °C (1650 °F) and furnace cooled. (e)	96	Room	...	0.007 (0.3)	53
44Co-31Cr-13W	(e)	96	Room	24 h	nil	53
44Co-31Cr-13W	Heat treated 4 h at 899 °C (1650 °F) and furnace cooled. (e)	96	Room	24 h	0.0076 (0.3)	53
50Co-20Cr-15W-10Ni	...	25	65 (150)	...	0.27 (11)	53
50Co-20Cr-15W-10Ni	...	25	66 (150)	...	0.279 (11)	53
50Co-20Cr-15W-10Ni	...	77	Room	...	nil	53
50Co-20Cr-15W-10Ni	...	77	Room	...	nil	53
50Co-20Cr-15W-10Ni	...	96	Room	...	nil	53
50Co-20Cr-15W-10Ni	...	96	Room	...	nil	53
53Co-30Cr-4.5W	(e)	25	65 (150)	...	0.025 (1)	53
53Co-30Cr-4.5W	Heat treated 4 h at 899 °C (1650 °F). (e)	25	65 (150)	...	0.025 (1)	53
53Co-30Cr-4.5W	(e)	25	66 (150)	24 h	0.254 (1)	53
53Co-30Cr-4.5W	Heat treated 4 h at 899 °C (1650 °F) and furnace cooled. (e)	25	66 (150)	24 h	0.254 (1)	53
53Co-30Cr-4.5W	(e)	77	Room	...	nil	53
53Co-30Cr-4.5W	(e)	77	Room	24 h	nil	53
53Co-30Cr-4.5W	Heat treated 4 h at 899 °C (1650 °F) and furnace cooled. (e)	77	Room	24 h	...	53
53Co-30Cr-4.5W	(e)	96	Room	...	nil	53
53Co-30Cr-4.5W	Heat treated 4 h at 899 °C (1650 °F). (e)	96	Room	...	nil	53
53Co-30Cr-4.5W	(e)	96	Room	24 h	nil	53
53Co-30Cr-4.5W	Heat treated 4 h at 899 °C (1650 °F) and furnace cooled. (e)	96	Room	24 h	nil	53
Alloy 690	(f)	20	Room	7 d	0.05 (2)	57
Alloy 690	(f)	40	Room	7 d	<0.03 (<1)	57
Alloy 690	(f)	60	Room	7 d	0.05 (2)	57
Alloy 690	(f)	80	Room	7 d	<0.03 (<1)	57
Alloy 690	(f)	98	Room	7 d	0.5 (20)	57
Alloy 825	Metal pickling; field or plant test	10	48-71 (120-160)	23 d	0.013 in./yr	89
Alloy C-22	Plus 0.1% HCl	5	Boiling	...	0.660 (26)	63
Alloy C-22	Plus 0.5% HCl	5	Boiling	...	1.549 (61)	63
Alloy C-22	...	10	Boiling	...	0.279 (11)	63
Alloy C-22	Plus 1% HCl	10	70 (158)	...	<0.0254 (<1)	63
Alloy C-22	Plus 1% HCl	10	90 (194)	...	2.362 (93)	63
Alloy C-22	Plus 1% HCl	10	Boiling	...	5.715 (225)	63
Alloy C-22	Plus 2% HF	10	Boiling	...	0.737 (29)	63
Alloy C-22	Plus 1.2% HCl plus 1% FeCl$_3$ plus 1% CuCl$_2$	11.5	Boiling	...	0.076 (3)	63
Alloy C-22	...	20	66 (150)	...	<0.0254 (<1)	63
Alloy C-22	...	20	79 (174)	...	0.0254 (1)	63
Alloy C-22	...	20	Boiling	...	0.838 (33)	63
Alloy C-22	Plus 1.2% HCl plus 1% FeCl$_3$ plus 1% CuCl$_2$ (ASTM G28B)	23	Boiling	...	0.178 (7)	63
Alloy C-22	Plus 200 ppm Cl⁻	25	70 (158)	...	0.279 (11)	63
Alloy C-22	Plus 200 ppm Cl⁻	25	Boiling	...	5.740 (226)	63
Alloy C-22	...	30	66 (150)	...	0.0254 (1)	63
Alloy C-22	...	30	79 (174)	...	0.076 (3)	63

(Continued)

Corrosion Behavior of Various Metals and Alloys in Sulfuric Acid (Continued)

Material	Condition, other factors, comments	Concentration, %	Temperature, °C (°F)	Duration	Corrosion rate, mm/yr (mils/yr) or other	Ref
Alloy C-22	...	30	Boiling	...	1.626 (64)	63
Alloy C-22	...	40	38 (100)	...	<0.0254 (<1)	63
Alloy C-22	...	40	66 (150)	...	<0.0254 (<1)	63
Alloy C-22	...	40	79 (174)	...	0.152 (6)	63
Alloy C-22	...	50	38 (100)	...	<0.0254 (<1)	63
Alloy C-22	...	50	66 (150)	...	0.0254 (1)	63
Alloy C-22	...	50	79 (174)	...	0.406 (16)	63
Alloy C-22	Plus 42 g/L Fe₂(SO₄)₃ (ASTM G28A)	50	Boiling	...	0.610 (24)	63
Alloy C-22	...	60	38 (100)	...	<0.0254 (<1)	63
Alloy C-22	...	70	38 (100)	...	nil	63
Alloy C-22	...	80	38 (100)	...	nil	63
Alloy C-4	Plus 0.1% HCl	5	Boiling	...	1.245 (49)	63
Alloy C-4	Plus 0.5% HCl	5	Boiling	...	2.311 (91)	63
Alloy C-4	...	10	Boiling	...	0.787 (31)	63
Alloy C-4	Plus 1% HCl	10	70 (158)	...	0.610 (24)	63
Alloy C-4	Plus 1% HCl	10	90 (194)	...	1.676 (66)	63
Alloy C-4	Plus 1% HCl	10	Boiling	...	4.877 (192)	63
Alloy C-4	Plus 2% HF	10	Boiling	...	0.660 (26)	63
Alloy C-4	Plus 1.2% HCl plus 1% FeCl₃ plus 1% CuCl₂	11.5	Boiling	...	25.908 (1020)	63
Alloy C-4	...	20	66 (150)	...	<0.0254 (<1)	63
Alloy C-4	...	20	79 (174)	...	0.0508 (2)	63
Alloy C-4	...	20	Boiling	...	0.914 (36)	63
Alloy C-4	Plus 1.2% HCl plus 1% FeCl₃ plus 1% CuCl₂ (ASTM G28B)	23	Boiling	...	58.268 (2294)	63
Alloy C-4	Plus 200 ppm Cl⁻	25	70 (158)	...	0.940 (37)	63
Alloy C-4	Plus 200 ppm Cl⁻	25	Boiling	...	4.623 (182)	63
Alloy C-4	...	30	66 (150)	...	<0.0254 (<1)	63
Alloy C-4	...	30	79 (174)	...	0.076 (3)	63
Alloy C-4	...	30	Boiling	...	1.854 (73)	63
Alloy C-4	...	40	38 (100)	...	<0.0254 (<1)	63
Alloy C-4	...	40	66 (150)	...	0.254 (10)	63
Alloy C-4	...	40	79 (174)	...	0.381 (15)	63
Alloy C-4	...	50	38 (100)	...	<0.0254 (<1)	63
Alloy C-4	...	50	66 (150)	...	0.330 (13)	63
Alloy C-4	...	50	79 (174)	...	0.635 (25)	63
Alloy C-4	Plus 42 g/L Fe₂(SO₄)₃ (ASTM G28A)	50	Boiling	...	4.242 (167)	63
Alloy C-4	...	60	38 (100)	...	<0.0254 (<1)	63
Alloy C-4	...	70	38 (100)	...	0.0508 (2)	63
Alloy C-4	...	80	38 (100)	...	<0.0254 (<1)	63
Alloy C-625	...	50	79 (174)	...	1.32 (52)	63
Alloy 625	Plus 0.1% HCl	5	Boiling	...	3.835 (151)	63
Alloy 625	Plus 0.5% HCl	5	Boiling	...	11.024 (434)	63
Alloy 625	...	10	Boiling	...	1.168 (46)	63
Alloy 625	Plus 1% HCl	10	70 (158)	...	3.073 (121)	63
Alloy 625	Plus 1% HCl	10	90 (194)	...	8.280 (326)	63
Alloy 625	Plus 1% HCl	10	Boiling	...	22.073 (869)	63
Alloy 625	Plus 2% HF	10	Boiling	...	1.397 (55)	63
Alloy 625	Plus 1.2% HCl plus 1% FeCl₃ plus 1% CuCl₂	11.5	Boiling	...	42.266 (1664)	63
Alloy 625	...	20	66 (150)	...	<0.0254 (<1)	63
Alloy 625	...	20	79 (174)	...	<0.0254 <(1)	63
Alloy 625	...	20	Boiling	...	3.25 (124)	63
Alloy 625	Plus 1.2% HCl plus 1% FeCl₃ plus 1% CuCl₂ (ASTM G28B)	23	Boiling	...	98.399 (3847)	63
Alloy 625	Plus 200 ppm Cl⁻	25	70 (158)	...	1.794 (110)	63
Alloy 625	Plus 200 ppm Cl⁻	25	Boiling	...	8.255 (325)	63
Alloy 625	...	30	66 (150)	...	<0.0254 (<1)	63
Alloy 625	...	30	79 (174)	...	<0.0254 (<1)	63

(Continued)

Corrosion Behavior of Various Metals and Alloys in Sulfuric Acid (Continued)

Material	Condition, other factors, comments	Concentration, %	Temperature, °C (°F)	Duration	Corrosion rate, mm/yr (mils/yr) or other	Ref
Alloy 625	...	30	Boiling	...	6.045 (238)	63
Alloy 625	...	40	38 (100)	...	<0.0254 (<1)	63
Alloy 625	...	40	66 (150)	...	0.432 (17)	63
Alloy 625	...	40	79 (174)	...	0.889 (35)	63
Alloy 625	...	50	38 (100)	...	0.0254 (1)	63
Alloy 625	...	50	66 (150)	...	0.635 (25)	63
Alloy 625	Plus 42 g/L $Fe_2(SO_4)_3$ (ASTM G28A)	50	Boiling	...	0.584 (23)	63
Alloy 625	...	60	38 (100)	...	<0.0254 (<1)	63
Alloy 625	...	70	38 (100)	...	<0.0254 (<1)	63
Alloy 625	...	80	38 (100)	...	<0.0254 (<1)	63
Carpenter 20	Metal pickling; field or plant test; no aeration; no agitation; cast	8	54 (130)	47 d	0.0059 in./yr	89
Carpenter 20	Sugar processing; field or plant test. Approximately 10%	10	20-70 (68-152)	97 d	<0.0001 in./yr	89
Carpenter 20	Metal pickling; field or plant test	10	48-71 (120-160)	23 d	nil	89
Carpenter 20	Sugar processing; field or plant test. Approximately 10%	10	20-70 (68-152)	97 d	0.025 in./yr	89
Carpenter 20	Coal by-product processing; field or plant test; slight to moderate aeration; rapid agitation	15	15-30 (59-86)	212 d	0.0012 in./yr	89
Carpenter 20	Metal cleaning; field or plant test; strong aeration; rapid agitation	30	54 (130)	62 d	0.0002 in./yr	89
Carpenter 20	Metal cleaning; field or plant test; strong aeration; rapid agitation	30	54 (130)	62 d	0.0012 in./yr	89
Carpenter 20	Research; laboratory test; no aeration	50	32 (90)	...	0.0038 in./yr	89
Carpenter 20	Research; laboratory test; no aeration	66	32 (90)	...	0.0003 in./yr	89
Carpenter 20	Research; laboratory test; no aeration	77.6	32 (90)	...	0.0001 in./yr	89
Co-20Cr	...	11	Boiling	...	110 (4400)	35
Fe-47Cr (ferrite)	Reducing	10	Boiling	...	2939 $g/dm^2/d$	58
Fe-47Cr (sigma)	Reducing	10	Boiling	...	7422 $g/dm^2/d$	58
Fe-47Cr (ferrite)	Reducing	50	Boiling	...	5088 $g/dm^2/d$	58
Fe-47Cr (sigma)	Reducing	50	Boiling	...	5280 $g/dm^2/d$	58
Ferralium	1N	...	Boiling	...	1.15 (46)	51
Ferralium	...	5	66 (150)	...	nil	63
Ferralium	...	5	Boiling	...	0.30 (12)	63
Ferralium	...	10	66 (150)	...	nil	63
Ferralium	...	10	Boiling	...	1.0 (40)	63
Ferralium	...	20	66 (150)	...	nil	63
Hastelloy B	Plus 0-5% Na_2SO_4, 0-0.05% $ZnSO_4$, 0.02% CS_3, trace of H_2S	0-3	93 (200)	...	>0.25-0.51 (>10-20)	68
Hastelloy B	Plus 0.04% SO_2, and varying amounts of carbon on bottom tray of SO_2 scrubber in regeneration of alkylation acid	0.1	73-81 (164-177)	...	>1.27 (>50)	68
Hastelloy B	Saturated with NaCl. Maximum pitting, 0.35 mm/yr (14 mils/yr)	2	48-52 (118-126)	...	<0.05 (<2)	68
Hastelloy B	Plus 0.8-5.3% $AlSO_4$, 0-0.3% $KCr(SO_4)_2$, H_2O, moderate aeration	2.8-9.3	28 (83)	...	>0.25-0.51 (>10-20)	68
Hastelloy B	Plus 20 oz. $Na_2Cr_2O_7$ per 18 gal	5	21-29 (70-85)	...	<0.05 (<2)	68
Hastelloy B	Plus $FeSO_4$, 0.05% TiO_2 (0.008% solids)	5	32 (90)	...	>0.25-0.51 (>10-20)	68
Hastelloy B	Plus sulfate oils, traces of NaCl and Na_2SO_4	5	50 (122)	...	0.05-0.25 (2-10)	68
Hastelloy B	Plus 0.50-0.56 oz/gal Cu	5	80-85 (175-185)	...	>1.27 (>50)	68
Hastelloy B	Plus ore containing MnO and MnO_2	5	82 (180)	...	>0.25-0.51 (>10-20)	68
Hastelloy B	Steel pickling tank	8	49-60 (120-140)	...	0.05-0.25 (2-10)	68
Hastelloy B	Plus 1% HF, 3% Na_2SO_4, 1% $SiO_2 \cdot 2H_2O_2$, 0.5% Na_2SiF_6, balance water in separation of Na_2SiF_6	9	27-49 (80-120)	...	>1.27 (>50)	68
Hastelloy B	Plus Na_2SO_4 and glucose in rayon spin bath	10	45 (113)	...	<0.05 (<2)	68
Hastelloy B	SO_2 purge	10	38 (100)	...	>1.27 (>50)	68
Hastelloy B	SO_2 purge	10	65 (150)	...	>0.51-1.27 (>20-50)	68

(Continued)

Corrosion Behavior of Various Metals and Alloys in Sulfuric Acid (Continued)

Material	Condition, other factors, comments	Concen-tration, %	Temperature, °C (°F)	Duration	Corrosion rate, mm/yr (mils/yr) or other	Ref
Hastelloy B	SO$_2$ purge	10	93 (200)	...	>1.27 (>50)	68
Hastelloy B	SO$_2$ purge	10	Boiling	...	0.05-0.25 (2-10)	68
Hastelloy B	...	10	93 (200)	672 h	>1.27 (>50)	68
Hastelloy B	Nickel sulfide impurities	10	107 (225)	240 h	0.05-0.25 (2-10)	68
Hastelloy B	Plus 10-12% Na$_2$SO$_4$	10-12	349 (660)	...	<0.05 (<2)	68
Hastelloy B	Plus 10% CuSO$_4$, 52 ppm Cl$^-$. Average Baume 28.7, pH 1	10-20	86 (186)	90 d	>1.27 (>50)	68
Hastelloy B	Plus sugar from digestion of tuber barbasco. Process is for obtaining steroid used in hormone production	15	120 (248)	...	0.05-0.25 (2-10)	68
Hastelloy B	Dicyclopentadiene hydrate reaction. Pilot plant	15	115-130 (238-266)	220 h	>0.25-0.51 (>10-20)	68
Hastelloy B	To 5% (final before discarding), 0.09% (original) to 0.54% (final) FeSO$_4$. Inhibited with Acti-vol 3591	16	74 (165)	...	>1.27 (>50)	68
Hastelloy B	Zr-HF separation	20	Room	...	<0.05 (<2)	68
Hastelloy B	Plus CO$_2$(SO$_4$)$_3$, FeSO$_4$, trace CuSO$_4$	20	15-90 (59-194)	...	>0.51-1.27 (>20-50)	68
Hastelloy B	Plus 12% CO. Copper refining. Moderate aeration	20	52 (125)	90 d	>1.27 (>50)	68
Hastelloy B	Plus 1-2% Cu, 7000 oz/ton Ag, 200 oz/ton Au, 0.5% Sb, 0.5% Co, 1.0% 12% Te, 2% Cu. Traces Ag, Au, Sb, Co	20	52 (125)	90 d	>1.27 (>50)	68
Hastelloy B	Saturated with CuSO$_4$. Pickling copper and brass. Aeration, moderate agitation	20	60 (140)	120 d	0.05-0.25 (2-10)	68
Hastelloy B	Plus 8% CuSO$_4$, 52 ppm Cl. Copper refining	20	63 (145)	90 d	>0.25-0.51 (>10-20)	68
Hastelloy B	Plus 9.6% FeSO$_4$, 12% Ti as sulfate. Maximum pitting, 0.076 mm/yr (3 mils/yr)	24	19-21 (66-70)	...	<0.05 (<2)	68
Hastelloy B-2	Plus 0-5% Na$_2$SO$_4$, 0-0.05% ZnSO$_4$, 0.02% CS$_3$, trace of H$_2$S	0-3	93 (200)	...	>0.25-0.51 (>10-20)	68
Hastelloy B-2	Plus 0.04% SO$_2$, and varying amounts of carbon on bottom tray of SO$_2$ scrubber in regeneration of alkylation acid	0.1	73-81 (164-177)	...	>1.27 (>50)	68
Hastelloy B-2	Saturated with NaCl. Maximum pitting, 0.35 mm/yr (14 mils/yr)	2	48-52 (118-126)	...	<0.05 (<2)	68
Hastelloy B-2	Plus 0.8-5.3% AlSO$_4$, 0-0.3% KCr(SO$_4$)$_2$, H$_2$O, moderate aeration	2.8-9.3	28 (83)	...	>0.25-0.51 (>10-20)	68
Hastelloy B-2	Plus 20 oz Na$_2$Cr$_2$O$_7$ per 18 gal	5	21-29 (70-85)	...	<0.05 (<2)	68
Hastelloy B-2	Plus FeSO$_4$, 0.05% TiO$_2$ (0.008% solids)	5	32 (90)	...	>0.25-0.51 (>10-20)	68
Hastelloy B-2	Plus sulfate oils, traces of NaCl and Na$_2$SO$_4$	5	50 (122)	...	0.05-0.25 (2-10)	68
Hastelloy B-2	Plus 0.50-0.56 oz/gal Cu	5	80-85 (175-185)	...	>1.27 (>50)	68
Hastelloy B-2	Plus ore containing MnO and MnO$_2$	5	82 (180)	...	>0.25-0.51 (>10-20)	68
Hastelloy B-2	Steel pickling tank	8	49-60 (120-140)	...	0.05-0.25 (2-10)	68
Hastelloy B-2	Plus 1% HF, 3% Na$_2$SO$_4$, 1% SiO$_2$·2H$_2$O$_2$, 0.5% Na$_2$SiF$_6$, balance water in separation of Na$_2$SiF$_6$	9	27-49 (80-120)	...	>1.27 (>50)	68
Hastelloy B-2	Plus Na$_2$SO$_4$ and glucose in rayon spin bath	10	45 (113)	...	<0.05 (<2)	68
Hastelloy B-2	SO$_2$ purge	10	38 (100)	...	>1.27 (>50)	68
Hastelloy B-2	SO$_2$ purge	10	65 (150)	...	>0.51-1.27 (>20-50)	68
Hastelloy B-2	SO$_2$ purge	10	93 (200)	...	>1.27 (>50)	68
Hastelloy B-2	SO$_2$ purge	10	Boiling	...	0.05-0.25 (2-10)	68
Hastelloy B-2	...	10	93 (200)	672 h	>1.27 (>50)	68
Hastelloy B-2	Nickel sulfide impurities	10	107 (225)	240 h	0.05-0.25 (2-10)	68
Hastelloy B-2	Plus 10-12% Na$_2$SO$_4$	10-12	349 (660)	...	<0.05 (<2)	68
Hastelloy B-2	Plus 10% CuSO$_4$, 52 ppm Cl$^-$. Average Baume 28.7, pH 1	10-20	86 (186)	90 d	>1.27 (>50)	68
Hastelloy B-2	Plus sugar from digestion of tuber barbasco. Process is for obtaining steroid used in hormone production	15	120 (248)	...	0.05-0.25 (2-10)	68
Hastelloy B-2	Dicyclopentadiene hydrate reaction. Pilot plant	15	115-130 (238-266)	220 h	>0.25-0.51 (>10-20)	68

(Continued)

Corrosion Behavior of Various Metals and Alloys in Sulfuric Acid (Continued)

Material	Condition, other factors, comments	Concen-tration, %	Temperature, °C (°F)	Duration	Corrosion rate, mm/yr (mils/yr) or other	Ref
Hastelloy B-2	To 5% (final before discarding), 0.09% (original) to 0.54% (final) $FeSO_4$. Inhibited with Activol 3591	16	74 (165)	...	>1.27 (>50)	68
Hastelloy B-2	Zr-HF separation	20	Room	...	<0.05 (<2)	68
Hastelloy B-2	Plus $Co_2(SO_4)_3$, $FeSO_4$, trace $CuSO_4$	20	15-90 (59-194)	...	>0.51-1.27 (>20-50)	68
Hastelloy B-2	Plus 12% CO. Copper refining. Moderate aeration	20	52 (125)	90 d	>1.27 (>50)	68
Hastelloy B-2	Plus 1-2% Cu, 7000 oz/ton Ag, 200 oz/ton Au, 0.5% Sb, 0.5% Co, 1.0% 12% Te, 2% Cu. Traces Ag, Au, Sb, Co	20	52 (125)	90 d	>1.27 (>50)	68
Hastelloy B-2	Saturated with $CuSO_4$. Pickling copper and brass. Aeration, moderate agitation	20	60 (140)	120 d	0.05-0.25 (2-10)	68
Hastelloy B-2	Plus 8% $CuSO_4$, 52 ppm Cl. Copper refining	20	63 (145)	90 d	>0.25-0.51 (>10-20)	68
Hastelloy B-2	Plus 9.6% $FeSO_4$, 12% Ti as sulfate. Maximum pitting, 0.076 mm/yr (3 mils/yr)	24	19-21 (66-70)	...	<0.05 (<2)	68
Hastelloy C	Plus 0-5% Na_2SO_4, 0-0.05% $ZnSO_4$, 0.02% CS_3, trace of H_2S	0-3	93 (200)	...	0.025 (1)	68
Hastelloy C	Hot H_2SO_4, pH 3.0, containing tungsten and molybdenum salts with 2-3 g/L fluorides, moderate aeration	0-4	60 (140)	...	<0.05 (<2)	68
Hastelloy C	Plus 0.04% SO_2, and varying amounts of carbon on bottom tray of SO_2 scrubber in regeneration of alkylation acid	0.1	73-81 (164-177)	...	<0.05 (<2)	68
Hastelloy C	Spent pickle solutions. Cold wash water with salts picked up in steel pickling (0.097% ferrous, 0.003% ferric)	0.26	Room	...	0.001 (0.05)	68
Hastelloy C	Plus $CuSO_4$ to saturation	0.4-8.0	77-104 (170-220	...	0.015 (0.6)	68
Hastelloy C	Plus vegetable fats, greases	1-5	104 (220)	...	nil	68
Hastelloy C	As scrubbing liquid, moderate aeration	1-23	150 (302)	...	>0.51-1.27 (>20-50)	68
Hastelloy C	Plus 0.1% $CuSO_4$ and some alcohols	2.5	93-121 (200-250)	...	0.2 (8.2)	68
Hastelloy C	Plus 0.8-5.3% $AlSO_4$, 0-0.3% $KCr(SO_4)_2$, H_2O, moderate aeration	2.8-9.3	28 (83)	...	<0.05 (<2)	68
Hastelloy C	Plus 20 oz $Na_2Cr_2O_7$ per 18 gal	5	21-29 (70-85)	...	0.0017 (0.07)	68
Hastelloy C	Plus 3-4% zirconyl sulfate	5	32 (90)	15 d	<0.05 (<2)	68
Hastelloy C	Plus sulfate oils, traces of NaCl and Na_2SO_4	5	50 (122)	...	0.007 (0.3)	68
Hastelloy C	Aeration, lab test	5	58-67 (137-153)	29.5 d	<0.05 (<2)	68
Hastelloy C	Plus 0.50-0.56 oz/gal Cu	5	80-85 (175-185)	...	0.048 (1.9)	68
Hastelloy C	Plus ore containing MnO and MnO_2	5	82 (180)	...	<0.05 (<2)	68
Hastelloy C	Plus 15-25% Na_2SO_4, 1-5% organic salts	5-15	45-55 (113-131)	...	0.004 (0.16)	68
Hastelloy C	Plus Cu, 10-60 g/L (40 avg); Ag, 0-12 g/L (3.5 avg). Solids consist of precious metals, silica, $PbSO_4$, and a few % or less of Se, Te, As, Sb and Bi	5-150 g/L	71 (160)	...	<0.05 (<2)	68
Hastelloy C	Plus 0.35 oz/gal $NaNO_3$	6-9	68-79 (155-175)	...	0.863 (34)	68
Hastelloy C	Plus 0.8-0.9 oz/gal $NaNO_3$ in pickling tank	7-8	68-74 (155-165)	...	0.05 (2.1)	68
Hastelloy C	Plus 3% $Al_2(SO_4)$, 1% $Fe_2(SO_4)_3$, traces of $CaSO_4$ and $MgSO_4$	7.5-8	93-99 (200-210)	...	0.04 (1.6)	68
Hastelloy C	Steel pickling tank	8	49-60 (120-140)	...	0.12 (4.7)	68
Hastelloy C	Plus 1% HF, 3% Na_2SO_4, 1% $SiO_2 \cdot 2H_2O_2$, 0.5% Na_2SiF_6, balance water in separation of Na_2SiF_6	9	27-49 (80-120)	...	<0.05 (<2)	68
Hastelloy C	Plus Na_2SO_4 and glucose in rayon spin bath	10	45 (113)	...	0.005 (0.2)	68
Hastelloy C	Plus 10% $CuSO_4$	10	70 (158)	...	0.38 (15)	68
Hastelloy C	Plus 10% sulfate	10	70 (158)	...	>1.27 (>50)	68
Hastelloy C	Plus 10% Na_2SO_4	10	70 (158)	...	0.2 (8)	68

(Continued)

Corrosion Behavior of Various Metals and Alloys in Sulfuric Acid (Continued)

Material	Condition, other factors, comments	Concentration, %	Temperature, °C (°F)	Duration	Corrosion rate, mm/yr (mils/yr) or other	Ref
Hastelloy C	Plus 10% FeSO$_4$	10	70 (158)	...	0.86 (34)	68
Hastelloy C	SO$_2$ purge	10	38 (100)	...	<0.05 (<2)	68
Hastelloy C	SO$_2$ purge	10	65 (150)	...	0.05-0.25 (2-10)	68
Hastelloy C	SO$_2$ purge	10	93 (200)	...	>0.51-1.27 (>20-50)	68
Hastelloy C	SO$_2$ purge	10	Boiling	...	>1.27 (>50)	68
Hastelloy C	...	10	93 (200)	672 h	>0.25-0.51 (>10-20)	68
Hastelloy C	Lab test	10	Boiling	120 h	>0.25-0.51 (>10-20)	68
Hastelloy C	Nickel sulfide impurities	10	107 (225)	240 h	>1.27 (>50)	68
Hastelloy C	Plus 10-12% Na$_2$SO$_4$	10-12	349 (660)	...	0.002 (0.1)	68
Hastelloy C	Reacts with Fe$_2$O$_3$ to produce Fe$_2$(SO$_4$)$_3$. Field test. Aeration, moderate agitation, 6 ft/s	10-15	112 (234)	10 d	0.05-0.25 (2-10)	68
Hastelloy C	Plus 10% CuSO$_4$, 52 ppm Cl$^-$. Average Baume 28.7, pH 1	10-20	86 (186)	90 d	>0.25-0.51 (>10-20)	68
Hastelloy C	Top of acid spray section of conveyor-type spray pickling machine	12	85-91 (105-195)	...	0.1 (4)	68
Hastelloy C	Plus 13% by volume MnSO$_4$ and Mn$_2$O$_3$ in process for leaching crude MnO$_2$	13	27-99 (80-210)	...	0.457 (18)	68
Hastelloy C	Saturated with SO$_2$. Slight aeration	14-16	79 (175)	...	>0.25-0.51 (>10-20)	68
Hastelloy C	Dicyclopentadiene hydrate reaction. Pilot plant	15	115-130 (238-266)	220 h	>0.51-1.27 (>20-50)	68
Hastelloy C	To 5% (final before discarding), 0.09% (original) to 0.54% (final) FeSO$_4$. Inhibited with Actiol 3591	16	74 (165)	...	>0.25-0.51 (>10-20)	68
Hastelloy C	In pickling stainless foil plus 3% HCl. First pickle is followed by 15 min in 10% cold HNO$_3$	18	77-82 (170-180)	...	0.025 (1)	68
Hastelloy C	Plus 1.6-4.8% CuSO$_4$ for flash pickling of brass parts	19-28	60 (140)	...	0.04 (1.6)	68
Hastelloy C	Zr-HF separation	20	Room	...	<0.05 (<2)	68
Hastelloy C	Plus Co$_2$(SO$_4$)$_3$, FeSO$_4$, trace CuSO$_4$	20	15-90 (59-194)	...	0.3 (12)	68
Hastelloy C	Plus 12% CO. Copper refining. Moderate aeration	20	52 (125)	90 d	<0.05 (<2)	68
Hastelloy C	Plus 1-2% Cu, 7000 oz/ton Ag, 200 oz/ton Au, 0.5% Sb, 0.5% Co, 1.0% 12% Te, 2% Cu. Traces Ag, Au, Sb, Co	20	52 (125)	90 d	<0.05 (<2)	68
Hastelloy C	Saturated with CuSO$_4$. Pickling copper and brass. Aeration, moderate agitation	20	60 (140)	120 d	0.05-0.25 (2-10)	68
Hastelloy C	Plus 8% CuSO$_4$, 52 ppm Cl. Copper refining	20	63 (145)	90 d	<0.05 (<2)	68
Hastelloy C	Plus 2% Fe (ferrous and ferric in spray pickling machine)	20	77-82 (170-180)	...	0.434 (17.1)	68
Hastelloy C	Plus 0.5-3.5% CuSO$_4$ and abrasive anode mud from electrolytic copper refining	20-30	77-82 (170-180)	...	0.38 (15)	68
Hastelloy C-276	Plus 0.04% SO$_2$, and varying amounts of carbon on bottom tray of SO$_2$ scrubber in regeneration of alkylation acid	0.1	73-81 (164-177)	...	<0.05 (<2)	68
Hastelloy C-276	Spent pickle solutions. Cold wash water with salts picked up in steel pickling (0.097% ferrous, 0.003% ferric)	0.26	Room	...	<0.05 (<2)	68
Hastelloy C-276	Plus CuSO$_4$ to saturation	0.4-8.0	77-104 (170-220)	...	<0.05 (<2)	68
Hastelloy C-276	Plus 0-5% Na$_2$SO$_4$, 0-0.05% ZnSO$_4$, 0.02% CS$_3$, trace of H$_2$S	0-3	93 (200)	...	<0.05 (<2)	68
Hastelloy C-276	Hot H$_2$SO$_4$, pH 3.0, containing tungsten and molybdenum salts with 2-3 g/L fluorides, moderate aeration	0-4	60 (140)	...	<0.05 (<2)	68
Hastelloy C-276	Plus vegetable fats, greases	1-5	104 (220)	...	<0.05 (<2)	68
Hastelloy C-276	As scrubbing liquid, moderate aeration	1-23	150 (302)	...	>0.51-1.27 (>20-50)	68
Hastelloy C-276	Plus 0.1% CuSO$_4$ and some alcohols	2.5	93-121 (200-250)	...	0.05-0.25 (2-10)	68
Hastelloy C-276	Plus 0.8-5.3% AlSO$_4$, 0-0.3% KCr(SO$_4$)$_2$, H$_2$O, moderate aeration	2.8-9.3	28 (83)	...	<0.05 (<2)	68
Hastelloy C-276	Plus 20 oz Na$_2$Cr$_2$O$_7$ per 18 gal	5	21-29 (70-85)	...	<0.05 (<2)	68
Hastelloy C-276	Plus 3-4% zirconyl sulfate	5	32 (90)	15 d	<0.05 (<2)	68

(Continued)

Corrosion Behavior of Various Metals and Alloys in Sulfuric Acid (Continued)

Material	Condition, other factors, comments	Concentration, %	Temperature, °C (°F)	Duration	Corrosion rate, mm/yr (mils/yr) or other	Ref
Hastelloy C-276	Plus sulfate oils, traces of NaCl and Na_2SO_4	5	50 (122)	...	<0.05 (<2)	68
Hastelloy C-276	Aeration, lab test	5	58-67 (137-153)	29.5 d	<0.05 (<2)	68
Hastelloy C-276	Plus 0.50-0.56 oz/gal Cu	5	80-85 (175-185)	...	<0.05 (<2)	68
Hastelloy C-276	Plus ore containing MnO and MnO_2	5	82 (180)	...	<0.05 (<2)	68
Hastelloy C-276	Plus 15-25% Na_2SO_4, 1-5% organic salts	5-15	45-55 (113-131)	...	<0.05 (<2)	68
Hastelloy C-276	Plus Cu, 10-60 g/L (40 avg); Ag, 0-12 g/L (3.5 avg). Solids consist of precious metals, silica, $PbSO_4$, and a few % or less of Se, Te, As, Sb and Bi	5-150 g/L	71 (160)	...	<0.05 (<2)	68
Hastelloy C-276	Plus 0.35 oz/gal $NaNO_3$	6-9	68-79 (155-175)	...	>0.51-1.27 (>20-50)	68
Hastelloy C-276	Plus 0.8-0.9 oz/gal $NaNO_3$ in pickling tank	7-8	68-74 (155-165)	...	0.05-0.25 (2-10)	68
Hastelloy C-276	Plus 3% $Al_2(SO_4)_3$, 1% $Fe_2(SO_4)_3$, traces of $CaSO_4$ and $MgSO_4$	7.5-8	93-99 (200-210)	...	<0.05 (<2)	68
Hastelloy C-276	Steel pickling tank	8	49-60 (120-140)	...	0.05-0.25 (2-10)	68
Hastelloy C-276	Plus 1% HF, 3% Na_2SO_4, 1% $SiO_2 \cdot 2H_2O_2$, 0.5% Na_2SiF_6, balance water in separation of Na_2SiF_6	9	27-49 (80-120)	..	<0.05 (<2)	68
Hastelloy C-276	Plus Na_2SO_4 and glucose in rayon spin bath	10	45 (113)	...	<0.05 (<2)	68
Hastelloy C-276	Plus 10% $CuSO_4$	10	70 (158)	...	>0.25-0.51 (>10-20)	68
Hastelloy C-276	Plus 10% sulfate	10	70 (158)	...	>1.27 (>50)	68
Hastelloy C-276	Plus 10% Na_2SO_4	10	70 (158)	...	0.05-0.25 (2-10)	68
Hastelloy C-276	Plus 10% $FeSO_4$	10	70 (158)	...	>0.51-1.27 (>20-50)	68
Hastelloy C-276	SO_2 purge	10	38 (100)	...	<0.05 (<2)	68
Hastelloy C-276	SO_2 purge	10	65 (150)	...	0.05-0.25 (2-10)	68
Hastelloy C-276	SO_2 purge	10	93 (200)	...	>0.51-1.27 (>20-50)	68
Hastelloy C-276	SO_2 purge	10	Boiling	...	>1.27 (>50)	68
Hastelloy C-276	...	10	93 (200)	672 h	>0.25-0.51 (>10-20)	68
Hastelloy C-276	Lab test	10	Boiling	120 h	>0.25-0.51 (>10-20)	68
Hastelloy C-276	Nickel sulfide impurities	10	107 (225)	240 h	>1.27 (>50)	68
Hastelloy C-276	Plus 10-12% Na_2SO_4	10-12	349 (660)	...	<0.05 (<2)	68
Hastelloy C-276	Reacts with Fe_2O_3 to produce $Fe_2(SO_4)_3$, field test, aeration, moderate agitation, 6 ft/s	10-15	112 (234)	10 d	0.05-0.25 (2-10)	68
Hastelloy C-276	Plus 10% $CuSO_4$, 52 ppm Cl^-. Average Baume 28.7, pH 1	10-20	86 (186)	90 d	>0.25-0.51 (>10-20)	68
Hastelloy C-276	Top of acid spray section of conveyor-type spray pickling machine	12	85-91 (105-195)	...	0.05-0.25 (2-10)	68
Hastelloy C-276	Plus 13% by volume $MnSO_4$ and Mn_2O_3 in process for leaching crude MnO_2	13	27-99 (80-210)	...	>0.25-0.51 (>10-20)	68
Hastelloy C-276	Saturated with SO_2. Slight aeration	14-16	79 (175)	...	>0.25-0.51 (>10-20)	68
Hastelloy C-276	Dicyclopentadiene hydrate reaction. Pilot plant	15	115-130 (238-266)	220 h	>0.51-1.27 (>20-50)	68
Hastelloy C-276	To 5% (final before discarding), 0.09% (original) to 0.54% (final) $FeSO_4$. Inhibited with Activol 3591	16	74 (165)	...	>0.25-0.51 (>10-20)	68
Hastelloy C-276	In pickling stainless foil plus 3% HCl. First pickle is followed by 15 min in 10% cold HNO_3	18	77-82 (170-180)	...	<0.05 (<2)	68
Hastelloy C-276	Plus 1.6-4.8% $CuSO_4$ for flash pickling of brass parts	19-28	60 (140)	...	<0.05 (<2)	68
Hastelloy C-276	Plus 2% Fe (ferrous and ferric in spray pickling machine)	20	77-82 (170-180)	...	>0.25-0.51 (>10-20)	68
Hastelloy C-276	Plus 0.5-3.5% $CuSO_4$ and abrasive anode mud from electrolytic copper refining	20-30	77-82 (170-180)	...	>0.25-0.51 (>10-20)	68
Hastelloy C-276	Zr-HF separation	20	Room	...	<0.05 (<2)	68
Hastelloy C-276	Plus $Co_2(SO_4)_3$, $FeSO_4$, trace $CuSO_4$	20	15-90 (59-194)	...	>0.25-0.51 (>10-20)	68
Hastelloy C-276	Plus 12% CO. Copper refining. Moderate aeration	20	52 (125)	90 d	<0.05 (<2)	68

(Continued)

Corrosion Behavior of Various Metals and Alloys in Sulfuric Acid (Continued)

Material	Condition, other factors, comments	Concen-tration, %	Temperature, °C (°F)	Duration	Corrosion rate, mm/yr (mils/yr) or other	Ref
Hastelloy C-276	Plus 1-2% Cu, 7000 oz/ton Ag, 200 oz/ton Au, 0.5% Sb, 0.5% Co, 1.0% 12% Te, 2% Cu. Traces Ag, Au, Sb, Co	20	52 (125)	90 d	<0.05 (<2)	68
Hastelloy C-276	Saturated with CuSO$_4$. Pickling copper and brass. Aeration, moderate agitation	20	60 (140)	120 d	0.05-0.25 (2-10)	68
Hastelloy C-276	Plus 8% CuSO$_4$, 52 ppm Cl. Copper refining	20	63 (145)	90 d	<0.05 (<2)	68
Hastelloy C-4	Unwelded. Heat treated at 1066 °C (1950 °F), water quenched. (g)	10	Boiling	...	0.56 (22)	68
Hastelloy C-4	As welded. Gas tungsten arc welded. (g)	10	Boiling	...	0.64 (25)	68
Hastelloy C-4	Aged. Aged 100 h at 899 °C (1650 °F). (g)	10	Boiling	...	0.51 (20)	68
Hastelloy C-4	Unwelded. Heat treated at 1066 °C (1950 °F), water quenched. (g)	85	75 (167)	...	0.58 (23)	68
Hastelloy C-4	As welded. Gas tungsten arc welded. (g)	85	75 (167)	...	0.43 (17)	68
Hastelloy C-4	Aged. Aged 100 h at 899 °C (1650 °F). (g)	85	75 (167)	...	0.53 (21)	68
Hastelloy G	0.057% HCl, pH 2 to 5, incineration of munici-pal waste	0.19	60 (140)	2360 h	<0.05 (<2)	68
Hastelloy G	As scrubbing liquid, moderate aeration	1-23	150 (302)	...	>1.27 (>50)	68
Hastelloy G	Aeration, lab test	5	58-67 (137-153)	29.5 d	<0.05 (<2)	68
Hastelloy G	SO$_2$ purge	10	38 (100)	...	<0.05 (<2)	68
Hastelloy G	SO$_2$ purge	10	65 (150)	...	<0.05 (<2)	68
Hastelloy G	SO$_2$ purge	10	93 (200)	...	<0.05 (<2)	68
Hastelloy G	SO$_2$ purge	10	Boiling	...	>1.27 (>50)	68
Hastelloy G	3% chromic acid in deionized water	10	80 (175)	...	<0.05 (<2)	68
Hastelloy G	3% chromic acid in deionized water	10	80-82 (175-180)	...	<0.05 (<2)	68
Hastelloy G	Lab test	10	Boiling	120 h	>0.25-0.51 (>10-20)	68
Hastelloy G	Reacts with Fe$_2$O$_3$ to produce Fe$_2$(SO$_4$)$_3$, field test, aeration, moderate agitation, 6 ft/s	10-15	112 (234)	10 d	<0.05 (<2)	68
Hastelloy G	Plus 10% CuSO$_4$, 52 ppm Cl$^-$. Average Baume 28.7, pH 1	10-20	86 (186)	90 d	<0.05 (<2)	68
Hastelloy G	Plus 12% CO. Copper refining. Moderate aera-tion	20	52 (125)	90 d	<0.05 (<2)	68
Hastelloy G	Plus 1-2% Cu, 7000 oz/ton Ag, 200 oz/ton Au, 0.5% Sb, 0.5% Co, 1.0% 12% Te, 2% Cu. Traces Ag, Au, Sb, Co	20	52 (125)	90 d	<0.05 (<2)	68
Hastelloy G	Plus 8% CuSO$_4$, 52 ppm Cl. Copper refining	20	63 (145)	90 d	<0.05 (<2)	68
Hastelloy G-3	0.057% HCl, pH 2 to 5, incineration of munici-pal waste	0.19	60 (140)	2360 h	<0.05 (<2)	68
Hastelloy G-3	As scrubbing liquid	1-23	150 (302)	...	>1.27 (>50)	68
Hastelloy G-3	Aeration, lab test	5	58-67 (137-153)	29.5 d	<0.05 (<2)	68
Hastelloy G-3	SO$_2$ purge	10	38 (100)	...	<0.05 (<2)	68
Hastelloy G-3	SO$_2$ purge	10	65 (150)	...	<0.05 (<2)	68
Hastelloy G-3	SO$_2$ purge	10	93 (200)	...	<0.05 (<2)	68
Hastelloy G-3	SO$_2$ purge	10	Boiling	...	>1.27 (>50)	68
Hastelloy G-3	3% chromic acid in deionized water	10	80 (175)	...	<0.05 (<2)	68
Hastelloy G-3	3% chromic acid in deionized water	10	80-82 (175-180)	...	<0.05 (<2)	68
Hastelloy G-3	Lab test	10	Boiling	120 h	>0.25-0.51 (>10-20)	68
Hastelloy G-3	Reacts with Fe$_2$O$_3$ to produce Fe$_2$(SO$_4$)$_3$, field test, aeration, moderate agitation, 6 ft/s	10-15	112 (234)	10 d	<0.05 (<2)	68
Hastelloy G-3	Plus 10% CuSO$_4$, 52 ppm Cl$^-$. Average Baume 28.7, pH 1	10-20	86 (186)	90 d	<0.05 (<2)	68
Hastelloy G-3	Plus 12% CO. Copper refining. Moderate aera-tion	20	52 (125)	90 d	<0.05 (<2)	68
Hastelloy G-3	Plus 1-2% Cu, 7000 oz/ton Ag, 200 oz/ton Au, 0.5% Sb, 0.5% Co, 1.0% 12% Te, 2% Cu. Traces Ag, Au, Sb, Co	20	52 (125)	90 d	<0.05 (<2)	68
Hastelloy G-3	Plus 8% CuSO$_4$, 52 ppm Cl. Copper refining	20	63 (145)	90 d	<0.05 (<2)	68
Hastelloy G-30	...	2	Boiling	...	0.203 (8)	63
Hastelloy G-30	...	10	Boiling	...	0.787 (31)	63
Hastelloy G-30	Nitric acid plus 8% HCl	18	80 (176)	...	0.0508 (2)	63

(Continued)

Corrosion Behavior of Various Metals and Alloys in Sulfuric Acid (Continued)

Material	Condition, other factors, comments	Concentration, %	Temperature, °C (°F)	Duration	Corrosion rate, mm/yr (mils/yr) or other	Ref
Hastelloy G-30	...	20	Boiling	...	1.372 (54)	63
Hastelloy G-30	Nitric acid plus 11% HCl	25	80 (176)	...	0.5842 (23)	63
Hastelloy G-30	Plus 42 g/L Fe$_2$(SO$_4$)$_3$	50	Boiling	...	0.178 (7)	63
Hastelloy G-30	Plus 10% nitric acid	50	Boiling	...	0.406 (16)	63
Hastelloy G-30	...	50	107 (225)	...	0.939 (37)	63
Hastelloy G-30	Nitric acid plus 3% HCl	59	80 (176)	...	0.127 (5)	63
Hastelloy G-30	Plus 5% nitric acid	60	Boiling	...	1.143 (45)	63
Hastelloy G-30	Plus 5% nitric acid	70	Boiling	...	3.378 (133)	63
Hastelloy G-30	Plus 8% nitric acid plus 4% HF	77	54 (129)	...	0.0102 (0.4)	63
Hastelloy G-30	...	80	52 (125)	...	0.305 (12)	63
Hastelloy G-30	...	99	130 (226)	...	1.092 (43)	63
Hastelloy G-30	...	99	140 (284)	...	1.168 (46)	63
Haynes No. 25	(h)	2	Room	24 h	nil	68
Haynes No. 25	(h)	2	66 (150)	24 h	nil	68
Haynes No. 25	(h)	2	Boiling	24 h	1.24 (49)	68
Haynes No. 25	(h)	5	Room	24 h	nil	68
Haynes No. 25	(h)	5	66 (150)	24 h	nil	68
Haynes No. 25	(h)	5	Boiling	24 h	1.32 (52)	68
Haynes No. 25	(h)	10	Room	24 h	nil	68
Haynes No. 25	(h)	10	66 (150)	24 h	nil	68
Haynes No. 25	(h)	10	Boiling	24 h	2.34 (92)	68
Haynes No. 25	(h)	25	Room	24 h	nil	68
Haynes No. 25	(h)	25	66 (150)	24 h	0.28 (11)	68
Haynes No. 25	(h)	25	Boiling	24 h	5.16 (203)	68
Haynes No. 25	(h)	50	Room	24 h	nil	68
Haynes No. 25	(h)	50	66 (150)	24 h	0.76 (30)	68
Haynes No. 25	(h)	50	Boiling	24 h	>25.4 (>1000)	68
Haynes No. 25	(h)	60	Room	24 h	nil	68
Haynes No. 25	(h)	60	66 (150)	24 h	0.74 (29)	68
Haynes No. 25	(h)	60	Boiling	24 h	>25.4 (>1000)	68
Haynes No. 25	(h)	77	Room	24 h	nil	68
Haynes No. 25	(h)	77	66 (150)	24 h	1.40 (55)	68
Haynes No. 25	(h)	77	Boiling	24 h	>25.4 (>1000)	68
Haynes No. 25	(h)	80	Room	24 h	nil	68
Haynes No. 25	(h)	80	66 (150)	24 h	1.55 (61)	68
Haynes No. 25	(h)	80	Boiling	24 h	>25.4 (>1000)	68
Haynes No. 25	(h)	85	Room	24 h	nil	68
Haynes No. 25	(h)	85	66 (150)	24 h	2.31 (91)	68
Haynes No. 25	(h)	85	Boiling	24 h	>25.4 (>1000)	68
Haynes No. 25	(h)	90	Room	24 h	nil	68
Haynes No. 25	(h)	90	66 (150)	24 h	3.12 (123)	68
Haynes No. 25	(h)	90	Boiling	24 h	18.7 (735)	68
Haynes No. 25	(h)	96	Room	24 h	nil	68
Haynes No. 25	(h)	96	66 (150)	24 h	2.64 (104)	68
Haynes No. 25	(h)	96	Boiling	24 h	8.08 (318)	68
Inco alloy G	Plus 3 vol% HCl + 1% FeCl$_3$ + 1% CuCl$_2$	7	70 (158)	...	1200 (30.5)	40
Inco alloy G	...	10	Boiling	...	14 (0.36)	40
Inco alloy G	...	50	Boiling	...	108 (2.74)	40
Inco alloy G-3	Plus 3 vol% HCl + 1% FeCl$_3$ + 1% CuCl$_2$	7	70 (158)	24 h	30; 40 (0.76; 1.02)	40
Inco alloy G-3	Duplicate specimens	10	Boiling	1 week	20; 23 (0.51; 0.58)	40
Inco alloy G-3	Duplicate specimens	50	Boiling	1 week	49; 23 (0.51; 0.58)	40
Incoloy 825	Mixture of sulfuric acid and sebacic acid pH 1	...	Room	30 d	0.003 (0.1)	43
Incoloy 825	12% sulfuric acid pickling solution containing copper sulfate up to 11.2%. Immersed inside tank of Mesta pickler	...	82 (180)	26 d	0.005 (0.2)	43
Incoloy 825	Evaporation of aluminum sulfate solution from 28.2 to 57.7% Al$_2$(SO$_4$)$_3$, containing 0.1% Fe$_2$O$_3$, 0.3% FeO, and traces of Cr$_2$O$_3$ and Al$_2$O$_3$	...	91-121 (195-250)	44 d	0.020 (0.8)	43

(Continued)

Corrosion Behavior of Various Metals and Alloys in Sulfuric Acid (Continued)

Material	Condition, other factors, comments	Concentration, %	Temperature, °C (°F)	Duration	Corrosion rate, mm/yr (mils/yr) or other	Ref
Incoloy 825	Aqueous solution	0.5	99 (210)	45 d	0.051 (2.0)	43
Incoloy 825	Plus 20-25% ammonium sulfate plus 10-15% sodium sulfate. Immersed in tank	1-4	35-40 (95-104)	...	0.003 (0.1)	43
Incoloy 825	Spent acid liquor from tall oil splitting. Plus 1% tall oil and 2-3% lignin by volume. Acid discharge line from centrifuge	1	121 (250)	33 d	0.003 (0.1)	43
Incoloy 825	Plus 91.6% benzene sulfonic acid. Immersed in glass-lined vessel	3.5	60 (140)	7 d	1.14 (45.0)	43
Incoloy 825	Plus 10-300 mesh ore of MnO$_2$ and MnO. Attached to steam coil in leaching tank	5	82 (180)	245 d	0.013 (0.5)	43
Incoloy 825	Plus 0.25% copper sulfate in pickling of brass. Immersed in continuous strip pickler	5-10	38-93 (100-200)	162 d	0.003 (0.1)	43
Incoloy 825	Plus 1% hydrofluoric acid, 3% sodium sulfate, 1% silica, 0.5% sodium fluosilicate and balance water. Immersed in tank near entrance	9	27-49 (80-120)	62 d	0.025 (1.0)	43
Incoloy 825	Plus 4% sodium dichromate. Immersed in cleaning solution for aluminum	20	66-71 (150-160)	77 d	0.483 (19.0)	43
Incoloy 825	Plus 100 g/L CuSO$_4$, 10 g/L NiSO$_4$, and trace of chloride. Treatment of copper residue in nickel refining. Immersed in concentration-plant air blowers	20	91 (195)	7 d	0.127 (5.0)	43
Incoloy 825	Plus 25-100 g/L MnSO$_4$, 1-3 g/L Fe$_2$(SO$_4$)$_3$. Immersed in sump in MnO$_2$ electrolysis circuit. Flow 100 gal/min (380 L/min)	25-50g/L	93 (200)	119 d	0.071 (2.8)	43
Incoloy 825	In uranium ore leach tank in mixture containing 60% solids, 5-10 g/L ferric ion, some ferrous ion, 0.1% sodium chlorate	28-55 g/L	45 (113)	41 d	0.003 (0.1)	43
Incoloy 825	28% oxalic acid, 32% water and 4% ash. On agitator support in vacuum evaporation plan. Alternately immersed and exposed	36	60 (140)	171 d	0.061 (2.4)	43
Incoloy 825	In vacuum evaporator. Recovery of sulfuric acid in paper making	39	49 (120)	120 d	nil	43
Incoloy 825	In vacuum evaporator. Recovery of sulfuric acid in paper making	42	57 (135)	120 d	0.008 (0.3)	43
Incoloy 825	Plus 22% nitric acid and 19% water. Immersed in laboratory tests	50	66 (150)	6 d	0.013 (0.5)	43
Incoloy 825	Plus 22% nitric acid and 19% water. Immersed in laboratory tests	50	83 (182)	5 d	0.109 (4.3)	43
Incoloy 825	In vacuum evaporator. Recovery of sulfuric acid in paper making	55	71 (160)	120 d	0.102 (4.0)	43
Incoloy 825	Plus gas mixture containing 44% propylene and 56% propane. In outlet piping from second stage reactor circulating pumps, pressure 400 psi (2.8 MPa)	67	52 (125)	170 d	0.005 (0.2)	43
Incoloy 825	Plus traces of benzene sulfonic acid in bottom of acid settling tank	78	38-54 (100-130)	56 d	0.013 (0.5)	43
Incoloy 825	Plus 3.5% hydrogen peroxide plus various salts of iron, manganese, chromium and nickel in holding tank	78	38-54 (100-130)	8 d	0.127 (5.0)	43
Incoloy 825	Plus small amounts of phosphine, ammonia and hydrogen sulfate. In exit of packed tower in falling acid stream	79-93	10-32 (50-90)	189 d	0.056 (2.2)	43
Incoloy 825	Plus 40-100 g/L selenious acid, small amount sulfurous acid	100-200 g/L	21-27 (70-80)	90 d	nil	43
Inconel 600	Unaerated	0.16	100 (212)	...	0.094 (3.7)	64
Inconel 600	Air-saturated	0.16	100 (212)	...	...	64
Inconel 600	Unaerated. Velocity, 15.5 fpm	1	30 (86)	120 h	...	64
Inconel 600	Unaerated. Velocity, 15.5 fpm	1	78 (172)	22 h	...	64
Inconel 600	Air-saturated. Velocity, 15.5 fpm	1	30 (86)	120 h	1.245 (49)	64
Inconel 600	Air-saturated. Velocity, 15.5 fpm	1	78 (172)	22 h	2.794 (110)	64
Inconel 600	Unaerated. Velocity, none	5	18 (65)	100 h	0.061 (2.4)	64
Inconel 600	Unaerated. Velocity, 15.5 fpm	5	30 (86)	20 h	0.229 (9)	64
Inconel 600	Unaerated. Velocity, 16.0 fpm	5	30 (86)	23 h	...	64
Inconel 600	Unaerated. Velocity, none	5	60 (140)	100 h	0.254 (10)	64
Inconel 600	Air-saturated. Velocity, none	5	18 (65)	100 h	...	64

(Continued)

Corrosion Behavior of Various Metals and Alloys in Sulfuric Acid (Continued)

Material	Condition, other factors, comments	Concen-tration, %	Temperature, °C (°F)	Duration	Corrosion rate, mm/yr (mils/yr) or other	Ref
Inconel 600	Unaerated. Velocity, 16.0 fpm	5	80 (176)	20 h	0.762 (30)	64
Inconel 600	Air-saturated. Velocity, 15.5 fpm	5	30 (86)	20 h	...	64
Inconel 600	Air-saturated. Velocity, 16.0 fpm	5	30 (86)	23 h	1.981 (78)	64
Inconel 600	Air-saturated. Velocity, none	5	60 (140)	100 h	...	64
Inconel 600	Air-saturated. Velocity, 16.0 fpm	5	80 (176)	20 h	3.81 (150)	64
Inconel 600	Unaerated. Velocity, none	10	...	24 h	0.107 (4.2)	64
Inconel 600	Air-saturated. Velocity, none	10	...	24 h	...	64
Inconel 600	Unaerated. Velocity, 15.5 fpm	70	30 (86)	20 h	1.169 (46)	64
Inconel 600	Air-saturated. Velocity, 15.5 fpm	70	30 (86)	20 h	...	64
Inconel 600	Unaerated. Velocity, 15.5 fpm	93	30 (86)	20 h	6.858 (270)	64
Inconel 600	Air-saturated. Velocity, 15.5 fpm	93	30 (86)	20 h	0.254 (10)	64
Inconel 617	Average of two tests	5	80 (175)	...	...	44
Inconel 617	Average of two tests	5	Boiling	...	0.61 (24)	44
Inconel 617	Average of two tests	10	80 (175)	...	0.05 (2)	44
Inconel 617	Average of two tests	10	Boiling	...	0.71 (28)	44
Inconel 617	Average of two tests	20	80 (175)	...	0.81 (32)	44
Inconel 617	Average of two tests	20	Boiling	...	2.46 (97)	44
Inconel 617	Average of two tests	30	80 (175)	...	1.12 (44)	44
Inconel 617	Average of two tests	30	Boiling	...	11.89 (468)	44
Inconel 617	Average of two tests	40	80 (175)	...	1.02 (40)	44
Inconel 617	Average of two tests	40	Boiling	...	21.29 (838)	44
Inconel 617	Average of two tests	50	80 (175)	...	2.39 (94)	44
Inconel 617	Average of two tests	50	Boiling	...	...	44
Inconel 625	...	15	80 (176)	...	0.188 (7.4)	64
Inconel 625	...	50	80 (176)	...	0.432 (17)	64
Inconel 625	...	60	80 (176)	...	0.711 (28)	64
Inconel 625	...	70	80 (176)	...	1.626 (64)	64
Inconel 625	...	80	80 (176)	...	2.286 (90)	64
Inconel 706	Annealed	10	Boiling	...	3.12 (123)	146
Monel 400	(j)	2	135 (275)	4 d	0.033 (1.3)	64
Monel 400	...	5	101 (214)	23 h	0.086 (3.4)	134
Monel 400	...	10	102 (216)	23 h	0.061 (2.4)	134
Monel 400	(j)	10	170 (338)	19 d	0.079 (3.1)	64
Monel 400	Plant test. Plus precipitated basic alum in auto-clave under 225 psig pressure. Pitted to maximum depth of 0.004 in.	10	200 (392)	14 d	1.448 (57)	64
Monel 400	...	19	104 (219)	23 h	0.191 (7.5)	134
Monel 400	Plant test. Mixture of 1 part weak organic base and 3 parts 22% sulfuric acid solution in auto-clave under 260 psig pressure	22	225-230 (437-446)	272 h	4.826 (190)	64
Monel 400	Laboratory test. In autoclave under 50 psig pres-sure. Velocity, 17 fpm	39	158 (317)	...	>25.4 (>1000)	64
Monel 400	...	50	123 (253)	20 h	16.51 (650)	134
Monel 400	...	75	182 (360)	20 h	58.42 (2300)	134
Monel 400	...	96	293 (560)	3 h	83.82 (3300)	134
Nickel 200	Unaerated. Velocity, 15.5 fpm	1	30 (86)	...	...	44
Nickel 200	Unaerated. Velocity, 15.5 fpm	1	78 (172)	...	...	44
Nickel 200	Air-saturated. Velocity, 15.5 fpm	1	30 (86)	...	1.245 (49)	44
Nickel 200	Air-saturated. Velocity, 15.5 fpm	1	78 (172)	...	2.794 (110)	44
Nickel 200	Air-saturated. Velocity, none	2	21 (70)	...	...	44
Nickel 200	Unaerated. Velocity, none	2	21 (70)	...	0.0508 (2)	44
Nickel 200	Unaerated. Velocity, none	5	18 (65)	...	0.0559 (2.2)	44
Nickel 200	Unaerated. Velocity, 16.0 fpm	5	30 (86)	...	0.229 (9)	44
Nickel 200	Unaerated. Velocity, none	5	60 (140)	...	0.254 (10)	44
Nickel 200	Unaerated. Velocity, 15.5 fpm	5	60 (140)	...	...	44
Nickel 200	Unaerated. Velocity, 16.0 fpm	5	71 (160)	...	...	44
Nickel 200	Unaerated. Velocity, none	5	77 (170)	...	0.053 (21)	44
Nickel 200	Unaerated. Velocity, 15.5 fpm	5	78 (172)	...	0.762 (30)	44
Nickel 200	Air-saturated. Velocity, none	5	18 (65)	...	...	44

(Continued)

Corrosion Behavior of Various Metals and Alloys in Sulfuric Acid (Continued)

Material	Condition, other factors, comments	Concentration, %	Temperature, °C (°F)	Duration	Corrosion rate, mm/yr (mils/yr) or other	Ref
Nickel 200	Air-saturated. Velocity, 16.0 fpm	5	30 (86)	...	1.549 (61)	44
Nickel 200	Air-saturated. Velocity, none	5	60 (140)	...	...	44
Nickel 200	Air-saturated. Velocity, 15.5 fpm	5	60 (140)	...	2.235 (88)	44
Nickel 200	Air-saturated. Velocity, 16.0 fpm	5	71 (160)	...	2.616 (103)	44
Nickel 200	Air-saturated. Velocity, none	5	77 (170)	...	...	44
Nickel 200	Air-saturated. Velocity, 15.5 fpm	5	78 (172)	...	5.08 (200)	44
Nickel 200	Unaerated. Velocity, none	10	21 (70)	...	0.0432 (1.7)	44
Nickel 200	Unaerated. Velocity, 15.0 fpm	10	60 (140)	...	...	44
Nickel 200	Unaerated. Velocity, none	10	77 (170)	...	0.305 (12)	44
Nickel 200	Unaerated. Velocity, none	10	80 (176)	...	...	44
Nickel 200	Air-saturated. Velocity, none	10	21 (70)	...	...	44
Nickel 200	Air-saturated. Velocity, 15.0 fpm	10	60 (140)	...	2.261 (89)	44
Nickel 200	Air-saturated. Velocity, none	10	77 (170)	...	...	44
Nickel 200	Air-saturated. Velocity, none	10	80 (176)	...	3.048 (120)	44
Nickel 200	Unaerated. Velocity, none	20	21 (70)	...	0.1016 (4)	44
Nickel 200	Air-saturated. Velocity, none	20	21 (70)	...	...	44
Nickel 200	Unaerated. Velocity, 26.0 fpm	25	82 (180)	...	...	44
Nickel 200	Air-saturated. Velocity, 26.0 fpm	25	82 (180)	...	2.108 (83)	44
Nickel 200	Unaerated. Velocity, none	48	70 (158)	...	0.4572 (18)	44
Nickel 200	Air-saturated. Velocity, none	48	70 (158)	...	...	44
Nickel 200	Unaerated. Velocity, 16.0 fpm	50	30 (86)	...	...	44
Nickel 200	Air-saturated. Velocity, 16.0 fpm	50	30 (86)	...	0.4064 (16)	44
Nickel 200	Unaerated. Velocity, 15.5 fpm	70	38 (100)	...	0.7366 (29)	44
Nickel 200	Air-saturated. Velocity, 15.5 fpm	70	38 (100)	...	...	44
Nickel 200	Unaerated. Velocity, 15.5 fpm	93	30 (86)	...	...	44
Nickel 200	Unaerated. Velocity, none	93	65 (149)	...	3.708 (146)	44
Nickel 200	Air-saturated. Velocity, 15.5 fpm	93	30 (86)	...	0.254 (10)	44
Nickel 200	Air-saturated. Velocity, none	93	65 (149)	...	...	44
Nickel 200	Unaerated. Velocity, none	95	21 (70)	...	1.803 (71)	44
Nickel 200	Air-saturated. Velocity, none	95	21 (70)	...	...	44
Lead, tin, and magnesium						
Lead	Evaporator. Plus 17% Na$_2$SO$_4$, 30% other inorganic sulfates	6	40 (104)	...	0.125 (5)	48
Lead	Evaporator. Concentrated bath plus 30% Na$_2$SO$_4$	20	55 (130)	...	0.1 (4)	48
Lead	Plus 6.7% NaCl	33	24 (75)	...	0.15 (6)	49
Lead	Plus 6.7% NaCl	33	60 (140)	...	0.3 (12)	49
Lead	Plus 6.7% NaCl	33	80 (176)	...	0.9 (36)	49
Tin	Fuming	...	20 (68)	...	Unsuitable	94
Tin	Fuming	...	60 (140)	...	Unsuitable	94
Tin	Fuming	...	100 (212)	...	Unsuitable	94
Tin	Hydrogen	6	...	...	35 mg/dm^2/d	59
Tin	Oxygen	6	...	...	4300 mg/dm^2/d	59
Tin	...	<50	20 (68)	...	Unsuitable	94
Tin	...	<50	60 (140)	...	Unsuitable	94
Tin	...	<50	100 (212)	...	Unsuitable	94
Tin	...	70	20 (68)	...	Unsuitable	94
Tin	...	70	60 (140)	...	Unsuitable	94
Tin	...	70	100 (212)	...	Unsuitable	94
Tin	...	95	20 (68)	...	Unsuitable	94
Tin	...	95	60 (140)	...	Unsuitable	94
Tin	...	95	100 (212)	...	Unsuitable	94
Magnesium	...	All	Room	...	Unsuitable	119
Tantalum and hafnium						
Hafnium	...	60	...	8 d	0.005 (0.2)	11
Hafnium	...	60	...	8 d	0.005 (0.2)	11
Ta-Mo alloy	Contains 0% Ta. (k)	Conc	55 (131)	...	0.8 mg/dm^2/d	56

(Continued)

Corrosion Behavior of Various Metals and Alloys in Sulfuric Acid (Continued)

Material	Condition, other factors, comments	Concen-tration, %	Temperature, °C (°F)	Duration	Corrosion rate, mm/yr (mils/yr) or other	Ref
Ta-Mo alloy	Contains 10.1% Ta. (k)	Conc	55 (131)	...	0.9 mg/dm^2	56
Ta-Mo alloy	Contains 20.1% Ta. (k)	Conc	55 (131)	...	0.8 mg/dm^2/d	56
Ta-Mo alloy	Contains 30.0% Ta. (k)	Conc	55 (131)	...	1.0 mg/dm^2/d	56
Ta-Mo alloy	Contains 40.0% Ta. (k)	Conc	55 (131)	...	0.9 mg/dm^2/d	56
Ta-Mo alloy	Contains 50.0% Ta. (k)	Conc	55 (131)	...	0.0 mg/dm^2/d	56
Ta-Mo alloy	Contains 61.2% Ta. (k)	Conc	55 (131)	...	0.0 mg/dm^2/d	56
Ta-Mo alloy	Contains 71.5% Ta. (k)	Conc	55 (131)	...	0.0 mg/dm^2/d	56
Ta-Mo alloy	Contains 82.8% Ta. (k)	Conc	55 (131)	...	0.0 mg/dm^2/d	56
Ta-Mo alloy	Contains 91.4% Ta. (k)	Conc	55 (131)	...	0.0 mg/dm^2/d	56
Ta-Mo alloy	Contains 100% Ta. (k)	Conc	55 (131)	...	0.0 mg/dm^2/d	56
Tantalum	Fuming 15% SO$_3$	...	23 (73)	...	0.0127 (0.5)	42
Tantalum	...	...	70 (158)	...	Rapid	42
Tantalum	...	1	Boiling	...	0.02 (1)	37
Tantalum	...	5	Boiling	...	<0.02 (<1)	37
Tantalum	...	5	190 (375)	...	<0.02 (<1)	37
Tantalum	...	10	Boiling	...	<0.02 (<1)	37
Tantalum	...	10	190 (375)	...	<0.02 (<1)	37
Tantalum	...	10	25 (76)	...	nil	42
Tantalum	...	20	94-100 (205-212)	4 d	nil	74
Tantalum	...	30	Boiling	...	<0.02 (<1)	37
Tantalum	...	30	190 (375)	...	<0.02 (<1)	37
Tantalum	Commercial sheet. (a)	30	Boiling	48 h	<0.025 (<1)	33
Tantalum	High purity. (a)	30	Boiling	48 h	<0.025 (<1)	33
Tantalum	...	40	25 (76)	...	nil	42
Tantalum	...	50	19-26 (65-80)	35 d	nil	74
Tantalum	...	50	Boiling	...	<0.02 (<1)	37
Tantalum	...	50	190 (375)	...	<0.02 (<1)	37
Tantalum	Commercial sheet. (a)	50	Boiling	48 h	<0.025 (<1)	33
Tantalum	High purity. (a)	50	Boiling	48 h	<0.025 (<1)	33
Tantalum	Commercial sheet. (a)	60	Boiling	48 h	<0.025 (<1)	33
Tantalum	High purity. (a)	60	Boiling	48 h	<0.025 (<1)	33
Tantalum	...	70	Boiling	...	<0.02 (<1)	37
Tantalum	...	70	190 (375)	...	<0.05 (<2)	37
Tantalum	...	75	Boiling	...	<0.05 (<2)	37
Tantalum	...	75	190 (375)	...	<0.05 (<2)	37
Tantalum	(m)	80	Boiling	...	<0.12 (<5)	37
Tantalum	...	80	190 (375)	...	<0.12 (<5)	37
Tantalum	(m)	85	Boiling	...	<1.2 (<50)	37
Tantalum	...	85	190 (375)	...	<0.05 (<2)	37
Tantalum	...	98	19-26 (65-80)	36 d	nil	74
Tantalum	...	98	21 (70)	...	nil	74
Tantalum	...	98	145 (295)	30 d	nil	74
Tantalum	...	98	175 (345)	30 d	0.0002 (0.01)	74
Tantalum	...	98	200 (390)	30 d	0.04 (1.5)	74
Tantalum	...	98	250 (480)	6 h	0.74 (29)	74
Tantalum	...	98	300 (570)	...	8.7 (342)	74
Tantalum	...	98	25 (76)	...	nil	42
Tantalum	...	98	50 (122)	...	nil	42
Tantalum	...	98	100 (212)	...	nil	42
Tantalum	...	98	200 (392)	...	0.0762 (3)	42
Tantalum	...	98	250 (482)	...	Rapid	42
Tantalum	(m)	Conc	Boiling	...	>5.0 (>200)	37
Tantalum	...	Conc	190 (375)	...	<0.05 (<2)	37
Noble metals						
Gold	...	All	250 (480)	...	<0.05 (<2)	8
Iridium	...	Conc	Room-100 (212)	...	nil	29

(Continued)

Corrosion Behavior of Various Metals and Alloys in Sulfuric Acid (Continued)

Material	Condition, other factors, comments	Concen-tration, %	Temperature, °C (°F)	Duration	Corrosion rate, mm/yr (mils/yr) or other	Ref
Osmium	...	Conc	100 (212)	...	nil	17
Palladium	...	Conc	Room	...	<0.25 (<10)	17
Palladium	...	Conc	100 (212)	...	1.6 (63)	17
Rhodium	...	Conc	100 (212)	...	<0.25 (<10)	29
Ruthenium	...	95	100 (212)	...	nil	18
Silver	...	10	Boiling	...	0.003 (0.12)	4
Silver	...	10	Boiling	...	0.003 (0.12)	4
Silver	...	50	Boiling	...	0.034 (1.3)	4
Silver	...	50	Boiling	...	0.034 (1.3)	4
Silver	...	60	Boiling	...	0.88 (34.6)	4
Silver	...	60	Boiling	...	0.88 (34.6)	4
Silver	...	95	Room	...	0.14 (5.5)	4
Silver	...	95	Room	...	0.14 (5.5)	4
Others						
Cb alloy	Wrought 100% Cb; laboratory button; annealed at 1175 °C (2140 °F) for 30 min. Sample embrittled. (a)	30	Boiling	48 h	0.27 (11)	33
Cb alloy	Wrought 100% Cb; arc melted; annealed at 1400 °C (2552 °F) for 1 h. Sample embrittled. (a)	30	Boiling	48 h	0.22 (9)	33
Cb alloy	Wrought 100% Cb; electron-beam melted; annealed at 1400 °C (2552 °F) for 1 h. (a)	30	Boiling	48 h	0.22 (9)	33
Cb alloy	Wrought 8% Ti, bal Cb; arc melted; annealed at 1400 °C (2552 °F) for 1 h. (a)	30	Boiling	48 h	0.32 (13)	33
Cb alloy	Wrought 0.75% Zr, bal Cb; arc melted; annealed at 1400 °C (2552 °F) for 1 h. Sample embrittled. (a)	30	Boiling	48 h	0.25 (10)	33
Cb alloy	Wrought 6.9% Ti, 0.81% Zr, bal Cb; arc melted; annealed at 1400 °C (2552 °F) for 1 h. (a)	30	Boiling	48 h	0.37 (15)	33
Cb alloy	Wrought 50% V, 50% Cb; arc melted. Sample not tested for embrittlement. (a)	30	Boiling	48 h	1.57 (63)	33
Cb alloy	Wrought 100% Cb; laboratory button; annealed at 1175 °C (2140 °F) for 30 min. Sample embrittled. (a)	50	Boiling	48 h	0.8 (32)	33
Cb alloy	Wrought 100% Cb; electron-beam melted; annealed at 1400 °C (2552 °F) for 1 h. Sample embrittled. (a)	50	Boiling	48 h	0.57 (23)	33
Cb alloy	Wrought 100% Cb; arc melted; annealed at 1400 °C (2552 °F) for 1 h. Sample embrittled. (a)	50	Boiling	48 h	0.85 (34)	33
Cb alloy	Wrought 0.75% Zr, bal Cb; arc melted; annealed at 1400 °C (2552 °F) for 1 h. Sample embrittled. (a)	50	Boiling	48 h	0.9 (36)	33
Cb alloy	Wrought 8% Ti, bal Cb; arc melted; annealed at 1400 °C (2552 °F) for 1 h. (a)	50	Boiling	48 h	1.57 (63)	33
Cb alloy	Wrought 6.9% Ti, 0.81% Zr, bal Cb; arc melted; annealed at 1400 °C (2552 °F) for 1 h. (a)	50	Boiling	48 h	4.67 (187)	33
Cb alloy	Wrought 100% Cb; laboratory button; annealed at 1175 °C (2140 °F) for 30 min. Sample embrittled. (a)	60	Boiling	48 h	1.75 (70)	33
Cb alloy	Wrought 100% Cb; arc melted; annealed at 1400 °C (2552 °F) for 1 h. Sample embrittled. (a)	60	Boiling	48 h	1.72 (69)	33
Cb alloy	Wrought 100% Cb; electron-beam melted; annealed at 1400 °C (2552 °F) for 1 h. (a)	60	Boiling	48 h	1.6 (64)	33
Cb alloy	Wrought 0.75% Zr, bal Cb; arc melted; annealed at 1400 °C (2552 °F) for 1 h. Sample embrittled. (a)	60	Boiling	48 h	1.7 (68)	33
Cb alloy	Wrought 8% Ti, bal Cb; arc melted; annealed at 1400 °C (2552 °F) for 1 h. (a)	60	Boiling	48 h	2.85 (114)	33
Cobalt	Static	5	25 (77)	...	0.22 (9)	54
Columbium	...	1	190 (375)	...	<0.02 (<1)	37
Columbium	...	1	190 (375)	...	<0.02 (<1)	37
Columbium	...	5	190 (375)	...	<0.02 (<1)	37
Columbium	(m)	10	Boiling	...	<0.12 (<5)	37
Columbium	(m)	10	190 (375)	...	<0.2 (<10)	37

(Continued)

Corrosion Behavior of Various Metals and Alloys in Sulfuric Acid (Continued)

Material	Condition, other factors, comments	Concen-tration, %	Temperature, °C (°F)	Duration	Corrosion rate, mm/yr (mils/yr) or other	Ref
Columbium	(m)	20	190 (375)	...	<0.7 (<30)	37
Columbium	(m)	30	Boiling	...	<0.38 (<15)	37
Columbium	(m)	30	190 (375)	...	>1.2 (>50)	37
Columbium	(m)	40	190 (375)	...	>2.5 (>100)	37
Columbium	(m)	50	Boiling	...	<1.2 (<50)	37
Columbium	(m)	50	190 (375)	...	>7.6 (>300)	37
Columbium	(m)	60	190 (375)	...	>10 (>400)	37
Columbium	(m)	70	Boiling	...	>6.35 (>250)	37
85WC-15Co	...	10	22 (72)	48 h	1.4 g/m^2/h (0.91 mg/in.^{2}/h)	34
85WC-15Co	...	10	22 (72)	48 h	0.68g/m^2/h (0.44 mg/in.^{2}/h)	34
94WC-6Co	...	10	22 (72)	48 h	0.19 g/m^2/h (0.12 mg/in.^{2}/h)	34
94WC-6Ni	...	10	22 (72)	48 h	0.05 g/m^2/h (0.03 mg/in.^{2}/h)	34
Niobium	...	5-40	Room	...	nil	2
Niobium	...	10	Boiling	...	0.125 (5.0)	2
Niobium	Combined with 7% HCl and 100 ppm F⁻	20	Boiling	...	0.25 (10)	2
Niobium	...	20	94-100 (205-212)	4 d	0.0005 (0.02)	74
Niobium	Plus 7% HCl + 50 ppm F⁻	20	Boiling	...	0.236 (9.3)	61
Niobium	Plus 7% HCl + 100 ppm F⁻	20	Boiling	...	0.246 (9.7)	61
Niobium	...	25	Boiling	...	0.25 (10)	2
Niobium	...	40	Boiling	...	0.5 (20)	2
Niobium	Combined with 2% FeCl$_3$	40	Boiling	...	0.25 (10)	2
Niobium	Plus 20% HNO$_3$	50	50-80 (120-175)	...	nil	2
Niobium	Plus 20% HNO$_3$	50	Boiling	...	0.25 (10)	2
Niobium	Plus 20% HNO$_3$	50	50 (122)	...	nil	61
Niobium	Plus 20% HNO$_3$	50	80 (176)	...	nil	61
Niobium	Plus 20% HNO$_3$	50	Boiling	...	0.241 (9.5)	61
Niobium	...	60	Boiling	...	1.25 (50)	2
Niobium	Combined with 0.1 to 1% FeCl$_3$	60	Boiling	...	0.5 (20)	2
Niobium	Plus 3% CrO$_3$	72	100 (212)	...	0.025 (1.0)	2
Niobium	Plus 3% CrO$_3$	72	125 (255)	...	0.125 (5.0)	2
Niobium	Plus with 3% CrO$_3$	72	Boiling	...	3.75 (150)	2
Niobium	...	98	Room	...	Embrittlement	2
Niobium	...	98	19-26 (65-80)	36 d	0.0005 (0.02)	74
Niobium	Tarnished	98	145 (295)	30 d	4.6 (180)(b)	74

(a) Average of three 48-h test periods. (b) Five 48-h test periods. (c) Sulfuric acid test samples activated before tests and hydrochloric acid test samples tested without activation. (d) May be considered in place of a copper metal when some property, other than corrosion resistance, governs its use. (e) As cast, based on five 24-h test periods with cast specimens 38 mm x 25 mm x 6 mm (1.5 in. x 1 in. x 0.25 in.), 120-grit abrasive finish. (f) Average for duplicate specimens tested at 25 °C (77 °F). (g) Determined in laboratory tests. It is recommended that samples be tested under actual plant conditions. (h) Specimens prepared from 12-gage, solution heat-treated sheet. Five 24-h test periods. (j) Plant test. Plus 12% pyroligneous liquor in pressure digestion of wood under 30 psig pressure. (k) Solutions saturated with oxygen. (m) Susceptible to embrittlement.

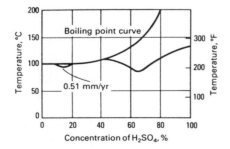

Nickel-base alloy. Isocorrosion diagram for Illium B in sulfuric acid. Source: "The Corrosion Resistance of Nickel-Containing Alloys in Sulfuric Acid and Related Compounds," *Corrosion Engineering Bulletin 1*, The International Nickel Company, 1983.

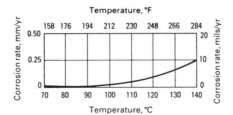

Nickel-base alloy. Corrosion of alloy 55 in 98% sulfuric acid. Source: "The Corrosion Resistance of Nickel-Containing Alloys in Sulfuric Acid and Related Compounds," *Corrosion Engineering Bulletin 1*, The International Nickel Company, 1983.

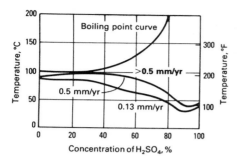

Nickel-base alloy. Isocorrosion diagram for Inconel 625 in sulfuric acid. Source: J.R. Crum and M.E. Adkins, "Correlation of Alloy 625 Electrochemical Behavior with the Sulfuric Acid Isocorrosion Chart," in *Proceedings of the NACE Corrosion/85 Symposium on Corrosion in Sulfuric Acid*, National Association of Corrosion Engineers, Houston, 1985, 23.

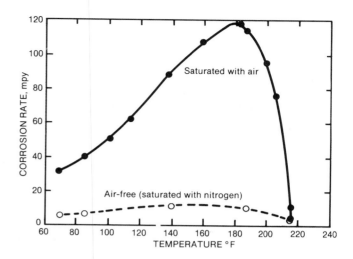

Nickel-base alloy. Effect of temperature on corrosion of Monel 400 in sulfuric acid. Concentration, 5 to 6%; velocity, 15.5 to 16.5 ft/min. Source: Inco Alloys International, 1985.

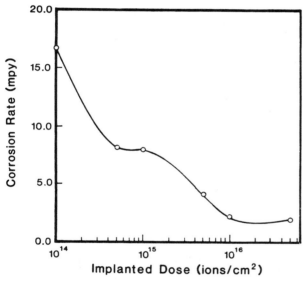

Nickel-base alloy. Corrosion rate of Inconel 600 tested in 1.0N sulfuric acid vs. the implanted dose of 100 keV BF_2+ ions. Source: J.D. Rubio, R.R. Hart, *et al.*, "Effects of BF_2+ Ion Implantation on the Corrosion Resistance of Inconel 600," *Corrosion*, Vol 42, Sept 1986, 557-558.

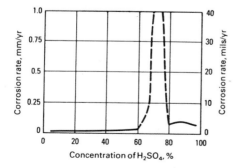

Nickel-base alloy. Corrosion rates of alloy 66 in sulfuric acid solutions at 100 °C (212 °F). Source: "The Corrosion Resistance of Nickel-Containing Alloys in Sulfuric Acid and Related Compounds," *Corrosion Engineering Bulletin 1*, The International Nickel Company, 1983.

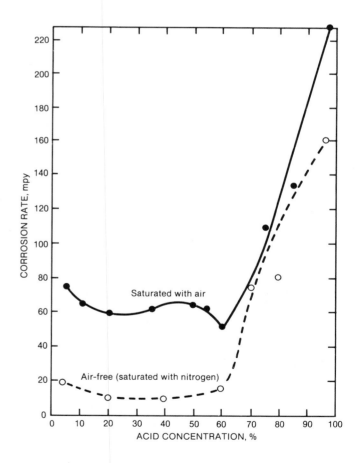

Nickel-base alloy. Corrosion of Monel 400 in sulfuric acid at 95 °C (203 °F); velocity, 16.5 ft/min. Source: Inco Alloys International, 1985.

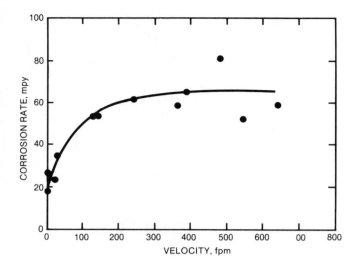

Nickel-base alloy. Effect of velocity on corrosion of Monel 400 in sulfuric acid. 5% concentration, air-saturated solution at room temperature. Source: Inco Alloys International, 1985.

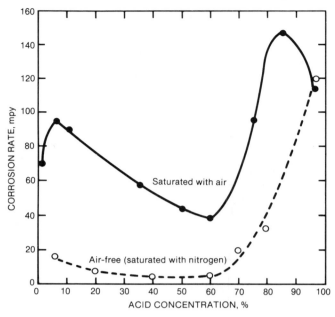

Nickel-base alloy. Corrosion of Monel 400 in sulfuric acid at 60 °C (140 °F); velocity, 16.5 ft/min. Source: Inco Alloys International, 1985.

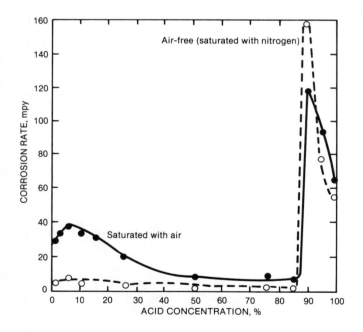

Nickel-base alloy. Corrosion of Monel 400 in sulfuric acid at 30 °C (86 °F); velocity, 17 ft/min. Source: Inco Alloys International, 1985.

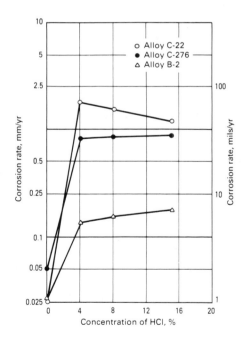

Nickel-base alloys. Effect of hydrochloric acid on the corrosion of various alloys in 15% sulfuric acid at 80 °C (175 °F). Source: N. Sridhar, Paper 182, presented at Corrosion/86, National Association of Corrosion Engineers, Houston, 1986.

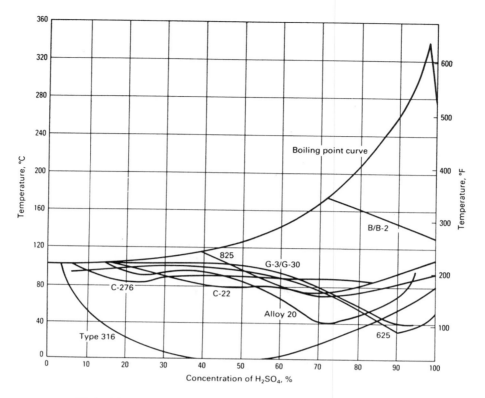

Nickel-base alloys. Comparative behavior of several nickel-base alloys in pure sulfuric acid. The isocorrosion lines indicate a corrosion rate of 0.5 mm/yr (20 mils/yr). Source: J.R. Crum and M.E. Atkins, *Materials Performance*, Vol 25 (No. 2), 1986, 27-32.

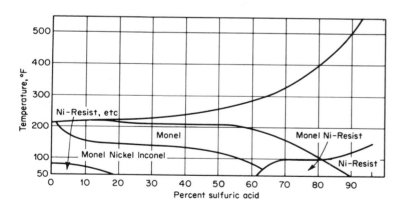

Nickel-base alloys. Corrosion of several nickel alloys by sulfuric acid as a function of concentration and temperature. Source: M.G. Fontana and N.D. Greene, *Corrosion Engineering*, McGraw-Hill, New York, 1967, 233.

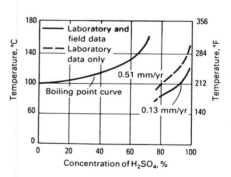

Nickel-base alloy. Isocorrosion diagram for alloy 55 in sulfuric acid. Source: "The Corrosion Resistance of Nickel-Containing Alloys in Sulfuric Acid and Related Compounds," *Corrosion Engineering Bulletin 1*, The International Nickel Company, 1983.

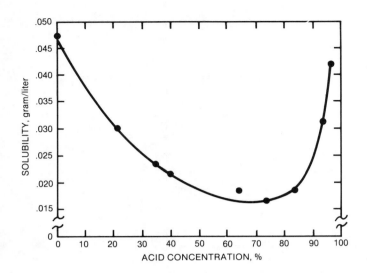

Monel 400. Solubility of oxygen in sulfuric acid at 15 °C (60 °F) at atmospheric pressure. Source: Inco Alloys International, 1985.

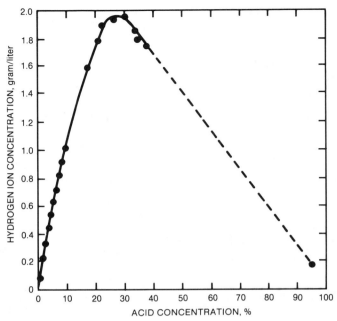

Monel 400. Hydrogen-ion concentration of sulfuric acid at 25 °C (77 °F). Source: Inco Alloys International, 1985.

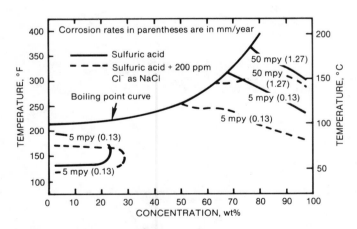

Hastelloy B-2. Corrosion resistance of Hastelloy B-2 to sulfuric acid with 200 ppm chloride ions. All test specimens were solution heat treated and in the unwelded condition. Source: Haynes International, 1984.

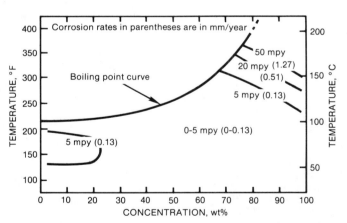

Hastelloy B-2. Corrosion resistance of Hastelloy B-2 to sulfuric acid. All test specimens were solution heat treated and in the unwelded condition. Source: Haynes International, 1984.

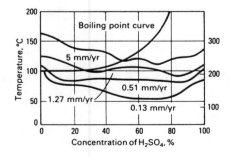

Hastelloy C-276. Isocorrosion diagram for Hastelloy C-276 in sulfuric acid. Source: *Metals Handbook*, 9th ed., Vol 13, Corrosion, ASM International, Metals Park, OH, 1987, 1152.

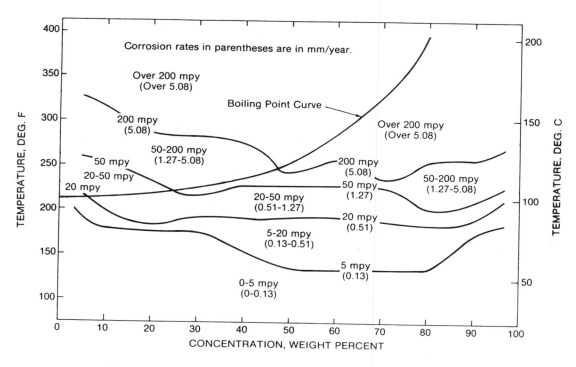

Hastelloy C-276. Resistance to sulfuric acid. All test specimens were solution heat treated and in the unwelded condition. Source: Haynes International, 1984.

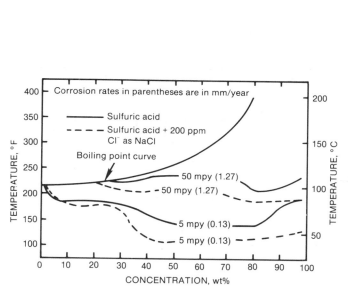

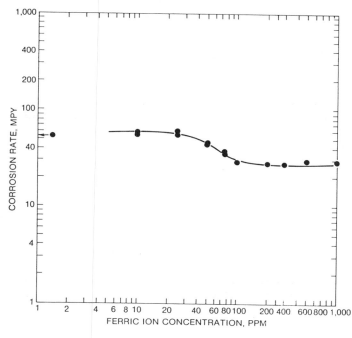

Hastelloy C-276. Resistance to sulfuric acid with 200 ppm chloride ions. All test specimens were solution heat treated and in the unwelded condition. Source: Haynes International, 1984.

Hastelloy C-276. Effect of ferric ion concentration on corrosion rate in boiling 30% sulfuric acid. All test specimens were solution heat treated and in the unwelded condition. Source: Haynes International, 1984.

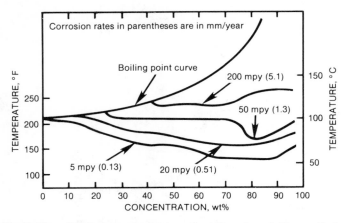

Hastelloy C-22. Corrosion resistance of Hastelloy C-22 to sulfuric acid. All test specimens were heat treated at 1121 °C (2050 °F), rapid quenched, and in the unwelded condition. Source: Haynes International, 1987.

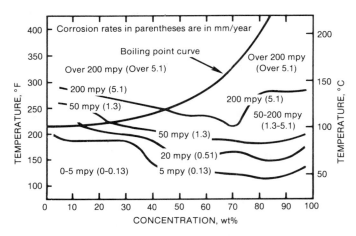

Hastelloy C-4. Corrosion resistance of Hastelloy C-4 to sulfuric acid. All test specimens solution heat treated at 1066 °C (1950 °F), rapid quenched, and in the unwelded condition. Source: Haynes International, 1984.

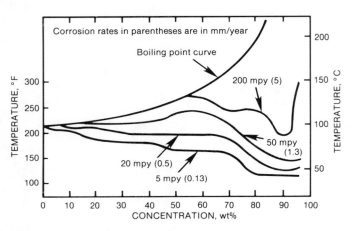

Hastelloy G-30. Corrosion resistance of Hastelloy G-30 to sulfuric acid. All test specimens were heat treated at 1177 °C (2150 °F), rapid quenched, and in the unwelded condition. Source: Haynes International, 1987.

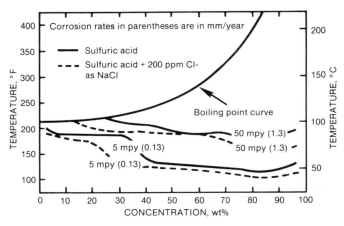

Hastelloy C-4. Corrosion resistance of Hastelloy C-4 to sulfuric acid with 200 ppm chloride ions. All test specimens were solution heat treated at 1066 °C (1950 °F), rapid quenched, and in the unwelded condition. Source: Haynes International, 1984.

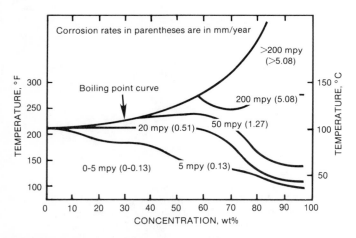

Hastelloy G-3. Corrosion resistance of Hastelloy G-3 to sulfuric acid. All test specimens were solution heat treated and in the unwelded condition. Source: Haynes International, 1984.

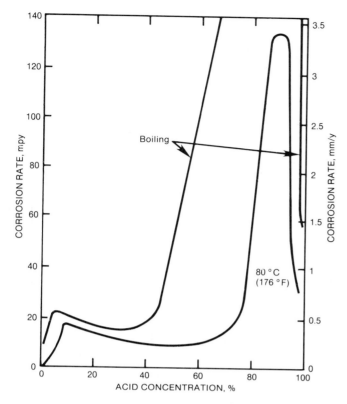

Incoloy 825. Corrosion rates of Incoloy 825 from laboratory tests in chemically pure sulfuric acid. Source: Inco Alloys International, 1987.

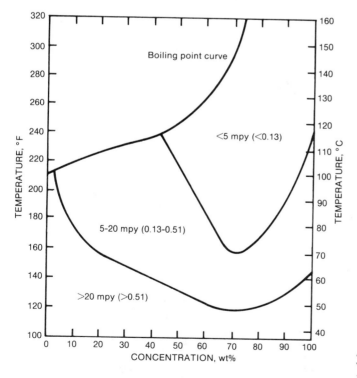

Incoloy 825. Isocorrosion chart for Incoloy 825 in sulfuric acid (based on laboratory tests in pure acid). Source: Inco Alloys International, 1987.

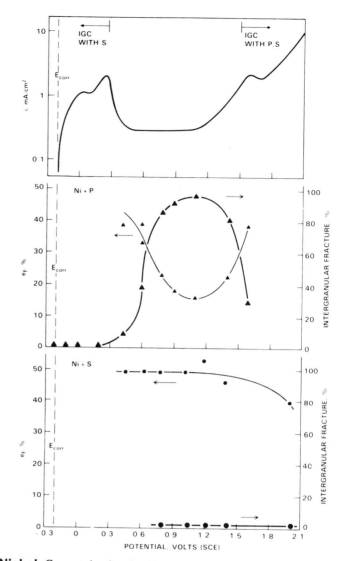

Nickel. Current density, ductility, and percent intergranular fracture for Ni and Ni + P vs. electrochemical potential (SCE). Slow strain rate testing in 1N sulfuric acid at 25 °C. Source: R.H. Jones, M.J. Danielson, et al., "Role of Segregated P and S in Intergranular Stress Corrosion Cracking of Ni," *Journal of Materials for Energy Systems*, Vol 8, Sept 1986, 188.

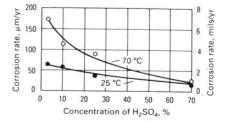

Aluminum. Corrosion of C65500 in sulfuric acid solutions. Specimens were immersed for 48 h at the indicated temperatures. The solution was not agitated or intentionally aerated. Source: *Metals Handbook*, 9th ed., Vol 2, Properties and Selection: Nonferrous Alloys and Pure Metals, American Society for Metals, Metals Park, OH, 1979, 473.

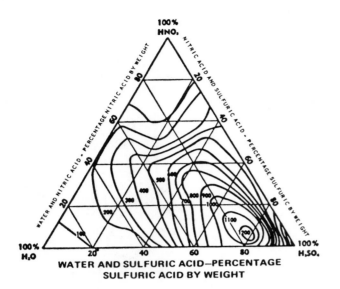

Aluminum. Resistance of alloy 1100 in various ratios of mixed nitric acid, sulfuric acid, and water. The contours show the average penetration in mils/yr. Source: *Guidelines for the Use of Aluminum with Food and Chemicals*, 5th ed., The Aluminum Association, Washington, DC, 1984, 844.

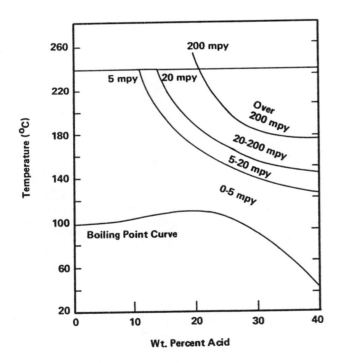

Zirconium. Isocorrosion curves for Grade 702 zirconium in sulfuric acid. Source: B.J. Moniz, "Corrosion Resistance of Zirconium in Chemical Processing Equipment," in *Industrial Applications of Titanium and Zirconium* (STP 830), R.T. Webster, C.S. Young, Ed., ASTM, Philadelphia, 1983, 194.

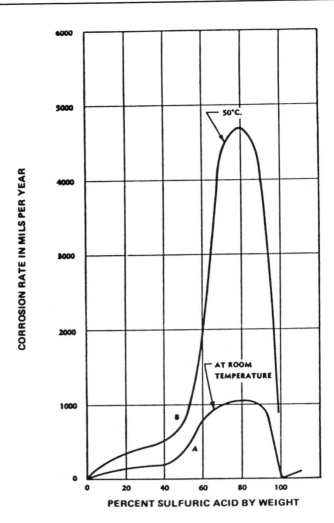

Aluminum. Effect of concentration and temperature on the resistance of alloy 1100 in sulfuric acid. Source: *Guidelines for the Use of Aluminum with Food and Chemicals*, 5th ed., The Aluminum Association, Washington, DC, 1984, 58.

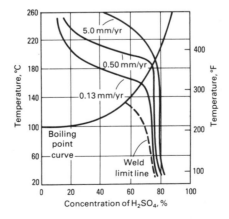

Zirconium. Corrosion of zirconium by sulfuric acid as a function of temperature and acid concentration. Source: *Metals Handbook*, 9th ed., Vol 13, Corrosion, ASM International, Metals Park, OH, 1987, 1154.

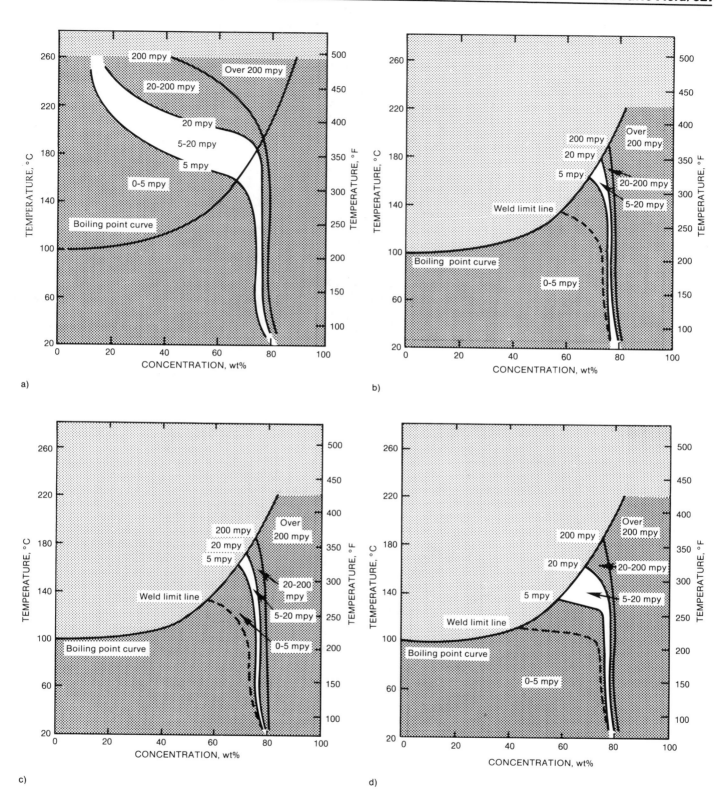

Zirconium. Corrosion of Zircadyne alloys in sulfuric acid solutions. (a) and (b) Zircadyne 702; (c) Zircadyne 704; (d) Zircadyne 705. Source: "Zircadyne Corrosion Properties," Source: Teledyne Wah Chang Albany, 1986.

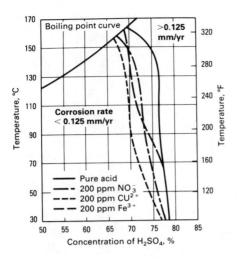

Zirconium. Effect of 200 ppm of various impurities on the 0.125 mm/yr isocorrosion line for zirconium in sulfuric acid. Source: *Metals Handbook,* 9th ed., Vol 13, Corrosion, ASM International, Metals Park, OH, 1987, 709.

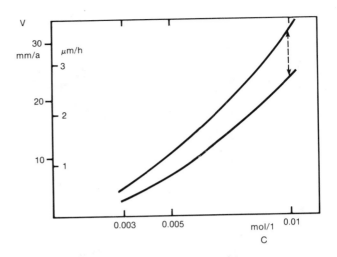

Zirconium. Corrosion rates of Zircaloy-4 as a function of sodium fluoride concentration in sulfuric acid (anodic polarization 1000 mV). Source: J. Vehlow, "Corrosion of Zircaloy-4 in H_2SO_4-NaF and Its Application for Measuring the Distribution Pattern of Fission Products in Zircaloy-4 Fuel Hulls," *Werkstoffe und Korrosion,* Vol 36, May 1985, 197.

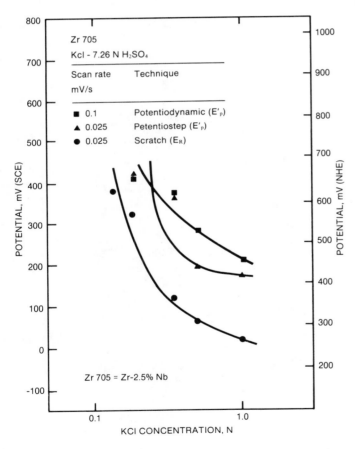

Zirconium. Comparison of pitting potential of Zr705, as determined by the scratch method, potentiodynamic method, and the potentiostep method. Source: J.S. Chen, A. Bronson, *et al.,* "Pitting Corrosion on Zirconium in KCl and KCl-H_2SO_4 Solutions," *Corrosion,* Vol 41, Aug 1985, 441.

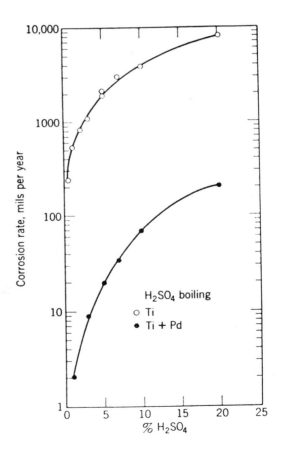

Titanium. Comparison of titanium and Ti-0.20Pd alloy in boiling sulfuric acid. Source: H. Godard, W. Jepson, *et al., The Corrosion of Light Metals,* John Wiley & Sons, New York, 1976.

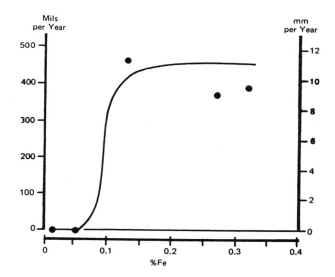

Titanium. Effect of iron content of CP titanium on corrosion rate in boiling 1% sulfuric acid. Source: RMI Titanium Company, 1982.

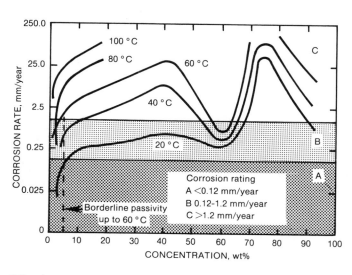

Titanium. Corrosion rate of titanium in sulfuric acid solutions (natural aeration). Source: Imperial Metal Industries (Kynoch) Ltd.

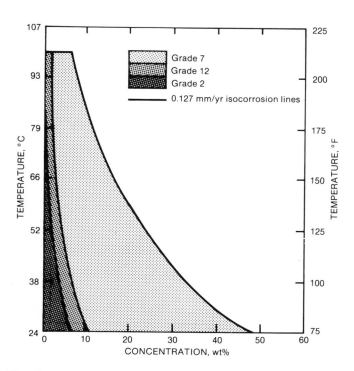

Titanium. Isocorrosion diagram for titanium alloys in pure, naturally aerated sulfuric acid solutions. The 0.127 mm/yr (5 mils/yr) isocorrosion lines are shown. Source: *Metals Handbook*, 9th ed., Vol 13, Corrosion, ASM International, Metals Park, OH, 1987, 680.

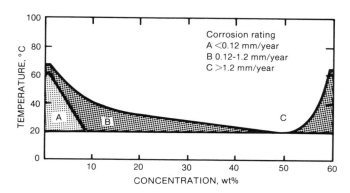

Titanium. Isocorrosion chart for titanium in sulfuric acid (natural aeration). Source: Imperial Metal Industries (Kynoch) Ltd.

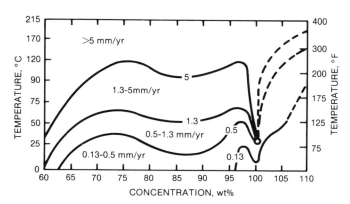

Steel. Corrosion of steel by sulfuric acid as a function of temperature and acid concentration. Source: *Metals Handbook*, 9th ed., Vol 13, Corrosion, ASM International, Metals Park, OH, 1987, 1149.

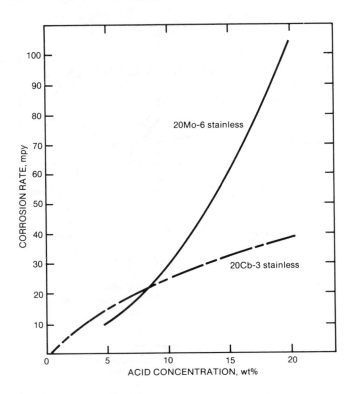

Stainless steel. Typical corrosion resistance of Carpenter 20Mo-6 in boiling reagent grade sulfuric acid. Source: Carpenter Technology, 1987.

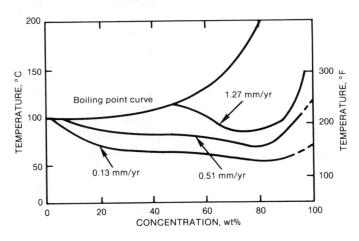

Stainless steel. Isocorrosion diagram for ACI CN-7M in sulfuric acid. Source: "The Corrosion Resistance of Nickel-Containing Alloys in Sulfuric Acid and Related Compounds," *Corrosion Engineering Bulletin 1*, The International Nickel Company, 1983.

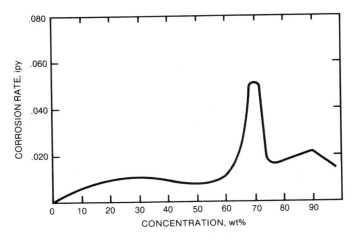

Stainless steel. Corrosion of 20Cb-3 in nonaerated sulfuric acid at 80 °C (176 °F). Source: Carpenter Technology, 1977.

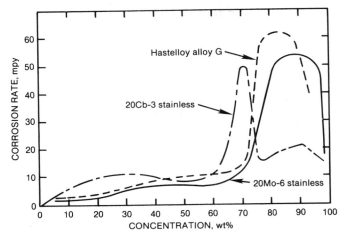

Stainless steel. Typical isocorrosion chart to 20Mo-6 stainless in nonaerated sulfuric acid. Source: Carpenter Technology, 1987.

Regions outlined exhibit corrosion rates less than .25 mm/a (10 mpy) and self-repassivation

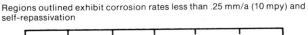

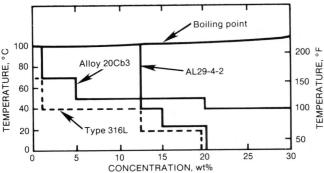

Stainless steel. Comparison of corrosion resistance of AL29-4-2, 20Cb-3, and type 316L stainless steel in sulfuric acid. Source: Allegheny Ludlum Corporation, 1982.

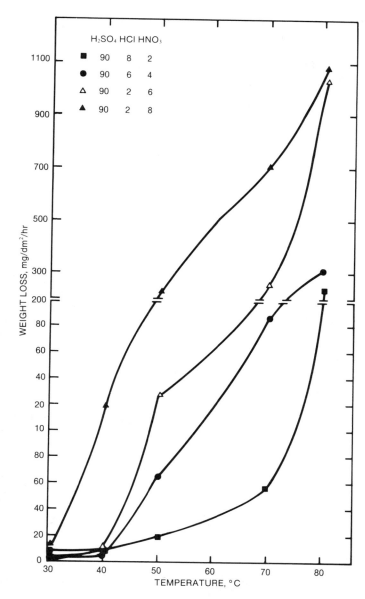

Stainless steel. Effect of temperature on corrosion of AISI 304 stainless steel immersed in ternary mixture of hydrochloric acid, sulfuric acid, and nitric acid. Source: M. Vajpeyi, S. Gupta, *et al.*, "Corrosion of Stainless Steel (AISI 304) in Sulfuric Acid Contaminated with HCl and HNO₃," *Corrosion Prevention and Control*, Vol 32, Oct 1985, 104.

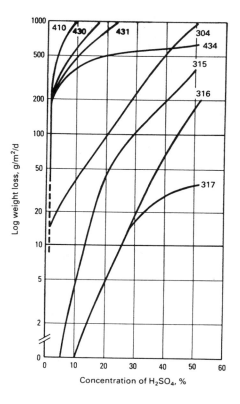

Stainless steel. Corrosion rates of various stainless steels in unaerated sulfuric acid at 20 °C (70 °F). Source: J.E. Truman, in *Corrosion: Metal-Environment Reactions*, Vol 1, L.L. Shreir, Ed., Newness-Butterworths, 1976, 352.

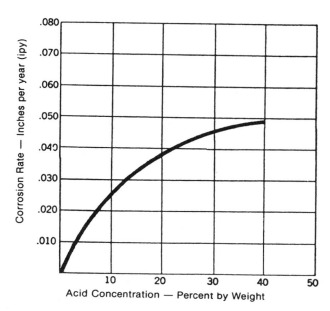

Stainless steel. Corrosion rate of 20Cb-3 vs. concentration of boiling sulfuric acid. Source: Carpenter Technology, 1977.

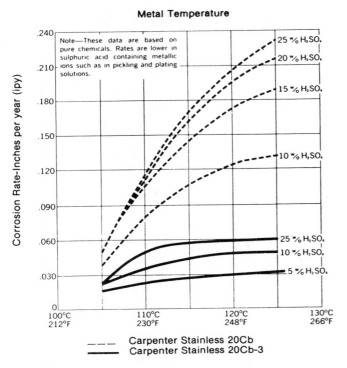

Metal Temperature

Note—These data are based on pure chemicals. Rates are lower in sulphuric acid containing metallic ions such as in pickling and plating solutions.

- - - Carpenter Stainless 20Cb
——— Carpenter Stainless 20Cb-3

Stainless steel. Corrosion of annealed 20Cb and improved 20Cb-3 to boiling sulfuric acid as a function of metal temperature and concentration. Source: Carpenter Technology, 1977.

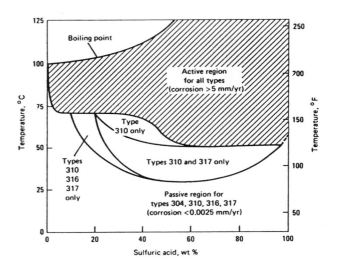

Stainless steel. Active and passive corrosion regions for stainless steels in aerated sulfuric acid solutions. Source: *Metals Handbook*, 9th ed., Vol 3, Properties and Selection: Stainless Steels, Tool Materials, and Special-Purpose Metals, American Society for Metals, Metals Park, OH, 1980, 91.

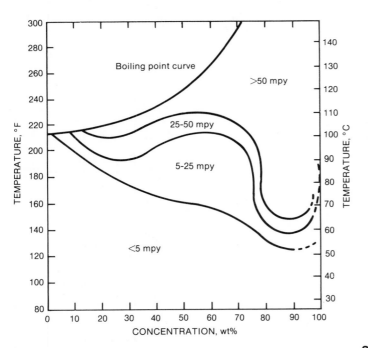

Stainless steel. Typical isocorrosion chart for 20Mo-6 stainless in nonaerated sulfuric acid. Source: Carpenter Technology, 1987.

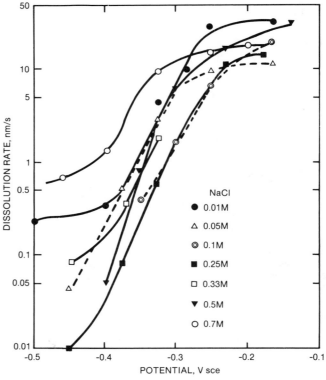

Stainless steel. Average (uniform) dissolution rate potential curves for AISI 304 obtained from the weight loss in $2M$ H_2SO_4-NaCl for 30-min exposure at 90 °C. Source: M. Asawa, "Stress Corrosion Cracking Regions

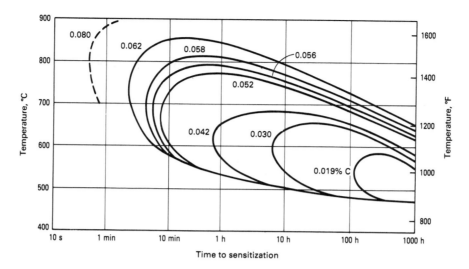

Stainless steel. Time-temperature-sensitization curves for type 304 stainless steel in a mixture of $CuSO_4$ and H_2SO_4 containing free copper. Curves show the times required for carbide precipitation in steels with various carbon contents. Carbides precipitate in the areas to the right of the various carbon content curves. Source: *Metals Handbook*, 9th ed., Vol 13, Corrosion, ASM International, Metals Park, OH, 1987, 551.

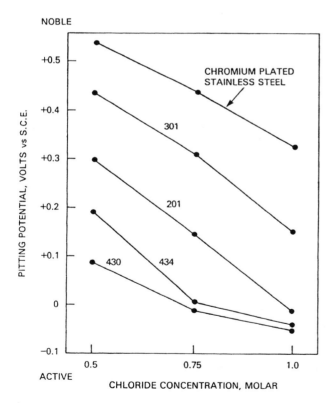

Stainless steel. Effect of chloride concentration on the pitting potential of various stainless steels in sulfuric acid solution containing chloride at the levels indicated. Source: A.J. Sedriks, "Effects of Alloy Composition and Microstructure on the Passivity of Stainless Steels," *Corrosion*, Vol 42, July 1986, 378.

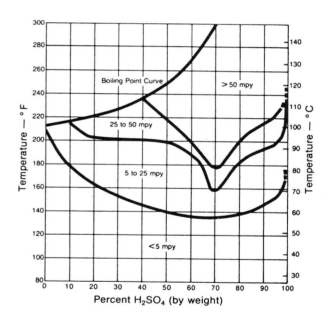

Stainless steel. Isocorrosion chart for 20Cb-3 in sulfuric acid. Source: Carpenter Technology, 1977.

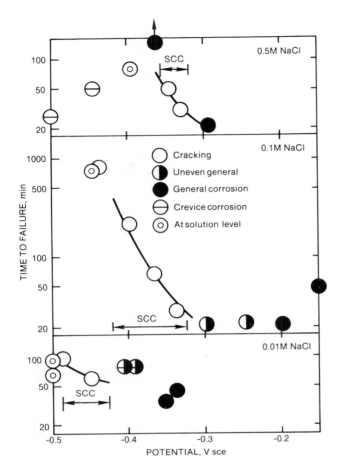

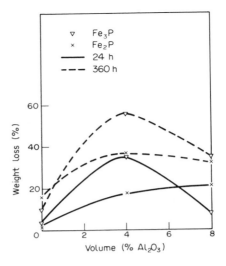

Stainless steel. Percentage weight loss of 0.5 wt% P (either as Fe_3P or Fe_2P) in $1N$ sulfuric acid at room temperature for different periods. Source: S.K. Mukherjee, G.S. Upadhyaya, "Corrosion Behaviour of Sintered 434L Ferritic Stainless Steel, Al_2O_3 Composites Containing Phosphorus," *Corrosion Science*, Vol 25, Sept 1985, 464.

Stainless steel. Effects of potential and NaCl concentration on time to fracture and the fracture mode on AISI 304 in $2M$ H_2SO_4-NaCl solution at 95 °C at a constant load of 225 N (initial stress of 324 MPa). The double circles and circles with horizontal lines represent fracture by local corrosion at the testing solution (air interface) and by crevice corrosion in the rubber plug, respectively. Source: M. Asawa, "Stress Corrosion Cracking Regions on Contour Maps of Dissolution Rates for AISI 304 Stainless Steel in Sulfuric Acid Solutions with Chloride, Bromide, or Iodide," *Corrosion*, Vol 43, April 1987, 199.

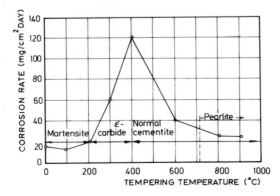

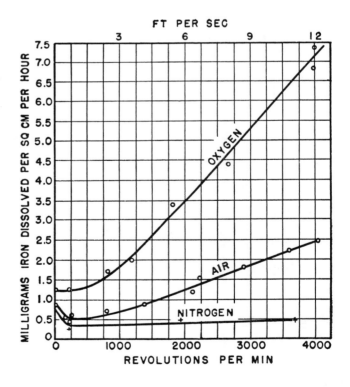

Steel. Effect of heat treatment on corrosion of 0.95% carbon steel in 1% sulfuric acid. Specimen area 18.5 cm^2; specimen weight 29 g; tempering time 2 h. Source: G. Wranglen, *An Introduction to Corrosion and Protection of Metals*, Chapman Hall, New York, 1985, 73.

Steel. Effect of velocity on corrosion of mild steel (0.12% carbon) in $0.33N$ sulfuric acid under air, oxygen or nitrogen. Source: H.H. Uhlig, "Iron and Steel," in *The Corrosion Handbook*, H.H. Uhlig, Ed., John Wiley & Sons, New York, 1948, 137.

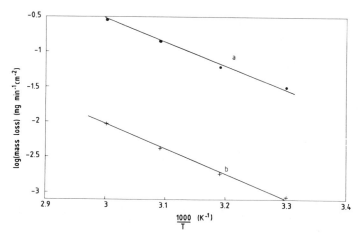

Steel. Arrhenius plot of the corrosion rate of steel in 2.5*N* sulfuric acid (a) in the absence and (b) in the presence of 1 x 10^{-3} M compound IV. Compound IV = 4-amino-3-phenyl-5-mercapto-1,2,4-triazoline. Source: B. Abd-El-Nabey, A. El-Toukhy, *et al.*, "4-Amino-3-Substituted-5-Mercapto-1,2,4-Triazolines as Inhibitors for the Acid Corrosion of Steel," *Surface Coating Technology*, Vol 27, April 1986, 333.

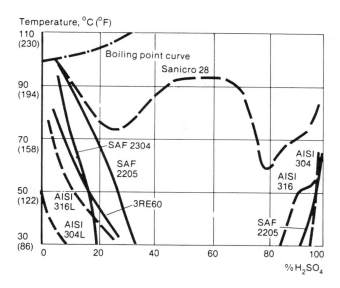

Duplex stainless steel. Isocorrosion diagram for duplex and austenitic stainless steels in stagnant sulfuric acid in contact with air. At the curves, the corrosion rate is 0.3 mm/yr. Source: S. Bernhardsson, P. Norberg, *et al.*, "Stainless Steels in the Petrochemical Industries," *Iron and Steel International*, Vol 58, Feb 1987, 8.

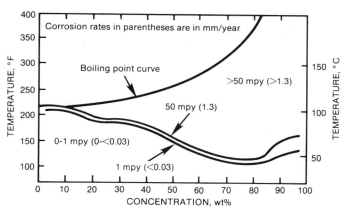

Duplex stainless steel. Corrosion resistance of Hastelloy alloy 255 and Ferralium to sulfuric acid. Source: Haynes International, 1987.

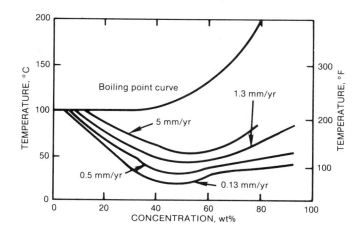

Duplex stainless steel. Isocorrosion diagram for ACI CD-4MCu in sulfuric acid. Source: *Corrosion Engineering Bulletin 1*, The International Nickel Company, 1983.

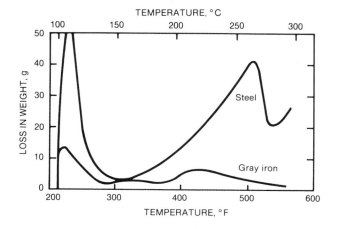

Gray iron. Corrosion of gray iron and steel by sulfuric acid at temperatures up to 315 °C (600 °F). Source: C. Walton, T. Opar, *Iron Castings Handbook*, Iron Castings Society, 1981, 507.

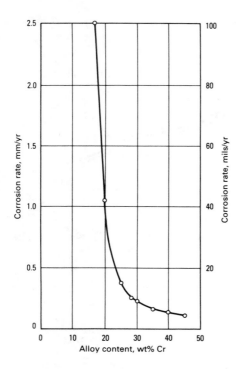

Iron-chromium alloys. The effect of chromium content on the corrosion behavior of iron-chromium alloys in boiling 50% sulfuric acid with $Fe_2(SO_4)_2$. Source: R.F. Steigerwald, *Metallurgical Transactions*, Vol 5, 1974, 2265-2269.

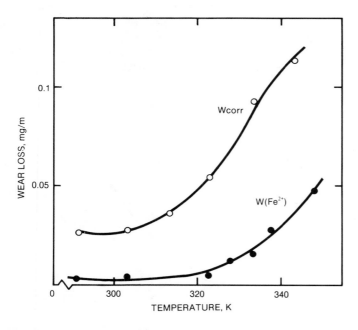

Cast iron. Wear loss and the effect of temperature in 65% sulfuric acid at 0.13 m/s and 1.7 MPa. Source: Y. Yahagi and Y. Mizutani, "Corrosive Wear of Cast Iron in Sulphuric Acid," *Journal of Tribology*, Vol 109, April 1987, 238-242.

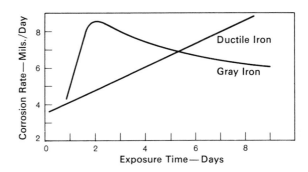

Iron. Effect of exposure time on the corrosion rate in 0.5% sulfuric acid at room temperature. Source: "Physical and Corrosion Properties," in *Source Book on Ductile Iron*, A.H. Rauch, Ed., American Society for Metals, Metals Park, OH, 1977, 363.

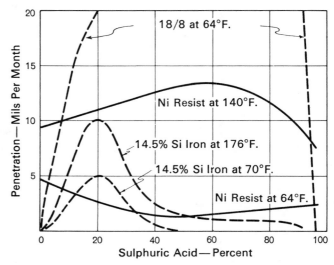

Iron. Corrosion rates of nickel and silicon high alloy irons at selected temperatures compared to 18-8 stainless steel in different concentrations of sulfuric acid. Source: "Physical and Corrosion Properties," in *Source Book on Ductile Iron*, A.H. Rauch, Ed., American Society for Metals, Metals Park, OH, 1977, 366.

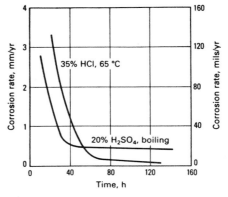

Cast iron. Corrosion rates of high-silicon cast irons as a function of time and media. Source: *Metals Handbook*, 9th ed., Vol 13, Corrosion, ASM International, Metals Park, OH, 1987, 567.

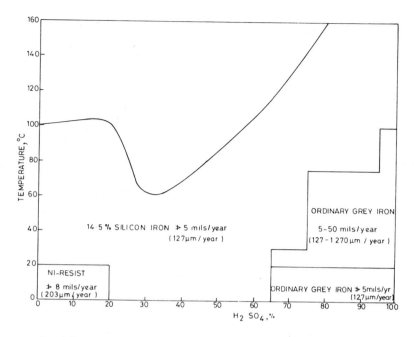

Cast iron. Corrosion rates of cast iron in sulfuric acid. Source: H.T. Angus, *Cast Iron: Physical and Engineering Properties,* 2nd ed., Butterworths, London, 1976, 313.

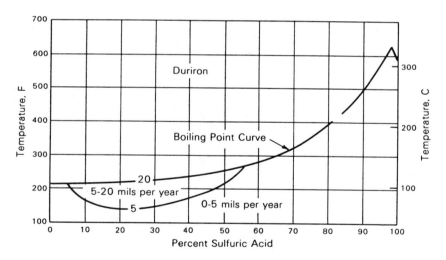

Cast iron. Effect of concentration and temperature on corrosion of high-silicon cast iron by sulfuric acid. Source: C. Walton and T. Opar, *Iron Castings Handbook*, Iron Castings Society, 1981, 510.

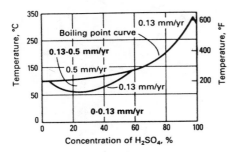

Cast iron. Corrosion by sulfuric acid as a function of temperature and acid concentration. Source: "The Corrosion Resistance of Nickel-Containing Alloys in Sulfuric Acid and Related Compounds," *Corrosion Engineering Bulletin 1*, The International Nickel Company, 1983.

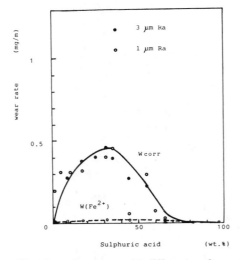

Cast iron. Wear loss of cast iron with different surface roughness (1 μm Ra and 3 μm Ra) in sulfuric acid, 0.13 m/s, 1.7 MPa, and 291 K. Source: Y. Yahagi and Y. Mizutani, "Corrosive Wear of Cast Iron in Sulphuric Acid," *Journal of Tribology*, Vol 109, April 1987, 239.

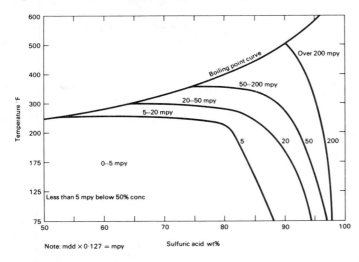

Note: mdd × 0·127 = mpy

Lead. Corrosion resistance of lead in sulfuric acid. Source: *Lead for Corrosion Resistant Applications: A Guide*, Lead Industries Association, New York.

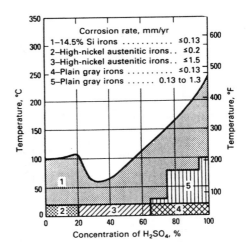

Cast iron. Corrosion of high-nickel austenitic cast iron in sulfuric acid as a function of acid concentration and temperature. Source: E.C. Miller, *Liquid Metals Handbook*, 2nd ed., Government Printing Office, Washington, DC, 1952, 144.

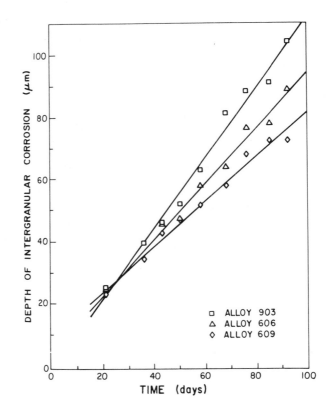

Lead alloy. Depth of intergranular corrosion as a function of time. The rate of intergranular corrosion decreases with increasing tin to calcium ratio and/or increasing tin content. Corrosion testing was carried out at 50 °C in 1.27 (+0.02) specific gravity sulfuric acid, at a constant anodic overpotential of 200 mV. Source: D. Kelly, P. Niessen, *et al.*, "The Influence of Composition and Microstructure on the Corrosion Behavior of Pb-Ca-Sn Alloys in Sulfuric Acid Solutions," *Journal of The Electrochemical Society*, Vol 132, Nov 1985, 2535.

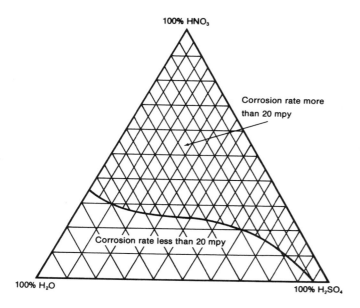

Lead. Corrosion rate of lead in mixed acids. Source: *Lead for Corrosion Resistant Applications: A Guide*, Lead Industries Association, New York.

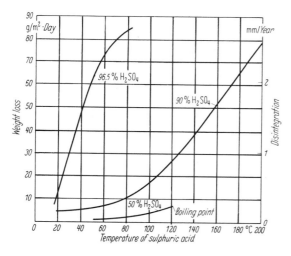

Lead. Effect of temperature and concentration on corrosion of lead in sulfuric acid. Source: W. Hofmann, *Lead and Lead Alloys: Properties and Technology*, G. Vibrans, Ed., Springer-Verlag, New York, 1970, 274.

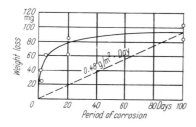

Lead. Course of corrosion vs. time of lead in 80% sulfuric acid at room temperature. Source: W. Hofmann, *Lead and Lead Alloys: Properties and Technology*, G. Vibrans, Ed., Springer-Verlag, New York, 1970, 273.

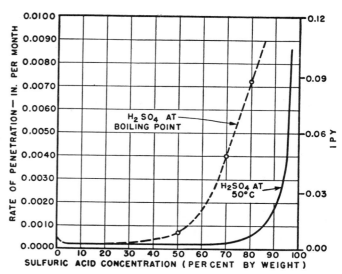

Lead. Corrosion of lead in sulfuric acid. The specimens were removed daily for 14 days and the protective sulfate coating was dissolved in acidified ammonium acetate solution (5%, hot). The corrosion rates are maximums for total immersion in sulfuric acid. Although these values are excessively high, they serve as a guide for commercial practice. Source: G.O. Hiers, "Lead and Lead Alloys," in *The Corrosion Handbook*, H.H. Uhlig, Ed., John Wiley & Sons, New York, 1948, 212.

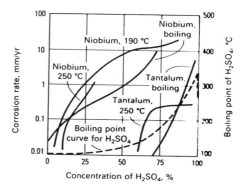

Niobium and tantalum. Corrosion of niobium and tantalum in sulfuric acid at various concentrations and temperatures. Source: C.R. Bishop, *Corrosion*, Vol 14, 1963, 308.

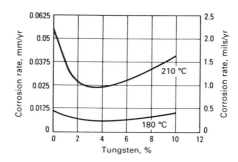

Tantalum-tungsten alloy. Corrosion rate vs. tungsten content for tantalum-tungsten alloys exposed to concentrated sulfuric acid at 180 °C (360 °F) and 210 °C (405 °F). Source: *Metals Handbook*, 9th ed., Vol 13, Corrosion, ASM International, Metals Park, OH, 1987, 736.

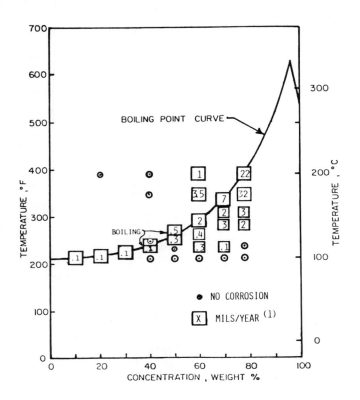

Tantalum. Corrosion resistance of KBI alloy 40 in sulfuric acid. KBI alloy 40 is a Ta-40Nb alloy. Source: R.H. Burns, F.S. Shuker, Jr., *et al.,* "Industrial Applications of Corrosion-Resistant Tantalum, Niobium, and Their Alloys," in *Refractory Metals and Their Industrial Applications* (STP 849), R.E. Smallwood, Ed., ASTM, Philadelphia, 1984, 63.

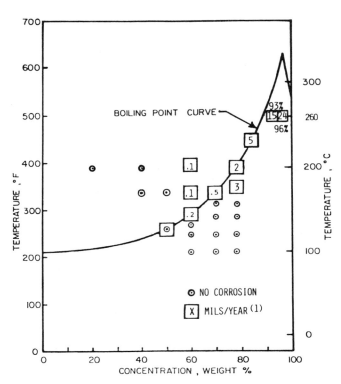

Tantalum. Corrosion resistance of tantalum in sulfuric acid. Source: R.H. Burns, F.S. Shuker, Jr., *et al.,* "Industrial Applications of Corrosion-Resistant Tantalum, Niobium, and Their Alloys," in *Refractory Metals and Their Industrial Applications* (STP 849), R.E. Smallwood, Ed., ASTM, Philadelphia, 1984, 62.

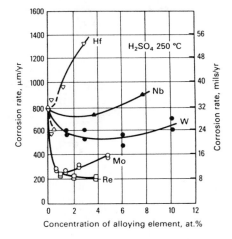

Tantalum alloy. Influence of alloying elements on the corrosion rate of binary tantalum alloys exposed 3 days to 95% sulfuric acid at 250 °C (480 °F). Source: L.A. Gypen, M. Brabers, and A. Deruyttere, "Corrosion Resistance of Tantalum Base Alloys, Elimination of Hydrogen Embrittlement in Tantalum by Substitutional Alloying," *Werkstoffe und Korrosion,* Vol 35, 1984, 37-46.

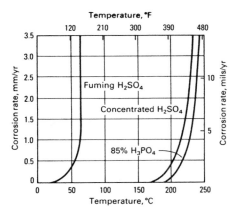

Tantalum. Corrosion rates of tantalum in fuming sulfuric acid (oleum) and concentrated sulfuric acid. Source: D.F. Taylor, "Tantalum: Its Resistance to Corrosion," Paper presented at the Chicago Section, The Electrochemical Society, May 1956.

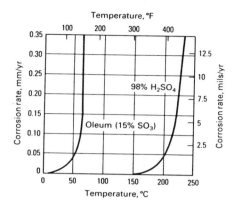

Tantalum. Corrosion of tantalum in 98% sulfuric acid and in oleum. Source: *Metals Handbook*, 9th ed., Vol 13, Corrosion, ASM International, Metals Park, OH, 1987, 1154.

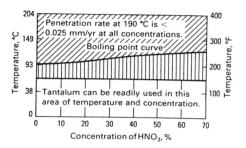

Tantalum. Corrosion resistance of tantalum in sulfuric acid. Source: R.H. Burns, F.S. Shuker, Jr., *et al.*, "Industrial Applications of Corrosion-Resistant Tantalum, Niobium and Their Alloys," in *Refractory Metals and Their Industrial Applications* (STP 849), R.E. Smallwood, Ed., ASTM, Philadelphia, 1984, 62.

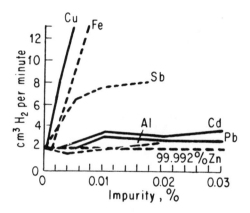

Zinc. Effect of impurities on the corrosion rate of zinc in dilute (18 g/L) sulfuric acid at room temperature. Original purity of the zinc was 9.982%. Source: N.D. Tomashov, *Theory of Corrosion and Protection of Metals*, B. Tytell, I. Geld, *et al.*, Ed., McMillan, New York, 1966, 633.

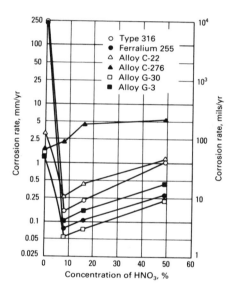

Various alloys. Effect of HNO$_3$ on the corrosion of various alloys in a boiling 30% sulfuric acid solution. Source: *Metals Handbook*, 9th ed., Vol 13, Corrosion, ASM International, Metals Park, OH, 1987, 649.

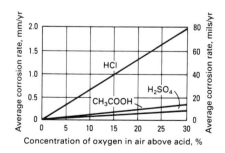

Copper. Effect of oxygen on corrosion rates for copper in 1.2N solutions of nonoxidizing acids. Specimens were immersed for 24 h at 24 °C (75 °F). Oxygen content of the solutions varied from test to test, depending on the concentration of oxygen in the atmosphere above the solutions. Source: *Metals Handbook*, 9th ed., Vol 13, Corrosion, ASM International, Metals Park, OH, 1987, 627.

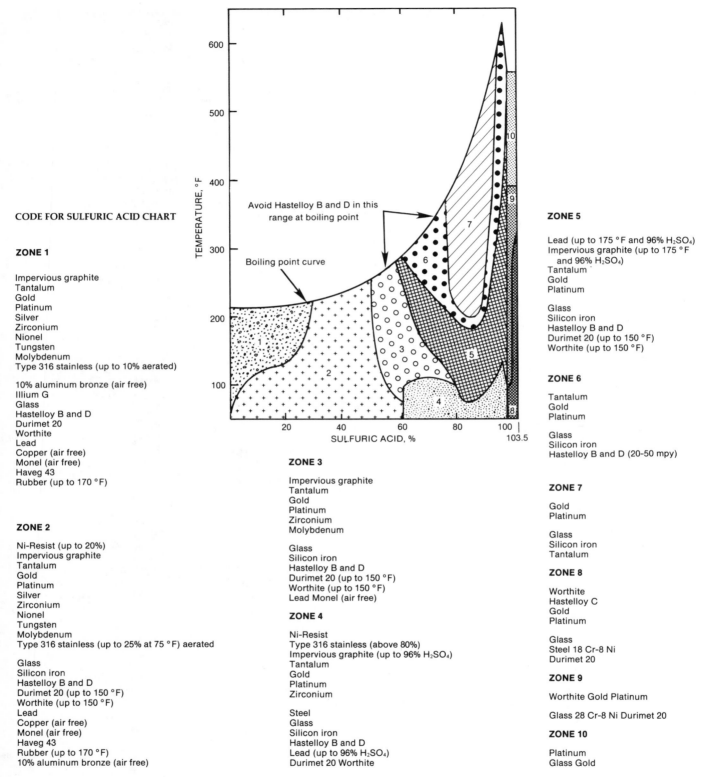

CODE FOR SULFURIC ACID CHART

ZONE 1

Impervious graphite
Tantalum
Gold
Platinum
Silver
Zirconium
Nionel
Tungsten
Molybdenum
Type 316 stainless (up to 10% aerated)

10% aluminum bronze (air free)
Illium G
Glass
Hastelloy B and D
Durimet 20
Worthite
Lead
Copper (air free)
Monel (air free)
Haveg 43
Rubber (up to 170 °F)

ZONE 2

Ni-Resist (up to 20%)
Impervious graphite
Tantalum
Gold
Platinum
Silver
Zirconium
Nionel
Tungsten
Molybdenum
Type 316 stainless (up to 25% at 75 °F) aerated

Glass
Silicon iron
Hastelloy B and D
Durimet 20 (up to 150 °F)
Worthite (up to 150 °F)
Lead
Copper (air free)
Monel (air free)
Haveg 43
Rubber (up to 170 °F)
10% aluminum bronze (air free)

ZONE 3

Impervious graphite
Tantalum
Gold
Platinum
Zirconium
Molybdenum

Glass
Silicon iron
Hastelloy B and D
Durimet 20 (up to 150 °F)
Worthite (up to 150 °F)
Lead Monel (air free)

ZONE 4

Ni-Resist
Type 316 stainless (above 80%)
Impervious graphite (up to 96% H_2SO_4)
Tantalum
Gold
Platinum
Zirconium

Steel
Glass
Silicon iron
Hastelloy B and D
Lead (up to 96% H_2SO_4)
Durimet 20 Worthite

ZONE 5

Lead (up to 175 °F and 96% H_2SO_4)
Impervious graphite (up to 175 °F
   and 96% H_2SO_4)
Tantalum
Gold
Platinum

Glass
Silicon iron
Hastelloy B and D
Durimet 20 (up to 150 °F)
Worthite (up to 150 °F)

ZONE 6

Tantalum
Gold
Platinum

Glass
Silicon iron
Hastelloy B and D (20-50 mpy)

ZONE 7

Gold
Platinum

Glass
Silicon iron
Tantalum

ZONE 8

Worthite
Hastelloy C
Gold
Platinum

Glass
Steel 18 Cr-8 Ni
Durimet 20

ZONE 9

Worthite Gold Platinum

Glass 28 Cr-8 Ni Durimet 20

ZONE 10

Platinum
Glass Gold

Materials in shaded zones have a reported corrosion rate of less than 20 mpy

Various metals. Corrosion resistance of various metals to sulfuric acid. Corrosion rates are less than 20 mils/yr. Source: M.G. Fontana, *Corrosion Engineering*, 3rd ed., McGraw-Hill, New York, 1986, 330.

Sulfurous Acid

Sulfurous acid, H_2SO_3, is an unstable, water-soluble, colorless liquid with a strong sulfur aroma. It is derived from absorption of sulfur dioxide (SO_2) in water. Reagent grade sulfurous acid contains about 6% sulfur dioxide in solution. Sulfurous acid is a strong reducing agent. It is readily oxidized to sulfuric acid and is itself reduced to hydrogen sulfide by zinc and dilute sulfuric acid. Sulfurous acid is used in the synthesis of medicines and chemicals, in the manufacture of paper and wine, in brewing, in metallurgy, in ore flotation, as a bleach and analytical reagent, and for refining of petroleum products.

Material Summaries

The following material summaries were compiled from a survey of the available literature. Inclusion of a material description under a given environment does not imply that it is the most appropriate material for corrosion service in that environment. Likewise, exclusion of a given material does not imply that it is not suitable for corrosion service applications in that environment.

Stainless Steels. Although sulfurous acid is a reducing agent, several stainless steels have provided satisfactory service in sulfurous acid environments. Conventional austenitic stainless steels have been used in sulfite digestors, and types 316 and 317 stainless steels, 20Cb-3, and cast ACI CF-8M and CN-7M stainless steels have been used in wet sulfur dioxide and sulfurous acid environments. Service life is improved by eliminating crevices, including those from settling of suspended solids, or by using molybdenum-containing grades. In some environments, stress-corrosion cracking is also a possibility.

Aluminum. In laboratory tests, dilute aqueous solutions of sulfurous acid caused corrosion of alloy 1100, which increased with concentration. At 0.1% sulfurous acid, the attack was mild (~4 mils/yr), whereas at 8% the attack was moderate (~12 mils/yr). Sulfurous acid condensed from gases containing sulfur dioxide and moisture will cause corrosion of aluminum alloys.

Lead. Lead has high corrosion resistance to sulfurous acid. It performs well at acid concentrations up to 95% at ambient temperatures, up to 85% at 220 °C (428 °F), and up to 93% at 150 °C (302 °F). Below a concentration of 5%, the corrosion rate increases, but it is still relatively low. Lead exhibits the same excellent corrosion resistance to higher concentrations of sulfurous acid at elevated temperatures.

Nickel. A wide variety of nickel alloys are available for use in flue gas desulfurization applications. Incoloy 825 and Hastelloy G are significantly more corrosion resistant in sulfurous and sulfuric acids than austenitic stainless steels.

Niobium. Niobium is completely resistant in dilute sulfurous acid at 100 °C (212 °F). In concentrated acid at the same temperature, it has a corrosion rate of 0.25 mm/yr (10 mils/yr).

Tin. Tin is attacked by sulfurous acid.

Titanium. Titanium alloys exhibit good resistance to most mildly reducing acid solutions whether or not they are inhibited, including sulfurous acid. Near-nil corrosion rates can be expected over the full concentration range to temperatures well beyond the boiling point of sulfurous acid.

Additional Reading

D.C. Agarwal, F.G. Hodge, and I.J. Storey, Combating Dewpoint Corrosion With High-Performance Ni-Cr-Mo-Type Alloys, in *Dewpoint Corrosion,* Ellis Horwood, Market Cross House, West Sussex, 125-136, 1985. MetAbs No. 86-350944. **Abstract:** One of the prices of technological development is the cost of abating pollution-pollution in the form of sulphur oxides from fossil-fired power stations or in the form of combustion products of hazardous wastes. The failure mode identified in an extensive field corrosion testing programme was localized attack which corresponds with failures in actual operating systems.

R.N. Britton and R.L. Stevens, Materials Requirements for Condensing Boilers, in *Dewpoint Corrosion,* Ellis Horwood, Market Cross House, West Sussex, 159-177, 1985. MetAbs No. 86-350946. **Abstract:** Condensing the moisture content of the flue products in a gas boiler offers the prospect of a step change in thermal efficiency and reduced running costs for customers. An assessment program to identify promising materials (some Al alloys and stainless steels) and to evaluate their corrosion behavior, fabrication routes etc., is described.

A.G.C. Kobussen, Corrosion in Condensing Gas-Fired Central Heating Boilers, in *Dewpoint Corrosion,* Ellis Horwood, Market Cross House, West Sussex, 178-190, 1985. MetAbs No. 86-350947. **Abstract:** From the analysis of flue gas condensate samples from 327 Dutch condensing boilers, two factors influencing corrosion have been identified. Corrosion of materials is studied in condensing corrosion rigs with an acceleration factor of 3.5. Special attention is paid to evaporation of condensate and addition of HCl to simulate field conditions.

Prevention of Corrosion in Flue Gas Systems, *Processing, 31*(9), 21, 1985. MetAbs No. 86-350977. **Abstract:** Research work at CEGB and UMIST identified areas affected by ADP corrosion and studied the effects of temperature, air ingress, pulverized fuel ash, moisture levels and the presence of chlorine in coal on the ADP corrosion rate in coal-fired plant. Recent developments in electrochemical monitoring of ADP corrosion have been successfully applied to a range of combustion plants.

C.E. Stevens and R.W. Ross Jr., Production, Fabrication, and Performance of Alloy 625 Clad Steel for Aggressive Corrosive Environments, *J. Mater. Energy Syst., 8*(1), 7-16, 1986. MetAbs No. 86-351699. **Abstract:** Methods used to manufacture, fabricate, and weld Inconel alloy 625 clad plate are described. Field test evaluation programs conducted at six power plant scrubber systems are also reported.

B.S. Phull and T.S. Lee, Localized Corrosion of Stainless Steels and Nickel Alloys in Flue Gas Desulfurization Environments, *Mater. Perform., 25*(8), 30-35, 1986. MetAbs No. 86-352234. **Abstract:** The results of a planned interval test of 90 days duration in a model flue gas desulfurization system are discussed. Corrosion in absorber and outlet duct zones is outlined in terms of relative tendencies of localized corrosion propagation for six alloys.

F. Mansfeld, and S.L. Jeanjaquet, Effects of Trace Elements on the Corrosion Behavior of Flue Gas Desulfurization Materials, *Corrosion, 43*(5), 298-304, 1987. MetAbs No. 87-351920. **Abstract:** Results of testing in simulated flue gas desulfurization environments are discussed. The effects of 13 trace elements on the corrosion behavior of Ferralium 255, Hastelloy G3, AISI 317L stainless, Monit and Ti Grade 2 are given.

W.H.D. Plant, Opportunities for Stainless Steel in Flue Gas Desulfurization Equipment, *Stainless Steel Ind.*, 15(86), 18-19, 1987. MetAbs No. 87-352592. **Abstract:** The existing technology in flue gas desulfurization developed in West Germany, the USA and Japan is discussed. The suitability of stainless steels, particularly the high-alloy grades, for much of the equipment which will be required worldwide in the next decade is discussed.

W.H.D. Plant, Life-Cycle Costing Approach to the Use of Stainless Steels in Flue Gas Desulfurization, *Steel Times*, 215(6), 284, 1987. MetAbs No. 87-352593. **Abstract:** A report by the Nickel Development Institute considers the economic viability of using stainless steel for flue gas disulfurization equipment.

Corrosion Behavior of Various Metals and Alloys in Sulfurous Acid

Material	Condition, other factors, comments	Concentration, %	Temperature, °C (°F)	Duration	Corrosion rate, mm/yr (mils/yr) or other	Ref
Stainless steels						
Type 304 stainless steel	Field or pilot plant test; slight to moderate aeration; rapid agitation. Sulfurous and sulfuric acids, pH ~2.5 (clay dust washer)	...	349-365 (660-690)	8.3 d	>1.0 in./yr	89
Type 304 stainless steel	Field or pilot plant test; slight to moderate aeration; rapid agitation; sensitized specimens. Sulfurous and sulfuric acids, pH ~2.5 (clay dust washer)	...	349-365 (660-690)	8.3 d	>1.0 in./yr	89
Type 304 stainless steel	Field or pilot plant test; slight to moderate aeration; rapid agitation. Sulfurous and sulfuric acids, pH ~2.5 (clay dust washer). Crevice attack: tendency to concentration-cell corrosion	...	349-365 (660-690)	8.1 d	0.27 in./yr	89
Type 304 stainless steel	Field or pilot plant test; slight to moderate aeration; rapid agitation; sensitized specimens. Sulfurous and sulfuric acids, pH ~2.5 (clay dust washer). Crevice attack: tendency to concentration-cell corrosion	...	349-365 (660-690)	8.1 d	0.43 in./yr	89
Type 304 stainless steel	Chemical processing; field or pilot plant test; no aeration; no agitation. Dilute sulfurous acid, in propylene-glycol solution	...	26 (80)	30 d	<0.0001 in./yr	89
Type 304 stainless steel	Power industry; field or pilot plant test; slight to moderate aeration; rapid agitation. Sulfurous acid and caustic soda in varying concentrations, water effluent of air heater washing, pH 1.1-12.6	...	65 (150)	2.4 d	0.0001 in./yr	89
Type 304 stainless steel	Synthetic resin processing; field or pilot plant test; no aeration; no agitation	~0.01	104 (219)	41.5 d	<0.0001 in./yr	89
Type 304 stainless steel	Chemical processing; field or pilot plant test; strong aeration; rapid agitation. Plus seawater, 1.7% sodium chloride. Slight pitting: maximum depth of pits from incipient to 0.005 in. Crevice attack: tendency to concentration-cell corrosion	~2.05	13 (55)	30 d	0.0015 in./yr	89
Type 304 stainless steel	Synthetic resins processing; field or pilot plant test; no aeration; no agitation. Sulfur-dioxide scrubber	2.6	52 (127)	41.5 d	<0.0001 in./yr	89
Type 304 stainless steel	Annealed. All solutions from CP chemicals. Tests made in the laboratory	6	90 (194)	...	0.460 (18)	19
Type 304 stainless steel	Annealed. All solutions from CP chemicals. Tests made in the laboratory	6	40 (104)	...	0.0025 (0.1)	19
Type 304 stainless steel	Synthetic resin processing; field or pilot plant test; no aeration; no agitation. With carbon over the standard maximum. Sulfur-dioxide scrubber	90.3	87 (189)	41.5 d	0.00022 in./yr	89
Type 316 stainless steel	Chemical processing; field or pilot plant test; no aeration; no agitation. Dilute sulfurous acid, in propylene-glycol solution	...	26 (80)	30 d	<0.0001 in./yr	89
Type 316 stainless steel	Field or pilot plant test; slight to moderate aeration; rapid agitation. Sulfurous and sulfuric acids, pH ~2.5 (clay dust washer). Crevice attack: tendency to concentration-cell corrosion	...	349-365 (660-690)	8.1 d	0.012 in./yr	89
Type 316 stainless steel	Field or pilot plant test; slight to moderate aeration; rapid agitation; sensitized specimens. Sulfurous and sulfuric acids, pH ~2.5 (clay dust washer)	...	349-365 (660-690)	8.1 d	0.011 in./yr	89
Type 316 stainless steel	Field or pilot plant test; slight to moderate aeration; rapid agitation. Sulfurous and sulfuric acids, pH ~2.5 (clay dust washer)	...	349-365 (660-690)	8.3 d	0.0054 in./yr	89
Type 316 stainless steel	Field or pilot plant test; slight to moderate aeration; rapid agitation; sensitized specimens. Sulfurous and sulfuric acids, pH ~2.5 (clay dust washer)	...	349-365 (660-690)	8.3 d	0.0059 in./yr	89

(Continued)

Corrosion Behavior of Various Metals and Alloys in Sulfurous Acid (Continued)

Material	Condition, other factors, comments	Concen-tration, %	Temperature, °C (°F)	Duration	Corrosion rate, mm/yr (mils/yr) or other	Ref
Type 316 stainless steel	Power industry; field or pilot plant test; slight to moderate aeration; rapid agitation. Sulfurous acid and caustic soda in varying concentrations, water effluent of air heater washing, pH 1.1-12.6	...	65 (150)	2.4 d	<0.0001 in./yr	89
Type 316 stainless steel	Synthetic resin processing; field or pilot plant test; no aeration; no agitation	~0.01	104 (219)	41.5 d	<0.0001 in./yr	89
Type 316 stainless steel	Synthetic resin processing; field or pilot plant test; no aeration; no agitation; welded specimens	~0.01	104 (219)	41.5 d	<0.0001 in./yr	89
Type 316 stainless steel	Chemical processing; field or pilot plant test; strong aeration; rapid agitation. Plus seawater, 1.7% sodium chloride. Crevice attack: tendency to concentration-cell corrosion	~2.05	13 (55)	30 d	0.00013 in./yr	89
Type 316 stainless steel	Synthetic resins processing; field or pilot plant test; no aeration; no agitation. Sulfur-dioxide scrubber	2.6	52 (127)	41.5 d	<0.0001 in./yr	89
Type 316 stainless steel	Synthetic resins processing; field or pilot plant test; no aeration; no agitation; welded specimens. Sulfur-dioxide scrubber	2.6	52 (127)	41.5 d	<0.0001 in./yr	89
Type 316 stainless steel	Synthetic resin processing; field or pilot plant test; no aeration; no agitation. Sulfur-dioxide scrubber	90.3	87 (189)	41.5 d	<0.0001 in./yr	89
Type 316 stainless steel	Synthetic resin processing; field or pilot plant test; no aeration; no agitation; welded specimens. Sulfur-dioxide scrubber	90.3	87 (189)	41.5 d	<0.0001 in./yr	89
Type 317 stainless steel	Power industry; field or pilot plant test; slight to moderate aeration; rapid agitation. Sulfurous acid and caustic soda in varying concentrations, water effluent of air heater washing, pH 1.1-12.6	...	65 (150)	2.4 d	0.0002 in./yr	89
Type 317 stainless steel	Chemical processing; field or pilot plant test; strong aeration; rapid agitation. Plus seawater, 1.7% sodium chloride. Crevice attack: tendency to concentration-cell corrosion	~2.05	13 (55)	30 d	0.0001 in./yr	89
Type 410 stainless steel	...	...	Room	...	Slightly attacked	121
Aluminum						
Aluminum (>99.5%)	Pure solution	...	20 (68)	...	Satisfactory	92
Aluminum-manganese alloys	Pure solution	...	20 (68)	...	Satisfactory	92
Coppers						
70-30 cupronickel	...	...	...	...	Fair	93
90-10 cupronickel	...	...	...	...	Fair	93
Admiralty brass	(a)	...	...	...	Good	93
Aluminum bronze	(a)	...	...	...	Good	93
Ampco 8, aluminum bronze	Generally suitable. Conditions such as aeration or temperature could restrict use	...	...	...	<0.5 (<20)	96
Architectural bronze	...	...	...	...	Not suitable	93
Brass	(a)	...	...	...	Good	93
Cartridge brass	...	...	...	...	Not suitable	93
Commercial bronze	(a)	...	...	...	Good	93
Electrolytic copper	(a)	...	...	...	Good	93
Free-cutting brass	...	...	...	...	Not suitable	93
Muntz metal	...	...	...	...	Not suitable	93
Naval brass	...	...	...	...	Not suitable	93
Nickel silver	...	18	...	...	Fair	93
Phosphor bronze	5% Sn. (a)	...	...	...	Good	93
Phosphor bronze	8% Sn. (a)	...	...	...	Good	93
Phosphor copper	(a)	...	...	...	Good	93
Red brass	(a)	...	...	...	Good	93
Silicon bronze	Low. (a)	...	...	...	Good	93
Silicon bronze	High. (a)	...	...	...	Good	93
Titanium						
Titanium	...	6	Room	...	nil	90

(Continued)

Corrosion Behavior of Various Metals and Alloys in Sulfurous Acid (Continued)

Material	Condition, other factors, comments	Concen-tration, %	Temperature, °C (°F)	Duration	Corrosion rate, mm/yr (mils/yr) or other	Ref
Heat- and corrosion-resistant alloys						
Carpenter 20	Power industry; field or pilot plant test; slight to moderate aeration; rapid agitation. Sulfurous acid and caustic soda in varying concentrations, water effluent of air heater washing, pH 1.1-12.6	...	65 (150)	2.4 d	<0.0001 in./yr	89
Carpenter 20	Synthetic resin processing; field or pilot plant test; no aeration; no agitation; cast specimens	~0.01	104 (219)	41.5 d	<0.0001 in./yr	89
Carpenter 20	Chemical processing; field or pilot plant test; strong aeration; rapid agitation; cast specimens. Plus seawater, 1.7% sodium chloride. Crevice attack: tendency to concentration-cell corrosion	~2.05	13 (55)	30 d	<0.0001 in./yr	89
Carpenter 20	Synthetic resins processing; field or pilot plant test; no aeration; no agitation; cast specimens. Sulfur-dioxide scrubber	2.6	52 (127)	41.5 d	<0.0001 in./yr	89
Carpenter 20	Synthetic resin processing; field or pilot plant test; no aeration; no agitation; cast specimens. Sulfur-dioxide scrubber	90.3	87 (189)	41.5 d	0.0001 in./yr	89
Incoloy 800	Solutions were prepared with reagent-grade chemicals. Test specimens were cold-rolled, annealed sheet, 2.84 mm (0.112 in.) thick. No pitting	5	80 (176)	7 d	1.09 (43.0)	44
Inconel 601	Pitting attack. Average of two tests	6	80 (176)	7 d	1.427 (56.2)	64
Inconel 690	...	6	80 (176)	...	1.14 (45)	57
Zirconium						
Zr702	...	6	Room	...	<0.13 (<5)	15
Zr702	...	Saturated	192 (380)	...	0.13-1.3 (5-50)	15
Lead, tin, and zinc						
Lead	With 3% SO₂	...	24 (75)	...	0.025 (1)	49
Noble metals						
Gold	...	All	100 (212)	...	<0.05 (<2)	8
Silver	...	All	90 (195)	...	<0.05 (<2)	4
Silver	...	All	90 (195)	...	<0.05 (<2)	4
Others						
Magnesium	...	All	Room	...	Unsuitable	119

(a) May be considered in place of a copper metal when some property, other than corrosion resistance, governs its use.

Tannic Acid

Tannic acid, $C_{14}H_{10}O_9$, also known as digallic acid, tannin, and gallo-tannin, is a yellowish powder that decomposes at 210 °C (410 °F). Tannic acid is derived from nutgalls. It is soluble in water and alcohol, and is insoluble in acetone and ether. Tannic acid is used in tanning, textiles, and as an alcohol denaturant. An amorphous form of tannic acid, also known as pentadigalloylglucose, exists with the formula $C_{76}H_{52}O_{46}$. It is a yellowish to brownish powder that is very soluble in alcohol and ether. It also decomposes between 210 to 215 °C (410 to 419 °F). This form is used to clarify wine or beer, as a reagent, and as a mordant in dyeing.

Material Summaries

The following material summaries were compiled from a survey of the available literature. Inclusion of a material description under a given environment does not imply that it is the most appropriate material for corrosion service in that environment. Likewise, exclusion of a given material does not imply that it is not suitable for corrosion service applications in that environment.

Aluminum. During laboratory tests run at ambient temperature and 100% relative humidity, aluminum alloys 3003 and 5154 were mildly attacked (0.05 mm/yr, or 2 mils/yr) by solid tannic acid. Aqueous solutions of 0.01 to 20% tannic acid produced mild attack (0.05 mm/yr, or 2 mils/yr) of aluminum alloy 1100 at ambient temperature, moderate attack (0.23 mm/yr, or 9 mils/yr) at 50 °C (122 °F), and aggressive attack at 100 °C (212 °F). The tanning industry utilizes aluminum alloy processing equipment.

Zirconium. Zirconium resists corrosion in tannic acid.

Corrosion Behavior of Various Metals and Alloys in Tannic Acid

Material	Condition, other factors, comments	Concentration, %	Temperature, °C (°F)	Duration	Corrosion rate, mm/yr (mils/yr) or other	Ref
Stainless steels						
Type 304 stainless steel	...	10	21 (70)	...	Good	121
Type 316 stainless steel	...	10	21 (70	...	Good	121
Type 410 stainless steel	...	10	21 (70)	...	Good	121
Type 430 stainless steel	...	10	21 (70)	...	Good	121
Aluminum						
Aluminum (99.0-99.5%)	...	...	...	...	Satisfactory	92
Aluminum-manganese alloys	...	...	...	...	Satisfactory	92
Coppers						
70-30 cupronickel	...	...	...	...	Suitable	93
90-10 cupronickel	...	...	...	...	Suitable	93
Admiralty brass	...	...	...	...	Suitable	93
Aluminum bronze	...	...	...	...	Suitable	93
Ampco 8, aluminum bronze	Generally suitable	...	...	...	<0.05 (<2)	96
Architectural bronze	(a)	...	...	...	Good	93
Brass	...	...	...	...	Suitable	93
Cartridge brass	(a)	...	...	...	Good	93
Commercial bronze	...	...	...	...	Suitable	93
Electrolytic copper	...	...	...	...	Suitable	93
Free-cutting brass	(a)	...	...	...	Good	93
Magnesium	...	3	Room	...	Unsuitable	119
Muntz metal	(a)	...	...	...	Good	93
Naval brass	(a)	...	...	...	Good	93
Nickel silver	...	18	...	...	Suitable	93
Phosphor bronze	5% Sn	...	...	...	Suitable	93
Phosphor bronze	8% Sn	...	...	...	Suitable	93
Phosphor copper	...	...	...	...	Suitable	93
Red brass	...	...	...	...	Suitable	93
Silicon bronze	Low	...	...	...	Suitable	93
Silicon bronze	High	...	...	...	Suitable	93
Titanium						
Titanium	...	25	100 (212)	...	nil	90
Zirconium						
Zr702	...	25	35-100 (95-212)	...	<0.025 (<1)	15
Lead, tin, and zinc						
Tin	...	10	20 (68)	...	Resistant	94
Tin	...	10	60 (140)	...	Resistant	94
Tin	...	10	100 (212)	...	Unsuitable	94
Others						
Magnesium	...	3	Room	...	Unsuitable	119

(a) May be considered in place of a copper metal when some property, other than corrosion resistance, governs its use.

Tartaric Acid

Tartaric acid, $HOOC(CHOH)_2COOH$, is a water- and alcohol-soluble colorless crystalline solid with an acid taste and a melting temperature of 170 °C (338 °F). It is also known as dihydroxysuccinic acid. Tartaric acid is used as a chemical intermediate and a sequestrant, as well as in tanning, effervescent beverages, baking powder, ceramics, photography, textile processing, mirror silvering, and metal coloring.

Material Summaries

The following material summaries were compiled from a survey of the available literature. Inclusion of a material description under a given environment does not imply that it is the most appropriate material for corrosion service in that environment. Likewise, exclusion of a given material does not imply that it is not suitable for corrosion service applications in that environment.

Stainless Steels. Type 304 stainless steel has been used in tartaric acid (and in citric acid) at moderate temperatures. Type 316 stainless steel has been suggested for all concentrations up to the boiling point of tartaric acid.

Copper and its alloys corrode rather slowly when exposed to various concentrations of tartaric acid.

Aluminum. Aluminum alloys 3003 and 5154 were resistant to solid tartaric acid in laboratory tests conducted under conditions of 100% relative humidity at ambient temperature. In other laboratory tests, 1100 alloy was resistant to aqueous solutions (0.1 to 55%) at ambient temperature, but these solutions were corrosive at 50 °C (122 °F) and very corrosive at 100 °C (212 °F). Tartaric acid has been processed in aluminum alloy filters and crystallizers and has been stored in aluminum alloy tanks.

Additional Reading

M.A. Elmorsi, E.M. Mabrouk, R.M. Issa, and M.M. Ghoneim, Electrochemical Studies of the Corrosion of Some Cu-Zn Alloys in Organic Acids, *Surf. Coat. Technol., 30*(3), 277-287, 1987. MetAbs No. 87-351667. **Abstract:** The electrochemical corrosion parameters (e.g., corrosion current density, corrosion rate and polarization resistance) of 63Cu-37Zn, 70Cu-30Zn and 58.81Cu-39.53Zn-1.66Pb alloys were measured in aqueous solutions of weak organic acids (oxalic, tartaric and succinic acid). Potentiodynamic, Tafel plot and polarization resistance techniques were used with the model 350A-PARC corrosion measurement system. The effect of acid concentration and temperature on the corrosion parameters of such alloys is discussed.

J.D. Talati and A.S. Patel, Corrosion of Copper by Food Acids Containing Colourants and Sweetening Agents. II. Corrosion by Tartaric Acid, *Werkst. Korros., 37*(9), 504-510, 1986. MetAbs No. 87-351795. **Abstract:** The corrosion of copper in tartaric acid solutions containing various food colorants and/or sweetening agents has been studied with respect to the concentration of the acid and the colorant and temperature.

Corrosion Behavior of Various Metals and Alloys in Tartaric Acid

Material	Condition, other factors, comments	Concentration, %	Temperature, °C (°F)	Duration	Corrosion rate, mm/yr (mils/yr) or other	Ref
Stainless steels						
Type 304 stainless steel	...	10	21 (70)	...	Very good	121
Type 304 stainless steel	Chemical processing; field or plant test; no aeration; rapid agitation. Commercial grade	...	202 (395)	5 d	0.002 in./yr	89
Type 304 stainless steel	Chemical processing; field or plant test; no aeration; rapid agitation. Vapors over tartaric acid, decomposition products, acetic and formic acids, etc.	...	202 (395)	5 d	0.003 in./yr	89
Type 316 stainless steel	...	10	21 (70)	...	Good	121
Type 316 stainless steel	Chemical processing; field or plant test; no aeration; rapid agitation. Commercial grade	...	202 (395)	5 d	0.0045 in./yr	89
Type 316 stainless steel	Chemical processing; field or plant test; no aeration; rapid agitation. Vapors over tartaric acid, decomposition products, acetic and formic acids, etc.	...	202 (395)	5 d	0.0006 in./yr	89
Type 317 stainless steel	Chemical processing; field or plant test; no aeration; rapid agitation. Commercial grade	...	202 (395)	5 d	0.0063 in./yr	89
Type 317 stainless steel	Chemical processing; field or plant test; no aeration; rapid agitation. Vapors over tartaric acid, decomposition products, acetic and formic acids, etc.	...	202 (395)	5 d	0.001 in./yr	89
Type 410 stainless steel	...	10	21 (70)	...	Good	121
Type 430 stainless steel	...	10	21 (70)	...	Good	121
Aluminum						
Aluminum (>99.5%)	Solution	...	...	...	Satisfactory	92
Coppers						
70-30 cupronickel	...	...	...	...	Suitable	93
90-10 cupronickel	...	...	...	...	Suitable	93
Admiralty brass	...	...	...	...	Suitable	93
Aluminum bronze	...	...	...	...	Suitable	93
Ampco 8, aluminum bronze	Generally suitable	...	...	...	<0.05 (<2)	96
Architectural bronze	...	...	...	...	Fair	93
Brass	...	...	...	...	Suitable	93
C26000, C23000	...	10	25 (75)	...	0.05 max (2 max)	63

(Continued)

Corrosion Behavior of Various Metals and Alloys in Tartaric Acid (Continued)

Material	Condition, other factors, comments	Concentration, %	Temperature, °C (°F)	Duration	Corrosion rate, mm/yr (mils/yr) or other	Ref
C26000, C23000	...	30	25 (75)	...	0.5-1.25 (20-50)	63
C26000, C23000	...	50	25 (75)	...	0.5-1.25 (20-50)	63
C26000, C23000	...	100	25 (75)	...	0.05 max (2 max)	63
C71000	...	5	25 (75)	...	0.025 max (1 max)	63
C71300	...	2	25 (75)	...	0.04 (1.6)	63
Cartridge brass	...	...	...	...	Fair	93
Commercial bronze	...	...	...	...	Suitable	93
Electrolytic copper	...	...	...	...	Suitable	93
Free-cutting brass	...	...	...	...	Fair	93
Muntz metal	...	...	...	...	Fair	93
Naval brass	...	...	...	...	Fair	93
Nickel silver	...	18	...	...	Suitable	93
Phosphor bronze	5% Sn	...	...	...	Suitable	93
Phosphor bronze	8% Sn	...	...	...	Suitable	93
Phosphor copper	...	...	...	...	Suitable	93
Red brass	...	...	...	...	Suitable	93
Silicon bronze	Low	...	...	...	Suitable	93
Silicon bronze	High	...	...	...	Suitable	93
Titanium						
Titanium	...	10-50	100 (212)	...	<0.127 (<5.08)	90
Titanium	...	10	60 (140)	...	0.003 (0.12)	90
Titanium	...	25	60 (140)	...	0.003 (0.12)	90
Titanium	...	50	60 (140)	...	0.001 (0.04)	90
Titanium	...	10	100 (212)	...	0.003 (0.12)	90
Titanium	...	25	100 (212)	...	nil	90
Titanium	...	50	100 (212)	...	0.0121 (0.484)	90
Heat- and corrosion-resistant alloys						
Incoloy 800	No pitting. (a)	10	80 (176)	7 d	<0.003 (<0.1)	44
Inconel 690	...	10	25 (77)	...	<0.03 (<1)	57
Nickel 200	In vacuum evaporating pan	57	54 (130)	...	0.187 (7.5)	44
Zirconium						
Zr702	...	10-50	35-100 (95-212)	...	<0.025 (<1)	15
Lead, tin, and zinc						
Tin	Nonaerated solutions	...	20 (68)	...	Resistant	94
Tin	...	...	60 (140)	...	Resistant	94
Tin	...	...	100 (212)	...	Unsuitable	94
Noble metals						
Silver	...	All	100 (212)	...	<0.05 (<2)	4
Silver	Oxygen increases attack in dilute tartaric acid at room temperature	All	100 (212)	...	<0.05 (<2)	4
Gold	...	All	Boiling	...	<0.05 (<2)	8
Others						
Magnesium	...	All	Room	...	Unsuitable	119
Niobium	...	20	Room	...	nil	2
Niobium	...	20	Boiling	...	nil	2

(a) Solutions were prepared with reagent-grade chemicals. Test specimens were cold-rolled, annealed sheet, 2.84 mm (0.112 in.) thick.

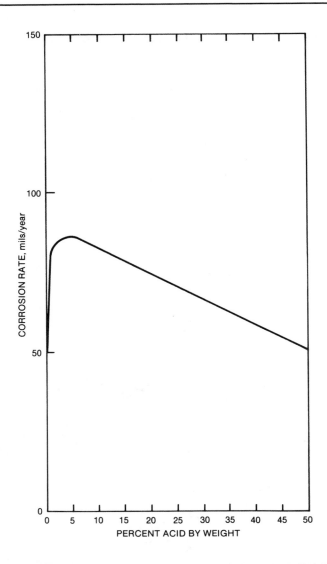

Aluminum. Effect of tartaric acid on alloy 1100 at 100 °C (212 °F). Source: *Guidelines for the Use of Aluminum with Food and Chemicals: Compatibility Data on Aluminum in the Food and Chemical Process Industries*, 5th ed., The Aluminum Association, Washington, DC, 1984, 25.

Trichloroethylene

Trichloroethylene, $CHCl:CCl_2$, is a heavy, stable toxic liquid with a chloroform aroma. It is slightly soluble in water, is soluble in greases and common organic solvents, and boils at 87 °C. Trichloroethylene is used in metal degreasing, solvent extraction, and dry cleaning, and as a fumigant and chemical intermediate.

Material Summaries

The following material summaries were compiled from a survey of the available literature. Inclusion of a material description under a given environment does not imply that it is the most appropriate material for corrosion service in that environment. Likewise, exclusion of a given material does not imply that it is not suitable for corrosion service applications in that environment.

Aluminum. In limited laboratory tests, 3003 alloy was resistant to trichloroethylene in the dry condition at ambient temperature, at 50 °C (122 °F), and under refluxing conditions. The presence of water accelerates the corrosive effects of trichloroethylene. Aluminum alloy tank cars have been used for transporting dry trichloroethylene. Inhibited trichloroethylene has been used for degreasing of aluminum alloy products. *Caution:* Under certain conditions, some hydrocarbons may produce a rapid rate of corrosion of aluminum or a violent reaction. Consequently, the service conditions to ensure safety should be recognized or established before aluminum alloys are used with any halogenated hydrocarbons.

Zirconium. Zirconium resists corrosion in trichloroethylene.

Additional Reading

H.W. White, Study of Corrosion and Corrosion Inhibitor Species on Aluminum Surfaces, in *Tunneling Spectroscopy—Capabilities, Applications and New Techniques*, Plenum Press, New York, 287-309, 1982. MetAbs No. 85-352371. **Abstract:** Applications of tunneling spectroscopy to the provision of fundamental data on the corrosion of aluminum and aluminum alloys in chlorinated solvents and acid media are reviewed, the mechanism of surface-reaction inhibition by chemical additives discussed, and the results are related to the development of improved inhibitors and more resistant alloy compositions. Particular media studied include CCl_4, trichloroethylene, and HCl, and the inhibitors considered comprise formamide for the CCl_4 and acridine and thiourea for the HCl.

Corrosion Behavior of Various Metals and Alloys in Trichloroethylene

Material	Condition, other factors, comments	Concentration, %	Temperature, °C (°F)	Duration	Corrosion rate, mm/yr (mils/yr) or other	Ref
Stainless steels						
Type 410 stainless steel	...	100	Room	...	Attacked	121
Aluminum						
Aluminum (99.0-99.5%)	Liquid	...	20 (68)	...	Restricted applications	92
Aluminum alloys	Liquid	...	20 (68)	...	Restricted applications	92
Coppers						
70-30 cupronickel	Moist	...	...	...	Suitable	93
90-10 cupronickel	Dry	...	...	...	Suitable	93
90-10 cupronickel	Moist. (a)	...	...	...	Good	93
Admiralty brass	Dry	...	...	...	Suitable	93
Admiralty brass	Moist. (a)	...	...	...	Good	93
Aluminum bronze	Dry	...	...	...	Suitable	93
Aluminum bronze	Dry	...	...	...	Suitable	93
Aluminum bronze	Moist. (a)	...	...	...	Good	93
Ampco 8, aluminum bronze	Generally suitable. Conditions such as aeration or temperature could restrict use	...	...	...	<0.5 (<20)	96
Architectural bronze	Dry	...	...	...	Suitable	93
Architectural bronze	Moist	...	...	...	Fair	93
Brass	Dry	...	...	...	Suitable	93
Brass	Moist. (a)	...	...	...	Good	93
Cartridge brass	Dry	...	...	...	Suitable	93
Cartridge brass	Moist	...	...	...	Fair	93
Commercial bronze	Dry	...	...	...	Suitable	93
Commercial bronze	Moist. (a)	...	...	...	Good	93
Electrolytic copper	Dry	...	...	...	Suitable	93
Electrolytic copper	Moist. (a)	...	...	...	Good	93
Free-cutting brass	Dry	...	...	...	Suitable	93
Free-cutting brass	Moist	...	...	...	Fair	93
Muntz metal	Dry	...	...	...	Suitable	93
Muntz metal	Moist	...	...	...	Fair	93
Naval brass	Dry	...	...	...	Suitable	93
Naval brass	Moist	...	...	...	Fair	93
Nickel silver	Dry	18	...	...	Suitable	93
Nickel silver	Moist. (a)	18	...	...	Good	93
Phosphor bronze	5% Sn. Dry	...	...	...	Suitable	93
Phosphor bronze	8% Sn. Dry	...	...	...	Suitable	93
Phosphor bronze	5% Sn. Moist. (a)	...	...	...	Good	93
Phosphor bronze	8% Sn. Moist. (a)	...	...	...	Good	93
Phosphor copper	Moist. (a)	...	...	...	Good	93
Phosphor copper	Dry	...	...	...	Suitable	93
Red brass	Dry	...	...	...	Suitable	93
		(Continued)				

Corrosion Behavior of Various Metals and Alloys in Trichloroethylene (Continued)

Material	Condition, other factors, comments	Concen-tration, %	Temperature, °C (°F)	Duration	Corrosion rate, mm/yr (mils/yr) or other	Ref
Red brass	Moist. (a)	...	...	...	Good	93
Silicon bronze	Low. Dry	...	...	...	Suitable	93
Silicon bronze	High. Dry	...	...	...	Suitable	93
Silicon bronze	Low. Moist. (a)	...	...	...	Good	93
Silicon bronze	High. Moist. (a)	...	...	...	Good	93
Titanium						
Titanium	...	99	Boiling	...	<0.13 (<5)	20
Titanium	...	99	Boiling	...	0.003-0.127 (0.12-5.08)	90
Titanium	Plus 50% H_2O	50	25 (77)	...	0.001 (0.04)	90
Zirconium						
Zr702	BP 87 °C (189 °F)	99	Boiling	...	<0.13 (<5)	15
Others						
Magnesium	...	100	Room	...	Suitable	119
Niobium	...	99	Boiling	...	nil	2

(a) May be considered in place of a copper metal when some property, other than corrosion resistance, governs its use.

Trichloroacetic Acid

Trichloroacetic acid, CCl_3COOH, is a colorless deliquescent crystalline solid that has a melting point of 57.5 °C (134 °F) and a boiling point of 198 °C (388 °F). Soluble in water, alcohol, and ether, it is toxic with a strong pungent odor. Trichloroacetic acid is used as a laboratory reagent, a herbicide, in medicine, and in microscopy.

Additional Reading

K.P. Soni and I.M. Bhatt, Corrosion and Inhibition of Copper, Brass and Aluminium in Nitric Acid, Sulfuric Acid and Trichloroacetic Acid, *J. Electrochem. Soc. India*, 34(1), 76-77, 1985. MetAbs No. 86-350473. **Abstract:** Corrosion of 99.6% copper, brass (36.7% zinc) and aluminum in acid, alkali and neutral solutions was investigated. Various organic and inorganic substances have also been studied as inhibitors.

J.D. Talati, G.A. Patel, and D.K. Gandhi, Maximum Utilization Current Density in Cathodic Protection. I. Aluminum in Acid Media, *Corrosion*, 40(2), 88-92, 1984. MetAbs No. 84-351165. **Abstract:** Cathodic protection of aluminum alloy AA 2017 in 2.5M HCl containing various dyes and of AA 2017 and AA 3003 in 2.0M trichloroacetic acid containing various amines as inhibitors has been studied.

A.S. Fouda and L.H. Madkour, Inhibitive Action of Some Amines and Hydrazines Towards Corrosion of Zinc in Trichloroacetic Acid Solution, *Bull. Soc. Chim. Fr.*, I(5), 745-749, 1986. MetAbs No. 87-350695. **Abstract:** The inhibitive action of some amines and hydrazines toward the corrosion of zinc in trichloroacetic acid was tested by thermometric and weight loss methods.

H. Mansour, H.M. Moustafa, A. El-Wafa, and G.A. Noubi, Corrosion of Aluminium in Chloroacetic Acids, *Bull. Electrochem.*, 2(5), 449-451, 1986. MetAbs No. 87-350962. **Abstract:** The corrosion of aluminium in mono-, di-, and trichloroacetic acids was studied. The effects of time and temperature and various inhibitors were investigated.

Corrosion Behavior of Various Metals and Alloys in Trichloroacetic Acid

Material	Condition, other factors, comments	Concen-tration, %	Temperature, °C (°F)	Duration	Corrosion rate, mm/yr (mils/yr) or other	Ref
Aluminum						
Aluminum (>99.5%)	...	...	...	...	Restricted applications	92
Coppers						
70-30 cupronickel	(a)	...	...	...	Good	93
90-10 cupronickel	(a)	...	...	...	Good	93
Admiralty brass	...	...	...	...	Fair	93
Aluminum bronze	(a)	...	...	...	Good	93

(Continued)

Corrosion Behavior of Various Metals and Alloys in Trichloroacetic Acid (Continued)

Material	Condition, other factors, comments	Concentration, %	Temperature, °C (°F)	Duration	Corrosion rate, mm/yr (mils/yr) or other	Ref
Architectural bronze	...	...	...	...	Not suitable	93
Brass	...	...	...	...	Fair	93
Cartridge brass	...	...	...	...	Not suitable	93
Commercial bronze	(a)	...	...	...	Good	93
Electrolytic copper	(a)	...	...	...	Good	93
Free-cutting brass	...	...	...	...	Not suitable	93
Muntz metal	...	...	...	...	Not suitable	93
Naval brass	...	...	...	...	Not suitable	93
Nickel silver	(a)	18	...	...	Good	93
Phosphor bronze	5% Sn. (a)	...	...	...	Good	93
Phosphor bronze	8% Sn. (a)	...	...	...	Good	93
Phosphor copper	(a)	...	...	...	Good	93
Red brass	(a)	...	...	...	Good	93
Silicon bronze	Low. (a)	...	...	...	Good	93
Silicon bronze	High. (a)	...	...	...	Good	93
Titanium						
Titanium	...	100	Boiling	...	14.6 (584)	90
Zirconium						
Zr702	...	10-40	Room	...	<0.05 (<2)	15
Zr702	...	100	Boiling	...	>1.3 (>50)	15
Zr702	BP 195 °C (383 °F)	100	100 (212)	...	>1.3 (>50)	15

(a) May be considered in place of a copper metal when some property, other than corrosion resistance, governs its use.

Urea

Urea, $CO(HN_2)_2$, also known as carbamide, is a white crystalline powder that has a melting point of 132.7 °C (270 °F). It is a natural product of animal protein metabolism and is the chief nitrogen constituent of urine. Commercially, urea is produced by the reaction of ammonia and carbon dioxide. It is soluble in water, alcohol, and benzene. Although urea is best known for its use in the preparation of fertilizers and plastics, it is used in medicine, adhesives, explosives, and as a flameproofing agent.

Material Summaries

The following material summaries were compiled from a survey of the available literature. Inclusion of a material description under a given environment does not imply that it is the most appropriate material for corrosion service in that environment. Likewise, exclusion of a given material does not imply that it is not suitable for corrosion service applications in that environment.

Stainless Steels. Types 304 and 316 stainless steels have been recommended as good choices for service in urea.

Aluminum. Tested at ambient temperature and 100% relative humidity, aluminum alloy 3003 resisted attack by solid urea, whereas alloy 5154 was mildly attacked. Aluminum alloy 3003 also resisted attack by urea in solution during other tests at ambient temperature. Urea has been distilled, dried, shipped, and stored in aluminum alloy equipment.

Zirconium. Zirconium resists corrosion in urea.

Additional Reading

K. Matsumoto and T. Shinohara, Electrochemical Study of Stainless Steels in High-Temperature Urea Solutions, *Corrosion, 40*(8), 387-393, 1984. MetAbs No. 84-352696. **Abstract:** The corrosion of stainless steels (17Cr-13Ni-2Mo, 25Cr-5Ni-1.5Mo and 30Cr-2Mo, etc.) in high-temperature and high-pressure urea solutions was studied by electrochemical measurements together with immersion tests to elucidate the corrosion mechanism and to rationalize the corrosion prevention methods.

S.K. Bhowmik, Materials of Construction in Urea Plants and the Areas Where Maximum Corrosion Takes Place, *Corros. Maint., 8*(1), 11-22, 1985. MetAbs No. 86-350489. **Abstract:** The suitability of high chromium (25%) austenitic stainless steel, titanium and zirconium as construction materials for urea plants is discussed to counteract the problems of carbamate handling and corrosion of the reactor, decomposition unit, separators, valuers and joints. Selection of materials is discussed in terms of corrosion resistance, workability, welding and economy. The different urea processes in Indian plants, the mechanisms of corrosion, and various case histories of corrosion are described.

F. Mancia and A. Tamba, Electrochemical Behavior of Special Stainless Steels Under Urea Synthesis Conditions and Comparison With Huey Test Results, *Corrosion, 43*(3), 165-173, 1987. MetAbs No. 87-351816. **Abstract:** A study has been made of the corrosion behavior of the following classes of stainless steels: AISI 316 urea grade, 25Cr-22Ni-2MoN super-austenitic, 21 to 25Cr-6-7Ni and 1.5 to 3 Mo duplex, and 21 to 25 chromium extra-low interstitial ferritic niobium and niobium plus titanium stabilized steels. Electrochemical measurements were conducted under simulated urea synthesis service conditions. The Huey test was also applied.

Corrosion Behavior of Various Metals and Alloys in Urea

Material	Condition, other factors, comments	Concentration, %	Temperature, °C (°F)	Duration	Corrosion rate, mm/yr (mils/yr) or other	Ref
Stainless steels						
Type 304 stainless steel	Chemical processing; field or plant test; slight to moderate aeration; rapid agitation. Plus 31% ammonia, 17% water, 8% carbon dioxide	44	32 (90)	42 d	0.0001 in./yr	89
Type 304 stainless steel	Chemical processing; field or plant test; no aeration; slight to moderate agitation. Plus 32% ammonia, 7% carbon dioxide, water remainder, heat-exchanger head	43	32-121 (90-250)	100 d	<0.0001 in./yr	89
Type 304 stainless steel	Petrochemical processing; field or plant test; slight to moderate aeration. Plus 32.2% ammonia, 20.5% water, 19% carbon dioxide, 0.3% inerts	28	179-182 (355-360)	150 d	<0.0001 in./yr	89
Type 304 stainless steel	Chemical processing; field or plant test; no aeration; rapid agitation. Plus ammonia, carbon dioxide, oil, urea stripper reboiler	...	121-154 (250-310)	56 d	0.028 in./yr	89
Type 316 stainless steel	Chemical processing; field or plant test; slight to moderate aeration; rapid agitation. Plus 31% ammonia, 17% water, 8% carbon dioxide	44	32 (90)	42 d	0.0002 in./yr	89
Type 316 stainless steel	Chemical processing; field or plant test; no aeration; slight to moderate agitation. Plus 32% ammonia, 7% carbon dioxide, water remainder, heat-exchanger head	43	32-121 (90-250)	100 d	<0.0001 in./yr	89
Type 316 stainless steel	Petrochemical processing; field or plant test; slight to moderate aeration. Plus 32.2% ammonia, 20.5% water, 19% carbon dioxide, 0.3% inerts	28	179-182 (355-360)	150 d	<0.0001 in./yr	89
Type 316 stainless steel	Chemical processing; field or plant test; no aeration; rapid agitation. Plus ammonia, carbon dioxide, oil, urea stripper reboiler	...	121-154 (250-310)	56 d	0.027 in./yr	89
Titanium						
Ti-3Al-2.5V	ASTM Grade 9	50	150 (302)	...	0.005 (0.2)	91
Titanium	Plus 32% NH_3 + 20.5% H_2O, 19% CO_2	28	182 (360)	...	0.079 (3.16)	90
Titanium	...	50	150 (302)	...	nil	91
Heat- and corrosion-resistant alloys						
20Cr-25Ni-4.5Mo-1.5Cu	Plus 17.5% CO_2, 33% NH_3, 19.5% H_2O. Oxygen added for passivation during test. Crevice corrosion under washer	30	185 (365)	62.5 d	0.12 (4.8)	80
Alloy 825	Chemical processing; field or plant test; slight to moderate aeration; rapid agitation. Plus 31% ammonia, 17% water, 8% carbon dioxide	44	32 (90)	42 d	<0.0001 in./yr	89
Alloy 825	Chemical processing; field or plant test; no aeration; slight to moderate agitation. Plus 32% ammonia, 7% carbon dioxide, water remainder, heat-exchanger head	43	32-121 (90-250)	100 d	<0.0001 in./yr	89
Alloy 825	Petrochemical processing; field or plant test; slight to moderate aeration. Plus 32.2% ammonia, 20.5% water, 19% carbon dioxide, 0.3% inerts	28	179-182 (355-360)	150 d	<0.0001 in./yr	89
Carpenter 20	Petrochemical processing; field or plant test; slight to moderate aeration. Plus 32.2% ammonia, 20.5% water, 19% carbon dioxide, 0.3% inerts	28	179-182 (355-360)	150 d	<0.0001 in./yr	89
E-Brite	Plus 17.5% CO_2, 33% NH_3, 19.5% H_2O. Oxygen added for passivation during test. No corrosion	30	185 (365)	62.5 d	0.06 (2.3)	80
Zirconium						
Zr702	17% NH_3, 15% CO_2, 10% H_2O	58	193 (380)	...	<0.025 (<1)	15
Others						
Magnesium	...	100	Room	...	Suitable	119
Magnesium	Cold aqueous solution	All	...	...	Suitable	119
Magnesium	Warm aqueous solution	All	...	...	Unsuitable	119

Water

Water, H_2O, is a clear, odorless, tasteless liquid that is essential for most animal and plant life and is an excellent solvent for many substances. Water has a melting point of 0 °C (32 °F) and a boiling point of 100 °C (212 °F). This chemical compound may also be termed hydrogen oxide.

Naturally occurring waters are seldom pure. Even rainwater, which is distilled by nature, contains nitrogen, oxygen, carbon dioxide, and other gases, as well as entrained dust and smoke particles. Water that runs over the ground carries with it eroded soil, decaying vegetation, living microorganisms, dissolved salts, and colloidal and suspended matter. Water that seeps through soil contains dissolved carbon dioxide and becomes acidic. Groundwater also contains salts of calcium, magnesium, iron, and manganese

All of these foreign substances in natural waters affect the structure and composition of the resulting films and corrosion products on the surface of metals, which in turn control the corrosion of the metal involved. In addition to these substances, such factors as pH, time of exposure, temperature, motion, and fluid agitation influence the aqueous corrosion of the metal.

Cooling Water. The quality of water used in shell and tube heat exchangers can vary from season to season and year to year, particularly if the water is taken from a river that discharges into a bay or sea. In one case, for example, a plant had 64 identical AISI type 304 stainless steel condensers that were cooled on the shell side with river water that varied in chloride content from less than 50 ppm to as high as 2000 ppm. The stainless steel tubes failed by external pitting at the baffles. It was discovered that an almost perfect correlation could be obtained by plotting the average monthly chloride content against the number of leaking condensers retubed that month.

In a similar case, a series of stainless steel heat exchangers cooled with recirculating treated water had been in service for more than 10 years. During an emergency, untreated river water was used to cool the units for about 48 h. Several weeks later, five of the coolers failed by massive chloride stress-corrosion cracking. There was a large buildup of dried mud in the units, which caused reduced heat transfer and higher tube wall temperatures.

Vacuum Pumps. Liquid ring vacuum pumps typically have ductile cast iron rotors and gray cast iron casings. From a corrosion standpoint, it is desirable to use fresh seal water. Paper machine white water is considered unsuitable for seal water use because of its high temperature and low pH. Even fresh water may be corrosive if the flow rate is so low that the temperature increases inside the pump or if the fresh water becomes contaminated by excessive white water carryover. A discharge seal water temperature of 50 °C (122 °F) and/or a pH less than 4.5 can cause accelerated cast iron corrosion. High discharge seal water conductivity may indicate excessive white water carryover. Accelerated impeller corrosion can occur at rotor tip speeds above 27 m/s (80 ft/s). The presence of sand or grit in the water will also shorten liquid ring vacuum pump life because of erosion.

Material Summaries

The following material summaries were compiled from a survey of the available literature. Inclusion of a material description under a given environment does not imply that it is the most appropriate material for corrosion service in that environment. Likewise, exclusion of a given material does not imply that it is not suitable for corrosion service applications in that environment.

Aluminum. Suitability of the more corrosion-resistant aluminum alloys for use with high-purity water at room temperature is well established. The slight reaction with water that occurs initially ceases almost completely within a few days after development of a protective oxide film of equilibrium thickness. After this conditioning period, the amount of metal dissolved by the water becomes negligible.

Corrosion resistance of aluminum alloys in high-purity water is not significantly decreased by dissolved carbon dioxide or oxygen in the water or, in most cases, by the various chemicals added to high-purity water in the steam power industry to provide the required compatibility with steel. These additives include ammonia and neutralizing amines for pH adjustment to control carbon dioxide, hydrazine and sodium sulfate to control oxygen, and filming amines (long-chain polar compounds) to produce nonwettable surfaces. Somewhat surprisingly, the effects of alloying elements on corrosion resistance of aluminum alloys in high-purity water at elevated temperatures are opposite to their effects at room temperature; elements (including impurities) that decrease resistance at room temperature improve it at elevated temperatures.

At 200 °C (390 °F), high-purity aluminum of sheet thickness disintegrates completely within a few days by reaction with high-purity water to form aluminum oxide. In contrast, aluminum-nickel-iron alloys have the best elevated temperature resistance to high-purity water of all aluminum metals; for example, alloy X8001 (1.0Ni-0.5Fe) has good resistance at temperatures as high as 315 °C (600 °F).

Erosion-Corrosion. In noncorrosive environments such as high-purity water, the stronger aluminum alloys have the greatest resistance to erosion-corrosion, because resistance is controlled almost entirely by the mechanical components of the system. In a corrosive environment, such as seawater, the corrosion component becomes the controlling factor; thus, resistance may be greater for the more corrosion-resistant alloys even though they are lower in strength.

Stress-Corrosion Cracking. Water or water vapor is the key environmental factor required to produce stress-corrosion cracking in aluminum alloys. Halide ions have the greatest effects in accelerating attack. Chloride is the most important halide ion because it is a natural constituent of marine environments and is present in other environments as a contaminant. Because it accelerates stress-corrosion cracking, Cl^- is the principal component of environments used in laboratory tests to determine susceptibility of aluminum alloys to this type of attack. In general, susceptibility is greater in neutral solutions than in alkaline solutions and is greater still in acidic solutions.

Natural Waters. Aluminum alloys of the 1xxx, 3xxx, 5xxx, and 6xxx series are resistant to corrosion by many natural waters. The more important factors controlling the corrosivity of natural waters to aluminum include water temperature, pH, and conductivity, availability of cathodic reactants, presence or absence of heavy metals, and the corrosion potentials and pitting potentials of the specific alloys. Various correlations of the corrosivity of natural waters to aluminum have been attempted, but none predicts the corrosivity of all natural waters reliably.

Beryllium that is clean and free of surface impurities has very good resistance to attack in low-temperature high-purity water. The corrosion rate in good-quality water is typically less than 0.025 mm/yr (1 mil/yr).

Beryllium has been reported to perform without problems for 10 years in slightly acidified demineralized water in a nuclear test reactor. This high-purity water environment also produced no evidence of accelerated corrosion with the beryllium galvanically coupled with stainless steel or aluminum.

Beryllium of normal commercial purity, however, is susceptible to attack, primarily in the form of localized pitting, when exposed to impure water. Chloride and sulfate ions are the most critical contaminants in aqueous solutions. Because these contaminants are present in tap water, most processing specifications warn against its use. Early processors encountered serious problems of pitting or surface corrosion in beryllium that was allowed to stand in tap water, or was rinsed off with tap water and, after drying, was allowed to stand in a damp atmosphere where water condensation could easily occur on the contaminated surfaces. More recently, an airframe manufacturer experienced a major production problem when water vapor, condensing on overhead piping, dripped onto structures in the processing line. In cases where tap water can be used, the final rinses are done in deionized water to ensure that the chloride or sulfate impurities are not retained on the subsequently dried metal surface.

The pitting of beryllium in aqueous baths containing chloride or sulfate ions has generally been attributed to attack in areas anodic to the bulk of the metal. In an investigation consisting of 12-month corrosion tests in water at 85 °C (185 °F), the pitting attack was attributed to a lack of metal purity. Years later, in a study prompted by rejection of beryllium components for the presence of hard inclusions, pitting corrosion was shown to be associated with points of silicon and aluminum segregation.

On the basis of the examination of pitted specimen surfaces by microprobe analysis, the following general conclusions were drawn:

* Pitting corrosion is determined by the distribution of alloy impurities.

* Sites that have high concentrations of iron, aluminum, or silicon (probably in solid solution) tend to form corrosion pits.

* Corrosion sites are often characterized by the presence of alloy-rich particles, which are probably beryllides; however, the particles themselves do not appear to be corrosion active.

* Pitting density is believed to be related to the number of segregated regions in the matrix containing concentrations of iron, aluminum, or silicon higher than concentrations present in the surrounding areas.

Segregated impurities, such as Be_2C particles, intermetallic compounds, or alloy-rich zones, can contribute to localized attack when present in an exposed beryllium surface. Be_2C forms a gelatinous corrosion product in an aqueous environment. As the purity of beryllium has improved during the years of its commercialization, the problem of localized corrosion at segregated particles and inclusions has significantly decreased.

The effects of the surface finish of beryllium on aqueous corrosion were investigated. The specimen conditions included (1) as-machined, (2) pickled in chromic-phosphoric acid after machining, and (3) machined, annealed beryllium reannealed in vacuum for 1 h at 825 °C (1515 °F). The results of long-term tests in demineralized water at 85 °C (185 °F) showed that the pickled specimens corroded at a higher rate than the others during the first 60 days of testing. The machined and annealed specimens initially corroded faster than the as-machined specimens. It was found, however, that with extended exposure times the magnitude of attack for all the types of surfaces reached about the same value—0.0025 to 0.005 mm/yr (0.1 to 0.2 mil/yr).

Extensive information on the behavior of beryllium under the combined effects of stress and chemical environment is not readily available. The first reported work involved the use of extruded material in water containing $0.005M$ hydrogen peroxide at pH 6 to 6.5 at 90 °C (195 °F). No evidence of cracking was noted even though stresses up to 90% of the yield strength were used. Stress corrosion has been reported on cross-rolled sheet when synthetic seawater was used as the test medium. Studies of time to failure versus applied stress revealed that the time decreased from 2340 to 40 h as the applied stress was increased from 8.4 to 276 MPa (1220 to 40,000 psi, or 70% of yield strength). Failure appeared to be closely associated with random pitting attack. Certain pits appeared to remain active, which promoted severe localized attack.

Cast Irons. Unalloyed and low-alloy cast irons are the primary cast irons used in water. The corrosion resistance of unalloyed cast iron in water is determined by its ability to form protective scales. In hard water, corrosion rates are generally low because of the formation of calcium carbonate scales on the surface of the iron. In softened or deionized water, the protective scales cannot be fully developed, and some corrosion will occur.

In industrial waste waters, corrosion rates are primarily a function of the contaminants present. Acid pH waters increase corrosion, but alkaline pH waters lower corrosion rates. Chlorides increase the corrosion rates of unalloyed cast irons, although the influence of chlorides is small at a neutral pH.

Carbon Steels. Carbon steel pipe and vessels are often required to transport water, or they are submerged in water to some extent during service. This exposure can be under conditions of varying temperature, flow rate, pH, and so on, all of which can alter the rate of corrosion. The relative acidity of the solution is probably the most important factor to be considered. At low pH, the evolution of hydrogen tends to eliminate the possibility of protective film formation so that steel continues to corrode, but in alkaline solutions, the formation of protective films greatly reduces the corrosion rate. The greater the alkalinity, the slower the rate of attack becomes. In neutral solutions, other factors, such as aeration, become rate determining so that generalization becomes more difficult.

Stainless Steels. The chloride contents of waters such as brackish water or seawater pose the danger of pitting or crevice corrosion of stainless steels. When the application involves moderately increased temperatures, even as low as 45 °C (110 °F), and particularly when there is heat transfer into the chloride-containing medium, there is the possibility of stress-corrosion cracking. It is useful to consider water with two general levels of chloride content—fresh water, which can have chloride levels up to approximately 600 ppm, and seawater, which encompasses brackish and severely contaminated waters. The corrosivity of a particular level of chloride can be strongly affected by the other chemical constituents present, making the water either more or less corrosive.

Permanganate ion, which is associated with the dumping of chemicals, has been related to pitting of type 304 stainless steel. The presence of sulfur compounds and oxygen or other oxidizing agents can affect the corrosion of copper and copper alloys, but does not have very significant effects on stainless steels at ambient or slightly elevated temperatures (up to approximately 250 °C, or 500 °F).

In fresh water, type 304 stainless steel has provided excellent service for such items as valve parts, weirs, fasteners, and pump shafts in water and wastewater treatment plants. Custom 450 stainless steel has been used as shafts for large butterfly valves in potable water. The higher strength of precipitation-hardenable stainless steel permits reduced shaft diameter and increased flow. Type 201 stainless steel has seen service in revetment mats to reduce shoreline erosion in fresh water. Type 316 stainless steel has been used as wire for microstrainers in tertiary sewage treatment and is suggested for waters containing minor amounts of chloride.

Cemented Carbides. The major applications of cemented carbides actually involve environments that are inherently corrosive. For example, the major use of cemented carbides is for metal-cutting (machining) applications. In these applications, extreme heat is generated whether or not coolants are used, and when coolants are used, the corrosive attack of the coolant is a factor in the performance of the cutting tool. In general, however, very little heed is paid to this factor; cemented carbides are more often chosen for their wear resistance in such applications as mining and oil well drilling. In actuality, there is a corrosive environment to be contended with in mining and oil well drilling; the natural waters and other fluids involved are often very corrosive.

Copper is extensively used for handling fresh water. Copper tubing in the K-gage range with flared fittings was designed for underground water service and, along with type L tubing, has not become standard for this application. The largest single application of copper tubing is for hot and cold water distribution lines in homes and other buildings, although considerable quantities are also used in heating lines (including radiant heating lines for homes), drain tubes, and fire safety systems.

Minerals in water combine with dissolved carbon dioxide and oxygen and react with copper to form a protective film. Therefore, the corrosion rate is low (5 to 25 μm/yr, or 0.2 to 1.0 mil/yr) in most exposures. In distilled water or very soft water, protective films are less likely to form; therefore, the corrosion rate may vary from less than 2.5 to 125 μm/yr (0.1 to 5 mils/yr) or more, depending on oxygen and carbon dioxide contents.

Copper-Zinc Alloys. The corrosion resistance of the brasses is good in unpolluted fresh water—normally 2.5 to 25 μm/yr (0.1 to 1.0 mil/yr). Corrosion rates are somewhat higher in nonscaling water containing carbon dioxide and oxygen. Uninhibited brasses of high zinc content (35 to 40% Zn) are subject to dezincification when used with stagnant or slow moving brackish or slightly acid waters. On the other hand, inhibited admiralty metals and brasses containing 15% Zn or less are highly resistant to dezincification and are used very successfully in these waters. Inhibited admiralty metal (C44300, C44400, and C44500) has good corrosion resistance and is extensively used for tubing in various services, especially steam condensers cooled with fresh, salt, or brackish water. Several cases of the stress-corrosion cracking of admiralty brass heat exchanger tubing have been documented. The environments in which such stress-corrosion cracking was observed included stagnant water, stagnant water contaminated with NH_3, and water accidentally contaminated with a nitrate. Inhibited yellow brasses are widely used in Europe and are gaining acceptance in North America. Alloy C68700 (arsenical aluminum brass, an inhibited 77Cu-21Zn-2Al alloy) has been successfully used for condenser and heat exchanger tubes.

Copper nickels generally have corrosion rates under 25 μm/yr (1 mil/yr) in unpolluted water. Alloy C71500 (Cu-30Ni) has the best general resistance to aqueous corrosion of all the commercially important copper alloys, but C70600 (Cu-10Ni) is often selected because it offers good resistance at lower cost. Both of these alloys, although well suited to applications in the chemical industry, have been most extensively used for condenser tubes and heat exchanger tubes in recirculating steam systems. Copper nickels are sometimes used to resist impingement attack where severe velocity and entrained-air conditions cannot be overcome by changes in operating conditions or equipment design.

Copper-silicon alloys (silicon bronzes) also have excellent corrosion resistance, and for these alloys, the amount of dissolved oxygen in the water does not influence corrosion significantly. If carbon dioxide is also present, the corrosion rate will increase (but not excessively), particularly at temperatures above 60 °C (140 °F). Corrosion rates for silicon bronzes are similar to those for copper.

Copper-Aluminum Alloys. The aluminum bronzes have been used in many waters, from potable water to brackish water to seawater. Softened waters are usually more corrosive to these materials than hard waters. Alloys C61300 and C63200 are used in cooling tower hardware in which the makeup water is sewage effluent. Aluminum bronzes resist oxidation and impingement corrosion because of the aluminum in the surface film.

Nickel Silvers. The two most common nickel silvers—C75200 (65Cu-18Ni-17Zn) and C77000 (55Cu-18Ni-27Zn)—have good resistance to corrosion in fresh water.

Hafnium. The corrosion resistance of hafnium in water is superior to that of zirconium and Zircaloy alloys.

Lead. Distilled water free of oxygen and carbon dioxide does not attack lead. Distilled water containing carbon dioxide but not oxygen also has little effect on lead. The corrosion behavior of lead in distilled water containing dissolved carbon dioxide and dissolved oxygen depends on the carbon dioxide concentration. This dependency, which causes many different reactions to take place in a narrow range of concentration, explains the contradictory nature of much of the corrosion data reported in the literature.

For example, lead steam coils that handle pure water condensate are not severely corroded in systems in which all condensate is returned to the boiler and negligible makeup water is used. However, if makeup water is used, dissolved oxygen can be introduced to the condensate, and corrosion can be severe. Carbon dioxide can also be generated from the breakdown of carbonates and bicarbonates in boiler water, decreasing the severity of corrosion of lead. The oxygen level in the makeup water is usually controlled by adding oxygen scavengers, such as hydrazine or sodium sulfite.

In general, the corrosion rate in natural and domestic waters depends on the degree of water hardness. Water hardness is primarily caused by calcium and magnesium salts in the water. These salts, if present in at least moderate amounts (> 125 ppm), form films on lead that adequately protect it against corrosive attack. Silicate salts present in the water increase both the hardness and the protective value of the film. In contrast, nitrate and chloride ions either interfere with the formation of the protective film or penetrate it, thus increasing corrosion.

In soft, aerated natural and domestic waters, the corrosion rate depends on both the hardness and the oxygen content of the water. When water hardness is less than 125 ppm, the corrosion rate, like the rate in distilled water, depends on the relative proportions of dissolved carbon dioxide and dissolved oxygen. Potable waters, in which lead content is not permitted to exceed 0.05 ppm, often have hardnesses below 125 ppm and often contain considerable amounts of carbon dioxide and oxygen; thus, lead frequently cannot be used for pipe or containers that handle potable waters. This problem of contamination limits the use of lead in such applications, even though from a service point of view, the corrosion rate is negligible.

The corrosion rates of chemical lead (99.9% Pb) in several industrial and domestic waters were investigated. It was found that corrosion rates were relatively low, even where water hardness was below 125 ppm.

Magnesium. In stagnant distilled water at room temperature, magnesium alloys rapidly form a protective film that prevents further corrosion. Small amounts of dissolved salts in water, particularly chlorides or heavy metal salts, will break down the protective film locally, which usually results in pitting.

Dissolved oxygen plays no major role in the corrosion of magnesium in either fresh water or saline solutions. However, agitation or any other means of destroying or preventing the formation of a protective film leads to corrosion. When magnesium is immersed in a small volume of stagnant water, its corrosion rate is negligible. When the water is constantly replenished so that the solubility limit of $Mg(OH)_2$ is never reached, the corrosion rate may increase.

The corrosion of magnesium alloys by pure water increases substantially with temperature. At 100 °C (212 °F), the AZ alloys corrode typically at 0.25 to 0.50 mm/yr (10 to 20 mils/yr). Pure magnesium and alloy ZK60A corrode excessively at 100 °C (212 °F) with rates up to 25 mm/yr (1000 mils/yr). At 150 °C (302 °F), all alloys corrode excessively.

Nickel and nickel-base alloys generally have very good resistance to corrosion in distilled water and fresh water. Typical corrosion rates for Nickel 200 (commercially pure nickel) in a distilled water storage tank at ambient temperature and domestic hot water service are <0.0025 mm/yr (<0.1 mil/yr) and <0.005 mm/yr (<0.2 mil/yr), respectively. Nickel-copper alloys such as 400 and R-405 also have very low corrosion rates and are used in fresh water systems for valve seats and other fittings.

Because of the cost of nickel alloys, less expensive stainless steels or other materials are usually specified for pure or freshwater applications, unless increased resistance to stress-corrosion cracking or pitting is required. Alloys 600 and 690, for example, are used for increased stress-corrosion cracking resistance in high-purity water nuclear steam generators. Stress-corrosion cracking of these alloys has occurred in such environments and is generally intergranular. This phenomenon also extends to stainless steels and other nickel-base alloys. Although alloy 600 is susceptible to cracking in steam generators, it is much more resistant than type 304 stainless steel.

Niobium reacts with water to form niobium oxide. There is a direct transition from immunity to passivity without an intermediate region where corrosion occurs. Niobium reacts with water vapor at temperatures above 300 °C (570 °F).

Silver is resistant to attack by water or steam at temperatures up to 600 °C (1110 °F).

Tantalum is not attacked by fresh water, mine waters (which are usually acidic), or seawater, either cold or hot. Tantalum shows no corrosion in deionized water at 40 °C (100 °F). For tantalum equipment exposed to boiler waters and condensates, the alkalinity must be controlled. The pH should be less than 9 and preferably no more than 8.

Tin. In hot or cold distilled water, the only action of tin is the slow growth of an oxide film, with a negligible amount of metal entering solution. Water that was freshly distilled in tin was found to have less than 1 ppb tin in solution. Storage in tin-lined or tinned copper tanks for 24 h produced, in the worst instances, only a few ppb, but in some cases, the tin content remained below 1 ppb.

In tap water of 7.2 pH at 25 °C (75 °F), specimens of 99.99% cold rolled tin showed a weight gain of 0.04 mils/yr in 50 days and the formation of an insoluble film. With harder tap waters of 7.4 and 8.6 pH, weight losses on the order of 0.09 and 0.02 mils/yr, respectively, were incurred in 50 days. Precipitated carbonate was mainly responsible for localized water line attack with hot and cold hard waters because no attack occurred without the precipitate.

Tin-Lead Solders. Natural waters and commercial treated waters that are aggressive to lead are likely to corrode solder at a rate that increases slowly, in proportion to its lead content, up to about 70% Pb, then more rapidly at higher lead contents. Selective dissolution of lead can also occur in distilled, demineralized, or naturally soft waters, causing serious weakening of joints. In commercial waters, the ability of lead to form insoluble oxides, sulfates, and carbonates usually protects solders against serious attack. Although rare, selective dissolution of tin has been reported during prolonged contact of solders with solutions of anionic surface-active agents.

When freshly exposed to water, solders are anodic to copper, but soldered joints in copper pipes are widely used without trouble in conventional commercial and domestic cold and hot water systems. Despite this generally good corrosion resistance, it has been demonstrated that, under adverse conditions, lead may be leached from the commonly used 50Sn-50Pb plumbing solder into water traveling through the pipe; this is a cause of increasing concern.

Soldered joints in brass usually perform well in domestic waters, but good joint design is imperative. In automobile radiators in which there are no inhibitors, ethylene glycol, although not directly aggressive, does appear able to detach protective deposits that may form on soldered joints. Sodium nitrite, which is used as an inhibitor for some metals, will attack solders and must be used in conjunction with sodium benzoate.

Titanium and its alloys are fully resistant to water, all natural waters, and steam at temperatures in excess of 315 °C (600 °F). Slight weight gain is usually experienced in these benign environments, along with some surface discoloration at higher temperatures from finite passive film thickening. The immunity to attack of alpha alloys is observed regardless of oxygen level or in high-purity water, such as that normally used in nuclear reactor coolant systems. The typical contaminants encountered in natural water streams, such as iron and manganese oxides, sulfides, sulfates, carbonates, and chlorides, do not compromise the passivity of titanium. In media containing chloride levels greater than 1000 ppm (for example, seawater) at temperatures of about 75 °C (165 °F), consideration should be given to possible crevice corrosion when tight crevices exist in service.

Stress-Corrosion Cracking. Under certain metallurgical conditions, several titanium alloys have been shown to be susceptible to stress-corrosion cracking in distilled water. These include Ti-8Al-1Mo-1V, Ti-5Al-2.5Sn, and Ti-11.5Mo-6Zr-4.5Sn. Microstructural variation for each alloy affects the degree of susceptibility. For example, mill-annealed Ti-8Al-1Mo-1V is less susceptible than step-cooled Ti-8Al-1Mo-1V.

Stress-corrosion cracking of Ti-8Al-1Mo-1V has been extensively studied because of its sensitivity to microstructure. The martensitic structures produced by quenching from a high-temperature solution treatment are immune to stress-corrosion cracking. Lower temperature solution treatment produces an equiaxed alpha-beta structure that is susceptible to stress-corrosion cracking. The degree of susceptibility is determined by the grain size, volume fraction, and mean free path of the susceptible alpha phase. Tempered martensitic structures, produced by annealing a martensitic microstructure, are also susceptible to stress-corrosion cracking. Basket-weave or Widmanstätten microstructures produced by working and/or heat treatment above the beta transus generally exhibit better toughness both in and out of an aqueous environment.

In general, titanium alloys with higher aluminum, oxygen, and tin contents are the most susceptible to stress-corrosion cracking. Molybdenum is usually beneficial in increasing stress-corrosion cracking resistance. Microstructural effects in these alloys are similar to those discussed for Ti-8Al-1Mo-1V.

With the exception of Ti-13V-11Cr-3Al, all of the commercial beta titanium alloys are immune to stress-corrosion cracking in the beta-phase condition. However, aging decomposes the beta phase and produces a variety of phases. The omega phase produced by low-temperature aging of many beta alloys does not induce stress-corrosion cracking susceptibility. Aging at higher temperatures produces the alpha phase, which nearly always leads to stress-corrosion cracking. The degree to which a given beta alloy in the beta + alpha condition is susceptible appears to be related to the alloy chemistry and to the quantity and morphology of the alpha phase.

Aging at higher temperatures produces a coarser alpha, which is less susceptible to stress-corrosion cracking than the finer alpha. Alloys containing molybdenum are less susceptible to stress-corrosion cracking, especially those without tin.

Ionic Species. The anions Cl⁻, Br⁻, and I⁻ are some of the species shown to promote and/or induce stress-corrosion cracking in titanium alloys. The few alloys susceptible to cracking in distilled water become more susceptible, whereas alloys that are not susceptible in distilled water may become susceptible when these species are present.

Zinc. The corrosion of zinc in water is largely controlled by the impurities present in the water. In addition, such factors as pH, time of exposure, temperature, motion, and fluid agitation influence the aqueous corrosion of zinc.

As in the atmosphere, the corrosion resistance of a zinc coating in water depends on its initial ability to form a protective layer by reacting with the environment. In distilled water, which cannot form a protective scale to reduce the access of oxygen to the zinc surface, the attack is more severe than in most types of domestic or river water, which do contain some scale-forming salts.

The scale-forming ability of water depends principally on three factors: the hydrogen ion concentration (pH value), the total calcium content, and the total alkalinity. If the pH value is below that at which the water would be in equilibrium with calcium carbonate, the water will tend to dissolve rather than to deposit scale. Waters with a high content of free carbon dioxide also tend to be aggressive toward zinc.

Water hardness is an important variable in zinc corrosion. The corrosion rate of zinc in hard water may be 15 μm/yr (0.6 mil/yr), but in soft water, it can be 150 μm/yr (6 mils/yr). Hard waters are usually less corrosive toward zinc because they deposit protective scales on the metallic surface. Softer waters do not deposit these scales. Similarly, seawater also deposits protective scales on zinc and is less corrosive than soft water.

Softer waters, with their higher content of dissolved oxygen and carbon dioxide, generally attack zinc more vigorously than the fairly hard waters. River waters have been found to deposit scale more easily than well waters. The normal corrosion product of zinc in water is $ZnCO_3$.

Agitation, Aeration, and Carbon Dioxide. With respect to distilled water, under conditions in which the oxygen content cannot be replaced as quickly as it is consumed by the corrosion process, such as in stagnant water, zinc is attacked rapidly at local areas, and this causes pitting. As more oxygen is made available, the corrosion becomes more uniform. With further increases in the oxygen content of the water, the corrosion rate increases. For example, when thin films of moisture condense on a zinc surface, the concurrent rapid supply of oxygen at the corroding surface has an accelerating effect on the corrosion rate.

Experimentation has shown that with test pieces immersed in water through which oxygen was bubbled corrosion occurred about eight times as fast as with specimens in water that was boiled to remove gases and then cooled out of contact with air. Although the corrosion rate increased when oxygen was bubbled through the water, the attack was uniform. The presence of oxygen in the water accelerates the corrosion by depolarization of the cathodic areas. The rate of corrosion is then controlled by diffusion of oxygen through the film of $Zn(OH)_2$ corrosion products.

Temperature. In practical applications involving distilled water, the temperature of the water has been shown to be a very important factor affecting the rate of corrosion of zinc. In one study, a marked increase in corrosion rate was found to occur at a temperature of about 60 °C (140 °F), followed by a decrease in corrosion at higher temperature. At temperatures near 70 °C (160 °F), a reversal in potential may occur where zinc coatings become cathodic to iron. Low oxygen and high bicarbonate contents favor reversal, but the presence of oxygen, sulfates, and chlorates tends to maintain the natural anodic state of the zinc.

The results of this study were obtained on 99.9% pure zinc immersed for 15 days in aerated distilled water. The water was continuously aerated by air bubbling through it, and no attempt was made to remove carbon dioxide from the air. Also, the specimens were supported on a wooden disk that was rotated through the test water at 56 rpm. Thus, all of the factors that cause increased corrosion, as discussed above, were present in these tests. The temperature, however, seems to have been the controlling factor in this experiment.

Tests showed that the observed corrosion peak at approximately 65 °C (150 °F) occurs both in waters under a pure oxygen atmosphere and under a carbon dioxide free air atmosphere. In contrast, under an oxygen-free nitrogen atmosphere, the peak disappears completely. Additional experiments showed that, as the partial pressure of oxygen over the water was reduced from that in air, the peak decreased in magnitude and shifted to lower temperatures that involve the decreased solubility of oxygen in water at elevated temperatures.

This is consistent with the observation that decreased oxygen supplies (caused by reduced oxygen pressure over the water) lower the corrosion peak temperature. As the oxygen partial pressure is lowered, the equilibrium oxygen content in the water is lowered for any temperature. The reduced oxygen content of the water thus lowers the temperature at which depolarization becomes rate limiting, because the critical oxygen level for depolarization is reached at a lower temperature.

Cold Domestic Water. Galvanized pipe is widely used in handling domestic water supplies, and the results have been satisfactory. Therefore, quantitative corrosion rates are not of primary interest, and only limited data are available in the literature. Hard domestic waters contain dissolved salts that may affect the corrosion of zinc. Carbonates and bicarbonates tend to deposit protective films that stifle corrosion, and it is generally agreed that soft or distilled waters are more corrosive than hard water.

Hot Domestic Water. In domestic water systems, for which zinc is widely adopted as a protective coating, the sacrificial dissolution of zinc at discontinuities in the coating in the presence of calcium bicarbonate (a normal constituent of hard water supplies) leads to the deposition of an insoluble layer of $CaCO_3$ on the exposed surfaces. Because this layer is impervious to the passage of ions and electrons, it inhibits any further corrosive action. This reaction, which depends on the presence of dissolved calcium bicarbonate in the water, cannot occur in systems in soft water areas, and it is generally agreed that soft or distilled water is more corrosive than hard water. Other constituents in natural waters, such as nitrates, sulfates, and chlorides, may tend to increase corrosion, but their effects are usually overcome by the carbonates that form films of relatively low solubility in close contact with the zinc surface.

Changing the temperature of a solution can influence the corrosion tendency. For example, historically, household water heater tanks were made of galvanized steel. The zinc coating on the carbon steel base offered some cathodic protection to the underlying steel, and the service life (usually judged by how long it took to produce rusty water) was considered to be adequate. Water tanks were seldom operated above 60 °C (140 °F).

Natural Water. The factors influencing the corrosion of zinc by tap or supply waters discussed in the preceding paragraphs also apply to natural waters, such as lake and river waters.

Zirconium. Corrosion and oxidation of unalloyed zirconium in water and steam are reported to be irregular. This behavior is probably caused by variations in the impurity content in the metal. Nitrogen and carbon impurities are particularly harmful. The corrosion rate of zirconium increases markedly when nitrogen and carbon concentrations exceed 40 and 300 ppm, respectively.

Zircaloy-2 is superior to unalloyed zirconium in high-temperature water and steam. Zircaloy-4 differs in composition from Zircaloy-2 only in that it has no nickel and a slightly greater iron content. Both variations are intended to reduce hydrogen pickup in reactor operation. The corrosion behavior of Zircaloy-4 is very similar to that of Zircaloy-2. However, hydrogen pickup for Zircaloy-4 is significantly lower, particularly when the alloy is exposed to water at 360 °C (680 °F). At this temperature, hydrogen pickup for Zircaloy-4 is about 25% of theoretical, or less than half that for Zircaloy-2. In addition, hydrogen pickup for Zircaloy-4 is less sensitive to hydrogen overpressure than that for Zircaloy-2. For both Zircaloys, hydrogen pickup is markedly decreased when dissolved oxygen is present in the corrosion medium.

Alloy Zr-2.5Nb is considered to be somewhat less resistant to corrosion than the Zircaloys. Nevertheless, Zr-2.5Nb is acceptable for many applications. An example is the use of Zr-2.5Nb pressure tubes in the primary loops of some reactors. The corrosion resistance of Zr-2.5Nb can be substantially improved by heat treatment. Also, Zr-2.5Nb is superior to Zircaloys in steam at temperatures above 400 °C (750 °F).

Additional Reading

L.A. Luini, Stress Corrosion Cracking of An Aluminum-Zinc Magnesium Alloy, University of Connecticut, *Diss. Abstr. Int.*, *41*(8), 68, 1981. MetAbs No. 81-351276. **Abstract:** The stress-corrosion cracking of a high-strength type 7039 Al-Zn-Mg alloy has been studied as a function of heat treatment, test temperature and environment. For each of four heat treatments, plots of crack velocity vs. stress-intensity factor were obtained for testing in both distilled water and 3.5% NaCl + H₂O.

K. Goto, Y. Shimizu, and G. Ito, Effect of Metallurgical Factors on the Initiation of Pitting Corrosion of Aluminum in Fresh Water, *Trans. Natl. Res. Inst. Met. (Jpn.)*, *22*(4), 270-276, 1980. MetAbs No. 81-351491. **Abstract:** Various metallurgical factors governing the initiation of pitting corrosion were examined by electron microscopy and cathodic polarization measurements.

G.M. Scamans and C.D.S. Tuck, Embrittlement of Aluminum Alloys Exposed to Water Vapor, *Environment-Sensitive Fracture of Engineering Materials*, 464-483, 1979. MetAbs No. 81-351667. **Abstract:** Exposure of unstressed aluminium and aluminium alloys to water vapor saturated air at 70 °C results in the formation of a duplex hydroxide film that initiates by hydrogen-induced blistering of the protective amorphous oxide. For Al-Zn-Mg alloys, this reaction results in three distinct forms of intergranular penetration.

M. Khobaib, C.T. Lynch, and F.W. Vahldiek, Inhibition of Corrosion Fatigue in High-Strength Aluminum Alloys, *Corrosion*, *37*(5), 285-292, 1981. MetAbs No. 81-351962. **Abstract:** The effects of environment on the crack growth rate of several high-strength Al alloys (7075-T6, 7075-T73 and 2024-T3) were studied in distilled water, tap water, aqueous sodium chloride, aqueous inhibitors with and without sodium chloride, and ambient air.

L. Christodoulou and H.M. Flower, In Situ HVEM Observations of Hydrogen Embrittlement in Al-Zn-Mg Alloys, in *Hydrogen Effects in Metals*, TMS/AIME, Warrendale, PA, 26-31, 1980. MetAbs No. 82-350288. **Abstract:** An investigation into the effect of exposure of Al-Zn-Mg alloys to water vapor has shown that H produced by the reaction is absorbed by the alloy. It is proposed that the interaction of stress and environmental variables governs the environmental failure of Al-Zn-Mg alloys in aqueous and water-vapor-containing environments.

R.C. Salvarezza, M.F.L. de Mele, and H.A. Videla, Redox Potential and the Microbiological Corrosion of Aluminium and Its Alloys in Fuel/Water Systems, *Br. Corros. J.*, *16*(3), 162-168, 1981. MetAbs No. 82-350626. **Abstract:** The redox potential, generally employed in microbiological studies, is used to assess whether corrosion conditions can be reached in fuel/water systems.

R.J. Gray, J.C. Griess, R.S. Crouse, and J.H. DeVan, Examination of Aluminum Tubing Pitted in Stagnant Water (Retroactive Coverage), in *Microstructural Science*, Vol 6, Elsevier, New York, 19-20, 1977. MetAbs No. 82-350801. **Abstract:** A demonstration is being conducted to determine the feasibility of an annual cycle energy system as an energy balance system for heating and cooling a house. The initial demonstration involved testing of ½-in.-diam series 1100 Al alloy finned tubing as the basic thermal transfer via a 15% methanol brine solution.

M.O. Speidel, Influence of Environment on Fracture, in *Advances in Fracture Research (Fracture 81)*, Vol 6, Pergamon Press, Oxford, 29, 1982. MetAbs No. 82-351678. **Abstract:** A review of the phenomena and most important influential parameters of environment-assisted subcritical crack growth, particularly stress-corrosion cracking, creep crack, growth and corrosion fatigue is presented.

P. Mauret and P. Lacaze, Water Corrosion Studies of AlMg (5154) and AlCuMg (2024) Aluminium Alloys by Gas Chromatography, *Corros. Sci.*, *22*(4), 321-329, 1982. MetAbs No. 82-351752. **Abstract:** An original method, based on gas chromatography, is used to study the water corrosion of 5154 and 2024 foils. The honeycomb composite structures (i.e., NIDA), widely used in the aircraft industry, can come under strong attack from water corrosion if they are used without protective coating or if the coating is damaged.

W. Chu, Y. Wang, and C. Hsiao, Research of Hydrogen-Induced Cracking and Stress Corrosion Cracking in an Aluminum Alloy, *Corrosion*, *38*(11), 561-570, 1982. MetAbs No. 83-350292. **Abstract:** For a high-strength Al alloy (7075, LC4), the dynamic processes of nucleation and propagation of hydrogen-induced delayed cracking of a charged and modified WOL specimen were followed metallographically.

H. Hirano, N. Aoki, and T. Kurosawa, The Effect of Dissolved Oxygen and NO₃⁻ Anions on the Stress Corrosion Cracking of Type 304 Stainless Steel in Water at 290 °C, *Corrosion*, *39*(8), 313-322, 1983. MetAbs No. 83-352518. **Abstract:** The effect of dissolved oxygen and NO₃⁻ anions on the intergranular stress-corrosion cracking and transgranular stress-corrosion cracking of 304 stainless steel has been studied in water at 290 °C using the constant extension rate test method.

B.C.S. Rao and D.H. Buckley, "Cavitation Pitting and Erosion of Aluminum 6061-T6 in Mineral Oil and Water," NASA Tech. Paper No. 2146, National Aeronautics and Space Administration, 1983. MetAbs No. 83-352529. **Abstract:** Cavitation erosion studies of Al 6061-T6 in mineral oil and in ordinary tap water are presented.

J.B. Lee and R.W. Staehle, Open-Circuit Potential Measurements for Type 304, Alloy 600, Nickel and Platinum in 250 °C Water: The Effect of Chromate and Nitrate Additions, *Corrosion*, *39*(10), 406-408, 1983. MetAbs No. 84-350295. **Abstract:** An investigation of the effect of chromate and nitrate on the open-circuit potentials of Type 304, Alloy 600, Ni and Pt in pressurized water at 250 °C is discussed.

R.A. Page, Stress Corrosion Cracking of Alloys 600 and 690 and No. 82 and 182 Weld Metals in High-Temperature Water, *Corrosion, 39(10),* 409-421, 1983. MetAbs No. 84-350296. **Abstract:** The relative susceptibilities of Alloy 600 and 690 base metals and I-82 and I-182 weld metals to intergranular stress-corrosion cracking in pure water at 288 °C were evaluated.

A.V. Karlashov, A.D. Gnatyouk, and A.B. Kardash, Corrosion Fatigue Strength of Aluminium Alloys, in *Corrosion Fatigue*, The Metals Society, London, 19-22, 1980. MetAbs No. 84-350322. **Abstract:** Studies at the Liev Institute of Civil Aviation on the corrosion-fatigue of the D1T, D16T, D16AT, D16ATV, V95T, V92T, and V93 Al construction alloys in water, NaCl, aircraft condensates, superphosphate hydrates, typical boring solutions, and an argillaceous medium are reported.

J. Hickling, The Effect of Fluid Flow on the Stress Corrosion Cracking of ASTM A508 Cl2 Steel in High-Temperature Water, *Corrosion, 40(1),* 36-38, 1984. MetAbs No. 84-351094. **Abstract:** The effect of fluid flow on the stress-corrosion cracking of ASTM A508 C12 steel in high-temperature water is discussed.

T. Kawakubo and M. Hishida, Crack Initiation and Growth Analysis by Direct Optical Observation During SSRT in High-Temperature Water, *Corrosion, 40(3),* 120-126, 1984. MetAbs No. 84-351482. **Abstract:** The stress-corrosion cracking behavior during the slow strain rate test has been investigated in high-temperature water on center-notched thin plate specimens of sensitized 304 stainless steel.

M.A. Stranick, The Corrosion Inhibition of Metals by Molybdate. I. Mild Steel, *Corrosion, 40(6),* 296-302, 1984. MetAbs No. 84-352378. **Abstract:** The effect of molybdate ion on the corrosion of mild steel (1010) in an aggressive, low-hardness water was investigated electrochemically.

R. Bandy and D. Van Rooyen, Stress Corrosion Cracking of Inconel Alloy 600 in High-Temperature Water—An Update, *Corrosion, 40(8),* 425-430, 1984. MetAbs No. 84-352702. **Abstract:** An experimental program on stress-corrosion cracking aimed at the development of a quantitative model for predicting the behavior of Inconel 600 tubing in high-temperature water is currently underway at Brookhaven National Laboratory.

D.E. Davies and R.M. Prigmore, The Effect of Sodium Fluoride on the Localized Corrosion of Aluminum in Distilled Water and 50% Ethanediol Solution, in *International Congress on Metallic Corrosion*, Vol 4, National Research Council of Canada, Ottawa, 3-7, 1984. MetAbs No. 84-353006. **Abstract:** Aluminum (99.9%) has been potentiostatically polarized in distilled water and in 50% ethanediol in the presence of 100 ppm sodium fluoride.

H.D. Solomon, Transgranular, Granulated and Intergranular Stress Corrosion Cracking in AISI 304 SS, *Corrosion, 40(9),* 493-506, 1984. MetAbs No. 84-353071. **Abstract:** The stress-corrosion cracking observed when slow strain rate tests were run on AISI 304 stainless steel specimens in oxygenated 288 °C water is discussed.

E.A. Loria, Influence of Composition on Continuous Cooling Sensitization of AISI 304 Stainless Steel, *Corrosion, 40(12),* 669-672, 1984. MetAbs No. 85-350471. **Abstract:** A comprehensive study of the effect of carbon content on continuous cooling sensitization found in the literature is discussed.

M.E. Indig and J.E. Weber, Effects of H_2 Additions on Stress Corrosion Cracking in a Boiling Water Reactor, *Corrosion, 41(1),* 19-30, 1985. MetAbs No. 85-350553. **Abstract:** Controlled amounts of hydrogen were injected into the Dresden-2 boiling water reactor during a 5-week period. The effect of the H-modified water chemistry on major structural alloys was studied.

O. Hollander and R.C. May, The Chemistry of Azole Copper Corrosion Inhibitors in Cooling Water, *Corrosion, 41(1),* 39-45, 1985. MetAbs No. 85-350555. **Abstract:** The behavior of benzotriazole and tolyltriazole as effective inhibitors of Cu corrosion in near neutral, low conductivity aqueous media was studied under typical cooling water conditions. Relationships between chemical properties and inhibition behavior are discussed and a modified theory of the mechanism of inhibition is proposed.

F. Mansfeld, M.W. Kendig, and W.J. Lorenz, Corrosion Inhibition in Neutral, Aerated Media, *J. Electrochem. Soc., 132(2),* 290-296, 1985. MetAbs No. 85-350787. **Abstract:** The concepts of interface and interphase inhibition as two different types of corrosion inhibition mechanisms are discussed.

J.R. Keiser and A.R. Olsen, Corrosion Studies in Coal Liquefaction Plants, Corrosion, Microstructure and Metallography, in *Microstructural Science,* Vol 12, American Society for Metals, 173-186, 1985. MetAbs No. 85-350797. **Abstract:** Studies of coal liquefaction pilot plants have revealed chloride and polythionic acid stress-corrosion cracking, waterside pitting, sulfidation, and a chloride-related acid attack of stainless steels and superalloys.

C. Matz, Stability of Adhesive Joints in High-Strength Aluminium Alloys to Aging and Chemical Attack, *Aluminium, 61(2),* 118-121, 1985. MetAbs No. 85-351003. **Abstract:** Climatic influences on the aging behavior of adhesive joints in aircraft can be estimated satisfactorily by simple controlled-climate aging tests. The determination of resistance to chemical attack relates mainly to the effect of water, corrosive aqueous solutions, fuels, and hydraulic liquids on the strength of the adhesive bond.

M.B. Hintz, L.J. Nettleton, and L.A. Heldt, Stress Corrosion Cracking of Alpha-Beta Brass in Distilled Water and Sodium Sulfate Solutions, *Metall. Trans. A, 16A(5),* 971-978, 1985. MetAbs No. 85-351019. **Abstract:** Specimens of a Cu-42 wt% Zn alpha-beta alloy have been tested to failure in uniaxial tension at constant extension rates in a variety of environments.

L. Evans,"A Review of the Materials of Construction for Plant and Equipment Handling Natural Waters," UK National Corrosion Conference 1982, 16-18, 1982. MetAbs No. 85-351221. **Abstract:** Selection of materials for construction and plant equipment depends on the corrosivity of the water that will be handled and the stresses and strains to which the equipment will be subjected. Materials selection is discussed.

G.P. Sheldon and N.W. Polan, Field Testing of Power Utility Condenser Tube Alloys, *J. Mater. Energy Syst., 6(4),* 313-319, 1985. MetAbs No. 85-351443. **Abstract:** The performances of various Cu alloys (C71500, C70600, C19400, C443) after four years exposure in condenser stream-side and cooling water environments of three operating power utility plants are described.

M. Miksch, E. Lenz, and R. Lohberg, Loading Conditions in Horizontal Feedwater Pipes of LWRs Influenced by Thermal Shock and Thermal Stratification Effects, Fracture Prevention and Availability, *Nucl. Eng. Des., 84(2),* 179-187, 1985. MetAbs No. 85-351553. **Abstract:** A study of crack formation in pressurized and boiling water reactors on the internal surfaces of horizontal lengths of feedwater piping upstream of steam generators and reactor pressure vessels is described.

J. Meessen and J.K. Reichert, Influence of NTA on Household Plumbing Piping (Copper, Lead and Hot-Galvanized Steel Pipes), *Environ. Technol. Lett.*, 6(1), 31-36, 1985. MetAbs No. 85-351611. **Abstract:** Experiments have shown that the nitrilotriacetic acid contents in soft potable water lead to significantly increased corrosion of Cu, Pb and hot-galvanized steel pipes in plumbing systems.

R.A. Page, Stress Corrosion of I-182 Weld Metal in High Temperature Water—The Effect of a Carbon Steel Couple, *Corrosion*, 41(6), 338-344, 1985. MetAbs No. 85-351733. **Abstract:** The effect of a carbon steel couple on the stress-corrosion cracking behavior of I-182 weld metal in oxygen-containing pure water at 288 °C was investigated.

B.A. Abd-El-Nabey, N. Khalil, and E. Khamis, The Acid Corrosion of Aluminium in Water—Organic Solvent Mixtures, *Corros. Sci.*, 25(4), 225-232, 1985. MetAbs No. 85-351892. **Abstract:** The corrosion behavior of aluminum metal in water-organic solvent mixtures containing HCl were studied chemically using thermometric, hydrogen evolution and weight loss methods and electrochemically using a Tafel extrapolation method.

T. Kawakubo and M. Hishida, Elastic-Plastic Fracture Mechanics Analysis on Environmentally Accelerated Cracking of Stainless Steel in High Temperature Water, *J. Eng. Mater. Technol. (Trans. ASME)*, 107(3), 240-245, 1985. MetAbs No. 85-352056. **Abstract:** Stress-corrosion crack growth during slow strain rate testing was investigated using elastic-plastic fracture mechanics. Thin compact and center-notched specimens of sensitized Type 304 stainless steel were examined at different extension rates in high-temperature oxygenated water.

C.D.S. Tuck, The Embrittlement of Al-Zn-Mg and Al-Mg Alloys by Water Vapor, *Metall. Trans. A*, 16A(8), 1503-1514, 1985. MetAbs No. 85-352059. **Abstract:** Al-4.5Zn-1.5Mg and Al-5Mg were reacted in water-vapor saturated air at 120 °C and tensile tested.

Y. Ando, Japanese Efforts in Relation to BWR Pipe Cracking, Safety and Reliability of Pressure Components, *Nucl. Eng. Des.*, 87, 239-248, 1985. MetAbs No. 85-352263. **Abstract:** The experiences of pipe cracking, development of remedies and/or countermeasures, examples of their application to the units and the fracture mechanistic research on piping are shown.

N.A. Zreiba and D.O. Northwood, The Corrosion/Hydriding Behavior of Zr-2.5 wt% Nb Nuclear Reactor Pressure Tubing in Pressurized Lithiated Water (pH 12.3) at 300 °C, *J. Mater. Energy Syst.*, 7(2), 104-122, 1985. MetAbs No. 85-352279. **Abstract:** The corrosion/hydriding behavior of Zr-2.5Nb nuclear reactor pressure tubing has been studied in the cold worked and heat treated conditions.

S.P. Lynch, Mechanisms of Stress-Corrosion Cracking and Liquid-Metal Embrittlement in Al-Zn-Mg Bicrystals, *J. Mater. Sci.*, 20(9), 3329-3338, 1985. MetAbs No. 85-352287. **Abstract:** Metallographic and fractographic studies of intercrystalline fracture in high-purity Al-6Zn-3Mg bicrystals in inert, liquid metal, and water environments are described.

R.N. Parkins, C.M. Rangel, and J. Yu, Stress Corrosion Cracking of Alpha-Brass in Waters With and Without Additions, *Metall. Trans. A*, 16A(9), 1671-1681, 1985. MetAbs No. 85-352302. **Abstract:** Slow strain rate stress-corrosion tests on a 0.032% arsenic brass in SO_2 solutions of increasing dilution are discussed.

A. McMinn, F.F. Lyle Jr., and G.R. Leverant, Stress Corrosion Crack Growth in NiCrMoV Turbine Disc Steels, *Corrosion*, 41(9), 493-503, 1985. MetAbs No. 85-352342. **Abstract:** A study was made of the effects of metallurgical and environmental variables on stress-corrosion cracking propagation rates in NiCrMoV turbine disc steels.

W.H. Hocking, F.W. Stanchell, E. McAlpine, and D.H. Lister, Mechanisms of Corrosion of Stellite-6 in Lithiated High Temperature Water, *Corros. Sci.*, 25(7), 531-557, 1985. MetAbs No. 85-352392. **Abstract:** The corrosion of the cobalt-based alloy Stellite-6 in lithiated high-temperature water, simulating a regime of an operating pressurized water reactor coolant circuit, has been investigated using a combination of surface analytical, microscopic and radiotracer techniques.

M. Hishida, J. Takabayashi, T. Kawakubo, and Y. Yamashina, Polarization Curve Measurement in High Purity Water at Elevated Temperatures, *Corrosion*, 41(10), 570-574, 1985. MetAbs No. 86-350064. **Abstract:** A polarization technique in high-purity water at elevated temperature was studied for corrosion research on boiling water reactor materials.

T. Fujii, T. Kodama, and H. Baba, The Influence of Water Quality and Hydraulic Factors on Corrosion of Carbon Steel Pipes in Fresh Water, *Trans. Natl. Res. Inst. Met. (Jpn.)*, 27(2), 125-129, 1985. MetAbs No. 86-350105. **Abstract:** In cold water supply systems, the corrosion of the steel substrate after disappearance of the galvanized layer leads to a "red water" problem and loss of carrying capacity due to tuberculation. In this respect, the corrosion rate measurements for steel pipes were made in cold soft water by using a once-through testing apparatus.

T. Ishihara and S. Ohashi, Combined Effects of Environmental Factors and Cyclic Stress on Intergranular Stress Corrosion Cracking of Sensitized Type 304 Stainless Steel in High Temperature Water, *Trans. Natl. Res. Inst. Met. (Jpn.)*, 27(2), 130-137, 1985. MetAbs No. 86-350106. **Abstract:** The combined effects of time-dependent environmental and stress conditions on intergranular stress-corrosion cracking of sensitized Type 304 stainless steel were studied in high-temperature water.

J.C. Ginocchio, Protection Against Corrosion in Drinking Water Distribution Systems, *Anti-Corros. Methods Mater.*, 32(8), 14-16, 1985. MetAbs No. 86-350136. **Abstract:** Measures to counteract corrosion caused by drinking water in iron pipes belonging to distribution systems of towns and villages are discussed.

H.P. Hermansson and I. Falk, Release Rates of Cobalt From Inconel 718 and X750 in Oxidizing Nuclear Reactor Water Environments, *Scand. J. Metall.*, 14(4), 209-213, 1985. MetAbs No. 86-350189. **Abstract:** The release of alloy constituents and metallic compounds from the surface of structural materials in contact with the water in a reactor system is of considerable importance for the build-up of radioactive surface deposits. Experiments to determine the release rates of metals from structural materials under the various chemical and physical conditions to which they can be subjected in a reactor system are described.

H.M. Shalaby and V.K. Gouda, Effect of Chloride Concentration and pH on Fatigue Crack Initiation Morphology of Type 403 Stainless Steel, *Br. Corros. J.*, 20(3), 125-132, 1985. MetAbs No. 86-350262. **Abstract:** Corrosion fatigue studies have been conducted on martensitic Type 403 turbine blade alloy in air, deaerated distilled water, and deaerated 0.01 and 1M NaCl solutions at pH 2, 7, and 10 at 100 °C.

J. Kuniya, I. Masaoka, R. Sasaki, H. Itoh, and T. Okazaki, Stress Corrosion Cracking Susceptibility of Low Alloy Steels Used for Reactor Pressure Vessel in High Temperature Oxygenated Water, *J. Pressure Vessel Technol. (Trans. ASME)*, 107(4), 430-435, 1985. MetAbs No. 86-350376. **Abstract:** Studies have been done on stress-corrosion cracking susceptibility of low-alloy steels in water containing dissolved oxygen. The effects of applied stress, strain rate, dissolved oxygen concentration, and test temperature on the susceptibility were examined utilizing uniaxial constant load tensile tests, and slow strain rate tests.

R. Bandy and D. Van Rooyen, Mechanisms of Stress Corrosion Cracking and Intergranular Attack in Alloy 600 in High Temperature Caustic and Pure Water, *J. Mater. Energy Syst., 7*(3), 237-245, 1985. MetAbs No. 86-350480. **Abstract:** Several studies have been conducted on the intergranular stress-corrosion cracking and intergranular attack of Alloy 600. A combination of attack has been observed in Alloy 600 tubing on the hot leg of some operating steam generators in pressurized water reactor nuclear power plants, and sodium hydroxide along with several other chemical species have been implicated in the tube degradations.

K. Fujiwara, H. Tomari, and K. Shimogori, Stress Corrosion Cracking Behavior of Weldments of Ferritic Stainless Steels in High Temperature Pure Water, *Trans. Iron Steel Inst. Jpn., 25*(4), 333-339, 1985. MetAbs No. 86-350495. **Abstract:** Considering the application of a ferritic stainless steel as heat exchanger tubing for a moisture separator reheater of light water reactors, stress-corrosion cracking behavior at the weldment of commercial ferritic stainless steels in a high-temperature pure water was studied. The double U-bend method was used for the study and the relationship with microstructure was discussed.

C.L. Briant, C.S. O'Toole, and E.L. Hall, The Effect of Microstructure on the Corrosion and Stress Corrosion Cracking of Alloy 600 in Acidic and Neutral Environments, *Corrosion, 42*(1), 15-27, 1986. MetAbs No. 86-350593. **Abstract:** A study of corrosion and stress-corrosion cracking of Alloy 600 is presented. The primary purpose is to relate the corrosion susceptibility of the alloy after various heat treatments to the microstructure produced by these heat treatments.

C.W. Jewett and A.E. Pickett, The Benefit of Hydrogen Addition to the Boiling Water Reactor Environment on Stress Corrosion Crack Initiation and Growth in Type 304 Stainless Steel, *J. Eng. Mater. Technol. (Trans. ASME), 108*(1), 10-19, 1986. MetAbs No. 86-350624. **Abstract:** Intergranular stress-corrosion cracking in Type 304 stainless steel in high-temperature, high-purity water requires the simultaneous presence of sensitized material, high tensile stress and oxygen. The purpose of this program was to verify the benefit of H additions on the stress-corrosion crack behavior.

J.Y. Park, W.E. Ruther, T.F. Kassner, and W.J. Shack, Stress Corrosion Crack Growth Rates in Type 304 Stainless Steel in Simulated BWR Environments, *J. Eng. Mater. Technol. (Trans. ASME), 108*(1), 20-25, 1986. MetAbs No. 86-350625. **Abstract:** Stress-corrosion cracking of Type 304 stainless steel has been studied with fracture-mechanics-type standard 25.4-mm thick compact tension specimens in simulated boiling-water reactor environments at 289 °C and 8.3 MPa.

D.A. Hale, The Effect of BWR Startup Environments on Crack Growth in Structural Alloys, *J. Eng. Mater. Technol. (Trans. ASME), 108*(1), 44-49, 1986. MetAbs No. 86-350628. **Abstract:** To assess the impact of startup practice on environmental cracking in the structural materials used in the boiling water reactor, a program was performed to evaluate crack growth at representative environmental conditions for both conventional and vacuum deaeration startup practices. Types 304 and 316 nuclear grade stainless steel, Inconel 600, carbon steel, and A508-2 low-alloy steel were studied.

R.M. Horn, Evaluation of Crack Growth in Oxygenated High Temperature Water Using Full Size Pipe Tests, *J. Eng. Mater. Technol. (Trans. ASME), 108*(1), 50-56, 1986. MetAbs No. 86-350629. **Abstract:** Full-size pipe tests have been conducted as part of EPRI research programs at the General Electric Company to verify intergranular stress-corrosion crack growth predictions made using a linear elastic fracture mechanics model. Tests on 304 stainless steel pipe were performed in oxygenated, high-temperature, high-purity water.

G.A.A. van Osch and W.M.M. Huijbregts, Corrosion Potential Measurements in Boiler Water: The Influence of Oxygen Content, *Corrosion, 42*(2), 120-123, 1986. MetAbs No. 86-350815. **Abstract:** The corrosion potentials of AISI 304 stainless steel, Pt, and 17MnMoV64 steel were measured in boiler water.

W.J. Shack, T.F. Kassner, P.S. Maiya, J.Y. Park, and W.E. Ruther, BWR Pipe Crack and Weld Clad Overlay Studies, *Nucl. Eng. Des., 89*(2-3), 295-303, 1985. MetAbs No. 86-350841. **Abstract:** Topics pertaining to the problem of stress-corrosion cracking of piping in boiling water reactors are addressed—the effects of impurities, dissolved oxygen content, and strain rate on susceptibility of "nuclear grade" Type 316NG and sensitized Type 304 stainless steel; finite-element analyses and experimental measurement of residual stresses in weldments with weld overlays; and analysis of field components to assess effectiveness of in-service inspection techniques and the in-reactor performance of weld overlays.

J.T.A. Roberts, R.L. Jones, M. Naughton, and A.J. Machiels, BWR Pipe Crack Control Using Hydrogen Water Chemistry: Status Report on Dresden-2 Program, *Nucl. Eng. Des., 89*(2-3), 505-512, 1985. MetAbs No. 86-350844. **Abstract:** One of the proposed remedies for intergranular stress-corrosion cracking of stainless steel piping in BWRs is an alternative water chemistry called hydrogen water chemistry that involves suppression of reactor water dissolved oxygen via H injection to the feedwater in conjunction with control of conductivity.

S. Narain, Water Management Considerations in Sulfuric Acid Plants Using Anodically Protected Shell and Tube Type Stainless Steel Acid Coolers, *Corros. Maint., 8*(3), 161-169, 1985. MetAbs No. 86-350966. **Abstract:** Metallurgical and water management design considerations are discussed for sulfuric acid production plants with anodically protected shell and tube type stainless steel acid coolers.

G.L. Rajani, Waterside Corrosion and Scaling Problems and Its Control in Industrial Boilers, *Corros. Maint., 8*(3), 195-202, 1985. MetAbs No. 86-350969. **Abstract:** Waterside scaling and corrosion in industrial boilers is influenced by boiler design and type, heat flux, boiler feedwater treatment scheme and operation and monitoring of BFW treatment. The case histories of two boilers that failed due to waterside corrosion and scaling are discussed.

C.J. Thomas, R.G.J. Edyvean, R. Brook, and W.G. Ferguson, Environmentally Assisted Crack Growth in a Martensitic Stainless Steel, *Mater. Sci. Eng., 78*(1), 55-63, 1986. MetAbs No. 86-351021. **Abstract:** The response of a martensitic stainless steel (En56C) to environmental stress cracking as a function of heat treatment has been examined. The as-quenched, 400, 550 and 650 °C temper conditions were studied. The threshold stress intensity for stress-corrosion cracking was determined in dry H_2S gas and the crack growth rate measured in distilled water and in acidified 3.5% NaCl solution at pH 3.

A. Talaat El-Mallah, M.E. Abou Hassan, A.S. Salem, and A. Hossam El-Din, Some Aspects of Corrosion Inhibition of Potable Water, *Corros. Prev. Control, 32*(5), 100-105, 1985. MetAbs No. 86-351102. **Abstract:** Methods of improving potable water and reducing corrosion of water mains are discussed as well as details of corrosion inhibiting reactions.

P.D. Hicks and F.P.A. Robinson, Corrosion Fatigue in Pressurized Water Reactors, *Rev. Coatings Corros., 6*(2), 184-202, 1985. MetAbs No. 86-351106. **Abstract:** The corrosion and stress interactions present in PWRs have led to a large number of tests being carried out in simulated environments. A review of some topics of interest with respect to corrosion fatigue in PWR vessels (A508-3 and A533B-1 steels) is presented.

R.A. Page and A. McMinn, Relative Stress Corrosion Susceptibilities of Alloys 690 and 600 in Simulated Boiling Water Reactor Environments,

Metall. Trans. A, 17A(5), 877-887, 1986. MetAbs No. 86-351112. **Abstract:** The relative susceptibilities of alloys 600 and 690 to intergranular stress-corrosion cracking in pure water and a simulated resin intrusion environment at 288 °C were evaluated.

G.B. Evans, Design Against Corrosion, *Aerospace, 12*(9), 23-28, 31-34, 1985. MetAbs No. 86-351178. **Abstract:** The selection of materials, types of corrosion and measures to counter corrosion are described with reference to aircraft. Fatigue crack growth rates of Al alloys 2024-T3 and 7075-T6 in dry air, wet air, distilled water and 3.5% NaCl solution are given.

G. Hultquist, Hydrogen Evolution in Corrosion of Copper in Pure Water, *Corros. Sci., 26*(2), 173-177, 1986. MetAbs No. 86-351194. **Abstract:** The corrosion of Cu in pure water has been studied.

V.S. Sastri, R. Beauprie, and M. Desgagne, Molybdate as a Pipeline Corrosion Inhibitor for Coal-Water Slurry Systems, *Mater. Perform., 25*(6), 45-47, 1986. MetAbs No. 86-351640. **Abstract:** Wear rates of AISI 1010 steel in coal-water slurries, both in the presence and absence of sodium molybdate, were obtained.

J.G. Stoecker and D.H. Pope, Study of Biological Corrosion in High Temperature Demineralized Water, *Mater. Perform., 25*(6), 51-56, 1986. MetAbs No. 86-351642. **Abstract:** The results of a multi-disciplinary study are presented concerning the localized biological corrosion of AISI 304 stainless steel.

S.C. Dexter, Corrosion in Marine and Natural Waters, in *Encyclopedia of Materials Science and Engineering*, Vol 2, Pergamon Press, Oxford, 880-881, 1986. MetAbs No. 86-351933. **Abstract:** Controlling corrosion on structures in natural waters is becoming increasingly difficult as the search for mineral and fossil-fuel resources is extended further offshore, and as more sophisticated technology demands increasing performance from existing structural materials.

H.P. Goddard, Corrosion of Aluminium Alloys, in *Encyclopedia of Materials Science and Engineering*, Vol 2, Pergamon Press, Oxford, 895, 1986. MetAbs No. 86-351940. **Abstract:** Commercial aluminum (approximately 99.6% Al) and the common alloys (Al-Mn, Al-Mg, Al-Mg-Si) have good corrosion resistance in natural environments—the atmosphere, fresh waters, seawater and most soils unlike Al-Cu and Al-Zn. Methods of increasing corrosion resistance are discussed.

H. Leidheiser, Corrosion of Copper Alloys, in *Encyclopedia of Materials Science and Engineering*, Vol 2, Pergamon Press, Oxford, 895-896, 1986. MetAbs No. 86-351941. **Abstract:** Copper alloys find application under a variety of corrosive conditions. Some of the more important applications are discussed.

R.A.E. Hooper, Corrosion of Iron and Steel, in *Encyclopedia of Materials Science and Engineering*, Vol 2, Pergamon Press, Oxford, 901-904, 1986. MetAbs No. 86-351943. **Abstract:** The main environments to which iron and steel are exposed are the natural media of air, water and soils. The rate of corrosion of unalloyed iron and steel is primarily determined by the aggressivity of the environment; variations in metal composition and microstructure have a much smaller effect.

W.M.M. Huijbregts and P.J.C. Letschert, Deposition of CRUD in BWR Water on Various Steels Exposed in the Dodewaard Nuclear Power Plant, *Kema Sci. Tech. Rep., 4*(2), 15-25, 1986. MetAbs No. 86-352150. **Abstract:** A rack composed of different materials and surface treatments was exposed in the reactor vessel of the GKN boiling-water reactor in Dodewaard for one reactor cycle to study the corrosion residual unidentified deposit (CRUD) deposition.

N. Totsuka, E. Lunarska, G. Cragnolino, and Z. Szklarska-Smialowska, A Sensitive Technique for Evaluating Susceptibility to IGSCC of Alloy 600 in High Temperature Water, *Scr. Metall., 20*(7), 1035-1040, 1986. MetAbs No. 86-352190. **Abstract:** A comparative study was conducted to evaluate the sensitivity of two types of specimens in detecting intergranular stress-corrosion cracking in alloy 600 exposed to high-temperature water.

M. Hishida, M. Saito, K. Hasegawa, K. Enomoto, and Y. Matsuo, Experimental Study on Crack Growth Behavior for Austenitic Stainless Steel in High Temperature Pure Water, *J. Pressure Vessel Technol. (Trans. ASME), 108*(2), 226-233, 1986. MetAbs No. 86-352203. **Abstract:** Crack growth behavior of type 304 stainless steel in a simulated BWR water environment was investigated for the quantitative characterization of subcritical flaw growth in BWR piping systems.

R.C. Newman, W.P. Wong, and A. Garner, A Mechanism of Microbial Pitting in Stainless Steel, *Corrosion, 42*(8), 489-491, 1986. MetAbs No. 86-352261. **Abstract:** The localized corrosion of AISI 304 in newsprint paper machines results from contamination of the white water by thiosulfate ions. Pitting can occur at ionic strengths in the same range as natural fresh water.

J.H. Bulloch and D. Alexander, Corrosion Fatigue Behavior of A508 Class III Steel in a Simulated PWR Water Environment at 325 °C, *Int. J. Pressure Vessels Piping, 24*(4), 283-302, 1986. MetAbs No. 86-352263. **Abstract:** Fatigue crack growth data collected in a simulated PWR environment for A508 Class III steel at 325 °C exhibited agreement with crack growth data recorded for A533B steel at 288 °C.

K. Hattori, M. Tsubota, and T. Okada, Effect of Chloride on the Stress Corrosion Cracking Susceptibility of Inconel X-750 in High-Temperature Water, *Corrosion, 42*(9), 531-532, 1986. MetAbs No. 86-352577. **Abstract:** The stress-corrosion cracking susceptibility of Inconel X-750 and sensitized AISI 304 has been investigated in relation to very low levels of chloride in high-temperature water.

T.R. Weber, M.A. Stranick, and M.S. Vukasovich, Molybdate Corrosion Inhibition in Deaerated and Low-Oxygen Waters, *Corrosion, 42*(9), 542-545, 1986. MetAbs No. 86-352579. **Abstract:** The inhibiting effect of sodium molybdate on mild steel corrosion in deaerated and low-oxygen concentration waters at pH 9.0 and 60 °C was investigated using weight loss and electrochemical test methods.

G. Pallos and G. Wallwork, Inhibitors and Inhibition Mechanisms for Mild Steel in Cooling Water Systems, *Corros. Rev., 6*(3), 237-278, 1985. MetAbs No. 87-350026. **Abstract:** A review of corrosion inhibitors and their mechanism of inhibition, with a discussion of attempts to design more ecologically acceptable inhibitors, is provided.

M. Erve, W. Brettschuh, H. Henzel, H. Sporl, and E. Lenz, Provisions to Prevent Strain-Induced Corrosion Cracking in Ferritic Piping Systems of Boiling Water Reactors, *Nucl. Eng. Des., 96*(2-3), 217-224, 1986. MetAbs No. 87-350119. **Abstract:** Based on failure analyses of 15MnNi63, 15NiCuMoNb5, 20MnMoNi55, and 17MnMoV64 low-alloy steels and evaluations of laboratory test results, system areas are as susceptible to strain-induced corrosion cracking.

S.G. Glover and S. McFiggans, Corrosion in Breweries: Cases, Causes and Cures, *Ind. Corros., 4*(1), 11-12, 1986. MetAbs No. 87-350189. **Abstract:** Evidence is presented of the nature and scale of corrosion in breweries. The replacement of cast iron by stainless steel for water storage vessels and of Cu by austenitic stainless steel for coppers is examined.

J.F. Moresby and M.K. Peck, Protection of a Type 5005 Aluminum Heat Exchanger Using Benzoate Inhibited Cooling Water, *Ind. Corros., 4*(4),

12-13, 1986. MetAbs No. 87-350193. **Abstract:** A heat exchanger of type 5005 aluminum used in heat transfer experiments was cooled by water circulated from a concrete tank. Corrosion resistance is discussed.

J.S. Abel, M.C. Strait, and J. Gilman, Applicability of Pipelocks as a Remedy for Intergranular Stress Corrosion Cracking in BWRs, *Int. J. Pressure Vessels Piping*, 25(1-4), 25-46, 1986. MetAbs No. 87-350335. **Abstract:** Design, analyses and first application of the pipelock as long-term multicycle protection for piping systems in boiling water reactor plants damaged by intergranular stress-corrosion cracking is described.

D.F. Bowers, Aqueous Corrosion of Cast Iron. I., *Mod. Cast.*, 76(11), 37-39, 1986. MetAbs No. 87-350359. **Abstract:** The properties of cast iron that make it a preferred choice for handling clean water and the major form of its corrosion are described.

B.E. Wilde, Influence of Silicon on the Intergranular Stress Corrosion Cracking Resistance of 18Cr-8Ni Base Stainless Steel, *Corrosion*, 42(11), 678-681, 1986. MetAbs No. 87-350382. **Abstract:** AISI 304 stainless steel is known to be susceptible to intergranular stress-corrosion cracking when exposed to certain types of nuclear reactor environments in the sensitized condition. The corrosion performance of Si-modified AISI 304 stainless steel in high-temperature water was investigated.

A. McMinn, Stress Corrosion of High-Chromium Nickel-Base Weld Metals and AISI 316 Nuclear Grade Stainless Steel in Simulated Boiling Water Reactor Environments, *Corrosion*, 42(11), 682-689, 1986. MetAbs No. 87-350383. **Abstract:** The stress-corrosion cracking susceptibility of AISI 316 NG (nuclear grade) stainless steel, which had been welded with three high-Cr Ni-base weld metals (I-72, R-127, and R-135), was investigated by a series of slow strain rate tests.

J. Morley, Corrosion of Steel Foundation Caissons From the Old Redheugh Bridge in Newcastle Upon Tyne, *Br. Corros. J.*, 21(3), 177-183, 1986. MetAbs No. 87-350406. **Abstract:** With particular emphasis on underground exposures because of their relevance to steel foundation structures, the total thickness loss corrosion rates, together with some chemical and metallurgical test results, were obtained from an examination of two old Redheugh Bridge steel foundation caissons recovered after 89 years of service in a tidal section of the River Tyne.

M. Hoshi, E. Tachikawa, and T. Suwa, Crud Behaviors in High Temperature Water. II. Characterization of Corrosion Layer on Type 304 Stainless Steel and Zircaloy-2, *J. Nucl. Sci. Technol. (Jpn.)*, 23(7), 612-621, 1986. MetAbs No. 87-350507. **Abstract:** Sample specimens of type 304 stainless steel and Zircaloy-2 were exposed to the OWL-1 loop water at 280 °C for 23 days. Corrosion data are presented.

R.E. Gold and L. Van Hulle, SCC of Mill Annealed Inconel 600 in Pure and Primary Water Environments and Accelerated SCC of Alloy 600 in 400 °C Superheated Steam, *ATB Metall.*, 26(1-2), 17-21, 1986. MetAbs No. 87-350814. **Abstract:** A study to identify test media that could lead to intergranular stress-corrosion cracking in mill-annealed alloy 600 at rates that significantly exceeded the conventional thermally accelerated pressurized water tests at 360 °C by raising the temperature to 400 °C above the critical point of water into the regime of superheated steam is discussed.

D.R. Diercks and D.L. Smith, Corrosion Behavior of Vanadium-Base Alloys in Pressurized Water at 288 °C, *J. Nucl. Mater.*, 617-621, 1986. MetAbs No. 87-350878. **Abstract:** The aqueous corrosion behavior of two heats each of V-15Cr-5Ti and V-20Ti and of a single heat of VANSTAR-7 was investigated at 288 °C in high-purity pressurized water.

D.F. Bowers, Aqueous Corrosion of Cast Iron. II., *Mod. Cast.*, 76(12), 28-30, 1986. MetAbs No. 87-350911. **Abstract:** Recirculation process water can corrode unalloyed Fe process equipment, pumps, and piping.

The treatment and control of process water to prevent excessive corrosion of cast irons is explored.

Fresh-Water Pitting—Corrosion-Resistant Copper Alloy, *New Materials Developed in Japan*, 431-432, 1986. MetAbs No. 87-350935. **Abstract:** "KS 1263" is a Cu alloy with excellent pitting corrosion resistance that has been developed for fresh-water pipe materials and heat-exchanger materials. Its unique properties are discussed.

T. Okada, S. Hattori, and S. Yamagishi, The Notch Effect on Corrosion—Fatigue Strength of High-Strength Steels, *Bull. Jpn. Soc. Mech. Eng.*, 29(255), 2765-2770, 1986. MetAbs No. 87-350970. **Abstract:** The notch effect on corrosion-fatigue strength was investigated with high-strength steels HT50 and HT80.

S.B. Adeloju and H.C. Hughes, The Corrosion of Copper Pipes in High Chloride-Low Carbonate Main Water, *Corros. Sci.*, 26(10), 851-870, 1986. MetAbs No. 87-351019. **Abstract:** Thermodynamic and electrochemical methods were used to derive fundamental information about the likely corrosion processes of copper pipes in high chloride/low carbonate main water under conditions of varying temperature and solution composition.

M. Akkaya and J.R. Ambrose, An Electrochemical Technique for the Prediction of Long-Term Corrosion Resistance of Copper Plumbing Systems, *Mater. Perform.*, 26(3), 9-13, 1987. MetAbs No. 87-351342. **Abstract:** The Langelier Index, a measurement of the degree of saturation of waters regarding calcium carbonate, is no longer applicable as a universal criterion for predicting the corrosivities of natural and potable waters. A new method, cyclic current reversal voltammetry, is discussed.

A.A. Stein, Predicting Stress Corrosion Cracking of Alloy 600 Steam Generator Tubing in Primary Water, *Corros. Prev. Control*, 33(6), 139-141, 1986. MetAbs No. 87-351370. **Abstract:** The stress-corrosion cracking behavior of alloy 600 steam generator tubing in primary water is analyzed by comparing experimental test data with actual service performance.

K. Asahi, M. Kitamura, E. Ibe, Y. Asakura, and S. Uchida, Characterization of Oxide Films on Stainless Steel Surfaces of Boiling Water Reactor Primary Cooling Systems, *Nucl. Sci. Eng.*, 95(4), 257-265, 1987. MetAbs No. 87-351384. **Abstract:** Oxide films on Type 304 stainless steel and carbon steel exposed to boiling water reactor primary cooling water were analyzed, and mechanisms of corrosion and ^{60}Co accumulation were proposed.

J.F. Gulich, Erosion-Corrosion Rates on Unalloyed Steels in Boiler Feedwater, *Sulzer Tech. Rev.*, 68(4), 19-22, 1986. MetAbs No. 87-351562. **Abstract:** Erosion-corrosion on unalloyed steels in alkalyzed boiler feedwater may be regarded as a dissolution of the thin magnetite layer grown on the surface of the steel. A procedure is described whereby the corrosion rate can be estimated via mass transfer correlations.

L. Tomlinson and C.B. Ashmore, Erosion-Corrosion of Carbon and Low Alloy Steels by Water at 300 °C, *Br. Corros. J.*, 22(1), 45-52, 1987. MetAbs No. 87-351704. **Abstract:** Examination of ferrules used to control the flow of water at 300 °C through individual tubes in an evaporator unit has shown that carbon steels can undergo high rates of erosion-corrosion under these conditions.

J.H. Bulloch, A Brief Review of Corrosion-Fatigue Phenomena in Simulated Pressurized Water-Reactor Environments, *J. S. Afr. Inst. Min. Metall.*, 87(2), 29-39, 1987. MetAbs No. 87-351821. **Abstract:** A review is given of the effects of corrosion fatigue on the low-alloy steel materials used in pressurized water-reactor vessels.

Reducing SC Cracking in Alloy 600, *Mater. Eng. (Cleveland), 43*, 45, 1987. MetAbs No. 87-351847. **Abstract:** The intergranular stress-corrosion cracking susceptibility of Alloy 600 in primary water is discussed.

E. Mattsson, Focus on Copper in Modern Corrosion Research, *Mater. Perform., 26*(4), 9-16, 1987. MetAbs No. 87-351869. **Abstract:** A survey is given of recent developmental work on the corrosion of Cu and its alloys using X-ray photoelectron spectroscopy and the quartz crystal microbalance technique.

C.E. Jaske and A.P. Castillo, Corrosion Fatigue of Cast Suction-Roll Alloys in Simulated Paper-Making Environments, *Mater. Perform., 26*(4), 37-43, 1987. MetAbs No. 87-351871. **Abstract:** Suction rolls in modern paper machines must meet the demands of performing under cyclic loading in increasingly corrosive environments. Methods of evaluating corrosion fatigue behavior in suction-roll shells are discussed.

V.M. Liss, Preventing Corrosion Under Insulation, *Chem. Eng. (NY), 94*(4), 97-98, 100, 1987. MetAbs No. 87-351912. **Abstract:** Three types of corrosion (galvanic, acidic or alkaline, and chloride) are discussed that can occur under insulation. Intruding water is the key problem and care must be taken to prevent water from entering the system.

T. Enjo, T. Kuroda, and Y.M. Yeon, Stress Corrosion Cracking of SUS304 Stainless Steel in High Temperature Water. Effect of Dissolved Oxygen and Strain Rate, *Trans. JWRI, 15*(2), 318-325, 1986. MetAbs No. 87-351913. **Abstract:** This study was made to investigate the effects of dissolved oxygen, strain rate and solution treatment temperature on the stress-corrosion cracking of the sensitized SUS 304 stainless steel.

S.H. Shim and Z. Szklarska-Smialowska, Effect of Fluid Flow on the Stress Corrosion Cracking of AISI 304 Stainless Steel in Pure Water and $0.01N$ Na_2SO_4 Solutions Differing in pH, *Corrosion, 43*(5), 286-290, 1987. MetAbs No. 87-351917. **Abstract:** The effect of fluid flow on stress-corrosion cracking of sensitized AISI 304 stainless steel was studied in air-saturated pure water and in air-saturated acidified and alkaline $0.01M$ Na_2SO_4 solutions under open circuit conditions at 250 °C, using slow strain rate tensile tests.

R.K. Fuller and J.W. McCarthy, Recovery From Low pH Excursions in Cooling Water Systems Using All-Organic Treatment, *Mater. Perform., 26*(5), 11-16, 1987. MetAbs No. 87-351952. **Abstract:** Detailed procedures are given for repassivation of systems using all-organic corrosion inhibitors to minimize fouling, recovery time, and corrosion in an open recirculating cooling water system.

M.J. Esmacher, Stress-Enhanced Corrosion of Boiler Tubing, *Mater. Perform., 26*(5), 17-20, 1987. MetAbs No. 87-351953. **Abstract:** Five case histories are presented on the effect of residual stresses (from fabrication or welding) on the waterside corrosion performance of carbon steel boiler tubing.

D. Thierry, Field Observations of Microbiologically Induced Corrosion in Cooling Water Systems, *Mater. Perform., 26*(5), 35-41, 1987. MetAbs No. 87-351955. **Abstract:** Microbial corrosion has been studied by means of corrosion monitoring techniques in three different cooling water systems. Results were obtained with polarization and electrical resistance and weight loss measurements and are discussed in view of monitoring microbial corrosion.

T. Fujii, T. Kodama, and H. Baba, Application of Electrochemical Techniques to the Study of Pitting Corrosion of Copper Tube in Fresh Water, *Mater. Sci. Forum, 8*, 125-131, 1986. MetAbs No. 87-352150. **Abstract:** The results of monitoring electrode potential of copper tubes in cold and hot soft water are discussed to evaluate pitting of copper tube.

N. Totsuka, E. Lunarska, G. Cragnolino, and Z. Szklarska-Smialowska, Effect of Hydrogen on the Intergranular Stress Corrosion Cracking of Alloy 600 in High Temperature Aqueous Environments, *Corrosion, 43*(8), 505-514, 1987. MetAbs No. 87-352847. **Abstract:** Slow strain rate tests on differently shaped tensile specimens machined from two heats of Alloy 600 tubing were conducted at 350 °C in deaerated aqueous solutions containing small amounts of lithium hydroxide and boric acid at different partial pressures of hydrogen, using a recirculating autoclave system.

W.J. Tomlinson, F.T. Moule, and G.N. Blount, Cavitation Erosion of a Nitrided Steel in Salt Water and Emulsion, *J. Mater. Sci. Lett., 6*(8), 877-878, 1987. MetAbs No. 87-352851. **Abstract:** An investigation was made of cavitation erosion of a nitrided steel (Fe-0.3C-0.45Mn-3Cr-0.3Ni-0.4Mo) in distilled water, water containing 1.0% NaCl and a 5% emulsion containing 1.0% NaCl. The erosion damage as a function of time was shown for the three erosion fluids.

T. Honda, K. Ohashi, Y. Furutani, and A. Minato, Suppression of Radiation Buildup on Stainless Steel in a Boiling Water Reactor, *Corrosion, 43*(9), 564-570, 1987. MetAbs No. 88-350054. **Abstract:** Deposition of radioactive corrosion products, such as Co-60, causes radiation field buildup in boiling water reactors plants. Deposition kinetics of Co-60 and elemental cobalt ions on stainless steels (AISI 304) and the effects of pre-oxidation on the suppression were evaluated in actual reactor water and laboratory autoclaves.

K. Ogino, A. Hida, and S. Kishima, Effects of pH on Cavitation Corrosion of Medium Carbon Steel in Distilled Water and Sodium Chloride Solutions, *Corrosion, 43*(11), 652-655, 1987. MetAbs No. 88-350469. **Abstract:** Effects of pH on cavitation corrosion of 0.23% carbon steel in distilled water and in 3 to 20% NaCl solutions were investigated.

G.I. Ogundele and W.E. White, Observations on the Influences of Dissolved Hydrocarbon Gases and Variable Water Chemistries on Corrosion of an API-L80 Steel, *Corrosion, 43*(11), 665-673, 1987. MetAbs No. 88-350472. **Abstract:** Accelerated electrochemical techniques were used to study the corrosion of API-5A-L80 and 4340 steels in laboratory-simulated aqueous environments representing typical waters from natural gas production wells.

J. Kuniya, I. Masaoka, and R. Sasaki, Effect of Cold Work on the Stress Corrosion Cracking of Nonsensitized AISI 304 Stainless Steel in High-Temperature Oxygenated Water, *Corrosion, 44*(1), 21-28, 1988. MetAbs No. 88-350926. **Abstract:** The effect of cold work on the stress-corrosion cracking of solution-annealed (nonsensitized) AISI 304 stainless steel in 288 °C oxygenated pure water was studied using creviced bent beam tests.

L.G. Ljungberg, D. Cubicciotti, and M. Trolle, Effects of Impurities on the IGSCC of Stainless Steel in High-Temperature Water, *Corrosion, 44*(2), 66-72, 1988. MetAbs No. 88-351083. **Abstract:** The effects of dissolved impurities in simulated boiler water reactor water on the intergranular stress-corrosion cracking of sensitized 304 stainless steels were studied by constant elongation rate tensile tests with notched specimens.

M. Tsubota, K. Hattori, and T. Kaneko, Study on SCC Susceptibility of Inconel X-750 in High-Temperature Pure Water: Effects of Aging Temperature and Time, *Corrosion, 44*(2), 73-78, 1988. MetAbs No. 88-351084. **Abstract:** The stress-corrosion cracking behavior of Inconel X-750 in high-temperature water has been examined in relation to aging conditions.

N. Totsuka and Z. Szklarska-Smialowska, Hydrogen Induced IGSCC of Two Unsensitized Austenitic Stainless Steels in High-Temperature

Water, *Corrosion*, 44(2), 124-126, 1988. MetAbs No. 88-351090. **Abstract:** The results of preliminary experiments undertaken to check whether face-centered cubic materials, namely unsensitized stainless steels, suffer intergranular stress-corrosion cracking on exposure to aqueous environments at high temperature are reported.

F.E. Goodwin, Corrosion Resistance of Lead Alloys Under Nuclear Waste Repository Conditions, *Corros. Prev. Control*, 32(2), 21-24, 1985. MetAbs No. 85-351789. **Abstract:** Corrosion characteristics of lead and lead alloys that are relevant to the use of lead in deep geologic radioactive waste disposal applications are discussed.

J.C. Ginocchio, Protection Against Corrosion in Drinking Water Distribution Systems, *Anti-Corros. Methods Mater.*, 32(8), 14-16, 1985. MetAbs No. 86-350136. **Abstract:** It has been established that the internal corrosion of iron pipes belonging to distribution systems of towns and villages is attributable to a variety of factors. These variables are discussed.

R.S. Glass, G.E. Overturf, R.A. Van Konynenburg, and R.D. McCright, Gamma Radiation Effects on Corrosion. I. Electrochemical Mechanisms for the Aqueous Corrosion Processes of Austenitic Stainless Steels Relevant to Nuclear Waste Disposal in Tuff, *Corros. Sci.*, 26(8), 577-590, 1986. MetAbs No. 87-350211. **Abstract:** The effects of gamma irradiation on the corrosion mechanisms of 304L and 316L stainless steels in groundwater from a proposed nuclear waste repository site in tuffaceous rock are presented. The electrochemical mechanisms involved in the corrosion potential shifts, as well as the subsequent effect on pitting resistance, are considered.

N.C. Subramanyam and S.M. Mayanna, Azoles as Corrosion Inhibitors for Mild Steel in Alkaline Mine Water, *Corros. Sci.*, 25(3), 163-169, 1985. MetAbs No. 85-351834. **Abstract:** The corrosion of mild steel in alkaline mine water containing various concentrations of benzotriazole, benzimidazole and imidazole has been studied by weight loss and polarization techniques at 303 K.

Corrosion Behavior of Various Metals and Alloys in Water

Material	Condition, other factors, comments	Concentration, %	Temperature, °C (°F)	Duration	Corrosion rate, mm/yr (mils/yr) or other	Ref
Irons and steels						
Carbon steel	Clean Mississippi water	...	...	...	0.2-0.3 mil/month	179
Carbon steel	Polluted Monongahela water	...	...	...	0.2-0.5 mil/month	179
Carbon steel	Natural hard water	...	...	...	0.5 mil/month	179
MF-1 carbon steel	Clean Mississippi water	...	...	...	0.008 mil/month	179
MF-1 carbon steel	Polluted Monongahela water	...	...	...	0.008 mil/month	179
MF-1 carbon steel	Natural hard water	...	...	...	Negligible	179
Stainless steels						
Type 410 stainless steel	Mine water	...	Room	...	Unattacked	121
Type 410 stainless steel	Seawater	...	Room	...	Attacked	121
Type 410 stainless steel	...	...	Room	...	Unattacked	121
Aluminum						
Aluminum (>99.5%)	Fresh tap water	...	...	...	Satisfactory	92
Coppers						
70-30 cupronickel	Potable	...	...	...	Suitable	93
70-30 cupronickel	Carbonated. (a)	...	...	...	Good	93
90-10 cupronickel	Carbonated. (a)	...	...	...	Good	93
90-10 cupronickel	Potable	...	...	...	Suitable	93
Admiralty brass	Carbonated. (a)	...	...	...	Good	93
Admiralty brass	Potable	...	...	...	Suitable	93
Aluminum bronze	Carbonated. (a)	...	...	...	Good	93
Aluminum bronze	Potable	...	...	...	Suitable	93
Ampco 8, aluminum bronze	Fresh. Generally suitable	...	...	...	<0.05 (<2)	96
Ampco 8, aluminum bronze	Salt (includes polluted harbor). Generally suitable	...	...	...	<0.05 (<2)	96
Architectural bronze	Carbonated	...	...	...	Fair	93
Architectural bronze	Potable	...	...	...	Fair	93
Brass	Carbonated. (a)	...	...	...	Good	93
Brass	Potable	...	...	...	Suitable	93
Cartridge brass	Carbonated	...	...	...	Fair	93
Cartridge brass	Potable	...	...	...	Fair	93
Commercial bronze	Carbonated. (a)	...	...	...	Good	93
Commercial bronze	Potable	...	...	...	Suitable	93
Electrolytic copper	Carbonated. (a)	...	...	...	Good	93
Electrolytic copper	Potable	...	...	...	Suitable	93

(Continued)

Corrosion Behavior of Various Metals and Alloys in Water (Continued)

Material	Condition, other factors, comments	Concentration, %	Temperature, °C (°F)	Duration	Corrosion rate, mm/yr (mils/yr) or other	Ref
Free-cutting brass	Carbonated	...	...	...	Fair	93
Free-cutting brass	Potable	...	...	...	Fair	93
Muntz metal	Carbonated	...	...	...	Fair	93
Muntz metal	Potable	...	...	...	Fair	93
Naval brass	Carbonated	...	...	...	Fair	93
Naval brass	Potable	...	...	...	Fair	93
Nickel silver	Carbonated. (a)	18	...	...	Good	93
Nickel silver	Potable	18	...	...	Suitable	93
Phosphor bronze	5% Sn. Carbonated. (a)	...	...	...	Good	93
Phosphor bronze	8% Sn. Carbonated. (a)	...	...	...	Good	93
Phosphor bronze	5% Sn. Potable	...	...	...	Suitable	93
Phosphor bronze	8% Sn. Potable	...	...	...	Suitable	93
Phosphor copper	Potable	...	...	...	Suitable	93
Phosphor copper	Carbonated. (a)	...	...	...	Good	93
Red brass	Carbonated. (a)	...	...	...	Good	93
Red brass	Potable	...	...	...	Suitable	93
Silicon bronze	Low. Carbonated. (a)	...	...	...	Good	93
Silicon bronze	High. Carbonated. (a)	...	...	...	Good	93
Silicon bronze	Low. Potable	...	...	...	Suitable	93
Silicon bronze	High. Potable	...	...	...	Suitable	93
Titanium						
Ti-3Al-2.5V	Seawater, ASTM Grade 9	...	Boiling	...	nil	91
Titanium	Seawater	...	Boiling	...	nil	91
Titanium	Degassed	...	316 (601)	...	nil	90
Titanium	River. Saturated with Cl	...	93 (200)	...	nil	90
Titanium	Chlorine saturated	...	75 (165)	...	0.003 (0.12)	27
Titanium	Welded sample. Chlorine saturated	...	88 (190)	...	0.002 (0.08)	27
Titanium	Chlorine saturated	...	97 (207)	...	0.07 (2.8)	27
Titanium	Chlorine saturated	Saturated	97 (207)	...	nil	90
Lead, tin, and zinc						
Chemical lead	Mine water: pH 8.3, 110 ppm hardness, aerated with slow agitation	...	20 (68)	...	0.007 (0.26)	13
Chemical lead	Mine water: 160 ppm hardness, aerated with slow agitation	...	19 (67)	...	0.007 (0.28)	13
Chemical lead	Mine water: 110 ppm hardness, aerated with slow agitation	...	22 (72)	...	0.006 (0.25)	13
Chemical lead	Cooling tower water, oxygenated, from Lake Erie; complete aeration; no agitation	...	16-29 (60-85)	...	0.134 (5.3)	13
Chemical lead	Los Angeles aqueduct water, treated with Cl and $CuSO_4$; 150 mm/s (0.5 ft/s) agitation	...	Ambient	...	0.009 (0.38)	13
Chemical lead	Spray cooling water, chromate treated, aerated	...	16 (60)	...	0.009 (0.37)	13
Chemical lead	Condensed steam. Traces of acid. No aeration. Slow agitation	...	21-38 (70-100)	...	0.85 mils/yr	178
Chemical lead	Mine water: pH 8.3, 110 ppm hardness. Aerated. Slow agitation	...	20 (68)	...	0.26 mils/yr	178
Chemical lead	Mine water: 160 ppm hardness. Aerated. Slow agitation	...	19 (67)	...	0.28 mils/yr	178
Chemical lead	Mine water: 110 ppm hardness. Aerated. Slow agitation	...	22 (72)	...	0.25 mils/yr	178
Chemical lead	Cooling tower, oxygenated Lake Erie water. Complete aeration. No agitation	...	16-29 (60-85)	...	5.3 mils/yr	178
Chemical lead	Los Angeles aqueduct water, treated with Cl and $CuSO_4$; Agitation, 0.5 ft/s	...	Ambient	...	0.38 mils/yr	178
Chemical lead	Spray cooling water, chromate treated. Aerated	...	16 (60)	...	0.37 mils/yr	178
Tin	Distilled	...	20 (68)	...	Resistant	94
Tin	Distilled	...	60 (140)	...	Resistant	94
Tin	Distilled	...	100 (212)	...	Resistant	94
Tin	Soft	...	20 (68)	...	Resistant	94
Tin	Soft	...	60 (140)	...	Resistant	94

(Continued)

Corrosion Behavior of Various Metals and Alloys in Water (Continued)

Material	Condition, other factors, comments	Concentration, %	Temperature, °C (°F)	Duration	Corrosion rate, mm/yr (mils/yr) or other	Ref
Tin	Soft	...	100 (212)	...	Resistant	94
Tin	Hard. Pitting possible in stagnant solutions	...	20 (68)	...	Resistant	94
Tin	Hard	...	60 (140)	...	Resistant	94
Tin	Hard	...	100 (212)	...	Resistant	94
Zinc	Appearance of corrosion film: gelatinous, very adherent. (b)	...	20 (68)	15 d	0.019 (0.78)	177
Zinc	Appearance of corrosion film: less gelatinous, adherent. (b)	...	50 (122)	15 d	0.069 (2.74)	177
Zinc	Appearance of corrosion film: mostly granular, nonadherent. (b)	...	55 (131)	15 d	0.386 (15.2)	177
Zinc	Appearance of corrosion film: granular to flaky, nonadherent. (b)	...	65 (149)	15 d	2.9 (115.4)	177
Zinc	Appearance of corrosion film: granular, flaky, nonadherent. (b)	...	75 (167)	15 d	2.33 (92)	177
Zinc	Appearance of corrosion film: compact, dense, nonadherent. (b)	...	95 (203)	15 d	0.297 (11.7)	177
Zinc	Appearance of corrosion film: very dense and adherent. (b)	...	100 (212)	15 d	0.119 (4.7)	177
Zinc	Cast, 99.97%. Conductivity 3.8 x 10^{-6} mho. Distilled water, quiet	...	...	3 d	0.279 (11)	177
Zinc	Cast, 99.97%. Conductivity 3.8 x 10^{-6} mho. Distilled water, quiet	...	...	1 d	0.386 (15.2)	177
Zinc	Cast, 99.97%. Conductivity 3.8 x 10^{-6} mho. Distilled water, air bubbled through	...	...	1 d	0.929 (36.6)	177
Zinc	Cast, 99.97%. Distilled water, CO_2 bubbled through	...	...	1 d	0.726 (28.6)	177
Zinc	Cast, 99.97%. Distilled water, air washed in KOH bubbled through	...	...	1 d	0.167 (6.6)	177
Zinc	Cast, 99.97%. Distilled water, solution rotated	...	...	1 d	1.0 (39.4)	177
Zinc	Cast, 99.97%. Conductivity water atmosphere free from carbon dioxide	...	...	1 d	0.101 (4.0)	177
Zinc	Distilled water, quiet	...	...	30 d	0.121 (4.8)	177
Zinc	Distilled water, specimen rotated	...	...	30 d	0.162 (6.4)	177
Zinc	Distilled water, aerated	...	...	30 d	0.127 (5)	177
Zinc	Distilled water, aerated. Specimen rotated 6 rpm	...	...	30 d	0.119 (4.7)	177
Zinc	Various grades. 99.99% rolled and cast zinc, also with up to 0.1% lead and galvanized steel. No effect due to composition. Plus 0.6 ppm free CO_2. Conductivity water: <0.1 x 10^{-6} mho	...	...	56 d	0.264 (10.4)	177
Zinc	Various grades. 99.99% rolled and cast zinc, also with up to 0.1% lead and galvanized steel. No effect due to composition. Conductivity water. Plus 0.8 ppm free CO_2	...	...	56 d	0.254 (10)	177
Zinc	Various grades. 99.99% rolled and cast zinc, also with up to 0.1% lead and galvanized steel. No effect due to composition. Conductivity water. Plus 8.0 ppm free CO_2	...	...	56 d	0.309 (12.2)	177
Zinc	Various grades. Electrolytic 99.98% zinc and refined zinc containing 1% lead. Conductivity water. Plus 36 ppm free CO_2	...	...	56 d	0.944 (37.2)	177
Zinc	Several grades. Electrolytic 99.98% zinc and refined zinc containing 1% lead. Distilled water	...	...	20 d	0.106 (4.2)	177
Zinc	Several grades. Electrolytic 99.98% zinc and refined zinc containing 1% lead. Distilled water	...	...	60 d	0.073 (2.9)	177
Zinc	Several grades. Electrolytic 99.98% zinc and refined zinc containing 1% lead. Distilled water. Plus 0.6 mg/L CO_2	...	...	10 d	0.081 (3.2)	177
Zinc	Several grades. Electrolytic 99.98% zinc and refined zinc containing 1% lead. Distilled water. Plus 0.6 mg/L CO_2	...	...	30 d	0.066 (2.6)	177
Zinc	Several grades. Electrolytic 99.98% zinc and refined zinc containing 1% lead. Distilled water. Plus 27 mg/L CO_2	...	...	30 d	0.038 (1.5)	177
Zinc	Several grades. Electrolytic 99.98% zinc and refined zinc containing 1% lead. Distilled water. Plus 34 mg/L CO_2	...	...	10 d	0.021 (0.84)	177

(Continued)

Corrosion Behavior of Various Metals and Alloys in Water (Continued)

Material	Condition, other factors, comments	Concen-tration, %	Temperature, °C (°F)	Duration	Corrosion rate, mm/yr (mils/yr) or other	Ref
Zinc	Several grades. Electrolytic 99.98% zinc and refined zinc containing 1% lead. Distilled water. Plus 34 mg/L CO_2	...	...	30 d	0.008 (0.33)	177
Zinc	Several grades. Electrolytic 99.98% zinc and refined zinc containing 1% lead. Distilled water. Plus 162 mg/L CO_2	...	...	10 d	0.026 (1.04)	177
Zinc	Several grades. Electrolytic 99.98% zinc and refined zinc containing 1% lead. Distilled water. Plus 162 mg/L CO_2	...	...	30 d	0.009 (0.39)	177
Tantalum and hafnium						
Tantalum	Chlorine saturated	...	25 (76)	...	nil	42
Tantalum	Oxalic acid	...	21 (70)	...	nil	42
Tantalum	Oxalic acid	...	96 (205)	...	0.00254 (0.1)	42
Others						
Cobalt	Static. Distilled	...	25 (77)	...	0.005 (0.2)	54
Magnesium	...	100	Boiling	...	Unsuitable	119
Magnesium	Distilled	100	Room	...	Suitable	119
Magnesium	Rain	100	Room	...	Suitable	119

(a) May be considered in place of a copper metal when some property, other than corrosion resistance, governs its use. (b) Rolled high-grade zinc. Immersed in distilled water aerated by air bubbles.

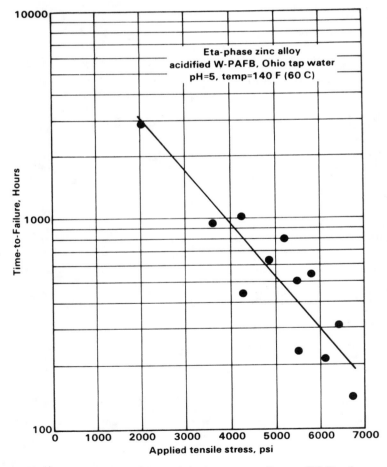

Zinc. Stress vs. time to failure of zinc in tap water. Source: C.J. Slunder and W.K. Boyd, *Zinc: Its Corrosion Resistance*, 2nd ed., T.K. Christman and J. Payer, Ed., International Lead Zinc Research Organization, New York, 1983, 153.

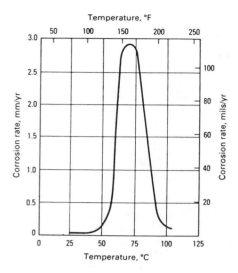

Zinc. Effect of temperature on corrosion of zinc in distilled water. Source: H. Grubitsch and O. Illi, The Hot Water Corrosion of Zinc II, *Korrosion Metall.*, Vol 16, 1940, 197.

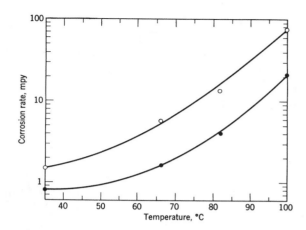

Magnesium. Corrosion rate of magnesium alloys in distilled water as a function of temperature. Circle: M1A alloy. Square: AZ61A alloy. Source: H.P. Godard, M.R. Bothwell, *et al.*, *The Corrosion of Light Metals*, John Wiley & Sons, New York, 1967, 284.

	Corrosion rate (mpy)	
Alloy	100°C[a]	150°C[b]
Pure magnesium	640	–
Ferrosilicon magnesium		Destroyed
A3A[c]	38	Destroyed
AZ31*B*	17	1200
AZ91	–	1100
AZ92*A*	14	–
HK31*A*	11	–
HZ31*A*	–	440
ZK60*A*	1000	–
M1A	78	2400

[a] 14 days stagnant immersion.
[b] 1.7 to 5.0 days stagnant immersion.
[c] A special-purity magnesium–3% aluminum alloy for nuclear applications.

Magnesium. Corrosion of magnesium alloys in hot deionized water. Source: H.P. Godard, M.R. Bothwell, *et al.*, *The Corrosion of Light Metals*, John Wiley & Sons, New York, 1967, 284.

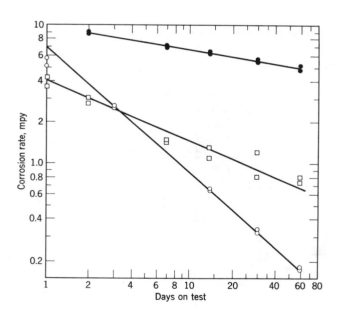

Magnesium. Corrosion rate as a function of time in distilled water (area of solution surface and test coupon surface are about equal). Closed circle: pure magnesium in distilled water vented to air through a caustic trap. Open circle: pure magnesium. Square: AZ92A-T6 alloy in distilled water exposed to atmospheric carbon dioxide. Source: H.P. Godard and M.R. Bothwell, *et al.*, *The Corrosion of Light Metals*, John Wiley & Sons, New York, 1967, 283.

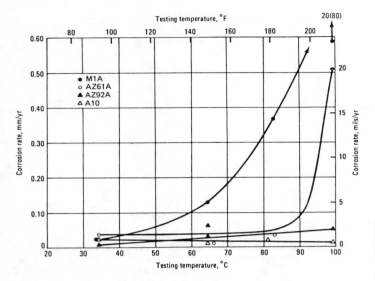

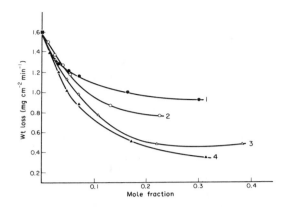

Magnesium. Effects of temperature on corrosion rates of magnesium alloys M1A, AZ61A, AZ92A, and A10 in tap water. Source: *Metals Handbook*, 9th ed., Vol 2, Properties and Selection: Nonferrous Alloys and Pure Metals, American Society for Metals, Metals Park, OH, 1979, 602.

Aluminum. Relationship between the weight loss of aluminum strip in 2M water and the mole fraction of the organic solvent in the medium. (1) Water-ethanol, (2) water-isopropanol, (3) water-methanol, (4) water-ethylene glycol. Composition: 99.5Al-0.22Si-0.16Fe. Source: B.A. Abd-El-Nabey, N. Khalil, *et al.,* "The Acid Corrosion of Aluminium in Water-Organic Solvent Mixtures," *Corrosion Science,* Vol 25, 1985, 229.

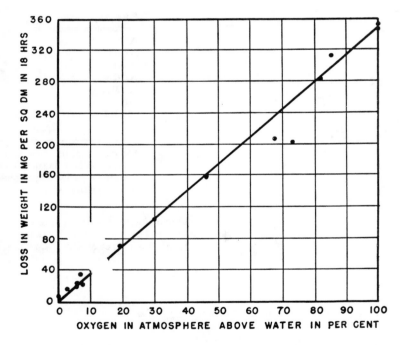

Lead. Effect of oxygen on corrosion of lead submerged in distilled water at 25 °C. Source: G.O. Hiers, "Lead and Lead Alloys," in *The Corrosion Handbook*, H.H. Uhlig, Ed., John Wiley & Sons, New York, 1948, 210.

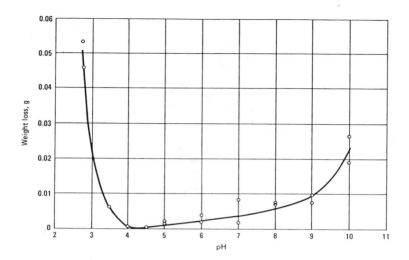

Aluminum. Weight loss of alloy 3004-H14 exposed 1 week in distilled water and in solutions of various pH values. Specimens were 1.6 x 13 x 75 mm (0.06 x 0.5 x 3 in.). The pH values of solutions were adjusted with HCl and NaOH. Test temperature was 60 °C (140 °F). Source: *Metals Handbook*, 9th ed., Vol 2, Properties Selection: Nonferrous Alloys and Pure Metals, American Society for Metals, Metals Park, OH 1979, 205.

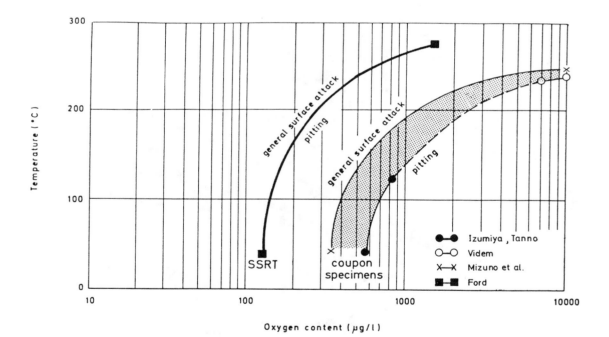

Low-alloy steels. Effect of oxygen content and temperature on pitting of unalloyed and low-alloy steels in stagnant BWR-quality water. Source: J. Hickling, "Strain-Induced Corrosion Cracking of Low-Alloy Steels in LWR Systems: Case Histories and Identification of Conditions Leading to Susceptibility," *Nuclear Engineering and Design*, Vol 91, Feb 1986, 329.

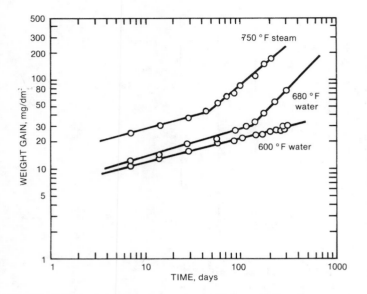

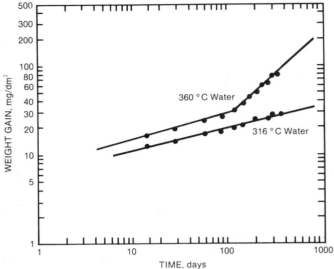

Zirconium. Corrosion behavior of Zircaloy-2 in high-temperature water and steam. Source: Stanley Kass, The Development of the Zircaloys, in *Corrosion of Zirconium Alloys* (STP 368), ASTM, Philadelphia, 1964, 15.

Zirconium. Corrosion behavior of Zircaloy-4 in water. Source: *ASTM Manual on Zirconium and Hafnium* (STP 639), J.H. Schemel, Ed., ASTM, Philadelphia, 1977, 24.

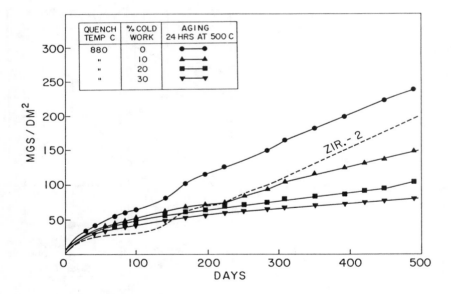

Zirconium. Effect of cold work and aging time on corrosion of 2.5Nb zirconium in water at 360 °C, 2750 psig. Source: J.E. LeSurf, "The Corrosion Behavior of 2.5Nb Zirconium Alloy," in *Applications-Related Phenomena in Zirconium and Zirconium Alloys* (STP 458), ASTM, Philadelphia, 1969, 291.

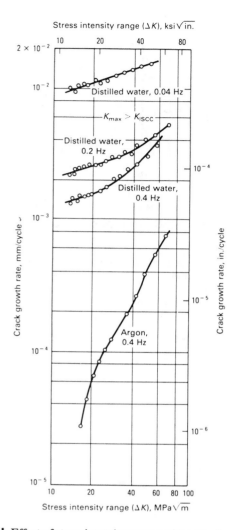

4340 steel. Effect of stress intensity range and loading frequency on corrosion fatigue crack growth in ultrahigh-strength 4340 steel exposed to distilled water at 23 °C (73 °F). Source: C.S. Kortovich, Corrosion Fatigue of 4340 and D6AC Steels Below K$_{ISCC}$, in *Proceedings of the 1974 Triservice Conference on Corrosion of Military Equipment*, AFML-TR-75-42, Air Force Materials Laboratory, Wright-Patterson Air Force Base, 1975.

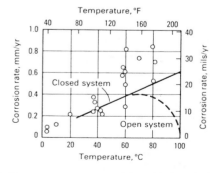

Steel. Effect of temperature on corrosion of steel in water. Data points are from actual plant measurements of corrosion under insulation. Source: *Metals Handbook*, 9th ed., Vol 13, Corrosion, ASM International, Metals Park, OH, 1987, 1145.

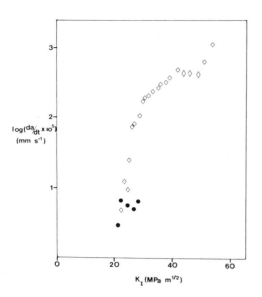

Stainless steel. Variation in crack velocity with the stress intensity factor for En56C (AISI 420) martensitic stainless steel tempered at 400 °C. Tested in water (diamond) and in NACE solution (closed circle). Source: C.J. Thomas, R.G.J. Edyvean, *et al.*, "Environmentally Assisted Crack Growth in a Martensitic Stainless Steel," *Materials Science and Engineering*, Vol 78, Feb 1986, 58.

GASEOUS AND AQUEOUS CORROSION

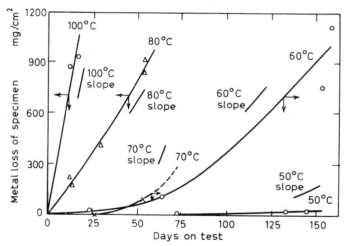

Uranium. Corrosion of standard uranium in aerated distilled water. Source: J.H. Gittus, *Uranium*, Butterworths, Washington, 1963, 406.

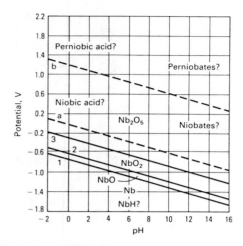

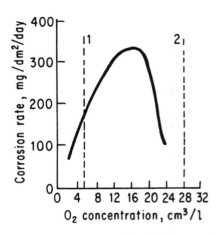

Niobium. Pourbaix (potential-pH) diagram for niobium in water at 25 °C (75 °F). Source: M. Pourbaix, *Atlas of Electrochemical Equilibria in Aqueous Solutions*, Pergamon Press, New York, 1966.

Iron. Effect of oxygen concentration in distilled water (pH 7) on the corrosion rate of iron at 25 °C. The dashed lines show the oxygen content of water upon contact with air (1) and with pure oxygen (2). Source: N.D. Tomashov, *Theory of Corrosion and Protection of Metals*, B. Tytell, I. Geld, *et al.*, Ed., The McMillan Co., New York, 1966, 505.

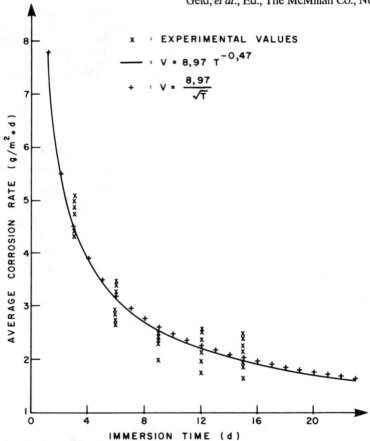

Cast iron. Average corrosion rate of cast iron as a function of immersion time and in the presence of chlorides and nitrates. $(Cl^-) = 157$ mg/L; $(NO_3^-) = 199.0$ mg/L. Source: D.L. Piron and R. Desjardins, "Corrosion Rate of Cast Iron and Copper Pipe by Drinking Water," in *Corrosion Monitoring in Industrial Plants Using Nondestructive Testing and Electrochemical Methods* (STP 908), G.C. Moran and P. Labine, Ed., ASTM, Philadelphia, 1986, 364.

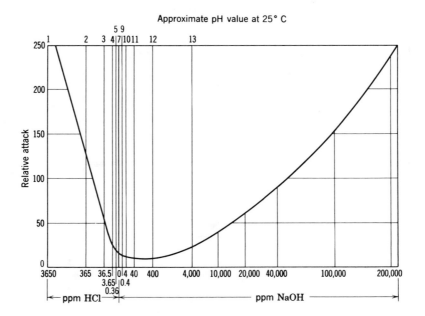

Iron. Corrosion of iron by water at 310 °C (590 °F) at various pH values measured at 25 °C. Source: H.H. Uhlig and R.W. Revie, *Corrosion and Corrosion Engineering: An Introduction to Corrosion Science and Engineering,* 3rd ed., John Wiley & Sons, New York, 1985.

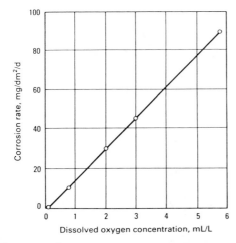

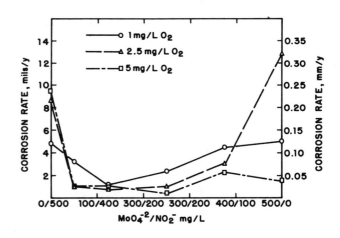

Low-carbon steel. Effect of oxygen concentration on the corrosion of low-carbon steel in slowly moving water containing 165 ppm calcium chloride. The 48-h test was conducted at 25 °C (75 °F). Source: H.H. Uhlig and R.W. Revie, *Corrosion and Corrosion Control,* 3rd ed., Wiley Interscience, New York, 1985, 108.

Carbon steel. Corrosion rate of SAE 1010 steel in 60 °C test water of pH 9 inhibited with MoO_4^{-2}/NO_2^- combinations in the presence of 0, 1, 2.5, and 5 mg/L oxygen. Source: T.R. Weber, M.A. Stranick, *et al.,* "Molybdate Corrosion Inhibition in Deaerated and Low-Oxygen Waters," *Corrosion,* Vol 42, Sept 1986, 543.

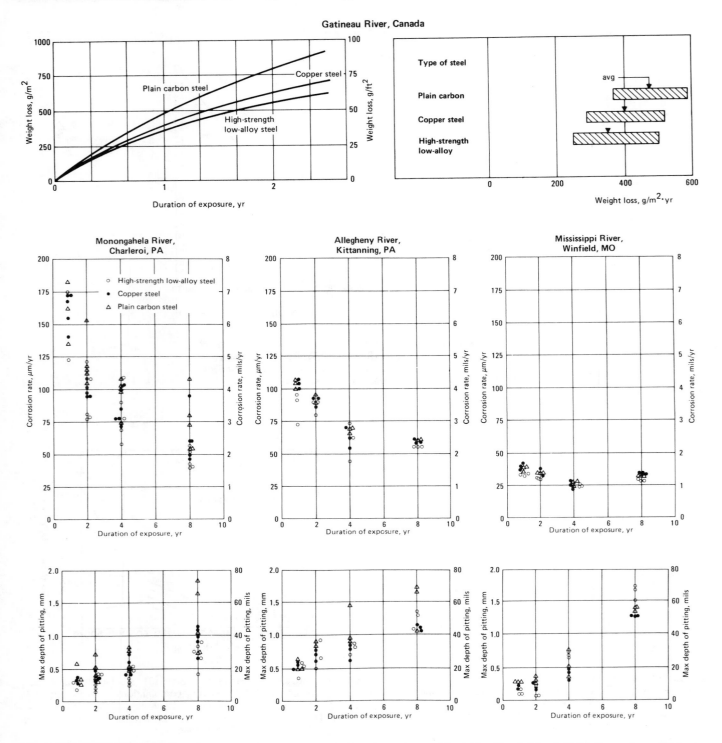

Low-carbon steel. Corrosion of three types of low-carbon steel in four rivers. Source: *Metals Handbook*, 9th ed., Vol 1, Properties and Selection: Irons and Steels, American Society for Metals, Metals Park, OH, 1978, 737.

References Used in Compiling the Environment Introduction and Summaries

G.S. Brady and H.R. Clauser, Ed., *Materials Handbook*, 11th ed., McGraw-Hill, New York, 1977, 1011 pages

C.D. Hodgman, R.C. Weast and S.M. Selby, Ed., *Handbook of Chemistry and Physics*, 42nd ed., The Chemical Rubber Publishing Co., Cleveland, 1961, 3481 pages

S.P. Parker, Ed., *McGraw-Hill Dictionary of Chemistry*, McGraw-Hill, New York, 1984, 665 pages

R.L. Shriner, R.C. Fuson, and D.Y. Curtin, *The Systematic Identification of Organic Compounds: A Laboratory Manual*, 5th ed., John Wiley & Sons, New York, 1964, 458 pages

H.H. Sister, C.A. VanderWerf, and A.W. Davidson, *College Chemistry: A Systematic Approach*, 2nd ed., MacMillan, New York, 1961, 709 pages

Metals Handbook, 9th ed., Vol 13, Corrosion, ASM International, Metals Park, OH, 1987

Guidelines for the Use of Aluminum with Food and Chemicals 5th ed., The Aluminum Association, Inc., Washington, DC, 1984

Lead for Corrosion Resistant Applications: A Guide, Lead Industries Association, New York, NY

Zinc: Its Corrosion Resistance, International Lead Zinc Research Organization, Inc., New York, NY, 1983

Product literature from the following producers: INCO Alloys International, Allegheny Ludlum Corporation, Carpenter Technology Corporation, Haynes International, Teledyne Wah Chang, Ampco Metal Company, Dow Chemical, Cyclops Corp., Metallwerk Plansee GmbH, Imperial Metals Industries, Ltd., Jessop Steel Company, Climax Molybdenum, The Duriron Company, Inc., Armco, Inc.

Cited References

1   N.D. Tomashov and P.M. Altovskii, *Corrosion and Protection of Titanium*, Government Scientific-Technical Publication of Machine-Building Literature (Russian translation), 1963; *Corrosion Resistance of Titanium*, Technical Handbook, Imperial Metals Industries (Kynoch) Ltd., Birmingham, UK; L.C. Covington and R.W. Schultz, "Corrosion of Resistance of Titanium," TIMET Corporation, 1982; R.L. Kane, The Corrosion of Titanium, in *The Corrosion of Light Metals*, The Corrosion Monograph Series, John Wiley & Sons, 1967; as cited in *Metals Handbook*, Ninth Edition, Vol 13, *Corrosion*, ASM International, Metals Park, OH, 1987, p 684

2   *Metals Handbook*, Ninth Edition, Vol 13, *Corrosion*, ASM International, Metals Park, OH, 1987, p 723-724

3   P.J. Gegner and W.L. Wilson, *Corrosion*, Vol 15 (No. 7), 1959; as cited in *Metals Handbook*, Ninth Edition, Vol 13, *Corrosion*, ASM International, Metals Park, OH, 1987, p 1179

4   *Metals Handbook*, Ninth Edition, Vol 13, *Corrosion*, ASM International, Metals Park, OH, 1987, p 795

5   *Metals Handbook*, Ninth Edition, Vol 13, *Corrosion*, ASM International, Metals Park, OH, 1987, p 802

6   *Metals Handbook*, Ninth Edition, Vol 13, *Corrosion*, ASM International, Metals Park, OH, 1987, p 803

7   *Metals Handbook*, Ninth Edition, Vol 13, *Corrosion*, ASM International, Metals Park, OH, 1987, p 800

8   *Metals Handbook*, Ninth Edition, Vol 13, *Corrosion*, ASM International, Metals Park, OH, 1987, p 798

9   *Metals Handbook*, Ninth Edition, Vol 13, *Corrosion*, ASM International, Metals Park, OH, 1987, p 796

10   *Metals Handbook*, Ninth Edition, Vol 13, *Corrosion*, ASM International, Metals Park, OH, 1987, p 797

11   *Metals Handbook*, Ninth Edition, Vol 13, *Corrosion*, ASM International, Metals Park, OH, 1987, p 720

12   *Metals Handbook*, Ninth Edition, Vol 2, *Properties and Selection: Nonferrous Alloys and Pure Metals*, American Society for Metals, Metals Park, OH, 1979, p 601

13   *Metals Handbook*, Ninth Edition, Vol 13, *Corrosion*, ASM International, Metals Park, OH, 1987, p 785

14   *Metals Handbook*, Ninth Edition, Vol 2, *Properties and Selection: Nonferrous Alloys and Pure Metals*, American Society for Metals, Metals Park, OH, 1979, p 599

15   *Metals Handbook*, Ninth Edition, Vol 13, *Corrosion*, ASM International, Metals Park, OH, 1987, p 711-715

16   Haynes International, 1983

17   *Metals Handbook*, Ninth Edition, Vol 13, *Corrosion*, ASM International, Metals Park, OH, 1987, p 804

18   *Metals Handbook*, Ninth Edition, Vol 13, *Corrosion*, ASM International, Metals Park, OH, 1987, p 806

19   *Metals Handbook*, Ninth Edition, Vol 3, *Properties and Selection: Stainless Steels, Tool Materials and Special-Purpose Metals*, American Society for Metals, Metals Park, OH, 1980, p 88

20   N.D. Tomashov and P.M. Altovskii, Corrosion and Protection of Titanium, Government Scientific-Technical Publication of Machine-Building Literature (Russian translation), 1963; L.C. Covington and R.W. Schultz, "Corrosion Resistance of Titanium," TIMET Corporation, 1982; R.L. Kane, The Corrosion of Titanium, in *The Corrosion of Light Metals*, The Corrosion Monograph Series, John Wiley & Sons, 1967; *Corrosion Resistance of Titanium*, Technical Handbook, Imperial Metals Industries (Kynoch) Ltd., Birmingham, UK; D.W. Stough, F.W. Fink, and R.S. Peoples, "The Corrosion of Titanium," Report 57, Titanium Metallurgical Laboratory, Battelle Memorial Institute, 1956; R.L. LaQue and H.R. Copson, *Corrosion Resistance of Metals and Alloys*, 2nd ed., ACS Monograph, Reinhold, 1963, p 646-661; as cited in *Metals Handbook*, Ninth Edition, Vol 13, *Corrosion*, ASM International, Metals Park, OH, 1987, p 685

21 S.W. Ciaraldi, M.R. Berry, and J.M. Johnson, Paper 98, presented at Corrosion/82, National Association of Corrosion Engineers, Houston, 1982

22 *Metals Handbook*, Ninth Edition, Vol 13, *Corrosion*, ASM International, Metals Park, OH, 1987, p 1161

23 *Metals Handbook*, Ninth Edition, Vol 13, *Corrosion*, ASM International, Metals Park, OH, 1987, p 661

24 R. Jasinski, Corrosion of N80-type Steel by CO_2/Water Mixture, *Corrosion*, Vol 43, April, 1987, p 216

25 F. King and C.D. Litke, unpublished research, 1985; also *Metals Handbook*, Ninth Edition, Vol 13, *Corrosion*, ASM International, Metals Park, OH, 1987, p 621

26 *Metals Handbook*, Ninth Edition, Vol 13, *Corrosion*, ASM International, Metals Park, OH, 1987, p 807

27 *Corrosion Resistance of Titanium*, Technical Handbook, Imperial Metals Industries (Kynoch) Ltd., Birmingham, UK; T.F. Degnan, Materials for Handling Hydrofluoric, Nitric, and Sulfuric Acids, in *Process Industries Corrosion*, National Association of Corrosion Engineers, Houston, 1975, p 229; S.H. Weiman, *Corrosion*, Vol 22, April 1966, p 98-106; as cited in *Metals Handbook*, Ninth Edition, Vol 13, *Corrosion*, ASM International, Metals Park, OH, 1987, p 679

28 *Metals Handbook*, Ninth Edition, Vol 13, *Corrosion*, ASM International, Metals Park, OH, 1987, p 627

29 *Metals Handbook*, Ninth Edition, Vol 13, *Corrosion*, ASM International, Metals Park, OH, 1987, p 805

30 Carpenter Technology Corp., 1985

31 G. Trabanelli, A. Frifnani, G. Brunoro, C. Monticelli, and F. Zucchi, *Mater. Perform.*, Vol 24 (No. 6), 1985, p 33; as cited in *Metals Handbook*, Ninth Edition, Vol 13, *Corrosion*, ASM International, Metals Park, OH, 1987, p 1168

32 J.A. Petit *et al.*, *Corros. Sci.*, Vol 21 (No. 4), 1981, p 279-299; V.P. Gupta, Process for Decreasing the Rate of Titanium Corrosion, U.S. Patent 4,321,231, 1982; R.W. Schultz and L.C. Covington, Hydrometallurgical Applications of Titanium, in *Industrial Applications of Titanium and Zirconium: Third Conference*, STP 830, American Society for Testing and Materials, Philadelphia, 1984, p 29-47; as cited in *Metals Handbook*, Ninth Edition, Vol 13, *Corrosion*, ASM International, Metals Park, OH, 1987, p 682

33 R.W. Schultz and J.S. Grauman, Fundamental Corrosion Characterization of High-Strength Titanium Alloys, in *Industrial Applications of Titanium and Zirconium: Fourth Volume*, STP 917, ASTM, Philadelphia, 1986, p 130-143; L.C. Covington and R.W. Schultz, "Corrosion Resistance of Titanium," TIMET Corporation, 1982; F.M. Reinhart, "Corrosion of Materials in Hydrospace, Part III, Titanium and Titanium Alloys," Technical Note N-921, U.S. Naval Civil Engineering Laboratory, Sept 1967; *Corrosion Resistance of Titanium*, Technical Handbook, Imperial Metals Industries (Kynoch) Ltd., Birmingham, UK; R.L. LaQue and H.R. Copson, *Corrosion Resistance of Metals and Alloys*, 2nd ed., ACS Monograph, Reinhold, 1963, p 646-661; R.W. Schultz, J.A. Hall, and T.L. Wardlaw, "TI-CODE 12, An Improved Industrial Alloy," Paper presented at the Japan Titanium Society 30th Anniversary International Symposium, Japan Titanium Society, Aug 1982; D.E. Thomas, *et al.*, Beta-C: An Emerging Titanium Alloy for The Industrial Marketplace, in *Industrial Applications of Titanium and Zirconium: Fourth Volume*, STP 917, ASTM, Philadelphia, 1986, p 144-163; as cited in *Metals Handbook*, Ninth Edition, Vol 13, *Corrosion*, ASM International, Metals Park, OH, 1987, p 705-706

34 S.C. Britton and R.M. Angles, *J. Electrodep. Tech. Soc.*, Vol 27, 1951, p 293; S.C. Britton and R.M. Angles, *Metallurgia*, Vol 44, 1951, p 185; as cited in *Metals Handbook*, Ninth Edition, Vol 7, *Powder Metallurgy*, American Society for Metals, Metals Park, OH, 1984, p 778

35 A. Davin and D. Coutsourdis, *Cobalt*, Vol 52, Sept 1971, p 160; as cited in *Metals Handbook*, Ninth Edition, Vol 13, *Corrosion*, ASM International, Metals Park, OH, 1987, p 660

36 *Corrosion and Corrosion Protection Handbook*, P. Schweitzer, Ed., Marcel Dekker, New York, 1983, p 204

37 M. Stern and C. Bishop, Corrosion and Electrochemical Behavior, in *Columbium and Tantalum*, F. Sisco and E. Epremian, Ed., John Wiley & Sons, New York, 1963, p 306

38 M. Stern and C. Bishop, Corrosion and Electrochemical Behavior, in *Columbium and Tantalum*, F. Sisco and E. Epremian, Ed., John Wiley & Sons, New York, 1963, p 307

39 *Metals Handbook*, Ninth Edition, Vol 13, *Corrosion*, ASM International, Metals Park, OH, 1987, p 634

40 Inco Alloys International, 1986

41 J.B. Lee, J.F. Smith, *et al.*, An Analytical Electron Microscope Examination of Sensitized AISI 430 Stainless Steel, *Corrosion*, Vol 41, Feb, 1985, p 77

42 P.A. Schweitzer, Tantalum, in *Corrosion and Corrosion Protection Handbook*, P.A. Schweitzer, Ed., Marcel Dekker, New York, 1983, p 182-183

43 Inco Alloys International, 1987

44 Inco Alloys International, 1979

45 S.R. Seagle, *Pulp Paper*, Vol 53 (No. 10), Sept 1979

46 P.J. Gegner and W.L. Wilson, *Corrosion*, Vol 15 (No. 7), 1959

47 Carpenter Technology Corp., Specialty Steels Technical Data, 1986

48 *Lead for Corrosion Resistant Applications: A Guide*, Lead Industries Association, New York, p 64

49 *Lead for Corrosion Resistant Applications: A Guide*, Lead Industries Association, New York, p 67

50 S.W. Ciaraldi, M.R. Berry, and J.M. Johnson, Paper 98, presented at Corrosion/82, National Association of Corrosion Engineers, Houston, 1982; Corrosion Engineering Bulletin 6, International Nickel Company; as cited in *Metals Handbook*, Ninth Edition, Vol 13, *Corrosion*, ASM International, Metals Park, OH, 1987, p 648

51 R.M. Davison and J.D. Redmond, The Application of Ferritic and Duplex Stainless Steels, *Second Symposium on Shell and Tube Heat Exchangers*, W.R. Apblett, Jr., Ed., American Society for Metals, Metals Park, OH, 1982, p 86

52 R.M. Davison and J.D. Redmond, The Application of Ferritic and Duplex Stainless Steels, *Second Symposium on Shell and Tube Heat Exchangers*, W.R. Apblett, Jr., Ed., American Society for Metals, Metals Park, OH, 1982, p 82

53 J.S. Pettibone, Other Metals, in *Corrosion Resistance of Metals and Alloys*, 2nd Edition, F.L. LaQue and H.R. Copson, Ed., Reinhold Publishing, New York, 1963, p 629

54 J.S. Pettibone, Other Metals, in *Corrosion Resistance of Metals and Alloys*, 2nd Edition, F.L. LaQue and H.R. Copson, Ed., Reinhold Publishing, New York, 1963, p 628

55 *Metals Handbook*, Ninth Edition, Vol 3, *Properties and Selection: Stainless Steels, Tool Materials and Special-Purpose Metals*, American Society for Metals, Metals Park, OH, 1980, p 81

56 M. Stern and C. Bishop, Corrosion and Electrochemical Behavior, in *Columbium and Tantalum*, F. Sisco and E. Epremian, Ed., John Wiley & Sons, New York, 1963, p 325

57 Inco Alloys International, 1980

58 R.F. Steigerwald, *Metalloved. Term. Obrab. Met.*, No. 7, 1973, p 16-20; R.F. Steigerwald and M.A. Streicher, Paper presented at the Annual Meeting, St. Louis, National Association of Corrosion Engineers, 1965; as cited in *Metals Handbook*, Ninth Edition, Vol 13, *Corrosion*, ASM International, Metals Park, OH, 1987, p 126

59 R.M. Burns and W.W. Bradley, *Protective Coatings for Metals*, Third Edition, Reinhold Publishing, New York, 1967, p 211

60 Haynes International, 1986

61 R.T. Webster, "The Applications of Zirconium and Niobium", Second Symposium on Shell and Tube Heat Exchangers, W.R. Apblett, Jr., Ed., American Society for Metals, Metals Park, OH, 1982, p 62

62 R.T. Webster, "The Applications of Zirconium and Niobium," Second Symposium on Shell and Tube Heat Exchangers, W.R. Apblett, Jr., Ed., American Society for Metals, Metals Park, OH, 1982, p 60

63 Haynes International, 1987

64 Inco Alloys International, 1985

65 Corrosion Engineering Bulletin, No. 6, International Nickel Company, Inc.

66 Metals Handbook, Ninth Edition, Vol 3, Properties and Selection: Stainless Steels, Tool Materials and Special-Purpose Metals, American Society for Metals, Metals Park, OH, 1980, p 80

67 Haynes International, 1982

68 Haynes International, 1984

69 Metals Handbook, Ninth Edition, Vol 2, Properties and Selection: Nonferrous Alloys and Pure Metals, American Society for Metals, Metals Park, OH, 1979, p 476

70 Metals Handbook, Ninth Edition, Vol 13, Corrosion, ASM International, Metals Park, OH, 1987, p 629

71 Z.A. Foroulis and R.J. Franco, High Temperature Internal Corrosion of an Acetone Plant Furnace Outlet Tube: Failure Analysis and Laboratory Simulation, Materials Performance, Vol 25, Oct, 1985, p 56

72 Metals Handbook, Ninth Edition, Vol 13, Corrosion, ASM International, Metals Park, OH, 1987, p 631

73 D.E. Gluck, R.B. Herchenroeder, G.Y. Lai, and M.F. Rothman, Met. Prog., Sept 1985, p 35

74 Metals Handbook, Ninth Edition, Vol 13, Corrosion, ASM International, Metals Park, OH, 1987, p 730

75 F.L. LaQue, Corrosion by Seawater, Behavior of Metals and Alloys in Seawater, in The Corrosion Handbook, H.H. Uhlig, Ed., John Wiley & Sons, 1948, p 383-430; S.C. Britton, Anti-Corrosion Manual, Scientific Surveys, Ltd., 1958; C.L. Baker, Ind. Eng. Chem., Vol 27, 1935, p 1358; as cited in Metals Handbook, Ninth Edition, Vol 13, Corrosion, ASM International, Metals Park, OH, 1987, p 772

76 Metals Handbook, Ninth Edition, Vol 13, Corrosion, ASM International, Metals Park, OH, 1987, p 632

77 Metals Handbook, Ninth Edition, Vol 2, Properties and Selection: Nonferrous Alloys and Pure Metals, American Society for Metals, Metals Park, OH, 1979, p 478

78 Allegheny Ludlum Corporation, 1981

79 W.Z. Friend, Corrosion of Nickel and Nickel-base Alloys, John Wiley & Sons, New York, 1980, p 67

80 Allegheny Ludlum Corporation, 1980

81 Allegheny Ludlum Corporation, 1982

82 S.R. Seagle, Pulp Paper, Vol 53, (No. 10), Sept 1979; "Resistance of Nickel and High Nickel Alloys to Corrosion by Hydrochloric Acid, Hydrogen Chloride and Chlorine," Corrosion Engineering Bulletin CEB-3, The International Nickel Company; as cited in Metals Handbook, Ninth Edition, Vol 13, Corrosion, ASM International, Metals Park, OH, 1987, p 1180

83 M.H. Brown, Q.B. DeLong, and J.R. Auld, Ind. Eng. Chem., Vol 39 (No. 7), 1947, p 839

84 K.L. Tseitlin and J.A. Strunkin, J. Appl. Chem. (USSR), Vol 29 (No. 11), 1956, p 1793

85 C. Chakrabarty, M.M. Singh, and C.U. Agarwal, J. Electrochem. Soc., Vol 31, 1982, p 165-169

86 Corrosion Resistance of Titanium, Technical Handbook, Imperial Metals Industries (Kynoch) Ltd., Birmingham, UK

87 Metals Handbook, Ninth Edition, Vol 3, Properties and Selection: Stainless Steels, Tool Materials and Special-Purpose Metals, American Society for Metals, Metals Park, OH, 1980, p 82

88 N. Sridhar, J. Kolts, et al., A Duplex Stainless Steel for Chloride Environments, Journal of Metals, Vol 37, March 1985, p 33

89 "A Guide to Corrosion Resistance," Climax Molybdenum Company, Greenwich, CT, 1981

90 N.D. Tomashov and P.M. Altovskii, Corrosion and Protection of Titanium, Government Scientific-Technical Publication of Machine-Building Literature (Russian translation), 1963; L.C. Covington and R.W. Schultz, "Corrosion Resistance of Titanium," TIMET Corporation, 1982; R.L. Kane, The Corrosion of Titanium, in The Corrosion of Light Metals, The Corrosion Monograph Series, John Wiley & Sons, 1967; Corrosion Resistance of Titanium, Technical Handbook, Imperial Metals Industries (Kynoch) Ltd., Birmingham, UK; S.H. Weiman, Corrosion, Vol 22, April 1966, p 98-106; H. Keller and K. Risch, The Corrosion Behavior of Titanium in Nitric Acid at High Temperatures, Werkst. Korros., Vol 9, 1964, p 741-743; R.L. LaQue and H.R. Copson, Corrosion Resistance of Metals and Alloys, 2nd ed., ACS Monograph, Reinhold, 1963, p 646-661; J.D. Jackson and W.K. Boyd, "Corrosion of Titanium," DMIC Memorandum 218, Defense Materials Information Center, Battelle Memorial Institute, Sept 1966; as cited in Metals Handbook, Ninth Edition, Vol 13, Corrosion, ASM International, Metals Park, OH, 1987, p 701-705

91 "Titanium," Teledyne Wah Chang Albany, 1988

92 F. King, Aluminium and Its Alloys, Ellis Horwood, Chichester, England, 1987, p 282-291

93 H. Leidheiser, Jr., The Corrosion of Copper, Tin and Their Alloys, John Wiley & Sons, New York, 1971, p 90-96

94 H. Leidheiser, Jr., The Corrosion of Copper, Tin and Their Alloys, John Wiley & Sons, New York, 1971, p 287-290

95 Lead for Corrosion Resistant Applications: A Guide, Lead Industries Association, Inc., New York, p 72

96 "Stock Metals," Ampco Metal Company, 1988

97 "Jessop JS700 (UNS NO8700)," Jessop Steel Company, Washington, PA, 1987

98 Allegheny Ludlum Corporation, 1986

99 Metals Handbook, Ninth Edition, Vol 13, Corrosion, ASM International, Metals Park, OH, 1987, p 662

100 Metals Handbook, Ninth Edition, Vol 3, Properties and Selection: Stainless Steels, Tool Materials and Special-Purpose Metals, American Society for Metals, Metals Park, OH, 1980, p 84

101 Metals Handbook, Ninth Edition, Vol 13, Corrosion, ASM International, Metals Park, OH, 1987, p 649

102 Metals Handbook, Ninth Edition, Vol 13, Corrosion, ASM International, Metals Park, OH, 1987, p 1158

103 R.W. Schultz, J.A. Hall, and T.L. Wardlaw, "TI-CODE 12, An Improved Industrial Alloy," Paper presented at the Japan Titanium Society 30th Anniversary International Symposium, Japan Titanium Society, Aug 1982; as cited in Metals Handbook, Ninth Edition, Vol 13, Corrosion, ASM International, Metals Park, OH, 1987, p 687

104 R.I. Higgins, Corrosion of Cast Iron, J. Res., Feb 1956, p 165-177

105 Metals Handbook, Ninth Edition, Vol 13, Corrosion, ASM International, Metals Park, OH, 1987, p 736

106 J.H. Gittus, Uranium, Butterworths, Washington, 1963, p 407

107 Metals Handbook, Ninth Edition, Vol 13, Corrosion, ASM International, Metals Park, OH, 1987, p 575

108 C. Briggs, Ed., Steel Casting Handbook, 4th Edition, Steel Founders' Society of America, 1970, 662-667

109 W.Z. Friend, *Corrosion of Nickel and Nickel-base Alloys*, John Wiley & Sons, New York, 1980, p 71

110 *Metals Handbook*, Ninth Edition, Vol 13, *Corrosion*, ASM International, Metals Park, OH, 1987, p 636

111 P.J. Gegner and W.L. Wilson, *Corrosion*, Vol 15 (No. 7), 1959

112 "Corrosion Resistance of Nickel and Nickel-Containing Alloys in Caustic Soda and other Alkalies," Corrosion Engineering Bulletin CEB-2, The International Nickel Company, Inc., 1973

113 Ampco Metal Division, Ampco-Pittsburgh, unpublished research, 1951; as cited in *Metals Handbook*, Ninth Edition, Vol 13, *Corrosion*, ASM International, Metals Park, OH, 1987, p 1175

114 P.J. Gegner, "Corrosion Resistance of Materials in Alkalies and Hypochlorites," Paper 27, Process Industries Corrosion Short Course, National Association of Corrosion Engineers, Houston, 1974

115 F.L. LaQue and H.R. Copson, *Corrosion Resistance of Metals and Alloys*, Reinhold Publishing, New York, 1963

116 *Metals Handbook*, Ninth Edition, Vol 13, *Corrosion*, ASM International, Metals Park, OH, 1987, p 1174; and Ampco Metal Division, Ampco-Pittsburgh, unpublished research, 1951.

117 P.J. Gegner, "Corrosion Resistance of Materials in Alkalies and Hypochlorites," Paper 27, Process Industries Corrosion Short Course, National Association o Corrosion Engineers, 1974; F.L. LaQue and H.R. Copson, *Corrosion Resistance of Metals and Alloys, Reinhold, 1963; E. Heyn* and D. Bauer, *Mitt. Kgl. Material Prufungsamt Prussia*, Vol 26, 1908; as cited in *Metals Handbook*, Ninth Edition, Vol 13, *Corrosion*, ASM International, Metals Park, OH, 1987, p 1177

118 "Resistance of Nickel and High Nickel Alloys to Corrosion by Hydrochloric Acid, Hydrogen Chloride and Chlorine," Corrosion Engineering Bulletin CEB-3, The International Nickel Company, Inc., 1972

119 Dow Chemical Co., Midland, MI

120 Allegheny Ludlum Steel Corp.

121 Cyclops Corp., Universal-Cyclops Specialty Steel Division

122 *Metals Handbook*, Ninth Edition, Vol 13, *Corrosion*, ASM International, Metals Park, OH, 1987, p 635

123 E. Hibner, Paper 181, presented at Corrosion/82, Houston, National Association of Corrosion Engineers, 1986; as cited in *Metals Handbook*, Ninth Edition, Vol 13, *Corrosion*, ASM International, Metals Park, OH, 1987, p 646

124 Haynes International, 1984

125 C.P. Larrabee and S.K. Coburn, The Atmospheric Corrosion of Steels as Influenced by Changes in Chemical Composition, in *Metallic Corrosion—First International Conference on Corrosion*, Butterworths, 1962, p 276-284; as cited in *Metals Handbook*, Ninth Edition, Vol 13, *Corrosion*, ASM International, Metals Park, OH, 1987, p 532

126 W.Z. Friend, *Corrosion of Nickel and Nickel-Base Alloys*, John Wiley & Sons, New York, 1980, 393

127 F.L. McGeary, E.T. Englehart, and P.J. Ging, Weathering of Aluminum, *Mater. Protec.*, Vol 6 (No. 6), 1967, p 33; as cited in *Metals Handbook*, Ninth Edition, Vol 13, *Corrosion*, ASM International, Metals Park, OH, 1987, p 599

128 G.O. Hiers and E. Minarcik, *Symposium on Atmospheric Corrosion of Nonferrous Metals*, STP 175, ASTM, 1956, p 135; W.E. Boggs, R.H. Kachik, and G.E. Pellisier, *J. Electrochem. Soc.*, Vol 110 (No. 1), 1963, p 4; as cited in *Metals Handbook*, Ninth Edition, Vol 13, *Corrosion*, ASM International, Metals Park, OH, 1987, p 771

129 *Lead For Corrosion Resistant Applications: A Guide*, Lead Industries Association, New York, p 46

130 *Lead For Corrosion Resistant Applications: A Guide*, Lead Industries Association, New York, p 65

131 *Lead For Corrosion Resistant Applications: A Guide*, Lead Industries Association, New York, p 63

132 J.H. Weber, *High Temperature Oxide Dispersion Strengthened Alloys*, Proceedings of the 25th National SAMPE Symposium and Exhibition, Society for the Advancement of Material and Process Engineering, 1980, p 752-763; as cited in *Metals Handbook*, Ninth Edition, Vol 13, *Corrosion*, ASM International, Metals Park, OH, 1987, p 839

133 Inco Alloys International, 1962

134 Inco Alloys International, 1984

135 Englehard Industries Division, Englehard Corporation; and *Metals Handbook*, Ninth Edition, Vol 13, *Corrosion*, ASM International, Metals Park, OH, 1987, p 794

136 *Stainless Steels*, R.A. Lula, Ed., American Society for Metals, Metals Park, OH, p 79

137 *Metals Handbook*, Ninth Edition, Vol 3, *Properties and Selection: Stainless Steels, Tool Materials and Special-Purpose Metals*, American Society for Metals, Metals Park, OH, 1980, p 85

138 *Metals Handbook*, Ninth Edition, Vol 2, *Properties and Selection: Nonferrous Alloys and Pure Metals*, American Society for Metals, Metals Park, OH, 1979, p 476-477

139 *Metals Handbook*, Ninth Edition, Vol 3, *Properties and Selection: Stainless Steels, Tool Materials and Special-Purpose Metals*, American Society for Metals, Metals Park, OH, 1980, p 87

140 C.J. Slunder and W.K. Boyd, *Zinc: Its Corrosion Resistance*, Second Edition, T.K. Christman and J. Payer, Ed., International Lead Zinc Research Organization, New York, 1983, p 115

141 H.H. Uhlig and R.W. Revie, *Corrosion and Corrosion Engineering: An Introduction to Corrosion Science and Engineering*, Third Edition, John Wiley & Sons, New York, 1985, p 270

142 H. Grafen and D. Kuron, Development of High Corrosion Resistance Lead Alloys Containing Palladium, in *Lead 71: Proceedings, Fourth International Conference on Lead*, European Lead Development Committee, London, 1971, p 135

143 *Steel Castings Handbook*, Fifth Edition, P. Wieser, Ed., Steel Founder's Society of America, Rocky River, OH, 1980

144 F.A. Lowenheim, R.A. Woodter, *et al.*, Tin and Tin Plate, in *Corrosion Resistance of Metals and Alloys*, Second Edition, F.L. LaQue and H.R. Copson, Ed., Reinhold Publishing, New York, 1963, p 261

145 Carpenter Technology Corp., 1987

146 Inco Alloys International, 1974

147 K. Takao and K. Terasaki, Chemical Resistance of Various Cemented Carbides, *Nippon Tungsten Rev.*, Vol 10, 1977; Y. Masumoto, K. Takechi, and S. Imassato, Corrosion Resistance of Cemented Carbide, *Nippon Tungsten Rev.*, Vol 19, 1986; as cited in *Metals Handbook*, Ninth Edition, Vol 13, *Corrosion*, ASM International, Metals Park, OH, 1987, p 857

148 M. Yasuda, S. Tokunaga, *et al.*, Corrosion Behavior of 18-8 Stainless Steels in Hot Concentrated Caustic Soda Solutions Under Heat-Transfer Conditions, *Corrosion*, Vol 41, 1985, p 713

149 *Metals Handbook*, Ninth Edition, Vol 1, *Properties and Selection: Irons and Steels*, American Society for Metals, Metals Park, OH, 1978, p 742

150 W.H. Ailor, Jr., Ten-Year Seawater Tests on Aluminum in *Corrosion in Natural Environments* (STP 558), ASTM, Philadelphia, 1974, p 117

151 W.Z. Friend, *Corrosion of Nickel and Nickel-Base Alloys*, John Wiley & Sons, New York, 1980, p 402

152 W.Z. Friend, *Corrosion of Nickel and Nickel-Base Alloys*, John Wiley & Sons, New York, 1980, p 401

153 *Metals Handbook*, Ninth Edition, Vol 13, *Corrosion*, ASM International, Metals Park, OH, 1987, p 628

154 *Lead For Corrosion Resistant Applications: A Guide,* Lead Industries Association, New York, p 62

155 *Metals Handbook,* Ninth Edition, Vol 3, *Properties and Selection: Stainless Steels, Tool Materials and Special-Purpose Metals,* American Society for Metals, Metals Park, OH, 1980, 87

156 "Corrosion Resistance of Nickel-containing Alloys in Phosphoric Acid," The International Nickel Company, 1976

157 L.D. Yates, "Corrosion Tests of Metals and Ceramics," Tennessee Valley Authority Chemical Engineering Report No. 9, Wilson Dam, Alabama, 1951

158 W.G. Renshaw and R.A. Lula, The Corrosion Properties of Chromium-Nickel-Manganese Austenitic Stainless Steels, *Proceedings ASTM,* Vol 52, 1956, p 866

159 N.D. Groves, C.M. Eisenbrown, and L.R. Scharfstein, Corrosion by Weak Acids under Heat Transfer Conditions, *Corrosion,* Vol 17, 1961, p 173

160 D. Warren, Corrosion and Weldability Studies on Chromium-Manganese Austenitic Stainless Steels, *Corrosion,* Vol 16, 1960, p 119

161 International Nickel Company, unpublished data

162 A.R. Morgan, Jr., Corrosion of Types 316 and 317 Stainless Steel by 75 and 85% Phosphoric Acid, *Corrosion,* Vol 15, 1959, p 351

163 J.D. Kemp and H.P. Zeh, U.S. Patent 2,653,177, Sept 22, 1953

164 H.F. Ebling and M.A. Scheil, A Standard Laboratory Corrosion Test for Metals in Phosphoric Acid Service, *Trans. Am. Soc. Mech. Eng.,* Vol 73, 1951, p 975

165 R.B. Leonard, Developing A New Alloy, *Chemical Engineering,* Vol 71 (No. 22), 1964, p 150

166 M.E. Rothman and G.Y. Lai, *Ind. Heat.,* Aug 1986, p 29

167 Physical and Corrosion Properties, in *Source Book on Ductile Iron,* A.H. Rauch, Ed., American Society for Metals, Metals Park, OH, 1977, 370

168 W.J.D. Shaw, Corrosion Behavior of the IN-9021 Aluminum Alloy, *Corrosion,* Vol 42, Sept 1986, p 555

169 Allegheny Ludlum Corporation, 1984

170 *Metals Handbook,* Ninth Edition, Vol 2, *Properties and Selection: Nonferrous Alloys and Pure Metals,* American Society for Metals, Metals Park, OH, 1979, 598

171 International Nickel Company; as cited in *Metals Handbook,* Ninth Edition, Vol 13, *Corrosion,* ASM International, Metals Park, OH, 1987, p 333

172 J.R. Bryant and C.B. Chitwood, Paper 58, presented at Corrosion/83, National Association of Corrosion Engineers, Houston, 1983

173 D.B. Anderson and K.D. Efird, Proceedings of the Third International Congress on Marine Corrosion and Fouling, National Bureau of Standards, Washington, DC, Oct 1972

174 M.A. Pelensky, J.J. Jawarski, and A. Gallaccio, Air, Soil, and Sea Galvanic Corrosion Investigation at Panama Canal Zone, in *Galvanic and Pitting Corrosion—Field and Laboratory Studies* (STP 576), ASTM, Philadelphia, 1967, p 94

175 H.B. Bomberger, P.J. Cambourelis, and G.E. Hutchinson, Corrosion Properties of Titanium in Marine Environments, *J. Electrochem. Soc.,* Vol 101, 1954, p 442; as cited in *Metals Handbook,* Ninth Edition, Vol 13, *Corrosion,* ASM International, Metals Park, OH, 1987, p 695

176 F.L. LaQue, Corrosion by Seawater, Behavior of Metals and Alloys in Seawater, in *The Corrosion Handbook,* H.H. Uhlig, Ed., John Wiley & Sons, New York, 1948, p 383-430

177 C.J. Slunder and W.K. Boyd, *Zinc: Its Corrosion Resistance,* Second Edition, T.K. Christman and J. Payer, Ed., International Lead Zinc Research Organization, New York, 1983, p 117

178 *Lead for Corrosion Resistant Applications: A Guide,* Lead Industries Association, New York, p 52

179 Allegheny Ludlum Corporation, 1974

180 *Petroleum Engineer International,* Oct 1986

181 R. Jasinski and K.D. Efird, Electrochemical Corrosion Probe for High Resistivity Hydrocarbon/Water Mixtures, *Corrosion Engineering,* Feb 1988, 658

182 J.P. Carter *et al., Corrosion,* 40(5), May 1984

183 *Metals Handbook,* Ninth Edition, Vol 13, *Corrosion,* ASM International, Metals Park, OH, 1987, p 654

184 M.A. Streicher, Analysis of Crevice Corrosion Data From Two Sea Water Exposure Tests on Stainless Alloys, *Mater. Perform.,* Vol 22, May 1983, p 37-50; H.O. Teeple, Corrosion by Some Organic Acids and Related Compounds, *Corrosion,* Vol 8, Jan 1952, p 14-28; as cited in *Metals Handbook,* Ninth Edition, Vol 13, *Corrosion,* ASM International, Metals Park, OH, 1987, p 556

185 R.L. Kane, The Corrosion of Titanium, in *The Corrosion of Light Metals,* The Corrosion Monograph Series, John Wiley & Sons, 1967; F.M. Reinhart, "Corrosion of Materials in Hydrospace, Part III, Titanium and Titanium Alloys," Technical Note N-921, U.S. Naval Civil Engineering Laboratory, Sept 1967; H.B. Bomberger, P.J. Cambourelis, and G.E. Hutchinson, Corrosion Properties of Titanium in Marine Environments, *J. Electrochem. Soc.,* Vol 101, 1954, p 442; W.L. Wheatfall, "Metal Corrosion in Deep-Ocean Environments," Research and Development Phase Report 429/66, U.S. Navy Marine Engineering Laboratory, Jan 1967; M.A. Pelensky, J.J. Jawarski, and A. Gallaccio, Air, Soil, and Sea Galvanic Corrosion Investigation at Panama Canal Zone, in *Galvanic and Pitting Corrosion—Field and Laboratory Studies,* STP 576, ASTM, 1967, p 94; *Corrosion Resistance of Titanium,* Technical Handbook, Imperial Metals Industries (Kynoch) Ltd., Birmingham, UK; as cited in *Metals Handbook,* Ninth Edition, Vol 13, *Corrosion,* ASM International, Metals Park, OH, 1987, p 677